BED & BREAKFAST

The Official Where to stay guide 2001

Scotland is split into eight tourist areas. You will find accommodation listed alphabetically by location within each of these areas. There is an index at the back of this book which may also help you.

INTRODUCTION

ACCOMMODATION

APPENDIX

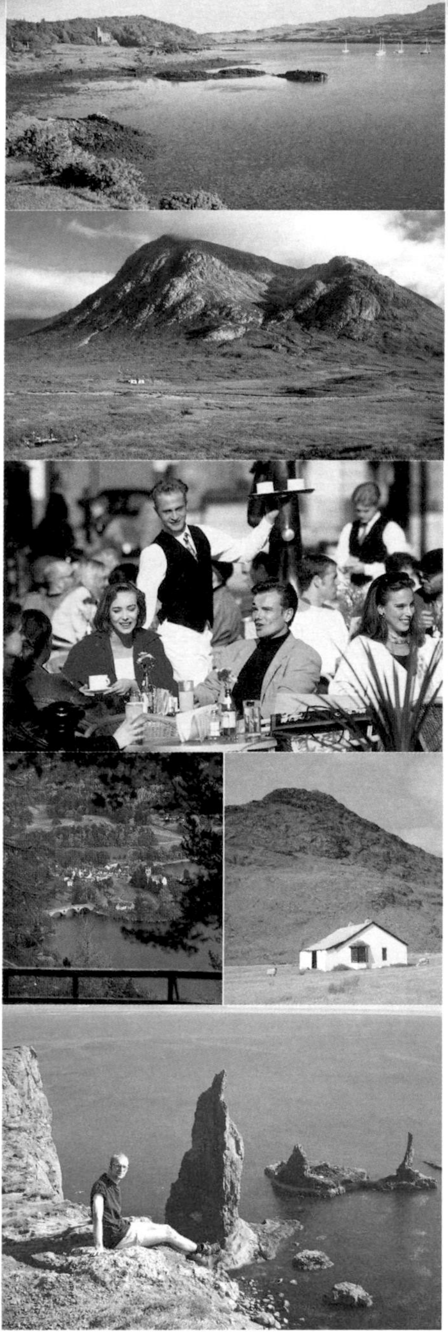

A BED AND BREAKFAST IS PERFECT FOR A SHORT HOLIDAY – an escape to the country, a city break in Edinburgh or Glasgow, or a place to unwind after a day's travel or business. It's also the ideal accommodation for stopping on a touring holiday to take in the history and scenery that make Scotland famous.

THERE'S A WIDE RANGE of bed and breakfasts to choose from around the country, wherever you may travel – whether it be a farmhouse in a highland glen, a croft on a remote Scottish island, or in the heart of Scotland's buzzing city-life.

FRIENDLY, HOSPITABLE and always economical, the bed and breakfast is one of the best ways you can get to know Scotland – and the Scots. The family home atmosphere, where the owner's touch makes all the difference, offers good food, comfortable surroundings, together with local knowledge, advice and information. It's a great combination, offering good value for money.

WELCOMING DOORS – to suit every taste – are awaiting you, so start making your choices now from the hundreds available in this book!

WHERE TO STAY...?

Over 1500 answers to the age-old question!

REVISED ANNUALLY, th_s is the most comprehensive guide to bed and breakfast establishments in Scotland.

EVERY PROPERTY in the guide has been graded and classified by Scottish Tourist Board inspectors. See page vi for details

HOW TO FIND ACCOMMODATION

This book split into eight areas of Scotland:

ACCOMMODATION

THE MAP on page xix shows these areas. Within each area section you will find accommodation listed alphabetically by location.

ALTERNATIVELY THERE IS an index at the back of this book listing alphabetically all accommodation locations in Scotland.

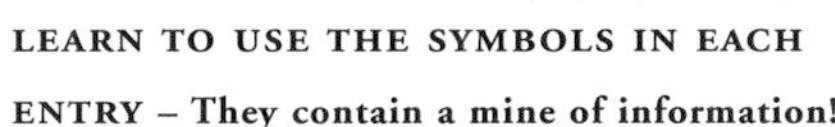

LEARN TO USE THE SYMBOLS IN EACH ENTRY – They contain a mine of information!

THERE IS A KEY TO SYMBOLS ON THE BACK FLAP.

NATURALLY, IT IS always advisable to confirm with the establishment that a particular facility is still available.

PRICES IN THE GUIDE are quoted per person and represent the minimum and maximum charges expected to apply to most rooms in the establishment. They include VAT at the appropriate rate and service charges where applicable.

THE PRICES OF accommodation, services and facilities are supplied to us by the operators and were, to the best of our knowledge, correct at the time of going to press. However, prices can change at any time during the lifetime of the publication, and you should check again when you book.

BOOKINGS CAN BE made direct to the establishment, through a travel agent, or through a local Tourist Information Centre.

REMEMBER, WHEN you accept accommodation by telephone or in writing, you are entering a legally binding contract which must be fulfilled on both sides. Should you fail to take up accommodation, you may not only forfeit any deposit already paid, but may also have to compensate the establishment if the accommodation cannot be re-let.

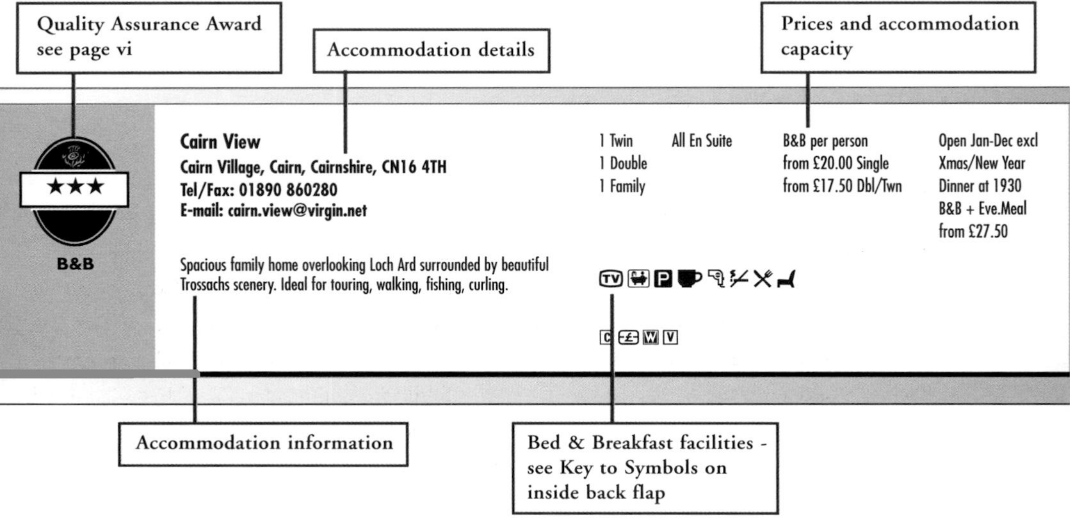
Quality Assurance Award see page vi
Accommodation details
Prices and accommodation capacity
★★★
B&B
Cairn View
Cairn Village, Cairn, Cairnshire, CN16 4TH
Tel/Fax: 01890 860280
E-mail: cairn.view@virgin.net
Spacious family home overlooking Loch Ard surrounded by beautiful Trossachs scenery. Ideal for touring, walking, fishing, curling.
1 Twin
1 Double
1 Family
All En Suite
B&B per person
from £20.00 Single
from £17.50 Dbl/Twn
Open Jan-Dec excl
Xmas/New Year
Dinner at 1930
B&B + Eve.Meal
from £27.50
Accommodation information
Bed & Breakfast facilities - see Key to Symbols on inside back flap

FOLLOW THE STARS AND YOU WON'T BE DISAPPOINTED WHEN YOU GET TO THE INN.

THE SCOTTISH TOURIST BOARD STAR SYSTEM is a world-first. Quality is what determines our star awards, not a checklist of facilities. We've made your priorities our priorities.

QUALITY MAKES or breaks a visit. This is why the most important aspects of your stay; the warmth of welcome, efficiency and friendliness of service, the quality of the food and the cleanliness and condition of the furnishings, fittings and decor earn Scottish Tourist Board Stars, not the size of the accommodation or the range of available facilities.

THIS EASY to understand system tells you at a glance the quality standard of all types and sizes of accommodation from the smallest B&B and self-catering cottage to the largest countryside and city centre hotels.

Quality Assurance awards correct at end September 2000

LOOK OUT FOR THIS DISTINCTIVE SIGN OF QUALITY ASSURED ACCOMMODATION

THE STANDARDS YOU CAN EXPECT.

★★★★★	**Exceptional**
★★★★	**Excellent**
★★★	**Very good**
★★	**Good**
★	**Fair and Acceptable**

A TRAINED SCOTTISH TOURIST BOARD QUALITY ADVISOR grades each property every year to give you the reassurance that you can choose accommodation of the quality standard you want.

TO HELP YOU further in your choice the Scottish Tourist Board System also tells you the type of accommodation and the range of facilities and services available.

PLEASE TURN OVER FOR DETAILS.

FOR FURTHER INFORMATION call into any Tourist Information Centre, or contact the Scottish Tourist Board.

MORE DETAILS AVAILABLE FROM:

Quality Assurance Department
Scottish Tourist Board
Thistle House
Beechwood Park North
INVERNESS
IV2 3ED
TEL: **01463 723040**
FAX: **01463 717244**
EMAIL: **qa@stb.gov.uk**

ACCOMMODATION TYPES

SELF CATERING

A HOUSE, cottage, apartment, chalet or similar accommodation which is let normally on a weekly basis to individuals where facilities are provided to cater for yourselves.

SERVICED APARTMENTS

SERVICED APARTMENTS are essentially self catering apartments where services such as a cleaning service is available and meals and drinks may be available. Meals and drinks would normally be provided to each apartment or in a restaurant and/or bar which is on site.

GUEST HOUSE

A GUEST HOUSE is usually a commercial business and will normally have a minimum of 4 letting bedrooms, of which some will have ensuite or private facilities. Breakfast will be available and evening meals may be provided.

B&B

ACCOMMODATION OFFERING bed and breakfast, usually in a private house. B&B's will normally accommodate no more than 6 guests, and may or may not serve an evening meal.

HOTEL

A HOTEL WILL NORMALLY HAVE a minimum of twenty letting bedrooms, of which at least half must have ensuite or private bathroom facilities. A hotel will normally have a drinks license (may be a restricted licence) and will serve breakfast, dinner and normally lunch.

SMALL HOTEL

A SMALL HOTEL WILL normally have a maximum of twenty letting bedrooms and a minimum of six. At least 50% of the bedrooms will have ensuite or private facilities. A small hotel will be licenced (may be a restricted license) and will serve breakfast, dinner and normally lunch. It will normally be run by owner(s) and reflect their style and personal input.

INTERNATIONAL RESORT HOTEL

A HOTEL ACHIEVING a 5 Star quality award which owns and offers a range of leisure and sporting facilities including an 18 hole golf course, swimming and leisure centre and country pursuits.

LODGE

PRIMARILY PURPOSE-BUILT overnight accommodation, often situated close to a major road or in a city centre. Reception hours may be restricted and payment may be required on check in. There may be associated restaurant facilities.

INN

BED AND BREAKFAST accommodation provided within a traditional inn or pub environment. A restaurant and bar will be open to non-residents and will provide restaurant or bar food at lunchtime and in the evening.

RESTAURANT WITH ROOMS

IN A RESTAURANT WITH ROOMS, the restaurant is the most significant part of the business. It is usually open to non-residents. Accommodation is available, and breakfast is usually provided.

CAMPUS ACCOMMODATION

CAMPUS ACCOMMODATION is provided by colleges and universities for their students and is made available-with meals-for individuals, families or groups at certain times of the year. These typically include the main Summer holiday period as well as Easter and Christmas.

SERVICED ACCOMMODATION

FACILITY AND SERVICE SYMBOLS

- TV in bedrooms
- Satellite/cable TV
- Tea/coffee making facilities in bedrooms
- Telephone in bedrooms
- Hairdryer in bedrooms
- Evening meal available
- Room service
- Restaurant
- Leisure facilities
- Indoor swimming pool
- Laundry service
- Porterage
- Lounge
- TV Lounge
- Full alcohol drinks license
- Restricted alcohol drinks license
- Non-smoking establishment
- Smoking restricted
- Payphone provided
- Washbasin in bedrooms
- Ensuite bath and/or shower for all bedrooms
- Ensuite bath and/or shower for some bedrooms
- Private bath and/or shower for all bedrooms
- Private bath and/or shower for some bedrooms
- Private parking
- Limited parking
- No TV

YOU NOT ONLY WANT TO BE SURE OF THE STANDARD OF ACCOMMODATION YOU CHOOSE TO STAY IN, which ever type it may be, you want to be sure you make the most of your time.

THE SCOTTISH TOURIST BOARD not only inspects every type of accommodation every year, but also a wide range of visitor attractions every second year to grade the standard of customer care provided for visitors.

THE INSPECTION SCHEME for visitor attractions provides you with the assurance that an attraction has been assessed for the condition and standard of the facilities and services provided – the warmth of welcome, efficiency of service, level of cleanliness, standard of visitor interpretation and of the toilets, restaurant and shop, if provided.

A LARGE WORLD FAMOUS CASTLE, or small local museum can attain high grades if their services for the visitor are of a high standard.

THE STANDARDS YOU CAN EXPECT.

★★★★★	**Exceptional**
★★★★	**Excellent**
★★★	**Very good**
★★	**Good**
★	**Fair and Acceptable**

IN ADDITION TO THE STAR GRADES, every attraction is categorised under one of the following types to help give the visitor an indication of the type of experience on offer:

Visitor Attraction
Castle
Historic Attraction
Museum
Tour
Garden
Activity Centre
Tourist Shop
Leisure Centre
Arts Venue
Historic House

LOOK FOR THE SCOTTISH TOURIST BOARD SIGN OF QUALITY:

VISITORS WITH PARTICULAR MOBILITY NEEDS MUST BE ABLE TO BE SECURE IN THE KNOWLEDGE THAT SUITABLE ACCOMMODATION IS AVAILABLE TO MATCH THESE REQUIREMENTS. Advance knowledge of accessible entrances, bedrooms and facilities is important to enable visitors to enjoy their stay.

ALONG WITH THE QUALITY awards which apply to all the establishments in this, and every Scottish Tourist Board guide, we operate a national accessibility scheme. By inspecting establishments to set criteria, we can identify and promote places that meet the requirements of visitors with mobility needs.

THE THREE CATEGORIES of accessibility – drawn up in close consultation with specialist organisations are:

Unassisted wheelchair access for residents

Assisted wheelchair access for residents

Access for residents with mobility difficulties

LOOK OUT FOR these symbols in establishments, in advertising and brochures. They assure you that entrances, ramps, passageways, doors, restaurant facilities, bathrooms and toilets, as well as kitchens in self catering properties, have been inspected with reference to the needs of wheelchair users, and those with mobility difficulties. Write or telephone for details of the standards in each category – address on page vii.

FOR MORE INFORMATION about travel, specialist organisations who can provide information and a list of all the Scottish accommodation which has had the access inspection write (or ask at a Tourist Information Centre) for the Scottish Tourist Board booklet "Accommodation for Visitors with Mobility Difficulties".

Holiday Care
2nd Floor
Imperial Buildings
Victoria Road
Horley
Surrey RH6 7PZ
TEL: **01293 774535**
FAX: **01293 784647**
EMAIL: **holiday.care@virgin.net**
WEB: **www.holidaycare.org.uk**

IN ADDITION, a referral service to put enquirers in touch with local disability advice centres is:

UPDATE
27 Beaverhall Road
Edinburgh
EH7 4JE
TEL: **0131 558 5200**
EMAIL: **info@update.org.uk**
WEB: **www.update.org.uk**

OVER 900 QUALITY ASSURED ACCOMMODATION PROVIDERS ARE OFFERING AN EXTRA WARM WELCOME FOR VISITORS who are cycling or walking for all, or part, of their holiday in Scotland.

AS WELL AS having had the quality of the welcome, service, food and comfort assessed by the Scottish Tourist Board, they will be able to offer the following:-

- ★ hot drink on arrival
- ★ packed lunch/flask filling option
- ★ late evening meal option
- ★ early breakfast option
- ★ drying facilities for wet clothes
- ★ local walking and/or cycling information
- ★ daily weather forecast
- ★ local public transport information
- ★ secure, lockable, covered area for bike storage
- ★ details of local cycle specialists

Walkers Welcome Scheme

Cyclists Welcome Scheme

LOOK OUT FOR the logos in this guide and other accommodation listings.

Green Tourism

IN RESPONSE TO the increasing need for businesses throughout the world to operate in an environmentally friendly way, the Scottish Tourist Board has developed the Green Tourism Business Scheme.

WHERE OWNERS OF accommodation are taking steps to reduce waste and pollution, to recycle and to be efficient with resources they are credited in this Scheme with a "Green Award". In our assessment of the degree of environmental good practice the business is demonstrating they are awarded one of the following;

BRONZE AWARD	BRONZE for achieving a satisfactory level
SILVER AWARD	SILVER for achieving a good level
GOLD AWARD	GOLD for achieving a very good level

FROM SCOTLAND'S NATURAL LARDER COMES A WEALTH OF FINE FLAVOURS.

THE SEA YIELDS crab and lobster, mussels and oysters, haddock and herring to be eaten fresh or smoked. From the lochs and rivers come salmon and trout.

SCOTCH BEEF AND LAMB, venison and game are of prime quality, often adventurously combined with local vegetables or with wild fruits such as redcurrants and brambles. Raspberries and strawberries are cultivated to add their sweetness to trifles and shortcakes, and to the home-made jams that are an essential part of Scottish afternoon tea.

THE SCOTS HAVE a sweet tooth, and love all kinds of baking – rich, crisp shortbread, scones, fruit cakes and gingerbreads. Crumbly oatcakes make the ideal partner for Scottish cheeses, which continue to develop from their ancient farming origins into new – and very successful – styles.

AND IN OVER a hundred distilleries, barley, yeast and pure spring water come together miraculously to create malt whisky – the water of life.

MANY SCOTTISH HOTELS and restaurants pride themselves on the use they make of these superb natural ingredients – around 400 are members of the Taste of Scotland Scheme which encourages the highest culinary standards, use of Scottish produce and a warm welcome to visitors. Look for the Stockpot symbol at establishments, or write to Taste of Scotland for a copy of their guide.

In Shops		**£8.99**
By Post:	**UK**	**£9.50**
	Europe	**£10.50**
	US	**£12.00**

TASTE OF SCOTLAND SCHEME
33 Melville Street
EDINBURGH, EH3 7JF
TEL: **0131 220 1900**
FAX: **0131 220 6102**
E-MAIL: **tastescotland@sol.co.uk**
WEB: **www.taste-of-scotland.com**

THE SCOTCH BEEF CLUB is an international association of restaurants of considerable repute.

THE MEMBERSHIP PROFILE is wide and varied – ranging from intimate establishments, through beautiful country houses, to city centre hotels. The membership includes 5 Star golf resorts, former vicarages, cottages, a bakehouse and even a station. Their styles are individual but what they all have in common is a recognised excellence and a commitment to using only the finest quality produce in their award winning kitchens. This commitment is demonstrated by their choice of beef – Scotch Beef.

GIVE YOURSELF a treat and try one of the Scotch Beef dishes on the menu at a Scotch Beef Club member.

SCOTLAND HAS SOME OF THE FINEST FOOD PRODUCTS IN THE WORLD. Our seafood, beef, lamb, venison, vegetables and soft fruit are renowned for their high quality. These fine indigenous raw materials and a wide assortment of international food products are skillfully combined by cooks and chefs into the vast range of cuisine available in Scotland.

AS YOU TRAVEL throughout the country you will find an excellent standard of cooking in all sorts of establishments from restaurants with imaginative menus to tea rooms with simple wholesome home-baking.

YOU WILL FIND some of these culinary gems by reading of their reputation in newspapers and magazines, from advice given by Tourist Information Centre staff, by looking for the Taste of Scotland logo, or by using your own instinct to discover them yourself.

THE SCOTTISH TOURIST BOARD has recognised that it would be helpful to you, the visitor, to have some assurance of the standards of food available in every different type of eating establishment; and indeed to be able to find a consistent standard of food in every place you choose to eat.

WE LAUNCHED THE NATURAL COOKING of Scotland as a long-term initiative to encourage eating places to follow the lead of those who are best in their field in providing a consistently high standard of catering.

WE HAVE HARNESSED the skills of chefs, the experience of restaurateurs and the expertise of catering trainers to introduce a series of cooking skills courses which will encourage the use of fresh, local produce, cooked in a simple and satisfying way. We are providing advice and guidance to eating places throughout Scotland on high quality catering and the skills involved in efficient food service and customer care. Many more initiatives are being planned to support this enhancement of Scottish cooking standards and a high dependency on the food available on our own doorsteps.

WHILST YOU WILL appreciate the food experiences you will find in eating your way around Scotland this year, the Natural Cooking of Scotland will ensure that the profile of fine Scottish cooking is even greater in future years.

SCOTLAND IS A SMALL COUNTRY AND TRAVEL IS EASY. There are direct air links with UK cities, with Europe and North America. There is also an internal air network bringing the islands of the North and West within easy reach.

SCOTLAND'S RAIL NETWORK not only includes excellent cross-border InterCity services but also a good internal network. All major towns are linked by rail and there are also links to the western seaboard at Mallaig and Kyle of Lochalsh (for ferry connections to Skye and the Western Isles) and to Inverness, Thurso and Wick for ferries to Orkney and Shetland.

ALL THE USUAL DISCOUNT CARDS are valid but there are also ScotRail Rovers (multi journey tickets allowing you to save on rail fares) and the Freedom of Scotland Travelpass, a combined rail and ferry pass allowing unlimited travel on ferry services to the islands and all of the rail network. In addition Travelpass also offers discounts on bus services and some air services.

INTERCITY SERVICES are available from all major centres, for example: Birmingham, Carlisle, Crewe, Manchester, Newcastle, Penzance, Peterborough, Preston, Plymouth, York and many others.

THERE ARE FREQUENT InterCity departures from Kings Cross and Euston stations to Edinburgh and Glasgow. The journey time from Kings Cross to Edinburgh is around 4 hours and from Euston to Glasgow around 5 hours.

COACH CONNECTIONS include express services to Scotland from all over the UK; local bus companies in Scotland offer explorer tickets and discount cards. Postbuses (normally minibuses) take passengers on over 130 rural routes throughout Scotland.

FERRIES TO AND AROUND the islands are regular and reliable, most ferries carry vehicles, although some travelling to smaller islands convey only passengers.

CONTACT the Information Department, Scottish Tourist Board, 23 Ravelston Terrace, Edinburgh EH4 3TP, or any Tourist Information Centre, for details of travel and transport.

MANY VISITORS CHOOSE to see Scotland by road – distances are short and driving on the quiet roads of the Highlands is a new and different experience. In remoter areas, some roads are still single track,and passing places must be used. When vehicles approach from different directions, the car nearest to a passing place must stop in or opposite it. Please do not use passing places to park in!

SPEED LIMITS ON Scottish roads:
Dual carriageways 70mph/112kph;
single carriageways 60mph/96kph;
built-up areas 30mph/48kph.

THE DRIVER AND front-seat passenger in a car must wear seatbelts; rear seatbelts, if fitted, must be used. Small children and babies must at all times be restrained in a child seat or carrier.

OPENING TIMES

PUBLIC HOLIDAYS: Christmas and New Year's Day are holidays in Scotland, taken by almost everyone. Scottish banks, and many offices, may close in 2001 on 1 and 2 January, 13 and 16th April, 7 and 28th May, 27th August. Scottish towns also take Spring and Autumn holidays which may vary from place to place, but are usually on a Monday.

BANKING HOURS: In general, banks open Monday to Friday, 0930 to 1600, with some closing later on a Thursday. Banks in cities, particularly in or near the main shopping centres, may be open at weekends. Cash machines in hundreds of branches allow you to withdraw cash outside banking hours, using the appropriate cards.

PUBS AND RESTAURANTS: Pubs and restaurants are allowed to serve alcoholic drinks between 1100 hours and 2300 hours Monday through to Saturday; Sundays 1230 hours until 1430 hours then again from 1830 hours until 2300 hours.

RESIDENTS IN HOTELS may have drinks served at any time, subject to the proprietors discretion.

EXTENDED LICENSING HOURS are subject to local council applications.

TELEPHONE CODES

IF YOU ARE CALLING from abroad, first dial your own country's international access code (usually 00, but do please check). Next, dial the UK code, 44, then the area code except for the first 0, then the remainder of the number as normal.

QUARANTINE REGULATIONS

IF YOU ARE COMING to Scotland from overseas, please do not attempt to bring your pet on holiday with you. British quarantine regulations are stringently enforced, and anyone attempting to contravene them will incur severe penalties as well as the loss of the animal.

SCOTLAND ON THE NET

VISIT OUR WEB SITE AT:

www.visitscotland.com

"THE SCOTTISH TOURIST BOARD IS COMMITTED TO ENSURING THAT OUR NATURAL ENVIRONMENT, UPON WHICH OUR TOURISM IS SO DEPENDANT, IS SAFEGUARDED FOR FUTURE GENERATIONS TO ENJOY."

ACCOMMODATION

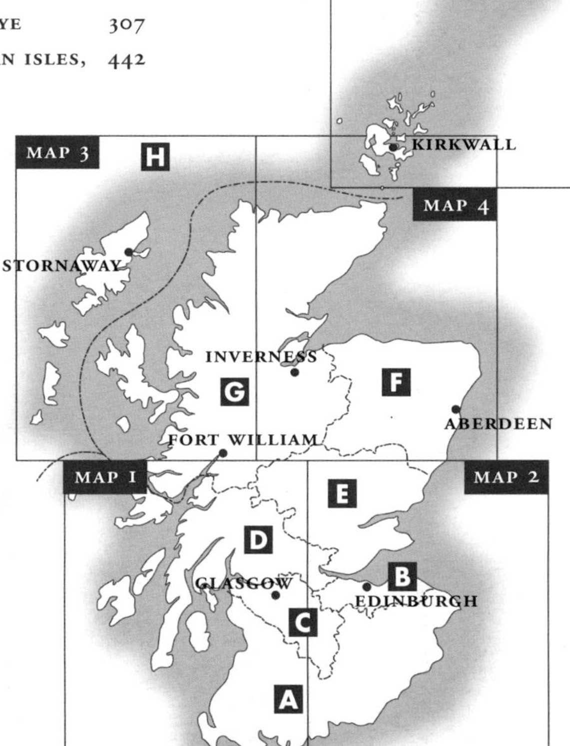

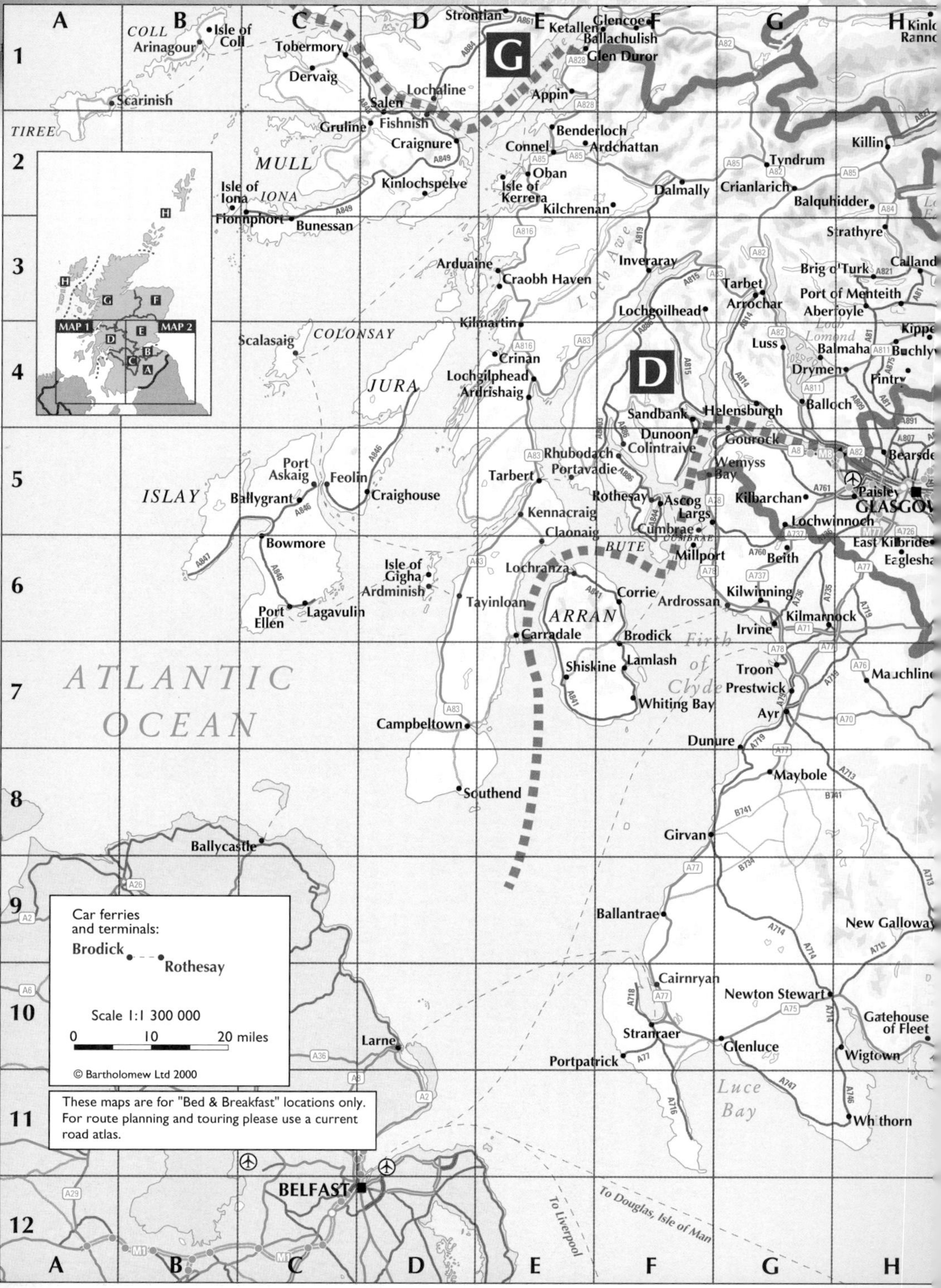

Car ferries and terminals:
Brodick
Rothesay
Scale 1:1 300 000
0 10 20 miles
© Bartholomew Ltd 2000
These maps are for "Bed & Breakfast" locations only. For route planning and touring please use a current road atlas.
MAP 1
MAP 2
ATLANTIC OCEAN
COLL
Arinagour
Isle of Coll
Scarinish
TIREE
MULL
Isle of Iona
IONA
Fionnphort
Bunessan
Tobermory
Dervaig
Salen
Gruline
Fishnish
Lochaline
Craignure
Kinlochspelve
Strontian
Ketallen
Glencoe
Ballachulish
Glen Duror
Appin
Benderloch
Connel
Ardchattan
Oban
Isle of Kerrera
Kilchrenan
Dalmally
Tyndrum
Crianlarich
Killin
Balquhidder
Strathyre
Callander
Brig o'Turk
Port of Menteith
Aberfoyle
Arduaine
Craobh Haven
Inveraray
Loch Awe
Lochgoilhead
Tarbet
Arrochar
Kilmartin
Crinan
Lochgilphead
Ardrishaig
Scalasaig
COLONSAY
JURA
Luss
Loch Lomond
Balmaha
Buchlyvie
Drymen
Fintry
Balloch
Sandbank
Helensburgh
Dunoon
Colintraive
Gourock
Rhubodach
Portavadie
Wemyss Bay
Tarbert
Rothesay
Ascog
Largs
Kilbarchan
Paisley
GLASGOW
Bearsden
Lochwinnoch
Port Askaig
Feolin
ISLAY
Ballygrant
Craighouse
Kennacraig
Claonaig
Cumbrae
Millport
BUTE
Bowmore
Beith
East Kilbride
Eaglesham
Isle of Gigha
Ardminish
Lochranza
Corrie
Ardrossan
Kilwinning
Tayinloan
ARRAN
Kilmarnock
Port Ellen
Lagavulin
Carradale
Brodick
Irvine
Lamlash
Shiskine
Firth of Clyde
Troon
Prestwick
Mauchline
Whiting Bay
Ayr
Campbeltown
Dunure
Maybole
Southend
Girvan
Ballycastle
Ballantrae
New Galloway
Cairnryan
Newton Stewart
Gatehouse of Fleet
Stranraer
Glenluce
Portpatrick
Wigtown
Larne
Luce Bay
Whithorn
BELFAST
To Liverpool
To Douglas, Isle of Man

A
B
C
D
E
F
G
H
1
2
3
4
5
6
7
8
9
10
11
12
Pitlochry
Grandtully
Aberfeldy
Dunkeld
Bridge of Cally
Blairgowrie
Alyth
Kirriemuir
Forfar
Glamis
Letham
Coupar Angus
Monikie
Arbroath
Carnoustie
Bankfoot
Stanley
Dundee
Broughty Ferry
NORTH SEA
Firth of Tay
E
Comrie
Crieff
Perth
Bridge of Earn
Forgandenny
Newburgh
Dairsie
Leuchars
Guardbridge
St Andrews
Auchterarder
Abernethy
Strathkinness
Kingsbarns
Ladybank
Peat Inn
Crail
Milnathort
Kinross
Falkland
Markinch
Lundin Links
Anstruther
St Monans
Leven
Dunblane
Blairlogie
Dollar
Tillicoultry
Ballingry
Firth of Forth
Kirkcaldy
Kinghorn
Burntisland
Dunfermline
Inverkeithing
Aberdour
Dalgety Bay
Limekilns
North Queensferry
South Queensferry
Falkirk
Linlithgow
Kilsyth
Gullane
Aberlady
North Berwick
Longniddry
East Linton
Dunbar
Winchburgh
Broxburn
EDINBURGH
Musselburgh
Haddington
Tranent
B
St Abbs
Eyemouth
Airdrie
East Calder
Lasswade
Harthill
Blackburn
Roslin
Abbey St Bathans
Ayton
Penicuik
Duns
Berwick-upon-Tweed
Motherwell
Hamilton
West Linton
C
Lauder
Greenlaw
Lanark
Peebles
Earlston
Biggar
Skirling
Galashiels
Melrose
Kelso
Yarrow
Selkirk
St Boswells
Abington
Jedburgh
Hawick
Moffat
A
Thornhill
Langholm
Lochmaben
Lockerbie
Dumfries
Ecclefechan
Annan
Gretna
Newcastle upon Tyne
Sunderland
Dalbeattie
Kippford
Auchencairn
Carlisle
Solway Firth
Middlesbrough

MAP 3

These maps are for "Bed & Breakfast" locations only. For route planning and touring please use a current road atlas.
MAP 3
MAP 4
OUTER HEBRIDES
LEWIS
HARRIS
NORTH UIST
BENBECULA
SOUTH UIST
BARRA
SKYE
RAASAY
CANNA
RUM
EIGG
MUCK
ARDNAMURCHAN
ASSYNT
The Minch
Loch Morar
Loch Lochy
Barvas
Gress
Back
Tolsta Chaolais
Breascleit
Stornoway
Melbost
Callanish
Aignish
Achmore
Tarbert
Scaristavore
Leverburgh
Berneray
Otternish
Lochmaddy
Grimsay
Kilaulay
Kilpheder
Lochboisdale
Ludag
Eriskay
North Bay
Castlebay
Kilmuir
Staffin
Uig
Waternish
Glenhinnisdale
Suladale
Kingsburgh
Treaslane
Bernisdale
Dunvegan
Portree
Penifiler
Struan
Raasay
Carbost
Sconser
Broadford
Elgol
Armadale
Ord
Sleat
Breakish
Kylerhea
Kyleakin
Glenelg
Kyle of Lochalsh
Plockton
Duirinish
Dornie
Achmore
Kishorn
Lochcarron
Strathcarron
Shieldaig
Diabaig
Torridon
Kinlochewe
Achnasheen
Loch Maree
Gairloch
Poolewe
Aultbea
Laide
Dundonnell
Ullapool
Stoer
Lochinver
Scourie
Mallaig
Morar
Arisaig
Acharacle
Kilchoan
Tomacharich
Corpach
Banavie
Fort William
Kinlochleven
Onich
Invergarry
Canni
A857
A858
A859
A865
A867
A888
A87
A850
A855
A863
A851
A830
A861
A832
A835
A837
A838
A894
A890
A896
A82
A B C D E F G H
1 2 3 4 5 6 7 8 9 10 11 12

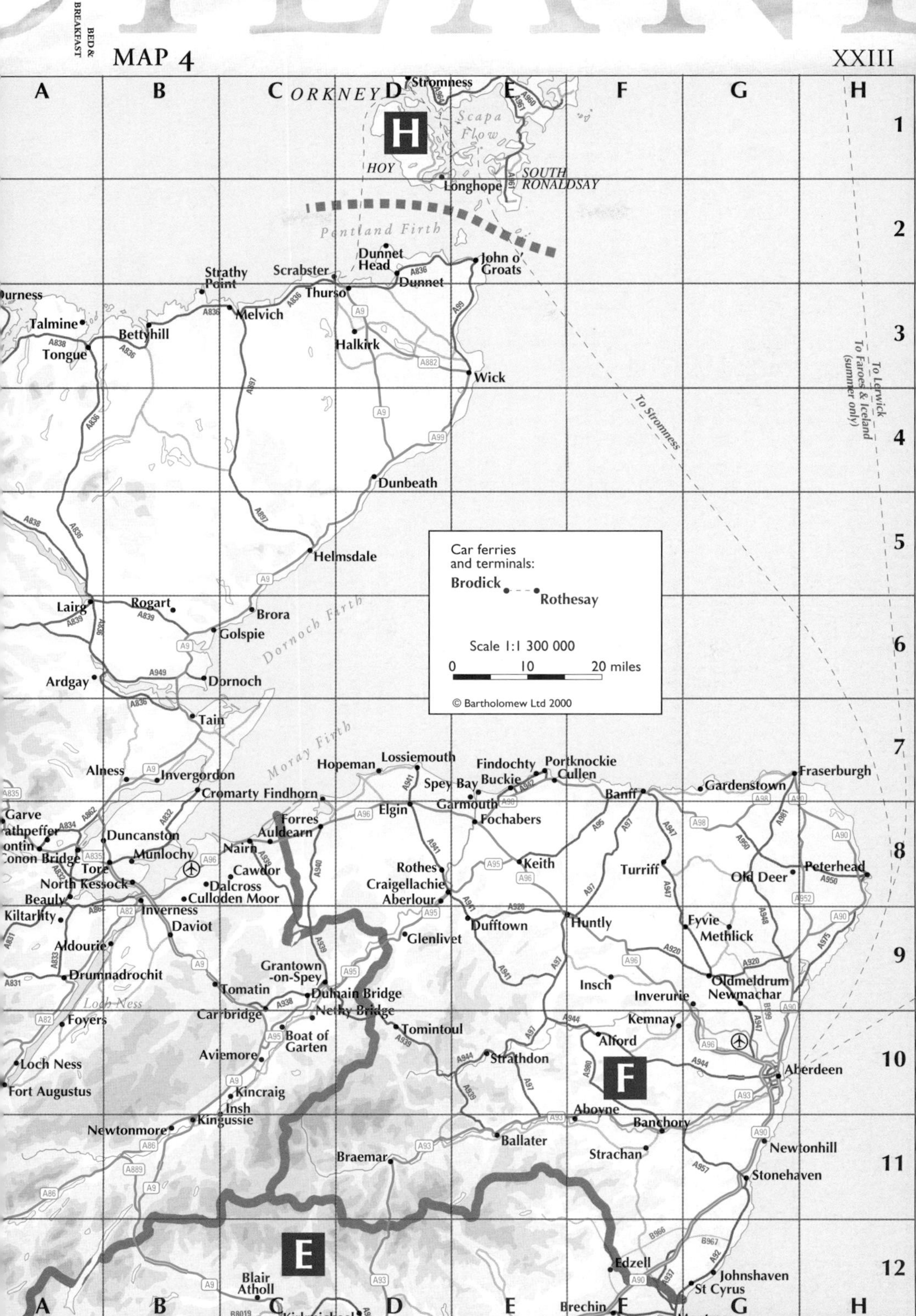
ORKNEY
Stromness
Scapa Flow
HOY
Longhope
SOUTH RONALDSAY
H
Pentland Firth
Dunnet Head
Dunnet
John o' Groats
Scrabster
Thurso
Strathy Point
Melvich
Durness
Talmine
Tongue
Bettyhill
Halkirk
Wick
Dunbeath
Helmsdale
Lairg
Rogart
Brora
Golspie
Dornoch Firth
Ardgay
Dornoch
Tain
To Stromness
To Lerwick
To Faroes & Iceland (summer only)
Car ferries and terminals:
Brodick
Rothesay
Scale 1:1 300 000
0
10
20 miles
© Bartholomew Ltd 2000
Moray Firth
Alness
Invergordon
Cromarty
Findhorn
Hopeman
Lossiemouth
Findochty
Portknockie
Cullen
Buckie
Spey Bay
Garmouth
Banff
Gardenstown
Fraserburgh
Garve
Strathpeffer
Contin
Conon Bridge
Duncanston
Munlochy
Tore
North Kessock
Beauly
Kiltarlity
Inverness
Nairn
Auldearn
Forres
Elgin
Fochabers
Cawdor
Dalcross
Culloden Moor
Daviot
Rothes
Craigellachie
Aberlour
Keith
Turriff
Old Deer
Peterhead
Dufftown
Huntly
Fyvie
Methlick
Glenlivet
Aldourie
Drumnadrochit
Loch Ness
Grantown-on-Spey
Tomatin
Dulnain Bridge
Nethy Bridge
Carrbridge
Boat of Garten
Tomintoul
Insch
Inverurie
Oldmeldrum
Newmachar
Kemnay
Alford
Foyers
Aviemore
Strathdon
Aberdeen
F
Loch Ness
Fort Augustus
Kincraig
Insh
Kingussie
Newtonmore
Aboyne
Banchory
Ballater
Braemar
Strachan
Newtonhill
Stonehaven
E
Edzell
Johnshaven
St Cyrus
Blair Atholl
Kirkmichael
Brechin
Montrose
A
B
C
D
E
F
G
H
1
2
3
4
5
6
7
8
9
10
11
12

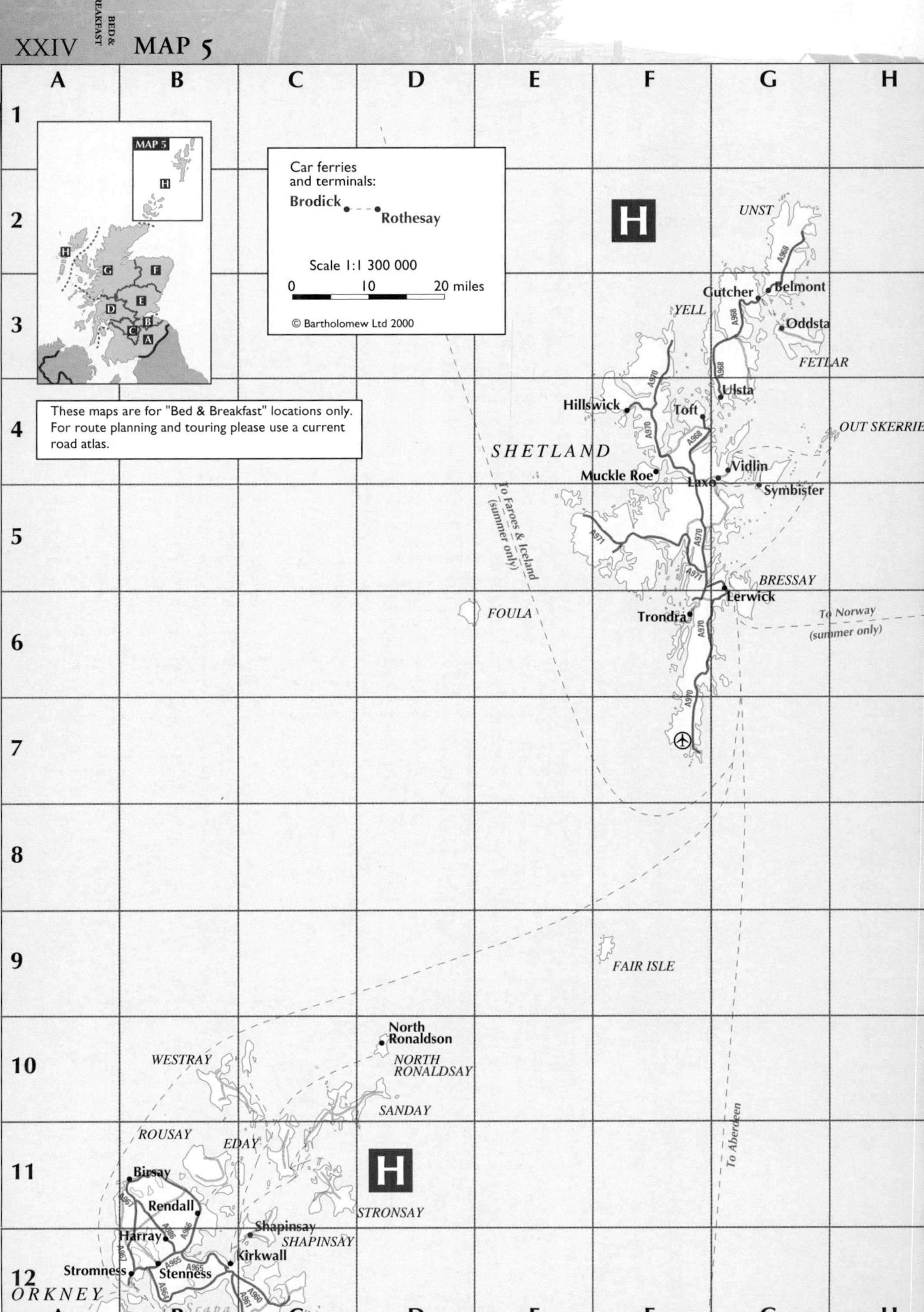

A B C D E F G H
1 2 3 4 5 6 7 8 9 10 11 12
MAP 5
H
G F E D B C A
Car ferries and terminals:
Brodick Rothesay
Scale 1:1 300 000
0 10 20 miles
© Bartholomew Ltd 2000
These maps are for "Bed & Breakfast" locations only. For route planning and touring please use a current road atlas.
UNST
Belmont
Cutcher
YELL
Oddsta
FETLAR
Ulsta
Hillswick
Toft
OUT SKERRIES
SHETLAND
Vidlin
Muckle Roe
Laxo
Symbister
To Faroes & Iceland (summer only)
BRESSAY
Lerwick
FOULA
Trondra
To Norway (summer only)
FAIR ISLE
North Ronaldson
NORTH RONALDSAY
WESTRAY
SANDAY
ROUSAY
EDAY
To Aberdeen
Birsay
Rendall
STRONSAY
Shapinsay
SHAPINSAY
Harray
Kirkwall
Stromness
Stenness
ORKNEY
Scapa Flow
A968 A970 A971 A965 A966 A986 A967 A964 A961 A960

SCOTLAND

BED & BREAKFAST

The Official
Where to stay guide
2001

SCOTLAND'S SOUTH WEST OFFERS A BEAUTIFUL AND UNCROWDED LANDSCAPE WHERE YOU CAN ENJOY A REAL FEELING OF SPACE.

River Tweed near Peebles

HERE YOU WILL find over 400 miles of the National Cycle network plus superb golf courses. There is also great walking country to be found, including the 212 mile coast-to-coast Southern Upland Way. This long-distance footpath begins in Portpatrick, goes through the Galloway Forest Park – the largest in Britain – then it crosses the Moffat Hills before it heads into the Scottish Borders. Back on the south-west coast, the tidal mudflats and sandy beaches of the Solway Firth are dotted with attractive villages and seaside towns including Kirkcudbright, with it's long artistic tradition as well as a thriving current arts scene. Dumfries is the main town in the region. Sometimes known as Queen of the South, this handsome red sandstone town has strong associations with Robert Burns. Other outstanding attractions are Caerlaverock Castle with four bird reserves nearby, Gretna Green and the Famous Old Blacksmith's Shop Visitor Centre, Threave Gardens and its new Countryside Centre, Wigtown (now a celebrated 'Book Town') and Sweetheart Abbey.

THE AYRSHIRE COAST has some excellent holiday attractions for all the family, including Vikingar! in Largs, and The Big Idea and the Magnum Leisure Centre both at Irvine Harbourside. For those interested in Scotland's national poet, Robert Burns, you can visit many attractions including his birthplace in Alloway. And you can relive some of his dramatic life at the Tam O' Shanter Experience. Less than an hour's sail will take you to the Isle of Arran which offers fine mountains, quiet beaches, the famous Brodick Castle and the Isle of Arran Distillery, Scotland's newest. For those who prefer a sporting holiday, the region offers horse-racing and football, while with over forty golf courses, golf is one of the biggest attractions. There are world famous courses at Troon, Turnberry and Prestwick.

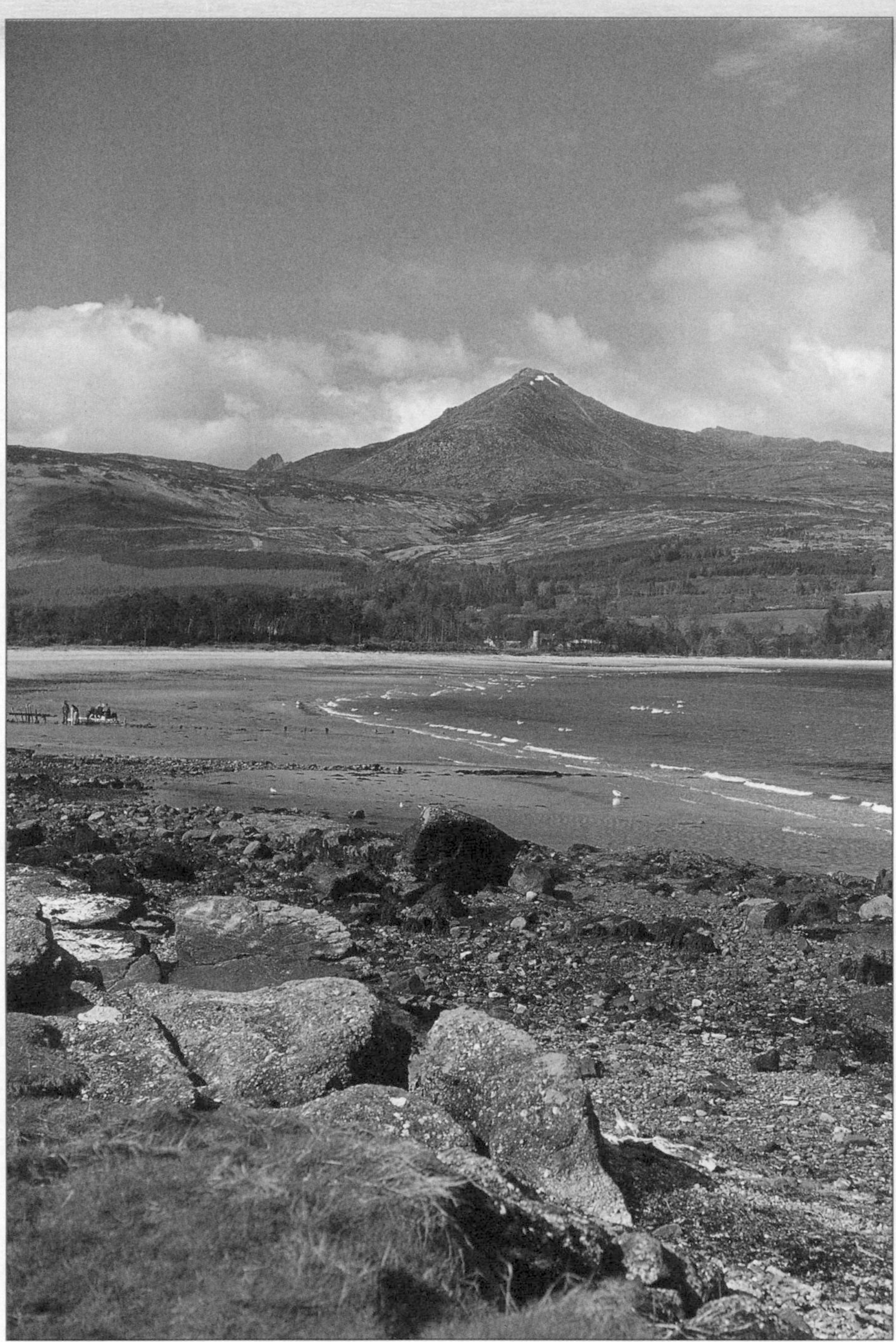

Goat Fell, seen from Brodick, Isle of Arran

Quiet road near New Galloway, Dumfries and Galloway

FIRST IMPRESSIONS of the Scottish Borders are of a surprisingly wild area, though river valleys with their woodlands and farms soon give a softer appearance. These borderlands were fought over until the 17th century and as a result there are many magnificent ruined abbeys and towered castles to visit.

There are also many fine stately homes such as the magnificent Edwardian mansion of Manderston and the superb Georgian house of Mellerstain. Market towns such as Kelso, Selkirk, Hawick and Melrose offer good shopping and accommodation facilities.

Close by are the magnificent ruins of Melrose Abbey and the distinctive triple peaks of the Eildon Hills, a landmark for miles around.

Below is the Tweed, one of Scotland's most famous salmon-fishing rivers. Sir Walter Scott's fascinating home of Abbotsford and the secluded Dryburgh Abbey where he is buried are just a few of the fascinating historical sites throughout this region.

The colourful past of the border towns is brought to life each year when the local residents re-enact the Common Ridings by dressing up in period costume and riding around the burgh boundaries. The landscape to the east is a beautiful mosaic of farmland and finally ends at the dramatic cliffs of St Abbs, a favourite place for bird watching.

EVENTS
SOUTH OF SCOTLAND (AYRSHIRE AND ARRAN, DUMFRIES AND GALLOWAY, SCOTTISH BORDERS)

14 APRIL
Venue-Arran
Isle of Arran Rugby Sevens
Annual Rugby Tournament.
TEL: **01770 302565**

*25 MAY-3 JUNE
Dumfries & Galloway Arts Festival
Various venues,
Dumfries & Galloway
Unique Arts Festival with various events.
Contact: Mrs Ruth Bell
TEL: **01387 260447**

9-16 JUNE
Guid Nychburris
Various venues, Dumfries
Annual burgh festival with street entertainment's, annual ride out and crowning of the Queen.
Contact: Stanley McEwen
TEL: **01387 254952**

15 JUNE
Selkirk Common Riding
Town Centre, Selkirk
The battle of Flodden in 1513 is commemorated with the casting of colours in the town market place plus the traditional riding of the marches.
Contact: Allan Douglas
TEL: **01750 21954**

9-14 JULY
Ayrshire Golf Classic
Various courses including the Ailsa Craig Course, Turnberry
4 day amateur golf event.
Contact: Celtic Links
TEL: **01292 671500**
EMAIL:
info@ayrshiregolfclassic.co.uk

16-27 AUGUST
Marymass Festival
Various venues, Irvine
Traditional festival featuring activities for all ages, including folk and other music events.
TEL: **01294 324482**

*
MID AUGUST - SEPTEMBER
Gaelforce
Various venues,
Dumfries & Galloway
Arts festival celebrating Scottish and Irish culture, featuring music, dance, theatre, exhibitions and much more.
Contact: Gracefield Arts Centre
TEL: **01387 262084**

8-15 SEPTEMBER
Borders Walking Festival
West Linton, Scottish Borders
Choice of guided walks each day plus evening entertainment.
Contact: Walking Development Officer, Tweed Horizons
TEL: **01835 824632**

*9-10 JUNE
Prestwick International Airshow
Prestwick Airport
2 day international airshow with the Red Arrows, parachute display teams, wing walkers, jet fighters, funfair and public catering.
Contact: The Airshow Office
TEL: **07769 974050**

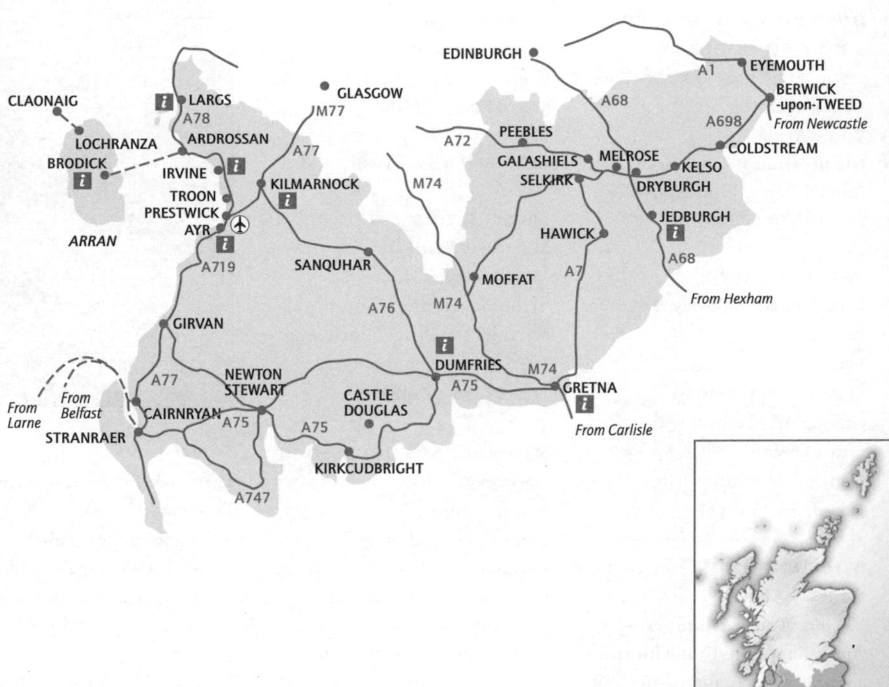

AYRSHIRE AND ARRAN TOURIST BOARD
Ayr Tourist Information Centre
22 Sandgate
AYR
KA7 1BW Jan – Dec

TEL: **01 292 28 86 88**
FAX: **01 292 28 86 86**
www.ayrshire-arran.com

DUMFRIES AND GALLOWAY TOURIST BOARD
64 Whitesands
Dumfries
DG1 2RS

TEL: **01 387 25 38 62**
FAX: **01 387 24 55 31**
www.dumfriesandgalloway.co.uk

SCOTTISH BORDERS TOURIST BOARD
Tourist Information Centre
Murray's Green
Jedburgh TD8 6BE

TEL: **08 70 60 70 250** (Brochure)
01 835 86 40 99 (Information)
FAX: **01 835 86 40 99**
www.scot-borders.co.uk

AYRSHIRE AND ARRAN TOURIST BOARD

AYR
22 Sandgate
TEL: **(01292) 288688**
Jan-Dec

BRODICK
The Pier
Isle of Arran
TEL: **(01770) 302140/302401**
Jan-Dec

GIRVAN
Bridge Street
TEL: **(01465) 714950**
Easter-Oct

IRVINE
New Street
TEL: **(01294) 313886**
Jan-Dec

KILMARNOCK
62 Bank Street
TEL: **(01563) 539090**
Jan-Dec

LARGS
Promenade
TEL: **(01475) 673765**
Jan-Dec

MILLPORT
28 Stuart Street
Isle of Cumbrae
TEL: **(01475) 530753**
Easter-Oct

DUMFRIES AND GALLOWAY TOURIST BOARD

CASTLE DOUGLAS
Markethill Car Park
TEL: **(01556) 502611**
Easter-Oct

DUMFRIES
Whitesands
TEL: **(01387) 253862**
Jan-Dec

GATEHOUSE OF FLEET
Car Park
TEL: **(01557) 814212**
Easter-Oct

GRETNA GREEN
Old Blacksmith's Shop
TEL: **(01461) 337834**

KIRKCUDBRIGHT
Harbour Square
TEL: **(01557) 330494**
Easter-end Oct

MOFFAT
Ladyknowe
TEL: **(01683) 220620**
Easter-end Oct

NEWTON STEWART
Dashwood Square
TEL: **(01671) 402431**
Easter-Oct

STRANRAER
Burns House
28 Harbour Street
TEL: **(01776) 702595**
Jan-Dec

SCOTTISH BORDERS TOURIST BOARD

COLDSTREAM
High Street
TEL: **(01890) 882607**
Easter-Oct

EYEMOUTH
Auld Kirk, Manse Road
TEL: **(018907) 50678**
April-Oct

GALASHIELS
St John Street
TEL: **(01896) 755551**
Easter-Oct

HAWICK
Drumlanrig's Tower
TEL: **(01450) 372547**
Easter-Oct

JEDBURGH
Murray's Green
TEL: **(01835) 863435/863688**
Jan-Dec

KELSO
Town House, The Square
TEL: **(01573) 223464**
Easter-Oct

MELROSE
Abbey House
TEL: **(01896) 822555**
Easter-Oct

PEEBLES
High Street
TEL: **(01721) 720138**
Jan-Dec

SELKIRK
Halliwell's House
TEL: **(01750) 20054**
Easter-Oct

Abbey St Bathans, by Duns, Berwickshire

Map Ref: 2E5

★★★ B&B

Quixwood Farmhouse

Abbey St.Bathans, Duns, Berwickshire, TD11 3RS
Tel: 01361 840233 Fax: 01361 840223

1 Family, 1 Twin | 1 En Suite fac, 1 Priv.NOT ensuite | B&B per person from £20.00 Single | Open Jan-Dec; B&B + Eve.Meal from £30.00

Spacious accommodation on working farm in rural peace and tranquility yet only 2.5 miles from A1. Easy access to coast, Edinburgh and all attractions of the Borders. Evening meals by arrangement.

C V

by Annan, Dumfriesshire

Map Ref: 2C10

★★★ B&B

Mrs M K Forrest, Hurkledale

Cummertrees, by Annan, Dumfriesshire, DG12 5QA
Tel: 01461 700228
E-mail: marykforrest@hotmail.com

1 Twin, 1 Double, 1 Family | 2 En Suite fac, 1 Priv.NOT ensuite | B&B per person from £22.00 Dbl/Twn | Open Jan-Dec excl Xmas/New Year; B&B + Eve.Meal from £32.00

Traditional farmhouse within a working farm on the outskirts of Cumertrees village, located 4 miles (6kms) from Annan. The area is steeped in history, Ruthwell Cross and the Savings Bank Museum are nearby. Birdwatching at Caerlaverock, golf at Powfoot and fishing on the River Annan. Solway Firth 1/4 mile. Evening meals by prior arrangement.

TV P

C W V

Brodick, Isle of Arran

Map Ref: 1F7

★★★ GUEST HOUSE

Allandale House

Brodick, Isle of Arran, KA27 8BJ
Tel: 01770 302278

1 Single, 1 Twin, 1 Double, 3 Family | 5 En Suite fac, 1 Priv.NOT ensuite | B&B per person £20.00-£26.00 Single, £20.00-£26.00 Dbl/Twn; Room only £18.00-£24.00 | Open 20Jan-Oct; B&B + Eve.Meal £34.00-£38.00

Comfortable guest house in south facing postion with well laid out garden, on the outskirts of Brodick. Only a few minutes walk from the ferry and Brodick centre yet in a peaceful location. Some ground floor annexe accommodation.

TV P

C V

Carrick Lodge

Brodick, Isle of Arran, KA27 8BH
Tel/Fax: 01770 302550

1 Single, 2 Twin, 2 Double, 1 Family | 5 En Suite fac, 1 Priv.NOT ensuite | B&B per person from £22.00 Single, from £22.00 Dbl/Twn; Room only per person from £18.00 | Open Feb-Oct

Lovely old red sandstone listed building with panoramic views of Brodick bay. Warm and friendly welcome with comfortable bedrooms. Central to all areas of Arran and only minutes from ferry terminal.

TV P

V

Brodick, Isle of Arran Map Ref: 1F7

GLEN CLOY FARMHOUSE

Glen Cloy, Brodick, Isle of Arran KA27 8DA
Tel: 01770 302351
e.mail: mvpglencloy@compuserve.com
Web: www.SmoothHound.co.uk/hotels/glencloy.html

Glen Cloy Farmhouse is situated in a peaceful glen just outside Brodick. Golf, castle and mountains nearby. Our bedrooms are comfortably furnished with tea and coffee making facilities and homemade shortbread. There is a large, cosy drawing room with an extensive library, and a bright dining room with glorious views where you can enjoy a farmhouse tea, and breakfast using home produced preserves, free range eggs from our hens and locally produced bacon and sausages.

Recommended by The Good Bed and Breakfast Guide.

GUEST HOUSE

Glen Cloy Farmhouse

Glen Cloy Road, Brodick, Isle of Arran, KA27 8DA
Tel: 01770 302351
E.mail: mvpglencloy@compuserve.com
Web: www.SmoothHound.co.uk/hotels/glencloy.html

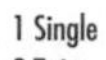

1 Single, 2 Twin, 2 Double

2 En Suite fac, 1 Pub Bath/Show

B&B per person from £22.00 Single, £22.00-£27.00 Dbl/Twn

Open Jan-Dec

Farmhouse full of character set in peaceful glen with views of hills and sea. Within easy reach of Brodick ferry. Mark and Vicki produce memorable breakfasts with homemade jams and bread, and eggs from their own hens. Embroidery courses held in spring and autumn.

SMALL HOTEL

Ormidale Hotel

Brodick, Isle of Arran, KA27 8BY
Tel: 01770 302293 Fax: 01770 302098
E-mail: reception@ormidale-hotel.co.uk
Web: www.ormidale-hotel.co.uk

1 Single, 3 Twin, 2 Double, 1 Fam/Trpl

4 En Suite fac, 1 Pub Bath/Show

B&B per person from £23.00 Single, from £23.00 Dbl/Twn. Room only per person from £18.00

Open Mar-Oct

Family run, set in mature woodland by the golf course. Excellent home cooked bar meals, children welcome. CAMRA approved. Good pub atmosphere.

B&B

Mrs Raeburn

Crovie, Corriegills, Brodick, Isle of Arran, KA27 8BL

1 Twin, 1 Double

1 Pub Bath/Show

B&B per person from £17.00 Single, from £17.00 Dbl/Twn. Room only per person from £15.00

Open Mar-Oct

Crovie is situated one mile from Brodick in Corriegills in a quiet location with panoramic views over the Firth of Clyde and Arran hills. Comfortable lounge with colour TV. Personal supervision and a warm Scottish welcome. No smoking in bedrooms.

Brodick, Isle of Arran

Map Ref: 1F7

★★ GUEST HOUSE

Tigh-na-Mara
The Seafront, Brodick, Isle of Arran, KA27 8AN
Tel: 01770 302538 Fax: 01770 302546
E-mail: arran.tighnamara@btinternet.com

2 Twin 5 Double 2 Family	2 En Suite fac 3 Pub Bath/Show	B&B per person from £18.00 Single from £18.00 Dbl/Twn	Open Jan-Dec

Personally supervised Guest House in a central position on the sea front, close to all amenities and good eating places. It has views over Brodick Bay to Goat Fell, a 5 minute walk from ferry terminal. There is a large Residents Lounge and dining area which both enjoy magnificent scenery over the bay. There is a ground floor double ensuite bedroom. Visa and Mastercard are accepted. Friendly welcome assured.

TV C £ V

Corrie, Isle of Arran

Map Ref: 1F6

★★ GUEST HOUSE

Blackrock Guest House
Corrie, Isle of Arran, KA27 8JP
Tel: 01770 810282

2 Single 1 Twin 1 Double 4 Family	3 En Suite fac 1 Pub Bath/Show	B&B per person from £18.00 Single from £18.00 Dbl/Twn	Open Mar-Nov

Where the mountains meet the sea... that is where we are, on the outskirts of 'the Prettiest village in Europe'. Come and enjoy our traditional Scottish guesthouse, established on shore edge in the 1930's. Ensuite accommodation; panoramic views; natural garden; red squirrels; otters and birdlife. Groups welcome – constant hot water. Boat Hire.

C

Lamlash, Isle of Arran

Map Ref: 1F7

★★ B&B

E Sloan
Westfield
Lamlash, Isle of Arran, KA27 8NN
Tel: 01770 600428

2 Single 1 Twin 1 Double	1 Pub Bath/Show	B&B per person from £16.00 Single from £16.00 Dbl/Twn	Open Jan-Dec

Small friendly, traditional Arran house on south side of village with secluded garden for guests' use and views to the hills. Close to all village amenities such as tennis, bowling green and shops. The Lamlash golf club is one mile away. Self catering also available.

P W V

Shiskine, Isle of Arran

Map Ref: 1E7

★★★ B&B

Glengarrion
Shiskine, Isle of Arran, KA27 8EP
Tel/Fax: 01770 860424
E-mail: sandra.judge@tesco.net

1 Twin	All En Suite	B&B per person from £18.00 Single	Open Mar-Oct

Detached bungalow in centre of quiet village with picturesque country views across the Shiskine valley and Machrie Moor. Accommodation on ground floor level. Ideally situated for golf, walking and cycling. Blackwaterfoot village is 1 1/2 miles away.

TV P V

Whiting Bay, Isle of Arran

Map Ref: 1F7

★★★ SMALL HOTEL

Burlington Hotel & Licensed Restaurant
Shore Road, Whiting Bay, Isle of Arran, KA27 8PZ
Tel: 01770 700255 Fax: 0374 595327
E-mail: burlhotel@aol.com
Web: www.milford.co.uk/scotland/accom/h-a-1737.html

2 Single 3 Twin 4 Double	8 En Suite fac 1 Priv.NOT ensuite	B&B per person £27.00-£37.00 Single £25.00-£34.00 Dbl/Twn Room only per person £19.00-£30.00	Open Apr-Oct B&B + Eve.Meal £40.00-£53.00

Enjoy the Arran experience and traditional Scottish hospitality in this seafront Edwardian Hotel. A delightful culinary experience using local produce organically orientated. Fine wines specially selected from international lists. A member of the Arran Taste Trail.

TV P C £ V

Important: Prices stated are estimates and may be subject to amendments

Whiting Bay, Isle of Arran

Map Ref: 1F7

GUEST HOUSE

View Bank House
Golf Course Road, Whiting Bay, Isle of Arran, KA27 8QT
Tel/Fax: 01770 700326

1 Single, 1 Twin, 2 Double, 3 Family | 4 En Suite fac, 2 Pub Bath/Show | B&B per person from £20.00 Single from £20.00 Dbl/Twn | Open Jan-Dec excl Xmas/New Year B&B + Eve.Meal from £32.00

Beautifully privately owned house where you can relax and enjoy superb home cooked fresh food, large garden with magnificent views across the Clyde. 500 yards down a country lane brings you onto the shore. Open most of the year with full central heating and warm atmosphere. Viewbank charms its guests back time and time again.

C V

Auchencairn, by Castle Douglas, Kirkcudbrightshire

Map Ref: 2A10

B&B

Mrs Bardsley
The Rossan, Auchencairn, by Castle Douglas, Kirkcudbrightshire, DG7 1QR
Tel: 01556 640269 Fax: 01556 640278
E-mail: bardsley@rossan.freeserve.co.uk

3 Family | 2 Pub Bath/Show | B&B per person from £20.00 Single from £15.00 Double | Open Jan-Dec B&B + Eve.Meal £25.00-£26.00

Former Victorian manse, with large gardens, on outskirts of the village. Convenient for touring. Vegetarian, gluten free and special diets available. Budget accommodation. Keen conservationists since the 1950s. Packed lunch on request. Clothes dried overnight and dogs welcome at no extra cost.

V

B&B

Bluehill Farmhouse
Bluehill. Auchencairn, Castle Douglas, DG7 1QW
Tel: 01556 640228
E-mail: caygillbluehill@aol.com
Web: www.milford.co.uk/go/bluehill.html

2 Twin, 2 Double | All En Suite | B&B per person from £25.00 from £20.00 Dbl/Twn | Open Jan-Dec excl Xmas/New Year

Quality en-suite accommodation with excellent breakfasts, on working farm in delightful rural area. Panoramic views towards Solway Firth and Lakeland Hills. Recreational activities nearby.

C W

B&B

Mrs F M Cannon
Collin Hill, Auchencairn, by Castle Douglas, Kirkcudbrightshire, DG7 1QN
Tel: 01556 640242 Mobile: 0797 7784040

1 Twin, 1 Double | All En Suite | B&B per person £21.00-£22.00 Dbl/Twn | Open Feb-Nov

Tastefully furnished bungalow with spectacular views over the Solway Firth to the Cumbrian Hills. Half mile to village and sea. Both rooms on ground floor with ensuite facilities.

V

B&B

Mains of Collin Farmhouse
Auchencairn, by Castle Douglas, Kirkcudbrightshire, DG7 1QN
Tel: 01556 640211
E-mail: fionawallace@mainsofcollin.freeserve.co.uk
Web: www.themains.co.uk

2 Double | All En Suite | B&B per person from £25.00 Single £17.00-£19.00 Double | Open Jan-Dec excl Xmas/New Year

A warm welcome assured in this friendly family home on upland farm in quiet location and within walking distance of village where pub meals are available. An ideal base for touring the beautiful Solway Coast. One of "Scotland's Best"!

C W V

VAT is shown at 17.5%: changes in this rate may affect prices.

Key to symbols is on back flap.

Auchencairn, by Castle Douglas, Kirkcudbrightshire

Map Ref: 2A10

B&B

Rascarrel Cottage
Auchencairn, Castle Douglas, Kirkcudbrightshire, DG7 1RJ
Tel: 01556 640214

1 Twin
1 Double

All En Suite

B&B per person
from £25.00 Single
from £20.00 Dbl/Twn

Open Mar-Oct

Have a relaxing break at our attractive cottage where you will find peace, comfort and wonderful views. Situated on an 18th century smuggling route overlooking Rascarrel Farm and the Solway Firth, it is 500 yards from the sea and 2 miles from the village where pub meals are available. Ground floor ensuite accommodation. Non smoking household.

W V

Torbay
Bluehill, Auchencairn, Castle Douglas, Kirkcudbrightshire, DG7 1QW
Tel: 01556 640180
E-mail: cannontorbay@aol.com

B&B

1 Twin
1 Double

All En Suite

B&B per person
from £30.00 Single
from £25.00 Dbl/Twn

Open May-Sep

A warm welcome awaits you at Torbay. Enjoy the tranquility of unspoilt countryside, and relax in the tastefully furnished rooms. Wonderful views across the Solway. Lovely walks. Village pub 0.5 mile, coast 1 mile.

TV P

Ayr

Map Ref: 1G7

B&B

Abilann Bed & Breakfast
2 Lansdowne Road, Ayr, KA8 8LS
Tel: 01292 266068

1 Twin
1 Double
1 Family

1 Limited ensuite
2 Pub Bath/Show

B&B per person
from £16.00 Single
from £16.00 Twin

Open Jan-Dec

Semi-detached villa in quiet side street yet handy for town centre and Northfield Bowling Green. Private Parking. One ground floor bedroom.

TV P

C V

BRONZE

B&B

Auld Ayr
11 Carrick Road, Ayr, KA7 2RA
Tel: 01292 283219

1 Twin
1 Double
1 Family

2 En Suite fac
1 Pub Bath/Show

B&B per person
from £20.00 Single
from £16.00 Dbl/Twn
Room only per person
from £14.00

Open Jan-Dec

Semi-detached Victorian family home, within easy walking distance of town centre. 5 minutes walk from the train station. Ideal base for touring Ayrshire.

TV P

GUEST HOUSE

Belmont Guest House
Mr Andrew Hillhouse (proprietor),
15 Park Circus, Ayr, KA7 2DJ
Tel: 01292 265588 Fax: 01292 290303
E-mail: belmontguesthouse@btinternet.com
Web: www.belmontguesthouse.co.uk

1 Twin
2 Double
2 Family

All En Suite

B&B per person
£20.00-£24.00 Single
from £20.00 Dbl/Twn
Room only per person
£15.00-£19.00

Open Jan-Dec excl Xmas/New Year

Victorian townhouse in a quiet tree lined conservation area, within easy walking distance of town centre. Ground-floor bedrooms, all with ensuite facilities. Guest lounge with extensive book collection. On street and private car parking.

TV

C W V

SILVER

Important: Prices stated are estimates and may be subject to amendments

Ayr | Map Ref: 1G7

B&B

Mrs W Campbell
Ferguslea, 98 New Road, Ayr, KA8 8JG
Tel: 01292 268551
E-mail: wilmacampb@uk.packardbell.org

1 Single 1 Priv.NOT ensuite
2 Twin 2 Pub Bath/Show

B&B per person
£15.00-£16.00 Single
£15.00-£16.00 Twin
Room only per person
£12.00-£14.00

Open Jan-Dec

Traditional Scottish hospitality in comfortable family home, within 10 minutes walk of town centre and all amenities.

B&B

The Crescent
26 Bellevue Crescent, Ayr, Ayrshire, KA7 2DR
Tel: 01292 287329 Fax: 01292 286779
Web: www.26crescent.freeserve.co.uk

2 Twin All En Suite
3 Double

B&B per person
from £32.00 Single
from £24.00 Dbl/Twn

Open Feb-Nov

Built in 1898 this refurbished Victorian terrace house is in a quiet location with easy access for town centre and beach. Charming rooms have all been individually styled and decorated in a manner befitting the opulence of the Victorian era.

GUEST HOUSE

Dargil Guest House
7 Queen's Terrace, Ayr, Ayrshire, KA7 1DU
Tel: 01292 261955 Fax: 01292 880510

2 Double 3 En Suite fac
3 Family 1 Pub Bath/Show

B&B per person
£20.00-£30.00 Single
£20.00-£23.00 Double

Open Jan-Dec

Small, friendly guest house with sea front location. Only a few minutes walk from the town centre. Private parking.

B&B

Deanbank
44 Ashgrove Street, Ayr, KA7 3BG
Tel: 01292 263745

1 Twin 1 Pub Bath/Show
1 Double

B&B per person
from £20.00 Single
from £18.00 Double

Open Jan-Dec excl Xmas/New Year

Semi-detached late Victorian town house in quiet residential street within easy walking distance of town centre and seafront. Deanbank offers a quality breakfast including home baking. Ideal holiday base for golfing, riverwalks and exploring Burns Country.

B&B

Dunduff
Dunure, Ayr, KA7 4LH
Tel: 01292 500225 Fax: 01292 500222

1 Twin 2 En Suite fac
2 Double 1 Priv.NOT ensuite

B&B per person
from £35.00 Single
from £24.00 Dbl/Twn

Open Feb-Nov

Dunduff is a Georgian country house set in a 650 acre estate dating as far back as the 15C. It stands proudly overlooking the firth of Clyde to Arran and the Mull of Kintyre of which all our bedrooms look onto. Many attractions nearby include Culzean Castle, Burns Heritage, golf and local walks. Breakfast has something for all, including our locally smoked kippers. So come and enjoy the ambience of the Ayrshire coastline.

Ayr — Map Ref: 1G7

B&B

The Dunn Thing
13 Park Circus, Ayr, KA7 2DJ
Tel: 01292 284531
E-mail: TheDunnThing@compuserve.com

Rooms	Facilities	Prices	Open
1 Twin 2 Double	All En Suite	B&B per person from £17.00 Dbl/Twn	Open Jan-Dec

The Dunn Thing offers a warm welcome and a cup of tea on arrival to all our guests. This is a Victorian town house close to the town centre and sea front, situated in quiet area of Ayr.

TV

C W V

B&B

Failte
9 Prestwick Road, Ayr, Ayrshire, KA8 8LD
Tel/Fax: 01292 265282
E-mail: wthomson9@netscapeonline.co.uk

Rooms	Facilities	Prices	Open
1 Twin 1 Double	Private fac Ensuite fac	B&B per person from £18.00 Single from £18.00 Dbl/Twn Room only per person from £15.00	Open Jan-Dec excl Xmas/New Year

Welcome to Failte, a family bed and breakfast situated in residential area on the Ayr-Glasgow road. Town centre with its variety of eating establishments 10-15 minutes walk. Prestwick Airport 5 minutes drive.

TV

V

GUEST HOUSE

Mrs M Ferguson
Kilkerran, 15 Prestwick Road, Ayr, Ayrshire, KA8 8LD
Tel: 01292 266477

Rooms	Facilities	Prices	Open
2 Single 2 Twin 2 Double 2 Family	2 En Suite fac 3 Pub Bath/Show	B&B per person from £20.00 Single £18.00-£20.00 Dbl/Twn Room only per person from £15.00	Open Jan-Dec

Family run guest house on main road from Ayr to Prestwick airport. Two minutes drive from town centre and convenient for Burns country. Television lounge with satellite TV. Some annexe accommodation.

TV

C W V

B&B

'Garth Madryn'
71 Maybole Road, Alloway, Ayr, KA7 4TB
Tel: 01292 443346

Rooms	Facilities	Prices	Open
2 Twin	All En Suite	B&B per person from £18.00 Twin	Open Jan-Dec

Modern semi detached villa with secluded conservatories. Some off street parking. All rooms en-suite. We are situated in a quiet area within close proximity to golf courses, bowling, sports facilities, and Alloway's Brig O'Doon.

TV P

W

GUEST HOUSE

Glenmore Guest House
35 Bellevue Crescent, Ayr, KA7 2DP
Tel/Fax: 01292 269830
E-mail: marie@glenmoreguesthouse.co.uk
Web: http://www.glenmoreguesthouse.co.uk

Rooms	Facilities	Prices	Open
1 Single 1 Twin 1 Double 2 Family	4 En Suite fac 1 Priv.NOT ensuite	B&B per person £25.00-£30.00 Single £20.00-£22.50 Dbl/Twn	Open Jan-Dec

Victorian terraced house, in broad, leafy, quiet street. Ground floor ensuite room. Central for town, beach and golf.

TV

C

Important: Prices stated are estimates and may be subject to amendments

Ayr Map Ref: 1G7

B&B

Greenan Lodge
39 Dunure Road, Doonfoot, Ayr, Ayrshire, KA7 4HR
Tel: 01292 443939

1 Twin
2 Double

All En Suite

B&B per person
from £30.00 Single
from £25.00 Dbl/Twn

Open Jan-Dec

A welcome cup of tea or coffee awaits you at Brenalder Lodge which is a large modern bungalow in a residential area with fine views of the Carrick Hills. Relax in the spacious lounge after a day exploring the places of historic and scenic interest in this picturesque South-west corner of Scotland. The Lodge has all-day access and offers ample off-street parking.

TV P
C W V

Iona Guest House

27 St Leonards Road, Ayr KA7 2PS
Tel: 01292 269541 Fax: 01292 269541
e.mail: iona.guesthouse@tesco.net

A warm Scottish welcome awaits at Iona, which is well placed for easy access to both town and countryside, including Burns Cottage, Culzean Castle and top class golf courses. Our hearty breakfast menu offers good choice. Stay 7 nights for the price of 6.

B&B

Iona Guest House
27 St Leonards Road, Ayr, KA7 2PS
Tel/Fax: 01292 269541
E-mail: iona.guesthouse@tesco.net

2 Single
1 Twin
1 Double

2 En Suite fac
1 Pub Bath/Show

B&B per person
from £18.00 Single
from £18.00 Dbl/Twn

Open Feb-Nov

Traditional family home in residential area, ideally situated for both the business and holiday traveller.

TV P
C W V

B&B

Jac-Mar
23 Dalblair Road, Ayr, KA7 1UF
Tel: 01292 264798

2 Single
1 Twin
1 Double

3 En Suite fac
1 Priv.NOT ensuite

B&B per person
from £25.00 Single
from £22.50 Dbl/Twn

Open Jan-Dec excl Xmas/New Year
B&B + Eve.Meal from £30.00

Friendly hosted family run bed and breakfast in terraced house within town centre. 5 minutes from sea front, convenient for railway station and Prestwick airport. Central base for exploring Burns country, Ayrshire and Isle of Arran. Centrally located for easy access to the numerous Golf Courses Ayrshire has to offer.

TV P

B&B

Jane Lennon
Monaco, 41 Seafield Drive, Ayr, KA7 4BJ
Tel: 01292 264295

1 Twin
1 Double

Pub Bath/Shower
Ensuite fac

B&B per person
from £24.00 Single
from £19.00 Dbl/Twn

Open Jan-Dec

Comfortable family home in quiet seafront location with superb panoramic sea views to Arran and Greenan Castle. Central base for exploring Burns Country, walking and golfing. 5 minutes by car to town centre. Private Parking.

TV P
C W V

VAT is shown at 17.5%: changes in this rate may affect prices.

Key to symbols is on back flap.

Ayr

Map Ref: 1G7

Wilson Hall

SAC, Auchincruive, Ayr, KA6 5HW
Tel: 01292 525203 Fax: 01292 525207
E-mail: c.steel@au.sac.ac.uk

Rooms	Facilities	Prices	Open
90 Single 9 Twin 1 Family	Pub Bath/Showers	B&B per person from £12.00 Single from £12.00 Twin	Open Easter and Jul-Sep

Situated in the heart of Burns country, the college enjoys all the benefits of a tranquil country estate, yet a short drive from Ayr town centre.

Ayton, Berwickshire

Map Ref: 1F9

★★
B&B

Springbank Cottage

Beanburn, Ayton, Berwickshire, TD14 5QZ
Tel: 018907 81263

Rooms	Facilities	Prices	Open
1 Twin 1 Family	1 Pub Bath/Show	B&B per person from £24.00 Single from £18.00 Dbl/Twn	Open Jan-Dec excl Xmas/New Year

Victorian cottage set in attractive gardens in peaceful village convenient for A1. Ideal centre for touring Borders. Close to coastal Nature Reserve.

Ballantrae, Ayrshire

Map Ref: 1F9

Mrs Georgina McKinley

Laggan Farm, Ballantrae, Ayrshire, KA26 0JZ
Tel/Fax: 01465 831402
E-mail: jandr@lagganfrm.freeserve.co.uk

Rooms	Facilities	Prices	Open
1 Double 1 Family	1 En Suite fac 1 Pub Bath/Show	B&B per person from £18.00 Single from £16.00 Double	Open May-Oct

Dairy farm with large comfortable farmhouse 0.5 miles south of Ballantrae on the Ayrshire coast. Guests have their own dining room and sitting room with colour tv. Tea/coffee making facilities plus home baking is available in the dining room in the evening. Ideal base for touring, golfing, woodland walks and fishing by arrangement.

Important: Prices stated are estimates and may be subject to amendments

Beith, Ayrshire

Map Ref: 1G6

★★★

B&B

Mrs Gillan

Shotts Farm, Barrmill, by Beith, Ayrshire, KA15 1LB

Tel: 01505 502273

2 Double 1 Family	1 En Suite fac 2 Pub Bath/Show	B&B per person from £15.00 Single from £14.00 Double Room only per person from £11.00	Open Jan-Dec

Family run farmhouse accommodation on a 200 acre dairy farm. Ideal base for Burns country, Arran and cultural Glasgow.

C V

Castle Douglas, Kirkcudbrightshire

Map Ref: 2A10

★★★★

B&B

Albion House

49 Ernespie Road, Castle Douglas, Kirkcudbrightshire, DG7 1LD

Tel/Fax: 01556 502360

1 Twin 2 Double	2 En Suite fac 1 Priv.NOT ensuite	B&B per person from £20.00 Single from £18.50 Dbl/Twn Room only per person from £16.00	Open Mar-Oct B&B + Eve.Meal from £28.00

Substantial house, at edge of Galloway's market town, yet within walking distance of towns amenities. Renovated to restore its original features, to provide a high standard of accommodation.

V

★★★

GUEST HOUSE

Rose Cottage Guest House

'Rose Cottage', Gelson, Castle Douglas Kirkcudbrightshire, DG7 1SH

Tel/Fax: 01556 502513

1 Single 1 Twin 2 Double	1 En Suite fac 1 Pub Bath/Show	B&B per person from £20.00 Single from £18.00 Dbl/Twn	Open Jan-Dec excl Xmas/New Year B&B + Eve.Meal from £29.00

Friendly welcome in personally run guest house, situated in quiet village. Ideal for walkers and birdwatchers. Ample private parking. All rooms on ground floor. 1 1/2 miles from Threave Gardens - National Trust for Scotland.

C W V

Castle Douglas, Kirkcudbrightshire — Map Ref: 2A10

Smithy House

The Buchan, Castle Douglas DG7 1TH Tel: 01556 503841
e.mail: enquiries@smithyhouse.co.uk Web: www.smithyhouse.co.uk

A warm welcome awaits at our home, a traditional old Galloway Cottage, carefully extended and renovated with ensuite facilities and comfortable guest sitting room. Beautiful views over Carlingwark Loch to the hills and a gentle stroll into town. Centrally situated for exploring Galloway's coast and countryside; weekly rates available. Non-smoking.

B&B

Smithy House
The Buchan, Castle Douglas, Kirkcudbrightshire, DG7 1TH
Tel: 01556 503841
E-mail: enquiries@smithyhouse.co.uk
Web: www.smithyhouse.co.uk

1 Twin | 2 En Suite fac | B&B per person | Open Jan-Dec
2 Double | 1 Priv.NOT ensuite | from £22.00 Dbl/Twn

A warm welcome awaits at our home, a traditional old Galloway cottage, carefully extended and renovated with en-suite facilities and a comfortable guest sitting room. Beautiful views over Carlingwark Loch to the hills and a gentle stroll into town. Centrally situated for exploring Galloway's coast and countryside; weekly rates available. Non smoking.

by Castle Douglas, Kirkcudbrightshire — Map Ref: 2A10

★★★

GUEST HOUSE

Airds Farm
Crossmichael, Castle Douglas, Kirkcudbrightshire, DG7 3BG
Tel/Fax: 01556 670418
E-mail: tricia@airds.com
Web: www.airds.com

1 Single | 2 En Suite fac | B&B per person | Open Jan-Dec
1 Twin | 1 Pub Bath/Show | from £23.00 Single
2 Double | | from £18.00 Dbl/Twn
1 Family

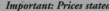

Superb views over Loch Ken and the picturesque village and church of Crossmichael will delight visitors to this traditional farmhouse. Lovers of nature will enjoy walking through the wooded glen and pastures nearby or relaxing in the conservatory. Gardens, castles and other attractions are within easy reach, fishing, boating and watersports are available on the loch. A warm welcome, in a comfortable and relaxing home.

Important: Prices stated are estimates and may be subject to amendments

by Castle Douglas, Kirkcudbrightshire Map Ref: 2A10

Craigadam, Castle Douglas DG7 3HU
Tel/Fax: 01556 650233
e.mail: inquiry@craigadam.com
Web: www.craigadam.com

Craigadam is an elegant country house within a working farm. Antique furnishings, log fires and friendly atmosphere. Relax in our elegant drawing room and enjoy the views across Galloway. All the bedrooms are ensuite. Dine in our oak panelled dining room where we specialise in venison, duck, salmon and sweets, not for the calorie conscious! Enjoy a game of billiards after dinner, catch a trout on our hill loch and have it for breakfast. All home-cooking using local produce. AA ♦♦♦♦

B&B

Craigadam
Castle Douglas, DG7 3HU
Tel/Fax: 01556 650233
E-mail: inquiry@craigadam.com Web: www.craigadam.com

3 Twin
2 Double
1 Family

All En Suite

B&B per person
£26.00-£30.00 Single
£23.00-£26.00 Dbl/Twn

Open Jan-Dec
B&B + Eve.Meal
£38.00-£40.00

18th century farmhouse with panoramic views of surrounding countryside. An ideal base for golfing, walking, fishing. All bedrooms are ensuite. There is a billiard room for after dinner entertainment. Come home in the evening to comfort, super food and good Scottish hospitality. We specialise in local produce including venison, pheasant, salmon. There is a trout loch on the estate.

B&B

Milton Park Farmhouse
Milton Park Farm, Haugh of Urr, Castle Douglas, Kirkcudbrightshire, DG7 3JJ
Tel: 01556 660212

1 Twin
2 Double

2 Pub Bath/Show

B&B per person
£20.00-£22.00 Single
£20.00-£22.00 Dbl/Twn

Open Apr-Oct

A warm welcome and good food awaits you in this comfortable farmhouse. Superb outlook over large garden and down the Urr Valley. Centrally situated, ideal base for walking, golf, birdwatching and touring around Galloway. Free trout fishing on river Urr.

Millport, Isle of Cumbrae Map Ref: 1F6

GUEST HOUSE

The College of the Holy Spirit
The College, Millport, Isle of Cumbrae, KA28 0HE
Tel: 01475 530353 Fax: 01475 530204
E-mail: tccumbrae@argyll.anglican.org

4 Single
7 Twin
5 Double
3 Family

7 Pub Bath/Show

B&B per person
from £17.00 Single
from £17.00 Dbl/Twn
Room only per person
from £12.50

Open Jan-Dec excl Xmas/New Year
B&B + Eve.Meal
from £26.00

Unique opportunity to stay in the smallest working cathedral in Europe. Some seperate accommodation in North college. Refectory style dining. Library. All the buildings are grade 'A' listed.

VAT is shown at 17.5%: changes in this rate may affect prices.

Key to symbols is on back flap.

Millport, Isle of Cumbrae

Map Ref: 1F6

★★

B&B

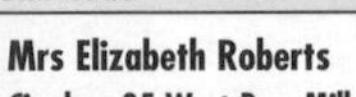

Mrs Elizabeth Roberts
Cirmhor, 35 West Bay, Millport, Isle of Cumbrae
Tel: 01475 530723

1 Twin
1 Double

2 Pub Bath/Show

B&B per person
from £20.00 Single
from £17.00 Dbl/Twn

Open Jan-Dec excl New Year
B&B + Eve.Meal from £25.00

On the edge of Millport with views to the Wee Cumbrae and Portencross. Ideal for walking, birdwatching & cycling. Bikes available. Attractive conservatory and garden available for guests. Packed lunches available.

by Dalbeattie, Kirkcudbrightshire

Map Ref: 2A10

Auchenskeoch Lodge

by Dalbeattie, Kirkcudbrightshire DG5 4PG
Tel: 01387 780277 Fax: 01387 780277

Former Victorian shooting lodge in 20 acre grounds including woodlands; formal gardens and productive vegetable garden. Fishing on own loch. Croquet lawn. Spacious comfortable bedrooms all ensuite and recently refurbished. Billiard room with full size table. Candlelit dinners; log fires. Traditional furnishings throughout. Peaceful secluded setting in unspoilt countryside.

★★★★

B&B

Auchenskeoch Lodge
by Dalbeattie, Kirkcudbrightshire, DG5 4PG
Tel/Fax: 01387 780277

2 Twin
1 Double

All En Suite

B&B per person
from £36.00 Single
from £30.00 Dbl/Twn

Open Easter-Oct
B&B + Eve.Meal from £46.00

Former shooting lodge, in 20 acres of secluded ground with private loch. Billiard room and croquet lawn. Dinners a speciality with home cooked dishes, which include vegetables picked from the garden. Good wine list.

Dumfries

Map Ref: 2B9

★★

B&B

Glencairn
45 Rae Street, Dumfries, DG1 1JD
Tel/Fax: 01387 262467
Web: http://go.to/glencairn

1 Single
1 Double
1 Family

2 En Suite fac

B&B per person
from £16.00 Single
from £18.00 Double

Open Jan-Dec

Comfortable 19c home within easy walking distance of town centre. Close to railway station and library. En-suite rooms available.

★★★

B&B

Hollybank Bed & Breakfast
23 Rae Street, Dumfries, DG1 1HY
Tel: 01387 264076 Fax: 01387 264075
Web: www.hollybank.com

2 Single
1 Double
1 Family

3 En Suite fac
1 Priv Bath/Show

B&B per person
£17.00-£20.00 Single
£17.50-£18.00 Dbl/Twn

Open Jan-Dec
B&B + Eve.Meal £23.50-£26.50

Traditional Scottish hospitality in this friendly family home close to town centre. The Robert Burns Heritage Trail starts in Dumfries which is a central base for touring the beautiful Solway Coast. All bedrooms have their own shower/bath rooms.

Important: Prices stated are estimates and may be subject to amendments

Dumfries — **Map Ref: 2B9**

★★ B&B

Mrs J Kempsell
The Cottage, 17 Rotchell Road, Dumfries, Dumfriesshire, DG2 7SE
Tel: 01387 255615

1 Single, 1 Twin, 1 Family — All En Suite

B&B per person £19.00-£21.00 Single, £19.00-£21,00 Twin. Room only per person from £15.00

Open Jan-Dec

Scottish hospitality in friendly family home. Close to museum and only a short walk to town centre. Central base for touring the beautiful Solway Coast and the Burns Heritage Trail.

★★ B&B

Annie M Sloan
30 Hardthorn Avenue, Dumfries, Dumfriesshire, DG2 9JA
Tel/Fax: 01387 253502
E-mail: anniesbandb@aol.com

1 Twin, 1 Double — 1 Pub Bath/Show

B&B per person from £16.50 Dbl/Twn. Room only per person from £13.00

Open Easter-Oct

A warm welcome awaits you at No30, a detached house in residential area, convenient for both town centre and by-pass.

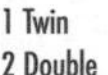

★ B&B

Smithy House
Shieldhill Road, Torthorwald, Dumfries, Dumfriesshire, DG1 3PT
Tel: 01387 750518

1 Twin, 2 Double, 1 Family — 1 En Suite fac, 2 Pub Bath/Show

B&B per person from £25.00 Single, from £16.50 Dbl/Twn

Open Apr-Nov. B&B + Eve.Meal from £25.00

Converted village smithy with annexe accommodation available. 3 miles (5km) from busy shopping town of Dumfries and local amenities.

★★★ B&B

Southpark Guest House
Quarry Road, Locharbriggs, Dumfries, DG1 1QG
Tel/Fax: 01387 711188
FREEPHONE: 0800 970 1588
E-mail: ewan@southparkhouse.co.uk
Web: www.southparkhouse.co.uk

1 Twin, 1 Double, 1 Family — 2 En Suite fac, 1 Priv.NOT ensuite

B&B per person £21.00-£24.00 Single, £18.00-£19.00 Dbl/Twn. Room only per person from £17.00

Open Jan-Dec

AA 4 diamond establishment. Situated edge of town enjoying panoramic views across the valleys, ample private parking. Easy access from all major routes. Credit Cards accepted, full laundry service. Activity holidays arranged. Edge of Caledonian Cycle Route and many fine walks. AA Host of the year finalists 2000.

VAT is shown at 17.5%: changes in this rate may affect prices.

Key to symbols is on back flap.

Dumfries

Map Ref: 2B9

B&B

Wallamhill House
Kirkton, by Dumfries, Dumfriesshire, DG1 1SL
Tel/Fax: 01387 248249
E-mail: wallamhill@aol.com
Web: www.wallamhill.co.uk

Spacious house in quiet countryside, beautiful views of Nith Valley. 2 miles from Dumfries town centre, safe parking. All rooms ground floor level, spacious, with ensuite shower rooms. Ideal and luxurious base to explore Dumfries and Galloway.

1 Twin, 1 Double, 1 Family — All En Suite

B&B per person from £25.00 Single, from £20.00 Dbl/Twn

Open Jan-Dec

C W V

by Dumfries

Map Ref: 2B9

B&B

Henderland Farmhouse B&B
Henderland, Crocketford, Dumfries, DG2 8QD
Tel: 01387 730270
Mobile: 07759 587591

Traditional Scottish hospitality in friendly family home. 19th Century Farmhouse on cattle and sheep farm, tours available. Close to A75 and only 7 miles from Dumfries.

1 Twin, 1 Double, 1 Family — 1 Ensuite fac, 1 Pub Bath/Show, 2 Limited ensuite

B&B per person from £20.00 Single, from £18.00 Dbl/Twn; Room only per person from £14.00

Open Jan-Dec excl Xmas/New Year; B&B + Eve.Meal from £26.00

C W

B&B

Locharthur House
Beeswing, Dumfries, Dumfriesshire, DG2 8JG
Tel: 01387 760235

A large Georgian house set in grounds of 3 acres, 6 miles West of Dumfries. The Solway coast is 12 miles away where there are numerous walks, beaches and places of interest. A central base for touring South West Scotland and the Burns Heritage Trail.

1 Twin, 1 Double, 1 Family — 2 Ensuite fac, 1 Priv.NOT ensuite

B&B per person from £20.00 Single, from £19.00 Single; Room only per person from £17.00

Open Jan-Dec; B&B + Eve.Meal from £26.00

C V

Dunure, by Ayr, Ayrshire

Map Ref: 1G7

B&B

Fisherton Farm B&B
Dunure, Ayrshire, KA7 4LF
Tel/Fax: 01292 500223
E-mail: lesleywilcox@hotmail.com
http://fishertonfarm.homestead.com/webpage.html

Traditional stone-built farmhouse on working mixed farm, with extensive sea views to Arran. 5 miles from Ayr and convenient for Prestwick Airport. Ground floor accommodation available. Central base for exploring Burns Country, places of historical interest, golfing, fishing and walking.

1 Twin, 1 Double — All En Suite

B&B per person from £20.00 Single, from £19.00 Dbl/Twn

Open Jan-Dec excl Xmas/New Year

C W V

Earlston, Berwickshire

Map Ref: 2D6

B&B

Mrs Sheila Hogg
Birkenside, Earlston, Berwickshire, TD4 6AR
Tel: 01896 849224

Traditional family farmhouse with spacious comfortable rooms and interesting architectural features. Set in the beautiful Borders countryside just off A68 between Earlston and Lauder. Ideally located for touring and visiting local Abbey's, Stately Homes and many craft centres around. Easy access to Edinburgh.

2 Twin — 1 En Suite fac, 1 Priv.NOT ensuite

B&B per person £17.00-£18.00 Single, £17.00-£18.00 Twin

Open Jan-Dec

C W

Important: Prices stated are estimates and may be subject to amendments

Ecclefechan, Dumfriesshire

Map Ref: 2C9

★

B&B

Carlyle House
Ecclefechan, Dumfriesshire, DG11 3DG
Tel/Fax: 01576 300322

1 Single
1 Twin
1 Family

2 Pub Bath/Show

B&B per person
£14.00 Single
£14.00 Twin
Room only per person
£10.50

Open Jan-Dec excl Xmas/New Year

Comfortable family accommodation convenient for A74. Children and pets welcome. Opposite Carlyle's birthplace.

Eyemouth, Berwickshire

Map Ref: 2F5

★★★

B&B

Mrs J MacKay
Hillcrest, Coldingham Road, Eyemouth, Berwickshire, TD14 5AN
Tel: 018907 50463

1 Twin
1 Double

1 Pub Bath/Show

B&B per person
from £17.00 Single
from £17.00 Dbl/Twn

Open Jan-Dec

Pleasantly situated with own garden in residential area of coastal town. Off street parking. Good location for all local amenities including harbour, nature reserve and touring the Border Counties.

Galashiels, Selkirkshire

Map Ref: 2D6

★★

B&B

Ettrickvale
33 Abbotsford Road, Galashiels, Selkirkshire, TD1 3HW
Tel: 01896 755224

2 Twin
1 Double

2 Pub Bath/Show

B&B per person
from £18.00 Single
from £16.00 Dbl/Twn

Open Jan-Dec excl Xmas/New Year
B&B+Eve.Meal from £22.00

Comfortable family run semi-detached bungalow with garden. By A7. On outskirts of town but only a short walk from local amenities. All accommodation on ground floor. Evening meals by arrangement.

★★

B&B

'Glenellwyn' Bed & Breakfast
89 Melrose Road, Galashiels, TD1 2BX
Tel: 01896 752964

2 Single
1 Family

1 Pub Bath/Show

B&B per person
from £20.00 Single
£18.00-£20.00 Double
Room only per person
from £12.00

Open Jan-Dec

Semi-detached 1930 house. Warm welcome. Convenient for touring all areas of the Scottish Borders.

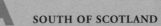

Galashiels, Selkirkshire

Map Ref: 2D6

B&B

Kirklands Bed & Breakfast, M McLauchlan
Gala Terrace, Galashiels, Selkirkshire, TD1 3JT
Tel/Fax: 01896 753762

Rooms	Facilities	Prices	Open
1 Single 1 Double 1 Family	1 Pub Bath/Show 3 Priv.NOT ensuite	B&B per person £16.50 Single £16.50 Double	Open Jan-Dec excl Xmas/New Year

Large house (1900), town centre area. 200 yds from Tourist Information Centre. Convenient for shops and restaurants. Easy parking. On Southern Upland Path. Open all year.

B&B

Wayside
37 Abbotsford Road, Galashiels, Selkirkshire, TD1 3HW
Tel: 01896 751952

Rooms	Facilities	Prices	Open
1 Twin 1 Double	All En Suite	B&B per person from £20.00 Single from £18.00 Dbl/Twn	Open Jan-Dec excl Xmas/New Year

Friendly, comfortable family home on A7, lounge has view to the Eildon Hills. Central location for touring the Borders. All rooms en-suite, ample parking, non-smoking in bedrooms.

B&B

Williamhope
Old Peel, Galashiels, Selkirkshire, TD1 3LL
Tel: 01896 850243
Fax: 01896 850461

Rooms	Facilities	Prices	Open
1 Double 1 Twin	1 En Suite fac 1 Priv.NOT ensuite	B&B per person £20.00-£22.00 Dbl/Twn	Open Jan-Dec B&B + Eve.Meal £32.00-£34.00

Peace and tranquility surround you in this former farmhouse deep in the Peeblesshire hills. 3 miles off the A72. Good home cooking with fresh local produce. Warm hospitality. The Scottish Borders is a wonderful location to enjoy Castles, Roman Forts, Strately Homes or Abbeys. For the walkers an extensive network of attractive footpaths.

by Galashiels, Selkirkshire

Map Ref: 2D6

B&B

Over Langshaw Farm
Langshaw, by Galashiels, Selkirkshire, TD1 2PE
Tel: 01896 860244

Rooms	Facilities	Prices	Open
1 Double 1 Family	1 En Suite fac 1 Priv.NOT ensuite	B&B per person from £25.00 Single from £22.00 Double	Open Jan-Dec

Beautifully situated traditional farmhouse on 500 acre mixed working farm. (FHB member). Welcoming, relaxing atmosphere. Near Melrose and Galashiels and only 35 miles from Edinburgh.

Gatehouse of Fleet, Kirkcudbrightshire

Map Ref: 1H10

B&B

The Bay Horse
9 Ann Street, Gatehouse-of-Fleet, Kirkcudbrightshire, DG7 2HU
Tel: 01557 814073

Rooms	Facilities	Prices	Open
1 Twin 2 Double	2 En Suite fac 1 Priv.NOT ensuite	B&B per person from £18.00 Single £20.00-£25.00 Dbl/Twn Room only per person from £18.00	Open Mar-Oct

The Bay Horse provides quiet and comfortable accommodation overlooking gardens and parkland yet convient to hotels, restaurants and gift shops. Gatehouse of Fleet is an ideal location for touring Galloway and the many local attractions include sandy beaches, sailing, walking, fishing, golf etc.

Girvan, Ayrshire — **Map Ref: 1F8**

B&B

Findlay & Kate McIntosh

Glendrissaig Guest House, Newton Stewart Road, by Girvan, Ayrshire, KA26 0HJ
Tel/Fax: 01465 714631

1 Twin / 1 Double / 1 Family — All En Suite — B&B per person from £23.00 Single, £22.00-£26.00 Dbl/Twn — Open Apr-Oct

Modern detached farmhouse with landscaped gardens in elevated position with excellent outlook westwards over Firth of Clyde towards Mull of Kintyre. Organic produce when available used in vegetarian meals. Ground floor bedroom available.

C V

B&B

Hawkhill Farm

Old Dailly, Girvan, Ayrshire, KA26 9RD
Tel: 01465 871232
Web: www.sujo.com/ctg/hawkhill.htm

1 Twin / 1 Double / 1 Family — 1 En Suite fac, 2 Priv.NOT ensuite — B&B per person from £20.00 Dbl/Twn — Open Apr-Oct

Large traditional farmhouse on arable farm, 3 miles (5 kms) from Girvan. The Adam-style lounge is a beautiful place to relax or watch TV after exploring the quiet corners of our area including Culzean Castle. Convenient for both the Irish and Arran Ferries. Friendly and informal atmosphere. Breakfast is made from fresh daily local produce. Bread, marmalade and jams are home made.

C W V

B&B

St Oswalds

5 Golf Course Road, Girvan, KA26 9HW
Tel: 01465 713786

1 Twin / 1 Double — 1 En Suite fac, 1 Priv.NOT ensuite — B&B per person £18.00-£22.00 Dbl/Twn — Open Jan-Dec

Guests are made most welcome at this comfortable semi-detached villa overlooking Ailsa Craig, Arran and Girvan Golf Course. The large double bedroom with private facilties has this wonderful view while the twin ensuite bedroom overlooks the town to the hills beyond. Excellent breakfast. Culzean 7 miles, Turnberry Golf Course 5 miles. Ideal touring area. Unrestricted street parking.

V

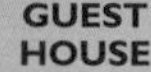

GUEST HOUSE

Thistleneuk Guest House

19 Louisa Drive, Girvan, Ayrshire, KA26 9AH
Tel/Fax: 01465 712137
E-mail: reservations@thistleneuk.freeserve.co.uk

1 Single / 2 Twin / 2 Double / 2 Family — All En Suite — B&B per person from £23.00 Single, from £23.00 Dbl/Twn — Open Easter-Oct, B&B + Eve.Meal from £31.00

A warm welcome from George and Margaret at Thistleneuk which is situated on the sea front with views of Ailsa Craig and is central for all Girvans amenities. In their Robert Burns dining room the emphasis is on traditional Scottish food using local produce when possible. Over the years Thistleneuk has established a reputation for comfort and good food.

C W V

by Girvan, Ayrshire — **Map Ref: 1F8**

B&B

Blair Farm

Barrhill, Girvan, Ayrshire, KA26 0RD
Tel: 01465 821247
Web: www.dalbeattie.com/farmholidays/qblfb.htm

1 Twn/Dbl / 1 Double — 1 En Suite fac, 1 Priv.NOT ensuite — B&B per person from £25.00 Single, from £20.00 Dbl/Twn — Open Easter-Nov

Enjoy peace, comfort and good home cooking at Blair, our family run farm situated off the A714, 1 mile south of Barrhill. Close to the Galloway Forest Park, Glentrool and the Ayrshire coast. Visitors lounge with TV and log fires for the cooler evening. Free fishing available.

C W

BRONZE

by Girvan, Ayrshire **Map Ref: 1F8**

B&B

Glengennet Farm
Barr, Girvan, Ayrshire, KA26 9TY
Tel/Fax: 01465 861220
E-mail: vsd@glengennet.fsnet.co.uk
Web: www.b-and-b-scotland.co.uk/dumfries.htm#glengennet

1 Twin
1 Double

All En Suite

B&B per person
£20.00-£22.00 Dbl/Twn

Open Apr-Oct

Original shooting lodge in peaceful situation with lovely views over the Stinchar Valley and the neighbouring Galloway Forest Park. Glengennet Farm is 1.5 miles from Barr with hotel for evening meals. A good base for visiting Glentrool, Culzean Castle and Country Park and the Ayrshire coast.

W V

B&B

Maxwelston Farm B&B
Maxwelston, by Dailly, Girvan, Ayrshire, KA26 9RH
Tel: 01465 811210
E-mail: maxwellston2@hotmail.com
Web: www.sujo.com/ctg/max.htm

1 Double
1 Family

1 Ensuite fac
1 Priv.NOT ensuite

Room only per person
from £18.00

Open Easter-Oct

A warm friendly welcome awaits you at this 18C Listed farmhouse on working sheep and beef farm, 5 miles (8kms) inland from Girvan. Our tastefully decorated home offers you warm cosy bedrooms, spacious lounge, large dining room where a hearty farmhouse breakfast is served and a large garden to enjoy. Within easy access to all attractions. Golf course situated opposite the farm.

C W V

Glenluce, Wigtownshire **Map Ref: 1G10**

B&B

Bankfield Farm
Glenluce, Newton Stewart, Wigtownshire, DG8 0JE
Tel/Fax: 01581 300281

1 Twin
1 Double
1 Family

2 En Suite fac
1 Priv.NOT ensuite

B&B per person
from £20.00 Single
from £18.00 Dbl/Twn

Open Jan-Dec excl Xmas/New Year

Farmhouse on 370 acre working farm conveniently situated between the village and the main A75 tourist route. 5 minutes walk into village with all amenities and 10 miles from Stranraer Ferry Port. Nearby attractions include Motor Museum, beautiful gardens at Glenwhan, Castle Kennedy and Botanic Gardens at Port Logan. Ideally situated for Southern Upland Way. Golf course, horse riding, fishing.

TV

Important: Prices stated are estimates and may be subject to amendments

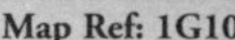

Glenluce, Wigtownshire — Map Ref: 1G10

HOTEL

Kelvin House Hotel

53 Main Street, Glenluce, Wigtownshire, DG8 0PP
Tel: 01581 300303 (office)/300528 (for residents use only)
Fax: 01581 300303
E-mail: kelvinhouse@lineone.net
Web: www.kelvin-house.co.uk

Located in tranquil village centre with easy access to major routes. Convenient for touring, either by car or bicycle, golfing, fishing, shooting and Irish ferries. Large family rooms available.

Rooms	Facilities	Prices	Open
2 Twin 4 Double	5 En Suite fac 1 Priv.NOT ensuite	B&B per person from £25.00 Single from £22.50 Dbl/Twn Room only per person from £20.00	Open Jan-Dec B&B + Eve.Meal from £35.00

GUEST HOUSE

Rowantree Guest House

38 Main Street, Glenluce, Wigtownshire, DG8 0PS
Tel: 01581 300244 Fax: 01581 300366

Family run house, popular with fishermen, golfers, tourists and ferry passengers. In village 15 minutes from Stranraer. Disabled facilities. Evening meal by prior arrangement.

Rooms	Facilities	Prices	Open
1 Twin 2 Double 2 Family	4 En Suite fac 1 Priv.NOT ensuite 1 Pub Bath/Show	B&B per person from £16.50 Single from £15.50 Dbl/Twn Room only per person from £12.50	Open Jan-Dec

Greenlaw, Duns, Berwickshire — Map Ref: 2E6

B&B

Bridgend House

36 West High Street, Greenlaw, Berwickshire, TD10 6XA
Tel/Fax: 01361 810270
E-mail: apropos des@fsbdial.co.uk

Built in 1816, this small and friendly Bed & Breakfast offers riverside trout fishing in the garden. On the A697 Newcastle to Edinburgh road, Greenlaw is set in the scenic Borders just 38 miles from Edinburgh.

Rooms	Facilities	Prices	Open
2 Twin 1 Double 1 Family	3 En Suite fac 1 Priv.NOT ensuite	B&B per person £18.00-£20.00 Dbl/Twn	Open Jan-Dec B&B + Eve.Meal £28.00-£30.00

Gretna, Dumfriesshire — Map Ref: 2C10

B&B

The Beeches

Loanwath Road, off Sarkfoot Road, Gretna, Dumfriesshire, DG16 5EP
Tel: 01461 337448

You are assured of a warm welcome at the Beeches, a former 19th century farmhouse located in a quiet part of Gretna, overlooking the Solway Firth and Lakeland hills. A non-smoking house with a homely and peaceful atmosphere. Ensuite facilities available.

Rooms	Facilities	Prices	Open
1 Dbl/Twn 1 Family	All En Suite	B&B per person from £21.00 Dbl/Twn	Open Feb-Dec excl Xmas/New Year

by Gretna, Dumfriesshire — Map Ref: 2C10

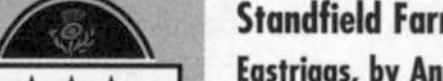

B&B

Standfield Farm

Eastriggs, by Annan, Dumfriesshire, DG12 6TF
Tel: 01461 40367

18th C farmhouse within working farm on outskirts of village of Eastriggs. Ideal base for touring. Families welcome. Gretna/M6 4 miles, Annan 4 miles, Dumfries 18 miles. Golf courses nearby. Good cycling country. Birdwatching at Caerlaverock 10 miles.

Rooms	Facilities	Prices	Open
2 Double 1 Family	1 En Suite fac 1 Pub Bath/Show	B&B per person from £18.00 Double	Open Mar-Oct

by Gretna, Dumfriesshire — Map Ref: 2C10

B&B

Thistlewood
Rigg, Gretna, Dumfriesshire, DG16 5JQ
Tel: 01461 337810

1 Twin, 2 Double — 2 Pub Bath/Show — B&B per person from £25.00 Single, from £18.00 Dbl/Twn — Open Jan-Dec

'Rural surroundings. Gretna two miles. Only five minutes from main tourist routes. Comfortable cosy bedrooms. (One four-poster). Extensive breakfast menu. Off-road parking'.

Hawick, Roxburghshire — Map Ref: 2D7

B&B

Craig-Ian
6 Weensland Road, Hawick, Roxburghshire, TD9 9NP
Tel: 01450 373506

1 Twin, 2 Double — 2 Pub Bath/Show — B&B per person from £15.00 Dbl/Twn — Open Jan-Dec excl Xmas/New Year

Large Victorian terraced house, set above main A698 tourist route and close to centre of historic Borders town.

Ellistrin
6 Fenwick Park, Hawick, Borders TD9 9PA
Tel: 01450 374216 Fax: 01450 373619
e.mail: ellistrin@compuserve.com Web: www.ellistrin.co.uk

Situated on the outskirts of the knitwear town of Hawick, this family house enjoys an elevated position with a lovely view. Three bedrooms all ensuite. All local amenities within easy walking distance. An attractive base for touring the lovely Borders countryside or walking in the Borders hills.

B&B

Ellistrin
6 Fenwick Park, Hawick, Roxburghshire, TD9 9PA
Tel: 01450 374216 Fax: 01450 373619
E-mail: ellistrin@compuserve.com
Web: www.ellistrin.co.uk

1 Twin, 2 Double — All En Suite, 1 Pub Bath/Show — B&B per person £18.00-£20.00 Single, from £18.00 Dbl/Twn — Open Apr-Oct

Comfortable Victorian villa set in extensive, well laid out gardens, in a commanding elevated position overlooking Hawick. All rooms ensuite. Private Parking.

B&B

Wiltonburn Farm B&B
Wiltonburn Farm, Hawick, Roxburghshire, TD9 7LL
Tel: 01450 372414 Fax: 01450 378098
Mobile: 07774 192551
Web: www.smoothhound.co.uk/hotels/wiltonbu

1 Family, 1 Double, 1 Twin/Dbl — En Suite, Priv. facilities, Pub.Bathroom — B&B per person from £22.00 Single, from £20.00 Dbl/Twn — Open Jan-Dec, Evening Meal from £10.00

Charming farmhouse situated in the peaceful surroundings of a working farm, yet only 2 miles from Hawick. Cashmere knitwear, farm shop, art and furniture gallery on site (discount for guests). Farm Holiday Bureau member. Welcome Host. En-suite available.

BRONZE

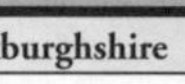

by Hawick, Roxburghshire

Map Ref: 2D7

★★ B&B

Kirkton Farmhouse

Kirkton, nr Hawick, Roxburghshire, TD9 8QJ
Tel/Fax: 01450 372421
E-mail: bell.kirkton@virgin.net

Spacious Border farmhouse with private sitting room, log fire and colour TV. Private loch fishing.Ideal touring base. Evening meal by prior arrangement.

Rooms	Facilities	Prices	Open
1 Twin 2 Double	1 Pub Bath/Show	B&B per person from £20.00 Single from £15.00 Dbl/Twn Room only per person from £15.00	Open Jan-Dec B&B + Eve.Meal from £22.50

C W V

Irvine, Ayrshire

Map Ref: 1G6

★★ B&B

Mrs D Daunt

The Conifers, 40 Kilwinning Road, Irvine, Ayrshire, KA12 8RY
Tel: 01294 278070

Bungalow with large well maintained garden. Ample off-street parking in safe location. All rooms can be let as singles. Central for bus routes, station and town centre with all its amenities including a variety of restaurants.

Rooms	Facilities	Prices	Open
1 Single 2 Twn/Dbl 1 Family	2 En Suite fac 1 Priv.NOT ensuite	B&B per person from £17.50 Single from £17.50 Dbl/Twn Room only £15.00	Open Jan-Dec excl Xmas/New Year

C V

Jedburgh, Roxburghshire

Map Ref: 2E7

B&B

Craigowen Bed & Breakfast

30 High Street, Jedburgh, Roxburghshire, TD8 6AG
Tel: 01835 862604

Personally run, with private parking, located in centre of town. Ideally situated for touring historic Borders area.

Rooms	Facilities	Prices	Open
1 Twin 1 Family	2 Priv.NOT ensuite	B&B per person from £17.00 Single from £17.00 Twin	Open Jan-Dec excl Xmas/New Year

C V

B&B

Mrs Margaret Crone (Bed & Breakfast)

15 Hartrigge Crescent, Jedburgh, Roxburghshire, TD8 6HT
Tel: 01835 862738

Warm hospitality in this friendly family house. In quiet residential area within walking distance of the town. Parking facilities near house.

Rooms	Facilities	Prices	Open
1 Twin 1 Double	1 Pub Bath/Show	B&B per person from £18.50 Single from £15.50 Dbl/Twn Room only per person from £12.50	Open Jan-Dec

C V

VAT is shown at 17.5%: changes in this rate may affect prices.

Key to symbols is on back flap.

Jedburgh, Roxburghshire Map Ref: 2E7

FROYLEHURST

The Friars, Jedburgh TD8 6BN
Tel/Fax: 01835 862477

An impressive Grade 'B' listed Victorian town house dated 1894, retaining original fireplaces, stained glass windows, cornices and tiled vestibule. Offering spacious and comfortable guest rooms and residents' lounge. Enjoying an elevated position in a large secluded garden in a quiet residential area with ample private off-street parking, yet only 2 minutes from town centre. All bedrooms have wash basins, shaver points, tea/coffee-making facilities, colour TV and radio. Full Scottish breakfast. This is a family home, and guests are made welcome by the owner, Mrs H Irvine.

B&B

Froylehurst
Friars, Jedburgh, Roxburghshire, TD8 6BN
Tel/Fax: 01835 862477

1 Twin
2 Double
1 Family

2 Pub Bath/Show

B&B per person
from £20.00 Single
from £18.00 Dbl/Twn

Open Mar-Nov

Detached Victorian house (retaining many original features) with large garden and private parking. Spacious rooms. Overlooking town, 2 minutes walk from the centre.

Jedburgh, Roxburghshire **Map Ref: 2E7**

KENMORE BANK

Oxnam Road, Jedburgh TD8 6JJ Telephone: 01835 862369
e.mail: joanne@diadembooks.com
Web: http://www.diadembooks.com

A charming Victorian villa with residential licence just off the A68. Situated beside the River Jed with panoramic views of the Abbey and ancient town of Jedburgh yet just five minutes' walk from shops, restaurants and pubs. Almost adjacent to the leisure centre with heated pool, sauna, gym and solarium. All bedrooms ensuite with colour TV. Central heating. Private parking.

Package golf holidays available on 17 courses.

Overnight from £19 B&B

Proprietors Charles and Joanne Muller.

★★ GUEST HOUSE 

★★ GUEST HOUSE

Kenmore Bank
Oxnam Road, Jedburgh, TD8 6JJ
Tel: 01835 862369
E.mail: joanne@diadembooks.com
Web: www.diadembooks.com

2 Twin, 2 Double, 2 Family — All En Suite — B&B per person from £29.00 Single, from £19 Dbl/Twn — Open Jan-Dec

Friendly, relaxing family run guest house with residential licence. Splendid views of the Abbey close by. Excellent base for touring the Borders. Just a few minutes walk to a good variety of pubs and restaurants.

★★★ B&B

Mrs Kinghorn
Riverview, Newmill Farm, Jedburgh, TD8 6TH
Tel: 01835 864607 (Mon-Fri 9am-6pm)
Tel: 01835 862145 (all other times)

2 Double, 1 Family — All En Suite — B&B per person from £25.00 Single, from £18.00 Double — Open Apr-Oct

Modern villa on quiet country road in rolling Scottish Borders Farmland. Overlooking the river Jed. Large residents lounge with balcony. Free trout fishing available for guests. Spacious car park area. Jedburgh 2 miles. Kelso 8 miles. Close to St Cuthberts Way (Grid ref NT659227)

Jedburgh, Roxburghshire | Map Ref: 2E7

THE SPINNEY GUEST HOUSE

Langlee, Jedburgh, Roxburghshire TD8 6PB
Telephone: 01835 863525 Fax: 01835 864883
e.mail: thespinney@btinternet.com

Quality accommodation in attractive and spacious surroundings. Friendly relaxed atmosphere. Ample parking. Two miles south of Jedburgh on A68.

B&B

The Spinney
Langlee, Jedburgh, Roxburghshire, TD8 6PB
Tel: 01835 863525 Fax: 01835 864883
E-mail: thespinney@btinternet.com

1 Twin	2 En Suite fac	B&B per person	Open Mar-Nov
2 Double	1 Priv.NOT ensuite	from £22.00 Dbl/Twn	

A warm welcome at this attractive house with large pleasant garden, lying just off the main A68 2 miles south of Jedburgh. All rooms have private facilities. Ample parking. Quality self-catering lodges available too.

TV P W V

WILLOW COURT

The Friars, Jedburgh, Roxburghshire TD8 6BN
Tel: 01835 863702 Fax: 01835 864601

Willow Court is set in 2 acres of peaceful gardens overlooking historic Jedburgh only 2 minutes walk from the town centre. Breakfast is served in the bright conservatory, which enjoys panoramic views to the wooded hillsides. The outlock is shared by the sitting rooms and some of the fresh ensuite bedrooms, most located on ground floor. Children welcome. Private parking. AA ♦♦♦♦ Selected.

GUEST HOUSE

Willow Court
The Friars, Jedburgh, Roxburghshire, TD8 6BN
Tel: 01835 863702 Fax: 01835 864601

1 Twin	3 En Suite fac	B&B per person	Open Jan-Dec
2 Double	1 Priv.NOT ensuite	from £25.00 Single	
1 Family		from £19.00 Dbl/Twn	
		Room only per person	
		from £18.00	

Set in 2 acres of garden above the town, with excellent views. Peaceful setting, yet close to all amenities including Abbey, Castle and a good selection of restaurants. All rooms are either ensuite or with private bathroom or shower-room. Most rooms are on the ground floor.

TV P C W V

Important: Prices stated are estimates and may be subject to amendments

Jedburgh, Roxburghshire — Map Ref: 2E7

★★★

B&B

'Windyridge'
39 Dounehill, Jedburgh, TD8 6LJ
Tel: 01835 864404
E.mail: jlowelowc6r@supanet.com

Rooms	Facilities	Prices	Open
1 Single 1 Twin 1 Double	1 En Suite fac 1 Pub Bath/Show	B&B per person from £18.00 Single from £19.00 Dbl/Twn	Open Jan-Dec

Within walking distance of the Abbey and town centre, this family home in a quiet, residential location, offers a warm welcome and panoramic views over Jedburgh. Garage and parking. Ideal location for outdoor activities. Families welcome.

by Jedburgh, Roxburghshire — Map Ref: 2E7

★

GUEST HOUSE

Ferniehirst Mill Lodge
by Jedburgh, Roxburghshire, TD8 6PQ
Tel/Fax: 01835 863279

Rooms	Facilities	Prices	Open
1 Single 4 Twin 3 Double 1 Family	All En Suite 1 Pub Bath/Show	B&B per person from £23.00 Single from £23.00 Dbl/Twn Room only per person from £20.00	Open Jan-Dec B&B + Eve.Meal from £37.00

Personally run, modern guest house, all rooms ensuite. Secluded riverside location, just two and a half miles South of Jedburgh. Haven for bird watchers and walkers. Specialists in home cooking using local produce. Trail riding centre.

Kelso, Roxburghshire — Map Ref: 2E6

★★★

GUEST HOUSE

Bellevue House
Bowmont Street, Kelso, Roxburghshire, TD5 7DZ
Tel/Fax: 01573 224588

Rooms	Facilities	Prices	Open
2 Twin 3 Double 1 Family	All En Suite	B&B per person from £25.00 Single from £23.00 Dbl/Twn	Open Jan-Dec excl Xmas/New Year

House of character in residential part of the historic town of Kelso. Minutes to the Tweed, town square and Floors Castle. Convenient for a good selection of restaurants, close to race course, ideally situated for local golf courses and fishing. Private parking. Non smoking.

★★★

B&B

'Clashdale'
26 Inchmead Drive, Kelso, Roxburghshire, TD5 7LW
Tel: 01573 223405

Rooms	Facilities	Prices	Open
1 Single 1 Double	1 Pub Bath/Show	B&B per person from £16.00 Single from £16.00 Dbl/Twn Room only per person from £11.00	Open Jan-Dec

Comfortable, double glazed, centrally heated accommodation in quiet cul-de-sac. 5 minutes from town centre. Tea on arrival and evening cuppa.

Kelso, Roxburghshire

Map Ref: 2E6

★★★ B&B

Craignethan House

Jedburgh Road, Kelso, TD5 8AZ
Tel: 01573 224818

1 Twin | 1 Priv.NOT ensuite | B&B per person from £18.50 Single from £18.50 Dbl/Twn | Open Jan-Dec
2 Double | 1 Pub Bath/Show

Experience a warm Scottish welcome at this delightful detached house overlooking the town and the river Tweed, with panoramic views of Floors Castle and surrounding countryside. Ground floor bedroom. Ample off street parking adjoining the house.

★★★ B&B

Goldilands

Roxburgh Road, Heiton, Kelso, Roxburghshire, TD5 8TP
Tel/Fax: 01573 450671
E-mail: jimbroth@aol.com

2 Twin | All En Suite | B&B per person £25.00 Single £20.00 Dbl/Twn | Open Jan-Dec
1 Double

Brand new centrally heated bungalow, all ground floor en-suite bedrooms, plus residents lounge. House separate from owners home in attractive gardens with ample private parking.

★★★ GUEST HOUSE

Diah & Douglas McAdam

Abbey Bank, The Knowes, Kelso, Roxburghshire, TD5 7BH
Tel/Fax: 01573 226550
E-mail: diah@abbeybank.freeserve.co.uk
Web: www.aboutscotland.com/kelso/abbeybank.html

1 Single | 4 En Suite fac | B&B per person £26.00-£32.00 Single £20.00-£26.00 Dbl/Twn | Open Jan-Dec
3 Twin | 1 Pub Bath/Show
2 Double

Elegant, historic 1820 town house. Full of character, providing a true Scottish welcome with oriental style comfort. 3 min walk to the Abbey, town centre and River Tweed. Ideal touring base. Private parking, lock up garage available on request.

by Kelso, Roxburghshire

Map Ref: 2E6

★★★ B&B

The Old Joiners Cottage

Eckford, Kelso, Roxburghshire, TD5 8LG
Tel/Fax: 01835 850323
E-mail: joiners.cottage@virgin.net

1 Double | All En Suite | B&B per person £18.00-£21.00 Single £18.00-£21.00 Double | Open Jan-Dec excl B&B + Eve.Meal from £25.50
1 Family

A charming Border style cottage situated midway between Jedburgh and Kelso, offering high quality accommodation and home cooking in a friendly atmosphere. Close to St Cuthbert's Way, one of Scotland's classic walks. Pets by arrangemet.

★★★★ B&B

Whitehill Farm

Nenthorn, by Kelso, Roxburghshire, TD5 7RZ
Tel/Fax: 01573 470203
E-mail: besmith@whitehillfarm.freeserve.co.uk

2 Single | 1 En Suite fac | B&B per person from £22.00 Single from £23.00 Twin | Open Jan-Dec excl Xmas/New Year B&B + Eve.Meal from £36.00
2 Twin | 1 Pub Bath/Show

18c farmhouse with superb views on mixed farm. Ideally placed for touring the Borders region and just off the Kelso/Edinburgh road. Real cooking, fresh food, meal by arrrangement.

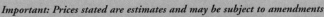

Important: Prices stated are estimates and may be subject to amendments

Kilmarnock, Ayrshire

Map Ref: 1G6

★★★ B&B

Aulton Farmhouse Bed & Breakfast
Aulton Farm, Kilmaurs, Kilmarnock, KA3 2PQ
Tel: 01563 538208

Pedigree Limousin cattle farm, close to the beaches and golf courses of Ayrshire, yet handy for Glasgow and Prestwick airports.

1 Twin | 2 Priv.NOT ensuite | B&B per person | Open Jan-Dec
2 Double | | from £18.00 Single |
1 Family | | from £18.00 Double |

C V

★★ GUEST HOUSE

Eriskay House
2 Dean Terrace, Kilmarnock, Ayrshire, KA3 1RJ
Tel: 01563 532061 Fax: 01563 544262
E-mail: eriskayhouse@hotmail.com

Detached villa conveniently situated on main bus route and close to Dean Park and Castle. Enclosed secure car park. Ideal base for touring Burns Country, Culzean Castle or taking the ferry to Arran.

2 Single | 4 En Suite fac | B&B per person | Open Jan-Dec
3 Twin | 1 Pub Bath/Show | from £15.00 Single | B&B + Eve.Meal
1 Double | | from £15.00 Dbl/Twn | from £23.00
1 Family | | Room only per person |
| | from £15.00 |

C V

★★★★ B&B

Hillhouse Farm B&B
Grassyards Road, Kilmarnock, Ayrshire, KA3 6HG
Tel: 01563 523370

The Howie family welcome you to their working farm in peaceful central location, 1 mile east of Kilmarnock. Large bedrooms, TV lounge and sun porch have superb views of the garden and open countryside. Farmhouse breakfasts and home baking for bedtime supper.

1 Twin | 2 En Suite fac | B&B per person | Open Jan-Dec
2 Family | 1 Priv.NOT ensuite | from £20.00 Single |
| 2 Pub Bath/Show | from £18.00 Twin |

C V

★★ B&B

Muirhouse Farm B&B
Gatehead, by Kilmarnock, Ayrshire, KA2 0BT
Tel/Fax: 01563 523975

Large family farmhouse on 170 acre dairy farm, 2 miles (3kms) from Kilmarnock. Quiet rural position. Near to Troon, ideal for golfers. Easy access to Glasgow also Arran Ferry. Choice of excellent eating places nearby.

1 Twin | 2 En Suite fac | B&B per person | Open Jan-Dec
1 Double | 1 Priv.NOT ensuite | from £17.00 Single |
1 Family | | from £17.00 Dbl/Twn |

C W V

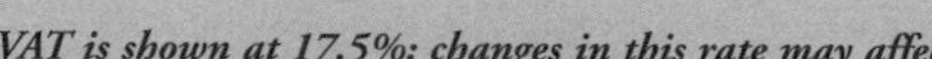

VAT is shown at 17.5%: changes in this rate may affect prices.

Key to symbols is on back flap.

Kilmarnock, Ayrshire

Map Ref: 1G6

"Tamarind"

24 ARRAN AVENUE, KILMARNOCK KA3 1TP

Tel: 01563 571788 Fax: 01563 533515

e.mail: James@tamarind25.freeserve.co.uk

The accommodation at 'Tamarind' was created with the International visitor in mind. Rooms are equipped with remote control TV and all are ensuite. A heated swimming pool (in season) is also available for your enjoyment. *Discerning travellers will feel at home here.*

★★★

B&B

Mrs C Turner

Tamarind, 24 Arran Avenue, Kilmarnock, Ayrshire, KA3 1TP
Tel: 01563 571788 Fax: 01563 533515
E-mail: James@tamarind25.freeserve.co.uk

1 Single
2 Twin
1 Family

All En Suite

B&B per person
£25.00-£30.00 Single
£35.00-£40.00 Twin

Open Jan-Dec

Ranch style bungalow with small heated swimming pool in residential area. Convenient base for touring, and centrally situated for Ayrshire's many golf courses.

Kilwinning, Ayrshire

Map Ref: 1G6

★★

B&B

Blairholme

45 Byres Road, Kilwinning, Ayrshire, KA13 6JU
Tel: 01294 552023
E-mail: t.cully@nationwideisp.net

1 Twin
1 Double

Priv.NOT Ensuite

B&B per person
£15.00-£20.00 Single
Room only per person
from £15.00

Open Jun-Dec excl Xmas/New Year

Turn of the century, semi detached bungalow. One ground floor room. Close to town centre. Ideal base for touring by car or train.

BRONZE

Kippford, by Dalbeattie, Kirkcudbrightshire

Map Ref: 2A10

ROSEMOUNT

ROSEMOUNT, KIPPFORD, DALBEATTIE DG5 4LN

Tel/Fax: 01556 620214

Sandy and Jess Muir extend a warm welcome for you to relax in our small friendly guest house. Ideal base for touring, walking, golfing, fishing and bird-watching. Home-cooked meals and preserves available to guests. Kippford is an unspoilt village with breathtaking sunsets and view. 10% reduction per week.

★★★

GUEST HOUSE

Rosemount

Kippford, Dalbeattie, Kirkcudbrightshire, DG5 4LN
Tel/Fax: 01556 620214

2 Twin
2 Double
1 Family

3 En Suite fac
2 Priv.NOT ensuite

B&B per person
from £25.00 Single
£19.00-£22.00 Dbl/Twn

Open Feb-Nov
B&B + Eve.Meal
£31.00-£34.00

Small friendly guest house on the Urr Estuary offering a superb view and spectacular sunsets. Smoking and non-smoking lounges.

Kirkcudbright — Map Ref: 2A10

★★★ B&B

Number 3 B&B
3 High Street, Kirkcudbright, Dumfries & Galloway, DG6 4JZ
Tel: 01557 330881
E-mail: ham_wwk@hotmail.com

Rooms	Facilities	B&B per person	Open
2 Twin 1 Double	2 Ensuite fac 1 Priv.Bath/Show	£30.00 Single £25.00 Dbl/Twn	Open Jan-Dec

A 'B' listed Georgian House with a 17th century dining area. Rich in ambience this property will charm those seeking warmth and comfort in delightful period surroundings. Opposite Broughton House, and in easy walking distance of the harbour and town centre.

Langholm, Dumfriesshire — Map Ref: 2D9

★★ B&B

Bush of Ewes Farmhouse
Ewes, Langholm, Dumfriesshire, DG3 0HN
Tel: 013873 81241

Rooms	Facilities	B&B per person	Open
2 Twin 1 Double		£15.00-£17.00 Single £15.00-£17.00 Dbl/Twn	Open Apr-Dec B&B + Eve.Meal from £25.00

Farmhouse on mixed working farm located 5 miles north of Langholm on the A7 tourist route to Edinburgh in the border country. 18 miles South of Hawick, ideal for walkers and bird watchers. Evening meal by prior arrangement.

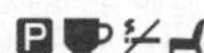

Largs, Ayrshire — Map Ref: 1F5

★★★ B&B

Belmont House
2 Broomfield Place, Largs, Ayrshire, KA30 8DR
Tel: 01475 676264

Rooms	Facilities	B&B per person	Open
1 Twin 3 Double	1 En Suite fac 2 Shared Bath 1 Priv.NOT ensuite	from £20.00 Single from £20.00 Dbl/Twn	Jan-Dec excl Xmas and New Year

Interesting old house on South Largs waterfront. Panoramic view over Clyde, busy with shipping and yacht traffic to islands and highlands. Spacious rooms, ground floor bedroom, sitting room available day time. Reductions for children, private parking, full facilities. Quiet location but only 5 minutes walk from shops, restaurants and ferry. Handy for airports.

★★ GUEST HOUSE

Carlton Guest House
10 Aubery Crescent, Largs, Ayrshire, KA30 8PR
Tel: 01475 672313 Fax: 01475 676128
E-mail: carlton.guesthouse@usa.net
Web: www.carltonguesthouse.com

Rooms	Facilities	B&B per person	Open
1 Single 1 Twin 1 Double 1 Family	1 En Suite fac	from £17.00 Single from £17.00 Dbl/Twn	Open Jan-Dec

On a quiet cul de sac on Largs promenade with full views to the ferries and the islands. Lounge with superb views situated on the first floor, has satellite T.V.

★★★ GUEST HOUSE

'Lea-Mar' Guest House
Douglas Street, Largs, Ayrshire, KA30 8PS
Tel/Fax: 01475 672447

Rooms	Facilities	B&B per person	Open
2 Twin 2 Double	All En Suite	from £23.00 Dbl/Twn	Open Jan-Dec excl Xmas/New Year, Feb

Detached bungalow in quiet area, yet close to town. 100 yards from the promenade and beach. Ideal base for touring. Private parking. All rooms ensuite.

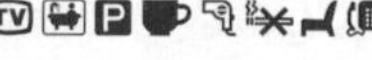

VAT is shown at 17.5%: changes in this rate may affect prices.

Key to symbols is on back flap.

Largs, Ayrshire

Map Ref: 1F5

GUEST HOUSE

Lilac Holm Guest House
14 Noddleburn Road (off Barr Cresc.), Largs, Ayrshire, KA30 8PY
Tel/Fax: 01475 672020
E-mail: LilacHolm@hotmail.com

1 Single, 2 Twin, 2 Double, 1 Family
2 Ensuite fac, 2 Pub Bath/Show
B&B per person: from £17.00 Single, from £17.00 Dbl/Twn
Open Jan-Dec excl Xmas/New Year

Detached bungalow style house in quiet residential area overlooking the Noddleburn, with views of the hills behind the town. Private parking. Personal attention of the owners.

B&B

The Old Rectory
Aubery Crescent, Largs, Ayrshire, KA30 8PR
Tel: 01475 674405
E-mail: ashrona@aol.com

1 Twin, 1 Family
1 Pub Bath/Show
B&B per person: from £20.00 Single, from £18.00 Dbl/Twn
Open Feb-Nov

A warm welcome at this family home situated on the sea front with views over Cumbrae to Arran. A five minute stroll along the promenade into town. Large garden with private parking area. Spacious residents lounge with seperate dining room and good sized bedrooms makes for a comfortable and relaxing stay.

GUEST HOUSE

St Leonard's Guest House
9 Irvine Road, Largs, Ayrshire, KA30 8JP
Tel: 01475 673318

2 Twin, 1 Double, 1 Family
1 En Suite fac, 1 Pub Bath/Show, 1 Pub Wc
B&B per person: from £21.00 Single, from £17.00 Dbl/Twn
Room only per person from £16.00
Open Jan-Dec excl Xmas/New Year

Elegant villa with off-street parking. Short walk away from town centre, restaurants, beach front and the railway station with its connections to Glasgow. Ideally placed for trips to Arran, Cumbrae and Bute by ferry, or in Summer sailing on the SS Waverly.

B&B

South Whittleburn Farm
Brisbane Glen, Largs, Ayrshire, KA30 8SN
Tel: 01475 675881 Fax: 01475 675080

1 Twin, 1 Double, 1 Family
All En Suite
B&B per person: from £20.00 Single, from £20.00 Dbl/Twn
Open Jan-Dec

Warm friendly hospitality, enormous delicious breakfasts. Ample parking. AA four diamonds, chosen by 'Which Best Bed & Breakfast'. Enjoy a great holiday on our working sheep farm, only five mins drive from the popular tourist resort of Largs. (45 minutes from Glasgow or Prestwick Airport). A warm welcome from Mary Watson.

B&B

Stonehaven Guest House
8 Netherpark Crescent, off Routenburn Road, Largs, KA30 8QB
Tel: 01475 673319
E-mail: stonehaven.martin@virgin.net

1 Single, 1 Twin, 1 Double
1 En Suite fac, 1 Pub Bath/Show
B&B per person: from £20.00 Single, from £23.00 Dbl/Twn
Open Jan-Dec excl Xmas/New Year

Situated in quiet residential area in front of Routenburn Golf Course, overlooking the Largs Bay, Isle of Cumbrae with the Isle of Arran and Ailsa Craig in the distance.

Important: Prices stated are estimates and may be subject to amendments

Largs, Ayrshire Map Ref: 1F5

Tigh-na-Ligh Guest House

104 Brisbane Road, Largs, Ayrshire KA30 8NN

Tel: 01475 673975 E.mail: tighnaligh@tinyonline.co.uk

Tigh-na-Ligh offers attractively decorated apartments. Dining room with individual tables where we serve a hearty Scottish breakfast. All bedrooms ensuite/private facilities with CTV and tea/coffee making facilities. Ample off-street private parking. Current fire certificate.

★★★ GUEST HOUSE

Tigh-na-Ligh Guest House

104 Brisbane Road, Largs, Ayrshire, KA30 8NN
Tel: 01475 673975
E-mail: tighnaligh@tinyonline.co.uk
Web: www.s-h-systems.co.uk/a06156

A warm and friendly welcome awaits you at Tigh-na-Ligh, situated in a quiet residential area. We pride ourselves on maintaining the highest standards and cleanliness. Most rooms have superb views of hills and countryside. All bedrooms have central heating, radio alarm, hairdryer etc. Pleasant dining room. All apartments recently refurbished. Mrs Gosling can suggest various day trips/outings. Easy access to the islands of the Clyde and Argyll peninsula. We are just five minutes stroll from the sea front.

2 Twin
2 Double
1 Family

4 En Suite fac
1 Priv.NOT ensuite

B&B per person
£30.00 single
from £23.00 Dbl/Twn

Open Feb-Nov
B&B + Eve.Meal
from £35.00

TV P C W V

★★★★ GUEST HOUSE

Whin Park Guest House

16 Douglas Street, Largs, Ayrshire, KA30 8PS
Tel: 01475 673437

Warm, comfortable and relaxing atmosphere, near seafront and Vikingar. Ground floor ensuite bedroom.

1 Single
1 Twin
2 Double
1 Family

All En Suite
1 Pub Bath/Show

B&B per person
from £26.00 Single
from £26.00 Dbl/Twn
Room only per person
from £21.00

Open Jan-Dec

TV P C £ W

Lauder, Berwickshire Map Ref: 2D6

★★ SMALL HOTEL

Black Bull Hotel

3 Market Place, Lauder, Berwickshire, TD2 6SR
Tel: 01578 722208 Fax: 01578 722419
E-mail: blackbullhotel@hotmail.com

Historic Coaching Inn circa 1500, traditionally furnished retaining its old world charm. In village centre on the A68 , only 25 miles south of Edinburgh centre.

6 Single
2 Double
1 Family

B&B per person
from £25.00 Single
from £20.00 Dbl/Twn

Open Jan-Dec

TV C £ V

★★★ B&B

Tricia & Peter Gilardi

The Grange, 6 Edinburgh Road, Lauder, Berwickshire, TD2 6TW
Tel/Fax: 01578 722649

Detached house standing in large garden with lovely views of surrounding countryside. A non-smoking house. Located on the Southern Upland Walk and close to several stately homes and castles. 45 minutes drive to Edinburgh.

2 Twin
1 Double

1 Pub Bath/Show

B&B per person
from £17.00 Single
from £17.00 Dbl/Twn

Open Jan-Dec excl Xmas

C W V

Lochmaben, Dumfriesshire — Map Ref: 2B9

★★★ B&B

Ardbeg Cottage

19 Castle Street, Lochmaben, Dumfriesshire, DG11 1NY
Tel/Fax: 01387 811855
Web: www.visitscotland.com/ardbeg

1 Twin 1 Double	All En Suite	B&B per person from £18.00 Single from £18.00 Dbl/Twn	Open Feb-Dec excl Xmas B&B + Eve.Meal from £25.00

Elma and Bill welcome you to their happy home, Ardbeg Cottage, which is situated in a residential area near the town centre. Evening meal by prior arrangement - served in the lounge/dining room.

TV W V

Lockerbie, Dumfriesshire — Map Ref: 2C9

★★★ B&B

Corrie Lodge Country House Bed & Breakfast

Corrie Road, Lockerbie, Dumfriesshire, DG11 2NG
Tel: 01576 710237

1 Twin 2 Double	2 Priv.NOT ensuite	B&B per person from £20.00 Single from £20.00 Dbl/Twn	Open Jan-Dec B&B + Eve.Meal from £30.00

A warm welcome is assured at this family run country house which retains much of its original character. Lockerbie 3 miles (5kms). Horses stabled if required, riding available. Golf course nearby. Evening meal by prior arrangement.

P

The Elms

Dumfries Road, Lockerbie, Dumfriesshire DG11 2EF
Tel: 01576 203898 Fax: 01576 203898
e.mail: theelms@gofornet.co.uk Web: www.lockerbie-lodging.com

Comfortable home in residential area a short walk from town centre. Private parking. Spacious lounge to relax in and attractive dining room to enjoy our hearty varied breakfasts. Completely refurbished bedrooms designed for comfort and with many extras. Excellent local golf, fishing, shooting and walking. Friendly personal welcome.

★★★★ B&B

The Elms

Dumfries Road, Lockerbie, Dumfriesshire, DG11 2EF
Tel/Fax: 01576 203898
E-mail: theelms@gofornet.co.uk
Web: www.lockerbie-lodging.com

1 Double 1 Twin	En Suite fac	B&B per person from £21.00 Dbl/Twn Room only per person from £16.00	Open Mar-Nov

A traditional Victorian house with all modern comforts yet retaining many period features. Very comfortable accommodation with seperate dining room and guests lounge. In easy walking distance of village centre. Hotel bar and restaurant next door, and off-road parking.

TV P V

★★ HOTEL

Ravenshill House Hotel

12 Dumfries Road, Lockerbie,
Dumfriesshire, DG11 2EF
Tel/Fax: 01576 202882
E-mail: Ravenshillhouse.hotel@virgin.net

3 Twin 3 Double 2 Family	7 En Suite fac 1 Priv.NOT ensuite	B&B per person £25.00-£35.00 Single £22.50-£25.00 Dbl/Twn Room only per person from £20.00	Open Jan-Dec excl Xmas/New Year B&B + Eve.Meal from £32.00

A family run hotel set in 2.5 acres of garden in a quiet residential area, yet convenient for town centre and M6/M74. With a chef proprietor the hotel enjoys a reputation for good food, comfortable accommodation and friendly service. Weekend, short and golfing breaks.

TV P C W V

Important: Prices stated are estimates and may be subject to amendments

Lockerbie, Dumfriesshire

Map Ref: 2C9

GUEST HOUSE

Rosehill Guest House
9 Carlisle Road, Lockerbie, Dumfriesshire, DG11 2DR
Tel/Fax: 01576 202378

1 Single, 2 Twin, 1 Double, 1 Family | 3 En Suite fac, 2 Priv.NOT ensuite | B&B per person £18.00-£20.00 Single, £18.00-£20.00 Dbl/Twn; Room only per person £16.00-£18.00 | Open Jan-Dec excl Xmas/New Year

Family guest house in residential area, 5 minutes walk from town centre. Ample car parking. Walking distance for a choice of restaurants.

by Lockerbie, Dumfriesshire

Map Ref: 2C9

B&B

Mrs C Hislop
Carik Cottage, Waterbeck, by Lockerbie, Dumfriesshire, DG11 3EU
Tel: 01461 600652

1 Single, 1 Double, 1 Family | 2 En Suite fac, 1 Priv.NOT ensuite | B&B per person £20.00-£22.00 Single, £20.00-£22.00 Double; Room only per person from £14.00 | Open Mar-Oct

Tastefully converted cottage in peaceful rural setting with beautiful views where in the summertime you can see our small herd of Belted Galloways. Only 3 miles(5km) from the M74. Ideal for touring south west Scotland or an overnight stop between North and South. Lounge available.

B&B

Nether Boreland Bed & Breakfast
Lockerbie, Dumfriesshire, DG11 2LL
Tel/Fax: 01576 610248
E-mail: amanda@chariots.org.uk

1 Twin, 2 Double | 2 En Suite fac, 1 Priv.NOT ensuite | B&B per person from £27.50 Single, from £22.50 Dbl/Twn; Room only per person from £20.00 | Open Jan-Dec

Welcome to quality accommodation in our comfortable farmhouse in peaceful, friendly surroundings 7 miles from M74. Our breakfast menu includes free range eggs. Equestrian, carriage driving and other activities available on the farm. Well appointed bedrooms with ensuite or private bathroom. TV, tea trays, hairdryers and clock/radios. Brochure available.

Mauchline, Ayrshire

Map Ref: 1H7

B&B

Treborane
Dykefield Farm, Mauchline, Ayrshire, KA5 6EY
Tel: 01290 550328

2 Family | 1 En Suite fac, 1 Pub Bath/Show | B&B per person £12.00-£15.00 Double; Room only per person from £10.00 | Open Jan-Dec; B&B + Eve.Meal £17.00-£20.00

Bed and breakfast accommodation in cottage on working farm in the heart of Burns Country. Friendly atmosphere, evening meal and ensuite bedroom. 1 mile from the village of Mauchline. 20 mins to the centre of Ayr town.

VAT is shown at 17.5%: changes in this rate may affect prices.

Key to symbols is on back flap.

Maybole, Ayrshire Map Ref: 1G8

★★★ B&B

Holmlea
62 Culzean Road, Maybole, Ayrshire, KA19 8AH
Tel: 01655 882736 Fax: 01655 883557
E-mail: gilmour_mck@msn.com

1 Double, 1 Family | 2 Pub Bath/Show | B&B per person from £22.00 Single, from £18.00 Double | Open Mar-Oct

Victorian family villa on B7023, 4 miles (6kms) North of Culzean Castle. Ideal centre for touring Burns Country. Convenient stopover point on the Carlisle to Glasgow cycle route.

C W

BRONZE

Melrose, Roxburghshire Map Ref: 2D6

★★★ B&B

Braidwood
Buccleuch Street, Melrose, Roxburghshire, TD6 9LD
Tel: 01896 822488

3 Double, 1 Fam/Twin | 2 En Suite fac, 2 Priv.NOT ensuite | B&B per person from £20.00 Double | Open Jan-Dec

Friendly welcome in attractive listed town house only a stones throw from Melrose Abbey and Priorwood Gardens. Home baking.

TV

W V

★★★★ GUEST HOUSE

Dunfermline House
Buccleuch Street, Melrose, TD6 9LB
Tel/Fax: 01896 822148
E-mail: bestaccom@dunmel.freeserve.co.uk
Web: www.dunmel.freeserve.co.uk

1 Single, 2 Twin, 2 Double | 4 En Suite fac, 1 Priv.NOT ensuite | B&B per person from £23.00 Single, from £23.00 Dbl/Twn | Open Jan-Dec

Overlooking Melrose Abbey. A highly respected and well established guest house offering very high standards. All rooms (except one) with en-suite facilities, the single room has a private bathroom. Traditional Scottish breakfasts with interesting variations. Non-smoking house.

TV

W V

BRONZE

★★★ B&B

The Gables B&B
Darnick, Melrose, Roxburghshire, TD6 9AL
Tel/Fax: 01896 822479

1 Single, 1 Twin, 1 Double | 1 Pub Bath/Show | B&B per person from £22.00 Single, from £18.00 Dbl/Twn | Open Jan-Dec

Georgian villa in centre of quiet village, 3/4 mile/1km from Melrose. Ideal base for touring the Borders. Home baking. Non-smoking.

TV

C W V

Important: Prices stated are estimates and may be subject to amendments

Melrose, Roxburghshire

Map Ref: 2D6

B&B

Torwood Lodge

30 High Cross Avenue, Melrose, Roxburghshire, TD6 9SU
Tel: 01896 822220
Web: www.torwoodlodge.co.uk

Large comfortable Victorian family house in attractive location. Easy walking distance to town, River Tweed and Eildon Hills. All ensuite facilities.

2 Twin, 1 Double | All En Suite | B&B per person from £28.50 Single, from £23.50 Dbl/Twn | Open Jan-Dec excl Xmas/New Year

V

Moffat, Dumfriesshire

Map Ref: 2B8

B&B

Alton House

Moffat, Dumfriesshire, DG10 9LB
Tel: 01683 220903/07850 129105 (mobile)

A historic country house set in 3 acres of secluded grounds on the outskirts of Moffat. A former home of the ancient chiefs of Clan Moffat. Furnished with antiques and works of art. Wonderful views. Accommodation is in a self-contained suite of private rooms at ground floor level.

1 Private/Suite | Ensuite fac | B&B per person £19.00-£24.00 Single, £19.00-£24.00 Double, Room only per person £17.00-£21.00 | Open Jan-Dec

C V

GUEST HOUSE

Barnhill Springs Country Guest House

Moffat, Dumfriesshire, DG10 9QS
Tel: 01683 220580

Barnhill Springs is an early victorian country house standing in its own grounds overlooking upper Annandale. It is a quiet family run guest house situated 1/2 a mile from the A74/M at the Moffat junction no.15. Barnhill Springs is ideally situated as a centre for touring Southern Scotland, for walking and cycling on the Southern Upland Way or for a relaxing overnight stop for holiday makers heading North or South. AA 3 diamonds.

2 Twin, 2 Double, 1 Family | 1 Priv.NOT ensuite, 2 Pub Bath/Show | B&B per person from £22.00 Single, from £22.00 Dbl/Twn | Open Jan-Dec, B&B + Eve.Meal from £36.00

V

B&B

Burnside

Well Road, Moffat, Dumfriesshire, DG10 9BW
Tel: 01683 221900

A Georgian House restored to its former glory set in an acre of attractive gardens. Accommodation of the highest standards, with hospitality and attention to detail to match. A quiet residential area in easy walking distance of the town centre.

1 Twin, 1 Double | All En Suite fac | B&B per person £22.50 Dbl/Twn | Open Mar-Nov

W V

Moffat, Dumfriesshire — Map Ref: 2B8

★★★★
B&B

Fiona Corlett
Craigie Lodge, Ballplay Road, Moffat, Dumfriesshire, DG10 9JU
Tel: 01683 221769
E-mail: craigielodge@aol.com

1 Twin
2 Double

All En Suite

B&B per person
£18.00-£21.00 Dbl/Twn

Open Jan-Dec excl Xmas/New Year
B&B + Eve.Meal
£30.00-£33.00

Large Victorian family house set in mature 1/2 acre garden. All rooms ensuite facilities. Ground floor accommodation available. Reduced rates 3 days. Evening meal by arrangement.

★★★★
B&B

Hazel Bank
Academy Road, Moffat, Dumfriesshire, DG10 9HP
Tel: 01683 220294 Fax: 01683 221675
E-mail: ruth@hazelbankmoffat.co.uk

1 Single
1 Double
1 Family

1 En Suite fac
ground floor

B&B per person
£23.00-£25.00 Single
£18.00-£20.00 Double

Open Jan-Dec

Family home, centrally situated 2 minutes from town centre. Many hotels and restaurants in the immediate vicinity. Good base for touring. Ground floor ensuite available.

★★★
B&B

Robert H Jackson
Ericstane, Moffat, Dumfriesshire, DG10 9LT
Tel: 01683 220127

1 Twin
1 Double

All En Suite

B&B per person
from £23.00 Single
from £18.00 Dbl/Twn

Open Jan-Dec

Period farmhouse on a working farm located in the peaceful valley of Annan Water. 4 miles (6kms) from Moffat, which offers a good range of shops, pubs, hotels and restaurants.

Moffat, Dumfriesshire — Map Ref: 2B8

WOODHEAD FARM

OLD CARLISLE ROAD, MOFFAT, DUMFRIESSHIRE DG10 9LU

Telephone/Fax: 01683 220225

Luxuriously appointed farmhouse just two miles from beautiful spa town of Moffat. Breakfast is served in conservatory overlooking garden. All rooms are ensuite and have views of surrounding hills. Murray and Sylvia extend a warm welcome to all their guests. Ample safe parking. 120-acre working stock farm.

B&B

Mrs Jackson
Woodhead Farm, Moffat, Dumfriesshire, DG10 9LU
Tel/Fax: 01683 220225

2 Twin
1 Double

All En Suite

B&B per person
to £30.00 Single
to £25.00-£27.50 Dbl/Twn

Open Jan-Dec
B&B + Eve.Meal
to £38.50-£43.50

Luxuriously furnished farmhouse situated on 100 acre working stock farm with commanding panoramic views of the surrounding countryside. All ensuite. Evening meal by prior arrangement.

B&B

Mrs S Long
Coxhill Farm, Old Carlisle Road, Moffat, Dumfriesshire, DG10 9QN
Tel: 01683 220471

1 Twin Ensuite
1 Double Ensuite

B&B per person
from £22.50 Dbl/Twn

Open Jan-Dec

Attractive modern farmhouse with en-suite bedrooms. Set in 70 acres of unspoilt countryside on a working sheep farm. Lovely views, beautiful rose gardens and ample parking. Walking distance to Moffat. 1/4 miles from Southern Upland Way. A peaceful base for South West Scotland and all sporting activities. Non-smoking.

B&B

Morag
19 Old Carlisle Road, Moffat, Dumfriesshire, DG10 9QJ
Tel: 01683 220690

1 Single
1 Twin
1 Double

1 Pub Bath/Show

B&B per person
£17.00-£19.00 Single
£16.00-£18.00 Dbl/Twn

Open Jan-Dec
B&B + Eve.Meal
£25.00-£28.00

A warm welcome is assured at this family run Victorian house located within quiet suburbs 1/2 mile from Moffat town centre. It is an excellent base for exploring the Moffat Water Valley and the Galloway countryside to the west. Golf, fishing, walking and other country pursuits available locally. Southern upland way 1/2 mile. Evening meals by arrangement. Non-smoking.

B&B

Queensberry House
12 Beechgrove, Moffat, Dumfriesshire, DG10 9RS
Tel: 01683 220538

3 Double

All En Suite
All on grd flr

B&B per person
from £22.00 Single
from £20.00 Double
Room only per person
from £18.00

Open Jan-Dec excl Xmas

A warm welcome is guaranteed at this nicely appointed Victorian house in a quiet area opposite the bowling green and within a few minutes walk from town centre.

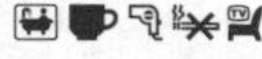

Moffat, Dumfriesshire — Map Ref: 2B8

★★
GUEST HOUSE

Rockhill Guest House
14 Beechgrove, Moffat, Dumfriesshire, DG10 9RS
Tel: 01683 220283
Web: www.moffatown.com/moffat/accommodation

Rooms	Facilities	B&B per person	Open
2 Single	5 En Suite fac	£17.00-£21.00 Single	Open Jan-Nov
1 Twin	2 Pub Bath/Show	£17.00-£21.00 Dbl/Twn	B&B + Eve.Meal
3 Double			£26.00-£30.00
4 Family			

Victorian house overlooking bowling green and park, in quiet area close to town centre. Open outlook to hills. Own private carpark. Ensuite rooms; some rooms with colour television. Pets welcome by arrangement. Evening meals available also by prior arrangement.

★★★
GUEST HOUSE

Seamore Guest House
Academy Road, Moffat, Dumfriesshire, DG10 9HW
Tel: 01683 220404 Fax: 01683 221313
Web: www.seamorehouse.co.uk

Rooms	Facilities	B&B per person	Open
1 Twin	4 En Suite fac	£20.00-£22.50 Single	Open Jan-Dec
3 Double	1 Priv.NOT ensuite	£16.00-£20.00 Dbl/Twn	
1 Family			

Comfortable family run guest house in centre of Moffat. All rooms with own private bathroom, plus a comfortable guests lounge. Children and pets welcome. Good centre for touring. Walkers welcome. Private off road parking.

by New Galloway, Kirkcudbrightshire — Map Ref: 1H9

HIGH PARK FARM

W

Balmaclellan, New Galloway, Castle Douglas DG7 3PT
Telephone/Fax: 01644 420298 e.mail: HIGH.PARK@farming.co.uk

HIGH PARK is a comfortable stone-built farmhouse built in 1838. The 171-acre dairy, sheep and stock rearing farm is situated by Loch Ken on the A713 amidst Galloway's beautiful scenery within easy reach of hills and coast. Good food guaranteed. All bedrooms have washbasins, shaver points, colour TV, tea/coffee facilities. Pets welcome.

★★ B&B **Brochure: Mrs Jessie E. Shaw at above address**

★★
B&B

High Park Farm
Balmaclellan, by New Galloway, Castle Douglas, DG7 3PT
Tel/Fax: 01644 420298
E.mail: HIGH.PARK@farming.co.uk

Rooms	Facilities	B&B per person	Open
1 Twin	1 Pub Bath/Show	from £16.00 Single	Open Apr-Oct
2 Double		from £16.00 Dbl/Twn	

Early 19c farmhouse on working dairy and sheep farm, situated by Loch Ken off A713, amidst beautiful Galloway scenery. Relax in the evening in the comfortable lounge/dining room after a busy day sightseeing.

Important: Prices stated are estimates and may be subject to amendments

by New Galloway, Kirkcudbrightshire | **Map Ref: 1H9**

B&B

Kalmar
Balmaclellan, Kirkcudbrightshire, DG7 3QF
Tel: 01644 420685 Fax: 01644 420244
E-mail: kalmar@dial.pipex.com
Web: www.kalmar.dial.pipex.com

2 Twin | All En Suite | B&B per person from £27.00 Single from £20.00 Twin | Open Jan-Dec B&B + Eve.Meal from £30.00

Modern warm village home all ensuite with baths and showers. Golf course 2 miles away and only 12 pounds per day . This area is world renowned for fishing, walking, sailing and bird watching. The owners enjoy cooking and will provide the very best of Scottish food, beautifully presented. Very quiet and peaceful, the whole area is almost a traffic free zone.

Newton Stewart, Wigtownshire | **Map Ref: 1G10**

B&B

Benera Bed & Breakfast
Corsbie Road, Newton Stewart, Wigtownshire, DG8 6JD
Tel: 01671 403443

1 Twin, 1 Double | 1 En Suite fac, 1 Priv.NOT ensuite | B&B per person from £20.00 Single from £18.50 Dbl/Twn Room only per person from £14.00 | Open Apr-Oct

Modern bungalow peacefully situated on the edge of the town with superb views of the Galloway Hills. Ideal location for golfing, fishing, walking, cycling and bird watching as well as exploring this scenic corner of Scotland.

B&B

Clugston Farm
Clugston Farm, Newton Stewart, Wigtownshire, DG8 9BH
Tel: 01671 830338

1 Twin, 1 Double | 2 Pub Bath/Show | B&B per person from £16.00 Single from £15.00 Dbl/Twn Room only from £20.00 | Open Mar-Oct B&B + Eve.Meal from £23.00

About 5 miles (8kms) off the A75. Near the sea, hill walking and easy access to 3 golf courses. Two ground floor rooms.

Newton Stewart, Wigtownshire | Map Ref: 1G10

CREEBRIDGE LODGE

***Minnigaff, Newton Stewart, Wigtownshire* DG8 6NR**
***Tel/Fax:* 01671 402319**

Creebridge Lodge is a beautiful listed house with private parking, a sunny breakfast room and comfortable bedrooms. All our ensuite bathrooms comprise a bath as well as a shower, wc etc. Ideally situated for evening meals, shops and golf. The perfect base for exploring this beautiful part of Scotland.

B&B

Creebridge Lodge
Minnigaff, Newton Stewart, Wigtownshire, DG8 6NR
Tel/Fax: 01671 402319

1 Twin, 2 Double | All En Suite | B&B per person from £23.00 Single, from £23.00 Dbl/Twn | Open Jan-Dec

A warm welcome and comfortable ensuite rooms await you in this beautiful period house. Ample parking, super breakfasts, elegant lounge. Good choice of evening meals nearby. Colour tv's/hairdryers/tea and coffee etc. in all rooms. Double glazed bedrooms, full central heating, lock-up area for bikes. Drying/ironing facilities available. Perfectly situated guest house for everything this area has to offer.

by Newton Stewart, Wigtownshire | Map Ref: 1G10

★★★ B&B

Challoch Farm
Newton Stewart, Wigtownshire, DG8 6RB
Tel: 01671 402109
E-mail: lmoses3561@aol.com

1 Twin, 1 Double, 1 Family | 1 Ensuite fac, 1 Pub Bath/Show, 1 Priv.NOT ensuite | B&B per person from £18.00 Single, from £18.00 Dbl/Twn | Open Jan-Dec excl Xmas/New Year

Situated only 2 miles north of Newton Stewart on the A714, Challoch Farmhouse offers you the chance to relax in comfort and seclusion. Well appointed bedrooms and spacious front lounge. Substantial breakfast will set you up for a days fishing, golfing, hillwalking, birdwatching or simply to explore our lovely corner of south west Scotland.

Peebles | Map Ref: 2C6

B&B

Mrs Sheila Goldstraw
Venlaw Farm, Peebles, EH45 8QG
Tel: 01721 722040

1 Twin, 1 Double, 1 Family | 2 En Suite fac, 1 Priv.NOT ensuite, 1 Pub Bath/Show | B&B per person from £20.00 Single, from £20.00 Dbl/Twn | Open Apr-Oct

Modern farmhouse accomodation on working farm within the boundary of Peebles town, yet in peaceful rural setting. With lovely walks and scenery.

B&B

Lindores
60 Old Town, Peebles, EH45 8JE
Tel/Fax: 01721 720441
E-mail: lane.lindores@virgin.net
Web: www.aboutscotland.co.uk/peebles/lindores.html

1 Single, 2 Twin, 3 Double, 1 Family | 2 En Suite fac, 2 Priv.NOT ensuite, 1 Pub Bath/Show | B&B per person from £20.00 Single, from £16.00 Dbl/Twn; Room only per person from £13.00 | Open Jan-Dec excl Xmas/New Year; B&B + Eve.Meal from £25.00

Stone built late Victorian town house near edge of town, situated on main A72 tourist route. Convenient for touring the Borders and Edinburgh. Private parking.

Important: Prices stated are estimates and may be subject to amendments

Peebles — Map Ref: 2C6

★★★ B&B

'Shalem'
March Street, Peebles, EH45 8EP
Tel/Fax: 01721 721047
E-mail: maclellan@shalem.freeserve.co.uk

1 Double 1 Family	1 Priv.NOT ensuite 1 Ensuite	B&B per person from £20.00 Single from £18.00 Double	Open Jan-Dec excl Xmas/New Year

Friendly family home deceptively spacious in central location offering comfortable relaxed atmosphere. 5 minutes walk from High Street. Ideal for sightseeing and walking. Only 25 miles from Edinburgh city centre.

C

★★★★ B&B

The Steading
Venlaw Castle Road, Peebles, EH45 8QG
Tel: 01721 720293

1 Twin 2 Double	All En Suite	B&B per person from £25.00 Single from £20.00 Dbl/Twn Room only per person from £16.00	Open Jan-Dec

Tastefully converted steading with spacious rooms peacefully situated on an elevated position with panoramic views over Peebles. 10 minutes walk to town centre and River Tweed. 22 miles from Edinburgh. Ample parking.

C

★★★ B&B

Whitestone House
Innerleithen Road, Peebles, EH45 8BD
Tel/Fax: 01721 720337
Web: www.aboutscotland.com/peebles/whitestone.html

1 Single 1 Twin 2 Double 1 Family	2 Pub Bath/Show	B&B per person from £19.00 Single from £17.50 Dbl/Twn	Open Jan-Dec

Spacious Victorian house with fine views to surrounding hills on the A72. A comfortable sitting/breakfast room to relax in. German and French spoken. Ideal base for fishing/walking and central for Edinburgh and the Borders. Private parking.

C V

Winkston Farmhouse
Edinburgh Road, Peebles, EH45 8PH
Tel: 01721 721264

1 Twin 2 Double	1 Ensuite fac 1 Pub Bath/Show	B&B per person from £20.00 Single from £17.00 Dbl/Twn	Open Apr-Oct

'B' Listed Georgian farmhouse of historical interest, in own grounds. Friendly family atmosphere. On main bus route, 21 miles (34kms) from Edinburgh.

C W V

Woodlands B&B
Venlaw Farm Road, Peebles, EH45 8QQ
Tel: 01721 729882

1 Twin 2 Double	2 En Suite fac 1 Priv.NOT ensuite	B&B per person from £24.00 Single from £18.00 Dbl/Twn	Open Jan-Dec excl Xmas/New Year

Modern detached house on edge of town in quiet rural location within walled garden. Pleasant homely atmosphere. Ample parking.

C W V

VAT is shown at 17.5%: changes in this rate may affect prices.

Key to symbols is on back flap.

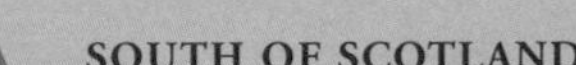

by Peebles

Map Ref: 2C6

B&B

Colliedean Bed & Breakfast

4 Elibank Road, Eddleston, Peebles, EH45 8QL
Tel: 01721 730281

1 Double
1 Family

1 Limited ensuite

B&B per person
from £18.00 Single
from £16.00 Double

Open Apr-Oct

Quietly situated in small village on main bus route to Edinburgh and Borders towns. Homely and friendly atmosphere. Good restaurant within walking distance.

B&B

Drochil Castle B&B

Drochil Castle Farm, Nr Romanno Bridge,
West Linton, Peeblesshire, EH46 7DD
Tel/fax: 01721 752249

1 Single
1 Twin
1 Double
1 Family

Ensuite fac
Pub Bath/Show

B&B per person
from £18.00 Single
£18.00-£20.00 Dbl/Twn

Open Jan-Dec

A warm welcome awaits you at this traditional working beef and sheep farm. Set amongst rolling borders hills with fine views down the Lyne & Tweed Valley. Located beside the ruins of the 16th century Drochil Castle.

B&B

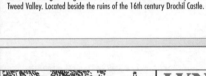

Lyne Farmhouse

Lyne Farm, Peebles, Peeblesshire, EH45 8NR
Tel/Fax: 01721 740255
E-mail: awaddell@farming.co.uk
Web: www.lynefarm.co.uk

1 Twin
2 Double

2 Pub Bath/Show

B&B per person
£18.00-£21.00 Single
£18.00-£20.00 Dbl/Twn
Room only per person
£18.00-£21.00

Open Jan-Dec

Victorian farmhouse on mixed farm with magnificent views over Stobo Valley. 4 miles (6kms) west of Peebles on A72. 23 miles (32kms) from Edinburgh.

Portpatrick, Wigtownshire

Map Ref: 1F10

GUEST HOUSE

Melvin Lodge Guest House

South Crescent, Portpatrick, DG9 8LE
Tel: 01776 810238

2 Single
1 Twin
3 Double
4 Family

5 En Suite fac
1 Pub Bath/Show

B&B per person
from £20.00 Single
from £23.00 Dbl/Twn

Open Jan-Dec

Families and pet lovers with their pets are made most welcome at this large Victorian villa with superb views over the harbour and Irish Sea. Relax in the comfort of the TV lounge before setting off on the Southern Upland Way.

Important: Prices stated are estimates and may be subject to amendments

Prestwick, Ayrshire

Map Ref: 1G7

B&B

Isobel Short
Bonhomie, 119 Ayr Road, Prestwick, Ayrshire, KA9 1TN
Tel: 01292 671406

1 Single, 1 Double, 1 Family — 1 En Suite fac, 2 Pub Bath/Show — B&B per person £16.00-£19.00 Single, £16.00-£22.00 Double — Open Jan-Dec

Comfort in style – breakfast with a smile on main route to Ayr. Next door to Centrum Icerink. 5 minutes Prestwick – pick-up and drop off service.

St Abbs, Berwickshire

Map Ref: 2F5

B&B

Murrayfield
7 Murrayfield, St Abbs, Berwickshire, TD14 5PP
Tel: 01890 771468 Mobile: 07719 703796

1 Double, 1 Family — 1 En Suite fac, 1 Pub Bath/Show — B&B per person from £21.50 Single, from £16.50 Double — Open Jan-Dec

Former fisherman's cottage in quiet village, close to beach, harbour and nature reserve. One room ensuite.

St Boswells, Roxburghshire

Map Ref: 2D7

B&B

Mainhill
by St Boswells, Roxburghshire, TD6 0HG
Tel: 01835 823788

2 Twin — 2 Priv.NOT ensuite — B&B per person from £20.00 Single, from £18.00 Twin — Open Jan-Dec

Traditional Georgian House set well away from the road in its own spacious grounds. Peaceful and relaxing atmosphere. Good touring base. 1 mile from St Boswells.

Selkirk

Map Ref: 2D7

B&B

Mrs P Chalmers
Sunnybrae House, 75 Tower Street, Selkirk, TD7 4LS
Tel: 01750 21156

1 Twin, 1 Double — All En Suite — B&B per person £21.00 Dbl/Twn — Open Jan-Dec, B&B + Eve.Meal £35.00

A warm welcome awaits you at Sunnybrae which has 2 suites, both with sitting room and en-suite bathroom. Bedrooms have views over the town to the hills beyond. Home cooking using local produce. Private parking.

★★

B&B

Dinsburn
1 Shawpark Road, Selkirk, TD7 4DS
Tel: 01750 20375 Mobile: 07790 728001

1 Twin, 1 Double, 1 Family — 2 En Suite fac, 1 Priv.NOT ensuite — B&B per person from £18.00 Single, from £17.00 Dbl/Twn — Open Jan-Dec, B&B + Eve.Meal from £25.00

Semi-detached, sandstone Victorian house in residential area on east side of town centre. Next to bowling green.

VAT is shown at 17.5%: changes in this rate may affect prices.

Key to symbols is on back flap.

Selkirk

Map Ref: 2D7

★★★ B&B

Mrs B Lamont
Ashkirktown Farm, Selkirk, Roxburghshire, TD7 4PB
Tel: 01750 32315

3 Double | 2 Pub Bath/Show | B&B per person £18.00 Single £18.00 Double | Open Jan-Dec

Situated halfway between Hawick and Selkirk, this friendly, family farm house is set well back from the main A7 in its own peaceful gardens.

★★ B&B

Mrs Janet F MacKenzie
Ivybank, Hillside Terrace, Selkirk, TD7 2LT
Tel/Fax: 01750 21270
E-mail: netta.mackenzie@ivybankselkirk.freeserve.co.uk

1 Twin, 1 Double | 1 En Suite fac, 1 Priv.NOT Ensuite | B&B per person from £18.00 Single from £18.00 Dbl/Twn Room only per person from £12.50 | Open Feb-mid Dec

Set back from A7 with fine views over the hills beyond. Private off-street parking. Ensuite or private bathroom facilities.

Skirling, by Biggar, Peeblesshire

Map Ref: 2B6

★★★★★ B&B

Skirling House
Skirling, by Biggar, Peebles-shire, ML12 6HD
Tel: 01899 860274 Fax: 01899 860255
Web: www.skirlinghouse.com

2 Twin, 2 Double | All En Suite | B&B per person from £45.00 Single from £35.00 Dbl/Twn | Open Mar-Dec B&B + Eve.Meal from £55.00

Open fires, peaceful gardens, rolling hills, fine cuisine. Unique Arts & Crafts house by village green. All rooms overlooking secluded gardens and woods.

Stranraer, Wigtownshire

Map Ref: 1F10

★★ B&B

Carlton Guest Hose
4 Carlton Terrace, London Road, Stranraer, DG9 8AG
Tel: 01776 706014

1 Single, 1 Twin, 1 Double, 1 Family | 1 En Suite fac, 1 Pub Bath/Show | B&B per person from £16.00 Single from £17.50 Dbl/Twn Room only from £12.00 | Open Jan-Dec

Friendly family run B&B centrally situated, 5 mins from ferries and town centre. Off street parking. Large bedroom suitable for families. Comfortable TV lounge. Pets welcome.

★★★ B&B

Ellarton
Royal Crescent, Stranraer, Wigtownshire, DG9 8HB
Tel: 01776 703001

2 Twn/Dbl | All En Suite | B&B per person £22.00-£25.00 Single £20.00-£22.00 Dbl/Twn | Open Jan-Dec excl Xmas/New Year

A friendly welcome awaits you at this family run B&B. 2 mins from Harbour. Private parking. Tea and coffee with homebakes served every evening in lounge.

Important: Prices stated are estimates and may be subject to amendments

Stranraer, Wigtownshire — **Map Ref: 1F10**

B&B

Mr & Mrs Farroll

Hawthorn Cottage, Stoneykirk Road, Stranraer, Wigtownshire, DG9 7BT
Tel: 01776 702032

2 Twin, 2 Double — 2 En Suite fac, 1 Pub Bath/Show

B&B per person from £21.00-£25.00 Single, £17.00-£20.00 Dbl/Twn. Room only per person £14.00-£17.00

Open Jan-Dec excl Xmas/New Year

A friendly welcome awaits you at Hawthorn Cottage, a two storey house, personally run, in residential area. Convenient for the town centre and ferries to Ireland. Private parking, non-smoking house.

B&B

Glenotter

Leswalt Road, Stranraer, Wigtownshire, DG9 0EP
Tel: 01776 703199
E-mail: glenotter.bb@talk21.com

1 Twin, 1 Double, 1 Family — All En Suite

B&B per person £21.00-£27.00 Single, £19.00-£22.00 Dbl/Twn

Open Jan-Dec excl Xmas/New Year

A warm and friendly welcome awaits you at Glenotter which is situated in a quiet residential area with large private car park, yet only 4-5 minutes drive from the town centre, P.O. and Stena ferries. Guests are welcome to relax in the spacious TV lounge or in the summer evenings to sit in the large colourful garden. Stranraer is an ideal centre for exploring beautiful Galloway with so much to do and see.

GUEST HOUSE

Harbour Guest House

Market Street, Stranraer, Wigtownshire, DG9 7RF
Tel: 01776 704626
E-mail: Harbourguesthouse@calinetuk.com
E-mail: reservations@harbourguesthouse.com
Web: www.Harbourguesthouse.com

3 Dbl/Twn, 1 Family — En Suite fac, Private fac, 1 Pub.Bath/Show

B&B per person £20.00-£25.00 Single, £19.00-£23.00 Twin. Room only per person £17.00-£19.00

Open Jan-Dec excl Xmas/New Year

The Harbour Guest House offers spacious and luxurious accommodation for the ultimate in relaxation. Within easy walking distance you will find the town centre should you require shops, restaurants, leisure facilities and pubs. Ideally situated for bus, train and ferry terminals for the scheduled traveller. Private secure parking available by arrangement. Family pets welcome by prior arrangement.

GUEST HOUSE

Hartforth

33 London Road, Stranraer, Wigtownshire, DG9 8AF
Tel: 01776 704832

1 Single, 2 Twin, 1 Double, 1 Family — 2 Pub Bath/Show

B&B per person from £16.00 Single, from £16.00 Dbl/Twn. Room only per person from £15.00

Open Jan-Dec

Family run guest house close to town centre, with private car-park and some lock-up space for bicycles and motor cycles, situated near ferry terminals. Good base for touring this south-west corner of Scotland with its gardens, beaches and golf courses.

B&B

Ivy House

3 Ivy Place, London Road, Stranraer, DG9 8ER
Tel: 01776 704176
Web: www.ivyhouse.web.com

1 Twin, 1 Double, 1 Family — 2 En Suite fac, 1 Pub Bath/Show, 1 Priv.NOT ensuite

B&B per person from £20.00 Single, from £16.00 Dbl/Twn. Room only per person from £14.00

Open Jan-Dec

A friendly welcome awaits you at this family run B&B situated close to town centre and Irish Ferry Terminals. Convenient base for visiting Castle Kennedy, Ardwell and Logan Botanic Gardens.

Stranraer, Wigtownshire — **Map Ref: 1F10**

★★
B&B

Lorenza

2 Station Street, Stranraer, Wigtownshire, DG9 7HN
Tel: 01776 703935

1 Twin 2 Double	2 En Suite fac 1 Pub Bath/Show	B&B per person from £16.00 Single from £18.00 Dbl/Twn	Open Jan-Dec excl Xmas/New Year

Terraced house in residential area, convenient for town centre and Irish Ferries, Port Logan, Botanic Gardens, Ardwell and Castle Kennedy gardens all within easy driving distance.

★★★★
B&B

Windyridge Villa

5 Royal Crescent, Stranraer, Wigtownshire, DG9 8HB
Tel/Fax: 01776 889900
E-mail: Windyridge_Villa@hotmail.com

1 Twin 1 Double	All En Suite	B&B per person from £25.00 Single from £20.00 Dbl/Twn	Open Jan-Dec excl Xmas/New Year

A very warm welcome awaits you at this family home overlooking the Garden of Friendship and Loch Ryan. A few minutes from Irish ferry terminals. Lock up garage available. Both ensuite rooms tastefully decorated with TV's. Tea-tray with home-bakes etc. wide variety of breakfast dishes available. Comfortable sea-facing guests lounge available.

★★
HOTEL

Torrs Warren Hotel

Stoneykirk, Stranraer, Wigtownshire, DG9 9DH
Tel: 01776 830204 Fax: 01776 830298
Web: www.torrswarren.co.uk

1 Single 1 Twin 3 Double 1 Family	All En Suite	B&B per person from £28.00 Single from £24.00 Dbl/Twn Room only per person from £19.50	Open Jan-Dec B&B + Eve.Meal from £34.00

Friendly, family run Country House Hotel on the edge of small rural Village, 5 miles from Stranraer and the Ferry Terminal to Ireland. You will be made most welcome, whether you are staying to enjoy golf, sea angling or a relaxing short break.

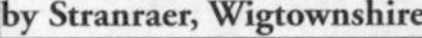

by Stranraer, Wigtownshire — **Map Ref: 1F10**

★★★★
B&B

Chlenry Farmhouse

Castle Kennedy, Stranraer, Wigtownshire, DG9 8SL
Tel: 01776 705316 Fax: 01776 889488
E-mail: WolseleyBrinton@aol.com

1 Twin 1 Double	2 Priv.Bathrooms	B&B per person £33.00 Single £27.50 Dbl/Twn	Open 5Jan-22Dec Dinner £22.50 Supper by arrangement £12.50

Peace. Tranquillity. Relaxation. Golf, gardens close by. Explore glorious Galloway from the comfort of Chlenry. Delicious dinner cooked by request. Breakfast served in the pretty dining room which also has comfortable armchairs, colour TV and an open fireplace, all for the guests exclusive use. On the Southern Upland Way. Packed lunches available.

★★★
B&B

East Challoch Farmhouse

Dunragit, Stranraer, Dumfriesshire, DG9 8PY
Tel: 01581 400391

1 Twin 1 Double	All En Suite	B&B per person from £25.00 Single from £20.00 Dbl/Twn	Open Jan-Dec B&B + Eve.Meal from £32.00

A warm welcome awaits you at our family run traditional farmhouse with views over Luce Bay. Spacious double or twin rooms with ensuite facilities. Both rooms with Tv's and tea trays. Comfortable lounge for guests' use. Evening meal available. Feel free to use our well established garden. Only 7 miles from Stranraer. Pony trekking, golf course within 1 mile.

Important: Prices stated are estimates and may be subject to amendments

nr Stranraer, Wigtownshire

Map Ref: 1F10

Kildrochet House
by Stranraer, Wigtownshire, DG9 9BB
Tel/Fax: 01776 820216
Web: www.kildrochet.co.uk

★★★★ B&B

1 Twin 2 Double	2 En Suite fac 1 Priv.NOT ensuite	B&B per person from £33.00 Single from £27.00 Dbl/Twn	Open Jan-Dec Evening Meal by arrangement £19.00

Early 18th century William Adam Dower House set in peaceful 6 acres of gardens, pasture and woods. The large garden room windows open out onto the terrace and croquet lawn which is surrounded by herbaceous borders, rhododendrons, azaleas and a backdrop of mature trees. Non smoking house. Evening meals by prior arrangement using fresh local produce when available.

by Thornhill, Dumfriesshire

Map Ref: 2A8

'The Bothy' at The Garth
Tynron, Thornhill, Dumfriesshire, DG3 4JY
Tel/Fax: 01848 200364
E-mail: chrisandmimi@supanet.com

★★★ B&B

1 Double	All En Suite	B&B per person from £22.00 Single	Open Jan-Dec excl Xmas/New Year

'B&B' with a difference. Your own self contained cottage adjoining the owners large country house. Cosy accommodation with 'closet' type double bed, sitting room, kitchen and shower room. Breakfast arrangements are flexible. Continental supplied in your cottage, or the Scottish breakfast in the owners delightful kitchen or garden room.

Troon, Ayrshire

Map Ref: 1G7

Advie Lodge
2 Bentinck Drive, Troon, Ayrshire, KA10 6HX
Tel: 01292 313635 Fax: 01292 310817
Web: www.advielodge.co.uk

★★★★ B&B

1 Twin 2 Dbl/Twn	All En Suite	B&B per person from £27.00 Single from £22.00 Dbl/Twn	Open Jan-Dec excl Xmas/New Year

A warm welcome awaits you in this listed Victorian lodge. Centrally situated for beach, shops, marina and golf courses. Spacious rooms individually styled, all ensuite. Twin / double on ground floor. Secluded garden for guests use. Close to railway station. Prestwick airport approx 5 miles. Private parking. Brochure available.

The Cherries
50 Ottoline Drive, Troon, Ayrshire, KA10 7AW
Tel: 01292 313312 Fax: 01292 319007
E-mail: thecherries50@hotmail.com

★★★ B&B

1 Family 1 Twin 1 Single	1 En Suite fac 2 Pub Bath/Show 1 Priv.NOT ensuite	B&B per person from £20.00 Single from £20.00 Twn/Fam Room only per person from £17.00	Open Jan-Dec

Warm welcome in family home. Quiet residential area backing onto golf course. Beach and a variety of restaurants nearby.

Copper Beech
116 Bentinck Drive, Troon, Ayrshire, KA10 6JB
Tel/Fax: 01292 317231
E-mail: gmclardy@aol.com
Web: www.eurogolfing.com

★★★★ B&B

1 Single 3 Twin	3 En Suite fac 1 Priv.NOT ensuite 1 Limited ensuite	B&B per person from £29.50 Single from £29.50 Twin	Open Jan-Dec excl Xmas/New Year

Secluded elegant villa with extensive oak panelling. Golfing trips arranged. Minutes from Royal Troon. Secure parking. Experience our breakfast.

Troon, Ayrshire

Map Ref: 1G7

B&B

Fordell, Mrs Morag Mathieson
43 Beach Road, Barassie, Troon, Ayrshire, KA10 6SU
Tel: 01292 313224 Fax: 01292 312141
E-mail: morag@fordell.junglelink.co.uk
Web: www.fordell.junglelink.co.uk

This traditional grey sandstone semi-villa offers a comfortable homely atmosphere directly overlooking the Firth of Clyde and the Island of Arran. It is situated within easy walking distance of the Barassie Railway Station, golf course and beach. Non smoking house.

2 Twin | Whb, 2 Pub Bath/Show | B&B per person from £20.00 pp. Reductions for long stay and repeat visit | Open Jan-Dec excl Xmas/New Year B&B + Eve.Meal from £23.00 by arrangement

W V

B&B

Mrs N Livingstone
Tigh Dearg, 31 Victoria Drive, Troon, Ayrshire, KA10 6JF
Tel/Fax: 01292 311552

Friendly accommodation in detached family villa, close to beach, golf courses, station and Prestwick airport. Arran ferry 20 minutes.

1 Single, 1 Twin, 1 Family | 2 En Suite fac, 1 Pub Bath/Show | B&B per person £16.00-£25.00 Single £16.00-£25.00 Twin | Open Jan-Dec

C V

B&B

Mossgiel
56 Bentinck Drive, Troon, Ayrshire, KA10 6HY
Tel/Fax: 01292 314937

Traditional house, centrally located. 5 minutes walking distance from all the towns golf courses. Two minutes walk from beach. Many extras in bedrooms. On street parking.

2 Twin, 1 Double | 2 En Suite fac, 1 Priv.NOT ensuite | B&B per person from £24.00 Single from £19.50 Dbl/Twn | Open Jan-Dec excl Xmas/New Year

C

Twynholm, Kirkcudbrightshire

Map Ref: 2A10

B&B

Mrs M McMorran
Miefield Farm, Twynholm, Kirkcudbrightshire, DG6 4PS
Tel: 01557 860254

Working sheep and beef farm at the head of a quiet glen. See sheep dogs and shepherds at work.

1 Twin, 1 Double, 1 Family | 1 Pub Bath/Show | B&B per person £14.50-£15.00 Single £14.50-£15.00 Dbl/Twn | Open Apr-Oct B&B + Eve.Meal from £20.00

C W V

West Linton, Peeblesshire

Map Ref: 2A10

B&B

'Jerviswood'
Linton Bank Drive, West Linton, Peeblesshire, EH46 7DT
Tel/Fax: 01968 660429

Comfortable modern house set in attractive garden in picturesque historic village with excellent eating places within easy walking distance. Within easy reach of Edinburgh and Scottish Borders. Ideal centre for walking, touring and golfing.

2 Twin, 1 Double | B&B per person £16.00-£17.00 Dbl/Twn | Open Jan-Dec excl Xmas/New Year

Important: Prices stated are estimates and may be subject to amendments

Whithorn, Wigtownshire

Map Ref: 1H11

B&B

Mrs E Forsyth

Baltier Farm, Whithorn, Wigtownshire, DG8 8HA
Tel: 01988 600241

1 Single, 1 Twin, 2 Double, 1 Family
1 En Suite fac, 1 Pub Bath/Show

B&B per person
£16.00-£20.00 Single
£16.00-£20.00 Dbl/Twn
Room only per person
from £14.00

Open Mar-Nov

Stone built house on dairy farm 0.3 miles from the main road. Large garden and sun room gives fine views over surrounding countryside towards the south and west. 3 miles from local town and village.

B&B

Old Bishopton

Whithorn, Newton Stewart, Wigtownshire, DG8 8DE
Tel: 01988 500754

1 Double
All En Suite

B&B per person
from £15.00 Single
from £21.00 Double
Room only
from £12.00

Open Apr-Oct

Stone built bungalow with open views of the rolling farmland to the historic town of Whithorn. After a busy days sightseeing, guests can relax in their own sun lounge or private walled garden. Ideal for couples. Only 10 miles from Wigtown which has created much interest in its selection as the Scottish Book Town.

Wigtown

Map Ref: 1H10

B&B

Brora Lodge B&B

Station Road, Wigtown, nr Newton Stewart, DG8 9DZ
Tel: 01988 402595

2 Twin, 1 Double
All En Suite

B&B per person
from £19.50 Single
from £18.50 Dbl/Twn
Room only per person
from £15.00

Open Jan-Dec excl Xmas/New Year
B&B + Eve.Meal from £30.00

Lesley and Peter welcome you to their home which is a detached bungalow situated on the edge of the town (Scotlands book town). Views over open fields to the river Bladnoch to the Solway firth beyond. All accommodation on the ground floor.

GUEST HOUSE

Glaisnock House

20 South Main Street, Wigtown, DG8 9EH
Tel/Fax: 01988 402249
E-mail: cairns@glaisnock.freeserve.co.uk

1 Single, 1 Dbl/Twn, 2 Family
2 En Suite fac, 1 Pub Bath/Show, 1 Shower

B&B per person
from £18.50 Single
from £17.50 Dbl/Twn

Open Jan-Dec excl Xmas/New Year
B&B + Eve.Meal £27.50-£28.50

The Cairns family welcome you to their home in the centre of town. A variety of meals including local shellfish when available is offered in their licenced restaurant. Good base for touring the area or browsing through the many bookshops in Scotland's booktown.

WITH A CITY SKYLINE EVERY BIT AS SPECTACULAR AS THE POSTCARDS SUGGEST, SCOTLAND'S CAPITAL IS SIMPLY OUTSTANDING IN WORLD TERMS.

Linlithgow Palace, West Lothian

IT IS NOW ALSO home to the new Scottish Parliament. Edinburgh Castle is one of the most famous symbols of Scotland, but it is only one of a whole range of attractions stretching down the Royal Mile in the heart of the Old Town. The city is steeped in history and culture, from the Palace of Holyroodhouse, where the tragic story of Mary Queen of Scots unfolded, to the narrow alleyways of the Old Town which were the inspiration for Robert Louis Stevenson's novel Dr Jekyll and Mr Hyde. Our Dynamic Earth, the Royal Yacht Britannia and the Museum of Scotland are just three of the city's newest visitor attractions.

THE MOST FAMOUS EVENTS the city host are the spectacular International Festival and the Festival Fringe, but it remains the liveliest of cities all year round with other events such as the Science Festival, Film Festival and the biggest New Year street party in the world. As a major cultural centre, Edinburgh has many art galleries, theatres and cinemas. There are many street cafés and restaurants specialising in both international and modern Scottish cuisine, while over 700 bars in the city offer fine locally brewed beers and, of course, a wide range of malt whiskies.

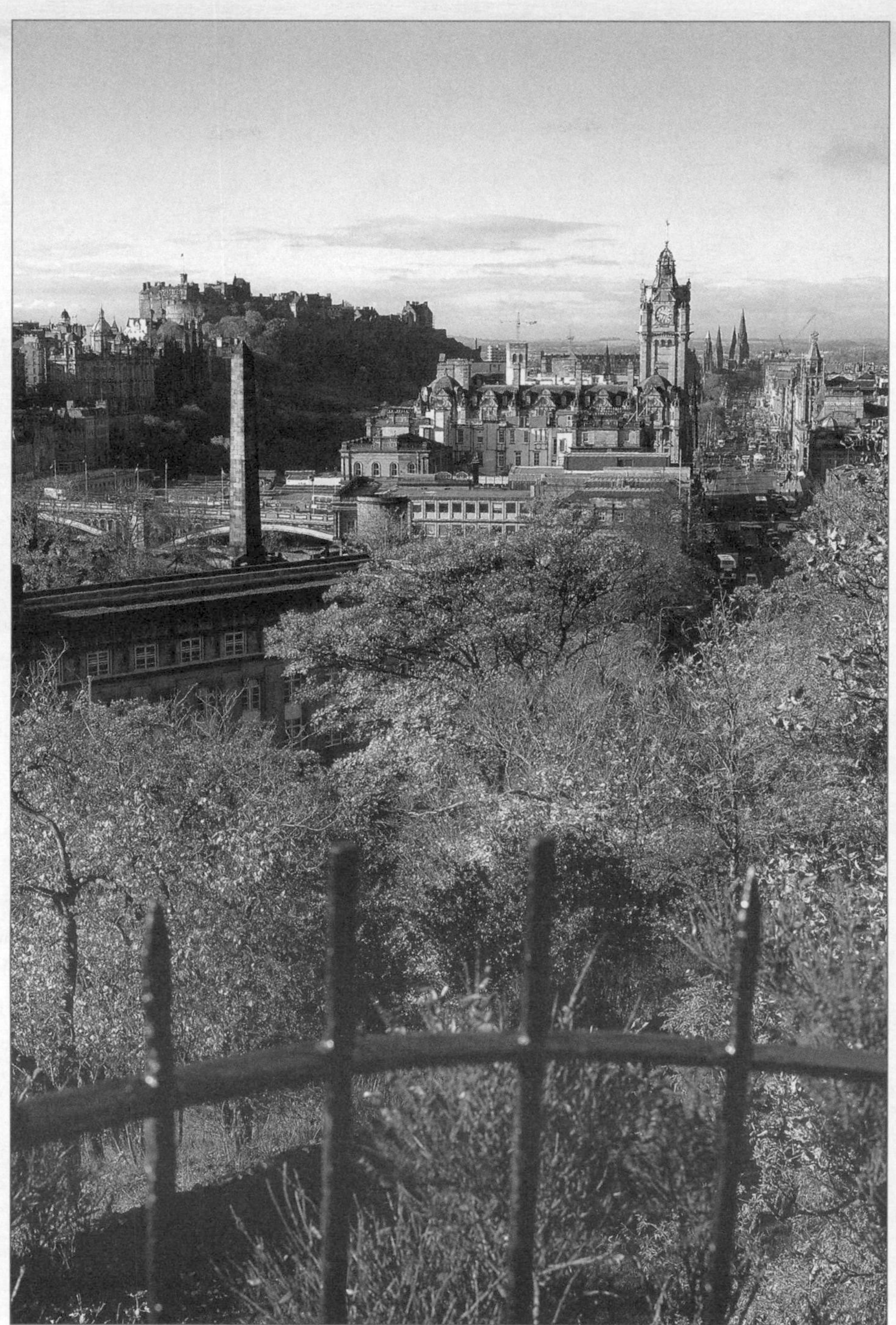

Edinburgh Skyline from Calton Hill

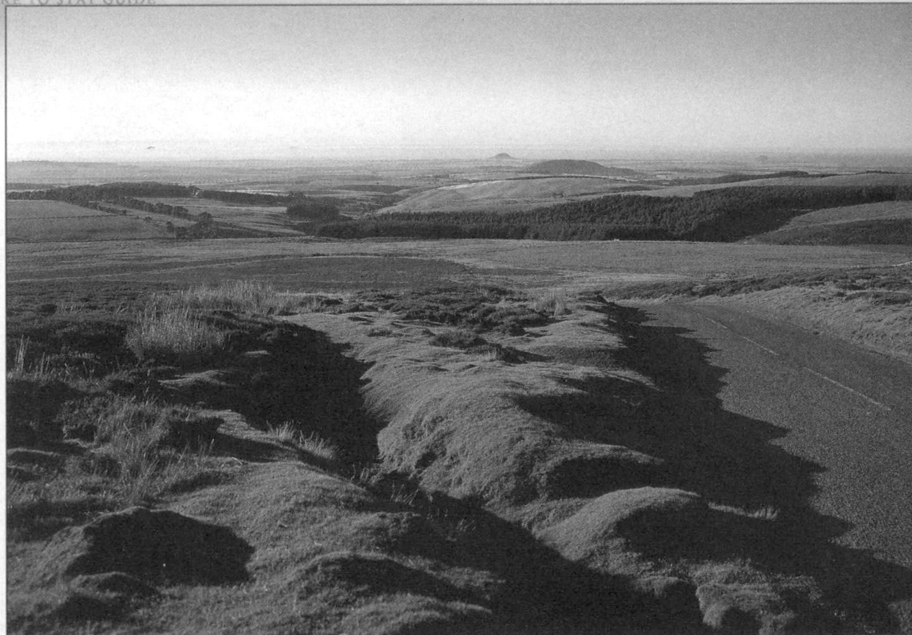

Firth of Forth and East Lothian landscape seen from the Lammermuir Hills

THIS FAST-PACED and cosmopolitan city offers superb shopping in the many department stores along the famous thoroughfare of Princes Street as well as Princes Mall and the many designer shops along elegantly proportioned George Street in the heart of the 18-century New Town. The village-like suburbs of Stockbridge and Bruntsfield offer small shops where a friendly welcome is guaranteed.
A relaxing alternative within the bustling city are the many quiet green spaces including Holyrood Park, Calton Hill, the Dean Village and the Royal Botanic Garden, which features Britain's tallest palm house and the world-famous Rock Garden.

WITHIN A FEW MILES of the city centre are the Lothians. This is soft rolling farmland with splendid hill-walking in the surrounding Pentland, Moorfoot and Lammermuir Hills. There are almost 70 miles of coastline along the Firth of Forth combining nature reserves, sandy beaches and seaside resorts. Dunbar has been officially recorded as Scotland's driest and sunniest town. The new Scottish Seabird Centre in North Berwick uses the latest technology to allow all the family to view the famous gannet colony on the nearby Bass Rock. To the west, South Queensferry is set in a dramatic location immediately below the gigantic structures of the famous Forth Bridges.

EXPERIENCE AND ENJOY one of Europe's most exciting regions, by combining city and countryside. With easy access by air, rail and road, Edinburgh and the Lothians is a year-round destination for everyone.

EVENTS EDINBURGH AND LOTHIANS

17 FEBRUARY
Scotland v Wales
Murrayfield Stadium, Edinburgh
As part of the Six Nation Championship.
Contact: Scottish Rugby Union
TEL: **0131 346 5000**
www.sru.org.uk

17 MARCH
Scotland v Italy
Murrayfield Stadium, Edinburgh
As part of the Six Nation Championship.
Contact: Scottish Rugby Union
TEL: **0131 346 5000**
www.sru.org.uk

1-12 APRIL
Edinburgh International Science Festival
Various venues, Edinburgh
Worlds largest event devoted to celebration of science. Lots of events for children.
Contact: Science Festival Office
TEL: **0131 530 2001**
www.edinburghfestivals.co.uk/science/

7 APRIL
Scotland v Ireland
Murrayfield Stadium, Edinburgh
As part of the Six Nation Championship.
Contact: Scottish Rugby Union
TEL: **0131 346 5000**
www.sru.org.uk

21-24 JUNE
Royal Highland Show
Royal Highland Centre, Edinburgh
The spectacular highlight of Scotland's country calendar, with a Scottish food exhibition, pedigree livestock, flower show, show jumping, craft fair and much more.
Contact: Royal Highland Centre
TEL: **0131 333 3036**

3-25 AUGUST
Edinburgh Military Tattoo
Edinburgh Castle Esplanade,
A unique blend of music, ceremony and theatre set against the magnificent backdrop of Edinburgh Castle, featuring display teams and bands from all over the World.
Contact: The Tattoo Office
TEL: **0131 225 1188**
www.edintattoo.co.uk

5-27 AUGUST
Edinburgh Festival Fringe
Various venues, Edinburgh
One of the largest arts festivals in the World, comprising three weeks of theatre, dance, music and comedy, with up to 1000 different shows a day played in over 200 venues throughout the city.
Contact: The Fringe Office
TEL: 0131 226 5257
EMAIL: admin@edfringe.com
www.edfringe.com

11-27 AUGUST
Edinburgh International Book Festival
Charlotte Square Gardens, Edinburgh
Annual celebration where writers and readers meet to celebrate the written word. Lectures, talks, discussions, readings and daily events for children.
Contact: Edinburgh International Book Festival
TEL: **0131 228 5444**
EMAIL: admin@edbookfest.co.uk
www.edbookfest.co.uk

12 AUGUST-1 SEPTEMBER
Edinburgh International Festival
Various venues, Edinburgh
For three weeks Edinburgh plays hosts to some of the World's finest theatre, opera, music and dance companies in one of Europe's premier arts festivals.
Contact: The Hub, Edinburgh's Festival Centre
TEL: **0131 473 2001** (information)
TICKET LINE: **0131 473 2000**
www.eif.co.uk

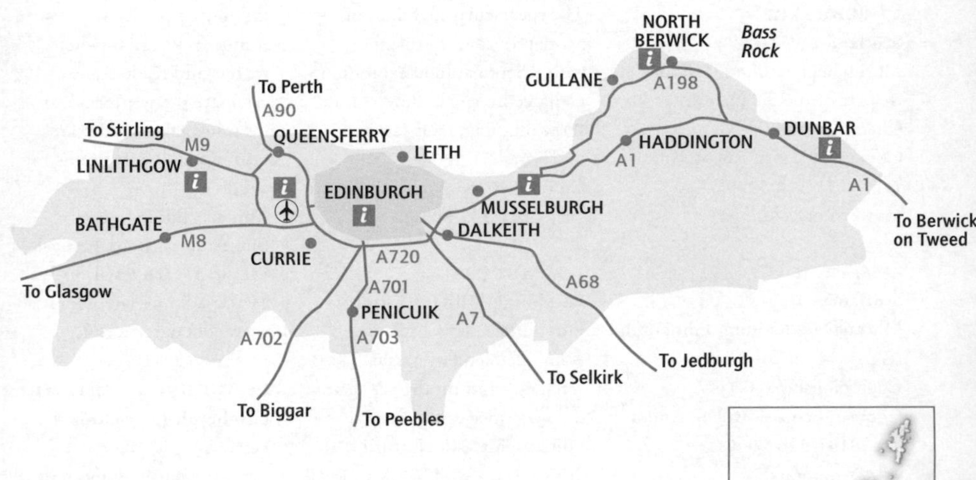

EDINBURGH AND LOTHIANS TOURIST BOARD
Edinburgh and Scotland Information Centre
3 Princes Street
Edinburgh
EH2 2QP

TEL: **0131 473 3800**
FAX: **0131 473 3881**
www.edinburgh.org

EDINBURGH AND LOTHIANS TOURIST BOARD

DUNBAR
143 High Street
TEL: **(01368) 863353**
Jan-Dec

EDINBURGH
Edinburgh and Scotland
Information Centre
3 Princes Street
TEL: **(0131) 473 3800**
Jan-Dec

EDINBURGH AIRPORT
Tourist Information Desk
TEL: **(0131) 333 2167**
Jan-Dec

NEWTONGRANGE
Scottish Mining Museum
Lady Victoria Colliery
TEL: **(0131) 663 4262**
Easter-Oct

NORTH BERWICK
Quality Street
TEL: **(01620) 892197**
Jan-Dec

OLD CRAIGHALL
Granada Service Area
A1
Musselburgh
TEL: **(0131) 653 6172**
Jan-Dec

PENICUIK
Edinburgh Crystal
Visitor Centre
Eastfield
TEL: **(01968) 673846**
Easter-Sept

Aberlady, East Lothian

Map Ref: 2D4

★★★
HOTEL

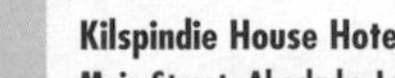

Kilspindie House Hotel
Main Street, Aberlady, Longidday, East Lothian, EH32 0RE
Tel: 01875 870682 Fax: 01875 870504
E-mail: info@kilspindie-golfscotland.com

Family run hotel in coastal conservation village of Aberlady. Ample parking and all rooms en-suite. Within easy reach of 17 local golf courses. 25 mins drive from Edinburgh. Full restaurant plus bar meals and high teas. Lovely area for walking, bird watching and interesting hillviews.

Rooms	Facilities	B&B per person	B&B + Eve.Meal
6 Single 16 Twin 4 Double	All En Suite	from £40.00 Single from £33.00 Dbl/Twn	from £50.00

Blackburn, West Lothian

Map Ref: 2B5

CRUACHAN BED & BREAKFAST

78 EAST MAIN STREET, BLACKBURN, WEST LOTHIAN EH47 7QS
Tel: 01506 655221 Fax: 01506 652395
e.mail: cruachan.bb@virgin.net Web: www.cruachan.co.uk

A relaxed and friendly base is provided at Cruachan from which to explore central Scotland. Hosts Kenneth and Jacqueline ensure you receive the utmost in quality of service, meticulously presented accommodation and of course a full Scottish breakfast. They look forward to having the pleasure of your company.

★★★
B&B

Cruachan Bed & Breakfast
78 East Main Street, Blackburn, West Lothian, EH47 7QS
Tel: 01506 655221 Fax: 01506 652395
E.mail: cruachan.bb@virgin.net
Web: www.cruachan.co.uk

Located on A705 in Blackburn. Cruachan is 1.5 miles from junction 4 of M8 allowing easy access to road links for Edinburgh and Glasgow, or enjoy the benefit of a 30 minute rail journey to Edinburgh from nearby Bathgate. An ideal central location for your visit to Scotland.

Rooms	Facilities	B&B per person	Open
3 Double 1 Family	3 En Suite fac 1 Priv.NOT ensuite	from £28.00 Single from £23.00 Double	Open Jan-Dec excl Xmas/New Year

Broxburn, West Lothian

Map Ref: 2B5

BANKHEAD FARMHOUSE B&B

Bankhead Farm, Dechmont, Broxburn, West Lothian EH52 6NB
Tel: 01506 811209
e.mail: Bankheadbb@aol.com Web: www.bankheadfarm.com

Perfectly placed for exploring Edinburgh and Scotland. Bankhead has 7 modern ensuite bedrooms in traditional farmhouse building. Panoramic views of local hills and over the Forth to Fife, yet close to 3 historic towns and less than 20 minutes from Edinburgh Airport. Easy access to main Scottish routes. Car essential.

★★★
B&B

Bankhead B&B
Bankhead Farm, Dechmont, Broxburn, West Lothian, EH52 6NB
Tel: 01506 811209
E-mail: Bankheadbb@aol.com
Web: www.bankheadfarm.com

Perfectly placed for Edinburgh and airport. Stay in a traditional farmhouse with modern en-suite bedrooms. Panoramic views of scottish countryside.

Rooms	Facilities	B&B per person	Open
2 Single 1 Twin 2 Double 2 Family	All En Suite	from £30.00 Single from £25.00 Dbl/Twn	Open Jan-Dec excl Xmas

Dunbar, East Lothian — Map Ref: 2E4

★★ SMALL HOTEL

The Goldenstones Hotel
Queens Road, Dunbar, East Lothian, EH42 1LG
Tel: 01368 862356 Fax: 01368 865644
E-mail: goldenstones@cs.com

19 Rooms

B&B per person
from £32.00 Single
from £30.00 Double

Open Jan-Dec
B&B + Eve.Meal
from £37.00

Family run hotel centrally situated in Dunbar. Near town centre and beaches. Golfing packages available.

★★ GUEST HOUSE

Springfield Guest House
Belhaven Road, Dunbar, East Lothian, EH42 1NH
Tel/Fax: 01368 862502
E-mail: smeed@tesco.net

1 Single
1 Twin
1 Double
2 Family

2 Priv.NOT ensuite
1 Pub Bath/Show

B&B per person
£20.00-£30.00 Single
£18.00-£22.00 Dbl/Twn
Room only per person
£16.00-£20.00

Open Jan-Nov excl New Year
B&B + Eve.Meal
£28.00-£32.00

An elegant 19c villa with attractive garden. Family run with home-cooking. Ideal base for families, golf and touring.

East Calder, West Lothian — Map Ref: 2B5

Near EDINBURGH –

OVERSHIEL FARM, EAST CALDER EH53 0HT

Telephone: 01506 880469 Fax: 01506 883006

PEACEFUL COUNTRY SETTING, 6 MILES WEST OF EDINBURGH. EASY ACCESS INTO CITY CENTRE BY CAR, BUS OR TRAIN (STATION 1.5 MILES). ALL ROOMS HAVE COLOUR TV PLUS TEA/COFFEE-MAKING FACILITIES. SAFE PARKING.

★★★ B&B

Mrs Jan Dick
Overshiel Farm, East Calder, West Lothian, EH53 0HT
Tel: 01506 880469 Fax: 01506 883006

2 Twin
1 Double

2 En Suite fac
1 Pub Bath/Show

B&B per person
£25.00-£30.00 Single
£18.00-£22.00 Dbl/Twn

Open Jan-Dec

Stone built farmhouse set in large garden and surrounded by arable farmland. 5 miles (8kms) from Edinburgh Airport. Easy access to M8 and M9. Non-smoking establishment. Wide range of eating places within short drive.

East Calder, West Lothian

Map Ref: 2B5

B&B

Whitecroft Bed & Breakfast

7 Raw Holdings, East Calder, West Lothian EH53 0ET
Tel: 01506 882494 Fax: 01506 882598
E-mail: Lornascot@aol.com

Family bungalow on 5 acre small holding adjacent to Almondell Country Park. On main bus route to Edinburgh (20 mins) and 5 minutes drive to Livingston. Private parking. Ground floor accommodation. No Smoking.

1 Twin
2 Double

B&B per person
from £30.00 Single
from £22.00 Dbl/Twn

Open Jan-Dec

East Linton, East Lothian

Map Ref: 2D4

B&B

Mrs M Henderson

Kiloran House, Drylaw Terrace, East Linton, East Lothian, EH40 3AY
Tel: 01620 860410 Fax: 01620 860881
E-mail: kiloran@btinternet.com

A Victorian house of great character, furnished to a high standard. Relaxed and friendly atmosphere. Non-smoking house. Short drive to all Lothians Golf Courses and beaches. Within half hour of Edinburgh.

2 Double All En Suite
1 Family

B&B per person
£25.00-£30.00 Single
£20.00-£25.00 Double
Room only per person
£20.00-£25.00

Open Jan-Dec

East Linton, East Lothian

Map Ref: 2D4

Kippielaw Farmhouse

East Linton, East Lothian EH41 4PY Tel/Fax: 01620 860368

Comfortable, welcoming, tastefully restored 18th-century farmhouse with stunning views over East Lothian countryside. Pleasant local walks to Traprain Law, Hailes Castle and East Linton village. The attractions of Edinburgh are only 30 minutes away. Relax and enjoy candlelit dinners in our log-fired dining room overlooking attractive gardens and courtyard.

B&B

Kippielaw Farmhouse
East Linton, East Lothian, EH41 4PY
Tel/Fax: 01620 860368

1 Twin	1 En Suite fac	B&B per person	Open Jan-Dec
1 Double	1 Priv.NOT ensuite	from £25.00 Single	B&B + Eve.Meal
		from £22.00 Dbl/Twn	from £42.00

18c farmhouse overlooking open farmland to the coast. 25 miles from Edinburgh. Interesting garden. Imaginative candlelit dinners. An ideal place to come and unwind and enjoy the peace and beauty of East Lothian.

P

C V

Edinburgh

Map Ref: 2C5

Abcorn Guest House

4 Mayfield Gardens, Edinburgh EH9 2BU

Tel: 0131 667 6548 Fax: 0131 667 9969

e.mail: abcorn@btinternet.com Web: www.btinternet.com/~abcorn

The Abcorn is a family run guest house in a detached Victorian villa, near to the city centre, with a private car park. All our rooms are ensuite and also have colour TV and tea/coffee-making facilities.

GUEST HOUSE

Abcorn Guest House
4 Mayfield Gardens, Edinburgh, EH9 2BU
Tel: 0131 667 6548 Fax: 0131 667 9969
E.Mail: abcorn@btinternet.com
Web: www.btinternet.com/~abcorn

1 Single	All En Suite	B&B per person	Open Jan-Dec
2 Twin		£24.00-£35.00 Single	
2 Double		£24.00-£35.00 Dbl/Twn	
2 Family			

Personally managed by the owners Jimmy and Marjorie Kellacher this detached guest house is centrally located on the main bus route 5 mins from the city centre. Ample private parking.

TV P

C V

B&B

Mrs Norah Aitchison
26 Duddingston Avenue, Edinburgh, EH15 1SQ
Tel: 0131 669 9689

1 Twin	2 Pub Bath/Show	B&B per person	Open Jun-Sep
		£16.00-£20.00 Twin	

Quiet comfortable accommodation, unrestricted parking close to major bus routes to city centre. Ground floor accommodation.

V

Edinburgh — Map Ref: 2C5

Albion House

6 Templeland Road, Corstorphine, Edinburgh EH12 8RP
Tel: 0131 539 0840 Fax: 0131 538 3325
e.mail: mavis@templeland.freeserve.co.uk

A friendly welcome and daily complimentary home baking await at our comfortable Edwardian home. Robes provided for private bathroom. Non-smoking. Three miles west of city centre, fast frequent bus service to town. Three miles from airport with easy access to main touring routes. Unrestricted street parking.

B&B

Albion

6 Templeland Road, Corstorphine, Edinburgh, EH12 8RP
Tel: 0131 539 0840 Fax: 0131 538 3325
E-mail: mavis@templeland.freeserve.co.uk

2 Twin, 1 Double | 2 En Suite fac, 1 Priv.NOT ensuite | B&B per person £22.00-£24.00 Dbl/Twn | Open Apr-Nov

A friendly welcome with complimentary home baking and biscuits awaits you at our comfortable Edwardian family home in peaceful location. Ground floor ensuite bedrooms with private sitting room. Non-smoking house. The house is situated 3 miles west of the city with fast frequent bus service to the centre. Airport 4 miles. Easy access to main touring routes.

TV V

GUEST HOUSE

The Alexander Guest House

35 Mayfield Gardens, Edinburgh, EH9 2BX
Tel: 0131 258 4028 Fax: 0131 258 1247
E-mail: alexander@guest68.freeserve.co.uk

2 Single, 3 Twin, 3 Double | 4 En Suite fac, 1 Pub Bath/Show, 1 Limited ensuite | B&B per person from £20.00 Single, from £20.00 Dbl/Twn | Open Jan-Dec

Elegantly furnished four star Victorian villa situated one mile from Edinburgh's famous Royal Mile, castle and Holyrood. Every detail has been thought of in our recently refurbished bedrooms, to make your stay a memorable one. Breakfast time is special at the Alexander with a wide variety of dishes on offer.

TV P V

B&B

Mrs Linda J Allan

10 Baberton Mains Rise, Edinburgh, EH14 3HG
Tel: 0131 442 3619
E-mail: LJA_bandb_edin@hotmail.com

1 Double | B&B per person from £22.00 Single, from £15.00 Double | Open Apr-Sep

Family home in quiet residential area. Unrestricted parking. Frequent bus service to Princes Street. Convenient for Golf courses and Heriot Watt University.

TV

GUEST HOUSE

Alness Guest House

27 Pilrig Street, Edinburgh, EH6 5AN
Tel: 0131 554 1187

1 Single, 1 Twin, 2 Double, 4 Family | 3 Pub Bath/Show | B&B per person £20.00-£25.00 Single, £20.00-£25.00 Dbl/Twn | Open Jan-Dec

Friendly family run guest house. On main bus route, 1 mile (2kms) from Princes Street and Castle. Close to Port of Leith and Britannia.

TV C V

Important: Prices stated are estimates and may be subject to amendments

Edinburgh Map Ref: 2C5

GUEST HOUSE

Amaragua Guest House
10 Kilmaurs Terrace, Edinburgh, EH16 5DR
Tel/Fax: 0131 667 6775

1 Single	Shared bathroom	B&B per person	Open Jan-Dec
1 Single	Private bathroom	£17.00-£25.00 Single	
1 Twin	Ensuite	£17.00-£29.00 Dbl/Twn	
2 Double	Ensuite		
1 Family	Ensuite		
1 Twin	Shared bathroom		

Victorian terraced house in residential area, close to Prestonfield Golf Course, Holyrood Park and Commonwealth Pool. Nearby bus routes to centre.

C V

GUEST HOUSE

Arden Guest House
126 Old Dalkeith Road, Edinburgh, EH16 4SD
Tel: 0131 664 3985 Fax: 0131 621 0866

1 Single	All En Suite	B&B per person	Open Jan-Dec
2 Twin		from £18.00 Single	
3 Double		from £18.00 Dbl/Twn	
2 Family			

Newly built, privately owned guest house with all rooms ensuite with ground floor level accommodation. On main A7 road, situated on south side of city 10 minutes away. Ideal base for business guests. Off-street parking. Easy access to all amenities.

C W V

B&B

Athena Guest House
4 Ormelie Terrace, Joppa, Edinburgh, EH15 2EX
Tel: 0131 657 3331
E.mail: lou-fi@msn.com
Web: www.athena-guesthouse.com

1 Dbl	All En Suite	B&B per person from	Open Jan-Dec
1 Family		£20.00 to £35.00 double	

Enjoy the fabulous facilities in and around Edinburgh whilst based at our family run B&B. There's the beautiful sandy beach at Joppa offering grand Victorian baths. Ideally situated to take advantage of touring the coastline and visiting all tourist attractions and excellent golf courses.

V

Edinburgh

Map Ref: 2C5

GUEST HOUSE

Ardgarth Guest House
1 St Mary's Place, Portobello, Edinburgh, EH15 2QF
Tel: 0131 669 3021 Fax: 0131 468 1221
Web: www.ardgarth.demon.co.uk

3 Single 4 Twin 1 Double 2 Family	4 En Suite fac	B&B per person from £16.00 Single from £16.00 Dbl/Twn	Open Jan-Dec

Comfortable accommodation in quiet and friendly guest house. Close to beach and golf course. Special diets catered for, ground floor ensuite disabled facilities with roll-in showers. Unrestricted parking, frequent buses give easy access to and from city centre. French spoken.

C W V

B&B

'Arisaig'
64 Glasgow Road, Corstorphine, Edinburgh, EH12 8LN
Tel: 0131 334 2610 Fax: 0131 334 1800
E-mail: helen_baird@hotmail.com

1 Twin 1 Double	All En Suite	B&B per person £28.00-£36.00 Single £23.00-£27.00 Dbl/Twn	Open Apr-Oct

Personally run comfortable and friendly accommodation in detached dormer bungalow. Good bus service to town centre, approx 3 miles (5 kms). Ideal base for exploring this historic city and enjoying the many events and attractions on offer. Ground floor accommodation available.

V

GUEST HOUSE

Arrandale House
28 Mayfield Gardens, Edinburgh, EH9 2BZ
Tel: 0131 667 6029 Fax: 0131 622 2262
E-mail: lis@arrandale.co.uk

2 Twin 3 Double 1 Family	5 En Suite fac 1 Priv.NOT ensuite	B&B per person from £20.00-£40.00 Single from £18.00 to £30.00 Dbl/Twn	Open Jan-Dec

Comfortable accommodation, en suite facilities, easy access to city centre. Completely non-smoking. Discounts available on some bookings.

Edinburgh **Map Ref: 2C5**

GUEST HOUSE

Ashdene House
23 Fountainhall Road, Edinburgh, EH9 2LN
Tel: 0131 667 6026
E-mail: Ashdene_House_Edinburgh@Compuserve.com
Web: http://welcome.to/ashdene_house

Very comfortable family run Edwardian town house retaining many features, in quiet residential conservation area. Convenient for bus route to city centre (10 minutes). Non-smoking establishment.

1 Single 5 En Suite fac
1 Twin
2 Double
1 Family

B&B per person
£42.00-£58.00 Single
£24.00-£40.00 Dbl/Twn

Open Jan-Dec excl Xmas/New Year

GOLD

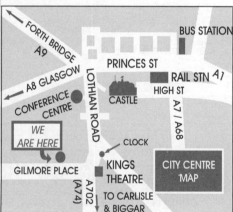

GUEST HOUSE

Averon Guest House
44 Gilmore Place, Edinburgh, EH3 9NQ
Tel: 0131 229 9932
E-mail: info@averon.co.uk
Web: www.averon.co.uk

Central location with private car park to rear. 10 minute walk to Princes Street and Castle. Near Kings Theatre and Conference Centre.

1 Single 6 En Suite fac
3 Twin 2 Pub Bath/Show
3 Double
3 Family

B&B per person
from £19.00 Single
from £19.00 Dbl/Twn

Open Jan-Dec

GUEST HOUSE

Ave Roxzannah
36 Minto Street, Edinburgh, EH9 2BS
Tel: 0131 667 8933
E-mail: averox@aol.com

B Listed Georgian villa, situated 5 minutes from city centre. Ideal location for all amenities and attractions. Parking facility for two cars.

1 Twin All En Suite
1 Double
2 Family

B&B per person
£25.00-£40.00 Single
£19.00-£30.00 Dbl/Twn

Open Jan-Dec

Edinburgh Map Ref: 2C5

★★★

B&B

Peter & Alison Ayres
21 Mayfield Road, Newington, Edinburgh, EH9 2NQ
Tel: 0131 667 8435 Fax: 0131 466 0579
E-mail: alisonayres@ndirect.co.uk
Web: www.ndirect.co.uk/~alisonayres

Warm welcome assured in traditionally furnished Victorian family home. 2 kms to city centre. Ground floor rooms. Private parking. Non smoking. Visa and mastercard accepted.

1 Double
1 Family

All En Suite

B&B per person
from £27.50 Double

Open Apr-Oct

★★★

GUEST HOUSE

Balmore House
34 Gilmore Place, Edinburgh, EH3 9NQ
Tel/Fax: 0131 221 1331
E-mail: Balmore@classicfm.net

Recently refurbished traditional Victorian terraced villa with conservatory dining room. 10 minutes to city centre. Close to Kings Theatre. Private parking.

1 Twin
3 Double
1 Family

All En Suite

B&B per person
from £25.00 Dbl/Twn

Open Jan-Dec

BALQUHIDDER GUEST HOUSE

94 Pilrig Street, Edinburgh EH6 5AY

Telephone: 0131 554 3377

Built in 1857 as a church manse, this charming centrally situated Victorian detached house offers a high standard of accommodation at very favourable terms. Personally supervised by same family for 20 years. Own keys with access to rooms at all times. B&B from £20 per person per night. *For details contact Proprietor: Mrs N. Ferguson.*

★★

GUEST HOUSE

Balquhidder Guest House
94 Pilrig Street, Edinburgh, EH6 5AY
Tel: 0131 554 3377

Detached house in its own grounds overlooking public park and on bus routes to the city centre.

1 Single
3 Twin
2 Double

5 En Suite fac
1 Limited ensuite
1 Pub Bath/Show

B&B per person
from £20.00 Single
from £20.00 Dbl/Twn

Open Jan-Dec excl
Xmas/New Year

Edinburgh **Map Ref: 2C5**

Belford Guest House

13 Blacket Avenue, Edinburgh EH9 1RR
Tel: 0131 667 2422 Fax: 0131 667 7508

Small and friendly family run guest house in quiet tree-lined avenue 1 mile from the city centre. Buses run from either end of the avenue to all attractions in the city. Four rooms ensuite. TV's and hairdryers in all rooms. ***Private parking. No smoking.***

Belford Guest House
13 Blacket Avenue, Edinburgh, EH9 1RR
Tel: 0131 667 2422 Fax: 0131 667 7508

4 Twin, 3 Family | 3 En Suite fac, 2 Pub Bath/Show | B&B per person from £25.00 Single, from £20.00 Twin | Open Jan-Dec

Family run guest house in quiet road just off main A7/A701. Conveniently situated for main tourist attraction and city centre, buses run to the city centre from either end of the avenue. Variety of eating establishments locally.

The Bellevue Guest House
8 East Claremont Street, Edinburgh, EH7 4JP
Tel: 0131 556 4862 Fax: 0131 558 1790

1 Single, 2 Twin, 2 Double, 1 Family | All En Suite | B&B per person £19.00-£30.00 Single, £19.00-£30.00 Dbl/Twn | Open Jan-Dec

Family run Victorian terraced townhouse within walking distance of city centre, Playhouse Theatre, and a variety of restaurants. Non-smoking establishment. Two rooms on the ground floor.

Ben Cruachan
17 McDonald Road, Edinburgh, EH7 4LX
Tel: 0131 556 3709

1 Twin, 1 Double, 1 Family | All En Suite | B&B per person from £35.00 Single, from £25.00 Twin | Open Apr-Oct

Centrally located, personally run, terraced house 0.5 mile (1 km) to Princes St. Unrestricted street parking. Excellent selection of restaurants nearby Playhouse Theatre, 0.25 mile.

Blossom House
8 Minto Street, Edinburgh, EH9 1RG
Tel: 0131 667 5353 Fax: 0131 667 2813

2 Twin, 2 Double, 4 Family | En Suite fac, Pub Bath/Show, En Suite fac | B&B per person from £20.00 Single, from £17.50 Dbl/Twn | Open Jan-Dec

Comfortable, family run guest house. City centre within walking distance. Excellent bus service. Private car park. Close to commonwealth pool.

VAT is shown at 17.5%: changes in this rate may affect prices.

Key to symbols is on back flap.

Edinburgh Map Ref: 2C5

★★★★ GUEST HOUSE

Bonnington Guest House
202 Ferry Road, Edinburgh, EH6 4NW
Tel/Fax: 0131 554 7610
E-mail: bonningtongh@netscapeonline.co.uk

1 Twin	3 En Suite fac	B&B per person	Open Jan-Dec
2 Double	1 Priv.NOT ensuite	£23.00-£35.00 Dbl/Twn	
3 Family	1 Pub Bath/Show		

Early Victorian Listed building with private parking. On the north side of the city. Convenient bus routes to centre. Well appointed rooms with many of the period features retained. Very comfortable accommodation of a high standard.

TV P C V

★★ B&B

Brambles
66 Pilrig Street, Edinburgh, Midlothian, EH6 5AS
Tel: 0131 554 1353
E-mail: Brambles@accom.freeserve.co.uk

1 Twin	1 En Suite fac	B&B per person	Open Apr-Oct
1 Double	2 Pub Bath/Show	£16.00-£25.00 Dbl/Twn	
1 Family			

Victorian terraced villa. Convenient for all theatres, Princes Street, Castle, city centre and Waverly Station. Easy, unrestricted parking.

TV V

★★★ GUEST HOUSE

Brodies Guest House
22 East Claremont Street, Edinburgh, EH7 4JP
Tel: 0131 556 4032 Fax: 0131 556 9739
E.mail: info@brodiesguesthouse.co.uk
Web: www.brodiesguesthouse.co.uk

1 Single	3 En Suite fac	B&B per person	Open Jan-Dec
1 Twin	1 Pub Bath/Show	£24.00-£30.00 Single	
1 Double		£24.00-£38.00 Dbl/Twn	
2 Family			

Small, friendly, family run Victorian town house in a cobbled street within 1/2 mile of Princes Street. Convenient for bus/railway station, playhouse theatre, pubs and restaurants nearby. Scottish breakfasts a speciality.

TV C V

Edinburgh Map Ref: 2C5

BUCHANAN GUEST HOUSE

97 Joppa Road, Edinburgh EH15 2HB
Tel: 0131 657 4117 Fax: 0131 669 9353
e.mail: BuchananHouse@bigfoot.com
Web: http://website.lineone.net/~buchananhouse/

A warm welcome is extended to all visitors by Margaret and Stewart Buchanan at their personally run Victorian guest house with panoramic view overlooking Firth of Forth. The bedrooms are well equipped with every comfort in mind and full Scottish breakfast is provided. Conveniently located. Frequent bus service to city centre and en-route to main golf courses. Businessmen welcome. FREE UNRESTRICTED PARKING.

GUEST HOUSE

Buchanan Guest House
97 Joppa Road, Edinburgh, EH15 2HB
Tel: 0131 657 4117 Fax: 0131 669 9353
E-mail: BuchananHouse@bigfoot.com
Web: http://website.lineone.net/~buchananhouse/

2 Twin	1 En Suite fac	B&B per person	Open Jan-Dec
1 Double	2 Pub Bath/Show	£18.00-£25.00 Single	
1 Family		£18.00-£25.00 Dbl/Twn	

Comfortable personally run guest house, on major bus route to city centre. Unrestricted parking. Front views overlooking sea. 5 minutes drive from A1.

C £ W V

BURNS B&B

Tel: 0131 229 1669
Fax: 0131 229 9225

67 Gilmore Place, Edinburgh EH3 9NU

Popular homely B&B in city centre close to Princes Street, Castle, E.I.C.C., tourist attractions, theatres and restaurants. Comfortable rooms all ensuite. Good breakfasts. Parking. Non-smoking. No pets. Access with your own keys. Low season offer – double rooms available as singles – £25 pppn. B&B from £22-£30 pppn. Open all year.

Write, telephone or fax Mrs Burns.

B&B

Burns Bed & Breakfast
67 Gilmore Place, Edinburgh, EH3 9NU
Tel: 0131 229 1669 Fax: 0131 229 9225

1 Twin	All En Suite	B&B per person	Open Jan-Dec
1 Double		from £22.00 Dbl/Twn	

Charming pre-victorian terraced house, personally run by Mrs Burns. Close to city centre, tourist attractions, Kings Theatre, E.I.C.C and local restaurants. All ensuite. Non-smoking.

£ V

VAT is shown at 17.5%: changes in this rate may affect prices.

Key to symbols is on back flap.

Edinburgh Map Ref: 2C5

B&B

Mrs C M Cairns
28 Cammo Road, Edinburgh, EH4 8AP
Tel: 0131 339 3613

2 Double

B&B per person
from £24.00 Single
from £20.00 Double

Open Mar-Oct

A warm welcome awaits you at this family home in quiet residential area with easy access to Queensferry Rd and Airport. Ideal base for touring Edinburgh and surrounding countryside. Ample parking.

GUEST HOUSE

Cameron Toll Guest House
299 Dalkeith Road, Edinburgh, EH16 5JX
Tel: 0131 667 2950 Fax: 0131 662 1987
E-mail: camerontoll@msn.com
Web: http://members.edinburgh.org/camerontoll

3 Single
2 Twin
3 Double
3 Family

10 En Suite fac
1 Priv.NOT ensuite

B&B per person
from £30.00 Single
from £22.00 Dbl/Twn

Open Jan-Dec
B&B + Eve.Meal
from £32.00

Andrew and Mary offer you a cosy bedroom in our friendly guest house with some private parking. Situated on the A7, there is a frequent bus service to the city centre. The Commonwealth Pool is nearby. Scottish hospitality to ensure a memorable stay. Gold award for environmental management.

C £ W V

GOLD

Important: Prices stated are estimates and may be subject to amendments

Edinburgh Map Ref: 2C5

CARRONVALE

38 Corstorphine Bank Drive, Edinburgh EH12 8RN
Telephone: 0131 334 3291 Fax: 0131 334 3883

Spacious, centrally heated bungalow with unrestricted parking in quiet residential area, three miles from city centre and four miles from airport. Ground-floor bedrooms, ensuite facilities, colour TV, tea and coffee provided. Residents' lounge, own keys. Full Scottish breakfast. Good bus service to city centre.

Carronvale
38 Corstorphine Bank Drive, Edinburgh, EH12 8RN
Tel: 0131 334 3291 Fax: 0131 334 3883

2 Twin	1 En Suite fac 1 Priv Bath/Show	B&B per person £18.00-£27.00 Twin	Open Apr-Oct

In quiet residential area, a delightful detached home with colourful gardens. A short walk to main bus route to city centre (4 miles). Convenient for Edinburgh zoo, airport and motorway network. Unrestricted street parking.

V

Castle Park Guest House

75 Gilmore Place, Edinburgh EH3 9NU
Telephone: 0131 229 1215 Fax: 0131 229 1223

Family run close to Kings Theatre and city centre conference centre. Always a warm welcome awaits you. All bedrooms have colour TV, Sky, tea and coffee. Central heating. Full Scottish breakfast. Children welcome. Special prices. Private lane parking. £17.50–£27 pppn.

Castle Park Guest House
75 Gilmore Place, Edinburgh, EH3 9NU
Tel: 0131 229 1215 Fax: 0131 229 1223

1 Single 2 Twin 3 Double 1 Family	4 En Suite fac 1 Pub Bath/Show	B&B per person from £17.50 Single from £20.00 Dbl/Twn Room only per person from £10.00	Open Jan-Dec

Family run guest house close to city centre. Convenient for Kings Theatre and Conference Hall. A variety of local restaurants and bistros. Children welcome.

C V

VAT is shown at 17.5%: changes in this rate may affect prices.

Key to symbols is on back flap.

Edinburgh

Map Ref: 2C5

CHARLESTON HOUSE

38 Minto Street, Edinburgh EH9 2BS
Tel: 0131 667 6589 Fax: 0131 668 3800
e.mail: joan_wightman@hotmail.com

Listed Georgian town house (1826) retaining many original features. Quick access to city centre by bus or on foot. Easy access to Borders, Highlands and Glasgow via city bypass. We offer a choice of standard or ensuite rooms all furnished traditionally to complement the period features. A traditional breakfast is served as well as alternatives. Colour TV with satellite, room refreshments, central heating and wash hand basin in all the rooms. Open over New Year. Special offers in the low season. This family run guest house offers a warm welcome.

GUEST HOUSE

Charleston House Guest House
38 Minto Street, Edinburgh, EH9 2BS
Tel: 0131 667 6589 Fax: 0131 668 3800
E-mail: joan_wightman@hotmail.com

2 Twin / 1 Double / 2 Family — 2 En Suite fac / 2 Pub Bath/Show / 1 Priv.NOT ensuite — B&B per person from £25.00 Single, from £20.00 Dbl/Twn — Open Jan-Dec excl Xmas

Traditionally furnished Georgian family home - 1826, 1- 1.5 miles from city centre. Excellent bus route, very frequent service.

BRONZE

B&B

Clarence St B&B
3a Clarence Street, Edinburgh, EH3 5AE
Tel: 0131 557 9368

1 Twin / 1 Family — Public Bath/Show / Priv.NOT ensuite — B&B per person from £18.00 Single, from £17.00 Twin — Open Apr-Oct

Garden flat in Georgian terrace in New Town. Central location yet in quiet area. Close to Botanic Gardens, sports grounds (Highland Games every weekend in Summer). Theatre workshop and numerous restaurants nearby. Private garden.

B&B

The Conifers
56 Pilrig Street, Edinburgh, EH6 5AS
Tel: 0131 554 5162

1 Twin / 1 Double / 1 Family — All En Suite — B&B per person £25.00-£30.00 Dbl/Twn — Open Jan-Dec

Friendly family home close to city centre. Recently refurbished, all rooms ensuite. Spacious superior quality ground floor bedroom retaining original features. Within walking distance of Playhouse Theatre. Non-smoking house.

Important: Prices stated are estimates and may be subject to amendments

Edinburgh Map Ref: 2C5

Braid Hills Cottage

20 Jordan Lane, Edinburgh EH10 4QZ
Telephone: 0131 447 3650
e.mail: l.cooper@zoom.co.uk

Georgian cottage in quiet corner near centre of Edinburgh. Full breakfasts with vegetarian choices always available. We are very friendly, have a large garden and welcome children. The city centre is 10 minutes away by bus.

★★

B&B

Lynn Cooper
20 Jordan Lane, Edinburgh, EH10 4QZ
Tel: 0131 447 3650
E-mail: l.cooper@zoom.co.uk

1 Single	1 En Suite fac	B&B per person	Open Jan-Dec
1 Twin	1 Pub Bath/Show	£22.00-£30.00 Single	
1 Double		£20.00-£28.00 Dbl/Twn	

Stone built 19c single storey house with large garden in quiet location on south side of city. Convenient bus routes to city centre. Full, continental or vegetarian breakfast available. Non-smoking house.

C V

Mrs Moira Conway

Crannoch But & Ben

467 QUEENSFERRY RD
EDINBURGH EH4 7ND
TEL/FAX: 0131 336 5688

STB Grade of 4 Stars and Classification of Bed & Breakfast has been awarded to this outstanding family home. This bungalow has private facilities for all rooms and residents' lounge. Near Airport on A90 and 3 miles from city centre with excellent bus service and car parking. *All guests receive a warm welcome.*

★★★★

B&B

Crannoch But & Ben
467 Queensferry Road, Edinburgh, EH4 7ND
Tel/Fax: 0131 336 5688
E-mail: moiraconway@cranoch467.freeserve.co.uk

1 Twin	All En Suite	B&B per person	Open Jan-Dec
1 Double		£25.00-£27.00 Single	
1 Family		£25.00-£27.00 Dbl/Twn	

Detached bungalow with warm and friendly atmosphere, on Forth Road Bridge route, 3 miles (5kms) from city centre. Non-smoking house. Ensuite bathrooms, parking.

C V

★★

GUEST HOUSE

Crioch Guest House
23 East Hermitage Place, Edinburgh, EH6 8AD
Tel/Fax: 0131 554 5494
E-mail: welcome@crioch.com
Web: www.crioch.com

1 Single	5 Ensuite fac	B&B per person	Open Jan-Dec
1 Twin	1 Priv.NOT ensuite	from £20.00 Single	
2 Double		from £18.50 Dbl/Twn	
2 Family			

Only 10 minutes from the city centre, Crioch overlooks the leafy park of Leith Links. Our recent major refurbishment means that all rooms now have ensuite shower or private bathroom, and you still receive the same warm welcome. Free parking and a frequent bus service leaves you to enjoy Edinburgh's sights on foot, and later a short stroll takes you to Leith's fine cafes, bars and restaurants.

TV C £ V

Edinburgh — Map Ref: 2C5

Crion Guest House

33 Minto Street,
Edinburgh EH9 2BT

Telephone: 0131 667 2708 Fax: 0131 662 1946
e.mail: w.cheape@gilmourhouse.freeserve.co.uk
Web: www.edinburghbedbreakfast.com

A warm friendly welcome awaits you at this family run guest house. Fully refurbished with your comfort in mind offering outstanding Bed & Breakfast value. Three ensuite rooms now available. Double ensuite prices from £20 to £36 max per person. Situated within 1½ miles of city centre on an excellent bus route near most tourist attractions, near University and Commonwealth Pool. For enquiries send SAE or telephone.

GUEST HOUSE

Crion Guest House

33 Minto Street, Edinburgh, EH9 2BT
Tel: 0131 667 2708 Fax: 0131 662 1946
E-mail: w.cheape@gilmourhouse.freeserve.co.uk
Web: www.edinburghbedbreakfast.com

Refurbished, friendly, family run guest house, close to Commonwealth Pool and University. On main bus route to city centre. Variety of local restaurants. Near most tourist attractions.

Rooms	Facilities	B&B per person	Open
1 Single	3 En Suite fac	from £21.00 Single	Open Jan-Dec
2 Twin	2 Priv.NOT ensuite	£20.00-£36.00 Dbl/Twn	
1 Double			
2 Family			

TV P C V

DORIS CROOK

2 SETON PLACE, EDINBURGH EH9 2JT
Telephone: 0131 667 6430 Fax: 0131 667 6652
e.mail: doriscrook@zoom.co.uk
Web: http://pages.zoom.co.uk/doriscrook

Detached Victorian villa within conservation area in the south side of Edinburgh surrounded by well maintained private garden with private parking. Rooms decorated to high standard with ensuite facilities, tea and coffee and colour TV. Non smoking friendly family home.

B&B

Mrs Doris Crook

2 Seton Place, Edinburgh, EH9 2JT
Tel: 0131 667 6430 Fax: 0131 667 6652
E.mail: doriscrook@zoom.co.uk
Web: http://pages.zoom.co.uk/doriscrook

Upper flatted villa at end of Georgian terrace in quiet residential area. Private parking and easy access to town centre.

Rooms	Facilities	B&B per person	Open
2 Twin	2 En Suite fac	£22.00-£26.00 Dbl/Twn	Open Jan-Dec
1 Double	1 Priv.NOT ensuite		

TV P C V

Important: Prices stated are estimates and may be subject to amendments

Edinburgh

Map Ref: 2C5

CRUACHAN GUEST HOUSE

53 Gilmore Place, Edinburgh EH3 9NT

Tel/Fax: 0131 229 6219 e.mail: janette@cruachan9.freeserve.co.uk

Janette and Graham promise you a warm welcome at their very homely guest house. Situated in the heart of Edinburgh, all attractions are in easy walking distance and Janette's Scottish breakfast served in the bright conservatory is not to be missed. Bed & Breakfast £20-£35 per person per night. Special 3 nights for 2 in Winter. Parking available.

★★★ GUEST HOUSE

Cruachan Guest House

53 Gilmore Place, Edinburgh, EH3 9NT
Tel/Fax: 0131 229 6219
E-mail: janette@cruachan9.freeserve.co.uk
Web: www.cruachan9.freeserve.co.uk

2 Single, 1 Twin, 2 Double, 1 Family

4 En Suite fac, 1 Pub Bath/Show

B&B per person from £20.00 Single, from £21.00 Dbl/Twn

Open Jan-Dec

Janette & Graham promises you a warm welcome at this non-smoking and homely Guest House. Being 10 minutes walk from the City Centre and its amenities it is ideal for short breaks. Two ensuite rooms on ground floor. Private parking 400m away.

★★★ GUEST HOUSE

Dene Guest House

7 Eyre Place, off Dundas Street, Edinburgh, EH3 5ES
Tel: 0131 556 2700 Fax: 0131 557 9876
E-mail: deneguesthouse@yahoo.co.uk

3 Single, 3 Twin, 3 Double, 2 Family

5 En Suite fac, 2 Pub Bath/Show

B&B per person from £19.50 Single, from £19.50 Dbl/Twn

Open Jan-Dec

Charming Georgian townhouse offering friendly service and a relaxed atmosphere. Perfectly located in city centre to experience Edinburgh's culture, history, restaurants and bars.

★ B&B

Mr & Mrs T Divine

116 Greenbank Crescent, Edinburgh, EH10 5SZ
Tel: 0131 447 9454
E-mail: mary@greenbnk.fsnet.co.uk

1 Single, 1 Twin

B&B per person from £17.00 Single

Open Mar-Oct

Family home in quiet residential area with easy access to city centre and bypass. Parking. On main bus routes.

★★ B&B

Doocote House

15 Moat Street, Edinburgh, EH14 1PE
Tel: 0131 443 5455

1 Twin, 1 Double, 1 Family

1 Pub Bath/Show, 1 Pub Shower

B&B per person from £16.00-£20.00 Dbl/Twn

Open March-Oct

Terraced house in quiet street just off main bus route. Approx. 2 miles (3kms) from city centre. Unrestricted street parking.

Edinburgh — Map Ref: 2C5

GUEST HOUSE

Dorstan Private Hotel
7 Priestfield Road, Edinburgh, EH16 5HJ
Tel: 0131 667 6721/5138 Fax: 0131 668 4644

Victorian villa in quiet residential area. Own car parking. 1 mile (2 kms) on main bus route from city centre. Most rooms en suite. Golf course adjacent. Ideal for visiting tourist attractions and surrounding area.

Rooms	Facilities	Prices	Open
5 Single 1 Twin 6 Double 2 Family	9 En Suite fac 3 Limited ensuite 3 Pub Bath/Show	B&B per person £32.00-£48.00 Single £36.00-£41.00 Dbl/Twn	Open Jan-Dec

SMALL HOTEL

Dunstane House Hotel
4 West Coates, Edinburgh, EH12 5JQ
Tel/Fax: 0131 337 6169
E-mail: reservations@dunstanehousehotel.co.uk

Impressive Listed Victorian mansion retaining many original features enjoying imposing position within large grounds on the A8 airport road (major bus route). 10 mins walk from city centre. Close to Edinburgh Conference Centre, Murrayfield and Edinburgh Zoo. Private secluded car park. Lounge bar. New seafood restaurant opening early 2001. Friendly service assured by proprietors Shirley and Derek Mowat.

Rooms	Facilities	Prices	Open
4 Single 2 Twin 5 Double 5 Family	All En Suite	B&B per person from £35.00 Single from £33.50 Dbl/Twn	Open Jan-Dec

B&B

Mrs Jean Durbin
4 Inverleith Row, Edinburgh, EH3 5LP
Tel: 0131 5565398 Fax: 0131 556 5398

Late Georgian town house with period furnishings. Boundary on Royal Botanic Gardens. The house has its own landscaped garden with sheltered seating areas. 5 minutes by bus to Princes Street, the heart of the city, or to the port of Leith, with its many restaurants and pubs and popular dockland developments.

Rooms	Facilities	Prices	Open
1 Single 1 Double	Priv. NOT En Suite	B&B per person £45.00 Single £30.00 Dbl	Open Jun-Sep

CAMPUS ACCOMMODATION

Edinburgh Conference Centre
Heriot-Watt University, Riccarton, Edinburgh, EH14 4AS
Tel: 0131 451 3669 Fax: 0131 451 3199
Web: www.ecc.scot.net

Situated in 370 acre picturesque campus of Heriot Watt University. 6 miles (10kms) west of the city centre, 3 miles (5kms) from Edinburgh Airport.

Rooms	Facilities	Prices	Open
1493 Sngl 98 Twin 35 Double	1231 Ensuite 465 Pub Bath/Show	B&B per person from £26.00 Single from £23.00 Dbl/Twn	Open Jan-Dec excl Xmas/New Year B&B + Eve.Meal from £35.00

Edinburgh | Map Ref: 2C5

HOTEL

Edinburgh First, University of Edinburgh

18 Holyrood Park Road, Edinburgh, EH16 5AY
Tel: 0800 028 7118 Fax: 0131 667 7271
E-mail: Edinburgh.First@ed.ac.uk

330 Rooms All En Suite

B&B per person
£27.00-£46.00 Single
£69.00-£75.00 Double

Open Mar-Apr, Jun-Sep

On campus in Holyrood Park beside Arthur's Seat. Close to Royal Commonwealth Pool, 3 km from city centre. In beautiful surroundings, we offer comfortable accommodation with en-suite facilities. Particularly suitable for groups. Alternative annexe accommodation available. Conference and meeting facilities.

C £ W V

GUEST HOUSE

Elder York Guest House

38 Elder Street, Edinburgh, EH1 3DX
Tel: 0131 556 1926

3 Single, 3 Twin, 4 Double, 1 Family

4 En Suite fac, 3 Limited ensuite, 3 Pub Bath/Show

B&B per person
£27.00-£32.00 Single
£24.00-£32.00 Dbl/Twn

Open Jan-Dec

Guest house in centre of city, short walk from Princes St, rail and bus station. Close to car park.

TV

C £ V

GUEST HOUSE

Ellesmere Guest House

11 Glengyle Terrace, Edinburgh, EH3 9LN
Tel: 0131 229 4823 Fax: 0131 229 5285
E-mail: celia@edinburghbandb.co.uk
Web: www.edinburghbandb.co.uk

1 Single, 2 Twin, 2 Double, 1 Family

All En Suite

B&B per person
from £25.00 Single
from £25.00 Dbl/Twn

Open Jan-Dec excl Xmas

City centre Victorian terraced house in quiet location overlooking Bruntsfield Links with frontage overlooking golf links. Kings Theatre, Conference Centre and all amenities within walking distance. All rooms en suite. Full Scottish Breakfast.

TV

W V

B&B

Elliston

5 Viewforth Terrace, Edinburgh, EH10 4LH
Tel: 0131 229 6698

2 Single, 1 Twin

1 Pub Bath/Show

B&B per person
from £22.00 Single
from £20.00 Twin

Open Apr-end Sep

Victorian villa approx 2 miles (3kms) from Princes Street. In quiet residential location, and within walking distance of restaurants and theatres. Close to bus route. Non smoking house. Television in twin bedroom.

C £ V

Edinburgh Map Ref: 2C5

Ellesmere House

11 Glengyle Terrace,
EDINBURGH

Tel: 0131 229 4823 EH3 9LN Fax: 0131 229 5285

e.mail: celia@edinburghbandb.co.uk Web: www.edinburghbandb.co.uk

"Your home away from home"

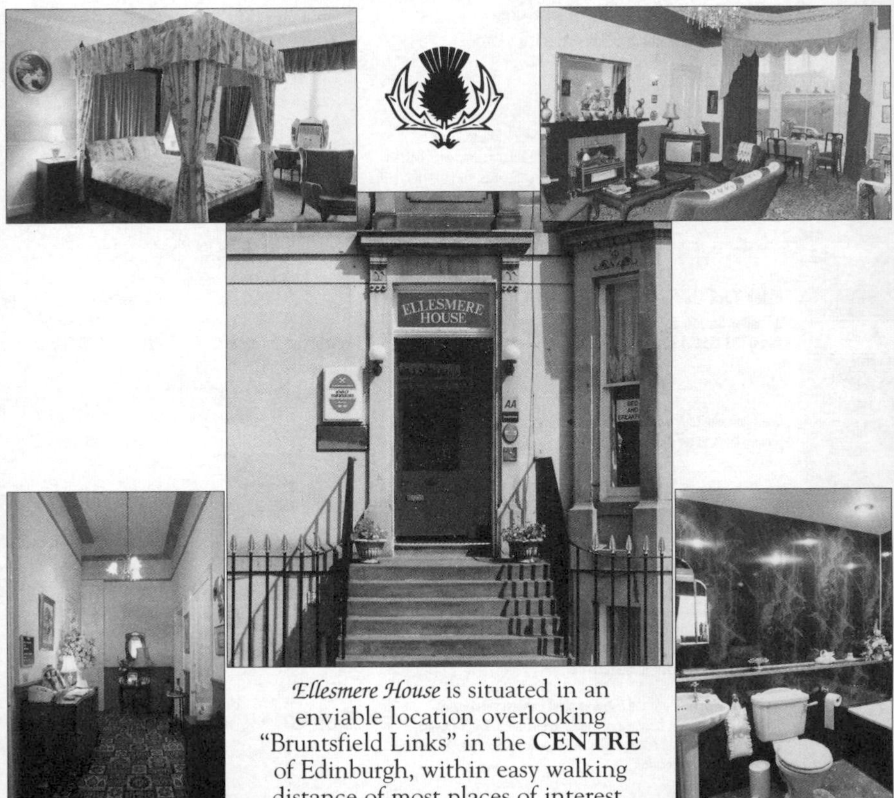

Ellesmere House is situated in an enviable location overlooking "Bruntsfield Links" in the **CENTRE** of Edinburgh, within easy walking distance of most places of interest. The International Conference Centre, theatres and various good restaurants are very close by. Rooms are all ensuite and are tastefully furnished and decorated to a very high standard and many extras added with your comfort in mind. For honeymooners or that special anniversary there is a four-poster bed available. Start the day with our delicious full Scottish breakfast.

Prices from £25, all rooms ensuite. Excellent value and competitive prices.

Personally run by Cecilia & Tommy Leishman who extend a very warm welcome to all of their guests.

STB ★★★★ AA ♦♦♦♦ Selected

Edinburgh

Map Ref: 2C5

B&B ★★

Emerald Guest House
3 Drum Street, Gilmerton, Edinburgh. EH17 8QQ
Tel: 0131 664 5918

Rooms	Facilities	B&B per person	Open
1 Family 1 Double 2 Twin 1 Treble	3 Ensuite fac 1 Pub Bath/Show	£20.00-£35.00 Single £20.00-£31.00 Dbl/Twn	Open Jan-Dec

Family run bed and breakfast located on convenient bus route to city centre. Private parking available.

Falcon Crest

70 South Trinity Road
Edinburgh EH5 3NX
Tel: 0131 552 5294

A friendly welcome awaits at our family run guest house in a quiet residential Victorian terrace. Located between the Royal Botanic Gardens, Newhaven Harbour and Granton Marina. Ten minutes by frequent bus service from the city centre. Good road links. Private parking. Special diets by prior request.

GUEST HOUSE

Falcon Crest Guest House
70 South Trinity Road, Edinburgh, EH5 3NX
Tel: 0131 552 5294

Rooms	Facilities	B&B per person	Open
1 Single 2 Twin 2 Double 1 Family	3 En Suite fac 2 Pub Bath/Show	from £16.00 Single from £16.00 Dbl/Twn Room only per person from £15.00	Open Jan-Dec excl Xmas

Victorian terraced family home in attractive residential area, near main bus route to city centre. Free on street parking.

B&B

Finlaystone
19 Meadowplace Road, Edinburgh, EH12 7UJ
Tel/Fax: 0131 334 8483

Rooms	Facilities	B&B per person	Open
1 Twin 1 Family	2 Pub Bath/Show	from £16.00 Twin	Open Jan-Nov

On the West side of the city, detached bungalow offering ground floor accommodation and off street parking. Excellent bus service to city centre and airport. Various type of eating establishments within walking distance.

B&B

Mrs D R Frackelton
17 Hope Park Terrace, Edinburgh, EH8 9LZ
Tel: 0131 667 7963

Rooms	Facilities	B&B per person	Open
1 Single 1 Double		from £22.00 Single from £21.00 Double	Open Apr-Oct

Ground floor flat 15 minutes walk to Princes Street (1 mile) 10 mins. Royal mile, 7 mins University and Royal College of Surgeons. Central to all attractions.

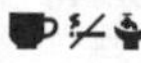

Edinburgh

Map Ref: 2C5

GUEST HOUSE

Galloway
22 Dean Park Crescent, Edinburgh, EH4 1TH
Tel/Fax: 0131 332 3672

1 Single
2 Twin
2 Double
5 Family

6 En Suite fac
1 Priv.NOT ensuite

B&B per person
from £25.00 Single
from £18.00 Dbl/Twn

Open Jan-Dec

Friendly, family run guest house, beautifully restored and situated in a residential area, 10 minutes walk from Princes Street and convenient for Edinburgh International Conference Centre. Free street parking.

C V

GUEST HOUSE

James & Heather McWilliams
Ben Craig House, 3 Craigmillar Park, Edinburgh, EH16 5PG
Tel: 0131 667 2593 Fax: 0131 667 1109
E.mail: bencraighouse@dial.pipex.com
Web: www.bencraighouse.co.uk

1 Twin
3 Double
1 Family

5 En Suite fac

B&B per person
£25.00-£45.00 Single
£25.00-£40.00 Dbl/Twn
Room only per person
£25.00-£36.00

Open Jan-Dec

Traditional detached sandstone Victorian villa with quiet gardens. On main route for city centre. (1.5 miles south of Princes Street.) Tastefully restored and decorated to high standard.

C V

GUEST HOUSE

Gifford House
103 Dalkeith Road, Edinburgh, EH16 5AJ
Tel/Fax: 0131 667 4688
E-mail: giffordhotel@btinternet.com

1 Single
2 Twin
2 Double
2 Family

All En Suite

B&B per person
from £25.00 Single
from £20.00 Dbl/Twn
Room only per person
from £18.00

Open Jan-Dec

A well appointed Victorian stone built house situated on one of the main routes into Edinburgh. Close to Holyrood Park and Arthur's Seat and only 300 metres from Royal Commonwealth Swimming Pool. Regular bus services to all city amenities. Well positioned for conference centre.

C V

GUEST HOUSE

Glenallan Guest House
19 Mayfield Road, Edinburgh, EH9 2NG
Tel: 0131 667 1667
E-mail: enquiries@Glenallan.co.uk
Web: www.Glenallan.co.uk

1 Single
1 Twin
2 Double
1 Family

3 En Suite fac
1 Priv.NOT ensuite
1 Pub Bath/Show

B&B per person
from £24.00 Single
from £22.00 Dbl/Twn

Open Jan-Dec

Conveniently situated on main bus route into city centre. Private car parking. Recently refurbished. Completely non-smoking. Under new ownership. French, Spanish, German and Polish spoken.

C W V

Important: Prices stated are estimates and may be subject to amendments

Edinburgh — Map Ref: 2C5

★★★★
GUEST HOUSE

Glenalmond Guest House
25 Mayfield Gardens, Edinburgh, EH9 2BX
Tel/Fax: 0131 668 2392

1 Single	All En Suite	B&B per person	Open Jan-Dec
2 Twin	4 F.Poster	£25.00-£40.00 Single	
4 Double	6 Canopy	£25.00-£40.00 Dbl/Twn	
3 Family			

Personally run guest house with private parking. On main bus routes to city centre.

TV P C £ V

GLENDEVON
50 GLASGOW ROAD, EDINBURGH EH12 8HN
Telephone/Fax: 0131 539 0491

A warm welcome awaits visitors at 'Glendevon'. A detached bungalow with attractive garden, open outlook and private parking. On good bus route to city centre and 3 miles from airport. All rooms centrally heated and tastefully furnished with W.H.B., tea/coffee making facilities and colour TV. Residents lounge available. Non-smoking.

B&B

'Glendevon'
50 Glasgow Road, Edinburgh, EH12 8HN
Tel/Fax: 0131 539 0491

1 Single	2 Pub Bath/Show	B&B per person	Open Apr-Oct
1 Twin		£18.00-£22.00 Single	
1 Double		£18.00-£22.00 Dbl/Twn	
		Room only per person	
		from £18.00	

1930's family bungalow on major bus route to city centre and 2 miles from the Airport. Private parking. Some ground floor accommodation. Non-smoking.

TV P

SMALL HOTEL

Glenora Hotel
14 Rosebery Crescent, Edinburgh, EH12 5JY
Tel: 0131 337 1186 Fax: 0131 337 1119
E-mail: edinburgh@purplenet.co.uk
Web: www.edinburgh.purplenet.co.uk

2 Single	All En Suite	B&B per person	Open Jan-Dec
3 Twin		from £17.50 Single	
3 Double		from £17.50 Dbl/Twn	
2 Family			

Victorian terraced house approximately a minutes walk to city centre and within easy reach of city's tourist attractions. Airport bus stops next to hotel.

TV C £ V

Edinburgh | Map Ref: 2C5

GUEST HOUSE

The Grange Guest House
2 Minto Street, Edinburgh, EH9 1RG
Tel/Fax: 0131 667 2125
E.mail: ash252@email.msn.com

3 Twin, 2 Double, 3 Family | All En Suite, 1 Pub Bath/Show | B&B per person £30.00-£35.00 Single, £18.00-£30.00 Dbl/Twn | Open Jan-Dec

Stone built Georgian House on main A7. On bus route for the city centre and all amenities. Continental breakfast only. Close to Commonwealth Pool and within walking distance to Holyrood Park.

C

B&B

Hamilton House
22 Craigmillar Park, Edinburgh, EH16 5PS
Tel: 0131 662 9324 Fax: 0131 466 0510
E-mail: dwwren@aol.com
Web: http://members.aol.com/dwwren/hamilton.htm

1 Single, 1 Twin, 1 Double | 1 Priv.not ensuite, 1 Pub Bath/Show | B&B per person from £18.00 Single, from £18.00 Dbl/Twn; Room only per person from £15.00 | Open Jan-Dec

Elegant victorian townhouse of great character. Situated on main bus route to city centre allowing easy access to Royal Mile, Princes Street, and the Castle. Garage Parking available.

C £ V

B&B

The Hedges
19 Hillside Crescent, Edinburgh, EH7 5EB
Tel: 0131 558 1481

1 Single, 1 Twin, 1 Double | All En Suite, 1 Priv.NOT ensuite | B&B per person £18.00-£27.50 Single, £18.00-£27.50 Dbl/Twn; Room only per person £18.00-£25.00 | Open Jan-Dec

Family house where children are welcome. 10 mins walk from Princes Street and 5 mins from Playhouse Theatre. Free on-street parking.

C V

HOTEL

Heriot-Watt University
Heriot-Watt University, Riccarton, Edinburgh, EH14 4AS
Tel: 0131 451 3669/3501 (eve) Fax: 0131 451 3199
E-mail: ecc@hw.ac.uk
Web: www.ecc.scot.net

1491 Single, 98 Twin, 35 Double | 1918 En Suite fac, 96 Pub Bath/Show | B&B per person £26.00-£40.00 Single, £23.00-£30.00 Dbl/Twn | Open Jan-Dec, B&B + Eve.Meal £35.00-£55.50

Situated in 370 acre picturesque campus of Heriot Watt University. 6 miles (10kms) west of city centre, 3 miles (5kms) from Edinburgh airport.

C £ V

Important: Prices stated are estimates and may be subject to amendments

Edinburgh **Map Ref: 2C5**

GUEST HOUSE

Highfield Guest House
83 Mayfield Road, Edinburgh, EH9 3AE
Tel: 0131 667 8717 Fax: 0131 668 3006
Web: www.ypr52.dial.pipex.com

1 Single, 1 Twin, 2 Double, 1 Family | 4 En Suite fac, 1 Priv.NOT ensuite | B&B per person from £20.00 Single, from £20.00 Dbl/Twn | Open Jan-Dec

Situated in a residential area this stone built Victorian house has been refurbished to a high standard. Friendly and hospitable hosts offering a full breakfast, including the choice of vegetarian haggis. Totally non smoking with all bedrooms en-suite/private facilities. 10 minutes to city centre on main bus routes 42 & 46.

C W V

GUEST HOUSE

Highland Park Guest House
16 Kilmaurs Terrace, Edinburgh, EH16 5DR
Tel/Fax: 0131 667 9204
E.mail: highlandparkhouse@hotmail.com

1 Single, 2 Twin, 1 Double, 1 Family | 1 En Suite fac, 2 Pub Bath/Show | B&B per person £18.00-£29.00 Single, £17.00-£29.00 Dbl/Twn; Room only per person from £15.00 | Open Jan-Dec excl Xmas

Victorian stone built house retaining many original features in quiet residential area. 1.5 miles (3kms) from city centre. On main bus routes. Non-smoking establishment. Ground floor en suite bedroom.

TV

C V

GUEST HOUSE

Hopetoun Guest House
15 Mayfield Road, Edinburgh, EH9 2NG
Tel: 0131 667 7691 Fax: 0131 466 1691
E-mail: hopetoun@aol.com
Web: http://members.aol.com/hopetoun

1 Double, 2 Family | 1 En Suite fac, 1 Priv.NOT ensuite, 1 Pub Bath/Show | B&B per person £20.00-£40.00 Single, £20.00-£30.00 Double | Open Jan-Dec

Completely non-smoking, small, friendly guest house on the south side of the city, 1.5 miles (2.5kms) from Princes Street. Choice of traditional, healthy or vegetarian breakfast. Guests are encouraged to make use of the owners wide knowledge of what the city has to offer.

TV P

C V

VAT is shown at 17.5%: changes in this rate may affect prices.

Key to symbols is on back flap.

Edinburgh — Map Ref: 2C5

HOUSE O'HILL GUEST HOUSE

7 HOUSE O'HILL TERRACE, QUEENSFERRY ROAD, EDINBURGH EH4 2AA
TEL: 0131 332 3674 FAX: 0131 343 3446
E.MAIL: chrissy@houseohill.freeserve.co.uk WEB: www.7houseohill.freeserve.co.uk

Enjoy warm Scottish hospitality at our elegant Victorian retreat, where you can relax in a warm, clean, friendly environment with personal service assured. All rooms ensuite, tastefully furnished to a high standard and well-equipped for your comfort. Conservatory breakfast room overlooking oriental garden, breakfasts freshly prepared to order. Central. Parking.

★★★★ GUEST HOUSE

House O'Hill Guest House

7 House O'Hill Terrace, Blackhall, Edinburgh, EH4 2AA
Tel: 0131 332 3674 Fax: 0131 343 3446
E-mail: chrissy@houseohill.freeserve.co.uk
Web: www.7houseohill.freeserve.co.uk

Family run semi-detached Victorian house situated approx 1.5 miles (2.5kms) from West End. Convenient access to city via Queensferry Road. City bypass, airport, train stations, sports stadiums, shopping complexes, leisure clubs and zoo within a 2 mile radius. Parking. Children welcome.

2 Twin 1 Double 1 Family	All En Suite	B&B per person from £25.00 Single from £23.00 Dbl/Twn	Open Jan-Dec

C £ V

INGLENEUK

31 DRUM BRAE NORTH, EDINBURGH EH4 8AT
Tel/Fax: 0131 317 1743 e.mail: ritchietype@cwcom.net
Web: www.accomodata.co.uk/110999.htm

For an enjoyable stay anytime, visit our comfortable home situated in a quiet residential area. As well as a double ensuite, we have a self contained annex with private entrance, comprising large twin bedded room with lounge/breakfasting area having two rooms off, a double bedroom and a shower room – ideal for two couples travelling together – family/double or twin. A full breakfast is served in your room giving a totally relaxed breakfast setting looking out onto a lovely landscaped garden. Ample private parking. Four miles from city, 3 miles from airport. Good bus service. Close to Forth Bridge.

★★ B&B

Ingleneuk

31 Drumbrae North, Edinburgh, EH4 8AT
Tel/Fax: 0131 317 1743
E-mail: ritchietype@cwcom.net
Web: www.accomodata.co.uk/110999.htm

On the west side of town, convenient for the Forth Bridge and the airport, this cottage styled B&B backs onto a private woodland garden alive with birds and squirrels in amongst the ornamental Japanese bridge. Both rooms have their own private entrance, one is a family suite suitable for four persons. Enjoy a relaxed breakfast, served in the comfort of your own room.

1 Twin 1 Double	All En Suite	B&B per person from £25.00 Single from £19.00 Dbl/Twn	Open Jan-Dec

Edinburgh Map Ref: 2C5

GUEST HOUSE

International Guest House
37 Mayfield Gardens, Edinburgh, EH9 2BX
Tel: 0131 667 2511 Fax: 0131 667 1112
E-mail: intergh@easynet.co.uk
Web: www.intermart.co.uk/international/

Stone built Victorian house in residential area with regular bus service to city centre. All rooms have ensuite facilities. Some private parking and on-street parking. Ground floor room available for persons with limited mobility.

4 Single
1 Twin
2 Double
2 Family

All En Suite

B&B per person
£25.00-£45.00 Single
£20.00-£40.00 Dbl/Twn

Open Jan-Dec

B&B

Invermark
60 Polwarth Terrace, Edinburgh, EH11 1NJ
Tel: 0131 337 1066

Georgian house situated in quiet residential area, 15 minutes by bus from city centre. Next to main bus route. Local hotels offer a range of evening meals. Convenient for Craiglockhart Sports Centre.

1 Single
1 Twin
1 Family

B&B per person
from £20.00 Single
from £20.00 Twin

Open Apr-Oct

GUEST HOUSE

Joppa Turrets Guest House
1 Lower Joppa (at beachend of Morton St),
Edinburgh, EH15 2ER
Tel/Fax: 0131 669 5806
Web: www.joppaturrets.demon.co.uk

What makes us special? Location right on sandy beach, sea views, fresh air and sounds of the waves, from our attractive, cosy bedrooms. Frequent nearby bus to beautiful city centre, returning to peace and quiet in our residential cul de sac and pretty private garden. Unrestricted on-street parking. NON SMOKING. Nearby are restaurants and pubs, plus indoor swimming, turkish baths and fitness centre. See our web-page.

4 Double
1 Family

3 En Suite fac
1 Pub Bath/Show

B&B per person
from £19.00 Single
from £19.00 Double
Room only per person
from £19.00

Open Jan-Dec excl Xmas

Edinburgh
Map Ref: 2C5

Edinburgh Map Ref: 2C5

Kingswood

30 Arboretum Place, Inverleith, Edinburgh EH3 5NZ
Telephone: 0131 332 7315

Luxury modern home situated in a quiet residential area next to the Royal Botanic Gardens overlooking Inverleith Park. Within easy walking distance of city centre and tourist attractions. Private car parking available and near main bus routes.

★★★

B&B

Mr & Mrs A M Kay
Kingswood, 30 Arboretum Place, Inverleith, Edinburgh, EH3 5NZ
Tel: 0131 332 7315

1 Twin | 2 Double
1 En Suite fac | 1 Pub Bath/Show
B&B per person £18.00-£30.00 Dbl/Twn
Open Apr-Oct

Comfortable family house of modern architectural design located in a quiet residential area adjacent to the Royal Botanic Garden and overlooking Inverleith Park. Ample private parking and un-restricted street parking. Easy access to the city centre and main attractions.

V

★★★

GUEST HOUSE

Kenvie Guest House
16 Kilmaurs Road, Edinburgh, EH16 5DA
Tel: 0131 668 1964 Fax: 0131 668 1926
E-mail: dorothy@kenvie.co.uk

2 Twin | 1 Double | 2 Family
3 En Suite fac | 2 Pub Bath/Show
B&B per person from £25.00 Single from £23.00 Dbl/Twn
Room only per person from £20.00
Open Jan-Dec

A charming, comfortable, warm, friendly family run Victorian town house in a quiet residential street. Very close to bus routes and the city by-pass. We offer for your comfort, lots of caring touches including complimentary tea / coffee, colour TV and no-smoking rooms. En-suite available and vegetarians catered for. You are guranteed a warm welcome from Richard and Dorothy.

W V

★★★

GUEST HOUSE

Kingsley Guest House
30 Craigmillar Park, Edinburgh, EH16 5PS
Tel: 0131 667 3177 Tel/Fax: 0131 667 8439
E-mail: lynredmayne@kingsleyguesthouse.co.uk

2 Twin | 1 Double | 2 Family
3 En Suite fac | 1 Priv.NOT ensuite | 1 Pub Bath/Show
B&B per person from £20.00 Dbl/Twn
Open Jan-Dec

Friendly, comfortable and family run Victorian villa with own private car park. Excellent bus service for all major attractions in the city. Close to university area and Commonwealth Pool.

C W V

Edinburgh | Map Ref: 2C5

KINGSVIEW GUEST HOUSE

28 Gilmore Place, Edinburgh EH3 9NQ Tel/ Fax: 0131 229 8004

Family run guest house in the heart of the city. A warm friendly welcome awaits. An impressive grill menu 100% Scottish produce. Parking can be arranged locally at a small charge. Small groups welcome, as are children and pets. All major credit cards accepted. Advanced reservation is recommended. A warm welcome awaits.

★★
GUEST HOUSE

Kingsview Guest House
28 Gilmore Place, Edinburgh, EH3 9NQ
Tel/Fax: 0131 229 8004
E-mail: kingsviewguesthouse@talk21.com
Web: www.kingsviewguesthouse.com.uk

Family run, city centre guest house conveniently situated near the Kings Theatre. Close to all main bus routes.

Rooms	Facilities	B&B per person	Open
1 Single	3 En Suite fac	B&B per person	Open Jan-Dec
2 Twin	1 Pub Show	from £18.00 Single	
2 Double	1 Limited ensuite	from £18.00 Dbl/Twn	
3 Family			

Kirkland Bed and Breakfast

6 Dean Park Crescent, Edinburgh EH4 1PN
Telephone: 0131 332 5017
e.mail: m.kirkland@cableinet.co.uk

Warm friendly Victorian home only 10 minutes' walk from city centre. The Botanical Gardens and many interesting local shops and restaurants are also nearby. Breakfast is ample and varied, and we are happy to meet any special needs you may have.

★★★
B&B

Kirkland B&B
6 Dean Park Crescent, Edinburgh, EH4 1PN
Tel: 0131 332 5017
E-mail: m.kirkland@cableinet.co.uk
Web: www.kirkland.purp.blueyonder.co.uk

Warm, friendly, Victorian home 10 minutes walk from centre. Interesting local shops, restaurants and pubs.

Rooms	Facilities	B&B per person	Open
1 Double	1 En Suite fac	B&B per person	Open Apr-Oct
1 Twin	1 Priv.NOT ensuite	from £45.00 Single	
1 Family	1 Pub Bath/Show	from £22.00 Dbl/Twn	

C V

★★
GUEST HOUSE

Kirklea Guest House
11 Harrison Road, Edinburgh, EH11 1EG
Tel: 0131 337 1129 Fax: 0131 337 6650
E-mail: vkielnar@compuserve.com

A family run guest house in Victorian terrace convenient for bus routes to city centre and all attractions. 1.25 miles (2kms) from Princes Street. Dutch, French, German and Italian spoken by the owners.

Rooms	Facilities	B&B per person	Open
2 Single	En Suite fac	B&B per person	Open Jan-Dec
2 Double	Pub Bath/Show	from £26.00 Single	
2 Family		from £21.00 Dbl/Twn	

C V

Edinburgh Map Ref: 2C5

GUEST HOUSE

Lauderville House
52 Mayfield Road, Edinburgh, EH9 2NH
Tel: 0131 667 7788 Fax: 0131 667 2636
E-mail: res@laudervilleguesthouse.co.uk
Web: www.LaudervilleGuestHouse.co.uk

Brian and Yvonne Marriott welcome visitors to their restored Victorian Town House, centrally situated with easy access to city centre. Comfortable rooms, excellent breakfast, including vegetarian. All bedrooms non-smoking.

1 Single, 2 Twin, 6 Double, 1 Family — All En Suite

B&B per person: £28.00-£45.00 Single; £25.00-£40.00 Dbl/Twn

Open Jan-Dec

B&B

I Laurie
59 Craigcrook Avenue, Edinburgh, EH4 3PU
Tel: 0131 467 4284 Fax: 0131 312 6775
E-mail: elaurie@virgin.net

Family home, conveniently located for city centre and airport. Breakfast served in the conservatory overlooking Corstorphine Hills. Private parking. Non smoking house.

1 Single, 2 Twin

B&B per person: from £22.00 Single; from £20.00 Twin

Open Mar-Oct

B&B

Lindenlea
6 St Mark's Place, Portobello, Edinburgh, EH15 2PY
Tel: 0131 669 6490
E-mail: betty@lindenlea6.freeserve.co.uk

Traditional stone-built Victorian villa set in quiet residential area within Portobello. All local amenities nearby with only a 2-minute walk to the beach, promenade and historic Victorian baths. Free on street parking with frequent bus services on the doorstep. Ideal base for enjoying the city's attractions and exploring the coastline of East Lothian.

1 Twin, 2 Double — 2 En Suite fac, 1 Priv.NOT ensuite

B&B per person: £22.00-£25.00 Single; £22.00-£25.00 Dbl/Twn
Room only per person: £20.00-£22.00

Open Jan-Dec

GUEST HOUSE

Lindsay Guest House
108 Polwarth Terrace, Edinburgh, EH11 1NN
Tel: 0131 337 1580 Fax: 0131 337 9174
E-mail: bill@lindsay-polwarth.demon.co.uk

Listed semi-detached sandstone house in residential area on bus route to city centre. 1.5 miles (3 kms) from Princes St. Car parking. TVs in all bedrooms.

1 Single, 1 Twin, 2 Double, 3 Family — 3 En Suite fac, 2 Pub Bath/Show

B&B per person: from £18.00 Single; from £18.00 Dbl/Twn

Open Jan-Dec

B&B

McCrae's B&B
44 East Claremont Street, Edinburgh, EH7 4JR
Tel: 0131 5562610
E-mail: mccraes.bandb@lineone.net
Web: http://website.lineone.net/~mccrae.bandb

Comfortable accommodation in the Victorian part of the New Town, conveniently located, 15 mins walk to city centre. Unrestricted on-street parking.

3 Twin — All En Suite

B&B per person: from £27.50 Single; from £24.50 Twin

Open Jan-Dec

Edinburgh

Map Ref: 2C5

GUEST HOUSE

The McDonald Guest House
5 McDonald Road, Edinburgh, EH7 4LX
Tel/Fax: 0131 557 5935
E-mail: 5mcdonaldroad@ukgateway.net

3 Double — En Suite fac
1 Twin — Priv.NOT ensuite

B&B per person
from £22.50 Single
£20.00-£22.50 Dbl/Twn
Room only per person
from £22.50

Open Feb-Dec

Comfortable accommodation 10 minutes walk from Princes Street. Adjacent to main bus routes. Many good restaurants locally. Playhouse Theatre nearby. Unrestricted street parking.

TV C V

121 CAPTAINS ROAD

Edinburgh EH17 8DT

Tel: 0131 658 1578

Bungalow situated in residential area served by excellent bus service. *'£1.40 unlimited travel for the day'.* Convenient city centre shopping, exploring Castle, Royal Mile, Holyrood Palace and Park, Dynamic Earth, art galleries, museums, observatory, Britannia, zoo. Venues, theatres, concert halls, rugby stadium. Activities easy access, swimming, golf, ski-centre, hill-walking. City-bypass 1/2 mile.

B&B

Dorothy M G McKay
'The Haven', 121 Captains Road, Edinburgh, Midlothian, EH17 8DT
Tel/Fax: 0131 658 1578

1 Double — 1 En Suite fac
1 Twin — 1 Pub Bath/Show

B&B per person
£18.00-£25.00 Single
£16.00-£22.00 Dbl/Twn

Open Jan-Dec

Mrs Mckay has been offering B&B in Edinburgh for many years now and recently moved to this modern semi detached bungalow, set back from the road and 1 mile from the city bypass. On main bus routes to the city centre.

TV P

C W V

B&B

Mrs K A Mather
17 Spottiswoode Street, Edinburgh, EH9 1EP
Tel: 0131 228 1845
E-mail: kate@meadowsbb.com

1 Double — En Suite fac
1 Double — Priv.NOT ensuite
1 Pub Bath/Show

B&B per person
£23.00-£25.00 Dbl/Twn

Open Apr-Oct

Small, friendly, newly refurbished Victorian main door flat with attractive garden in the Meadows area. Ideally situated for cinemas, theatres, galleries, city centre, teaching hospital, university and varied selection of restaurants. Free on street parking available. On bus route.

V

B&B

Meadow Place House
1 Meadow Place Road, Corstorphine, Edinburgh, EH12 7TZ
Tel/Fax: 0131 334 8459

1 Single — 2 Pub Bath/Show
1 Twin
1 Family

B&B per person
from £16.00 Single
£15.00-£18.00 Twin

Open Jan-Dec

Comfortable, personally run B&B close to major bus routes to city centre and airport. Own parking. Ideal base for touring.

TV P

C V

Important: Prices stated are estimates and may be subject to amendments

Edinburgh **Map Ref: 2C5**

★ GUEST HOUSE

Menzies Guest House (city centre)
33 Leamington Terrace, Edinburgh, EH10 4JS
Tel/Fax: 0131 229 4629
E-mail: menzies@cableinet.co.uk

1 Twin, 3 Double, 2 Family | 3 En Suite fac, 2 Pub Bath/Show | B&B per person from £20.00 Single, from £13.50 Dbl/Twn; Room only per person from £26.00 | Open Jan-Dec

City centre with private parking, 10 minutes walk to Princes Street, Edinburgh Castle, King's Theatre and all main attractions.

★★★ GUEST HOUSE

Milton House
24 Duddingston Crescent, Edinburgh, EH15 3AT
Tel: 0131 669 4072
E-mail: winenbru@supanet.com

1 Twin, 3 Double | 2 En Suite | B&B per person from £20.00 Single, from £20.00 Dbl/Twn | Open Jan-Dec

Friendly family atmosphere with off street parking and easy access to the city centre. Adjacent to 9 hole golf course. Dog friendly household.

★★ GUEST HOUSE

Mingalar
2 East Claremont St, Edinburgh, EH7 4JP
Tel: 0131 556 7000 Fax: 0131 556 4907
E.mail: mingalar@criper.com
Web: www.criper.com/mingalar

3 Double, 3 Family | All En Suite, 1 Pub Bath/Show | B&B per person from £22.50 Single, from £20.00 Double | Open Feb-Dec

Refurbished Georgian terraced house, 10 minutes from the city centre and all its ammenities. Surrounding streets have metered or free parking.

Edinburgh — **Map Ref: 2C5**

★★ B&B

Moores
44b Stevenson Drive, Edinburgh, EH11 3DJ
Tel: 0131 443 9370

1 Single 1 Twin	All En Suite	B&B per person from £20.00 Single from £18.00 Dbl/Twn	Open Jan-Dec excl Xmas/New Year

Comfortable, well furnished personally run bed and breakfast with both bedrooms ensuite. Unrestricted street parking. Door to door bus service to city centre.

No 29
29 Scotland Street, Edinburgh, Midlothian, EH3 6PY
Tel: 0131 556 7497 Fax: 0131 557 3040

1 Twin 1 Family 1 Double	2 Ensuite fac 1 Priv.NOT ensuite	B&B per person £35.00-£60.00 Single £30.00-£40.00 Twin	Open Jan-Dec

Elegant Georgian (1820's) city centre townhouse spacious rooms, traditional Scottish cuisine and hospitality. Quiet street.

'No 45' Bed & Breakfast
45 Gilmour Road, Edinburgh, Midlothian, EH16 5NS
Tel: 0131 667 3536 Fax: 0131 662 1946
E.mail: w.cheape@gilmourhouse.freeserve.co.uk
Web: www.edinburghbedbreakfast.com

1 Single 1 Double 1 Family	2 En Suite fac 1 Priv.NOT ensuite	B&B per person from £30.00 Single from £25.00 Double	Open Jan-Dec

Semi-detatched Victorian house in quiet residential street furnished to a very high standard with free parking yet close to main bus route. City centre 2 miles. University Kings buildings and Cameron Toll shopping centre nearby. Quality compact en-suite shower rooms.

Edinburgh Map Ref: 2C5

B&B

Number Five
5 Dean Park Crescent, Edinburgh, EH4 1PN
Tel: 0131 332 4620 Fax: 0131 315 4122
E-mail: mdmiller@sol.co.uk
Web: www.aboutedinburgh.com/deanpark/5.html

3 Double | 2 En Suite fac, 1 Priv.NOT ensuite | B&B per person from £32.00 Double | Open Apr-Oct

Lovely Victorian home with comfortable atmosphere situated close to city centre in delightful residential area with interesting shops and restaurants nearby. Enjoy breakfast in the comfort of your bedrooms.

B&B

Number17
17 Learmonth Terrace, Edinburgh, EH4 1PG
Tel: 0131 315 4088 Fax: 0131 315 3491
E.mail: alex@numberseventeen.co.uk
Web: www.numberseventeen.co.uk

1 Twin, 1 Double | All En Suite | B&B per person from £50.00 Single, from £35.00 Dbl/Twn | Open Feb-Dec excl Xmas/New Year

A listed Victorian townhouse offering luxurious accommodation and sumptuous breakfast in Edinburgh's West End, only a few minutes walk from Princes Street and city centre.

GUEST HOUSE

Parklands Guest House
20 Mayfield Gardens, Edinburgh, EH9 2BZ
Tel: 0131 667 7184 Fax: 0131 667 2011
E-mail: parklands_guesthouse@yahoo.com

2 Twin Ensuite fac, 2 Double Ensuite fac, 1 Family Ensuite fac, 1 Single Private fac | B&B per person from £20.00 Dbl/Twn | Open Jan-Dec

Look forward to a warm welcome at this late Victorian house with fine woodwork and ceilings. Situated on the south side, on main bus routes to city centre. Close to University.

B&B

Pentland View
69 Glasgow Road, Edinburgh, EH12 8LL
Tel: 0131 316 4712

1 Twin, 1 Family | 1 En Suite fac, 1 Priv.NOT ensuite | B&B per person from £25.00 Single, from £18.00 Twin | Open Apr-Oct

Comfortable family home. Convenient for airport and all major routes. Private parking. Ground floor accommodation. Ensuite available.

Edinburgh

Map Ref: 2C5

Pringle's Ingle
26 Morningside Park, Edinburgh, EH10 5HB
Tel: 0131 447 5847
E.mail: migpringle@aol.com

1 En Suite shower
1 private bath

B&B per person
£25.00-£35.00 pppn

The Roses B&B
46A Drumbrae South, Edinburgh, EH12 8SZ
Tel: 0131 539 0909

2 Twin | 1 En Suite fac | B&B per person £15.00-£18.00 Single £18.00-£25.00 Twin | Open Jan-Dec

Semi-detached villa on bus route to town (20 minutes). Off street parking. 10 minutes by car to city bypass and 15 minutes to airport.

C V

Rowan Guest House
13 Glenorchy Terrace, Edinburgh, EH9 2DQ
Tel/Fax: 0131 667 2463
Web: www.rowan-house.co.uk

2 Single, 2 Twin, 4 Double, 1 Family | 3 Ensuite fac, 2 Pub Bath/Show | B&B per person from £23.00 Single from £22.00 Dbl/Twn | Open Jan-Dec

Victorian town house in quiet residential area with unrestricted street parking. Convenient access by car or bus (10 min) to Edinburgh city centre with all its attractions. Variety of eating establishments available locally.

C £ W

St Leonards
480 Lanark Road, Edinburgh, Midlothian, EH14 5BL
Tel: 0131 453 1968 Fax: 0131 442 4406
E-mail: ann.r@virgin.net

1 Twin, 2 Double | All En Suite | B&B per person from £45.00 Single from £30.00 Dbl/Twn | Open Jan-Dec excl Xmas

Large detached Georgian style Victorian house with ample car parking in leafy suburb of city. Upstairs drawing room has uninterrupted views of the Pentland Hills. Impressive dining room with oak panelling and open fire in season.

C £ V

Edinburgh Map Ref: 2C5

★★★
GUEST HOUSE

Salisbury Guest House

45 Salisbury Road, Edinburgh, EH16 5AA
Tel/Fax: 0131 667 1264
E-mail: brenda.wright@btinternet.com
Web: http://members.edinburgh.org/salisbury/

Georgian Listed building in quiet conservation area, 1 mile (2kms) from city centre. Ensuite and private facilities. Private car park. Non-smoking house.

2 Single 3 Twin 4 Double 3 Family	9 En Suite fac 3 Priv.NOT ensuite	B&B per person from £30.00 Single from £25.00 Dbl/Twn Room only per person from £23.00	Open Feb-Dec excl Xmas

Salisbury View Hotel

64 Dalkeith Road, Edinburgh, EH16 5AE
Tel/Fax: 0131 667 1133
E-mail: enquiries@salisburyviewhotel.co.uk
Web: www.salisburyviewhotel.co.uk

Small privately run Georgian hotel in historical conservation area. Opposite Holyrood Park, Pollock Halls and Commonwealth Swimming Pool. Easy access to city centre. Approx 15 min walk to Royal Mile. Award winning chef and highly acclaimed restaurant. Private car park. Ground floor rooms available.

1 Single 2 Twin 6 Double 1 Family	All En Suite	B&B per person from £32.00 Single from £32.00 Dbl/Twn	Open Jan-Dec excl Xmas

Sandeman House

33 Colinton Road, Edinburgh, EH10 5DR
Tel/Fax: 0131 447 8080
E.mail: joycesandeman@freezone.co.uk
Web: www.freezone.co.uk/sandemanhouse

Victorian terraced house within easy reach of city centre. Warm welcome and relaxed family atmosphere. Unrestricted parking. Non-smoking. Wonderful breakfasts.

1 Single 1 Twin 1 Double	2 En Suite fac 1 Priv.NOT ensuite	B&B per person from £35.00 Single from £28.00 Dbl/Twn	Open Apr-Oct

Santa Lucia Guest House

14 Kilmaurs Terrace, Edinburgh, EH16 5DR
Tel: 0131 667 8694

Situated in very quiet residential area of city. Convenient for bus services to the city centre. Close to Commonwealth Swimming Pool.

1 Single 4 Twin 1 Double	3 Ensuite fac 2 Pub Bath/Show 1 Toilet	B&B per person £15.00-£25.00 Single £15.00-£25.00 Dbl/Twn Room only per person £12.00-£20.00	Open Jan-Dec excl Xmas/New Year

Edinburgh Map Ref: 2C5

GUEST HOUSE

Sherwood Guest House
42 Minto Street, Edinburgh, EH9 2BR
Tel: 0131 667 1200 Fax: 0131 667 2344
E-mail: sherwdedin@aol.com
Web: http://www.sherwood-edinburgh.com

A friendly and hospitable welcome is assured from Mrs Greig. The guest house has been fully refurbished throughout to a high standard. On main bus route to city centre 1.5 miles distance (2.5 kms). Limited parking.

2 Twin, 2 Double, 2 Family | 5 En Suite fac, 1 Priv.NOT ensuite | B&B per person £25.00-£55.00 Dbl/Twn | Open Jan-Dec

B&B

Mrs E C Simpson
17 Crawfurd Road, Edinburgh, EH16 5PQ
Tel: 0131 667 1191

Friendly welcome in this late Victorian family home, retaining many original features including fine plasterwork. Situated in quiet residential area with easy access to city centre. Unrestricted parking.

1 Twin, 1 Double | 2 Pub Bath/Show | B&B per person from £18.50 Dbl/Twn | Open May-Sep

B&B

Mrs Elizabeth G Smith
14 Lennel Avenue, Murrayfield, Edinburgh, EH12 6DW
Tel: 0131 337 1979

Personally run, beautiful home, quietly situated in residential area of Murrayfield. 2 miles (3 kms) from city centre. Regular bus service to all amenities. Unrestricted parking.

2 Twin, 1 Double | 2 Pub Bath/Show | B&B per person from £26.00 Single, from £21.00 Dbl/Twn | Open Apr-Oct

GUEST HOUSE

Smiths' Guest House
77 Mayfield Road, Edinburgh, EH9 3AA
Tel: 0131 667 2524 Fax: 0131 668 4455
E-mail: mail@smithsgh.com
Web: www.smithsgh.com

Victorian town house, recently refurbished. Free on street parking. Near to city centre.

2 Single, 2 Twin, 2 Double, 1 Family | 2 En Suite fac, 3 Pub Bath/Show | B&B per person from £16.00 Single, from £16.00 Dbl/Twn; Room only per person from £16.00 | Open Jan-Dec; B&B + Eve.Meal from £21.00

B&B

Spylaw Bank House
2 Spylaw Avenue, Colinton, Edinburgh, EH13 0LR
Tel: 0131 441 5022
E-mail: angela@spylawbank.freeserve.co.uk

Elegant listed Georgian House in mature walled gardens. Comfortable rooms with period furnishings and well appointed modern bathrooms. Quiet location close to Colinton village with magnificent views over the Pentland Hills. Ideally located for touring Scotland and the city. Ten minutes from the city centre and airport. Five minutes from city bypass and motorway system. Ample parking. Main bus routes nearby.

1 Single, 1 Twin, 1 Double | All En Suite | B&B per person from £35.00 Single, from £25.00 Dbl/Twn | Open Jan-Dec excl Xmas; B&B + Eve.Meal from £38.00

Important: Prices stated are estimates and may be subject to amendments

Edinburgh Map Ref: 2C5

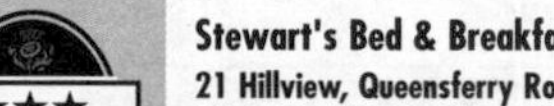

★★★ B&B

Stewart's Bed & Breakfast

21 Hillview, Queensferry Road, Edinburgh, EH4 2AF
Tel: 0131 539 7033 Fax: 0131 332 6624
E-mail: barbara@stewarts-bb.fsbusiness.co.uk

1 Twin 1 Double 1 Family	All En Suite	B&B per person from £18.00 Single from £18.00 Dbl/Twn	Open Jan-Dec excl Xmas/New Year

Attractive Edwardian terrace villa just 10 minutes from Edinburgh city centre. Near airport and bypass. Bus services pass door. Friendly welcome in a relaxed family home with comfortable rooms.

C V

★★★ B&B

Sure and Steadfast

76 Milton Road West, Edinburgh, EH15 1QY
Tel: 0131 657 1189/07710 506945 (mobile)
E-mail: a_t_taylor@ednet.co.uk

1 Twin 2 Double	1 Pub Bath/Show	B&B per person £25.00-£35.00 Single £17.50-£25.00 Dbl/Twn	Open Apr-Oct

Comfortable family home in Duddingston area of Edinburgh. Easy access from city by-pass and main A1 road.

£ V

★★ GUEST HOUSE

Sylvern Guest House

22 West Mayfield, Edinburgh, EH9 1TQ
Tel/Fax: 0131 667 1241

1 Twin 3 Double 2 Family	4 En Suite fac 2 Pub Bath/Show	B&B per person £17.00-£26.00 Dbl/Twn	Open Jan-Dec excl Xmas

Detached Victorian house in residential area. Private parking and convenient for main bus routes. Four rooms ensuite.

C V

Edinburgh Map Ref: 2C5

130 TRINITY ROAD

Edinburgh EH5 3LA

Tel: 0131 551 1662 e.mail: battersbyjoan@hotmail.com

Large twin bedded room and bathroom in terraced Georgian house in quiet area of Edinburgh close to the sea. No parking restrictions. Frequent bus service to town. Close to Botanic Gardens and the restaurants and art galleries of Leith. Children welcome. Vegetarians catered for. 12 minutes to town by bus.

B&B

130 Trinity Road

Edinburgh, EH5 3LA
Tel: 0131 551 1662
E-mail: battersbyjoan@hotmail.com

1 Twin | 1 Priv.NOT ensuite | B&B per person from £30.00 Single | Open Jan-Dec

A warm welcome is assured at this stone built terraced house situated close to sea and to city bus routes. Colourful garden in summer. Free on street parking.

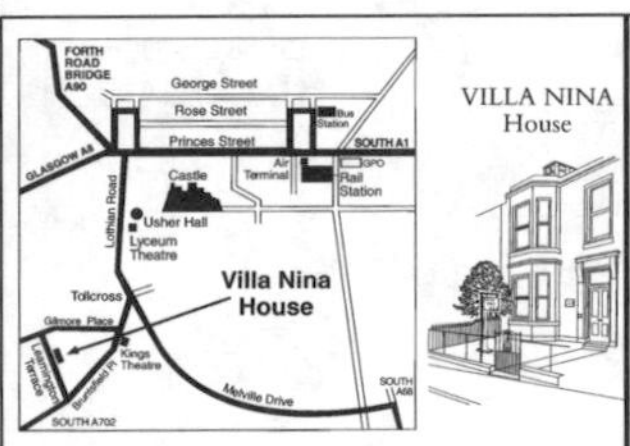

Villa Nina House

39 LEAMINGTON TERRACE, EDINBURGH EH10 4JS

Tel/Fax: 0131 229 2644 E.mail: villanina@amserve.net

Very comfortable Victorian terraced house situated in a quiet residential part of the city yet only ten minutes' walk to Princes Street, Edinburgh Castle, theatres, shops and major attractions. Some rooms with private showers. TV in all rooms. Full cooked breakfast.
Member of STB, GHA & AA. Closed for Christmas and New Year.
Bed and Breakfast from £17.50 per person.

GUEST HOUSE

Villa Nina Guest House

39 Leamington Terrace, Edinburgh, EH10 4JS
Tel: 0131 229 2644 Fax: 0131 229 2644
E-mail: villanina@amserve.net

2 Twin | 4 Limited ensuite | B&B per person | Open Jan-Dec excl
2 Double | 2 Pub Bath/Show | from £17.50 Dbl/Twn | Xmas/New Year

Terraced house. Approximately 0.5 mile (1 km) from city centre. Near Kings Theatre, the Castle and International Conference Centre. Showers in bedrooms.

by Edinburgh Map Ref: 2C5

ASHCROFT FARMHOUSE

EAST CALDER, NR EDINBURGH EH53 0ET
Tel: 01506 881810 Fax: 01506 884327
e.mail: ashcroft30538@aol.com
Web: www.ashcroft-farmhouse.com

New ranch-style farmhouse set in beautifully landscaped gardens, enjoying lovely views over surrounding farmland. 10m city centre, 5m airport, Ingliston, A720 City Bypass, M8/M9. Ideal base for touring, golfing, walking. Regular bus and train service nearby takes guests to the city centre within 20 minutes therefore no parking problems. All rooms are on ground floor. Bedrooms, including romantic four-poster are attractively furnished in antique pine with bright co-ordinating fabrics. Varied choice of breakfasts including home-made sausage, smoked salmon, kippers etc, even whisky marmalade. *Derek and Elizabeth extend a warm Scottish welcome to all guests. Sorry, no pets.*

AA ♦♦♦♦♦ NO SMOKING

★★★★ GUEST HOUSE

Ashcroft Farmhouse

East Calder, West Lothian, EH53 0ET
Tel: 01506 881810 Fax: 01506 884327
E-mail: ashcroft30538@aol.com
Web: www.ashcroft-farmhouse.com

3 Twin	All En Suite	B&B per person	Open Jan-Dec
1 Double		from £40.00 Single	
2 Family		from £28.00 Dbl/Twn	

A warm Scottish welcome awaits you at this modern bungalow with interesting landscaped garden and quality choice of breakfast. Half an hour by bus to Edinburgh city centre, 5 miles from the airport and within easy access to all major routes. Ample parking. Totally non-smoking.

TV P C W V

Gullane, East Lothian Map Ref: 2D4

JADINI GARDEN

1 Goose Green, Gullane, East Lothian EH31 2BA
Tel: 01620 843343 Fax: 01620 843453
e.mail: marychase@jadini.com Web: www.jadini.com

Located in the quiet coastal village of Gullane 30 minutes drive from Edinburgh. Jadini Garden is 2 minutes walk from the 3 famous golf courses and beautiful sandy beaches. Quiet secluded walled garden for the use of guests. Private parking. French, German and Spanish spoken.

★★★ B&B

Mrs M Chase

Jadini Garden, Goose Green, Gullane, East Lothian, EH31 2BA
Tel: 01620 843343
Fax: 01620 843453
E-mail: marychase@jadini.com
Web: www.jadini.com

1 Twin	1 En Suite fac	B&B per person	Open Jan-Dec
1 Double	1 Pub Bath/Show	£20.00-£25.00 Dbl/Twn	
1 Single		£25.00-£30.00 Single	

Family home located in a secluded walled garden, on the road to the beach. Only a few minutes walk from Gullane's three famous public golf courses. and a half hour drive from Edinburgh city centre. Comfortable rooms, garden facilities for the use of guests and private parking. French, Spanish and German spoken.

C

Gullane, East Lothian

Map Ref: 2D4

★★★★
B&B

Fausssetthill House

Main Street, Gullane, East Lothian, EH31 2DR
Tel/Fax: 01620 842396

2 Twin 1 Double	All En Suite	B&B per person from £40.00 Single from £26.00 Dbl/Twn	Open Mar-Dec

Detached Edwardian house with pleasant garden. Edinburgh 30 minutes by car. Sandy beaches and several golf courses nearby. Private parking. Non-smoking.

B&B

Hopefield House

Main Street, Gullane, East Lothian, EH31 2DP
Tel/Fax: 01620 842191
E-mail: iorad@inight.fsbusiness.co.uk

3 Twin	2 Ensuite fac 1 Priv.NOT ensuite	B&B per person from £30.00 Single from £24.00 Twin	Open Apr-Oct

Lovely stone house. Large sheltered garden. Village famous for golf and sandy bay. Edinburgh 30 minutes.

V

Haddington, East Lothian

Map Ref: 2D4

★★★★
B&B

Carfrae Farmhouse

Carfrae, Garvald, Haddington, East Lothian, EH41 4LP
Tel: 01620 830242 Fax: 01620 830320
E-mail: DgCarfrae@aol.com

1 Twin 2 Double	2 En Suite fac 1 Priv.NOT ensuite	B&B per person £20.00-£40.00 Single £25.00-£27.00 Dbl/Twn	Open Apr-Oct

19c listed farmhouse on a working farm with open aspect overlooking the walled garden. Furnished to a high standard. Edinburgh, the Borders and many golf courses within easy reach. Extremely peaceful location. All rooms have private or en suite facilities.

C

B&B

Mrs S A Clark

Fieldfare, Upper Bolton Farm, Haddington, East Lothian, EH41 4HW
Tel: 01620 810346

1 Twin 1 Double 1 Family	1 Priv.NOT ensuite	B&B per person from £20.00 Single from £17.00 Dbl/Twn	Open Jan-Dec excl Xmas

Victorian farm cottage in peaceful rural situation convenient for many sites of historic interest, only half an hour's drive from Edinburgh and 20 minutes drive to the coast. Pets welcome.

C V

B&B

Eaglescairnie Mains

Gifford, Haddington, East Lothian, EH41 4HN
Tel/Fax: 01620 810491
E-mail: williams.eagles@btinternet.com

2 Single 1 Twin 1 Double	2 En Suite fac 1 Pub Bath/Show	B&B per person from £25.00 Single from £20.00 Dbl/Twn	Open Jan-Dec excl Xmas/New Year

Beautiful house in quiet rural situation, on working mixed farm. Winner of National Conservation Awards. Farm walks with wonderful views. 4 miles (6kms) from Haddington, 30 mins drive from Edinburgh.

C W V

Important: Prices stated are estimates and may be subject to amendments

Haddington, East Lothian Map Ref: 2D4

Hamilton's

28 Market Street, Haddington EH41 3JE
Tel: 01620 822465 Fax: 01620 825613 e.mail: Hamil28mar@aol.com

Early Victorian building situated in centre of historic Haddington adjacent to A1, all local amenities within walking distance. Choice of breakfast with home-made bread and preserves. Comfortable base for touring quiet East Lothian countryside and unspoilt beaches. Regular bus service to Edinburgh 18 miles. Golf packages arranged. No smoking.

B&B

Hamilton's

28 Market Street, Haddington, East Lothian, EH41 3JE
Tel: 01620 822465 Fax: 01620 825613
E-mail: Hamil28mar@aol.com

1 Single, 1 Twin, 1 Family — 2 Ensuite fac, 1 Priv.NOT ensuite — B&B per person from £18.00 Single, from £20.00 Twin; Room only per person from £14.00 — Open Jan-Dec

1st floor flat in Victorian building set in a conservation area in the centre of the Royal Burgh of Haddington. Adjacent to the A1 and golf enthusiasts have the choice of 18 courses within easy reach. 18 miles south of Edinburgh.

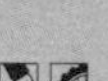

BRONZE

HOTEL

Maitlandfield Country House Hotel

24 Sidegate, Haddington, East Lothian, EH41 4BZ
Tel: 01620 826513 Fax: 01620 826713

3 Single, 10 Twin, 6 Double, 3 Triple — All En Suite — B&B per person from £50.00 Single, from £30.00 Dbl/Twn, from £60.00 – Feature room — Open Jan-Dec

A magnificent country house hotel privately owned and professionally managed. Ideally located for golfing, shooting and fishing. Splendid wedding and conference facilities also available.

SCHIEHALLION

19 Church Street, Haddington EH41 3EX
Telephone: 01620 825663 Fax: 01620 829663
E.mail: Catherine@schiehallion.fsbusiness.co.uk

Large Victorian house in the county town of East Lothian. Sandy beaches, golf courses nearby. Small towns and villages with excellent restaurants. Large lounge with a view of historic St. Mary's Cathedral. Library with TV. All rooms have wash basins, tea/coffee and TV facilities. Large walled garden available. Two old english sheepdogs in residence. ***Schiehallion welcomes all guests.***

B&B

Catherine Richards

Schiehallion, 19 Church Street, Haddington, East Lothian, EH41 3EX
Tel: 01620 825663 Fax: 01620 829663
E-mail: Catherine@schiehallion.fsbusiness.co.uk

1 Twin, 2 Double — 1 En Suite fac, 1 Pub Bath/Show — B&B per person from £25.00 Single, from £18.00 Dbl/Twn; Room only per person from £16.00 — Open Jan-Dec; B&B + Eve.Meal from £26.00

Large Victorian house in the country town of East Lothian. Sandy beaches, golf courses nearby. Small towns and villages with excellent restaurants. Large lounge with a view of historic St. Mary's Cathedral. Library with TV. All rooms have wash basins, tea/coffee and TV facilities. Large walled garden available. Two old english sheepdogs in residence. Edinburgh 17 miles.

Lasswade, Midlothian

Map Ref: 2C5

CARLETHAN HOUSE

WADINGBURN LANE, LASSWADE, MIDLOTHIAN EH18 1HG
Tel: 0131 663 7047 Fax: 0131 654 2657
e.mail: carlethan@aol.com

Margaret and Quin offer comfortable, friendly helpful hospitality in their beautiful Georgian home. The lovely one acre garden has a large patio and a peaceful pond and stream feature. Ideally placed for golf and sightseeing yet only 20 minutes from the city centre. Ample parking.

B&B

Carlethan House B&B

Wadingburn Lane, Lasswade, Midlothian, EH18 1HG
Tel: 0131 663 7047 Fax: 0131 654 2657
E-mail: carlethan@aol.com
Web: www.carlethan-house.co.uk

2 Twin
1 Double

2 En Suite fac
1 Priv.NOT ensuite

B&B per person
from £35.00 Single
from £25.00 Dbl/Twn
Room only per person
from £23.00

Open Dec-Oct

Carlethan house is a listed Georgian home, lovingly restored and set in tranquil rural surroundings only 5 miles from Edinburgh city centre. Ideally situated for approximately 40 golf courses within 30 minutes drive of many interesting historic sites including Roslyn chapel.

TV P

C V

B&B

Droman House

Lasswade, Midlothian, EH18 1HA
Tel: 0131 663 9239

1 Single
2 Double

1 Priv.NOT ensuite

B&B per person
from £20.00 Single
from £20.00 Double

Open May-Oct

Former Georgian manse in secluded setting. Informal and warm welcome assured. Ample private parking. Only 6 miles from Edinburgh city centre.

P

C

Linlithgow, West Lothian

Map Ref: 2B4

ARN HOUSE

Woodcockdale, Lanark Road, Linlithgow, West Lothian EH49 6QE
Tel: 01506 842088 Fax: 01506 842088
e.mail: arn-guest-house@euphony.net Web: www.arnhouse.co.uk

Look no further! Be among the many guests who return regularly to Arn House. Modern farmhouse on working farm. Restful scenic views. Easy access to Edinburgh airport and all tourist attractions in central Scotland. Phone now – 01506 842088.

B&B

Arn House

Woodcockdale, Lanark Road, Linlithgow, EH49 6QE
Tel/Fax: 01506 842088
E.mail: arn-guest-house@euphony.net
Web: www.arnhouse.co.uk

1 Twin
1 Double
2 Family

3 En Suite fac
1 Priv.NOT ensuite

B&B per person
from £18.00 Single
from £18.00 Dbl/Twn

Open Jan-Dec

Modern farmhouse on a working farm in rural area yet with easy access to Edinburgh, Glasgow and the Lothians. Edinburgh and Glasgow airports within easy reach. Full fire certificate held. Ground floor rooms.

TV P

C W V

Linlithgow, West Lothian — Map Ref: 2B4

B&B

Avila
13 Avon Place, Strawberry Bank, Linlithgow, EH49 6BL
Tel/Fax: 01506 848372
E-mail: dhogg@avila-scotland.co.uk
Web: www.avila-scotland.co.uk

2 Twin — 2 Ensuite fac
1 Double — 1 Priv.NOT ensuite

B&B per person
from £25.00 Single
from £23.00 Dbl/Twn

Open Jan-Dec excl Xmas

Large Victorian villa with modern spacious accommodation. Overlooking historic Linithgow Palace and centrally located for easy access to all local amenities, canal basin and loch. Within a few minutes from bus and rail stations. Easy access to motorways and Edinburgh / Glasgow and airports. Facilities include a beauty therapy room.

B&B

Belsyde Farm
Lanark Road, Linlithgow, West Lothian, EH49 6QE
Tel/Fax: 01506 842098
E-mail: belsyde.guesthouse@virgin.net

1 Family — ensuite fac
1 Double — 2 Pub Bath/Show
2 Single

B&B per person
from £18.00 Single
from £18.00 Double

Open Jan-Dec excl Xmas

Late 18c house with interesting garden,set on a 100 acre sheep farm beside Union Canal. Views over Forth Estuary and Ochil Hills. Easy access to M8, M9, M90 and Edinburgh Airport.

B&B

Bomains Farm
Linlithgow, West Lothian, EH49 7RQ
Tel: 01506 82188 Fax: 01506 824433

1 Twin — All En Suite
2 Double

B&B per person
from £30.00 Single
from £25.00 Dbl/Twn

Open Jan-Dec
B&B + Eve.Meal
from £37.00

A warm welcome to this family home. Rural but central location. Excellent views over the River Forth. Ideally located for motorways, Glasgow and Edinburgh. Gateway to the Highlands.

B&B

Pardovan House
Philpstoun, Linlithgow, West Lothian, EH49 7RU
Tel: 01506 834219
E-mail: alan.baker7@virgin.net

1 Family — Fam - Ensuite fac
1 Twin — Twin - Washbasin
1 Single — 1 Priv.Bath/Shower

B&B per person
from £16.00 Single
£18.00-£20.00 Dbl/Twn

Open Apr-Sep

A warm welcome at this spacious historic country house, set in 2 acres of ground with formal garden and natural woodland area. Easy access to all major routes. Only 15 minutes drive from Edinburgh Airport.

VAT is shown at 17.5%: changes in this rate may affect prices.

Key to symbols is on back flap.

Linlithgow, West Lothian

Map Ref: 2B4

Thornton

Edinburgh Road, Linlithgow, West Lothian EH49 6AA

Tel: 01506 844693 Fax: 01506 844876

Relaxed, friendly family home with ground floor accommodation. Located only 5 minutes walk along canal towpath from town centre and Linlithgow Palace (birthplace of Mary Queen of Scots). Large variety of pubs and restaurants nearby. Golf courses, country parks and historic houses within easy reach. Frequent trains to Edinburgh, Glasgow, Stirling.

B&B

Thornton

Edinburgh Road, Linlithgow, West Lothian, EH49 6AA
Tel: 01506 844693 Fax: 01506 844876
E.mail: inglisthornton@hotmail.com

1 Twin
1 Double

All En Suite

B&B per person
from £25.00 Single
from £22.50 Dbl/Twn

Open Jan-Dec excl Xmas/New Year

Comfortable, non-smoking family run Victorian house with original features retained. Large garden, private parking. 1km from rail station and town centre with its variety of eating establishments. Only 20 minutes by train to Edinburgh and 10 miles to the airport. Personal attention assured - a real home from home.

TV P W V C

Longniddry, East Lothian

Map Ref: 2D4

★★ B&B

Mr & Mrs George Playfair

The Spinney, Old School Lane, Longniddry, East Lothian, EH32 0NQ
Tel: 01875 853325

1 Twin
2 Family

1 En Suite fac
1 Pub Bath/Show

B&B per person
£20.00-£22.00 Single
£18.00-£20.00 Twin

Open Feb-Nov

Traditional Scottish breakfast in secluded bungalow in quiet village. Train, bus, beach, golf courses and hills within easy reach. Convenient for Edinburgh - train station 200 yards.

P C V

Musselburgh, East Lothian

Map Ref: 2C5

Mrs Elizabeth Aitken

★★ B&B

18 WOODSIDE GARDENS, MUSSELBURGH, EAST LOTHIAN EH21 7LJ
Telephone: 0131 665 3170/3344

Well-appointed bungalow within 6 miles of Edinburgh in quiet suburb with private parking. Excellent bus/train service to city. Two minutes from oldest golf course in world and race course. Easy access to beaches and beautiful countryside.

All rooms hot and cold water, colour TV and tea/coffee. Private parking.

B&B

Mrs E Aitken

18 Woodside Gardens, Musselburgh, East Lothian, EH21 7LJ
Tel: 0131 665 3170/3344

1 Twin
1 Double
1 Family

2 Pub Bath/Show

B&B per person
from £17.00 Single
from £17.00 Dbl/Twn

Open Jan-Dec

Detached bungalow in quiet residential area, close to Musselburgh Racecourse and golf course. Private parking. 7 - 8 miles from Princes Street, Edinburgh. Close to sandy beaches and river walks.

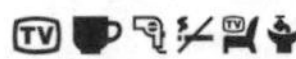

C V

Important: Prices stated are estimates and may be subject to amendments

Musselburgh, East Lothian — Map Ref: 2C5

ARDEN HOUSE

26 LINKFIELD ROAD, MUSSELBURGH, MIDLOTHIAN EH21 7LL
Telephone/Fax: 0131 665 0663
e.mail: ardenhouse@talk21.com Web: www.heimdall-scot.co.uk/ardenhouse

Ideally located for both Edinburgh's city centre attractions and surrounding beaches plus 32 golf courses. 15 minutes by car or bus to either. Arden House makes a superb base for exploring Southern and Central Scotland, however we will also try to make you feel very much at home.

GUEST HOUSE

Arden House
26 Linkfield Road, Musselburgh, Midlothian, EH21 7LL
Tel/Fax: 0131 665 0663
E-mail: ardenhouse@talk21.com
Web: www.heimdall-scot.co.uk/ardenhouse

A warm and friendly welcome awaits you at this Victorian stone turretted house. Situated 15 mins by car or bus from the hustle and bustle of Edinburgh city centre. Views overlooking the race course and golf course.

3 Twin, 2 Double, 2 Family
3 En Suite fac, 1 Priv.NOT ensuite
B&B per person: £20.00-£35.00 Single, £20.00-£25.00 Dbl/Twn
Room only per person: £18.00-£30.00
Open Jan-Dec

B&B

Eildon Bed & Breakfast
'Eildon', 109 Newbigging, Musselburgh EH21 7AS
Tel: 0131 665 3981
E-mail: eve@stayinscotland.net

A warm and helpful hostess awaits you at this beautifully restored B listed Georgian Townhouse. All bedrooms are traditionally furnished and the showerooms are elegant and spacious. Situated nearby is a sports centre and a swimming pool, superb riverside/beach walks and cycle paths. Convenient for frequent buses to Edinburgh City centre (20 minutes), free parking, cycle storage. Local award winning pub meals.

1 Twin, 1 Double, 1 Twin
1 En Suite fac, 2 Pub Bath/Show
B&B per person: £20.00-£35.00 Single, £16.00-£25.00 Dbl/Twn
Open Jan-Dec by arrangement

B&B

Melville House
103a North High Street, Musselburgh, Midothian, EH21 6JE
Tel: 0131 665 5187

Victorian house with accommodation on 2nd floor. Opposite Brunton Theatre. Shops and restaurants nearby. Frequent bus service to Edinburgh city centre. Easy access to East Lothian countryside.

1 Single, 3 Twin, 1 Double
2 Pub Bath/Show
B&B per person: from £20.00 Single, from £16.00 Dbl/Twn
Room only per person: from £14.00
Open Jan-Dec

B&B

Miss A R Mitchell, Craigesk Bed & Breakfast
10 Albert Terrace, Musselburgh, East Lothian
Tel: 0131 665 3344/3170 Fax: 0131 665 3344

Victorian terraced house with private parking, overlooking golf and race course. Convienent bus route to city centre (20 minutes). Within easy travel of East Lothian countryside and golf courses.

2 Twin, 2 Family
2 Pub Bath/Show
B&B per person: from £18.00 Single, from £17.00 Twin
Open Jan-Dec

Musselburgh, East Lothian

Map Ref: 2C5

B&B

Mr W Wilson
17 Windsor Park, Musselburgh, East Lothian, EH21 7QL
Tel/Fax: 0131 665 2194

3 Double | 1 En Suite fac, 1 Pub Bath/Show | B&B per person £16.00-£30.00 Single, £16.00-£25.00 Double | Open Jan-Dec

Personally run B & B. Comfortable accommodation in quiet residential area with unrestricted parking. Close to main bus route to Edinburgh city centre. Convenient for golf & race course.

TV C V

North Berwick, East Lothian

Map Ref: 2D4

B&B

Beehive Cottage B&B
12 Kingston, North Berwick, East Lothian, EH39 5JE
Tel: 01620 894785

1 Double | All En Suite | B&B per person from £25.00 Single, from £20.00 Double | Open Mar-Oct

200 year old cottage with pantiled roof and garden with extensive views. 2 miles (3km) drive to the sea and 20 miles to Edinburgh. Home-produced honey. Ground floor ensuite accommodation. Secure Parking.

TV P C V

SMALL HOTEL

Belhaven Hotel
28 Westgate, North Berwick, East Lothian, EH39 4AH
Tel: 01620 893009 Fax: 01620 895882
Web: www.belhavenhotel.co.uk

2 Single, 5 Twin, 2 Triple | 5 En Suite fac | B&B per person from £20.00 Single, from £20.00 Twin | Open Dec-Oct excl Xmas; B&B + Eve.Meal from £32.50

Family run hotel overlooking the 18th green and 1st tee of West Links Golf course. 5 minutes walk from town centre and railway station. Extensive sea views. Half an hour by road or rail to Edinburgh.

TV C

B&B

Chestnut Lodge B&B
2a Ware Road, North Berwick, East Lothian, EH39 4BN
E-mail: chestnutlodge@tinyonline.co.uk

1 Twin, 1 Double, 1 Family | All En Suite | B&B per person £22.00-£28.00 Single, £20.00-£26.00 Dbl/Twn | Open Mar-Dec excl Xmas/New Year

Modern well appointed house in quiet location. Ground floor ensuite available. Public transport nearby. Edinburgh 1/2 hour. Ideal base for golfing. Private parking. French and German spoken.

P C V

B&B

The Glebe House
Law Road, North Berwick, East Lothian, EH39 4PL
Tel/Fax: 01620 892608
E-mail: J.A.Scott@tesco.net

1 Twin, 2 Double | 2 En Suite fac, 1 Private fac | B&B per person £30.00-£35.00 pppn | Open Jan-Dec excl Xmas/New Year

Former Georgian manse (1780) furnished in period style and set in own grounds above North Berwick, with views of the sea and Berwick Law. Four poster bed available. 2 minutes walk to sandy beach and town centre. Numerous golf courses. 1/2 hour by car or train to Edinburgh city centre. All rooms private facilities.

TV P C V

North Berwick, East Lothian

Map Ref: 2D4

★★★
B&B

Palmerston B&B

28B St Andrew Street, North Berwick, East Lothian, EH39 4NX
Tel: 01620 892884 Fax: 01620 895561
E-mail: SandyIbbetson@cs.com

Spacious friendly home in town centre, well situated for all amenities. Beach, golf course and railway station within short walking distance. Private parking.

1 Twin
1 Double

All En Suite fac

B&B per person
from £28.00 Single
from £22.00 Dbl/Twn

Open Jan-Dec

The Studio

Grange Road, North Berwick, East Lothian, EH39 4QT
Tel: 01620 895150 Fax: 01620 895120
E-mail: johnvramsay@compuserve.com
Web: www.b-and-b-scotland.co.uk/studio.htm

Attractive listed building set in walled garden. Quiet peaceful location, private parking. Close to all amenities and local golf courses. All rooms are on the ground floor and have either private or en-suite facilities. Two rooms have their own separate entrances accessed from the garden. Extensive buffet breakfast choice together with full Scottish breakfast.

1 Twin
2 Double

2 Ensuite fac
1 Priv.NOT ensuite

B&B per person
from £30.00 Single
from £25.00 Dbl/Twn

Open Jan-Dec

V

Penicuik, Midlothian

Map Ref: 2C5

Braidwood Farm

Penicuik, Midlothian, EH26 9LP
Tel: 01968 679959 Fax: 01968 679805

Braidwood is an attractive modern farmhouse set in 240 acres on the edge of the Pentland hills only 10 miles from Edinburgh. Ideal base for visitors to both Edinburgh and the Borders. No children please.

3 Double
1 Twin

All En Suite

B&B per person
£25.00-£35.00 Dbl/Twn

Open Apr-Nov

by Penicuik, Midlothian

Map Ref: 2C5

★★★

B&B

Patieshill Farmhouse Bed & Breakfast

Carlops, Penicuik, Midlothian, EH26 9NB
Tel: 01968 660551 Fax: 01968 661162

1 Twin
2 Double

All En Suite

B&B per person
from £25.00 Single
from £20.00 Dbl/Twn

Open Jan-Dec

Panoramic views from this working hill farm just off A702. Set in the midst of the Pentland Hills only 13 miles (21kms) south of Edinburgh. New guest wing with accommodation on ground floor level. Non smoking house.

TV P C V

South Queensferry, West Lothian

Map Ref: 2B4

★★

GUEST HOUSE

Hawthorne House

15 West Terrace, South Queensferry, EH30 9LL
Tel: 0131 319 1447 Fax: 0131 319 2221
E-mail: hawthornehouse@yahoo.com

1 Single
1 Twin
2 Double
1 Family

2 En Suite fac

B&B per person
from £20.00 Single
from £22.50 Dbl/Twn

Open Jan-Dec

Refurbished 19th Century house centrally located in the High Street of the charming village of South Queensferry. Two large rooms with en-suite facilities offering beautiful views of River Forth and historic Forth Bridge. Easy access to Edinburgh by bus or train and 3 miles from Edinburgh Airport.

TV £ V

★★★

B&B

Mr MacLean

98 Provost Milne Grove, South Queensferry, EH30 9PL
Tel/Fax: 0131 331 1893

1 Twin
1 Double

1 Pub Bath/Show

B&B per person
£15.00-£20.00 Dbl/Twn

Open Jan-Dec

In residential estate, semi-detached modern house close to local shops and amenities. Two minutes drive to Forth Road Bridge and access to Scotlands motorway system. Suitable base for touring Kingdom of Fife, historic Dunfermline and Edinburgh. Interesting sea-front with many restaurants and a view of the famous bridges. Street parking.

TV V

Important: Prices stated are estimates and may be subject to amendments

South Queensferry, West Lothian **Map Ref: 2B4**

PRIORY LODGE

8 The Loan, South Queensferry EH30 9NS
Tel/Fax: 0131 331 4345
e.mail: calmyn@aol.com
Web: www.queensferry.com

A warm welcome is extended for guests old and new to this delightful purpose built guest house. Conveniently situated just off the cobbled high street in the picturesque village of South Queensferry which sits between the two famous bridges on the south side of the River Forth. The attractive bedrooms are maintained to a high standard and are comfortably furnished in antique pine. There is also a cosy guest room and visitors are welcome to use the modern kitchen facilities. A hearty Scottish breakfast is served at individual tables in the Bannockburn Room. The guest house is totally non-smoking.

GUEST HOUSE

Priory Lodge
The Loan, South Queensferry, West Lothian, EH30 9NS
Tel/Fax: 0131 331 4345
E.mail: calmyn@aol.com
Web: www.queensferry.com

Traditional Scottish hospitality in this friendly family run guest house located in the picturesque village of South Queensferry. Edinburgh city centre 7 miles: Airport / Royal Highland Exhibition grounds 3 miles. Priory Lodge is within walking distance of the village shops, variety of eating establishments, Forth Bridges and Dalmeny train station. Ground floor accommodation. Non-smoking establishment.

1 Twin
1 Double
3 Family

All En Suite

B&B per person
from £40.00 Single
from £27.00 Dbl/Twn

Open Jan-Dec

B&B

Mrs Anne-Marie Ross
5 Linn Mill, South Queensferry, West Lothian, EH30 9ST
Tel: 0131 331 2087
E-mail: amr@drossco.co.uk

Scandanavian style chalet. Garden with magnificent view over Firth of Forth to the famous bridges and Ochil hills. Short drive to variety of restaurants. Local walks nearby. Ideal touring base from edge of city and Hopetoun House 1 mile (2km) away.

1 Twin
1 Double

1 Pub Bath/Show

B&B per person
£20.00-£25.00 Dbl/Twn
Room only per person
from £15.00

Open Apr-Sep

Tranent, East Lothian **Map Ref: 2D5**

GUEST HOUSE

Mrs R Harrison
Rosebank Guest House, 161 High Street, Tranent, East Lothian, EH33 1LP
Tel: 01875 610967

Stone built house near centre of Tranent. Ten miles (16kms) to Edinburgh city centre with frequent bus service. Bus stop right outside house. Ideal base for golfing and touring East Lothian and Edinburgh.

1 Twin
3 Double
1 Family

2 Pub Bath/Show

B&B per person
£18.00 Single
£16.50 Dbl/Twn

Open Jan-Dec

Winchburgh, West Lothian

Map Ref: 2B5

★★★
B&B

Mr & Mrs R W Redwood

Turnlea, 123 Main Street, Winchburgh, Broxburn, West Lothian, EH52 6QP
Tel: 01506 890124 Fax: 01506 891573
E-mail: royturnlea@hotmail.com

Modern family villa on outskirts of a village 6 miles from Edinburgh Airport and the Royal Burgh of Linlithgow. 12 miles from the city centre. Easy access to all routes. Non-smoking house.

2 Twin
1 Double

All En Suite

B&B per person
£20.00-£25.00 Dbl/Twn
£25.00-£30.00 Single

Open Jan-Dec excl Xmas/New Year

TV P C £

★
B&B

West End House

Winchburgh, Broxburn, West Lothian, EH52 6TS
Tel: 01506 890528
E-mail: malcolm@mcvittiem.freeserve.co.uk

Comfortable accommodation in this family run B&B which is very convenient for Edinburgh Airport – only 5 miles away. Twin ensuite bedroom. Totally non smoking house. On main bus route to Edinburgh and Stirling.

1 Twin

All En Suite

B&B per person
from £18.00 Single
from £18.00 Twin

Open Jan-Dec excl Xmas/New Year
B&B + Eve.Meal from £25.00 by arrangement

TV P

FOR SHEER EXCITEMENT, GLASGOW IS ONE OF THE TOP UK DESTINATIONS. THIS FORWARD-THINKING AND STYLISH CITY OFFERS A CHOICE OF SHOPPING, ENTERTAINMENT AND CULTURE THAT SHOULD NOT BE MISSED. THE LEGENDARY GLASGOW FRIENDLINESS IS A BONUS, WHILE FIRST-TIME VISITORS WILL BE STRUCK BY THE CITY'S PANACHE.

Kelvingrove Gallery, Glasgow

GLASGOW'S ARCHITECTURE ranges from the magnificent Gothic style of Glasgow Cathedral to the imposing Italian Renaissance of the Victorian City Chambers.

As Britain's finest Victorian city, Glasgow offers 19th-century grandeur in its streets, squares and gardens while the fashionable and elegant terraces of the West End have been restored. In the 18th-century Merchant city, you will find cafés and boutiques and the chic Italian Centre with its exclusive designer shops. You can explore the St Enoch's Shopping Centre which is the largest glass-covered building in Europe as well as the Buchanan Galleries and stylish Princes Square. If you have any money left, head for a bargain in the famous Barras Market.

GLASGOW HAS AN unrivalled selection of more than 20 art galleries a museums to discover from the innovative Gallery of Modern Art to the internationally acclaimed Burrell Collection. Throughout the city, the unmistakable influence of two of the city's greatest sons – the architects Charles Rennie Mackintosh and Alexander 'Greek' Thomson can been seen. Visit Mackintosh's outstanding Glasgow School of Art and Thomson's newly restored Holmwood House.

Gourock and the Firth of Clyde

World Heritage Site, New Lanark

A YEAR-ROUND PROGRAMME of events including Celtic Connections, the Glasgow Folk Festival and the International Jazz Festival complements the arts scene in the city which is also home to Scottish Opera, Scottish Ballet and the Royal Scottish National Orchestra. Glasgow's cafés, bars and nightclubs offer plenty of opportunities to enjoy the friendliness and colourful character of the locals.

FROM GLASGOW, there is easy access to the rolling hills of Renfrewshire, the Inverclyde coastline and the fertile Clyde valley. At Paisley, you can visit the restored 12th-century abbey and learn about the famous Paisley textile pattern. Head upriver and the River Clyde changes its character tumbling over waterfalls into a rocky gorge at New Lanark Industrial Heritage Village, which is now a World Heritage site.

EVENTS GREATER GLASGOW AND CLYDE VALLEY

10–28 JANUARY
Celtic Connections
Various venues, Glasgow
Glasgow's annual celebration of Celtic music featuring international artists.
Contact: Celtic Connections
TEL: **0141 353 8050**

13-18 FEBRUARY
Scottish Curling Championships
Braehead Arena, Glasgow
The highlight of the Scottish curling year.
Contact: Royal Caledonian Curling Club
TEL: **0131 333 3003**

26-27 MAY
British Gold Panning Championships
Museum of Lead Mining, Wanlockhead, Biggar
Gold panning championships in Scotland's highest village – veterans, novices, adults and children alike can join the Scottish gold rush.
Contact:
Museum of Lead Mining
TEL: **01659 74387**
EMAIL:
wanlockhead@dial.pipex.com

2 JUNE
Shotts Highland Games
Hannah Park, Dykehead
Traditional Highland games including wrestling, side shows and the Clan Chieftains parade.
Contact: Mr Alex Hamilton
TEL: **01501 820280**

The Italian Centre, Glasgow

7 JUNE
Lanark Lanimer Day
Town centre, Lanark
Traditional procession and crowning of Lanimer Queen
Contact: Mr L Reid
TEL/FAX: **01556 663251**

9 JUNE
Bearsden & Milngavie Highland Games
Burnbrae, Milngavie
Traditional Highland Games, pipe bands, tug-o-war, athletics, heavy events and children's events.
Contact: Cameron Wallace
TEL: **0141 942 5177**

***9-24 JUNE**
West End Festival
Various venues, Glasgow
Music, theatre, exhibitions and free events, food, drink, and the midsummer Carnival Parade, in the West End of Glasgow
Contact: Festival Office
TEL: **0141 341 0844**

***4-8 JULY**
Glasgow Jazz Festival
Various venues, Glasgow
Glasgow's annual Jazz Festival, now in it's 15th Year.
Contact: Glasgow International Jazz Festival
TEL: **0141 287 5511 -**
TICKETLINE **0141 552 3592**
EMAIL: glasgow@jazzfest.co.uk
www.jazzfest.co.uk

***11 AUGUST**
World Pipe Band Championships
Glasgow Green, Glasgow.
The most prestigious event in the annual pipe band calendar, attracting some 200 bands from around the World.
Contact: Royal Scottish Pipe Band Association
TEL: **0141 221 5414**

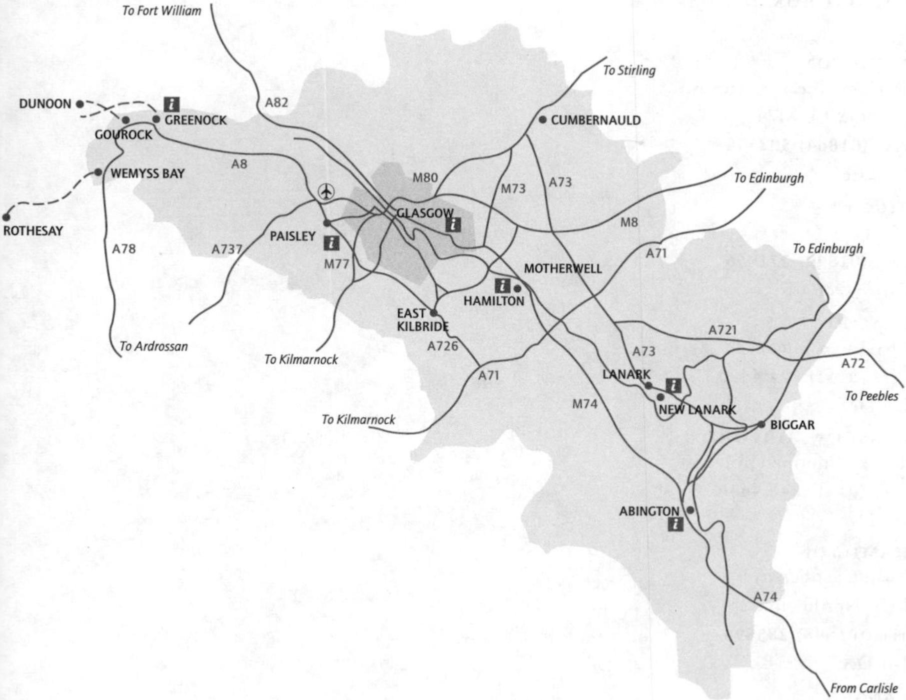

GREATER GLASGOW AND CLYDE VALLEY TOURIST BOARD
11 George Square
Glasgow
G2 1DY

TEL: **0141 204 4400**
FAX: **0141 204 4772**
www.seeglasgow.com

GREATER GLASGOW AND CLYDE VALLEY TOURIST BOARD

ABINGTON
Welcome Break Service Area
Junction 13, M74
TEL: **(01864) 502436**
Jan-Dec

BIGGAR
155 High Street
TEL: **(01899) 221066**
Easter-Oct

GLASGOW
11 George Square
TEL: **(0141) 204 4400**
Jan-Dec

GLASGOW AIRPORT
Tourist Information Desk
TEL: **(0141) 848 4440**
Jan-Dec

HAMILTON
Road Chef Services
M74 Northbound
TEL: **(01698) 285590**
Jan-Dec

LANARK
Horsemarket
Ladyacre Road
TEL: **(01555) 661661**
Jan-Dec

PAISLEY
9a Gilmour Street
TEL: **(0141) 889 0711**
Jan-Dec

Abington, Lanarkshire

Map Ref: 2B7

HOLMLANDS COUNTRY HOUSE

22 CARLISLE RD, CRAWFORD, BY ABINGTON, LANARKSHIRE ML12 6TW

Tel: 01864 502753 Fax: 01864 502313 Web: www.holmlandscotland.co.uk

If you enjoy good food, peaceful comfortable surroundings with an outstanding view, Holmlands is the place for you. We are situated within easy reach of Edinburgh and Glasgow and in the ideal spot for breaking the cross border journey and for touring the Borders and central areas.

B&B

Holmlands Country House

22 Carlisle Road, Crawford, Lanarkshire, ML12 6TW
Tel: 01864 502753 Fax: 01864 502313
E-mail: dan.davidson@holmlandscotland.co.uk
Web: www.holmlandscotland.co.uk

1 Twin, 1 Double, 1 Family | 2 En Suite fac, 1 Priv.not ensuite | B&B per person from £25.00 Single, from £20.00 Dbl/Twn; Room only per person from £15.00 | Open Jan-Dec; B&B + Eve.Meal from £30.00

Country house atmosphere, with splendid views over the Southern Uplands, just off Junction 14. Equidistant from Edinburgh and Glasgow (40 miles). Ideal base for touring the Borders, walking and golfing.

Townfoot Farm

B&B

Roberton, by Abington, Biggar, Lanarkshire, ML12 6RS
Tel: 01899 850655

2 Twin, 1 Double | 1 En Suite fac, 1 Pub Bath/Show | B&B per person from £17.50 Single, from £17.50 Dbl/Twn; Room only per person from £12.00 | Open Jan-Dec excl Xmas/New Year

In a delightfully quiet valley, set back from the main road, small and friendly with comfortable rooms. Some annexe accommodation with ensuite facilities. Easy access to M74 equidistant from Glasgow and Edinburgh. Ideal for touring the Scottish Borders.

Airdrie, Lanarkshire

Map Ref: 2A5

B&B

Mr & Mrs Aitken

Shawlee Cottage, 108 Lauchope Street, Chapelhall, Airdrie, ML6 8SW
Tel: 01236 753774

1 Single, 1 Twin, 3 Double | All En Suite | B&B per person £20.00-£27.00 Single, £20.00-£24.50 Dbl/Twn | Open Jan-Dec

Recently refurbished stone cottage, all accommodation on ground floor level with disabled access ramp. Convenient location with easy access to Glasgow (15 mins), Edinburgh (35 mins) and Stirling (45 mins). All rooms have direct-dial telephones and computer modem points and fax facility.

B&B

Easter Glentore Farm

Slamannan Road, Greengairs, by Airdrie, North Lanarkshire, ML6 7TJ
Tel/Fax: 01236 830243
Web: www.glentore.freeserve.co.uk

1 Twin, 2 Double | 2 En Suite fac, 1 Priv.NOT ensuite | B&B per person from £28.00 Single, from £21.00 Dbl/Twn; Room only per person from £19.00 | Open Jan-Dec excl Xmas/New Year

A warm welcome, home cooking and homely atmosphere can be experienced at this 245 acre farm set in unspoilt countryside. Enjoy panoramic views of the Campsie and Ochil Hills. Well placed for Glasgow, Stirling and Edinburgh. All rooms on ground floor. Non smoking house.

Airdrie, Lanarkshire — Map Ref: 2A5

★★★

B&B

Rowan Lodge
23 Condorrat Road, Glenmavis, Airdrie, ML6 0NS
Tel: 01236 753934
E.mail: june@rowanlodge.co.uk
Web: www.rowanlodge.co.uk

A friendly welcome awaits you at this family bungalow with all accommodation on ground floor level. Set in a quiet village within 2 minutes walk from a local restaurant. 15 miles from Glasgow. Easy access to all major routes.

1 Single, 1 Twin, 1 Double — All En Suite — B&B per person from £20.00 Single, from £20.00 Dbl/Twn — Open Jan-Dec excl Xmas/New Year

TV P

£ W

Bearsden, East Dumbartonshire — Map Ref: 1H5

★

CAMPUS ACCOMMODATION

University of Glasgow, St Andrew's Campus
Duntocher Road, Bearsden, Glasgow, Dunbartonshire, G61 4QA
Tel: 0141 330 3009/3400 Fax: 0141 330 3005

Hall of residence with conference facilities, lecture theatre, function rooms, indoor pool and gymnasium. Convenient access to city and airport.

203 Single, 105 Twin — 65 Pub Bath/Show — B&B per person from £16.00 Single, from £16.00 Twin — Open Easter, Jun-Sep

P

C £ V

Biggar, Lanarkshire — Map Ref: 2B6

★★★★

B&B

Mrs M E Stott
Lindsaylands, Biggar, Lanarkshire, ML12 6NR
Tel: 01899 220033/221221 Fax: 01899 221009
E-mail: elspeth@lindsaylands.co.uk
Web: www.lindsaylands.co.uk

Attractive country house William Leiper architecture. Set in 6 acres of garden, amidst lovely countryside with views to Border Hills. Hard tennis court and croquet lawn. Ideal base for touring Edinburgh, Glasgow and Scottish borders.

1 Twin, 2 Double — 2 En Suite fac, 1 Priv.NOT ensuite — B&B per person £28.00-£30.00 Single, £24.00-£26.00 Dbl/Twn — Open Mar-Nov

P

C W V

Important: Prices stated are estimates and may be subject to amendments

Biggar, Lanarkshire — **Map Ref: 2B6**

B&B

Walston Mansion Farmhouse
Walston, Carnwath, by Biggar, Lanarkshire, ML11 8NF
Tel/Fax: 01899 810338

1 Twin	2 En Suite fac	B&B per person	Open Jan-Dec
1 Double	1 Pub Bath/Show	from £20.00 Single	B&B + Eve.Meal
1 Family		£16.00-£18.00 Dbl/Twn	£24.50-£26.50

19c stone built farmhouse on a working farm situated on the edge of a small village in the shadow of the Pentland Hills. 5 miles from Biggar, 24 miles from Edinburgh, 30 miles from Glasgow and 16 miles from Peebles, an ideal holiday centre. Home cooking using home produced meat and organic vegetables. Evening meal provided by prior arrangement.

TV P C W V

Bothwell, Glasgow — **Map Ref: 2A5**

CRUACHAN

7 Croftbank Avenue, Bothwell G71 8RT
Telephone: 01698 850136 Fax: 01698 852443
e.mail: elizabeth@cruachanb-b.co.uk Web: www.cruachanb-b.co.uk

Donald and Betty extend a warm Scottish welcome to all their guests. Well-appointed rooms where attention to every little detail has been made. Large conservatory lounge overlooking the garden. Close to Strathclyde country park and M74. Convenient for M8, M73 and Glasgow. Several restaurants nearby. Off-street parking. Non-smoking.

B&B

Cruachan
7 Croftbank Avenue, Bothwell, nr Glasgow, G71 8RT
Tel: 01698 850136 Fax: 01698 852443
E.mail: elizabeth@cruachanb-b.co.uk
Web: www.cruachanb-b.co.uk

2 Double	2 Priv.NOT ensuite	B&B per person	Open Easter-Dec excl
		from £25.00 Single	Xmas/New Year
		from £20.00 Double	

Cosy, well-appointed rooms in this 1950's bungalow. Quiet residential area just off the M74 (Jn5) and within easy reach of M8 to Edinburgh and M73 to Stirling, only 9 miles south of Glasgow. Within walking distance of a wide choice of restaurants. Strictly non-smoking.

TV P W V

Eaglesham, by Glasgow, Renfrewshire — **Map Ref: 1H6**

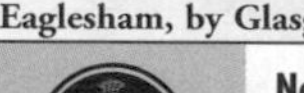

B&B

New Borland
Glasgow Road, Eaglesham, Renfrewshire, G76 0DN
Tel/Fax: 01355 302051
E-mail: newborland@dial.pipex.com

2 Single	1 Pub Bath/Show	B&B per person	Open Jan-Dec
2 Twin	2 En Suite fac	from £22.50 Single	
		from £24.00 Twin	
		Room only per person	
		from £20.00	

Near the picturesque, conservation village of Eaglesham a warm Scottish welcome is assured at this beautifully converted barn. Relaxing cosy lounge with wood burning stove, games room and comfortable dining room with open views over rolling farmland. Convenient for Glasgow Airport, Glasgow (9 miles), M74, Trossachs, Loch Lomond and Ayrshire (Burns and golf).

TV P W V

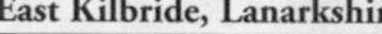

East Kilbride, Lanarkshire — **Map Ref: 1H6**

B&B

'Athbheoain'
189 Maxwellton Avenue, Maxwellton Village, Calderwood, East Kilbride, G74 3DX
Tel: 01355 228251/07720 186593
E-mail: scott@smaltman.fsnet.co.uk

1 Single	Priv.NOT ensuite	B&B per person	Open mid Jan-mid Dec
1 Twin		from £21.50 Single	
1 Double		from £17.50 Dbl/Twn	

Semi-detached traditional villa in quiet cul-de-sac in conservation village yet close to the other conservation village of East Kilbride and a 10 minute walk from the new town and its shops and restaurants.

TV P C V

VAT is shown at 17.5%: changes in this rate may affect prices.

Key to symbols is on back flap.

East Kilbride, Lanarkshire

Map Ref: 1H6

★★ B&B

Mrs C McLeavy
East Rogerton Lodge, Markethill Road, East Mains, East Kilbride, Lanarkshire, G74 4NX
Tel/Fax: 01355 263176

3 Twin | 1 Pub Bath/Show | B&B per person £20.00-£22.00 Single £15.00-£16.00 Twin | Open Jan-Dec

Farmyard conversion approximately 1 mile from the village and 6 miles south of Glasgow. Easy access to all major routes. All accommodation on ground floor level.

TV P C

Glasgow

Map Ref: 1H5

ADELAIDES

209 Bath Street, Glasgow G2 4HZ
Tel: 0141 248 4970 Fax: 0141 226 4247
Web: www.adelaides.co.uk

Part of stunning Baptist Church restoration. City centre guest house, centrally heated modern rooms, most ensuite, non-smoking, families welcome. Colour TV, complimentary tea and coffee in all rooms. Most of Glasgow's main attractions e.g. shops, theatres, museums of this revitalised city are within 10 minutes walk.

★★ GUEST HOUSE

Adelaide's
209 Bath Street, Glasgow, G2 4HZ
Tel: 0141 248 4970 Fax: 0141 226 4247
Web: www.adelaides.co.uk

2 Single, 2 Twin, 2 Double, 2 Family | 6 En Suite fac, 1 Pub Bath/Show | Room only per person £23.00-£39.50 | Open Jan-Dec

Guest house with self service eating facilities in redeveloped Victorian Church building, close to Kings Theatre and city centre. Parking arrangements available nearby.

TV C W V

★★ GUEST HOUSE

Alamo Guest House
46 Gray Street, Kelvingrove, Glasgow, G3 7SE
Tel: 0141 339 2395

2 Single, 1 Twin, 1 Double, 5 Family, 1 Triple | 2 En Suite fac, 1 Priv.NOT ensuite, 2 Pub Bath/Show | B&B per person from £21.00 Single from £18.00 Dbl/Twn | Open Jan-Dec

Friendly family run Victorian house, in quiet location overlooking park. Easy access to centre and within walking distance of SECC, galleries, Transport Museum, Glasgow University and a range of restaurants.

C V

★★ GUEST HOUSE

Alison House
26 Circus Drive, Glasgow, G31 2JH
Tel/Fax: 0141 556 1431

1 Single, 2 Twin, 2 Double, 2 Family | 1 En Suite fac | B&B per person £16.00-£18.00 Single £15,00-£18.00 Dbl/Twn | Open Jan-Dec

Victorian semi-villa in quiet residential area of East End, 10 minutes walk from Cathedral, Royal Infirmary, Strathclyde University Campus. One ground floor room. Limited access to kitchen available for takeaway's for evening dining.

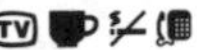

Glasgow Map Ref: 1H5

★★★ B&B

Avenue End B&B
21 West Avenue, Stepps, Glasgow, G33 6ES
Tel/Fax: 0141 779 1990
E-mail: AvenueEnd@aol.com

Rooms	Facilities	Prices	Open
1 Single 1 Double 1 Family	2 En Suite fac 1 Priv.NOT ensuite	B&B per person from £25.00 Single from £20.00 Dbl/Fam Room only per person from £20.00	Open Jan-Dec

Self built family home in quiet tree lined lane with easy access to motorway network and city centre. Near main route to Stirling, Loch Lomond and the Trossachs. Easy commuting by public or own transport. M8 exit 12.

C W V

★★ GUEST HOUSE

Belgrave Guest House
2 Belgrave Terrace, Gt Western Road, Glasgow, G12 8JD
Tel: 0141 337 1850/1741 Fax: 0141 337 1741

Rooms	Facilities	Prices	Open
3 Single 3 Twin 2 Double 3 Family	2 En Suite fac 1 Limited ensuite 3 Pub Bath/Show	B&B per person £21.00-£25.00 Single £18.50-£23.00 Dbl/Twn	Open Jan-Dec

Refurbished guest house, in the West End. Convenient for Botanic Gardens, other local attractions and amenities. 5 minute walk from two tube stations. Many restaurants, cafes and bus a few minutes walk away.

C £ V

★★★★ B&B

Margaret Bruce
24 Greenock Avenue, Glasgow, G44 5TS
Tel: 0141 637 0608

Rooms	Facilities	Prices	Open
1 Single 2 Twin 1 Double	2 En Suite fac 1 Pub Bath/Show 2 Priv.NOT ensuite	B&B per person from £22.50 Single from £22.50 Dbl/Twn	Open Apr-Oct

A modern architecturally designed villa with outstanding gardens and levels of comfort, situated within the conservation areas of Old Cathcart Village and Linn Park. But just 12 minutes by public transport to the city centre. Glasgow 20 mins. 10 mins from J22 - M8 Burrell collection 6 mins.

W V

★ CAMPUS ACCOMMODATION

Dalrymple Hall
Conference & Visitor Services, No 3 The Square, University of Glasgow, Glasgow, G12 8QQ
Tel: 0800 027 2030 Fax: 0141 334 5465
Web: www.gla/ac/uk/vacationaccommodation

Rooms	Facilities	Prices	Open
35 Single 21 Twin 1 Family	16 Pub Bath/Show	B&B per person from £22.50 Single	Open Mar, Apr, Jul, Sep B&B + Eve.Meal from £31.25

Hall of residence, part of Victorian terrace in West End of Glasgow, close to Botanic Gardens.

C £ W V

Glasgow **Map Ref: 1H5**

GUEST HOUSE

Enterprize Hotel
144 Renfrew Street, Glasgow, G3 6RF
Tel/Fax: 0141 332 8095

1 Single
1 Twin
2 Double
2 Family

All En Suite

B&B per person
from £45.00 Single
from £30.00 Dbl/Twn

Open Jan-Dec
B&B + Eve.Meal
from £55.00

Town house style guest house in quiet street behind Sauchiehall Street. Convenient for motorway, shops, theatres and restaurants.

GUEST HOUSE

Kirkland House
42 St Vincent Crescent, Glasgow, G3 8NG
Tel: 0141 248 3458 Fax: 0141 221 5174
E-mail: admin@kirkland.gispnet.com
Web: www.kirkland.gispnet.com

2 Single
1 Twin
1 Double
1 Family

3 En Suite fac
2 Limited ensuite

B&B per person
from £25.00 Single
from £25.00 Dbl/Twn

Open Jan-Dec

Ideally situated for city centre, S.E.C.C., University and Museums. Easy access to M8. Continental breakfast served in bedrooms.

Glasgow

Map Ref: 1H5

★★★

B&B

Lochgilvie House

117 Randolph Road, Glasgow, G11 7DS
Tel: 0141 357 1593 Fax: 0141 334 5828
E-mail: reservations@lochgilvie.demon.co.uk
Web: www.lochgilvie.demon.co.uk

1 Twin | All En Suite | B&B per person | Open Jan-Dec
1 Double | | £22.50-£30.00 Single |
1 Family | | from £22.50 Dbl/Twn |

Victorian townhouse in popular West End with bus and rail connections nearby. Easy access to A82 for Loch Lomond and Trossachs. Continental breakfast only served.

TV P V

★★

GUEST HOUSE

Lomond Hotel

6 Buckingham Terrace, Gt Western Road, Glasgow, G12 8EB
Tel: 0141 339 2339 Fax: 0141 339 5215
Web: www.scotland2000.com/lomondkelvin

8 Single | 6 En Suite fac | B&B per person | Open Jan-Dec
2 Twin | 6 Pub Bath/Show | £22.00-£38.00 Single |
3 Double | | £20.00-£27.00 Dbl/Twn |
4 Family | | Room only per person |
| | £19.00-£29.00 |

Victorian terraced house in the West End. Close to the BBC, Botanical Gardens and Glasgow University. On main bus routes to city centre and five minutes walk from underground, restaurants and shops.

TV

C V

★★★★

B&B

Park House

Victoria Park Gardens South, Glasgow, G11 7BX
Tel: 0141 339 1559 Fax: 0141 576 0915
E-mail: richardanddi.parkhouse.glasgow@dial.pipex.com

1 Twin | 2 En Suite fac | B&B per person | Open Apr-Sep
2 Double | 1 Priv.NOT ensuite | from £30.00 Single | B&B + Eve.Meal
| | from £25.00 Dbl/Twn | from £45.00

Large Victorian town house in quiet residential area. Convenient for Clydeside Expressway to city centre. Ideal base for touring. Off road parking.

TV P

W V

Glasgow **Map Ref: 1H5**

B&B

Mr & Mrs Robert & Anne Paterson (Paterson's)
16 Bogton Avenue, Muirend, Glasgow, G44 3JJ
Tel/Fax: 0141 637 4402
E-mail: apaterson@gofornet.co.uk

Set in a quiet suburb of Glasgow yet close to road, rail and bus services. (Only 12 mins by train to city centre). Convenient base for sightseeing to the nearby Burrell Collection or into the city for the shops, museums and galleries. Two minutes walk from supermarket and restaurants. Sandwiches/snacks available by request .

2 Single
1 Twin/Double

1 Priv.NOT ensuite

B&B per person
from £20.00 Single
from £19.00 Dbl/Twn
Room only per person
from £16.00

Open Jqan-Dec excl
Xmas/New Year
Evening Meal
£10.00 per person

TV V

HOTEL

The Terrace House
14 Belhaven Terrace, Glasgow, G12 0TG
Tel: 0141 337 3377 Fax: 0141 400 3378
Web: www.the-terrace.fsnet.co.uk

19c townhouse in West End of city within easy reach of main business centres and tourist attractions. Traditional values of comfort and service.

1 Single
3 Twin
3 Double
3 Family

2 Priv.NOT ensuite

B&B per person
from £49.00 Single
from £30.00 Dbl/Twn

Open Jan-Dec

TV C V

GUEST
HOUSE

The Town House
4 Hughenden Terrace, Glasgow, G12 9XR
Tel: 0141 357 0862 Fax: 0141 339 9605
E.mail: hospitality@thetownhouseglasgow.com
Web: www.thetownhouseglasgow.com

Glasgow's original and long established town house, situated in the desirable west end, offers a peaceful and luxurious base from which to enjoy all that Glasgow has to offer. A fine example of Victorian architecture. Free and ample parking.

4 Twin
4 Double
2 Family

All En Suite

B&B per person
from £60.00 Single
from £36.00 Dbl/Twn

Open Jan-Dec

TV C

Glasgow

Map Ref: 1H5

★ CAMPUS ACCOMMODATION

University of Strathclyde
Residence and Catering Services, 50 Richmond St., Glasgow, G1 1XP.
Tel: 0141 553 4148 Fax: 0141 553 4149
E-mail: rescat@mis.strath.ac.uk

833 Single, 135 Twin, 17 Double, 2 Family
308 En Suite fac, 679 Limited facs
B&B per person from £24.00 Single, from £19.75 Dbl/Twn
Open Jun-Sep

Modern, purpose-built halls of residence on campus. Ideal centre for exploring the city.

Hamilton, Lanarkshire

Map Ref: 2A5

★★ B&B

Mrs Margaret Jones
5a Auchingramont Road, Hamilton, Lanarkshire, ML3 6JP
Tel: 01698 285230

2 Single, 1 Twin, 2 Double, 1 Family
2 En Suite fac, 1 Priv.NOT ensuite
B&B per person from £22.00 Single, from £25.00 Dbl/Twn
Open Jan-Dec

Scandinavian split level villa, with private parking. Ensuite accommodation available. Satellite/Cable TV in lounge. 5 minutes from bus and train station.

★★★★ B&B

Mrs A McAuley
13/1 Auchingramont Road, Hamilton, Lanarkshire, ML3 6JP
Tel: 01698 457606

1 Single, 1 Double
2 Priv.NOT ensuite, 1 Pub Bath/Show
B&B per person £20.00-£22.00 Single to £25.00 Double
Open Jan-Dec

Recently converted old rectory. Ground floor flat with stairs leading down to the accommodation. Well-appointed rooms. Centrally situated, only 5 minutes walk from town centre, and convenient for access to M74 and major routes.

★★★ B&B

Mrs W McGuire
10A Auchingramont Road, Hamilton, Lanarkshire, ML3 6JT
Tel: 01698 424923
Fax: 01698 810550

1 Twin, 1 Family
Private fac., En suite
B&B per person £22.00-£25.00
Open Jan-Dec

Detached bungalow in peaceful location, set back off road. Families welcome (ensuite family room), large secure garden. 5 minutes walk from town centre, rail and bus station. Easy access to M74 and all major routes. Secure parking in owners garage. Homemade bread and preserves served at breakfast.

Harthill, by Shotts, Lanarkshire

Map Ref: 2A5

★★ GUEST HOUSE

Blairmains Guest House
Harthill, Lanarkshire, ML7 5TJ
Tel: 01501 751278 Fax: 01501 753383
E-mail: Heather@Blairmains.freeserve.co.uk

2 Single, 3 Twin, 1 Double
3 En Suite fac
B&B per person from £18.00 Single, from £16.00 Dbl/Twn
Open Jan-Dec, B&B + Eve.Meal from £21.00

Comfortable annexe accommodation set in an attractive farmhouse on small farm – 72 acres. Immediately adjacent to junction 5 of M8 motorway. Ideal centre for touring, with Edinburgh, Glasgow, Stirling 30 minute drive. Ample parking. Evening meals by prior arrangement.

VAT is shown at 17.5%: changes in this rate may affect prices.

Key to symbols is on back flap.

Kilbarchan, Renfrewshire

Map Ref: 1G5

B&B

Tower House

Milliken Park Road, Kilbarchan, Renfrewshire, PA10 2PB
Tel/Fax: 01505 703299

1 Single
1 Twin
1 Family

All En Suite

B&B per person
from £28.00 Single
from £25.00 Dbl/Fam
Room only per person
from £22.00

Open Jan-Dec

Late Georgian villa in quiet residential area. Easy access to motorway and only 10 minutes from Glasgow Airport. Frederic Chopin was a special guest at musical soiree here in the late August of 1848. French, German and Dutch spoken.

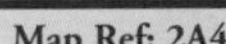

Kilsyth, North Lanarkshire

Map Ref: 2A4

B&B

Auchenrivoch Farm

Banton, Kilsyth, G65 0QZ
Tel: 01236 822113

2 Twin

1 Pub Bath/Show

B&B per person
£19.00-£20.00 Single
Room only per person
from £18.00

Open Jan-Dec excl Xmas/New Year

Working farm specialising in beef and sheep. Excellent country views strategically placed for the whole central belt. Only 10 miles from Historic Town of Stirling in Braveheart country. Glasgow and Edinburgh Airports easily accessible. Excellent bus service to Glasgow City Centre.

V

B&B

Mrs E MacGregor

Allanfauld Farm, Kilsyth, North Lanarkshire, G65 9DF
Tel: 01236 822155

1 Single
1 Family

1 Priv.NOT ensuite
1 Pub Bath/Show

B&B per person
£18.00 Single
£18.00 Double
Room only per person
£16.00

Open Jan-Dec

Working stock farm on Kilsyth Hills with large south facing garden. 12 miles (19kms) north of Glasgow. Centrally situated for day trips to Loch Lomond, Stirling and Edinburgh.

C

Lanark

Map Ref: 2A6

B&B

Jerviswood Mains Farm

Lanark, ML11 7RL
Tel: 01555 663987

1 Twin
2 Double

2 Pub Bath/Show

B&B per person
from £25.00 Single
from £18.00 Dbl/Twn

Open Jan-Dec

A warm welcome awaits you at this 19c stone built farmhouse of considerable character, 1 mile (2 kms) north of the historic market town of Lanark. Less than one hour's drive from both Glasgow and Edinburgh, is an exellent base for touring Scotland.

C V

Important: Prices stated are estimates and may be subject to amendments

by Lanark

Map Ref: 2A6

B&B

Corehouse Farm
Lanark, ML11 9TQ
Tel/Fax: 01555 661377
E-mail: corehouse@thegallop.com

1 Double
2 Family

All En Suite

B&B per person
from £22.00 Single
from £18.00 Dbl/Fam

Open Jan-Dec

Warm family welcome on traditional mixed farm (sheep, horses & cattle) close to Falls of Clyde and nature reserve. 3 miles (5km) from Lanark town and New Lanark Heritage Centre. All accommodation on ground level.

Lesmahagow, Lanarkshire

Map Ref: 2A6

B&B

Dykecroft
Dykecroft Farm, Boghead, Lesmahagow, Lanarkshire, ML11 0JQ
Tel: 01555 892226

1 Twin
2 Double

1 Pub Bath/Show

B&B per person
£21.00-£22.00 Single
£19.00-£20.00 Dbl/Twn

Open Jan-Dec

Modern farmhouse bungalow in rural situation 20 miles (32kms) South of Glasgow and airport. An hour's drive from Edinburgh, Stirling, Ayr and Loch Lomond, only 2 miles from the M74.

Lochwinnoch, Renfrewshire

Map Ref: 1G5

B&B

East Lochhead
Largs Road, Lochwinnoch, Renfrewshire, PA12 4DX
Tel/Fax: 01505 842610
E-mail: winnoch@aol.com
Web: www.eastlochhead.co.uk

1 Twin
1 Double
1 Dbl/Fam

All En Suite

B&B per person
from £35.00 Single
from £32.50 Dbl/Twn
Room only
from £60.00

Open Jan-Dec
B&B + Eve.Meal
from £60.00

Spacious Victorian country house overlooking Barr Loch. Easy access to Glasgow Airport and motorway network. Convenient for Ayrshire Coast, Burns Country, Loch Lomond and Glasgow.

B&B

Garnock Lodge
Boydstone Road, Lochwinnoch, PA12 4JT
Tel/Fax: 01505 503680
E-mail: garnocklodge@cwcom.net
Web: www.garnocklodge.cwc.net

1 Single
2 Twin
1 Double

2 En Suite fac
1 Priv.NOT ensuite

B&B per person
from £16.00 Single
from £20.00 Dbl/Twn
Room only per person
£12.00-£14.00

Open Jan-Dec excl
Xmas/New Year

1940's extended bungalow in peaceful situation, yet central for Glasgow airport and touring Loch Lomond, the Trossachs, Ayrshire & Burns country, Culzean Castle & ferries for the River Clyde islands.

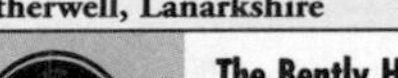

Motherwell, Lanarkshire — **Map Ref: 2A5**

HOTEL

The Bently Hotel
19 High Road, Motherwell, Lanarkshire, ML1 3HU
Tel: 01698 265588 Fax: 01698 253418

Privately owned, 19th c building centrally located, close to railway station and opposite the Motherwell Heritage Centre. Only 3 minutes drive from the M74, 15 miles south of Glasgow.

8 Single	All En Suite	B&B per person	Open Jan-Dec excl
4 Twin		from £35.00 Single	Xmas/New Year
5 Double		from £22.50 Dbl/Twn	B&B + Eve.Meal
1 Family		Room only per person	from £28.00
		from £20.00	

SMALL HOTEL

Dalziel Park Golf & Country Club
100 Hagen Drive, Motherwell, ML1 5RZ
Tel: 01698 862862 Fax: 01698 862863
Web: www.dalzielpark.co.uk

Newly built accommodation opposite the Clubhouse offering traditional contemporary en-suite bedrooms. Set in picturesque clubhouse woodland setting. Offering 15-bay floodlight driving range, hairdresser and 18 hole golf course. Approximately 20 mins drive to Glasgow and Edinburgh.

1 Single	All En Suite	B&B per person	Open Jan-Dec
4 Double		from £45.00 Single	
4 Family		from £25.00 Dbl/Twn	
		Room only	
		from £39.95	

HOTEL

Moorings Hotel
114 Hamilton Road, Motherwell, ML1 3DG
Tel: 01698 258131 Fax: 01698 254973

The Moorings House Hotel originates from a custom built 19th century home of one of Scotlands foremost steel families (The Colvilles). Ideally situated a few minutes from the M74 and M8 motorways. Ample parking.

2 Single	All En Suite	B&B per person	Open Jan-Dec
6 Twin		£30.00-£59.00 Single	B&B + Eve.Meal
20 Double		£25.00-£35.00 Dbl/Twn	£37.50-£66.50
2 Family			

CAMPUS ACCOMMODATION

Stewart Hall of Residence
Motherwell College, Dalzell Drive, Motherwell, Lanarkshire, ML1 2PP
Tel: 01698 261890 Fax: 01698 232527

On college campus and all on one level. Close to Strathclyde Park and M8/M74 motorway link for Glasgow and Edinburgh.

45 Single	1 En Suite fac	B&B per person	Open Jan-Dec excl
	44 Pri.NOT ensuite	from £19.00 Single	Xmas/New Year
		Room only per person	B&B + Eve.Meal
		from £16.00	to £23.00

Important: Prices stated are estimates and may be subject to amendments

Paisley, Renfrewshire

Map Ref: 1H5

★★ B&B

Acarra
75 Maxwellton Road, Paisley, PA1 2RB
Tel: 0141 887 7604 Fax: 0141 887 1589
Web: www.acarra.co.uk

Rooms	Facilities	Prices	Open
1 Single 1 Twin 1 Double	2 Pub Bath/Show	B&B per person from £25.00 Single from £20.00 Dbl/Twn	Open Jan-Dec

Listed terraced stone built house in quiet conservation area close to Paisley town centre, Royal Alexandra Hospital and Paisley University. Two miles (3km) from Glasgow Airport.

★★★ GUEST HOUSE

Ardgowan Town House Hotel
94 Renfrew Road, Paisley, Renfrewshire, PA3 4BJ
Tel/Fax: 0141 889 4763
Web: www.ardgowanhouse.com

Rooms	Facilities	Prices	Open
2 Twin 4 Double 2 Family	7 En Suite fac 1 Priv.NOT ensuite	B&B per person from £40.00 Single from £25.00 Dbl/Twn Room only per person from £20.00	Open Jan-Dec

Spacious modern amenities in this town house off Junction 27 of the M8. Large garden with fountains. Close to Glasgow airport with Glasgow city centre only 7 miles away.

Strathaven, Lanarkshire

Map Ref: 2A6

★★★ B&B

Georgie Rankin
Avonlea, 46 Millar Street, Glassford,
by Strathaven, Lanarkshire, ML10 6TD
Tel: 01357 521748/521369

Rooms	Facilities	Prices	Open
2 Twin	1 Pub Bath/Show	B&B per person £22.00-£25.00 Single £17.00-£19.00 Twin Room only per person £13.00-£15.00	Open Jan-Nov B&B + Eve.Meal £25.00-£35.00

Terraced house in quiet peaceful conservation village one and a half miles from Strathhaven. Traditional furnished bedrooms on 1st floor/ 18 miles South of Glasgow. 4 miles from M74 JN8. Evening meals can be provided by prior arrangement.

FROM THE GREEN SLOPES OF THE OCHIL HILLS IN THE EAST TO THE FAR-FLUNG HEBRIDEAN ISLANDS ON THE WESTERN SEABOARD, YOU WILL DISCOVER A REMARKABLY DIVERSE REGION WHERE HISTORY IS SET WITHIN A GLORIOUS NATURAL ENVIRONMENT.

Castle Stalker on Loch Linnhe, at Appin, north of Oban

IT IS HERE that the geological Highland boundary fault divides the lowland south from the mountainous north. Scenically, this area has everything, from the bonny banks of Loch Lomond, a playground for generations of visitors, to the bustling town of Stirling and western coastal resort of Oban.

A GOOD PLACE to begin is the Royal Burgh of Stirling. As a gateway to the Highlands and an important centre, Stirling has played a leading role in Scotland's story. Today, the castle with its newly restored Great Hall and the historic Old Town are just one of its many attractions. Nearby is the National Wallace Monument, telling the real story of Scotland's first freedom-fighter, William Wallace.

IN THE EARLY DAYS of tourism, the location of Loch Lomond and the Trossachs, a highly scenic area just beyond the Highland line, made them easy to reach. Often described as "The Highlands in Miniature', the Trossachs is still easy to reach with its gateway being the bustling and friendly town of Callander. At the Rob Roy and Trossachs Visitor Centre, you can uncover the legend of this celebrated folk hero. An excellent way to enjoy the captivating beauty of this area is on board the SS Sir Walter Scott which makes regular cruises across the placid waters of Loch Katrine. There are also plenty of cruising options on Loch Lomond, Scotland's largest loch (by surface area), which will shortly become part of Scotland's first national park.

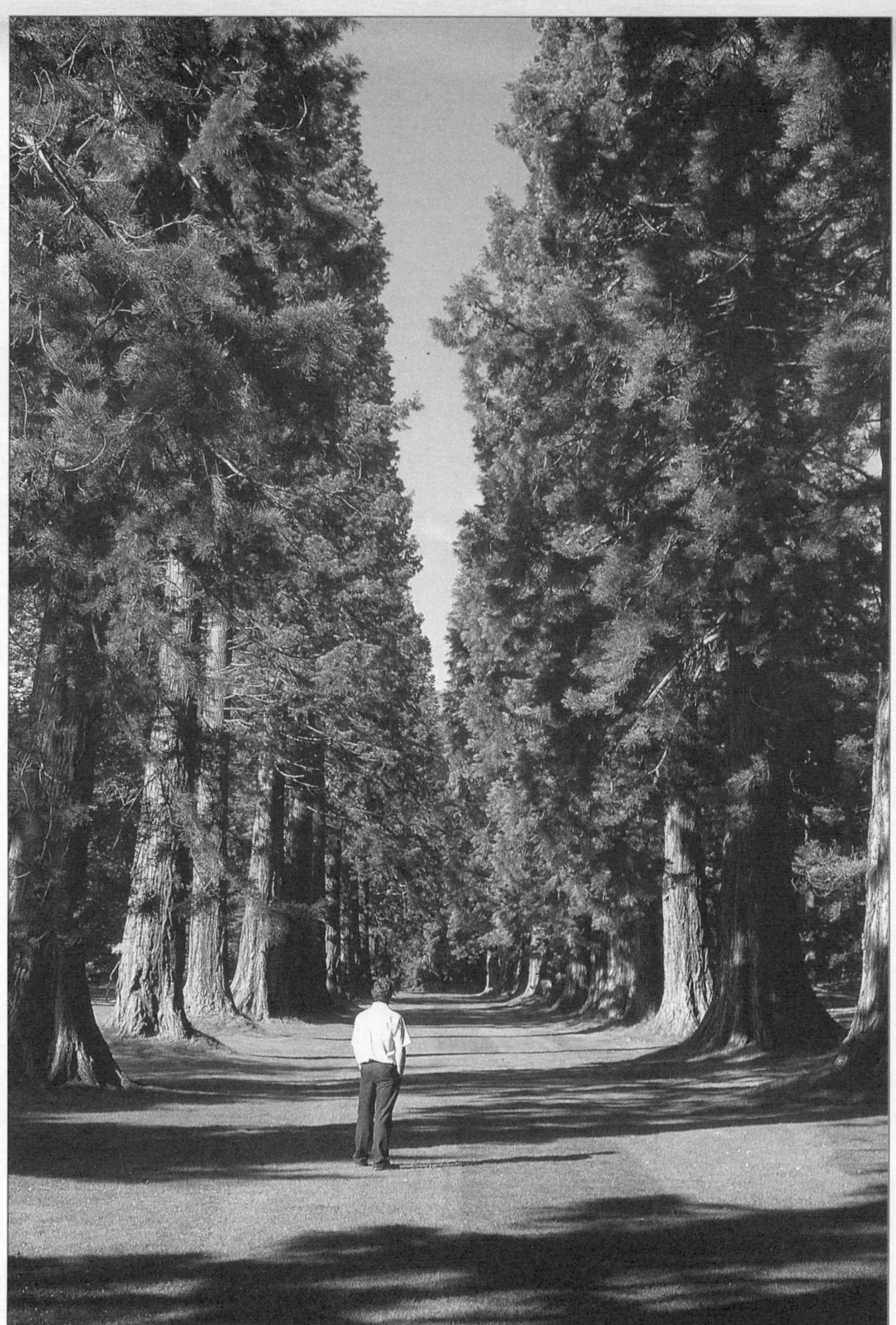

Younger Botanic Gardens, by Dunoon, Cowal Peninsula

Castle Campbell, by Dollar

FURTHER WEST IS the delightful Cowal Peninsula with the fine Victorian resort of Dunoon and the lovely Isle of Bute with its magnificent Victorian gothic mansion, Mount Stuart and pleasant seaside resort of Rothesay. Across the sheltered waters of Loch Fyne sits the Georgian planned village of Inveraray and to the south the beautiful peninsula of Kintyre offering miles of shoreline and beaches with unsurpassed views of the islands. Regular ferry services cross to the lively island of Islay, world-famous for its peaty malt whiskies and then to Jura, which in contrast, has one road, one distillery, one hotel and lots of space.

THE ROAD WEST will take you through a panorama of dramatic mountains which sweep down to the coastal resort of Oban. Romantic names and places such as Tobermory with its picture postcard harbour await the visitor to Mull and the island of Iona and Staffa are close by. You could venture further west for a real experience of island life and visit Colonsay, Tiree or Coll, but wherever you choose, you can be sure you will find a warm welcome in the heartland of Scotland.

EVENTS
WEST HIGHLANDS AND ISLANDS, LOCH LOMOND, STIRLING AND TROSSACHS

3-7 MAY
14th Isle of Bute Jazz Festival
Various venues, Bute
Annual jazz festival.
Contact: Ray & Linda Bruce
TEL: **01700 502800**

18-19 MAY
Alloa Ale Festival
Alloa Town Hall
Now in it's 5th year the Alloa Real Ale Festival is back with over forty real ales, scrumpy and wine with live music nightly.
Contact: Speirs Booking Office
TEL: **01259 213131**

26-27 MAY
Loch Fyne Seafood Fair
Loch Fyne, Argyllshire
A feast of West Coast seafood, plus live entertainment.
TEL: **01499 600264**

*15–17 JUNE
Royal Rothesay Regatta
Various venues, Rothesay
A celebration of the yacht clubs of the Clyde and their friends with plenty of shorebased entertainment.
Contact: Rothesay, Tourist Information Centre
TEL: **01700 502151**

28-29 JULY
Callander World Championship Highland Games
Callander Games Field,
Traditional Highland Games with caber tossing, hammer throwing, pipe bands, solo piping and highland dancing.
Contact: Mr D McKirgan
TEL: **01877 330919**

24-25 AUGUST
Cowal Highland Gathering
Dunoon, Argylshire
The largest and most spectacular Highland Games in the World, featuring the World Highland dancing championship, a major pipe band championship with over 150 pipe bands, also, solo piping, track & heavy athletics, shinty tournament together with a variety of trade stands and children's activities
Contact: Janet Fletcher, Cowal Highland Gathering
TEL: **01369 703206**
EMAIL info@cowalgathering.com
www.cowalgathering.com

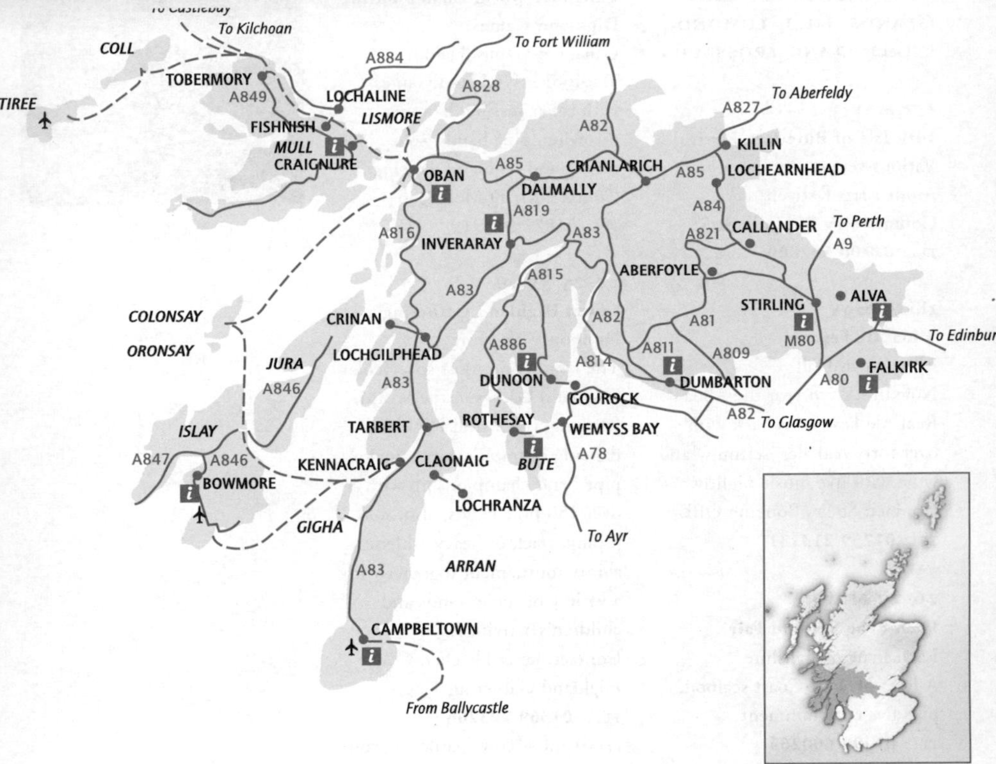

ARGYLL, THE ISLES, LOCH LOMOND, STIRLING AND TROSSACHS TOURIST BOARD

Old Town Jail
St John Street
Stirling
FK8 1EA

TEL: **01786 445222**
FAX: **01786 471301/446325**
www.visitscottish.heartlands.org

WEST HIGHLANDS, LOCH LOMOND, STIRLING AND TROSSACHS TOURIST BOARD

ABERFOYLE
Trossachs Discovery Centre
Main Street
TEL: **(01877) 382352**
Jan-Dec

ALVA
Mill Trail Visitor Centre
TEL: **(01259) 769696**
Jan-Dec

ARDGARTAN
Arrochar
TEL: **(01301) 702432**
April-Oct

BALLOCH
Balloch Road
TEL: **(01389) 753533**
April-Oct

BO'NESS
Seaview Car Park
TEL: **(01506) 826626**
April-Sept

BOWMORE
Isle of Islay
TEL: **(01496) 810254**
Jan-Dec

CALLANDER
Rob Roy and Trossachs Visitor Centre
Ancaster Square
TEL: **(01877) 330342**
Mar-Dec
Jan and Feb weekends only

CAMPBELTOWN
Mackinnon House
The Pier
Argyll
TEL: **(01586) 552056**
Jan-Dec

CRAIGNURE
The Pier
Isle of Mull
TEL: **(01680) 812377**
Jan-Dec

DRYMEN
Drymen Library
The Square
TEL: **(01360) 660068**
May-Sept

DUMBARTON
Milton
A82 Northbound
TEL: **(01389) 742306**
Jan-Dec

DUNBLANE
Stirling Road
TEL: **(01786) 824428**
May-Sept

DUNOON
7 Alexandra Parade
Argyll
TEL: **(01369) 703785**
Jan-Dec

FALKIRK
2-4 Glebe Street
TEL: **(01324) 620244**
Jan-Dec

HELENSBURGH
The Clock Tower
TEL: **(01436) 672642**
April-Oct

INVERARAY
Front Street
Argyll
TEL: **(01499) 302063**
Jan-Dec

KILLIN
Breadalbane Folklore Centre
TEL: **(01567) 820254**
March-end Oct
Feb weekends only

LOCHGILPHEAD
Lochnell Street
Argyll
TEL: **(01546) 602344**
April-Oct

OBAN
Argyll Square
Argyll
TEL: **(01631) 563122**
Jan-Dec

ROTHESAY
15 Victoria Street
Isle of Bute
TEL: **(01700) 502151**
Jan-Dec

STIRLING
Dumbarton Road
TEL: **(01786) 475019**
Jan-Dec

STIRLING (ROYAL BURGH)
The Esplanade
TEL: **(01786) 479901**
Jan-Dec

STIRLING
Pirnhall Motorway Service Area
Juntion 9, M9
TEL: **(01786) 814111**
April-Oct

TARBERT
Harbour Street
Argyll
TEL: **(01880) 820429**
April-Oct

TARBET-LOCH LOMOND
Main Street
TEL: **(01301) 702260**
April-Oct

TOBERMORY
Isle of Mull
TEL: **(01688) 302182**
April-Oct

TYNDRUM
Main Street
TEL: **(01838) 400246**
April-Oct

Aberfoyle, Perthshire

Map Ref: 1H3

GUEST HOUSE

Creag-Ard House
Aberfoyle, Stirling, FK8 3TQ
Tel/Fax: 01877 382297
E-mail: Creag-Ard@tinyonline.co.uk

2 Twin
4 Double

All En Suite

B&B per person
from £35.00 Single
from £27.00 Dbl/Twn

Open Easter-Oct
B&B + Eve.Meal
from £47.00

Nestling in 3 acres of gardens this lovely Victorian house enjoys superb views over Loch Ard and Ben Lomond. Own trout fishing plus boat hire. A haven of peace and tranquility. Home baking and evening meals by arrangement.

B&B

Forth House
Lochard Road, Aberfoyle, Stirlingshire, FK8 3TD
Tel: 01877 382696
E-mail: ForthLoft@aol.com

1 Double
1 Family

1 Priv.NOT ensuite

B&B per person
£20.00-£25.00 Single
£20.00-£25.00 Double

Open Jan-Dec

A warm welcome at this family run B&B situated a mile from Aberfoyle. A quiet rural setting with easy access to forest walks and cycle routes. TV lounge, open fire.

Appin, Argyll

Map Ref: 1E1

B&B

Lochside Cottage
Fasnacloich, Appin, Argyll, PA38 4BJ
Tel/Fax: 01631 730216
E-mail: broadbent@lochsidecottage.fsnet.co.uk
Web: www.lochsidecottage.fsnet.co.uk

2 Twin
1 Double

2 En Suite fac
1 Priv.NOT ensuite

B&B per person
from £22.00 Single
from £22.00 Dbl/Twn

Open Jan-Dec excl Xmas/New Year
B&B + Eve.Meal
from £39.50

The friendly atmosphere of the Broadbents' home welcomes you at the end of the day. Delicious home cooked dinner, a log fire and the certainty of a perfect night's sleep in an attractive and comfortable ensuite bedroom, all contribute to an unforgetable holiday at Lochside Cottage.

Important: Prices stated are estimates and may be subject to amendments

Appin, Argyll

Map Ref: 1E1

B&B

Lurignish Farm
Appin, Argyll, PA38 4BN
Tel: 01631 730365
E-mail: lurignish@amserve.net

1 Double, 1 Family | 1 Pub Bath/Show | B&B per person from £18.00 Single, from £18.00 Double | Open mid May-mid Sep

Family run 1000 acre hill farm overlooking Loch Linnhe, offering friendly highland hospitality with good home cooking and baking. Opportunities for hill walking , horse riding and water sports centre less than 1 mile from the farm and golfing midway between the farm and Fort William (28 miles). Oban 20 miles.

Ardchattan, Argyll

Map Ref: 1E2

Blarcreen Farmhouse

Ardchattan, Oban, Argyll PA37 1RG
Tel/Fax: 01631 750272
e.mail: j.lace@blarcreenfarm.demon.co.uk

Substantial Victorian farmhouse by the shores of Loch Etive. Quality guest house accommodation. Spacious, comfortable, relaxing. Excellent location. Superb views. Farmhouse cooking. Peace and tranquility; sweet fresh air and water in this most beautiful area of Scotland. We welcome you and offer assistance to make your stay in Scotland both excellent and memorable.

B&B

Blarcreen Farm Guest House
Ardchattan, by Oban, Argyll, PA37 1RG
Tel/Fax: 01631 750272
E-mail: j.lace@blarcreenfarm.demon.co.uk

1 Twin, 2 Double, 1 Family | 1 En Suite fac, 3 priv.NOT ensuite | B&B per person from £20.00 Single, from £20.00 Dbl/Twn; Room only per person from £18.00 | Open Mar-Dec; B&B + Eve.Meal from £27.50

Victorian farmhouse overlooking Loch Etive and the hills beyond. Ideal location for a quiet break fishing or hill walking. Personalised tours tailored to suit individual requirements.

Ardrishaig, by Lochgilphead, Argyll

Map Ref: 1E4

B&B

Mrs Hamilton
Seaview, St Clair Road, Ardrishaig, Argyll
Tel: 01546 603300

1 Twin, 2 Double | 1 En Suite fac, 2 Pub Bath/Show | B&B per person from £15.00 Dbl/Twn; Room only per person from £10.00 | Open Jan-Dec

Traditional stonebuilt house set above the village with open views over the harbour and loch. Home bakes and friendly welcome. Ideal base for touring West Coast of Scotland.

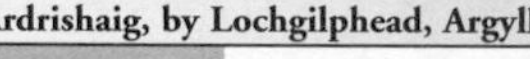

Arrochar, Argyll — Map Ref: 1G3

FERRY COTTAGE

Ardmay, Arrochar, Argyll & Bute G83 7AH
Tel: 01301 702428 Fax: 01301 702729
e.mail: CaroleBennetton@aol.com

Quietly situated at the gateway to the Highlands, the freshness of our non-smoking establishment is appreciated by smokers and non-smokers alike. In our centrally heated en-suite bedrooms (one features a waterbed) facilities include tea, coffee, toiletries and hairdryers – attention to detail alongside a warm welcome ensure a perfect stay. With panoramic views across Loch Long towards the Cobbler and the Arrochar Alps this is the idyllic location for touring and hill-walking. Loch Lomond is close by. For peace of mind we have a fire certificate and off-road parking. Payment by credit card is welcome (small fee applicable).
Non smoking establishment.

★★ B&B

Ferry Cottage
Ardmay, Arrochar, Argyll & Bute, G83 7AH
Tel: 01301 702428 Fax: 01301 702729
E-mail: CaroleBennetton@aol.com

1 Twin, 2 Double — All En Suite — B&B per person £20.00-£23.00 Dbl/Twn — Open Jan-Dec excl Xmas/New Year; B&B + Eve.Meal £31.50-£34.50

Refurbished 200 year old house with attractive bedrooms and ensuite shower-rooms. Scenic views across Loch Long. Major credit cards accepted. Private parking. Evening meals available & packed lunches. 5 minutes drive from Loch Lomond. Non smoking establishment.

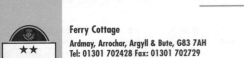

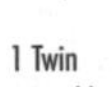

★★★ GUEST HOUSE

Lochside Guest House
Main Street, Arrochar, Argyll, G83 7AA
Tel/Fax: 01301 702467
E-mail: LochsideGH@aol.com

2 Single, 1 Twin, 3 Double, 1 Family — 4 En Suite fac, 1 Priv ensuite, 2 Pub Bath/Show — B&B per person £19.00-£26.00 Single, £19.00-£26.00 Dbl/Twn; Room only per person £19.00-£26.00 — Open Jan-Dec; B&B + Eve.Meal £29.00-£37.00

Warm friendly Scottish welcome at this lochside guest house with magnificent views across to the Arrochar Alps.

★★★ B&B

Rowantree Cottage
Main Street, Arrochar, G83 7AA
Tel/Fax: 01301 702540
E-mail: rowantreecottage@c.s.com

1 Twin, 1 Double, 1 Family — All En Suite, 1 Pub Bath — B&B per person from £20.00 Single, from £20.00 Dbl/Twn — Open Jan-Dec; B&B + Eve.Meal from £32.00

Comfortable refurbished cottage in centre of village with views across Loch Long to the Cobbler beyond.

Balloch, Dunbartonshire Map Ref: 1G4

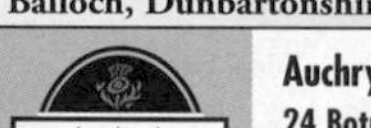

B&B

Auchry Bed & Breakfast
24 Boturich Drive, Balloch, Alexandria,
Dunbartonshire, G83 8JP
Tel: 01389 753208
E-mail: auchry@ic24.net

Comfortable accommodation in modern villa within minutes walking distance of Loch Lomond with its cruise boats for the day tripper. Close to all amenities, bus and rail stations with their connections to Glasgow.

1 Double Pub.Shower
1 Single

B&B per person
£17.00-£19.00 Single
£16.00-£19.00 Double

Open Jan-Dec excl Xmas/New Year

B&B

Ms Lillian Biddulph
Lachlan B&B, 15 Tullichewan Road, Balloch, G83 8SN
Tel: 01389 604402

Family run B&B in the heart of Balloch. 5 minutes walk to Lomond shores. Ideally positioned for public transport by bus or train, stroll to pubs, restaurants, shops, Loch Lomond cruises and Balloch Castle Country Park or visit Glasgow 40 minutes by train with galleries, restaurants and shopping centres.

1 Double All En Suite
1 Family/Twin

B&B per person
£16.00-£20.00 Double
Room only per person
from £14.00

Open Jan-Dec excl Xmas/New Year

OAKVALE B&B

OAKVALE, DRYMEN ROAD, BALLOCH G83 8JY
Tel: 01389 751615 e.mail: derek.feltham@talk21.com

Family run bed and breakfast offers quaint fresh comfortable accommodation in a cosy relaxed atmosphere. Hospitality and privacy guaranteed. Situated five minutes' walk from village and Loch Lomond shore. Visitors are well catered for with cruises, restaurants, pubs and beautiful unspoiled forest, mountain, river and loch scenery never far away.

B&B

Mrs J Feltham
Oakvale, Drymen Road, Balloch, Dunbartonshire, G83 8JY
Tel: 01389 751615
E-mail: derek.feltham@talk21.com

Extended 1940's bungalow near country park. 5 mins walk to Loch Lomond, cruises, restaurants and pubs.

1 Twin All En Suite
2 Double

B&B per person
£17.00-£22.00 Dbl/Twn
Room only per person
£16.00-£19.00

Open Jan-Dec

B&B

Glyndale Bed & Breakfast
6 McKenzie Drive, Lomond Road Estate, Balloch,
Dunbartonshire, G83 8HL
Tel: 01389 758238
E-mail: glyndale_b_and_b@tinyworld.co.uk

Modern family home in residential area, 10 minutes walk from Loch Lomond and Balloch Village with its shops, restaurants and loch cruises. 30 minute drive from Glasgow Airport. Close to Balloch railway station for trips to Glasgow City centre with its shops, restaurants and museums. Stirling and the Wallace Monument one hour's drive away.

1 Twin 1 Pub Bath/Show
1 Double

B&B per person
from £18.00 Single
from £16.00 Dbl/Twn

Open Jan-Dec excl Xmas/New Year

Balloch, Dunbartonshire — Map Ref: 1G4

★★★★ GUEST HOUSE

Gowanlea Guest House
Drymen Road, Balloch, Dunbartonshire, G83 8HS
Tel: 01389 752456 Fax: 01389 710543
Web: http://members.aol.com/gowanlea/gowanlea.htm

Situated in residential area of Balloch, close to world famous Loch Lomond. Friendly welcome. All rooms ensuite.

1 Twin
2 Double

All En Suite

B&B per person
from £20.00 Single
from £20.00 Dbl/Twn

Open Jan-Dec

★★★ GUEST HOUSE

Heathpete Guest House B&B
24 Balloch Road, Balloch, Dunbartonshire, G83 8LE
Tel: 01389 752195
E-mail: sheathpete@aol.com

Extended family bungalow in heart of village with all amenities close by. A few minutes walk to bus/rail stations, boat cruises and Country Park.

2 Double
2 Family

All En Suite

B&B per person
from £15.00 Single
from £15.00 Double

Open Jan-Dec

★★★ GUEST HOUSE

Kinnoul House
Drymen Road, Balloch, Dunbartonshire, G83 8HS
Tel/Fax: 01389 721116
E-mail: kinnoul-guesthouse.scotland@virgin.net
Web: http://freespace.virgin.net/kinnoul-guesthouse.scotland

Enjoy Scottish hospitality in this double Victorian house. Situated on an oak tree lined road at the quieter end of Balloch. Within walking distance of a variety of hotels, restaurants, Balloch Country Park and Loch Lomond itself. Within easy reach by car' Glasgow Airport 20 mins, Stirling 45 mins, Edinburgh 90 mins, Trossachs 30 mins. Oban 2 hrs. Balloch Railway Station has a half hourly service to and from Glasgow.

1 Twin
3 Double

3 En Suite fac
1 Priv.NOT ensuite

B&B per person
from £18.00 Dbl/Twn

Open Jan-Dec

Important: Prices stated are estimates and may be subject to amendments

Balloch, Dunbartonshire

Map Ref: 1G4

GUEST HOUSE

Norwood Guest House

60 Balloch Road, Balloch, Loch Lomond, Dunbartonshire, G83 8LE
Tel: 01389 750309 Fax: 01389 710469
E-mail: norwoodgh@aol.com

Centrally located overlooking Balloch Castle Country Park. Close to all local amenities including restaurants and shops.

2 Twin, 3 Double — All En Suite

B&B per person from £20.00 Single, from £18.00 Dbl/Twn

Open Jan-Dec

B&B

Sheildaig Farm

Upper Stoneymollen Road, Balloch, Alexandria, Dunbartonshire, G83 8QY
Tel: 01389 752459 Fax: 01389 753695
Mobile: 07711 317966
E-mail: sheildaig@talk21.com
Web: www.scotland2000.com/sheildaig

Totally refurbished farm courtyard buildings in secluded setting. Conveniently situated for touring Loch Lomond and the Trossachs. Easy access to A82 and Glasgow Airport. Candlelit dinners, with table license. 5 minutes from Balloch station with its service into Glasgow city centre.

3 Double — All En Suite

B&B per person from £40.00 Single, from £25.00 Double

Open Jan-Dec
B&B + Eve.Meal from £40.00

B&B

'Westville'

Riverside Lane, Balloch, Dunbartonshire, G83 8LF
Tel: 01389 752307

Mature bungalow, situated in quiet area of Balloch. Private parking. Overlooking the marina at River Leven at the southern end of Loch Lomond. A short flat stroll to shops, cruise boats and restaurants. Ideal location for touring to Inveraray, Oban, The Trossachs and Stirling with it's Castle.

1 Double, 1 Family — 1 Pub Bath/Show

B&B per person from £19.00 Single, from £18.00 Double

Open Jan-Dec excl Xmas/New Year

Balmaha, Stirlingshire

Map Ref: 1G4

B&B

Conic View Cottage

Balmaha Road, Balmaha, Stirlingshire, G63 0JQ
Tel: 01360 870297
Web: www.geocities.com/jenny_cronin

Modern bungalow in centre of village within sight of Loch Lomond. Convenient base for walking, touring, boating and fishing.

1 Single — 1 Priv.NOT ensuite
1 Double

B&B per person from £18.00 Single, from £18.00 Double

Open Mar-Nov

B&B

Critreoch

Rowardennen Road, Balmaha, by Drymen, Stirlingshire, G63 0AW
Tel: 01360 870309

Friendly family home in beautiful location set in mature gardens and close to shore of Loch Lomond, with magnificent views. West Highland Way crosses the foot of our drive. Ben Lomond the nearest Munro is 5 miles north of our home. Ideal base to tour Stirling, the Trossachs and Glasgow.

1 Twin — 1 En Suite fac
1 Double — 1 Priv.NOT ensuite

B&B per person from £25.00 Single, from £20.00 Dbl/Twn

Open May-Oct

VAT is shown at 17.5%: changes in this rate may affect prices.

Key to symbols is on back flap.

Balmaha, Stirlingshire

Map Ref: 1G4

★★★★ B&B

Mrs K MacFadyen

Dunleen, Milton of Buchanan, Balmaha, by Drymen, Stirlingshire, G63 OJE

Tel: 01360 870274

1 Twin, 1 Double | 1 Pub Bath/Show | B&B per person from £24.00 Single, £19.00-£20.00 Dbl/Twn | Open May-Oct

Comfortable modern ranch style home situated in secluded, lovely garden with a trout burn on its border that is overlooked by the guest lounge. On east side of Loch Lomond close to the West Highland Way. Rowardennan and Ben Lomond, the closest Munro are within 8 miles.

C W V

Balquhidder, Perthshire

Map Ref: 1H2

★★★★ B&B

Calea Sona

Balquhidder, Perthshire, FK19 8NY

Tel/Fax: 01877 384260

1 Twin, 1 Double | 1 En Suite fac, 1 Priv.NOT ensuite | B&B per person £28.00 Single, £23.00 Dbl/Twn | Open Jan-Dec excl Xmas

Cottage, an interesting blend of old and new, peacefully situated with superb views. Good walking area.

V

Benderloch, by Oban, Argyll

Map Ref: 1E2

★★★★ B&B

Barcaldine Castle

Benderloch, Oban, Argyll, PA37 1SA

Tel/Fax: 01631 720598

E-mail: barcaldine.castle@tesco.net

1 Double, 1 Family | 1 En Suite fac, 1 Priv.NOT ensuite | B&B per person from £25.00 Double

16th century tower house, the family seat of the Campbells of Barcaldine, set in an excellent location above the shores of Loch Creran, experience the delights of living in an historic building of considerable charm and character. Explore the secret passages and enjoy bed and breakfast with a difference.

C £ V

Blairlogie, by Stirling

Map Ref: 2A3

★★ B&B

Mrs Margaret Logan Farmhouse B&B

Blairmains Farm, Manor Loan, Blairlogie, Stirling

Tel: 01259 761338/07909 900481 (mobile)

2 Twin, 1 Double | 1 Pub Bath/Show | B&B per person from £20.00 Single, from £18.00 Dbl/Twn, Room only per person from £16.00 | Open Jan-Dec excl Xmas/New Year

Tradtional stone farmhouse on working dairy farm next to small conservation village. Close to Wallace Monument and University. Only five miles from Stirling. Ideal base for walkers touring central Scotland.

C V

Brig O'Turk, Perthshire

Map Ref: 1H3

★★★ B&B

Burnt Inn House

Brig o'Turk, by Callander, Perthshire, FK17 8HT

Tel: 01877 376212 Fax: 01877 376233

E-mail: burntinnhouse@aol.com

2 Twin, 1 Double | All En Suite | B&B per person from £20.00 Single, from £20.00 Dbl/Twn, Room only per person from £18.00 | Open Jan-Dec excl Xmas/New Year

Former Coach House dating back to the 1850's now recently refurbished family home offering comfortable en-suite accommodation. Set in the midst of the Trossachs with views to Ben Venue & Queen Elizabeth Forest Park. Enjoy breakfast in our traditional farmhouse kitchen, complete with welcoming Aga.

W V

Important: Prices stated are estimates and may be subject to amendments

Brig O'Turk, Perthshire

Map Ref: 1H3

★★★★ B&B

Frennich House
Brig o'Turk, Callander, Perthshire, FK17 8HD
Tel: 01877 376274

1 Twin Private fac
1 Double Ensuite fac

B&B per person
from £20.00 Single
from £20.00 Dbl/Twn

Open Apr-Oct

Frennich House is located in a secluded riverside position amidst 3 acres of mixed woodland, 7 miles from Callander in the heart of the scenic Trossachs. No Smoking.

Buchlyvie, Stirlingshire

Map Ref: 1H4

★★★ B&B

Gartinstarry
Buchlyvie, Stirlingshire, FK8 3PD
Tel/Fax: 01360 850252
E-mail: janey.leslie@ntlworld.com

2 Twin All En Suite

B&B per person
from £25.00 Single
from £20.00 Twin
Room only per person
from £20.00

Open Jan-Dec excl Xmas

Late 18th Century historic house in peaceful rural setting near Loch Lomond, Trossachs and Stirling. All accommodation on ground floor level.

Ascog, Isle of Bute

Map Ref: 1F5

★★★★ B&B

Mrs Watson
Ascog Farm, Ascog, Rothesay, Isle of Bute, PA20 9LL
Tel: 01700 503372

3 Single 2 Pub Bath/Show
1 Double

B&B per person
£17.00 Single
£17.00 Double
Room only per person
£17.00

Open Jan-Dec

A well appointed sympathetically restored 200-year-old farmhouse in a peaceful setting. Log fires and friendly welcome, come and be spoilt.

Rothesay, Isle of Bute

Map Ref: 1F5

★★★ GUEST HOUSE

The Commodore
12 Battery Place, Rothesay, Isle of Bute, PA20 9DP
Tel/Fax: 01700 502178

3 Twin All En Suite
3 Double

B&B per person
from £22.00 Single
from £18.00 Dbl/Twn
Room only per person
from £15.00 (sharing)

Open Jan-Dec

We are friendly and family run and are recommended by "Which" Good B&B Guide. Walking distance from pier and town centre.

Callander, Perthshire

Map Ref: 1H3

★★★ B&B

Almardon
Leny Road, Callander, Perthshire, FK17 8AJ
Tel: 01877 331597
E-mail: almardon@lenyroad.freeserve.co.uk

1 Twin All En Suite
2 Double

B&B per person
from £20.00 Dbl/Twn

Open Jan-Dec excl Xmas/New Year

Enjoy a relaxing stay in our spacious bungalow at the west end of town. Adjacent to Meadows Park and River Teith yet only minutes from shopping area and other amenities. Comfortable en-suite bedrooms with tea/coffee facilities, colour T.V, radio/alarm, hairdryer and iron. Ample parking within own grounds. Callander is so centrally situated, it makes an ideal base for touring the Central Highlands, walking, climbing and cycling.

VAT is shown at 17.5%: changes in this rate may affect prices.

Key to symbols is on back flap.

Callander, Perthshire — **Map Ref: 1H3**

★★★ GUEST HOUSE

Annfield Guest House
North Church Street, Callander, Perthshire, FK17 8EG
Tel: 01877 330204

2 Twin, 5 Double, 1 Family | 4 En Suite fac, 1 Priv.NOT ensuite, 2 Pub Bath/Show | B&B per person from £25.00 Single, from £21.00 Dbl/Twn | Open mid Jan-Dec excl Xmas

Centrally situated in a quiet area of the town in close proximity to shops and restaurants. Stepping stone to the Highlands.

C £ W V

★★★★ GUEST HOUSE

Arden House
Bracklinn Road, Callander, Perthshire, FK17 8EQ
Tel/Fax: 01877 330235
Web: www.SmoothHound.co.uk/hotels/arden.html

1 Single, 2 Twin, 2 Double, 1 Suite | All En Suite | B&B per person from £30.00 Single, from £27.50 Dbl/Twn | Open Mar-Nov

Elegant Victorian country house, peacefully set in attractive gardens with marvellous views of hills and countryside. Home of BBC TV's 'Dr Finlay's Casebook'. Ideal base for touring the Trossachs and western highlands.

TV P £ V

★★★★ B&B

Bennachie
19 Livingstone Avenue, Callander, Perthshire, FK17 8EP
Tel: 01877 330633

2 Twin | All En Suite | B&B per person from £20.00 Twin | Open Mar-Oct

Modern bungalow in quiet cul de sac overlooking golf course. Within walking distance of town centre and all amenities.

P W V

★★★ B&B

Bridgend Cottage
Kilmahog, Callander, Perthshire, FK17 8HD
Tel: 01877 330385

1 Twin, 2 Double | All En Suite | B&B per person £20.00-£22.00 Dbl/Twn | Open Jan-Dec

One mile from the Falls of Leny where the salmon leap. This traditional stone built gamekeepers cottage is set in a pretty, natural garden overlooking the river. Ideal base for touring the Trossachs. Lots of outdoor activities including hillwalking, cycling, private salmon fishing and golf.

TV P C V

★★★★ GUEST HOUSE

Brook Linn Country House
Leny Feus, Callander, Perthshire, FK17 8AU
Tel/Fax: 01877 330103
E-mail: derek@blinn.freeserve.co.uk
Web: www.brooklinn-scotland.co.uk

2 Single, 2 Twin, 2 Double, 1 Family | 6 En Suite fac, 1 Priv.NOT ensuite | B&B per person from £20.00 Single, from £20.00 Dbl/Twn | Open Easter-Oct

Comfortable, quiet family run Victorian house set in two acres of gardens with magnificent views. Short distance from town centre and all facilities. Non-smoking.

TV P C £ W V

Important: Prices stated are estimates and may be subject to amendments

Callander, Perthshire — Map Ref: 1H3

GUEST HOUSE

East Mains House

Manse Lane, Bridgend, Callander, Perthshire, FK17 8AG
Tel/Fax: 01877 330535
E-mail: east.mains@tesco.net

4 Double, 2 Family — 4 En Suite fac, 2 Priv.NOT ensuite, 1 Pub Bath/Show — B&B per person from £24.00 Single, from £22.00 Double — Open Jan-Dec

Built in 1773, East Mains is now a family run guesthouse, offering a range of comfortable accommodation. There is a large garden and ample off street parking. Located in Bridgend, the oldest part of Callander it is the ideal base from which to tour the Trossachs and Loch Lomond.

B&B

Mrs Megan Hughes

White Cottage, Bracklinn Road, Callander, Perthshire, FK17 8EQ
Tel: 01877 330896

2 Double — 1 Pub Bath/Show — B&B per person £22.00-£25.00 Single, £17.50 Double — Open Apr-Nov

Set within an acre of mature garden in elevated position 15 mins walk from Bracklinn Falls and town centre. Commanding views towards Ben Ledi and the Trossachs.

INVERTROSSACHS COUNTRY HOUSE

Invertrossachs, by Callander, Perthshire FK17 8HG
Telephone: 01877 331126 Fax: 01877 331229
e.mail: res@invertrossachs.freeserve.co.uk Web: www.invertrossachs.co.uk

Relax in the comfort of our elegant private country house. Stunning setting by Loch Venacher in the beautiful Trossachs. Perfect base for touring, offering walking, cycling and fishing in woodland estate with golf and sailing nearby. Also available self-catering apartments and cottage. Advanced booking recommended.

★★★★ B&B

B&B

Invertrossachs Country House

Invertrossachs, by Callander, Perthshire, FK17 8HG
Tel: 01877 331126
Fax: 01877 331229
E.mail: res@invertrossachs.freeserve.co.uk
Web: www.invertrossachs.co.uk

2 Rooms — Suites available — B&B per person £55.00-£85.00 Single, £39.50-£75.00 Dbl/Twn — Open Jan-Dec

Comfortable large rooms and suites within an Edwardian mansion offering country house bed & breakfast and enjoying privacy and seclusion by the shores of Loch Venachar. Spacious accommodation with outstanding loch or mountain views.

Callander, Perthshire — Map Ref: 1H3

LENY HOUSE

★★★★★ B&B

Callander, Perthshire FK17 8HA
Tel: 01877 331078 Fax: 01877 331335
e.mail: res@lenyestate.com Web: www.lenyestate.com

Historic Leny House, a family country mansion in Parkland. Paddocks with goats, sheep, horses. Built 1513, fortified 1691, extended 1845, restored 1999. First used for B&B by the Jacobites marching to the rebellion in 1745!! Magnificent views to mountains and glens. Private glen with abundant wildlife for intrepid visitors. Spacious, Victorian four poster bedrooms, with luxury ensuites. Antiques, tapestries, grand piano, baronial surroundings, open fires, warm welcomes. Own estate pub, restaurant and ceilidh music. Luxury self-catering also. Recommended by numerous books and guides including Which magazine. Winner of the Automobile Association Guest Accommodation of the year for Scotland and Ireland. Central for both coasts. Tranquil retreat to unwind. Enjoy our home with us. Price from £45.

★★★★★ B&B

Leny House
Leny Estate, Callander, Perthshire, FK17 8HA
Tel: 01877 331078 Fax: 01877 331335
E-mail: res@lenyestate.com
Web: www.lenyestate.com

1 Twin, 2 Double — All En Suite — B&B per person from £45.00 Dbl/Twn — Open Mar-Oct

A Jacobite Country House in the midst of idyllic rural scenery in the new National Park. Fascinating history and of architectural importance. Recently restored in close consultation with Historic Scotland to recreate rooms of Authentic Victorian Luxury. Ideal quiet location for walking and outdoor pursuits or just to relax. 'Winner of AA Best Accommodation in Scotland & N.Ireland Award'.

£ W V

★★★ B&B

Lenymede Bed & Breakfast
Leny Road, Callander, Perthshire, FK17 8AJ
Tel: 01877 330952 Fax: 08700 560464
Web: www.scotlands-best.com

2 Double, 1 Family — 1 En Suite fac, 1 Pub Bath/Show — B&B per person from £25.00 Single, from £18.00 Double — Open Jan-Dec excl Xmas

Relaxed,informal atmosphere in this spacious Victorian family home in mature grounds leading to river. Ground floor bedroom. One ground floor ensuite room.

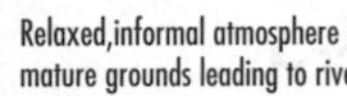

C W V

★★★★ SMALL HOTEL

Lubnaig Hotel
Leny Feus, Callander, Perthshire, FK17 8AS
Tel/Fax: 01877 330376
Web: www.lubnaighotel.co.uk

5 Twin, 5 Double — All En Suite — B&B per person from £30.00 Dbl/Twn — Open Apr-Oct

A relaxing family run country house, enhanced by its secluded location, large garden, private parking and within easy walking distance of the town centre. A genuine Scottish welcome awaits all guests. We offer a stress free holiday to enjoy Scotland.

£ V

Callander, Perthshire

Map Ref: 1H3

★★★★ B&B

The Misk
9 Katrine Crescent, Callander, Perthshire, FK17 8JR
Tel: 01877 330396

1 Twin | All En Suite | B&B per person from £20.00 Single from £20.00 Twin | Open Apr-Oct

A warm Scottish welcome assured in this friendly family home. Ground floor ensuite accommodation overlooking open farmland in modern house situated in quiet residential area on outskirts of town.

★★★ GUEST HOUSE

M Morgan
Dunmore, Leny Road, Callander, FK17 8AL
Tel: 01877 330756

1 Twin, 3 Double | All En Suite | B&B per person from £25.00 Single from £20.00 Dbl/Twn | Open Mar-Oct

A warm welcome at this traditional detached Victorian villa, overlooking Riverside Park. 5 minute walk from town centre and local amenities. Ample private parking.

★★★ GUEST HOUSE

Riverview Guest House
Leny Road, Callander, Perthshire, FK17 8AL
Tel/Fax: 01877 330635
Web: www.nationalparkscotland.co.uk

1 Single, 2 Twin, 2 Double | All En Suite | B&B per person from £21.00 Single from £21.00 Dbl/Twn | Open Feb-Dec B&B + Eve.Meal from £32.00

Detached stone built Victorian house set in its own garden with private parking. Close to town centre, leisure complex and local amenities. Within easy walking distance of pleasant riverside park and cycle track. Ideal base for exploring the beautiful Trossachs. Cycle storage available.

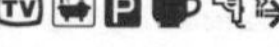

★★★★ GUEST HOUSE

Southfork Villa
25 Cross Street, Callander, Perthshire, FK17 8EA
Tel: 01877 330831

2 Twin, 2 Double, 2 Family | All Ensuite fac | B&B per person from £25.00 Single from £20.00 Dbl/Twn | Open Jan-Dec B&B + Eve.Meal from £32.50

Detached modern family home in centre of Callander. Ample secure private off-street parking. Local amenities and leisure centre close by. Ideal base for exploring the Trossachs. Outdoor activities including pony trekking, cycling and hillwalking. A warm welcome awaits.

★★★ B&B

Trean Farm
Callander, Perthshire, FK17 8AS
Tel/Fax: 01877 331160
E-mail: janette_trean@hotmail.com

1 Twin, 2 Double | 2 En Suite fac, 1 Priv.NOT ensuite | B&B per person £19.00-£21.00 Dbl/Twn | Open May-Oct

Farmhouse situated on a 235 acre working farm on the outskirts of Callander. Magnificent views of Ben Ledi. Within an easy 15 minutes walk to the town centre.

Campbeltown, Argyll

Map Ref: 1D7

★★★

B&B

Christlach Farmhouse

Southend, Kintyre, Argyll, PA28 6PJ
Tel: 01586 830664
E-mail: scotholidayskintyre@talk21.com

Rooms	Facilities	Prices	Open
1 Double 1 Family	2 Priv.NOT ensuite	B&B per person from £19.00 Single from £19.00 Double	Open Apr-Oct

A very warm welcome at this large traditional family run farmhouse in a countryside location. Surrounded by grassy fields and open views. 2 miles to safe sandy beach. Many interesting walks. Children and pets welcome. 2 Golf courses within an 8 mile radius. Evening meals available and special dietary requirements can be catered for.

★★

GUEST HOUSE

Mrs J. Scott-Dodd

Rosemount, Low Askomil, Campbeltown, Argyll, PA28 6EP
Tel: 01586 553552

Rooms	Facilities	Prices	Open
1 Twin 3 Double 1 Family	All En Suite	B&B per person from £25.00 Single from £21.00 Dbl/Twn	Open Jan-Dec

Georgian B listed home in elevated position with magnificent views over Campbeltown Loch and 10 minutes walk from town centre. Annexe cottage suite.

★★★

GUEST HOUSE

Westbank Guest House

Dell Road, Campbeltown, PA28 6JG
Tel/Fax: 01586 553660

Rooms	Facilities	Prices	Open
1 Single 2 Twin 3 Double 1 Family	5 En Suite fac 2 Priv.NOT ensuite	B&B per person from £23.00 Single from £18.00 Dbl/Twn	Open Jan-Dec

A well maintained Victorian villa in a quiet residential area, near to Machrihanish Golf Course. An ideal base for touring. 3 minutes walk to all town centre restaurants, shops and attractions.

Carradale, Argyll

Map Ref: 1E6

★★

B&B

Mains Farm

Carradale, Argyll, PA28 6QG
Tel: 01583 431216

Rooms	Facilities	Prices	Open
1 Single 1 Double 1 Family	1 Pub Bath/Show	B&B per person from £17.50 Single from £17.50 Double	Open Apr-Oct

Traditional farmhouse on working farm, on the outskirts of the village and a short walk from the beach. Panoramic views across to the Isle of Arran, near golf, fishing and forest walks. Restaurants available within walking distance.

Carron Bridge, Stirlingshire

Map Ref: 2A4

★

INN

Carronbridge Hotel

Carronbridge, by Denny, Stirlingshire, FK6 5JG
Tel: 01324 823459

Rooms	Facilities	Prices	Open
1 Twin 1 Double 1 Family	All En Suite	B&B per person from £25.00 Single from £20.00 Dbl/Twn	Open Jan-Dec

Family run hotel situated in picturesque Carron Valley. Ideal base for touring.

Important: Prices stated are estimates and may be subject to amendments

Bridge, Stirlingshire Map Ref: 2A4

Drum Farm

Carronbridge, Stirling, Stirlingshire FK6 5JL
Telephone and Fax: 01324 825518
e.mail: drumfarm@ndirect.co.uk Web: www.ndirect.co.uk/~drumfarm

Beautiful 200 year-old farmhouse situated in unspoilt countryside with views overlooking Carron Dam, just 15 minutes from Stirling and the M9 and M80, where you can start your tours around this beautiful part of Scotland.

B&B

Drum Farm
Carronbridge, Denny, Stirlingshire, FK6 5JL
Tel/Fax: 01324 825518
E.mail: drumfarm@ndirect.co.uk
Web: www.ndirect.co.uk/~drumfarm

1 Twin
1 Double

1 En Suite fac
1 Priv.NOT ensuite

B&B per person
from £28.00 Single
£19.00-£22.00 Dbl/Twn

Open Jan-Dec
B&B + Eve.Meal
£28.00-£31.00

Beautiful farmhouse situated in unspoilt countryside with views overlooking Carron Dam. Just 15 minutes from Stirling and the M9 & M80 where you can start your tours around this beautiful part of Scotland.

Coll, Isle of, Argyll Map Ref: 1B1

★★★

B&B

Achamore
Isle of Coll, Argyll, PA78 6TE
Tel: 01879 230430
E-mail: Jim@achamore.freeserve.co.uk

1 Twin
1 Double
can be a
family rm

2 Pub Bath/Show

B&B per person
from £19.00 Single
from £19.00 Dbl/Twn

Open Jan-Dec
B&B + Eve.Meal
from £29.00

Comfortably refurbished to a high standard, an old stone farmhouse, well placed for exploring this quiet and beautiful isle and half a mile from 9 hole golf course. Diving instruction available. Transport to and from ferry available. Evening meals available by prior arrangement, vegetarians catered for and pets welcome.

Connel, Argyll Map Ref: 1E2

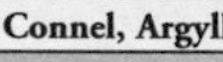

B&B

Ach-na-Craig
Grosvenor Crescent, Connel, PA37 1PQ
Tel: 01631 710588

2 Twin
1 Double

All En Suite

B&B per person
£18.00-£19.00 Dbl/Twn

Open Apr-Oct

Ach-na-craig is a modern family run house within a peaceful wooded glade in the quiet village of Connel, located 5 miles (8kms) from Oban. All rooms, including bedrooms are at ground floor level. There is ample secure parking.

VAT is shown at 17.5%: changes in this rate may affect prices.

Key to symbols is on back flap.

Connel, Argyll

Map Ref: 1E2

KILCHURN

Kilchurn, Connel, Argyll PA37 1PG
Telephone: 01631 710581 e.mail: kilchurn@msn.com

Kilchurn is a detached villa situated on the A85 over-looking Loch Etive and Ben Lora in the picturesque village of Connel which is 5 miles from Oban. The comfortable accommodation is decorated to a high standard and there is ample private parking.

B&B

Kilchurn
Connel, by Oban, Argyll, PA37 1PG
Tel: 01631 710581
E-mail: kilchurn@msn.com

1 Twin
2 Double

All En Suite

B&B per person
from £18.00 Dbl/Twn

Open Apr-Oct

Expect to receive a warm welcome into this family run Victorian villa, located on the edge of Connel village with pleasant views across Loch Etive, toward Ben Lora, and the Connel Bridge. Several hotels nearby for evening meals. House is well placed for exploring Oban, Kintyre, the islands and north towards Fort William.

W V

GUEST HOUSE

Ronebhal Guest House
Connel, by Oban, Argyll, PA37 1PJ
Tel: 01631 710310/813 Fax: 01631 710310
E-mail: ronebhal@btinternet.com
Web: www.argyllinternet.co.uk/ronebhal

1 Twin
3 Double
1 Family

4 En Suite fac
1 Priv.NOT ensuite

B&B per person
£20.00-£30.00 Single
£20.00-£28.50 Dbl/Twn
Room only per person
£18.00-£24.50

Open Feb-Nov

Victorian house with private parking. Magnificent views of Loch Etive and mountains beyond. Oban 5 miles (8kms).

C £ W V

B&B

Rosebank
Connel, by Oban, Argyll, PA37 1PA
Tel: 01631 710316

1 Single
1 Twin
1 Double

1 Pub Bath/Show

B&B per person
from £15.00 Single
from £14.00 Dbl/Twn

Open May-Sep

A warm welcome is to be expected into this family home in the heart of Connel village, close to hotels, post office and local shops. Railway station 100 metres walk. Oban 6 miles (9 km). Pets welcome.

C

Important: Prices stated are estimates and may be subject to amendments

Craobh Haven, by Lochgilphead, Argyll — Map Ref: 1E3

BUIDHE LODGE

Craobh Haven, by Lochgilphead, Argyll PA31 8UA
Tel: 01852 500291 e.mail: simone@buidhelodge.com
Web: www.buidhelodge.com

Beautiful Swiss-style lodge on perfect sealoch-side setting. Excellent home cooking, carefully selected wines. All six rooms ground level and ensuite. National Trust gardens, historic sites and boat trips nearby. Lodge featured in Which? Good Bed and Breakfast Guide.
Phone Nick or Simone for colour brochure. Let us spoil you!

GUEST HOUSE

Buidhe Lodge

Craobh Haven, by Lochgilphead, Argyll, PA31 8UA
Tel: 01852 500291
E-mail: simone@buidhelodge.com
Web: www.buidhelodge.com

Architect designed, timber lodge Guest House, on unique peaceful island setting connected by causeway to village. Evening meal by prior arrangement. Ideal for touring West Coast of Scotland.

Rooms	Facilities	Prices	Opening
4 Twin 2 Double	All En Suite	B&B per person from £33.00 Single from £23.00 Dbl/Twn	Open Jan-Dec excl Xmas B&B + Eve.Meal from £38.00

Lunga Estate

Craobh Haven, Argyll PA31 8QR
Telephone: 01852 500237 Fax 01852 500639
e.mail: colin@lunga.demon.co.uk

Lunga, a 17th-century mansion overlooking Firth of Lorne and Sound of Jura, home to the MacDougalls for over 300 years, who offer comfortable rooms for Bed and Breakfast and self-catering flats or cottages. Join us for our famous candle-lit dinners and share the facilities of this beautiful 3,000-acre coastal estate.

B&B

C Lindsay-MacDougall of Lunga

Lunga, Ardfern,by Lochgilphead, Argyll, PA31 8QR
Tel: 01852 500237 Fax: 01852 500639
E-mail: colin@lunga.demon.co.uk

18c mansion house on 3000 acre estate. Riding, fishing, sailing and hill-walking available. Annexe accommodation. Evening meal by arrangement.

Rooms	Facilities	Prices	Opening
1 Single 1 Twin 2 Double	All En Suite 1 Pub Bath/Show	B&B per person £17.50-£22.00 Single £17.50-£22.00 Dbl/Twn Room only per person £13.00-£16.50	Open Jan-Dec

Crianlarich, Perthshire

Map Ref: 1G2

B&B

Dunfraoich

Crianlarich, Perthshire, FK20 8RS
Tel: 01838 300277

1 Twin — 2 En Suite fac
2 Double — 1 Pub Bath/Show

A warm welcome in our traditional home in Crianlarich on the West Highland Way. Ideal location for touring a wide area of Scotland. Convenient for all public transport links.

GUEST HOUSE

Glenardran House

Crianlarich, Perthshire, FK20 8QS
Tel/Fax: 01838 300236
Web: www.championinternet.com/glenardran/

2 Twin — All En Suite
2 Double

B&B per person
from £30.00 Single
from £20.00 Dbl/Twn

Open Jan-Dec excl Xmas/New Year

Very comfortable late Victorian house in centre of village close to West Highland Way. Excellent base for touring, walking or climbing. Non-smoking.

Dalmally, Argyll

Map Ref: 1F2

★★★ GUEST HOUSE

Craig Villa Guest House

Dalmally, Argyll, PA33 1AX
Tel/Fax: 01838 200255
E.mail: craigvilla@loch-awe.com
Web: www.SmoothHound.co.uk/hotels/craigvilla.html

Personally run guest house in own grounds amidst breathtaking scenery. Good touring base. Home cooking. Evening meal by arrangement.

2 Twin, 2 Double, 2 Family | 5 En Suite fac, 1 Priv.NOT ensuite | B&B per person from £25.00 Single, from £19.00 Dbl/Twn | Open Easter-Oct, B&B + Eve.Meal from £31.50

★★ B&B

Cruachan

Monument Hill, Dalmally, Argyll, PA33 1AA
Tel: 01838 200496 Fax: 01838 200650
E-mail: mike@cruachan-dalmally.co.uk
Web: www.cruachan-dalmally.co.uk

Comfortable victorian family home in peaceful village offers warm welcome and excellent home cooking. Wonderful mountain views and walks. 2 ground floor en-suite rooms.

1 Twin, 2 Double | 2 En Suite fac, 1 Priv.NOT ensuite | B&B per person from £20.00 Single, from £16.50 Dbl/Twn | Open Jan-Dec, B&B + Eve.Meal from £29.00

★★★ B&B

Mrs MacDougall

Strathorchy, Dalmally, Argyll, PA33 1AE
Tel/Fax: 01838 200373

Recently built traditional style house in countryside setting beside No 1 tee on golf course. Good base for touring Argyll, the glens and islands. Close to the beautiful Kilchurn Castle at the head of Loch Awe. Walkers and cyclists welcome. Ideal base for Munro Baggers with 5 in the surrounding area. Loch fishing nearby.

1 Twin, 2 Double | 2 En Suite fac, 1 Pub Bath/Show | B&B per person £16.00-£19.00 Single, £16.00-£19.00 Dbl/Twn | Open Jan-Dec

★★ GUEST HOUSE

Orchy Bank

Dalmally, Argyll, PA33 1AS
Tel: 01838 200370
E-mail: aj.burke@talk21.com

Victorian House situated on the bans of the River Orchy and surrounded on 3 sides by mountains over 3000 feet. Fishing, golf, walking and bird-watching. Within 2 hours of Stirling, Glasgow, Fort William, Perth, Campbeltown and half an hour from Oban and Inveraray. Pets welcome.

2 Single, 2 Twin, 1 Double, 2 Family | 4 Pub Bath/Show | B&B per person from £17.00 Single, from £17.00 Dbl/Twn | Open Jan-Dec excl Xmas/New Year

VAT is shown at 17.5%: changes in this rate may affect prices.

Key to symbols is on back flap.

Dalmally, Argyll — Map Ref: 1F2

★★★

B&B

Portinnisherrich
Southeast Lochawe Side, by Dalmally, Argyll, PA33 1BW
Tel: 01866 844202

2 Family — All En Suite — B&B per person £19.00-£22.00 Double — Open Apr-Sep B&B + Eve.Meal £35.00-£38.00

Working farm peacefully situated on Lochaweside. Ideally positioned for forest walks and bird watching. Own jetty provides boating, fishing and sailing.

Dollar, Clackmannanshire — Map Ref: 2B3

★

B&B

The Lorne Tavern
17 Argyll Street, Dollar, Clackmannanshire, FK14 7AR
Tel: 01259 743423 Fax: 01259 743065
E-mail: jimnelson@talk21.com

Rooms	Facilities	B&B per person	Open
2 Single	with Washbasin	£15.00-£25.00 Single	Open Jan-Dec
1 Twin	Washbasin/Shower	£12.00-£18.00 Dbl/Twn	
1 Double	1 Pub Bath/Show		

Simple accommodation in rooms above friendly pub in the 'Old Town'.

Doune, Perthshire — Map Ref: 2A3

★★★★

B&B

Glenardoch House
Castle Road, Doune, Perthshire, FK16 6EA
Tel: 01786 841489

2 Double — All En Suite — B&B per person from £35.00 Single from £22.50 Double — Open May-Sep

Charming traditional 18th century stone built house by historical Doune Castle. Set in its own riverside gardens, with views of the old bridge. Peaceful location. Excellent base for exploring the Trossachs and Western Highlands.

Doune, Perthshire — **Map Ref: 2A3**

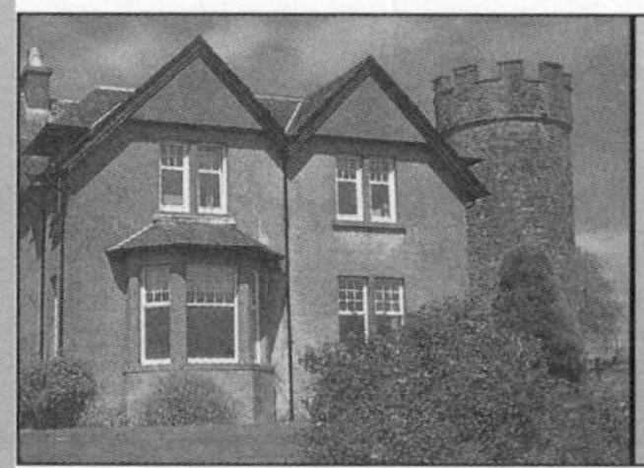

Inverardoch Farm House

INVERARDOCH MAINS FARM, DOUNE (B824), DUNBLANE FK15 9NZ

Telephone: 01786 841268

Working farm over looking Doune Castle with beautiful views from the bedrooms. Close to Doune Antique Centre and Safari Park. 4 miles from Dunblane and Bridge of Allan. 8 miles from Stirling and the Trossachs.

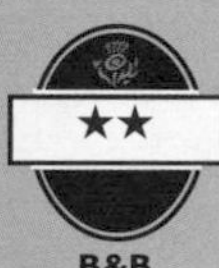

B&B

Inverardoch Farm House
Inverardoch Mains Farm, Doune (B824), Dunblane, Perthshire, FK15 9NZ
Tel: 01786 841268

1 Twin, 2 Double — 2 Limited ensuite, 1 Pub Bath/Show — B&B per person from £20.00 Single, from £20.00 Dbl/Twn — Open Apr-Oct

Tradtional rural farmhouse on a 200 acre working farm. In a pleasant rural setting with views over Doune Castle, Ben Ledi and the Campsie Hills. Convenient for Blair Drummond Safari Park and M9 motorway.

C W V

Drymen, Stirlingshire — **Map Ref: 1H4**

★★

RESTAURANT WITH ROOMS

Drymen Tandoori & Hotel
5-7 Stirling Road, Drymen, G63 0BW
Tel: 01360 660099 Fax: 01360 661162
Web: www.drymen-tandoori.co.uk

1 Single, 2 Twin, 2 Double — 1 Pub Bath/Show — B&B per person from £20.00 Single, from £20.00 Dbl/Twn — Open Jan-Dec, B&B + Eve.Meal from £33.00

One of the original village buildings, just off the square, this popular Indian restaurant is an ideal stop off point for West Highland Way walkers.

C £ W V

B&B

Easter Drumquhassle Farm
Gartness Road, Drymen, Stirlingshire, G63 0DN
Tel: 01360 660893 Fax: 01360 660282
Web: http://members.aol.com/juliamacx

1 Twin, 1 Double, 1 Family — All En Suite — B&B per person from £26.00 Single, from £18.50 Dbl/Twn — Open Jan-Dec, B&B + Eve.Meal from £27.50

Studio-type bedroom and accommodation in main house. Ideal base for touring Loch Lomond area. Quiet rural location. Spectacular views. Come and be well fed.

C W V

B&B

Elmbank
10 Stirling Road, Drymen, Stirlingshire, G63 0BN
Tel: 01360 660403

1 Single, 4 Twin, 1 Double — B&B per person from £25.00 Single, from £20.00 Dbl/Twn — Open Jan-Dec

Self-contained accommodation on first and second floors of traditional stone house in the centre of the village, run personally by the owners who live beneath, on the ground floor. Comfortable relaxed atmosphere.

Drymen, Stirlingshire — **Map Ref: 1H4**

HOTEL

Winnock Hotel

The Square, Drymen, Loch Lomond, G63 0BL
Tel: 01360 660245 Fax: 01360 660136
E-mail: winnockhotel@ic24.net
Web: www.winnockhotel.com

Traditional coaching Inn, dating in parts from early 18th C, situated centrally on the village green.

4 Single	All En Suite	B&B per person	Open Jan-Dec
16 Twin		from £49.00 Single	
21 Double		from £32.50 Dbl/Twn	
6 Family			

Dunblane, Perthshire — **Map Ref: 2A3**

Rokeby House

Doune Road, Dunblane
FK15 9AT
Tel: 01786 824447
Fax: 01786 821399

Web: http://www.aboutscotland.com/stirling/rokeby.html

Fine period Scottish country house set on the outskirts of this delightful village within walking distance of the Allan Water, the mediaeval cathedral and the old town. Personal warm friendly service in a very comfortable home where guests are made welcome with old fashioned hospitality. Guests may enjoy delicious home-cooking served in our lovely dining-room all offered at extremely good value. The gardens are being lovingly restored to their former splendour. Ideal for touring Stirling and The Trossachs. Edinburgh and Glasgow are less than one hour by train or car. Personally managed by the enthusiastic owner.

B&B

Rokeby House

Doune Road, Dunblane, Perthshire, FK15 9AT
Tel: 01786 824447 Fax: 01786 821399
Web: www.aboutscotland.com/stirling/rokeby.html

Charming Edwardian country house set in delightful gardens carefully restored by present owner. Situated within a 5 minute walk to the heart of the old town. Ideal base for exploring historic Stirling. Outdoor activities include fishing, hillwalking and water sports. A warm welcome within this opulent home of great character.

1 Twin	All En Suite	B&B per person	Open Jan-Dec
2 Double		from £65.00 Single	B&B + Eve.Meal
		from £45.00 Dbl/Twn	from £70.00

Dunoon, Argyll — **Map Ref: 1F5**

HOTEL

The Anchorage Hotel & Restaurant

Shore Road, Sandbank, Dunoon, Argyll, PA23 8QG
Tel: 01369 705108 Fax: 0870 7061099
E-mail: info@anchorage.co.uk

Stylish traditional stone villa c.1870 with magnificent open views over Holy Loch. Easy access from ferry terminal. High standard of service and accommodation.

1 Twin	All En Suite	B&B per person	Open Dec-Oct
4 Double		from £55.00 Dbl/Twn	

Important: Prices stated are estimates and may be subject to amendments

Dunoon, Argyll

Map Ref: 1F5

HOTEL

Enmore Hotel

Marine Parade, Kirn, Dunoon, Argyll, PA23 8HH
Tel: 01369 702230 Fax: 01369 702148
E-mail: enmorehotel@btinternet.com
Web: www.enmorehotel.co.uk

Personal attention assured at this elegant Georgian House set in its own garden overlooking the Firth of Clyde. Each room tastefully decorated and furnished to create a relaxing atmosphere. Award winning restaurant and Taste of Scotland member. Squash courts. Some bedrooms with their own double Jacuzzi/spa bath.

1 Single
3 Twin
5 Double
1 Family

All En Suite

B&B per person
from £35.00 Single
from £35.00 Dbl/Twn

Open Jan-Dec
B&B + Eve.Meal
from £60.00

B&B

Foxbank

Marine Parade, Hunters' Quay, Dunoon, PA23 8HJ
Tel: 01369 703858
E-mail: lawther:breathemail.net

A warm Scottish welcome assured in this comfortable family home on promenade overlooking the Firth of Clyde. Hearty breakfasts and evening meals. Fifteen minutes walk to town centre and convenient for both ferries.

2 Twin
1 Family

2 Pub Bath/Show

B&B per person
from £17.00 Single
from £17.00 Twin

Open Jan-Dec
B&B + Eve.Meal
from £24.00

Falkirk, Stirlingshire

Map Ref: 2A4

GUEST HOUSE

Ashbank Guest House

105 Main Street, Redding, Falkirk, Stirlingshire, FK2 9UQ
Tel: 01324 716649 Fax: 01324 712431
E-mail: ashbank@guest-house.freeserve.co.uk
Web: www.bandbfalkirk.com

Victorian family home - all rooms recently refurbished. North facing with views over Forth Valley to Braveheart country. Situated midway between Edinburgh & Glasgow. Ample off street parking.

1 Twin
2 Double

All En Suite fac

B&B per person
£23.00-£35.00 Single
£20.00-£25.00 Dbl/Twn

Open Jan-Dec
Evening meal on request.

B&B

Benaiah Bed & Breakfast

11 Culmore Place, Falkirk, FK1 2RP
Tel: 01324 621223 Mobile: 07718 300530/07931616854
E-mail: benaiahbb@falkirkscotland.fsbusiness.co.uk

Pleasant, friendly B&B with lovely views in quiet cul de sac on the outskirts of town - 2 1/2 miles from town centre. Only 1/2 hours travel to Edinburgh and Glasgow, and 1/4 hour to Stirling makes this an ideal base for touring central Scotland.

1 Twin
2 Family

1 Pub Bath/Show

B&B per person
£18.00-£25.00 Single
£15.00-£20.00 Dbl/Twn

Open Jan-Dec

B&B

Anna Burnside

Arbuthnot House, Dorrator Road, Falkirk, FK1 4BN
Tel: 01324 634785
E-mail: annaburnsi@yahoo.com
Web: www.milford.co.uk/go/arbuthnothouse.html

Large family home situated in mature gardens in a quiet peaceful location with a friendly relaxing atmosphere. Ample and safe off street parking. Within easy reach of Edinburgh and Glasgow by road or rail and only 10 miles from Stirling-makes an ideal base to explore Scotland.

2 Twin
1 Double

Ensuite fac
Private fac

B&B per person
from £25.00 Single
from £22.00 Dbl/Twn
Room only per person
from £15.00

Open Jan-Dec

Falkirk, Stirlingshire

Map Ref: 2A4

Darroch House

Camelon Road, Falkirk FK1 5SQ

Tel: 01324 623041 Fax: 01324 626288 e.mail: darroch@amserve.net

Exceptionally spacious and comfortable accommodation in Victorian manor peacefully situated in nine acres of grounds yet only ten minutes walk from town centre. Close to canal network and millennium link 'wheel' boatlift project. Centrally situated permitting easy day trips to Edinburgh, Glasgow, Stirling, St Andrews, Perth, Trossachs and much more.

★★★★

B&B

Darroch House

Camelon Road, Falkirk, Stirlingshire, FK1 5SQ
Tel: 01324 623041 Fax: 01324 626288
E-mail: darroch@amserve.net

1 Twin
2 Double

All En Suite

B&B per person
from £45.00 Single
from £25.00 Dbl/Twn
Room only per person
from £25.00

Open Jan-Dec

Built in 1838. Family home. Well-proportioned, Victorian manor house, set in 9 acres of garden and woodland in the heart of Falkirk. Traditional Scottish breakfast is served in the original dining room overlooking the donkey pasture.

★★★★

B&B

Denecroft Bed & Breakfast

8 Lochgreen Road, off Slamannan Road, Falkirk, FK1 5NJ
Tel/Fax: 01324 629258
E-mail: denecroft@tesco.net

1 Single
1 Twin
1 Double

All En Suite

B&B per person
from £26.00 Single
from £25.00 Dbl/Twn
Room only per person
from £20.00

Open Jan-Dec

A warm welcome awaits you at this family home, 1.5 miles from town centre. Quiet residential area within five minutes walk from Falkirk rail station, close to hospital. Only twenty minutes by train from Glasgow and Edinburgh.

★★

B&B

Mrs E Strain

Hawthorndean, Wallacestone Brae, Reddingmuirhead, Falkirk, Stirlingshire, FK2 0DQ
Tel/Fax: 01324 715840

1 Single
1 Twin
1 Family

1 En Suite fac
1 Pub Bath/Show

B&B per person
£20.00-£22.00 Single
£18.00-£20.00 Twin

Open Jan-Dec

Traditional renovated 19th century 2 storey cottage with log fire (seasonal). Quiet location in a residential area with interesting garden. Easy access to Motorway links throughout Central Scotland. Ample parking available and Sky Digital TV lounge.

Fintry, Stirlingshire

Map Ref: 1H4

★★★★

B&B

Mrs Helen Morris,

Netherton of Glenboig, Fintry, Stirlingshire, G63 0YH
Tel/Fax: 01360 860242
E-mail: morrish2@aol.com

1 Double

All En Suite

B&B per person
£25.00-£28.00 Single
£22.00-£25.00 Double

Open Jan-Dec excl Xmas/New Year

Comfortable spacious accommodation in 200 years old farmhouse. Relax over breakfast in the conservatory looking out across the open countryside towards the Campsie Fells. Ideal base for touring the Trossachs. Private trout and salmon fishing available.

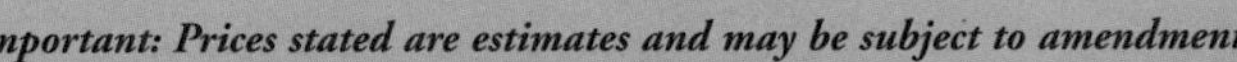

Important: Prices stated are estimates and may be subject to amendments

Gigha, Isle of, Argyll — Map Ref: 1D6

B&B

Post Office House

Isle of Gigha, Argyll, PA41 7AA
Tel: 01583 505251

Rooms	Facilities	Prices	Open
1 Single 1 Twin 1 Double 1 Family	All En Suite	B&B per person from £19.00 Single from £19.00 Dbl/Twn Room only per person from £10.00	Open Jan-Dec excl Xmas/New Year

Built in the 1850's this Victorian stone built house, formerly the school, is now the island post office and shop. Dinner, bed and breakfast is available using fresh local produce. Ideal base for a visit to this picturesque island and enjoy peace and tranquility, sandy beaches, nature spotting, wild flowers and the famous Achamore Gardens. Cycles available for hire. Self catering also available.

TV P C V

Glen Duror, Argyll — Map Ref: 1E1

SMALL HOTEL

Stewart Hotel

Glen Duror, Appin, Argyll, PA38 4BW
Tel/Fax: 01631 740268
Web: www.scotland2000.com/stewart

Rooms	Facilities	Prices	Open
6 Twin 4 Double 2 Family	All En Suite	B&B per person from £19.50 Single from £19.50 Dbl/Twn	Open Jan-Dec

Personally run hotel set in 5 acres of beautiful gardens 15 miles from Fort William and 25 miles from Oban. The hotel, which has been recently refurbished, offers a friendly, relaxed, informal style of service in both the bar and the restaurant.

TV P C W V

Helensburgh, Argyll — Map Ref: 1G4

GUEST HOUSE

Ardmore Guest House by the Sea

98 West Clyde Street, Helensburgh, Dunbartonshire, G84 8BE
Tel: 01436 673461 Fax: 01436 675739
E-mail: ardmore@fsbdial.co.uk
Web: www.scoot.co.uk/ardmore_guest_house

Rooms	Facilities	Prices	Open
4 Twin 1 Double 4 Family	3 En Suite fac 3 Pub Bath/Show 3 Priv.NOT ensuite	B&B per person from £20.00 Dbl/Twn Room only per person from £20.00	Open Jan-Dec B&B + Eve.Meal from £28.00

On the seafront with views over the River Clyde. Close to the town centre with its shops and restaurants. Relaxed, informal atmosphere. Off street parking. Loch Lomond 8 miles. Near Helensburgh railway station with its frequent service to Glasgow city centre. Full board terms available.

TV P C W V

B&B

Arran View, Colin & Janet Sanders

32 Barclay Drive, Helensburgh, Dunbartonshire, G84 9RA
Tel: 01436 673713 Fax: 01436 672595
E-mail: arranview@btinternet.com
Web: www.btinternet.com/~arranview

Rooms	Facilities	Prices	Open
1 Double 1 Twn/Dbl 2 Single	En Suite fac Adj.Bathroom 1 En Suite fac	B&B per person from £19.00 Single from £18.00 Dbl/Twn	Open Jan-Dec

A warm welcome at this comfortable detached home in the quiet residential area of upper Helensburgh West.

TV P W V

B&B

Eastbank B&B

10 Hanover Street, Helensburgh, Argyll, G84 7AW
Tel/Fax: 01436 673665
E-mail: dorothy-ross@breathemail.net

Rooms	Facilities	Prices	Open
1 Twin 1 Family	1 En Suite fac 1 Pub Bath/Show	B&B per person from £18.00 Single from £18.00 Twn/Fam Room only per person from £16.00	Open Jan-Dec

1st floor flat conversion with all accommodation on same level. Fine views from lounge across the Clyde to Greenock. Knitting instruction available.

TV P C W V

Helensburgh, Argyll

Map Ref: 1G4

B&B

Mrs M Richards

Ravenswood, 32 Suffolk Street, Helensburgh, Dunbartonshire, G84 9PA
Tel/Fax: 01436 672112

1 Single	2 En Suite fac	B&B per person	Open Jan-Dec
1 Twin	2 Priv.NOT ensuite	£25.00-£40.00 Single	B&B + Eve.Meal
2 Double	1 Pub Bath/Show	£25.00-£27.50 Dbl/Twn	£40.00-£55.00

Victorian family home. Quiet location with mature gardens, close to Hill House, town centre and Loch Lomond.

SILVER

Mrs Anne Urquhart

B&B

64 Colquhoun Street, Helensburgh, nr Loch Lomond G84 9JP
Tel: 01436 674922 Fax: 01436 679913
E-mail: theurquharts@sol.co.uk
Web: www.sol.co.uk/t/theurquharts

2 Twin	2 En Suite fac	B&B per person	Open Jan-Dec
1 Double	1 Priv.NOT ensuite	£26.00-£36.00 Single	
		£22.00-£26.00 Dbl/Twn	

In quiet area of beautiful garden town of Helensburgh. Enjoy friendly Scottish welcome, spacious comfortable rooms, good food, off-street parking, big leafy garden, no smoke (except the BBQ). Central for southern Highlands, Loch Lomond - 10 minutes drive, Rennie Macintosh's Hillhouse on same street. Glasgow 45 minutes, Airport 30 minutes. Special deals off-season.

Inveraray, Argyll

Map Ref: 1F3

SMALL HOTEL

Fernpoint Hotel

Round by the Pier, Inveraray, Argyll, PA32 8UY
Tel: 01499 302170 Fax: 01499 302366
E-mail: fernpoint.hotel@virgin.net

1 Single	6 En Suite fac	B&B per person	Open Mar-Jan excl Xmas
2 Twin	2 Priv.NOT ensuite	from £32.50 Single	B&B + Eve.Meal
4 Double		from £28.00 Dbl/Twn	from £45.00
1 Family		Room only per person	
		from £28.00	

Delightful Georgian House nestling in lochside gardens. Rooms with charming decor have breathtaking views of Loch Fyne and surrounding mountains. Bar meals served all day in stable bar or garden. Evening meals reflect chef's interest in local produce and vegetarian food. Children and pets welcome. B&B from £28-£45 per person per night.

B&B

Minard Castle

Minard, Argyll, PA32 8YB
Tel/Fax: 01546 886272
E-mail: reinoldgayre@bizonline.co.uk
Web: www.oas.co.uk/ukcottages/minardcastle/

2 Twin	All En Suite	B&B per person	Open Apr-Oct
1 Dbl/Fam		£30.00-£40.00 Single	
		£30.00-£40.00 Dbl/Twn	

This magnificent 19th century castle is set in 50 acres of private grounds on the shore of Loch Fyne, with panoramic views across the loch to the hills beyond. Retains original gothic revival architectural features, ornate ceilings, wood and plasterwork detail. Beautiful rooms with some interesting and antique furnishings. Outdoor pursuits include local forest walks, cycle trails, riding, fishing, beautiful gardens and archaeological attractions.

B&B

Newton Hall

Shore Road, Inveraray, Argyll, PA32 8UH
Tel: 01499 302484
E-mail: nh1961@aol.com

1 Twin	Ensuite fac	B&B per person	Open Jan-Dec excl
1 Double	Ensuite fac	£18.00-£22.00 Dbl/Twn	Xmas/New Year
1 Family	Private fac		

Sympathetically converted church overlooking Loch Fyne offering a warm friendly welcome. Ideal base for touring Argyll.

Iona, Isle of, Argyll — Map Ref: 1B2

★★ B&B

Finlay, Ross (Iona) Ltd
Martyr's Bay, Isle of Iona, Argyll, PA76 6SP
Tel: 01681 700357 Fax: 01681 700562

1 Single, 8 Twin, 2 Double, 2 Family
4 Ensuite fac, 3 Pub Bath/Show, 1 Priv.NOT ensuite
B&B per person from £24.00 Dbl/Twn
Open Jan-Dec

Purpose built rooms some with television all on one level and convenient for the ferry. Continental breakfast served. Also cottage annexe with TV lounge.

Ballygrant, Isle of Islay, Argyll — Map Ref: 1C5

★★★★★ GUEST HOUSE

Kilmeny Country Guest House
Ballygrant, Isle of Islay, Argyll, PA45 7QW
Tel/Fax: 01496 840668
Web: www.kilmeny.co.uk

1 Twin, 2 Double
All En Suite
B&B per person £36.00 Dbl/Twn
Open Jan-Dec excl Xmas/New Year
B&B + Dinner £60.00

Traditional farmhouse on 300 acre beef farm. Comfort, friendliness and peace. Emphasis on personal service, in a country house atmosphere. Non-smoking.

Bowmore, Isle of Islay, Argyll — Map Ref: 1C6

★★ SMALL HOTEL

Lochside Hotel
Shore Street, Bowmore, Isle of Islay, Argyll, PA43 7LB
Tel: 01496 810244 Fax: 01496 810390
E-mail: ask@lochsidehotel.co.uk
Web: www.lochsidehotel.co.uk
www.whisky4u.co.uk

5 Single, 1 Twin, 1 Double, 1 Family
All En Suite
B&B per person £25.00-£39.50 Single, £25.00-£34.50 Dbl/Twn
Open Jan-Dec

Personally run, on main street of the village with views over Loch Indaal from the bar and dining room. Ideal base for touring Islay.

Lagavulin, by Port Ellen, Isle of Islay, Argyll — Map Ref: 1C6

★★★ B&B

'Tigh-na-Suil'
Lagavulin, by Port Ellen, Isle of Islay, Argyll. PA42 7DX
Tel/Fax: 01496 302483

1 Twin, 1 Double
All En Suite
B&B per person £20.00-£30.00 Single, £20.00-£22.00 Dbl/Twn
Open Jan-Dec excl Xmas/New Year

Family home in peaceful, rural setting, with an abundance of wildlife and beautiful scenery. Distillery tours can be arranged.

Port Ellen, Isle of Islay, Argyll Map Ref: 1C6

Glenmachrie

Mrs Rachel Whyte, Port Ellen,
Isle of Islay, Argyll PA42 7AW
Tel/Fax: 01496 302560
e.mail: glenmachrie@lineone.net
Web: www.glenmachrie.com

THE TASTE OF SCOTLAND

★★★★ GUEST HOUSE

Glenmachrie (*'Which'* Hotel Guide – Best Island Hideaway in Britain) is a large traditional farmhouse set in a stone-walled garden by the river overlooking the famous Machrie golf links. Furnished to a high standard Glenmachrie offers total comfort, friendly welcomes and excellent local and farm-produced food. All bedrooms, tastefully decorated, have full ensuite facilities. The dining room, set with crystal and silverware, provides the ideal setting for our delicious food which has been awarded membership to the "Taste of Scotland". House guests enjoy free fly-fishing. Glenmachrie offers you true Highland hospitality, delicious local food and wonderful memories of an unforgettable Hebridean Holiday!

★★★★ GUEST HOUSE

Glenmachrie
Port Ellen, Isle of Islay, Argyll, PA42 7AW
Tel/Fax: 01496 302560
E-mail: glemachrie@lineone.net
Web: www.glenmachrie.com

2 Twin, 2 Double, 1 Family | All En Suite, 1 Pub Bath/Show | B&B per person from £40.00 Single, from £30.00 Dbl/Twn | Open Jan-Dec, B&B + Eve.Meal from £53.00

Farmhouse in quiet location, fine views westwards across Laggan Bay towards the Rhinns. Family run farm using the best of Islay's larder. Private fishing for wild brown trout.

GOLD

★★★ B&B

Tighcargaman
Port Ellen, Isle of Islay, Argyll, PA42 7BX
Tel/Fax: 01496 302345

1 Double, 2 Twin | 1 En Suite fac, 1 Priv.NOT ensuite, 1 Pub Bath/Show | B&B per person from £23.00 Dbl/Twn | Open Jan-Dec excl Xmas/New Year

Tighcargaman was built in 1842 and is set in its own grounds on the outskirts of Port Ellen, overlooking the bay. Small pottery on premises. 1/2 mile from ferry terminal and 4 miles from airport. Ground floor room available.

Craighouse, Isle of Jura, Argyll Map Ref: 1D5

★★ B&B

Gwen Boardman
7 Woodside, Craighouse, Isle of Jura, Argyll, PA60 7YA
Tel: 01496 820379

1 Twin, 1 Dbl/Fam | 1 Pub Bath/Show | B&B per person from £20.00 Single, from £20.00 Dbl/Twn | Open Apr-Oct

A warm welcome assured in a friendly informal home situated in Jura's only village. Hearty breakfasts. Meals available in nearby hotel.

Kilchrenan, Argyll | Map Ref: 1F2

★★★
B&B

Thistle-Doo
Kilchrenan, Taynult, by Oban, Argyll, PA35 1HF
Tel/Fax: 01866 833339

1 Twin All En Suite
2 Double

B&B per person from £20.00 Dbl/Twn

Open Jan-Dec excl Xmas/New Year

Modern family bungalow in idyllic secluded setting overlooking Loch Awe and set in an acre of garden. Village pub within walking distance. Oban 20 miles.

Killin, Perthshire | Map Ref: 1H2

Breadalbane House

Main Street, Killin, Perthshire FK21 8UT
Tel: 01567 820134 Fax: 01567 820798
e.mail: stay@breadalbane48.freeserve.co.uk

Set in the picturesque village of Killin in an incomparable region of beauty at the very heart of Scotland. The clans of MacNab, Campbell, MacGregor and McLaren all have connections with the area which is rich in history. Excellent base for touring with walking, hill-climbing, cycling, golf, fishing and watersports all on the doorstep. Friendly and caring hosts, Isabel and John, provide exceptionally comfortable accommodation with hearty and healthy breakfasts. Relaxing restaurants offering a variety of cuisine including local game and traditional Scottish fare are a few minutes walk away. Breadalbane House, for the discerning visitor to Scotland.

★★★
GUEST HOUSE

Breadalbane House
Main Street, Killin, Perthshire, FK21 8UT
Tel: 01567 820134 Fax: 01567 820798
E-mail: stay@breadalbane48.freeserve.co.uk

1 Twin All En Suite
2 Double
2 Family

B&B per person
£25.00-£30.00 Single
£20.00-£25.00 Dbl/Twn

Open Jan-Dec excl Xmas/New Year

Excellent accommodation in comfortable and well equipped ensuite rooms. Start your day with the healthy fruit and cereal buffet before enjoying our traditional Scottish breakfast. With walking, cycling, golf and watersports on your doorstep the relaxing lounge is the place to unwind after your day out. Rich in history and an ideal base for touring Central Scotland.

Killin, Perthshire

Map Ref: 1H2

★★★ GUEST HOUSE

Fairview House

Main Street, Killin, Perthshire, FK21 8UT
Tel: 01567 820667
E-mail: info@fairview-killin.co.uk
WEb: www.fairview-killin.co.uk

Family run guest house specialising in home cooking. Excellent touring centre, good walking and climbing area.

1 Single	5 En Suite fac	B&B per person	Open Jan-Dec
2 Twin	2 Private fac	£20.00-£24.00 Single	B&B + Eve.Meal
4 Double		£20.00-£24.00 Dbl/Twn	£35.00-£39.00

★★ HOTEL

Killin Hotel

Main Street, Killin, Perthshire, FK21 8TP
Tel: 01567 820296 Fax; 01567 820647
E-mail: killinhotel@btinternet.com
Web: www.killinhotel.com

Family run hotel in the village of Killin and overlooking the western end of Loch Tay. Trout and salmon fishing by arrangement. Come and experience our new Riverside Bistro.

6 Single	All En Suite	B&B per person	Open Jan-Dec
9 Twin		from £35.00 Single	B&B + Eve.Meal
13 Double		from £26.00 Dbl/Twn	from £35.00
4 Family		Room only per person	
		from £19.00	

Kippen, Stirlingshire

Map Ref: 1H4

★★★★ B&B

Sealladh Ard

Station Brae, Kippen, Stirlingshire, FK8 3DY
Tel: 01786 870291

Family home on the outskirts of conservation village within 5 mins walk of local hotels. Well laid out and interesting garden, full scottish breakfast served with home made bread and preserves, sit back and enjoy the spectacular views across the valley.

1 Twin	1 En Suite fac	B&B per person	Open Jan-Dec
1 Double	2 Pub Bath/Show	from £22.00 Single	
1 Family		from £20.50 Dbl/Twn	

Lochgilphead, Argyll

Map Ref: 1E4

★★★ B&B

Corbiere

Achnabreac, Lochgilphead, Argyll, PA31 8SG
Tel: 01546 602764

Detached family house in peaceful country location with lovely views across the surrounding farmlands. Ideal base for exploring historic Kilmartin Glen and the Kintyre Peninsula. Short drive to ferries for Inner Isles. Good walking with many forest tracks and the Crinan Canal nearby. Quiet roads to rough the beautiful Argyll countryside for the keen cyclist. Families and well behaved pets welcome.

1 Twin	2 Pub Bath/Show	B&B per person	Open Jan-Dec
1 Double		from £20.00 Single	
		from £16.50 Dbl/Twn	

Important: Prices stated are estimates and may be subject to amendments

Lochgilphead, Argyll

Map Ref: 1E4

★★★

B&B

'Somerled' Bed & Breakfast

Dunadd View, Bridgend, by Lochgilphead, Argyll, PA31 8QA
Tel: 01546 605226 Fax: 01546 605229

1 Twin
2 Double

All En Suite

B&B per person
from £19.00 Single
from £19.00 Dbl/Twn

Open Jan-mid Dec

Somerled is a new country house within the village of Bridgend, set in Kilmartin Glen 5 miles from Lochgilphead on the A816. Within walking distance lies Dunadd Fort. We are close to may forest walks and cycle routes. The area is a haven for wildlife and birds and there are many lochs for fishing. We are approximately 2 hours from Glasgow.
All bedrooms are ensuite and spacious. Two double and one twin.

Lochgoilhead, Argyll

Map Ref: 1F3

★★★★

B&B

Ben Bheula B&B

Lochgoilhead, Argyll, PA24 8AH
Tel: 01301 703508 Fax: 01301 703337
E-mail: benbheula@aol.com

3 Double

2 En Suite fac
1 Priv. fac

B&B per person
from £27.50 Single
from £25.00 Double

Open Mar-Jan

A warm welcome awaits you at our Victorian home set in the heart of Argyll Forest Park. Stunning views over loch and Cowal mountains. Superb walking country. Extensive lochside woodland garden attracts wildlife particularly red squirrels and deer. Many amenities in village include boat hire, fishing and leisure centre with indoor swimming pool, bowls, golf and pony trekking. Relax in tranquil friendly surroundings.

★

INN

Shore House Inn

Lochgoilhead, Argyll, PA24 8AJ
Tel/Fax: 01301 703340
E-mail: shorehouse,inn@fs13dial.co.uk

1 Single
2 Twin
2 Double
2 Family

3 En Suite fac
2 Pub Bath/Show

B&B per person
from £16.00 Single
from £20.00 Dbl/Twn

Open Jan-Dec

Peacefully situated on the shore of Loch Goil, with open views down the loch. Informal and friendly. Pets welcome. Bar and Restaurant.

Luss, Argyll & Bute — **Map Ref: 1G4**

B&B

Glenmollochan Farm

Mrs K R Wragg, Luss, by Alexandria,
Dunbartonshire, G83 8PB
Tel/Fax: 01436 860246

1 Twin | All En Suite | B&B per person | Open Apr-Oct
1 Double | £19.00-£25.00 Dbl/Twn

150 year old farmhouse, with well appointed rooms, situated 2 miles (3kms) from A82 on working farm, in Glen above Luss. Superb views of Loch Lomond and surrounding hills. Sit in the garden and enjoy peace and quiet, yet only 35 minutes from Glasgow Airport.

B&B

Polnaberoch B&B

Polnaberoch, Arden, by Luss, Loch Lomond, G83 8RQ
Tel/Fax: 01389 850615
E-mail: maclomond@sol.co.uk

1 Twin | All En Suite | B&B per person | Open Mar-Nov
1 Double | £23.00-£30.00 Dbl/Twn | B&B + Eve.Meal £40.00-£47.00

In tranquil rural setting with large garden. Short distance from Loch Lomond, golf courses and country walks. Several eating places within 10 minutes. Teas served in the garden.

B&B

Shantron Farm

Luss, Dunbartonshire, G83 8RH
Tel/Fax: 01389 850231
E-mail: rjlennox@shantron.u-net.com
Web: www.stayatlochlomond.com/shantron

1 Twin | 3 En Suite fac | B&B per person | Open Apr-Nov
1 Double | £22.00-£30.00 Dbl/Twn
1 Family

House in elevated position with panoramic views over Loch Lomond to the Campsie Fells. Farm is used regularly for filming of 'High Road'.

Important: Prices stated are estimates and may be subject to amendments

Bunessan, Isle of Mull, Argyll — Map Ref: 1C3

B&B

Ardness House

Bunessan, Isle of Mull, Argyll, PA67 6DU
Tel/Fax: 01687 700260
E-mail: ardness@supanet.com
Web: www.isleofmullholidays.com

A well appointed modern bungalow with all bedrooms ensuite. Guests lounge with panoramic views of Loch Caol and dramatic cliffs beyond. Three and a half miles from Iona ferry.

1 Twin, 2 Double — All En Suite

B&B per person: £18.00-£22.00 Dbl/Twn

Open Easter-Oct

Craignure, Isle of Mull, Argyll — Map Ref: 1D2

★★

B&B

Clachan House

Loch Don, Craignure, Isle of Mull, Argyll, PA64 6AP
Tel: 01680 812439

Converted crofter's house, 3 miles (5km's) from Craignure ferry. Magnificent view over Lochdon towards the mainland. Owners fresh eggs for breakfast.

1 Twin — 1 Ensuite fac
1 Double — 1 Pub Bath/Show

B&B per person: from £18.00 Single; from £18.00 Dbl/Twn

Open Jan-Dec

GUEST HOUSE

Pennygate Lodge

Craignure, Isle of Mull, Argyll, PA65 6AY
Tel: 01680 812333

Former Georgian manse set in 4.5 acres of landscaped garden with magnificent views of the Sound of Mull. Ideal base for touring, near main bus route and ferry terminal. Three night special breaks available.

3 Twin — En Suite fac
3 Double — 2 Pub Bath/Show
2 Family — Priv.NOT ensuite

B&B per person: from £22.00 Single; from £18.00 Dbl/Twn

Open Jan-Dec excl Xmas/New Year

B&B

Redburn

Lochdon, Craignure, Isle of Mull, Argyll, PA64 6AP
Tel/Fax: 01680 812370
E-mail: weir.c.lochdon@talk21.com

Converted croft house in quiet location on lochside. 3 miles (4.8 kms) from Craignure Ferry. Area for natural history enthusiasts. Home cooking.

1 Twin, 2 Double — All En Suite

B&B per person: from £25.00 Single; from £20.00 Dbl/Twn
Room only per person: from £25.00

Open Jan-Dec excl Xmas/New Year
Dinner at 1800
B&B + Eve.Meal from £30.00

by Craignure, Isle of Mull, Argyll — **Map Ref: 1D2**

★★★★ B&B

Inverlussa Bed & Breakfast
by Craignure, Isle of Mull, Argyll, PA65 6BD
Tel/Fax: 01680 812436

1 Twin 2 Single 2 Double 1 Family	1 En Suite fac 2 Pub Bath/Show	B&B per person from £20.00 Single from £20.00 Dbl/Twn	Open Apr-Oct

Personally run modern house in idyllic setting. 6 miles/10 minutes from Craignure ferry. Ideal base for touring Isle of Mull.

Dervaig, Isle of Mull, Argyll — **Map Ref: 1C1**

★★★ B&B

Achnacraig
Dervaig, Isle of Mull, Argyll, PA75 6QW
Tel: 01688 400309

1 Single 1 Twin 1 Double	1 Priv.NOT ensuite 1 Pub Bath/Show	B&B per person from £18.00 Single from £18.00 Dbl/Twn	Open Easter-Sep

Winding river, circling buzzards, stone farmhouse, stupendous views. Dinner available with prior arrangement featuring home grown organic produce and real cooking. Courtesy mountain bikes available. 4 miles (8 km) from Dervaig.

★★★★ B&B

Balmacara
Dervaig, Isle of Mull, Argyll, PA75 6QN
Tel/Fax: 01688 400363

1 Twin 2 Double	2 En Suite fac 1 Priv.NOT ensuite	B&B per person from £26.50 Dbl/Twn	Open Jan-Dec excl Xmas/New Year B&B + Eve.Meal from £41.00

Modern property set high above Dervaig village with magnificent views over Glen Bellart and Loch Cuin, framed by the hills and forests of North West Mull.

Dervaig, Isle of Mull, Argyll Map Ref: 1C1

CUIN LODGE

DERVAIG, ISLE OF MULL PA75 6QL
TEL: 01688 400346 E.MAIL: cuin-lodge@mull.com
WEB: www.cuin-lodge.mull.com

Cuin Lodge is a traditional 19th century former shooting lodge. One mile from Dervaig. You can relax and enjoy views of the Loch and Mull mountains from the conservatory. Ideally situated for walkers and wild life enthusiasts, you can be sure of a warm welcome and good home cooking.

B&B

Cuin Lodge
Dervaig, Isle of Mull, Argyll, PA75 6QL
Tel: 01688 400346
E-mail: cuin-lodge@mull.com
Web: www.cuin-lodge.mull.com

1 Single, 1 Twin, 1 Double, 1 Family

3 En Suite fac, 1 Pub Bath/Show

B&B per person: from £17.50 Single, from £21.00 Dbl/Twn

Open Jan-Dec excl Xmas/New Year
B&B + Eve.Meal £31.00-£34.50
Dinner £13.50

Converted 19th century shooting lodge on the edge of Loch Chumhainn, 1 mile from Dervaig. Conservatory extension offers panoramic views of the loch and mountains.

Fionnphort, Isle of Mull, Argyll Map Ref: 1C2

DINNER, BED AND BREAKFAST
SEAVIEW

Fionnphort, Isle of Mull PA66 6BL Tel: 01681 700235 • Fax: 01681 700669
e.mail: john@seaviewmull.f9.co.uk
Web: www.holidaymull.org/seaview/seaview.htm

Scottish granite house, Seaview offers friendly, comfortable accommodation in family run B&B. All bedrooms ensuite. Try our 'Fingal's Breakfast' in our dining room with splendid views across to Iona. A minutes walk to Iona and Staffa ferries. Spring and autumn D,B&B. special rates. Private parking. Pub/restaurant and shop nearby.

B&B

Seaview
Fionnphort, Isle of Mull, Argyll, PA66 6BL
Tel: 01681 700235 Fax: 01681 700669
E-mail: john@seaviewmull.f9.co.uk
Web: www.holidaymull.org/seaview/seaview.htm

2 Twin, 3 Double

4 En Suite fac, 1 Priv.NOT ensuite

B&B per person: from £19.00 Single, from £17.00 Dbl/Twn

Open Jan-Dec

Recently refurbished Scottish granite house with views over the Sound of Iona towards the Abbey. A minutes walk to Iona and Staffa Ferries.

B&B

Staffa House
Fionnphort, Isle of Mull, Argyll, PA66 6BL
Tel/Fax: 01681 700677

2 Twin, 1 Double

All En Suite

B&B per person: from £20.00 Single, from £20.00 Dbl/Twn

Open Mar-Oct
B&B + Eve.Meal from £32.50

Traditional Highland house with Edwardian style conservatory dining room. Views over sound of Iona and a short walk to ferries.

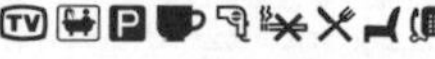

VAT is shown at 17.5%: changes in this rate may affect prices.

Key to symbols is on back flap.

Gruline, Isle of Mull, Argyll

Map Ref: 1D2

B&B

Gruline Home Farm

Gruline, nr Salen, Isle of Mull, PA71 6HR
Tel: 01680 300581 Fax: 01680 300573
E-mail: stb@gruline.com
Web: www.gruline.com

A former 19th century farmhouse set in $2^1/2$ acres of grounds at the foot of Mull's Mountain Range. Angela and Colin are totally committed to providing hospitality 'par excellence.' A warm, welcoming and comfortable home with excellent food and dinners prepared by Chef Proprietor using the best local produce.

2 Twin | All En Suite | B&B per person from £39.00 Single from £29.00 Twin | Open Jan-Dec B&B + Eve.Meal from £48.50

SILVER

Kinlochspelve, Isle of Mull, Argyll

Map Ref: 1D2

B&B

The Barn

Barrachandroman Kinlochspelve, Loch Buie,
Isle of Mull, Argyll, PA62 6AA
Tel: 01680 814220 Fax: 01680 814247
E-mail: edwards@lochbuie.org.uk

Luxuriously converted barn in secluded lochside location, both rooms with private facilities. Accent on fresh fish and seafood.

2 Double | 1 En Suite fac, 1 Priv.NOT ensuite | B&B per person from £25.00 Single from £25.00 Double | Open Feb-Dec excl Xmas B&B + Eve.Meal from £41.00

Salen, Aros, Isle of Mull, Argyll

Map Ref: 1D1

B&B

Duntulm

Salen, Aros, Isle of Mull, PA72 6JB
Tel: 01680 300513
Web: www.duntulm.ic24.net

2 Family | 1 Priv.NOT ensuite | B&B per person from £17.00 Single from £16.00 Dbl/Fam | Open Jan-Dec

by Salen, Aros, Isle of Mull, Argyll

Map Ref: 1D1

B&B

Callachally Farm

Salen, Aros, Isle of Mull, Argyll, PA72 6JN
Tel/Fax: 01680 300424

Comfortable bungalow in peaceful location overlooking surrounding farmland to hills beyond. Short walk to coast and sea views. Ideal for touring, walking, wildlife and birdwatching.

1 Twin, 1 Double | 1 Pub Bath/Show | B&B per person from £18.00 Dbl/Twn | Open Apr-Oct

Important: Prices stated are estimates and may be subject to amendments

Tobermory, Isle of Mull, Argyll — Map Ref: 1C1

★★★ GUEST HOUSE

Baliscate Guest House
Salen Road, Tobermory, Isle of Mull, Argyll, PA75 6QA
Tel: 01688 302048 Fax: 01688 302666
Web: www.baliscate.com

2 Double, 2 Family — All En Suite
B&B per person
from £20.00 Single
from £22.50 Double

Recently refurbished Victorian house set in 1.5 acres of garden and woodland, with magnificent views over The Sound of Mull. 15 minute down hill walk to Tobermory front and all amenities. 'Request' bus stop at bottom of garden.

★★★★ GUEST HOUSE

Fairways Lodge
Golf Course, Tobermory, Isle of Mull, Argyll, PA75 6PS
Tel/Fax: 01688 302238
E-mail: derekmcadam@fairwaysmull.com
Web: www.fairwaysmull.com

1 Single, 2 Twin, 1 Double, 1 Family — All En Suite
B&B per person
from £29.00 Single
from £29.00 Dbl/Twn
Open Jan-Dec excl Xmas

Fairways Lodge enjoys an outstanding position on Tobermory golf course with wonderful views over Tobermory Bay and the Sound of Mull. All bedrooms have private bathrooms, colour TV, welcome tray and every luxury. Our conservatory lounge is available to guests all day. Ideal centre for golf, fishing and touring. Visit Staffa and Iona. To find us follow signs to the golf course.

Oban, Argyll — Map Ref: 1E2

★★★ B&B

Bracker
Polvinister Road, Oban, Argyll, PA34 5TN
Tel: 01631 564302
Fax: 01631 571167
E.mail: cmacdonald@connectfree.co.uk

1 Twin, 2 Double — All En Suite
B&B per person
from £20.00 Single
from £17.00 Dbl/Twn
Open Mar-Oct

A warm welcome is assured at this modern family bungalow situated in a secluded residential area located a short distance from Oban town centre and all amenities. Private parking. Full en suite.

★★★ GUEST HOUSE

Corrie Mar House
Corrarm, Esplanade, Oban, Argyll, PA34 5AQ
Tel: 01631 562476 Fax: 01631 564339
E-mail: Corriemar@tinyworld.co.uk

2 Single, 4 Twin, 5 Double, 2 Family — All En Suite
B&B per person
£23.00-£35.00 Single
£18.00-£32.00 Dbl/Twn
Room only per person
from £15.00
Open Jan-Dec

Situated on the seafront, this large Victorian family run Guest House is only 10 minutes walk along the prom to the town centre. Spectacular Oban sunsets looking from the lounge over to Kerrara with the hills of Mull beyond.

Oban, Argyll

Map Ref: 1E2

★★★★

GUEST HOUSE

Don-Muir
Pulpit Hill, Oban, Argyll, PA34 4LX
Tel: 01631 564536 Fax: 01631 563739

1 Single, 1 Twin, 3 Double
3 En Suite fac, 1 Limited ensuite, 1 Pub Bath/Show
B&B per person: from £20.00 Single, from £21.00 Dbl/Twn
Open Feb-Oct
B&B + Eve.Meal £33.00-£50.00

Set in quiet residential area, high up on Pulpit Hill and close to public transport terminals. Parking available.

★★★

B&B

Drumriggend
Drummore Road, Oban, Argyll, PA34 4JL
Tel: 01631 563330 Fax: 01631 564217

1 Twin, 1 Double, 1 Family
All En Suite
B&B per person: £16.00-£20.00 Dbl/Twn
Open Jan-Dec

Detached house in quiet residential area. Situated on the south side of town about 1 mile (2kms) from the centre. Private car parking.

★★★★

B&B

Dungrianach
Pulpit Hill, Oban, Argyll, PA34 4LU
Tel/Fax: 01631 562840
E-mail: dungrianach@yahoo.co.uk
Web: www.dungrianach.yahoo.co.uk

1 Twin, 1 Double
All En Suite
B&B per person: from £23.00 Dbl/Twn
Open Apr-Sep

Secluded, in 4 acres of wooded garden on top of Pulpit Hill. Magnificent views over Oban Bay and the islands.

Oban, Argyll

Map Ref: 1E2

B&B

Mrs A Edwards

Rhumor, Drummore Road, Oban, Argyll, PA34 4JL
Tel: 01631 563544

1 Twin, 1 Double, 1 Family — All En Suite — B&B per person £18.00-£20.00 Dbl/Twn — Open Feb-Dec

Traditional bungalow with attic set in a quiet residential area on the outskirts of town. All amenities within 10 minutes walk. Comfortable rooms. Ample parking. Friendly family welcome. Non smoking house.

B&B

Firgrove

Ardconnel Road, Oban, Argyll, PA34 5DW
Tel/Fax: 01631 565250
E-mail: Wilson.Catering@lineone.net

2 Twin, 1 Double — 2 Pub Bath/Show — B&B per person from £18.50 Single, from £15.00 Twin; Room only per person from £12.50 — Open Jan-Dec

Victorian villa overlooking Oban Bay. Elevated position only 3 minutes walk to town centre and 2 minutes to leisure centre and swimming pool. Oban is an ideal base for visiting all Western Islands and the North of Scotland. Private parking.

GUEST HOUSE

Glenburnie House

Esplanade, Oban, Argyll, PA34 5AQ
Tel: 01631 562089
E-mail: Graeme.Strachan@btinternet.com

2 Single, 4 Twin, 8 Double — All En Suite — B&B per person from £30.00 Single, from £26.00 Dbl/Twn — Open Apr-Nov

Convenient for town centre and all amenities, this family run hotel has magnificient views of the bay and islands.Recently refurbished superior rooms.

B&B

Glengorm

Dunollie Road, Oban, Argyll, PA34 5PH
Tel: 01631 565361

1 Single, 1 Twin, 3 Double — 2 Pub Bath/Show — B&B per person from £14.00 Single, from £14.00 Dbl/Twn; Room only per person from £13.00 — Open Jan-Dec excl Xmas/New Year

Victorian terraced house on level ground near town centre, convenient for restaurants, entertainments, shops and ferries.

GUEST HOUSE

Glenroy Guest House

Rockfield Road, Oban, Argyll, PA34 5DQ
Tel: 01631 562585
E-mail: boydglen@ukonline.co.uk
Web: www.glenroy-guesthouse.co.uk

1 Twin, 5 Double — 4 Ensuite fac, 2 Pub Bath/Show, 2 Limited ensuite — B&B per person from £20.00 Dbl/Twn — Open Jan-Dec excl Xmas/New Year

Centrally situated family run guest house located only a very short distance from the town centre and all amenities. Owners are life-time locals with extensive local knowledge which they are happy to share with guests.

VAT is shown at 17.5%: changes in this rate may affect prices.

Key to symbols is on back flap.

Oban, Argyll Map Ref: 1E2

GREENCOURT GUEST HOUSE

BENVOULIN LANE, OBAN, ARGYLL PA34 5EF
TEL: 01631 563987 FAX: 01631 571276
E.MAIL: stay@greencourt-oban.fsnet.co.uk
WEB: www.greencourt-oban.fsnet.co.uk

Experience genuine Highland hospitality, comfortable rooms, delicious breakfasts and exceptional standards at this family-run property overlooking Oban's outdoor bowling green. Peaceful situation. Five minute stroll to amenities/promenade. Leisure centre adjacent. Ideal touring base. Brochure available. Credit cards accepted. Fiddle/accordion-playing hosts Joanie and Michael Garvin even provide a few tunes on request!

GUEST HOUSE

Greencourt Guest House

Benvoulin Lane, Oban, Argyll, PA34 5EF
Tel: 01631 563987 Fax: 01631 571276
E-mail: stay@greencourt-oban.fsnet.co.uk
Web: www.greencourt-oban.fsnet.co.uk

1 Single, 1 Twin, 4 Double | 5 Ensuite fac, 1 Priv.NOT ensuite | B&B per person £20.00-£26.00 Single, £20.00-£26.00 Dbl/Twn | Open Jan-Dec excl Xmas/New Year

Spacious family run property in quiet situation overlooking outdoor bowling green, a short stroll to town centre and adjacent to leisure centre. Attractive rooms, wholesome breakfasts, private parking. Ideal touring base.

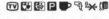

B&B

Harbour View Guesthouse

Shore Street, Oban, Argyll, PA34 4LQ
Tel: 01631 563462
E-mail: DilysMcDougall@aol.com

1 Twin, 1 Double, 3 Family | 2 Pub Bath/Show | B&B per person £15.00-£17.50 Single, £15.00-£17.50 Dbl/Twn | Open Jan-Dec excl Xmas/New Year

Centrally situated and convenient for a level stroll to ferry, railway station and shops.

B&B

Hawthorn

Benderloch, by Connel, Argyll, PA37 1QS
Tel: 01631 720452

1 Twin, 2 Double | 2 En Suite fac, 1 Priv.NOT ensuite | B&B per person from £25.00 Single, from £18.00 Dbl/Twn | Open Jan-Dec, B&B + Eve.Meal from £28.00

Family bungalow in peaceful rural setting 9 miles (14kms) from Oban and ferry terminals for the islands. 5 minutes walk from the excellent sandy beaches of Tralee Bay. Own restaurant adjacent. Ensuite rooms available.

Important: Prices stated are estimates and may be subject to amendments

Oban, Argyll

Map Ref: 1E2

Hawthornbank Guest House

Dalriach Road, Oban PA34 5JE

Tel: 01631 562041 e.mail: hawthornbank@aol.com

New owners, Brian and Valerie welcome you to their tastefully refurbished Victorian villa. Immaculate, well-equipped, en-suite rooms. Two feature rooms: Regency with 4-poster and Victorian with brass bed. Beautiful views over Oban Bay. Close to sports centre. Five minutes walk to town centre. Private parking. Non-smoking.

★★★★

GUEST HOUSE

Hawthornbank Guest House

Dalriach Road, Oban, Argyll, PA34 5JE
Tel: 01631 562041
E-mail: hawthornbank@aol.com
Web: http://www.SmoothHound.co.uk/hotels/hawthorn.html

Brian and Valerie look forward to welcoming you to Hawthornbank, a tastefully refurbished Victorian villa set in a quiet location yet only a short stroll from the town centre. Comfortable well equipped rooms some with stunning views over Oban Bay. How can you resist?

1 Single
1 Twin
6 Double

All En Suite

B&B per person
from £20.00 Single
from £22.00 Dbl/Twn

Open Jan-Dec

£ W V

★★★

B&B

Mrs Marie Johnston

Lower Soroba Farmhouse, Oban, Argyll, PA34 4LE
Tel: 01631 565349

Tastefully refurbished traditional (non-working) farmhouse within a quiet residential estate on the southern edge of Oban. 1 mile from town centre and all amenities. Excellent base for touring this beautiful part of Argyll. Warm welcome. Private parking. Evening meal by arrangement. Local bus route and hotel nearby.

1 Twin
1 Double
1 Family

All En Suite

B&B per person
from £17.00 Single
from £17.00 Dbl/Twn

Open Jan-Dec

TV P

C V

Oban, Argyll Map Ref: 1E2

Kilchrenan House

Corran Esplanade, Oban, Argyll PA34 5AQ
Tel/Fax: 01631 562663
e.mail: Kilchrenanhouse@supanet.com

Spacious Victorian house in excellent seafront location with uninterrupted views over Oban Bay and the Islands beyond. This 'B' listed building has been tastefully decorated to a high standard in keeping with the period. Kilchrenan House has a proven record of excellence and guests can be assured of the highest levels of comfort and service. Guest rooms are all ensuite with central heating, C.T.V., telephone and hospitality trays. Extensive breakfast menu catering for all dietary needs. Private car park. Under the personal supervision of the resident proprietors – Hugh and Sandra Maclean.

GUEST HOUSE

Kilchrenan House

Corran Esplanade, Oban, Argyll, PA34 5AQ
Tel/Fax: 01631 562663
E-mail: kilchrenanhouse@supenet.com

1 Single
2 Twin
6 Double
1 Family

All En Suite

B&B per person
£25.00-£32.00 Single
£23.00-£32.00 Dbl/Twn
Room only per person
£20.00-£28.00

Open Apr-Oct

Spacious Victorian house in excellent seafront location. Assured high standard of service and comfort. Uninterrupted views across Oban Bay towards the islands beyond. Oban town centre and all amenities within five minutes walk along the esplanade.

TV C V

LA CALA

GANAVAN ROAD, OBAN PA34 5TU
Telephone/Fax: 01631 562741

La Cala is a luxuriously appointed two storey Georgian style house situated on the northern outskirts of Oban. Beautiful situation by the sea with breathtaking panoramic sea views to the islands. Off street private parking. Single and standard double rooms let as unit for parties of three sharing. Private bathroom.

B&B

La Cala Bed & Breakfast

Ganavan Road, Oban, Argyll, PA34 5TU
Tel/Fax: 01631 562741

1 Single
2 Double

1 En Suite fac
2 Pub Bath/Show

B&B per person
£23.00-£28.00 Single
£23.00-£30.00 Double

Open Easter-Oct

Tastefully appointed Georgian style home set in pleasant gardens. Beautifully quiet situation by the sea with breathtaking panoramic views of the sounds of Mull, Kerrera and Lismore. 1.25 miles from Oban centre. Single and standard double rooms, let as a unit for 3 sharing, private bath room.

V

Important: Prices stated are estimates and may be subject to amendments

Oban, Argyll Map Ref: 1E2

★★★★ B&B

Mrs C McQuade
Ard Struan, Croft Road, Oban, Argyll, PA34 5JN
Tel: 01631 563689

1 Twin	All En Suite	B&B per person	Open Jan-Dec
3 Double		£18.00-£24.00 Dbl/Twn	

Modern detached villa with large garden in quiet residential area overlooking Oban Bay. Short distance from town centre. Broad base for touring west coast of Scotland and close to ferries for Mull, Iona and other islands.

B&B

Oakbank
Benvoulin Road, Oban, Argyll, PA34 5EF
Tel: 01631 563482 Fax: 01631 570917
E-mail: sadie@oakbankvilla.com
Web: www.oakbankvilla.com

1 Twin	1 limited ensuite	B&B per person	Open Jan-Dec excl
2 Double	1 Pub Bath/Show	£12.50-£17.50 Dbl/Twn	Xmas/New Year
		Room only per person	
		£12.50-£17.50	

Small family run bed and breakfast with fine views across Kerrera to the Isle of Mull, yet only 4 minutes walk from town centre, harbour and promenade. Visit the nearby sports centre and swimming pool or take a pleasant walk to McCaigs Tower.

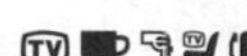

GUEST HOUSE

The Old Manse Guest House
Dalriach Road, Oban, Argyll, PA34 5JE
Tel: 01631 564886 Fax: 01631 570184
E-mail: oldmanse@obanguesthouse.co.uk
Web: www.obanguesthouse.co.uk

1 Twin	All En Suite	B&B per person	Open Mar-Nov
2 Double		£20.00-£30.00 Dbl/Twn	
1 Family			

Victorian detached Villa set in beautiful gardens, with views of sea and islands. Superior standard of hospitality and comfort. Only minutes walk to town centre. Private parking. Family suite available.

Oban, Argyll Map Ref: 1E2

B&B

Mrs B Ramsey

Glenstrae, Connel, by Oban, Argyll, PA37 1PG
Tel: 01631 710214
E.mail: glenstrae@btinternet.com
Web: www.btinternet.com/~glenstrae

1 Single | 2 En Suite fac | B&B per person | Open Easter-Oct
1 Twin | 1 Pub Bath/Show | £15.00-£17.50 Single
2 Double | | £17.50-£22.00 Dbl/Twn
Room only per person
£12.00-£18.00

Family run Victorian home in a pleasant location on the eastern edge of Connel Village having open views over Loch Etive to Ben Lora beyond. Situated 5 miles (8 kms) from Oban it is an excellent touring base with access to the many local amenities and attractions. Hillwalking, birdwatching, loch cruises and other activities available. Ample private parking.

GUEST HOUSE

Roseneath Guest House

Dalriach Road, Oban, Argyll, PA34 5EQ
Tel: 01631 562929 Fax: 01631 567218
Web: www.oban.org.uk/accommodation/roseneath/roseneath-guesthouse.html

2 Twin | All En Suite | B&B per person | Open Jan-Dec excl Xmas
6 Double | | £19.00-£26.00 Dbl/Twn

Personally run Victorian house in quiet area overlooking town and bay. Near seafront and shops. Private parking. Non-smoking.

HOTEL

Royal Hotel

Argyll Square, Oban, Argyll, PA34 4BE
Tel: 01631 563021 Fax: 01631 562811

15 Single | All En Suite | B&B per person | Open Jan-Dec
56 Twin | | £35.00-£65.00 Single
18 Double | | £35.00-£65.00 Dbl/Twn
2 Family

Imposing Victorian town centre hotel near to the water front. Easily accessible for ferry terminal, railway station and major roads.

Important: Prices stated are estimates and may be subject to amendments

Oban, Argyll — Map Ref: 1E2

B&B

Sheep Fank Cottage
Musdale Road, Kilmore, by Oban, Argyll, PA34 4XX
Tel: 01631 770308
E-mail: peter_gwen@tait-oban.freeserve.co.uk

2 Dbl/Twin All En Suite

B&B per person £23.00-£26.00 Dbl/Twn

Open May-Sep

Attractive, modern and tastefully appointed cottage set amongst a group of houses in the secluded green glen of Musdale, 5 miles south of Oban. Come and enjoy this peaceful, tranquil location. Perfect base for exploring Argyll and the Isles.

GUEST HOUSE

Thornloe Guest House
Albert Road, Oban, Argyll, PA34 5JD
Tel/Fax: 01631 562879
E-mail: thornloe@netscapeonline.co.uk
Web: www.smoothhound.co.uk/hotels/thornloe.html

1 Single, 2 Twin, 4 Double, 1 Family — 7 En Suite fac, 1 Priv.NOT ensuite

B&B per person from £18.00 Single, from £18.00 Dbl/Twn

Open Mar-Nov

Completely modernised Victorian semi-detached house with garden, in centrally situated residential area with fine views over Oban Bay towards the Isle of Mull. Within easy walking distance from town centre, leisure facilities and other amenities.

B&B

The Torrans
Drummore Road, Oban, Argyll, PA34 4JL
Tel: 01631 565342

1 Twin, 1 Double, 1 Family — All En Suite, 1 Priv.NOT ensuite

B&B per person £16.00-£20.00 Dbl/Twn

Open Jan-Dec

Comfortable family home in quiet residential cul-de-sac. 1 mile (2kms) from town centre and all amenities. Excellent views across Oban and the Islands.

Oban, Argyll

Map Ref: 1E2

B&B

Verulam
Drummore Road, Oban, Argyll, PA34 4JL
Tel: 01631 566115

2 Double | All En Suite | B&B per person £16.00-£20.00 Double | Open Easter-Oct

Modern family bungalow in quiet residential area, close to town centre. Private car park . All rooms ground floor.

GUEST HOUSE

Viewbank Guest House
Breadalbane Lane, Oban, Argyll, PA34 5PF
Tel: 01631 562328 Fax: 01631 570222

2 Twin, 1 Double, 2 Family | All En Suite | B&B per person from £18.00 Dbl/Twn; Room only per person from £16.00 | Open Jan-Dec

Viewbank is a spacious Victorian villa recently renovated, set in its own private garden with beautiful views over Oban Bay & Kerrera. All bedrooms ensuite. No smoking house.

by Oban, Argyll

Map Ref: 1E2

SMALL HOTEL

Ards House
Connel, by Oban, Argyll, PA37 1PT
Tel: 01631 710255
Web: www.ardshouse.com

1 Single, 3 Twin, 3 Double | 6 En Suite fac, 1 Priv.NOT ensuite | B&B per person from £35.00 Single, from £35.00 Dbl/Twn | Open Mar-Dec excl Xmas; B&B + Eve.Meal from £54.00

Warm friendly atmosphere in this family run house where husband is a keen cook. Large relaxing lounge, table licence, superb sea and sunset views. Taste of Scotland.

B&B

Invercairn
Musdale Road, Kilmore, Oban, Argyll, PA34 4XX
Tel/Fax: 01631 770301
E-mail: invercairn.kilmore@virgin.net

1 Twin, 2 Double | All En Suite | B&B per person from £20.00 Dbl/Twn | Open May-Sep

Warm Scottish welcome assured when you stay in this comfortable home, situated in a tranquil, picturesque Highland Glen. Perfect for touring. Enjoy the magnificent views, comfort and hospitality. Non smoking. Oban, the Gateway to the Isles, only 4 miles away.

Port of Menteith, Perthshire

Map Ref: 1H3

★★★ B&B

Collymoon Pendicle

Port of Menteith, by Kippen, Stirlingshire, FK8 3JY
Tel: 01360 850222
E-mail: gilliantough@compuserve.com

1 Double
1 Family

1 Pub Bath/Show

B&B per person
from £17.00 Double

Open Apr-Oct
B&B + Eve.Meal
from £27.00

Family run modern bungalow on traditional working farm in country setting with beautiful panoramic views over surrounding countryside to the Campsie Hills. Home cooking a speciality. All rooms on ground floor. Ideal base for touring the Highlands. Salmon and trout fishing available.

★★★ B&B

Mrs Norma Erskine

Inchie Farm, Port of Menteith, Perthshire, FK8 3JZ
Tel/Fax: 01877 385233
E-mail: inchiefarm@ecosse.net

1 Twin
1 Family

1 Pub Bath/Show

B&B per person
£17.00-£18.00 Dbl/Twn

Open Mar-Oct
B&B + Eve.Meal
from £27.00

A warm welcome and friendly hospitality at this family farm situated on the shore of Lake of Mentieth in a quiet location. Traditional 200 year old stone built house. Home baking and home cooking. Evening meals by arrangement. Non smoking house.

★★ B&B

Holly Cottage

Port of Menteith, by Stirling, FK8 3RA
Tel: 01877 385604

1 Twin
1 Double

All En Suite

B&B per person from
£18 Dbl/Twn

Open Jan-Dec

Detached spacious bungalow with large garden, near Scotland's only 'Lake'.

Sandbank, by Dunoon, Argyll

Map Ref: 1F5

★★ INN

The Cot House Hotel

Sandbank. Kilmun, Dunoon, Argyll, PA23 8QS
Tel/Fax: 01369 840260
Web: www.cothousehotel.co.uk

4 Single
3 Twin
4 Double
2 Family

All En Suite

B&B per person
from £25.00 Single
from £20.00 Dbl/Twn
Room only per person
from £18.00

Open Jan-Dec excl
Xmas/New Year

Personally run Inn in rural setting outside Dunoon. Ideally situated for exploring the Cowal Peninsula. Extensive a la carte menu including local ingredients. Well stocked bar with range of malt whiskies. Cosy log fire.

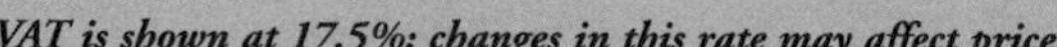

Southend, by Campbeltown, Argyll

Map Ref: 1D8

★★★ B&B

Low Cattadale Farmhouse
Southend, by Campbeltown, Argyll, PA28 6RN
Tel: 01586 830205

1 Twin, 2 Double — All En Suite

B&B per person from £20.00 Single, from £18.00 Dbl/Twn

Open Mar-Nov. B&B + Eve.Meal from £28.00

Distinctive black and white farmhouse with pretty, colourful garden situated on Southend Road. Evening meal available by arrangement. Quality cooking is a speciality. Vegetarians catered for.

Stirling

Map Ref: 2A4

★★★★ B&B

Ashgrove House
2 Park Avenue, Stirling, FK8 2LX
Tel/Fax: 01786 472640
E-mail: ashgrovehouse@strayduck.com
Web: www.ashgrove-house.com

1 Twin, 2 Double — All En Suite

B&B per person from £30.00 Single, from £23.50 Twin, from £25.00 Double

Open Feb-Nov

A warm welcome awaits you at this elegantly restored Victorian villa designed by renowned Scottish architect John Allan. 2 minutes to town centre and within walking distance of historical attractions including Stirling Castle. Ideal base for walking, golfing and exploring Loch Lomond and the Trossachs. Non-Smoking.

★★★ B&B

Carseview
16 Ladysneuk Road, Cambuskenneth, Stirling, Stirlingshire, FK9 5NF
Tel/Fax: 01786 462235

1 Single, 2 Twin — 1 Pub Bath/Show

B&B per person from £18.00 Single, from £18.00 Twin. Room only per person £12.00-£15.00

Open Jan-Dec

Comfortable country home evolved from turn of the century stables. In small conservation village within 15 minutes walk of Stirling town centre. Home baked bread served at breakfast.

★★★ GUEST HOUSE

Castlecraig B&B
50 Causewayhead Road, Stirling, FK9 5EY
Tel: 01786 475452

1 Twin, 1 Double, 1 Family — All En Suite

B&B per person £25.00 Single, £19.00-£20.00 Dbl/Twn

Open Jan-Dec

Purpose-built accommodation adjacent to tradtional stone semi-villa, only 5 minutes from Wallace Monument and University. Some ground floor rooms.

★★★★ GUEST HOUSE

Castlecroft
Ballengeich Road, Stirling, FK8 1TN
Tel: 01786 474933 Fax: 01786 466716

2 Twin, 3 Double, 1 Family — All En Suite, 1 Pub Bath/Show

B&B per person £35.00-£45.00 Single, £20.00-£25.00 Dbl/Twn, £65.00 Family

Open Jan-Dec excl Xmas/New Year

Nestling on elevated site under Stirling Castle, this comfortable modern house offers a warm welcome. Private facilities, some suitable for disabled.

Important: Prices stated are estimates and may be subject to amendments

Stirling | **Map Ref: 2A4**

★★★ B&B

Mrs Jennifer Dougall
14 Melville Terrace, Stirling, FK8 2NE
Tel/Fax: 01786 475361

1 Twin | 2 En Suite fac
1 Double | 1 Priv.NOT ensuite
1 Family

B&B per person
from £20.00 Dbl/Twn

Open Feb-Nov

Comfortable Georgian Town House located within 5 minutes walk to town centre and Railway Station. Off street parking.

C V

★★★ B&B

Firgrove
13 Clifford Road, Stirling, FK8 2AQ
Tel: 01786 475805 Fax: 01786 450733
E-mail: firgrovestirling@sblow.freeserve.co.uk

1 Twin | All En Suite
2 Double

B&B per person
£30.00-£35.00 Single
£22.00-£24.00 Dbl/Twn

Open Jan-Dec excl Xmas/New Year

Spacious family home with large comfortable rooms. Excellent parking within grounds. 5 minutes walk to town centre.

V

★★★★ B&B

Ian Galloway
X1 Victoria Square, Stirling, FK8 2RA
Tel: 01786 475545
E-mail: iain.galloway@tesco.net
Web: www.aboutscotland.com/stirling/victoriasquare.html

2 Twin/Double | All En Suite
1 Family

B&B per person
£40.00-£70.00 Single
£30.00-£35.00 Twin/Double

Open Jan-Dec

Victorian house with many original features situated in quiet residential area. 5 minutes walk from town centre, in Kings Park Close to Stirling Castle. One bedroom decorated in Charles Rennie Mackintosh art-deco style; and one spacious family room offering the 'Highland' theme with Tartan drapes.

C W V

★★★ GUEST HOUSE

Garfield House
12 Victoria Square, Stirling, FK8 2QU
Tel/Fax: 01786 473730

2 Twin | All En Suite
2 Double
2 Family

B&B per person
from £22.00 Dbl/Twn

Open Jan-Dec

Family run guest house in traditional stone built Victorian house overlooking quiet square close to the town centre, castle and all local amenities. Ideal base for exploring historic Stirling, Loch Lomond and the Trossachs.

C V

Stirling

Map Ref: 2A4

★★★
B&B

'Laurinda'
66 Ochilmount, Ochilview, Bannockburn, Stirling, FK7 8PJ
Tel: 01786 815612

1 Double	Private fac	B&B per person	Open Jan-Dec
1 Family	En Suite fac	£23.00-£24.00 Single	B&B + Eve.Meal
		£20.00-£21.00 Double	from £29.00

Modern detached villa in residential area of Bannockburn. Ideal location for touring all main cities and tourist attractions. Parking area.

★★
B&B

Mrs J MacGregor
27 King Street, Stirling
Tel/Fax: 01786 471082
E-mail: jennifer@sruighlea.demon.co.uk

1 Double	Private fac	B&B per person	Open Jan-Dec
1 Family	Pub Bath/Shower	£20.00-£25.00 Single	
		£16.00-£20.00 Double	

Comfortable Edwardian town house situated in the old town. Convenient for bus and rail station. 5 min walk from castle. Good touring base for Central Scotland. Convenient from motorway with ample parking nearby.

★★★★
B&B

Ravenscroft
21 Clarendon Place, Stirling, FK8 2QW
Tel: 01786 473815 Fax: 01786 450990
E-mail: dunbar@ravenscroft3.freeserve.co.uk

1 Twin	1 En Suite fac	B&B per person	Open Jan-Dec excl
1 Double	1 Priv.NOT ensuite	£35.00-£40.00 Single	Xmas/New Year
		from £23.50 Dbl/Twn	

Victorian family home with period furnishings and lots of character set in the conservation area. Close to town centre and historic sites. Non-smoking house.

★★
B&B

Rosemot
26 Cornton Road, Stirling, FK9 5AT
Tel/Fax: 01786 462796
E-mail: rsmeiklejohn@yahoo.co.uk

1 Twin	1 Pub Bath/Show	B&B per person	Open Jan-Dec excl
1 Double		from £18.00 Single	Xmas/New Year
		from £16.00 Dbl/Twn	

Comfortable family home with views of Stirling Castle and the River Forth. Ideally placed for Wallace Monument, University and town centre amenities. Private parking.

★★★★
B&B

Tiroran
45 Douglas Terrace, Stirling, FK7 9LW
Tel: 01786 464655

1 Twin	1 Pub Bath/Show	B&B per person	Open Apr-Oct
1 Double		from £18.00 Dbl/Twn	

A warm welcome in this family home situated in a quiet residential area, close to all local amenities, town centre and golf course. Ideal base for exploring Trossachs, Loch Lomond and historic Stirling. Tourist Award winner.

Stirling

Map Ref: 2A4

★★★ B&B

West Plean House
Denny Road, Stirling, FK7 8HA
Tel: 01786 812208 Fax: 01786 480550
E-mail: west.plean@virgin.net

1 Single, 1 Double, 1 Family	2 En Suite fac, 1 Priv.NOT ensuite	B&B per person £28.00-£30.00 Single, £23.00-£26.00 Double	Open Feb-Nov

200-year-old country house on working farm set in extensive grounds and woodlands. Offering warm Scottish farming hospitality.

C W V

★★★ GUEST HOUSE

Whitegables
112 Causewayhead Road, Stirling, FK9 5HJ
Tel/Fax: 01786 479838
E-mail: whitegables@b-j-graham.freeserve.co.uk

2 Double, 2 Family	All En Suite	B&B per person from £30.00 Single, from £20.00 Double; Room only per person from £20.00	Open Jan-Dec excl Xmas/New Year

Tudor-style detached house in residential area located midway between Stirling Castle and the Wallace Monument. Easily accessible to motorway links. Private off road car parking available. Non smoking house.

C £

Strathyre, Perthshire

Map Ref: 1H3

★★ B&B

Coire Buidhe
Strathyre, Perthshire, FK18 8NA
Tel: 01877 384288

1 Single, 2 Twin, 1 Double, 2 Family	2 En Suite fac, 2 Pub Bath/Show	B&B per person from £16.00 Single, £16.00-£19.00 Dbl/Twn	Open Jan-Dec excl Xmas

This former mill, now a personally run B & B in the village centre, offers traditional comfort. Ideal touring centre or base for wide range of outdoor activities.

C V

★★★★ GUEST HOUSE

Rosebank Guesthouse & Restaurant
Strathyre, Perthshire, FK18 8NA
Tel: 01877 384208 Fax: 01877 384201
E.mail: rosebank@tinyworld.co.uk
Web: www.SmoothHound.co.uk/hotels/roseban1.html

1 Single, 1 Twin, 2 Double, 1 Family	2 En Suite fac, 1 Priv.NOT ensuite	B&B per person from £19.00 Single, from £19.00 Dbl/Twn	Open Jan-Dec; B&B + Eve.Meal from £33.00

A warm welcome awaits you at this comfortable home in Trossachs village with scenic mountain and river views. Home baking. Log fires in lounge. Open fires in both lounge and dining room. Excellent touring centre for Scotland's first National Park.

C £ W V

Tarbert, Loch Fyne, Argyll — **Map Ref: 1E5**

B&B

Rhu House
Tarbert, Argyll, PA29 6YF
Tel/Fax: 01880 820231
E-mail: rhuhouse@ukonline.co.uk

1 Twin
2 Double

1 En Suite fac
1 Pub Bath/Show

B&B per person
from £19.00 Dbl/Twn

Open Mar-Nov

19th Century former shooting lodge situated in 40 acres of woodland on shores of West Loch Tarbert. Closest B & B to Islay ferry. Ideal for bird watchers and central base for touring beautiful Kintyre.

W V

B&B

Springside Bed & Breakfast
Pier Road, Tarbert, Loch Fyne, Argyll, PA29 6UE
Tel/Fax: 01880 820413
E-mail: marshall.springside@virgin.net

1 Single
1 Twin
1 Double
2 Family

3 En Suite fac
1 Priv.NOT ensuite
1 Pub Bath/Show

B&B per person
from £18.00 Single
£18.00-£22.00 pp
Dbl/Twn

Open Jan-Dec

Tranquility of traditional fishermans cottage, overlooking the harbour entrance, within walking distance of village. Convenient for ferries to Islay, Gigha, Cowal Peninsula and Arran. 3/4 hour drive to Campbeltown. Early breakfasts provided.

C V

Tarbet, by Arrochar, Dunbartonshire — **Map Ref: 1G3**

B&B

'Aye Servus'
Tyneloan, Tarbet, Loch Lomond, by Arrochar, G83 7DD
Tel: 01301 702819
E-mail: ayeservus@talk21.com

1 Twin
1 Double

B&B per person
from £17.00 Dbl/Twn

Open Jan-Dec excl
Xmas/New Year

Bungalow in elevated position, oversized lounge window with magnificent views over Ben and Loch Lomond. Large garden with outside seating. Cruise Loch Lomond and forest walks close by. West Highland railway line and bus stop are a 10 minute walk away.

C V

Tarbet, by Arrochar, Dunbartonshire   Map Ref: 1G3

BALLYHENNAN OLD TOLL HOUSE

TARBET, BY ARROCHAR G83 7DA
Telephone/Fax: 01301 702203
e.mail: jim@rawle1.freeserve.co.uk

Comfortable traditional guest house with beautiful views of Ben Lomond and Ben Reoch. The toll house is an ideal centre for touring, water activities, winter sports and walking. Having spent years walking in the area, the owner would be pleased to advise on some of the climbs and walks in and around the Arrochar Alps. Rail travellers will find the toll house five minutes walk from Arrochar and Tarbet station. There is ample off-road parking and all rooms have television, tea/coffee and ensuite facilities. There are several fine restaurants locally where you can sample fine Scottish cuisine.

B&B

Ballyhennan Old Toll House

Tarbet, by Arrochar, Dunbartonshire, G83 7DA
Tel/Fax: 01301 702203
E.mail: jim@rawle1.freeserve.co.uk

1 Twin — All En Suite
1 Double
1 Family

B&B per person
from £25.00 Single
from £17.50 Dbl/Twn

Open Jan-Dec excl Xmas/New Year

A warm welcome awaits in this comfortable house, convenient for Loch Lomond.

C W V

B&B

Bon Etive

Bemersyde Road, Tarbet, Arrochar, Dunbartonshire, G83 7DF
Tel: 01301 702219

1 Twin — 1 Pub Bath/Show
1 Double

B&B per person
£16.50-17.00 Dbl/Twn

Open Apr-Oct

Conveniently situated in quiet cul-de-sac close to the A82, with fine views of Loch Lomond and 'The Ben'. Close to station for trains to Glasgow or the scenic route of the West Highland line.

TV

C V

Tarbet, by Arrochar, Dunbartonshire — Map Ref: 1G3

LOMOND VIEW COUNTRY HOUSE

Tarbet, Loch Lomond, Arrochar, Argyll & Bute G83 7DG
Tel/Fax: 01301 702477 e.mail: lomondview@talk21.com

Welcome to our home in elevated position with all rooms overlooking Loch Lomond. All ensuite. Doubles with king-sized beds. Tastefully decorated in tartan with Norwegian pine furniture. Relax at your own table for breakfast overlooking the loch and enjoy a complimentary glass of sherry before dinner in our guests lounge.

★★★★ B&B

Lomond View Country House

Tarbet, Loch Lomond, Argyll & Bute, G83 7DG
Tel/Fax: 01301 702477
E-mail: lomondview@talk21.com
Web: www.lomondview.co.uk

1 Twin, 2 Double — All En Suite — B&B per person £25.00-£30.00 Dbl/Twn, £35.00-£45.00 Single — Open Jan-Dec

Welcome to our home which sits in an elevated position overlooking Loch Lomond. All bedrooms with picturesque views over Loch Lomond and Ben Lomond. Tastefully decorated in tartan with Norwegian pine furniture. Enjoy a complimentary sherry in the guests lounge. Ideal for day trips. Loch Lomond Golf Club 10 minutes drive.

Tillicoultry, Clackmannanshire — Map Ref: 2A3

Westbourne House

10 Dollar Road, Tillicoultry FK13 6PA
Telephone: 01259 750314 Fax: 01259 750642
e.mail: odellwestbourne@compuserve.com
Web: www.westbournehouse.co.uk

Victorian mill owner's mansion set in wooded grounds beneath Ochil Hills. Warm, friendly atmosphere. Delicious breakfasts. Log fires. Croquet lawn. TV/Radio, tea/coffee making facilities in all rooms, one on ground floor. Centrally situated for Edinburgh, Glasgow, Perth, Stirling and Trossachs – motorways fifteen minutes. Secure off-street parking. Single from £24. Double from £21.

★★★ B&B

Westbourne House

10 Dollar Road, Tillicoultry, Clackmannanshire, FK13 6PA
Tel: 01259 750314 Fax: 01259 750642
E-mail: odellwestbourne@compuserve.com
Web: www.westbourne.co.uk

2 Double, 1 Family — 2 Ensuite fac, 1 Pub Bath/Show — B&B per person from £24.00 Single, from £21.00 Dbl/Twn — Open Jan-Dec excl Xmas/New Year

Victorian mansion, full of character, on the Mill Trail and close to the new Sterling Mills 'Designer Outlet Village, nestling beneath the Ochil Hills. Home baking and cooking. Log fire. Secure off-road parking.

★★★★ B&B

Wyvis Bed & Breakfast

70 Stirling Street, Tillicoultry, Clackmannanshire, FK13 6EA
Tel: 01259 751513
E-mail: terrygoddard@netscape.co.uk

1 Double, 1 Twin — En Suite fac, Private fac — B&B per person £25.00-£28.00 Single, £21.00-£28.00 Dbl/Twn — Open Jan-Dec, B&B + Eve.Meal £35.00-£43.00

Cottage in conservation area overlooking the Ochil Hills and ideally situated for hillwalking. Friendly atmosphere, home cooking and baking. Evening meals by arrangement.

Tyndrum, by Crianlarich, Perthshire

Map Ref: 1G2

B&B

Glengarry House

Tyndrum, Perthshire, FK20 8RY
Tel: 01838 400224
E-mail: glengarry@altavista.net
Web: www.glengarryhouse.co.uk

A small family run Bed & Breakfast on the A82 on the outskirts of Tyndrum, the West Highland Way passes the door. Home cooking using fresh local produce.

1 Twin	2 Ensuite fac	B&B per person	Open Jan-Dec
1 Double	1 Priv.NOT ensuite	from £22.00 Single	B&B + Eve.Meal
1 Family		£18.00-£22.00 Dbl/Twn	£30.00-£34.00

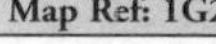

Invervey Hotel

Tyndrum, Perthshire FK20 8RY
Tel: 01838 400219 Fax: 01838 400280
Web: www.InverveyHotel.com

The Invervey Hotel is situated on the A82/85 at Tyndrum snuggling at the foot of some of the finest mountain scenery in Scotland. It is ideal for hill-walkers, climbers and ski enthusiasts (30 minutes by car to the ski tows). The lounge bar is large but cosy and is a wonderful meeting place for guests and locals. The games room, pool table, dart board and juke-box provides a separate and lively atmosphere for the young at heart.
Most of the bedrooms are ensuite and all have central heating, colour TV and telephone.
The restaurant is open all day and offers freshly prepared Scottish fayre and home baking.

HOTEL

The Invervey Hotel

Tyndrum, Perthshire, FK20 8RY
Tel: 01838 400219 Fax: 01838 400280
Web: www.InverveyHotel.com

Family hotel on main tourist route, surrounded on all sides by mountain scenery. An ideal base for fishing, shooting, walking. Climbing and ski-ing with 1/2 an hour drive.

5 Single	18 En Suite	B&B per person	Open Jan-Dec
7 Twin	1 Bathroom	from £20.00 Single	B&B + Eve.Meal
6 Double		from £20.00 Dbl/Twn	from £36.00
3 Family			

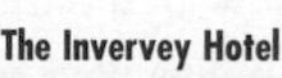

PLENTY OF CONTRASTS HERE: FROM THE WHITE-WALLED HARBOURFRONT HOUSES OF THE EAST NEUK FISHING VILLAGES TO THE HEATHERY SILENCE OF RANNOCH MOOR, FROM THE ARTS AND CULTURE OF DUNDEE TO THE TRANQUILLITY OF THE ANGUS GLENS. THIS AREA MAKES A GOOD PLACE FOR A BREAK, WITH A LITTLE OF EVERYTHING WITHIN EASY REACH.

Crail Harbour, East Neuk of Fife

PERTH IS AN IMPORTANT commercial centre for its hinterland both above and below the Highland line. Another Perthshire speciality are the little resort towns such as Dunkeld, Pitlochry or Aberfeldy, with their good range of visitor attractions such as the new Dewar's World of Whisky at Aberfeldy.

THE KINGDOM OF FIFE has plenty of character, with St Andrews noted as Scotland's oldest university and also often called 'the home of golf'. The town offers excellent shopping and is within easy reach of attractive East Neuk villages like Crail southwards and also the city of Dundee across the Tay Bridge to the north.

DUNDEE IS THE CITY of Discovery, with Discovery Point one of Scotland's top attractions while its new Science Centre, "Sensation" provides the whole family with hands-on fun. The Angus Glens are special places, with roads running deep into the hills through Glens Isla, Prosen, Clova or Esk – great country for walkers, birdwatchers and botanists. The coastline of Angus also offers plenty of interest, with spectacular cliffs and coves and small fishing ports such as Arbroath, home of the 'Arbroath smokie' – a fishy treat! Between hills and coast lie attractions such as Glamis Castle, birthplace of HM Queen Elizabeth the Queen Mother, and Edzell Castle with its unique garden.

Glenesk, Angus

Dunkeld and River Tay, Perthshire

SCATTERED ACROSS THE WHOLE area are a wide range of other attractions, such as Deep Sea World by North Queensferry (an aquarium featuring the world's largest walk-through tunnel), the birthplace cottage of the playwright JM Barrie in Kirriemuir, and also Scotland's National Garden at Perth (opening 2001).

EVENTS PERTHSHIRE, ANGUS & DUNDEE AND THE KINGDOM OF FIFE

18-23 APRIL
Kirkcaldy Links Market
Kirkcaldy Links
The longest street fair in Europe.
Contact: Mr J Haggart, Fife Community Services
TEL: **01592 417846**

23 JUNE
Ceres Highland Games
Ceres, Fife
The Worlds oldest Highland Games.
Contact: Ms M Glen
TEL: **01334 828811**

7-8 JULY
Game Conservancy Ltd Scottish Fair
Scone Palace, Nr Perth
Game fair with a wide spread of associated activities, competitions, demonstrations and trade stands.
TEL: **01620 850577**

14-15 JULY
Scottish Transport Extravaganza
Glamis Castle, Angus
Comprehensive display of vintage vehicles with trade & craft stalls, entertainment and amusements.
TEL: **01307 462496**

12 AUGUST
Perth Highland Games
Traditional Highland Games
Contact: Mr A Rettie
TEL: **01738 627782**
EMAIL: s.g.a@cableinet.co.uk

18-19 AUGUST
Arbroath Sea Fest
Arbroath Harbour
Weekend festival celebrating the maritime history, culture and seafood in Arbroath, with events for all the family.
Contact: Colin Stewart, Arbroath Sea Fest Company
TEL: **01241 870563**
EMAIL: cstewart@bsang.co.uk

15 SEPTEMBER
Battle of Britain
International Air Show
RAF Leuchars, Fife
Scotland's largest airshow featuring flying displays, exhibitions & aerobatics display teams.
Contact: Air Show Office
TEL: **01334 838559**
www.airshow.co.uk

22-23 SEPTEMBER
Fife Family History Fair
Various venues, Fife
Genealogy Fair
Contact: Janet Klack, Fife Central Area Libraries, East Fergus Place, Kirkcaldy, Fife, KY1 1XT (by post only)

*14-19 OCTOBER
Pitlochry Festival of Walking
Various venues, Pitlochry
The walking programme will consist of a selected series of graded walks, formulated and led by local guides. The routes will encompass hills, forests, lochs and rivers amidst the magnificent scenery of Highland Perthshire.
Contact: Pitlochry Tourist Information Centre.
TEL: **01796 472 215**

*24-30 NOVEMBER
St Andrews Week
Various venues, St Andrews
A week of festivities celebrating St Andrews day, including a festival of Scottish food and drink and an arts festival.
Contact: Ms Alison Laughlin, Project Co-ordinator
TEL: **01334 477872**

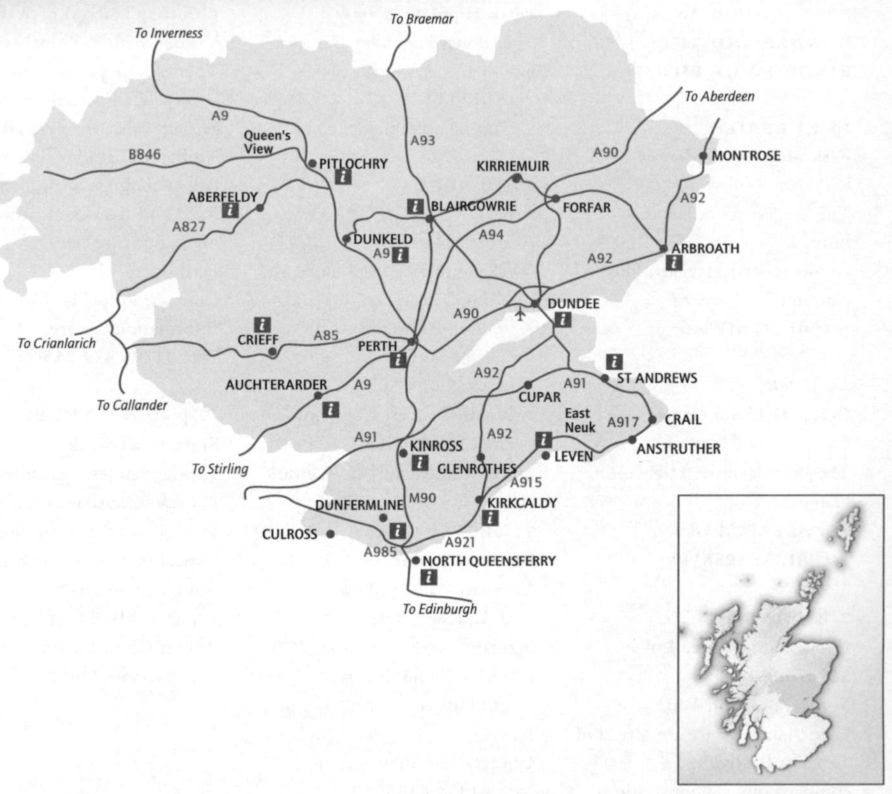

PERTHSHIRE TOURIST BOARD
Lower City Mills
West Mill Street
Perth
PH1 5QP

TEL: **01738 627958/9**
FAX: **01738 630416**
www.perthshire.co.uk

ANGUS AND DUNDEE TOURIST BOARD
21 Castle Street
Dundee
DD1 3AA

TEL: **01382 527527**
FAX: **01382 527550**
www.angusanddundee.co.uk

KINGDOM OF FIFE TOURIST BOARD
70 Market Street
St Andrews
KY16 9NU

TEL: **01334 472021**
FAX: **01334 478422**
www.standrews.com

ANGUS & CITY OF DUNDEE TOURIST BOARD

ARBROATH
Market Place
DD11 1HR
TEL: **(01241) 872609**
Jan-Dec

BRECHIN
Pictavia Centre
TEL: **(01356) 623050**
April-Sept

CARNOUSTIE
1b High Street
TEL: **(01241) 852258**
April-Sept

DUNDEE
7-21 Castle Street
TEL: **(01382) 527527**
Jan-Dec

FORFAR
45 East High Street
TEL: **(01307) 467876**
April-Sept

KIRRIEMUIR
St. Malcom's Wynd
TEL: **(01575) 574097**
April-Sept

MONTROSE
Bridge Street
TEL: **(01674) 672000**
April-Sept

KINGDOM OF FIFE TOURIST BOARD

ANSTRUTHER
Scottish Fisheries Museum
TEL: **(01333) 311073**
Easter-Sept

CRAIL
Museum and Heritage Centre
Marketgate
TEL: **(01333) 450859**
Easter-Sept

DUNFERMLINE
13/15 Maygate
TEL: **(01383) 720999**
April-Oct

FORTH BRIDGES
by North Queensferry
TEL: **(01383) 417759**
Jan-Dec

KIRKCALDY
19 Whytecauseway
TEL: **(01592) 267775**
Jan-Dec

ST ANDREWS
70 Market Street
TEL: **(01334) 472021**
Jan-Dec

PERTHSHIRE TOURIST BOARD

ABERFELDY
The Square
TEL: **(01887) 820276**
Jan-Dec

AUCHTERARDER
90 High Street
TEL: **(01764) 663450**
Jan-Dec

BLAIRGOWRIE
26 Wellmeadow
TEL: **(01250) 872960**
Jan-Dec

CRIEFF
Town Hall
High Street
TEL: **(01764) 652578**
Jan-Dec

DUNKELD
The Cross
TEL: **(01350) 727688**
Jan-Dec

KINROSS
Kinross Service Area
off Junction 6, M90
TEL: **(01577) 863680**
Jan-Dec

PERTH
Lower City Mills
West Mill Street
TEL: **(01738) 450600**
Jan-Dec

PERTH (INVERALMOND)
Caithness Glass
Inveralmond
A9 Western City Bypass
TEL: **(01738) 638481**
Jan-Dec

PITLOCHRY
22 Atholl Road
TEL: **(01796) 472215/472751**
Jan-Dec

Aberdour, Fife — Map Ref: 2C4

★★★★ B&B

Hawkcraig House
Hawkcraig Point, Aberdour, Fife, KY3 0TZ
Tel: 01383 860335

1 Twin | 1 Double — All En Suite

B&B per person: from £36.00 Single; from £26.00 Dbl/Twn

Open Apr-Oct. B&B + Eve.Meal from £48.00

Old ferryman's house situated at waters edge overlooking Aberdour Harbour and Inchcolm Island. Steep access. Totally non-smoking.

V

Aberfeldy, Perthshire — Map Ref: 2A1

★★★ B&B

'Ardtornish'
Kenmore Street, Aberfeldy, Perthshire, PH15 2BL
Tel: 01887 820629

2 Double | 1 Twin — 1 En Suite fac; 1 Pub Bath/Show

B&B per person: from £16.00 Dbl/Twn

Open Jan-Dec excl Xmas/New Year

Traditional town house near centre of Aberfeldy. Ideal for touring and all outdoor pursuits. Private parking.

V

★★★ B&B

Drumdewan Farmhouse
Drumdewan, Dull, Aberfeldy, Perthshire, PH15 2JQ
Tel/Fax: 01887 820071
E-mail: JDRiddell@aol.com

1 Dbl/Fam — En Suite fac

Open Jan-Dec excl Xmas/New Year

A warm Highland welcome to a traditional farmhouse in the heart of Perthshire with outstanding views. Central location for walking, touring, golf. We also operate award winning Highland Adventure Safaris which offer a unique journey of adventure & discovery. Ideal for families.

C V

★★★ B&B

Mavisbank B&B
Taybridge Drive, Aberfeldy, Perthshire, PH15 2BP
Tel: 01887 820223

1 Twin | 1 Double

B&B per person: £17.00-£18.00 Dbl/Twn

Open Mar-Oct

Friendly welcome in peaceful setting on outskirts of small country town. Beautiful views. Convenient for golfing, fishing, walking and birdwatching.

V

Important: Prices stated are estimates and may be subject to amendments

Aberfeldy, Perthshire Map Ref: 2A1

B&B

Oakbank
Kenmore Street, Aberfeldy, Perthshire, PH15 2BL
Tel: 01887 820298
Fax: 01887 829842

2 Double All En Suite
1 Family

B&B per person
from £25.00 Single
from £19.00 Double

Open Jan-Dec

Traditional stone built Victorian detached home. Short walk to town centre, swimming pool and recreation centre. Excellent for outdoor activities with watersports on Loch and River Tay and superb hillwalking including Ben Lawers and Schiehallion on the doorsteps. Or simply enjoy the peace and quiet of the tranquil surroundings.

B&B

Oakbank House
Grandtully, by Aberfeldy, Perthshire, PH15 2QZ
Tel: 01887 840265
E-mail: b&b@oakbank-house.freeserve.co.uk
Web: www.scotland2000.com/oakbank

1 Twin 1 En Suite fac
1 Double 1 Priv.NOT ensuite

B&B per person
£19.50 Single
£19.50 Dbl/Twn

Open Jan-Dec excl Xmas/New Year
B&B + Eve.Meal £29.00 pppn

Large Victorian mansion house set in almost 2 acres at Grandtully with scenic views to the river Tay valley. Half an hour drive from Perth; an ideal base for fishing, walking, golf and historic sites. Evening meal available. Enjoy eggs from our own flock of free-range black-rock hens.

B&B

Tighnabruaich
Taybridge Terrace, Aberfeldy, Perthshire, PH15 2BS
Tel: 01887 820456 Fax: 01887 829254

2 Single 2 Pub Bath/Show
1 Twin

B&B per person
from £18.00 Single
from £18.00 Twin

Open Apr-Nov

A Victorian stone built house with fine views over the golf course to the hills. Sympathetically furnished retaining the original wood doors and cornices making a comfortable home from home. Off road parking.

VAT is shown at 17.5%: changes in this rate may affect prices.

Key to symbols is on back flap.

Aberfeldy, Perthshire

Map Ref: 2A1

B&B

Tigh'n Eilean

Taybridge Drive, Aberfeldy, Perthshire, PH15 2BP
Tel/Fax: 01887 820109
Mobile: 07889 472248

1 Single
1 Twin
2 Double

All En Suite

B&B per person
from £20.00 Single
from £20.00 Dbl/Twn

Open Jan-Dec
B&B + Eve.Meal
from £34.00

Elegant Victorian house overlooking the river. Warm and comfortable, home cooking. One room with jacuzzi.

by Aberfeldy, Perthshire

Map Ref: 2A1

B&B

Boat of Cluny Bed & Breakfast

Boat of Cluny, by Aberfeldy, Perthshire, PH15 2JT
Tel/Fax: 01887 820944
E-mail: richard.cluny@virgin.net

1 Single
1 Double

1 Pub Bath/Show

B&B per person
from £18.00 Single
from £19.00 Double

Open Apr-Oct

Boat of Cluny, the former Cluny Ferry House, the last working ferry on the Tay, is situated in a beautiful setting on the banks of the River Tay. The area is renowned for its scenic beauty with golf, hill walking, pony trekking and fine gardens all within easy reach. Private fishing available.

B&B

Kinnighallen Farm

Duneaves Road, Fortingall, Aberfeldy, Perthshire, PH15 2LR
Tel: 01887 830619
E-mail: a.kininmonth@talk21.com

1 Twin
1 Double

1 Pub Bath/Show

B&B per person
from £16.50 Single
from £16.50 Dbl/Twn

Open Apr-Nov

Farmhouse set in beautiful countryside and woodland. Wide variety of wildlife in this peaceful backwater. Quiet garden for relaxation in the evening.

Abernethy, Perthshire

Map Ref: 2C3

B&B

Mrs MacKenzie Dawson

Gattaway Farm, Abernethy, Perthshire, PH2 9LQ
Tel: 01738 850746 Fax: 01738 850925
Mobile: 07976 830978
E-mail: tarduff@aol.com

1 Twin
2 Double

All En Suite

B&B per person
to £25.00 Single
to £20.00 Dbl/Twn

Open Jan-Dec
B&B + Eve.Meal
to £43.00

Georgian/Victorian farmhouse. Quiet rural location. Spectacular views. Ideal for touring and all outdoor activities. Ground floor ensuite twin bedroom with disabled (category 1) facilities available.

Important: Prices stated are estimates and may be subject to amendments

Alyth, Perthshire — Map Ref: 2C1

★★★ B&B

Craigellie House
Bamff Road, Alyth, Perthshire, PH11 8LA
Tel: 01828 632325

1 Twin, 1 Double — 1 Ensuite fac — B&B per person from £35.00 Dbl/Twn — Open Apr-Oct

Anstruther, Fife — Map Ref: 2D3

★★★★ GUEST HOUSE

Beaumont Lodge
43 Pittenweem Road, Anstruther, Fife, KY10 3DT
Tel/Fax: 01333 310315
E-mail: reservations@beau-lodge.demon.co.uk

2 Twin, 2 Double — All En Suite — B&B per person from £23.00 Dbl/Twn — Open Jan-Dec; B&B + Eve.Meal from £35.00

Family run guest house, maintained to a very high standard offering superb accommodation at affordable prices. 2 minutes walk to Anstruther's 9 hole golf course. Shore and harbour easily accessible. Private parking. Non-smoking.

★★★ B&B

Invermay Cottage
Common Road, Kilrenny, Anstruther, Fife, KY10 3JQ
Tel: 01333 312314
E-mail: invermay.kilrenny@talk21.com

1 Double, 1 Family — 1 Pub Bath/Show — B&B per person £25.00 Single, £18.00 Double; Room only per person £15.00 — Open Mar-Oct

Renovated 18th century cottage in peaceful location within walled garden. 9 miles from St Andrews. Situated within the East Neuk, between Crail and Anstruther.

Anstruther, Fife — Map Ref: 2D3

The Spindrift

Pittenweem Road, Anstruther, Fife KY10 3DT
Tel and Fax: 01333 310573
e.mail: info@thespindrift.co.uk Web: www.thespindrift.co.uk

Set on the western edge of Anstruther, The Spindrift has established a growing reputation for its unique brand of comfort, hospitality, freshly prepared food and service. Convenient for golf, walking, bird watching or exploring the picturesque and historic East Neuk.

Please contact Eric and Moyra McFarlane for reservations.

GUEST HOUSE

The Spindrift
Pittenweem Road, Anstruther, Fife, KY10 3DT
Tel/Fax: 01333 310573
E-mail: info@thespindrift.co.uk
Web: www.thespindrift.co.uk

Stone built Victorian house with wealth of original features, set in fishing village. Short walk from town centre. Ideal touring base. Non smoking. Private parking. Evening meal by arrangement.

2 Twin
5 Double
1 Family

All En Suite

B&B per person
from £30.00 Single
from £26.50 Dbl/Twn
Room only per person
from £20.00

Open Jan-Dec
B&B + Eve.Meal
from £40.00

B&B

Joyce & Tom Watson
8 Melville Terrace, Anstruther, Fife, KY10 3EW
Tel: 01333 310453

Victorian stone-built house in picturesque East Neuk fishing village. Varied and interesting breakfast. Small attractive garden with summer house where you can enjoy a read with your coffee.

1 Double
1 Family

1 Pub Bath/Show

B&B per person
from £17.00 Single
from £17.00 Double

Open Apr-Oct

Arbroath, Angus — Map Ref: 2D1

BAYVIEW

4 MONKBARNS DRIVE, ARBROATH DD11 2DS
TEL: 01241 879169 FAX: 01241 874037

In an excellent position overlooking the North Sea and West Links. Gracious house in the west end of town. Parking withing the grounds. Three large letting rooms, two of which have sea views. Bed and Breakfast prices from £18 per person per night.

B&B

Bayview
4 Monkbarns Drive, Arbroath, Angus, DD11 2DS
Tel: 01241 879169 Fax: 01241 874037

Situated in elevated position with outstanding views overlooking the River Tay. Private parking. Dogs welcome.

1 Twin
2 Double

B&B per person
from £18.00 Single
from £18.00 Dbl/Twn

Open Apr-Sep

Important: Prices stated are estimates and may be subject to amendments

Arbroath, Angus

Map Ref: 2D1

★ B&B

W Brookes

7 Helen Street, Arbroath, Angus, DD113AP

Tel: 01241 874912

1 Single, 1 Double | 1 Pub Bath/Show | B&B per person from £13.50 Single, from £13.50 Double; Room only per person from £11.00 | Open Mar-Oct

Modern terraced house, centrally situated close to railway and bus stations. Within walking distance of shops, beach and harbour. TV and tea/coffee making facilities in all rooms.

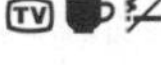

★★★ B&B

Mrs M Fergusson

20 Hillend Road, Arbroath, DD11 2AR

Tel: 01241 873991

1 Twin, 1 Double | 1 Pub Bath/Show | B&B per person from £16.00 Single, from £16.00 Dbl/Twn; Room only £14.00 Single, £25.00 Double | Open May-Sep

Spacious family house in quiet residential area within easy reach of all facilities in town. Off road parking. Gaelic and Spanish spoken. Non-smoking house. Hill walking and sea fishing can be arranged.

★★★ B&B

Mrs L Osborne

Hilltop, St Vigeans, Arbroath, Angus, DD11 4RD

Tel: 01241 873200

1 Twin, 1 Double, 1 Dbl/Ens | 1 Priv.NOT ensuite, 1 Pub Bath/Show | B&B per person from £22.50 Single, £20.00-£25.00 Dbl/Twn | Open Jan-Dec

Hilltop is beautifully situated in large gardens with rural setting. First class accommodation and warm hospitality guaranteeed. Central heating. Conveniently located for business, leisure and pleasure. Close to historic sites. Golf (3 courses) nearby.

Auchterarder, Perthshire

Map Ref: 2B3

★★★ B&B

Craiginver

1 Main Road, Aberuthven, Perthshire, PH3 1HE

Tel: 01764 662411

2 Twin | 1 En Suite fac, 1 Priv.NOT ensuite | B&B per person from £18.50 Single, from £17.50 Twin | Open Apr-Oct

Former manse dating back to 1854 and a 'C' listed building. Set in 1 1/4 acres of garden and woodland. Convenient base for touring Perthshire, Glasgow and Edinburgh an hour by car. Home made bread and preserves.

VAT is shown at 17.5%: changes in this rate may affect prices.

Key to symbols is on back flap.

Auchterarder, Perthshire — Map Ref: 2B3

★★ B&B

'Mamore'
10 The Grove, Auchterarder, Perthshire,P H3 1PT
Tel: 01764 662036

1 Twin | 1 Pub Bath/Show | B&B per person from £17.00 Single, from £17.00 Twin | Open Jan-Dec

Set in a quiet cul de sac yet close to the centre of the town with its restaurants and shops, this friendly Bed and Breakfast with its ground floor bedroom is an ideal base for golf and touring Perthshire and beyond.

Ballingry, nr Loch Leven, Fife — Map Ref: 2C3

★★ GUEST HOUSE

Navitie Guest House
by Ballingry, Lochgelly, Fife, KY5 8LR
Tel: 01592 860295 Fax: 01592 869769
E.mail: navitie@aol.com
Web: http://members.aol.com/navitie

1 Single, 2 Twin, 1 Double, 3 Family | All En Suite | B&B per person from £25.00 Single, from £22.00 Dbl/Twn | Open Jan-Dec, B&B + Eve.Meal from £32.00

Detached 200-year-old house in its own grounds overlooking Ballingry village. Only 4 miles (6kms) from the Edinburgh to Perth motorway. Centrally located only 30/40 minutes drive from Edinburgh, Stirling, Perth and St Andrews. Evening meal by arrangement.

Bankfoot, Perthshire — Map Ref: 2B2

★★★ B&B

Letham Farm
Bankfoot, Perth, PH1 4EF
Tel: 01738 787322

2 Twin, 1 Double | 1 En Suite fac, 1 Pub Bath/Show | B&B per person from £17.00 Twin | Open Mar-Nov

300 acre arable farm, in beautiful countryside, yet only 10 minutes from Perth. Warm welcome. Evening meal by prior arrangement.

★★ B&B

Mrs C McKay
Kayrene, Cairneyhill Road, Bankfoot, Perthshire, PH1 4AB
Tel/Fax: 01738 787338

2 Double | All En Suite | B&B per person £18.00-£18.50 Double | Open Jan-Dec excl Xmas/New Year

A friendly welcome at this personally run B & B. Private parking, ideal location for touring the Perthshire area. Fishing and golfing within easy reach.

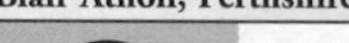

Blair Atholl, Perthshire

Map Ref: 4C12

★★

B&B

Beechwood

The Terrace, Blair Atholl, Perthshire, PH18 5SZ
Tel: 01796 481379

1 Twin — All En Suite
1 Double

B&B per person
£19.00-£20.00 Dbl/Twn

Open Jan-Dec

Bungalow in quiet side street of this picturesque town in rural Perthshire, surrounded by its magnificent scenery. Centrally situated to all main tourist routes. Both rooms with en suite.

T·H·E F·I·R·S

ST. ANDREWS CRESCENT, BLAIR ATHOLL PH18 5TA
Telephone: 01796 481256 Fax: 01796 481661
e.mail: geoff.crerar@lineone.net

Come and stay at our quiet family run guest house in Highland Perthshire. Set in beautiful scenery, just north of Pitlochry. Blair Atholl, famous for Blair Castle, offers golf, fishing, mountain bike hire, pony-trekking and endless walks in spectacular scenery.

★★★

GUEST HOUSE

The Firs

St Andrews Crescent, Blair Atholl, Perthshire, PH18 5TA
Tel: 01796 481256 Fax: 01796 481661
E-mail: geoff.crerar@lineone.net

1 Twin — All En Suite
2 Double
1 Family

B&B per person
from £18.50 Dbl/Twn

Open 2Jan-22Dec

Friendly family home with half an acre of garden, in a tranquil setting. Fine touring centre, close to Blair Castle.

Blairgowrie, Perthshire

Map Ref: 2B1

DUAN VILLA

Perth Road, Blairgowrie, Perthshire PH10 6EQ
Telephone: 01250 873053

Detached attractive Victorian villa – many original features intact – providing relaxing atmosphere to enjoy your stay in Blairgowrie. An ideal base for sight-seeing, touring, walking, golfing, ski-ing or fishing. There is ample parking and garden for guests' enjoyment. Situated ten minutes' walk from centre of town.

★★★

B&B

Duan Villa

Perth Road, Blairgowrie, Perthshire, PH10 6EQ
Tel: 01250 873053

1 Twin — 2 En Suite fac
2 Double — 1 Pub Bath/Show
1 Family

B&B per person
from £18.00 Single
from £17.00 Dbl/Twn

Open Jan-Dec excl New Year
B&B + Eve.Meal from £25.50

Traditional sandstone detached house retaining original cornices and wood panelling. On access route to Glenshee. Evening meal by arrangement.

Blairgowrie, Perthshire

Map Ref: 2B1

Duncraggan

Perth Road, Blairgowrie, Perthshire PH10 6EJ
Tel: 01250 872082 Fax: 01250 872098

Comfortable lovely furnished house with off road parking. An ideal location for tourists, hill-walkers, skiers and golfers alike or relax in our acre garden with small 9-hole putting green. No smoking house.

AA Selected ♦♦♦♦

★★★ GUEST HOUSE

Duncraggan
Perth Road, Blairgowrie, Perthshire, PH10 6EJ
Tel: 01250 872082 Fax: 01250 872098

1 Single, 1 Twin, 2 Double | 3 En Suite fac, 1 Pub Bath/Show, 1 Priv.NOT ensuite | B&B per person from £25.00 Single, from £20.00 Dbl/Twn | mid Mar-mid Oct

Comfortable lovely furnished house with off road parking an ideal location for tourists hillwalkers, skiers and golfers alike or relax in our acre gardens with small 9 hole putting green.

AA ♦♦♦♦

★★★ B&B

Eildon Bank
Perth Road, Blairgowrie, Perthshire, PH10 6ED
Tel/Fax: 01250 873648

1 Twin, 2 Double | 1 En Suite fac, 1 Pub Bath/Show | B&B per person from £16.00 Dbl/Twn | Open Jan-Dec excl Xmas

Comfortable family home, near to town centre, with ample private parking. Television in bedrooms. Good base for touring. Perthshire outdoor activities include walking,skiing, golf and fishing.

★★★ B&B

Garfield House
Perth Road, Blairgowrie, Perthshire, PH10 6ED
Tel: 01250 872999

1 Single, 1 Twin, 1 Double | 2 En Suite fac, 1 Priv.NOT ensuite | B&B per person £17.00-£20.00 Single, £17.00-£20.00 Dbl/Twn | Open mid Jan-mid Dec

Family run Bed and Breakfast, on main road entering Blairgowrie, in the heart of Perthshire. Ideal central base for touring, golfing etc. Off road parking available.

V

★★★ B&B

Gilmore House
Perth Road, Blairgowrie, Perthshire, PH10 6EJ
Tel: 01250 872791
E-mail: info@gilmorehouse.co.uk
Web: www.gilmorehouse.co.uk

1 Twin, 2 Double | All En Suite | B&B per person from £17.50 Dbl/Twn | Open Jan-Dec excl Xmas

Comfortable bedrooms in this recently refurbished traditional stone built house on the outskirts of Blairgowrie. Ideally situated for ski-ing at Glenshee, the whisky and castle trails, fishing on the rivers Ericht and Tay. Plenty golf courses in the area. Private parking.

W V

BRONZE

Blairgowrie, Perthshire | **Map Ref: 2B1**

★★★ HOTEL

Glenshieling House Hotel
Hatton Road, Rattray, Blairgowrie, Perthshire, PH10 7HZ
Tel: 01250 874605

Rooms	Facilities	Prices	Open
1 Twin 3 Double 2 Family	5 En Suite fac 1 Priv.NOT ensuite	B&B per person from £24.00 Single from £24.00 Dbl/Twn	Open Jan-Dec B&B + Eve.Meal from £36.50

Situated on the outskirts of Blairgowrie within large grounds, home to lots of wildlife. Home cooking using fresh local produce wherever possible. Golfing packages and tee off times can be arranged.

TV P C W V

★★★ GUEST HOUSE

The Laurels
Golf Course Road, Rosemount, Blairgowrie, Perthshire, PH10 6LH
Tel/Fax: 01250 874920
E-mail; laurels-blairgowrie@talk21.com

Rooms	Facilities	Prices	Open
1 Single 3 Twin 2 Double	4 En Suite fac 1 Pub Bath/Show	B&B per person from £20.00 Single from £19.50 Db/Twn	Open Feb-mid Nov B&B + Eve.Meal from £30.00

Originally a farmhouse dating from 1873, set back from main road, on outskirts of Blairgowrie with own large garden and ample parking. Rosemount Golf Course is a short walk away with a selection of 20 golf courses nearby. Ideal base for touring the beautiful Perthshire countryside. Fishing, shooting, mountaineering, ski-ing, pony trekking all in the local area.

TV P

by Blairgowrie, Perthshire | **Map Ref: 2B1**

★★★ B&B

Bankhead
Clunie, Blairgowrie, Perthshire, PH10 6SG
Tel/Fax: 01250 884281
E-mail: ian@ihwightman.freeserve.co.uk

Rooms	Facilities	Prices	Open
1 Twin 1 Family	All En Suite	B&B per person from £20.00 Single from £18.00 Twin	Open Jan-Dec excl Xmas/New Year B&B + Eve.Meal from £27.00

Farmhouse on working family farm between Loch Marlee and Clunie. Central base for touring, local fishing, golfing and skiing, osprey spotting at local Lowes Nature Reserve. Traditional farmhouse cooking and baking.

P V

★★★ B&B

Ridgeway B&B
Ridgeway, Wester Essendy, by Blairgowrie Perthshire, PH10 6RA
Tel: 01250 884734 Fax: 01250 884735
E-mail: Pam.Mathews@btinternet.com
Web: http://www.ridgewayb-b.co.uk

Rooms	Facilities	Prices	Open
1 Twin 1 Double	All En Suite	B&B per person from £22.00 Single from £22.00 Dbl/Twn Room only per person from £17.00	Open Jan-Dec excl Xmas/New Year

A warm welcome awaits. Detached bungalow with garden in peaceful country location. Views overlooking the spectacular scenery of Loch Marlee and surrounding farmland to the Grampian mountains. Only 3 miles from Blairgowrie. Ideal base for touring, hillwalking, golfing and fishing.

TV P W

Brechin, Angus

Map Ref: 4F12

★★★ B&B

Blibberhill Farmhouse
Blibberhill Farm, by Brechin, Angus, DD9 6TH
Tel/Fax: 01307 830323

1 Twin, 1 Double, 1 Family — All En Suite

B&B per person: from £18.00 Single; from £17.00 Dbl/Twn

Open Jan-Dec. B&B + Eve.Meal from £27.00

Stone built farmhouse in peaceful situation on mixed working farm. Homemade preserves and home baking and cooking. No smoking. Children welcome.

★★★★ B&B

Doniford
26 Airlie Street, Brechin, Angus, DD9 6JX
Tel: 01356 622361

1 Single, 1 Twin — All En Suite

Room only per person from £18.00

Open Jan-Dec. B&B + Eve.Meal from £29.00

A traditional Scottish welcome at this villa in quiet residential area. Ideal centre for touring the glens, fishing, golfing, castles and distilleries. Evening meals by arrangement. Plenty private parking.

by Brechin, Angus

Map Ref: 4F12

★★★ B&B

Brathinch Farm B&B
Brathinch Farm, by Brechin, Angus, DD9 7QX
Tel: 01356 648292 Fax: 01356 648003

1 Twin, 2 Double — 2 En Suite fac, 1 Priv.NOT ensuite, 1 Pub Bath/Show

B&B per person: £20.00-£25.00 Single; £18.00 Dbl; £19.00 Twn. Room only per person from £15.00

Open Jan-Dec

18c farmhouse on a family run working arable farm, with large garden. Easy access to Angus Glens. Ideally situated for golf, fishing, shooting, riding or just peace and quiet.

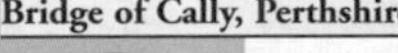

Bridge of Cally, Perthshire

Map Ref: 2B1

★★★ B&B

Tomlea Farm B&B
Ballintuim, by Bridge of Cally, Blairgowrie, Perthshire, PH10 7NL
Tel: 01250 881383 Fax: 01250 886383
E-mail: aliconstable@tomlea-farm.demon.co.uk
Web: www.tomlea-farm.demon.co.uk

2 Twin, 1 Family — 1 En Suite fac

B&B per person: from £20.00 Single; from £16.00 Twin

Open Jan-Dec

Traditional family-run hill farm in quiet and peaceful surroundings in the picturesque Glen of Strathardle. The area offers many outdoor activities including golf, fishing, skiing and hillwalking on the cateran trail. Ideal base for touring the castles and distilleries of Perthshire with Inverness and St Andrews only a day trip away.

Bridge of Earn, Perthshire

Map Ref: 2B2

★★★★ B&B

Battledown Bed & Breakfast
Battledown, Forgandenny,by Perth, Perthshire
Tel/Fax: 01738 812471

1 Twin, 2 Double — All En Suite

B&B per person: from £25.00 Single; from £20.00 Dbl/Twn

Open Jan-Dec

Quiet, comfortable cottage yet only seven miles from Perth. Private parking. Ideal for all outdoor pursuits. No smoking.

Important: Prices stated are estimates and may be subject to amendments

Broughty Ferry, Dundee

Map Ref: 2D2

★★ B&B

Dunrigh
1 Fyne Road, Broughty Ferry, Dundee, Tayside, DD5 3JF
Tel: 01382 778980

1 Single, 1 Twin — 1 Pub Bath/Show

B&B per person £16.00-£17.00 Single, £15.00-£16.00 Twin

Open Jan-Dec excl Xmas/New Year. Guest TV lounge

Modern semi-detached house in quiet residential area. Easy travelling distance to town centre and Discovery. Close to bus stop.

★★★ B&B

Invergarth
79 Camphill Road, Broughty Ferry, Dundee, Tayside, DD5 2NA
Tel: 01382 736278
E-mail: jill@oakley79.freeserve.co.uk

1 Twin, 1 Family — 2 Pub Bath/Show

B&B per person from £18.00 Single, from £17.00 Twin

Open Jan-Dec excl Xmas/New Year

Comfortable family accomodation in this quiet residential area yet nearby to beach and golf course. Convenient for all amenities in Dundee. Ideal base for touring the area.

★★★★ B&B

Mrs M H Laing
Auchenean, 177 Hamilton Street, Broughty Ferry, Dundee, Angus, DD5 2RE
Tel: 01382 774782

1 Single, 1 Twin — 1 Priv.NOT ensuite

B&B per person from £19.00 Single, from £19.00 Twin

Open Mar-Oct. B&B + Eve.Meal from £28.00

Detached house in quiet cul-de-sac. Border of Monifieth and Broughty Ferry. Central heating, private parking, double glazing. Residents lounge opening on to secluded garden. Morning/evening tea served free of charge.

Burntisland, Fife

Map Ref: 2C4

Gruinard

148 Kinghorn Road, Burntisland, Fife KY3 9JU
Tel: 01592 873877 e.mail: gruinard@dircon.co.uk
Web: www.s-h-systems.co.uk/hotels/gruinard.html

Situated on outskirts of the quiet coastal town of Burntisland, Gruinard offers excellent accommodation set in colourful garden. Overlooking river towards Edinburgh, accessible by train or road in approx 30 minutes. All meals include fresh local produce and are served in conservatory. Warm and friendly stay guaranteed. Sorry, no smoking.

★★★★ B&B

Gruinard
148 Kinghorn Road, Burntisland, Fife, KY3 9JU
Tel: 01592 873877
E-mail: gruinard@dircon.co.uk
Web: www.s-h-systems.co.uk/hotels/gruinard.html

1 Double, 1 Twin — All En Suite

B&B per person from £25.00 Single, from £21.00 Dbl/Twn

Open Mar-Nov. B&B + Eve.Meal from £32.50

Very well appointed traditional stone cottage (1904). Have breakfast in our conservatory overlooking the interesting and colourful garden. One room with extensive view across the Firth of Forth to the Edinburgh skyline. 30 minutes from Edinburgh and St Andrew's by car and easy access to Scotland's motorway system. "Scotland's Best" certificate.

Carnoustie, Angus

Map Ref: 2D2

★★★ B&B

Balhousie Farm
Carnoustie, Angus, DD7 6LG
Tel: 01241 853533 Fax: 01241 857533
E-mail: balhousie@msn.com
Web: www.balhousie-farm.co.uk

1 Twin, 1 Double, 1 Family — 1 pub show, 1 pub bath — B&B per person from £17.00 Single — Open Mar-Oct

Traditional Victorian family farmhouse on working farm, overlooking large gardens and extensive rural landscape. 3/4 mile off A92 giving easy access to coast, towns, Angus glens, golf courses and visitor attractions.

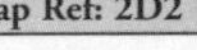

★★★★ B&B

The Old Manor
Panbride, Carnoustie, Angus, DD7 6JP
Tel: 01241 854804
E.mail: oldmanor@madasafish.com
Web: www.oldmanorcarnoustie.com
www.carnoustiecottage.com

3 Double — All En Suite — B&B per person from £35.00 Single, from £25.00 Double — Open Jan-Dec excl Xmas/New Year — B&B + Eve.Meal from £37.00

Spacious ensuite rooms in fully restored country house. Peaceful location close to Carnoustie. Convenient for golf, beaches and Angus glens. Non smoking house. Evening meals by arrangement using fresh local produce wherever possible.

★★★★ B&B

Park House
12 Park Avenue, Carnoustie, Angus, DD7 7JA
Tel/Fax: 01241 852101
E-mail: parkhouse@bbcarnoustie.fsnet.co.uk
Web: bbcarnoustie.fsnet.co.uk

2 Single, 1 Twin, 1 Double — All En Suite, 1 Pub Bath/Show — B&B per person from £25.00 Single, from £25.00 Dbl/Twn — Open Jan-Dec excl Xmas/New Year

A detached Victorian house in its own walled garden. Championship golf course and beach nearby. Private parking. Quiet location.

Important: Prices stated are estimates and may be subject to amendments

Comrie, Perthshire

Map Ref: 2A2

B&B

Langower B&B

Dalginross, Comrie, Perthshire, PH6 2ED
Tel: 01764 679990

1 Twin, 2 Double | 1 En Suite fac, 1 Pub Bath/Show | B&B per person from £20.00 Single, from £16.00 Dbl/Twn | Open Jan-Dec

Beautifully refurbished Victorian townhouse situated 100 yards from the River Earn. In the Perthshire Highlands village of Comrie. Ideal centre for golfers, walkers and fishermen.

Coupar Angus, Perthshire

Map Ref: 2C1

B&B

St Catherine's Croft

14 Union Street, Coupar Angus, by Blairgowrie, Perthshire, PH13 9AE
Tel/Fax: 01828 627753
E-mail: mary_broadley@yahoo.com

1 Single, 2 Twin, 1 Family | 2 En Suite fac, 1 Pub Bath/Show | B&B per person £17.00-£25.00 Single, £17.00-£22.00 Twn/Fam | Open Jan-Dec

Semi-detached stone built Victorian property in centre of Coupar Angus. Centrally situated for fishing, golfing, shooting, outdoor activities and an ideal touring base. Ensuite rooms available. Private parking.

Crail, Fife

Map Ref: 2D3

GUEST HOUSE

Caiplie Guest House

51-53 High Street, Crail, Fife, KY10 3RA
Tel/Fax: 01333 450564
Web: www.smoothhound.co.uk/hotels/caiplie.html

1 Single, 2 Twin, 3 Double, 1 Family | 3 En Suite fac, 1 Priv.NOT ensuite, 2 Pub Bath/Show | B&B per person from £18.00 Single, from £18.00 Dbl/Twn | Open Mar-Nov, B&B + Eve.Meal from £25.00

Very comfortable and friendly guest house renowned for its home cooking. with restricted table licence. On main street of fishing village near coastal path and picturesque harbour. Pets welcome by arrangement.

GUEST HOUSE

Hazelton House

29 Marketgate, Crail, Fife, KY10 3TH
Tel/Fax: 01333 450250
E-mail: admin@hazeltonhouse.com
Web: www.smoothhound.co.uk/hotels/hazelton.html

2 Twin, 1 Double, 2 Triple | 2 Pub Bath/Show | B&B per person from £20.00 | Open Jan-Dec

Fine Victorian merchant's house situated in the heart of historic Crail. Ideal base for touring East Neuk. St Andrews 15 minutes.

Crieff, Perthshire

Map Ref: 2A2

B&B

Ambleside Bed & Breakfast

3 Burrell Square, Crieff, Perthshire, PH7 4DP
Tel: 01764 652798
E-mail: ambleside@talk21.com

1 Single, 1 Double, 1 Family | B&B per person from £16.00 Single, from £16.00 Double; Room only per person from £12.00 | Open Jan-Dec

18C terraced town house in quiet cul-de-sac within 2 mins walk from town centre. Relaxed, friendly atmosphere. TV lounge with open fire.

Crieff, Perthshire — Map Ref: 2A2

★★ B&B

Concraig Farm

Muthill Road, Crieff, Perthshire, PH7 4HH
Tel: 01764 653237
E-mail: scott.concraig@tesco.net

2 Double, 1 Family — 1 En Suite fac, 2 Pub Bath/Show — B&B per person from £20.00 Single, from £17.00 Double — Open Apr-Oct

Comfortable farmhouse with spacious rooms. Peacefully situated just outside Crieff. Ideal location for golfing & touring.

V

★★★ B&B

Ann Coutts

'Number Five'
5 Duchlage Terrace, Crieff, Perthshire, PH7 3AS
Tel/Fax: 01764 653516
E-mail: number5@ecosse.net

1 Twin, 1 Family — All En Suite — B&B per person from £18.00 Single, from £18.00 Twin — Open Jan-Dec excl Xmas/New Year; B&B + Eve.Meal from £26.00

Centrally positioned in Crieff, offering excellent en-suite facilities and delicious breakfasts. Ideal for touring and golfing.

TV

C W V

★★ HOTEL

Leven House Hotel

Comrie Road, Crieff, Perthshire, PH7 4BA
Tel: 01764 652529

1 Single, 3 Twin, 6 Double — 8 En Suite fac, 2 Pub Bath/Show — B&B per person from £22.00 Single, from £22.00 Dbl/Twn — Open Feb-Nov; B&B + Eve.Meal from £37.00

Small family run hotel near town centre serving dinners and Scottish high teas. Ideally situated for touring and golf. Spacious car park.

TV

C W V

Crieff, Perthshire

Map Ref: 2A2

★★★★

B&B

Merlindale
Perth Road, Crieff, Perthshire, PH7 3EQ
Tel/Fax: 01764 655205
E-mail: merlin.dale@virgin.net

3 Double — All En Suite

B&B per person
from £35.00 Single
from £25.00 Double

Open Feb-Dec

John and Jackie provide a genuinely warm welcome at their comfortable family home with many touches of luxury. 6 languages spoken. By advance arrangement we offer a delicious four course dinner (Jackie is cordon bleu trained) and provide complimentary wine & liqueur. Extensive library with emphasis on Scotland. Jacuzzi bath. Relax and enjoy.

TV P

Culross, Fife

Map Ref: 2B4

★★★

B&B

St Mungo's
Low Causeway, Culross, Fife, KY12 8HY
Tel: 01383 882102
E-mail: martinpjackson@hotmail.com
Web: www.milford.co.uk/scotland/accom/h-a-1763.html

1 Twin — 1 En Suite fac
1 Double — 2 Pub Bath/Show
1 Family

B&B per person
from £20.00 Single
from £16.00 Double

Open Jan-Dec

17c home, with fine views overlooking the Forth. On outskirts of conservation village. Interesting garden. Ideal base for touring. Non smoking and private parking.

TV P

C W V

Dairsie, by Cupar, Fife

Map Ref: 2D2

★★★ B&B

Mrs C Scott

Easter Craigfoodie, Dairsie, by Cupar, Fife, KY15 4SW
Tel: 01334 870286

1 Twin | 1 Double | 1 Family

1 Pub Bath/Show

B&B per person
£18.00-£21.00 Single
£17.00-£19.00 Dbl/Twn

Open Jan-Dec

Traditional, Victorian farmhouse with panoramic views across Fife to Firth of Tay and Angus coast. 7 miles (11kms) from St Andrews. Ideal golf and touring base.

Dalgety Bay, Fife

Map Ref: 2B4

★★★★ B&B

Mr & Mrs Mead

The Coach House, 1 Hopeward Mews, Dalgety Bay, Fife, KY11 5TB
Tel: 01383 823584

2 Single | 1 Twin | 1 Double

2 Priv.NOT ensuite
2 Pub Bath/Show
Ensuite fac

B&B per person
£19.00-£21.00 Single
£19.00-£21.00 Dbl/Twn
£25.00-£26.00 Dbl Ens

Open Jan-Dec excl Xmas/New Year

Modern family bungalow in superb coastal location with excellent panoramic view south across the Firth of Forth to Edinburgh. Situated on the Fife Coastal Path, only 20 minutes travel from Edinburgh with excellent public transport links.. An ideal place to relax and unwind and watch the seals play at the foot of the garden.

Dundee, Angus

Map Ref: 2C2

★★★ GUEST HOUSE

Aberlaw Guest House, Beryl & Bruce Tyrie

230 Broughty Ferry Road, Dundee, Angus, DD4 7JP
Tel/Fax: 01382 456929
E-mail: AberlawGuesthouse1@activemail.co.uk

2 Single | 1 Twin | 2 Double

1 En Suite fac
1 Pub Bath/Show

B&B per person
from £22.00 Single
from £22.00 Dbl/Twn

Open Jan-Dec excl Xmas/New Year

Family run Victorian house with private parking. Close to city centre, overlooking River Tay. Five minutes on commuter bus to town centre. Ideal for golfing at Carnoustie and St. Andrews.

★★★ GUEST HOUSE

Abertay Guest House

65 Monifieth Road, Broughty Ferry, Dundee, Angus, DD5 2RW
Tel: 01382 730381

1 Single | 2 Twin | 1 Double | 2 Family

5 En Suite fac
1 Priv.NOT ensuite
1 Pub Bath/Show

B&B per person
from £25.00 Single
from £20.00 Dbl/Twn

Open Jan-Dec excl Xmas/New Year

Victorian terraced villa, approximately 5 miles from Dundee city centre and Universities. On main bus routes. Convenient for golf courses and beaches. Parking.

Dundee, Angus — Map Ref: 2C2

★★★ B&B

Anlast Three Chimneys
379 Arbroath Road, Dundee, DD4 7SQ
Tel: 01382 456710/077203 12412

Rooms	Facilities	Prices	Open
3 Twin	2 En Suite fac 1 Priv.	B&B per person £30.00-£35.00 Single £22.50-£25.00 Twin	Open Jan-Dec

A friendly welcome at this family villa on outskirts of Dundee. Only two miles from City centre. Private Parking. Non smoking house.

V

Ardmoy, Mrs Taylor
359 Arbroath Road, Dundee, Angus, DD4 7SQ
Tel: 01382 453249

Rooms	Facilities	Prices	Open
1 Single 2 Twin 1 Double	2 En Suite fac 1 Pub Bath/Show	B&B per person from £17.00 Single from £17.00 Dbl/Twn	Open Jan-Dec B&B + Eve.Meal from £23.00

Spacious stone built house in own garden on direct route to Carnoustie and Aberdeen. Private parking. Ideal touring base. Close to Discovery and city centre. Evening meal by prior arrangement.

C V

Ashvilla
216 Arbroath Road, Dundee, Angus, DD4 7RZ
Tel/Fax: 01382 450831

Rooms	Facilities	Prices	Open
1 Single 1 Twin 1 Double	1 Pub Bath/Show 1 Limited ensuite	B&B per person from £18.00 Single from £18.00 Dbl/Twn Room only per person from £16.00	Open Jan-Dec

Comfortable house, warm welcome, parking. Ideal situation on main route for both city centre and surrounding countryside. Children welcome.

C V

Mrs M Forgan
23 Castle Street, Tayport, Fife, DD6 9AE
Tel: 01382 552682 Fax: 01382 552006

Rooms	Facilities	Prices	Open
2 Twin 1 Double	2 Pub Bath/Show	B&B per person £16.00-£18.00 Single £15.00-£18.00 Dbl/Twn	Open Jan-Dec B&B + Eve.Meal £21.00-£25.00

Small and friendly. Situated in centre of Tayport and just a short walk from the harbour. Tea served on arrival and evening meals available. Easy commuting to Dundee, St Andrews and dozens of fine Golf Courses. Edinburgh 1 hour drive.

C W V

Hillside
43 Constitution Street, Dundee, DD3 6JH
Tel: 01382 223443 Fax: 01382 202149
E-mail: info@tildab.co.uk

Rooms	Facilities	Prices	Open
3 Dbl/Twn	2 Ensuite fac 1 Priv.NOT ensuite	B&B per person from £24.00 Single from £21.00 Dbl/Twn	Open Jan-Dec excl Xmas/New Year

Victorian family home in quiet residential area close to city centre and all amenities. Off street parking. Sunny conservatory dining room. Elegant residents lounge. Non smoking house.

Dundee, Angus | **Map Ref: 2C2**

★★★ GUEST HOUSE

Invermark House
23 Monifieth Road, Broughty Ferry, Dundee, Angus, DD5 2RN
Tel/Fax: 01382 739430
E-mail: sharon@invermarkhouse.fsnet.co.uk

1 Twin, 2 Double, 1 Family | All En Suite | B&B per person £25.00-£30.00 Single, £20.00-£22.50 Dbl/Twn | Open Jan-Dec excl Xmas/New Year

Privately run, in residential area near Dundee close to sandy beach shops and restaurants. Ideal for golfing and touring. Non smoking. Private car park.

★★ B&B

La-Little Flower B&B
52 Pitairlie Road, Midcraigie Estate, Dundee, DD4 8XP
Tel: 01382 501494

2 Single | 1 Pub Bath/Show | B&B per person from £17.50 Single | Open Jan-Dec excl Xmas/New Year

A warm and friendly welcome awaits at this comfortable family home. Ideal for cat lovers. Well situated for touring, central Scotland and further afield.

★★★ B&B

Nelson Guest House
8 Nelson Terrace, Dundee, DD1 2PR
Tel: 01382 225354

3 Twin | 1 Pub Bath/Show | B&B per person from £18.00 Single, from £16.00 Dbl/Twn | Open Jan-Dec

Family home in residential area, close to the town centre.

★ B&B

Sill Bed & Breakfast
47 Shaftsbury Road, Dundee, Angus, DD2 1JZ
Tel/Fax: 01382 566598
E-mail: freeservice@familystill

1 Single, 1 Twin | 1 Pub Bath/Show | B&B per person from £12.00 Single, from £12.00 Twin, Room only per person from £10.00 | Open Jan-Dec excl Xmas/New Year

In quiet residential area near city centre and University. Central heating, colour TV and tea and coffee making facilities in all rooms. Parking available.

★★★★ B&B

Mrs D Small
5 Fort Street, Dundee, Angus, DD2 1BS
Tel/Fax: 01382 566563

1 Twin, 1 Double | All En Suite | B&B per person £22.50-£27.50 Single, £20.00-£25.00 Dbl/Twn | Open Jan-Dec

A warm welcome at this family B & B. Quiet location. Fine views over the Tay. Many golf courses nearby. Ensuite rooms. Ideal base for touring Scotland.

Important: Prices stated are estimates and may be subject to amendments

Dunfermline, Fife

Map Ref: 2B4

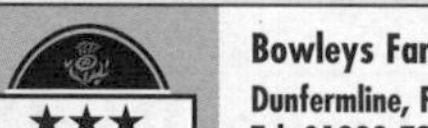

B&B

Bowleys Farm B&B
Dunfermline, Fife, KY12 0SG
Tel: 01383 721056

2 Family | 1 En Suite fac, 1 Priv.NOT ensuite | B&B per person from £25.00 Single, from £20.00 Dbl/Twn, Room only per person from £15.00 | Open Feb-Dec, B&B + Eve.Meal from £30.00

Quiet, peaceful and relaxing 19th century working stock farm. Warm welcome and homebaking. 5 miles (8kms) N of Dunfermline. Trout fishing available.

B&B

June & Bruce Hastings
Hopetoun Lodge, 141 Halbeath Road, Dunfermline, Fife, KY11 4LA
Tel: 01383 620906/01383 624252

2 Twin, 1 Family | 1 En Suite fac, 2 Pub Bath/Show | B&B per person £22.00-£28.00 Single, £20.00-£25.00 Twin | Open Jan-Dec

1920s bungalow with large Art Deco bathroom. Conveniently located for access to M90 and only 20 minutes by train from Edinburgh. Strictly non-smoking.

B&B

Hillview House
9 Aberdour Road, Dunfermline, Fife, KY11 4PB
Tel/Fax: 01383 726278
E-mail: hillviewbb@freenetname.co.uk
Web: www.HillviewhouseDunfermline.freeserve.co.uk

2 Twin, 1 Double | All En Suite | B&B per person £23.00-£27.00 Single, £20.00-£25.00 Dbl/Twn | Open Jan-Dec

An attractive detached villa on the outskirts of the town. Close to the M90, easy access to Edinburgh and Perth. Private parking. Italian spoken. All rooms en-suite. Complimentary videos. Benvenuti!

by Dunfermline, Fife

Map Ref: 2B4

B&B

Lochfitty Cottage B&B
Lassodie, Dunfermline, Fife, KY12 0SP
Tel: 01383 831081
Web: www.lochfittybandb.btinternet.co.uk

1 Double, 1 Family | 1 En-suite fac, 1 Priv.NOT ensuite | B&B per person from £18.00 Single, from £18.00 Dbl/Fam | Open Jan-Dec

Rural roadside location, with large natural garden, yet close to all local amenities and major attractions including Loch Fitty Trout Fishery, water skiing, numerous golf courses and Knockhill Racing Circuit. 3 kms from M90 (Junction 3 or Junction 4). Children and pets welcome.

by Dunfermline, Fife

Map Ref: 2B4

Roscobie Farmhouse B&B

Roscobie Farm, Dunfermline, Fife KY12 0SG

Tel: 01383 731571

Stay in a traditional farmhouse on a stock rearing farm with a warm relaxed friendly atmosphere and comfortable accommodation and excellent food. Enjoy magnificent views over the Forth Valley. Looking out towards the Pentland Hills a perfect central location for exploring beautiful Fife and central Scotland with easy access to M90 motorway.

★★

B&B

Roscobie Farmhouse B&B

Roscobie Farm, by Dunfermline, KY12 0SG
Tel: 01383 731571

1 Twin, 1 Family | 1 Pub Bath/Show | B&B per person £18.00-£20.00 Single, £18.00-£20.00 Twin | Open Jan-Dec excl Xmas/New Year

Traditional farmhouse, set on a 400 acre upland Beef and Sheep farm. Extensive rural views over Fife and South ward to the Lothians. Ideal location for exploring central Scotland, only 3 miles from junction on the M90 motorway, and close to Knockhill Race Track.

TV P

C V

Dunkeld, Perthshire

Map Ref: 2B1

★★★★

B&B

Mr & Mrs Peter Braney

The Pend, 5 Brae Street, Dunkeld, Perthshire, PH8 0BA
Tel: 01350 727586 Fax: 01350 727173
E-mail: react@sol.co.uk

1 Double, 2 Family | 2 Pub Bath/Show | B&B per person from £30.00 Single, from £30.00 Double | Open Jan-Dec, B&B + Eve.Meal from £50.00

Situated in the centre of Dunkeld, The Pend is a charming Georgian house full of character and retaining many original architectural features. Tastefully decorated and furnished using many fine antiques. Facilities include wash hand basin, shaver socket, hospitality tray, luxury bathrobe and colour television. Two large bathrooms.

TV P

C £ W V

★★★★

B&B

The Bridge Bed & Breakfast

10 Bridge Street, Dunkeld, Perthshire, PH8 0AH
Tel/Fax: 01350 727068
Web: www.visitscotland.com/TheBridge

2 Twin, 1 Double | All En Suite | B&B per person from £25.00 Single, £20.00-£25.00 Dbl/Twn | Open Jan-Dec

Welcome to the Bridge a beautiful restored Georgian home situated in the heart of historic Dunkeld. Ideally located for fishing, golf, cycling, walking, weddings, and enjoying the many attractions Perthshire has to offer. We will be happy to advise you. Fresh local produce available for breakfast, with tea, coffee and home baking available all day. All rooms are spacious and ensuite. Please note that we are strictly non smoking.

TV

C £ V

★★★

B&B

The Coppers

Inchmagrannachan, Dunkeld, Perthshire, PH8 0JS
Tel: 01350 727372 Fax: 01350 727021

1 Twin, 1 Double | 1 En Suite fac, 1 Pub Bath/Show | B&B per person from £16.00 Dbl/Twn | Open Apr-Oct

Typical Highland welcome and home baking in this bungalow with one ensuite bedroom. Comfortable lounge/conservatory with TV available for guests use and private parking. Quiet country location, which is easily accessible from the A9. Access to fishing, golf and superb walks.

P

W

Important: Prices stated are estimates and may be subject to amendments

Dunkeld, Perthshire

Map Ref: 2B1

★★★ B&B

Elwood Villa

Perth Road, Birnam, by Dunkeld, Perthshire, PH8 0BH
Tel: 01350 727330
E-mail: elwood7330@aol.com
Web: www.elwood-villa.co.uk

Edwardian, stone villa in residential area. Close to village amenitiesand River Tay, with easy access to forest and riverside walks. Friendly Scottish welcome with tea and home bakes. All rooms with wash-hand basins. Off Street Parking

1 Twin	1 Pub Bath/Show	B&B per person	Open Jan-Dec
1 Double		max £18.00 Single	
1 Family		max £18.00 Dbl/Twn	

★★★ B&B

Waterbury Guest House

Murthly Terrace, Birnam, by Dunkeld, Perthshire, PH8 0BG
Tel: 01350 727324 Fax: 01350 727023
E-mail: brian@waterbury-guesthouse.co.uk

Listed building in the centre of the rural village of Birnam, near Beatrix Potter Garden and Exhibition. Ideal holiday location in Highland Perthshire with many attractions and activities. Walking, cycling, birdwatching, fishing and golf and many others are on your doorstep.

2 Single	Standard	B&B per person	Open Jan-Dec
1 Twin	En Suite fac	from £20.00 Single	B&B + Eve.Meal
3 Double	En Suite fac	from £20.00 Dbl/Twn	from £31.00
2 Family	En Suite fac		
	2 Pub Bath/Show		

by Dunkeld, Perthshire

Map Ref: 2B1

★★★★ B&B

Mrs Jo Andrew

Letter Farm, Loch of the Lowes, Dunkeld, Perthshire, PH8 0HH
Tel: 01350 724254 Fax: 01350 724341
E-mail: Letterlowe@aol.com

Tastefully renovated farmhouse on working farm 1.5 miles (2.5 kms) from Scottish Wildfowl Trust Reserve. 3 miles (5kms) from Dunkeld. Peaceful location.

1 Twin	All En Suite	B&B per person	Open mid Jan-mid Dec
1 Double		£22.00-£27.00 Single	
1 Family		£22.00 Dbl/Twn	

Edzell, Angus

Map Ref: 4F12

★★★ B&B

Doune House

24 High Street, Edzell, Angus, DD9 7TA
Tel: 01356 648201
E-mail: johna@cameron21.freeserve.co.uk

A traditional Scottish welcome assured in this friendly family home where the emphasis is on quality and service. This victorian house is an ideal central base for touring the beautiful Angus glens, walking, golfing and fishing. Several eating places within a short stroll.

1 Twin	1 Priv.Shower	B&B per person	Open Jan-Dec excl
2 Family	1 Pub. Bath/Shower	from £16.50 Single	Xmas/New Year
		from £16.00 Family	

Edzell, Angus

Map Ref: 4F12

★★★ B&B

Elmgrove

Inveriscandye Road, Edzell, Angus, DD9 7TN
Tel/Fax: 01356 648266
Web: www.elmgrove.edzell.org.uk

2 Twin, 2 Double | 2 En Suite fac, 2 Pub Bath/Show | B&B per person £18.00-£22.00 Dbl/Twn | Open Jan-Dec excl Xmas/New Year

Set in a large garden, Elmgrove offers a quiet homely atmosphere. Rooms have tea/coffee, TVs and wash hand basins and there is a comfortable guest lounge. A warm welcome for all including children and pets. Off street parking available.

C V

★★★ B&B

Inchcape Bed & Breakfast

High Street, Edzell, Angus, DD9 7TF
Tel: 01356 647266
E-mail: inchcapebb.edzell@virgin.net

1 Single, 1 Twin, 1 Family | All En Suite | B&B per person from £18.00 Single, from £16.00 Twin | Open Jan-Dec excl Xmas/New Year

Semi-detached refurbished Edwardian villa on main street of quiet village, opposite golf course and near bowling green. 4 miles from main A90.

C V

Falkland, Fife

Map Ref: 2C3

★★ B&B

Templelands Farm

Falkland, Cupar, Fife, KY15 7DE
Tel: 01337 857383

1 Double, 1 Family | 2 Pub Bath/Show | B&B per person £15.00-£18.00 Single, from £15.00 Dbl/Twn | Open Easter-Oct

Farmhouse on Lomond Hills with superb panoramic views over Howe of Fife. 10 minutes walk from a variety of eating establishments. 20 miles (32 kms) from St Andrews. Central for touring.

C W

Forfar, Angus

Map Ref: 2D1

★★★ B&B

Atholl Cottage

2 Robertson Terrace, Forfar, Angus, DD8 3JN
Tel: 01307 465755 Mobile: 07957 913974

1 Double, 1 Family | All En Suite | B&B per person from £22.00 Single, from £18.00 Double | Open Jan-Dec

Situated in a quiet residential area, yet only 5 minutes walk to town centre, a warm welcome assured here. Off road parking available. Open all year.

C V

★★★ B&B

Colmar

9 Canmore Street, Forfar, Angus, DD8 3HT
Tel: 01307 463086

1 Single, 1 Twin, 1 Family | 2 En Suite fac, 1 Priv.NOT ensuite | B&B per person from £16.00 Single, from £17.50 Twn/Fam | Open Jan-Dec excl Xmas/New Year

Centrally situated friendly family run B&B with private parking. Ideal for Glamis Castle, walking in the glens with many golf courses nearby, including a championship course at Carnoustie (18 miles away).

Forfar, Angus — **Map Ref: 2D1**

★★★ B&B

Glencoul House
Justinhaugh, by Tannadice, Forfar, Angus, DD8 3SF
Tel/Fax: 01307 860248
E-mail: glencoul@waitrose.com

1 Twin, 1 Dbl/Fam — 2 Pub Bath/Show

B&B per person: from £20.00 Single; from £20.00 Dbl/Twn

Open Jan-Nov excl New Year. B&B + Eve.Meal from £29.50

Former Customs House on South Esk. Fishing available. Quiet and peaceful. Close to glens of Clova and Isla. Close to Forfar, Kirriemuir and Brechin. Evening meals available. A variety of golf courses within easy reach.

Farmhouse Bed & Breakfast

WEST MAINS OF TURIN, FORFAR DD8 2TE

Telephone: 01307 830229 Fax: 01307 830229 e.mail: cjolly3@cs.com
Web: www.s-h-systems.co.uk/hotels/farmho.html

Family run stock farm has a panoramic view over Rescobie Loch. Warm welcome awaits you. Good home cooking and baking ensures guests have an enjoyable stay. Ideal area for golfing (20 mins from Carnoustie), hillwalking, horse-riding, visiting Castles, National Trust properties and gardens. Snooker for evening entertainment.

B&B

Mrs C Jolly
West Mains of Turin, Rescobie, Forfar, Angus, DD8 2TE
Tel/Fax: 01307 830229
E.mail: cjolly3@cs.com
Web: www.s-h-systems.co.uk/hotels/farmho.html

1 Single, 1 Double, 1 Family — 1 En Suite fac, 1 Priv ensuite, 1 Pub Bath/Show

B&B per person: £17.00-£22.00 Single; £17.00-£20.00 Double

Open Mar-Oct. B&B + Eve.Meal £28.00-£32.00

Farmhouse on working stock farm, 4 miles (6kms) east of Forfar. In elevated position with panoramic views southwards over Rescobie Loch. Evening meals by arrangement. Plenty of golf courses nearby.

WEMYSS FARM

Montrose Road, Forfar DD8 2TB
Tel/Fax: Forfar 01307 462887 e.mail: Wemyssfarm@hotmail.com

Situated 2½ miles along the B9113, our 190-acre farm has a wide variety of animals. Glamis Castle nearby. Many other castles etc. within easy reach. Ideal touring base for Glens, Dundee (12 miles), Perth, St Andrews, Aberdeen, Edinburgh, Balmoral, Deeside and East Coast resorts. Hillwalking, shooting, golf and fishing nearby. Children welcome.

A warm welcome awaits!

B&B

Wemyss Farm
Montrose Road, Forfar, Angus, DD8 2TB
Tel/Fax: 01307 462887
E.mail: Wemyssfarm@hotmail.com

1 Double, 1 Family — 2 Pub Bath/Show

B&B per person: from £20.00 Single; from £17.00 Double

Open Jan-Dec. B&B + Eve.Meal from £29.00

Family farmhouse on working farm. Centrally situated for touring Angus and east coast. Home cooking and baking. Children welcome. Several castles and many golf courses within easy reach.

by Forfar, Angus Map Ref: 2D1

B&B

Finavon Farmhouse

Finavon, by Forfar, Angus, DD8 3PX
Tel: 01307 850269 Fax: 01307 850380
Web: www.b-and-b-scotland.co.uk/finavon.htm

1 Twin All En Suite
2 Double

B&B per person
from £21.00 Single
from £21.00 Dbl/Twn

Open Mar-Oct
B&B + Eve.Meal
from £30.00

Warm welcome assured in this modern house, in extensive secluded grounds at foot of Finavon Hill. Offers excellent facilities. Good base for touring. Excellent home cooking using fresh local and home grown produce. Conservatory dining room overlooking large interesting garden.

C W V

B&B

'Redroofs'

Balgavies, by Forfar, Angus, DD8 2TN
Tel/Fax: 01307 830268

1 Twin All En Suite
1 Double
1 Family

B&B per person
from £25.00 Single
from £20.00 Dbl/Twn

Open Jan-Dec excl
Xmas/New Year
B&B + Eve.Meal
from £27.50

House in woodland area. Ideal central base for outdoor activities. Children and pets welcome. Private parking. Less than an hours drive to Aberdeen. Plenty of beaches and golf courses nearby. All rooms on ground floor.

C W V

Forgandenny, Perthshire

Map Ref: 2B2

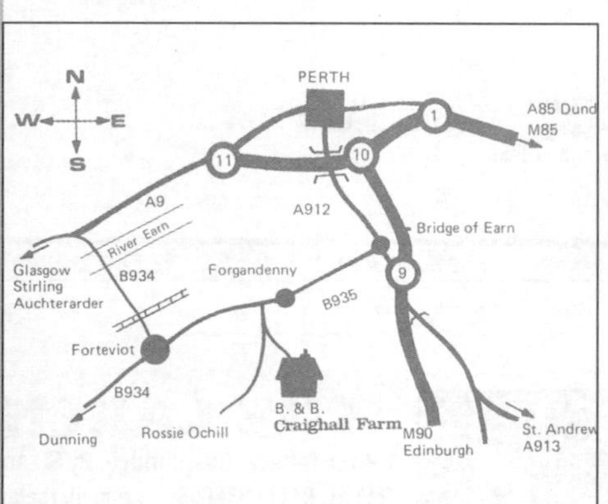

CRAIGHALL FARMHOUSE

Forgandenny, Bridge of Earn, Perth PH2 9DF
Tel: 01738 812415 Fax: 01738 812415

An ideal touring base – you can visit 90% of population of Scotland in 90 minutes. Situated on B935 ½ mile west from Forgandenny in the historic Valley of the Kings. At the foot of the hills we offer natural good humour and hospitality in our modern and tastefully furnished farmhouse. Through the windows, cattle, sheep and pigs graze in fields of our working farm. Golfers are well catered for with an abundance of courses within an hour's drive. Fishing by arrangement in private pond. Hillwalkers numerous routes through fields – healthy hearty breakfasts sets you up for the day with large and varied choice of home-grown produce. One of the few farmhouses to offer ground floor ensuite rooms.

★★★
B&B

Craighall Farmhouse
Craighalll, Fordandenny, Bridge of Earn, Perthshire, PH2 9DF
Tel/Fax: 01738 812415

1 Single	2 En Suite fac	B&B per person	Open Jan-Dec
3 Twin	1 Priv.NOT ensuite	from £25.00 Single	
1 Family	1 Pub Bath/Show	from £20.00 Twin	

Modern farmhouse, on mixed stock farm, with fine views over surrounding farmland and Ochil hills. All accommodation is on the ground floor. Home cooking. Non smoking establishment.

Fortingall, Perthshire

Map Ref: 2A1

★★
B&B

Mrs Tulloch
Fendoch, Fortingall, by Aberfeldy, Perthshire, PH15 2LL
Tel: 01887 830322
E-mail: Fendoch@eidosnet.co.uk

1 Twin	2 En Suite fac	B&B per person	Open Jan-Dec
1 Double	1 Priv.NOT ensuite	£16.00-£18.00 Single	B&B + Eve.Meal
1 Family	1 Pub Bath/Show	£16.00-£18.00 Dbl/Twn	£28.00-£30.00

A warm welcome and home cooking at this house, in quiet attractive village at foot of Glen Lyon. An ideal base for touring and outdoor activities.

Glamis, Angus

Map Ref: 2C1

★★★★
B&B

Mrs Grace Jarron
Hatton of Ogilvy, Glamis, by Forfar, Angus, DD8 1UH
Tel/Fax: 01307 840229

1 Twin	All En Suite	B&B per person	Open Apr-Oct
		£20.00-£22.00 Twin	

Ideal base for touring Angus and Glamis Castle. A warm welcome awaits at this traditional farmhouse on mixed farm. En-suite accommodation with sole use of guests lounge. Ideal base for the Angus glens, folk museum and many castles. Member of Scotland's Best.

Glamis, Angus — Map Ref: 2C1

B&B

The Tollhouse
Roundyhill, Glamis, Angus, DD8 1QE
Tel: 01307 840436 Fax: 01307 840762

1 Twin	2 En Suite fac	B&B per person	Open Jan-Dec
2 Double	1 Priv.NOT ensuite	£27.00 Single	
		£22.00 Dbl/Twn	

Come and unwind in totally renovated 18th century tollhouse. Enjoy Scottish hospitality and Kiwi informality. Delicious and interesting breakfasts. Beautiful countryside. Historic sites. Two miles north of Glamis on A928.

V

Guardbridge, by St Andrews, Fife — Map Ref: 2D2

"THE LARCHES"

7 River Terrace, Guardbridge, By St. Andrews KY16 0XA
Tel/Fax: 01334 838008 e.mail: thelarches@aol.com

"The Larches" is a beautiful former old Memorial Hall, situated in Guardbridge on the A919 between St. Andrews (3 miles) and Dundee (6 miles), convenient for golf, riding, glorious countryside and beaches. All rooms are ensuite or private bathroom, with colour TV, hairdryer, tea/coffee facilities, shaver points, hospitality tray, use of trouser press and ironing facilities, centrally heated throughout. Residents lounge with VCR and large selection of films, satellite TV. Conservatory recently built for residents use – available at all times. Children welcome, cot and high chair available at no extra charge. Come and sample our fantastic breakfasts! **Every home comfort!**

B&B

The Larches
7 River Terrace, Guardbridge, by St Andrews, Fife, KY16 0XA
Tel/Fax: 01334 838008
E-mail: thelarches@aol.com

1 Twin	2 En Suite fac	B&B per person	Open Jan-Dec
2 Double	1 Priv.NOT ensuite	£20.00-£32.00 Single	
	2 Pub Bath/Show	£20.00-£27.00 Dbl/Twn	

A beautiful old memorial hall, now converted into a family home, near centre of Guardbridge and R.A.F. Leuchars. 4 miles (6kms) from St. Andrews.

C V

Inverkeithing, Fife | **Map Ref: 2B4**

B&B

The Roods Guest House

16 Bannerman Avenue, Inverkeithing, Fife, KY11 1NG
Tel/Fax: 01383 415049
E-mail: isobel@theroods.com
Web: www.theroods.com

Quietly secluded family home. Close to rail station and M90. Well appointed bedrooms offering mini office and direct dial telephones. Evening meal by arrangement.

1 Twin
1 Double

All En Suite

B&B per person
from £22.00 Single
from £22.00 Dbl/Twn

Open Jan-Dec

C £ W V

Kinghorn, Fife | **Map Ref: 2C4**

B&B

Moir Cottage

6 Darney Terrace, Kinghorn, Fife, KY3 9RF
Tel: 01592 891556
E-mail: moircott@supanet.com

Traditional, fully refurbished, detached Victorian house offering comfortable accommodation, with sea views from the guest lounge. Situated close to all local amenities including train station, bus stops, sandy beach and golf course. Ideal base to explore the Fife coastline, St Andrews and Edinburgh.

1 Twin
1 Double

All En Suite

B&B per person
£18.00-£20.00 Single

Open Jan-Dec excl Xmas/New Year

Kingsbarns, by St Andrews, Fife | **Map Ref: 2D3**

B&B

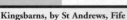

Mr Peter Erskine

Cambo House, St Andrews, Fife, KY16 8QD
Tel: 01333 450313 Fax: 01333 450987
E-mail: cambohouse@compuserve.com
Web: www.camboestate.com

Elegant Victorian mansion on wooded coastal estate, close to St Andrews with handsome four poster bed in principal guest bedroom. Evening meal by prior arrangement.

2 Double

1 En Suite fac
1 Priv.NOT ensuite

B&B per person
£38.00-£42.00 Single
£38.00-£42.00 Double

Open Jan-Dec
B&B + Eve.Meal
£65.50-£69.50

C £ V

Kinloch Rannoch, Perthshire — Map Ref: 1H1

GUEST HOUSE

Bunrannoch House
Kinloch Rannoch, Pitlochry, Perthshire, PH16 5QB
Tel/Fax: 01882 632407
E.mail: bun.house@tesco.net
Web: www.bunranoch.co.uk

Rooms	Facilities	Prices	Open
2 Twin 3 Double 2 Family	5 En Suite fac 2 Pub Bath/Show	B&B per person from £22.00 Single from £22.00 Dbl/Twn	Open Jan-Dec excl Xmas/New Year B&B + Eve.Meal from £38.00

'A Gem of a Place', set in beautiful surroundings, Burannoch House is renowned for its genuine, warm hospitality and excellent food. Explore the hills, where wildlife abounds. Discover castles, antiques, history and folklore. Cycle, walk, fish. Return to log fires, a fresh, home-baked tea tray and peace and relaxation. We would love to welcome you!

Kinross, Perthshire — Map Ref: 2B3

RESTAURANT WITH ROOMS

The Grouse & Claret Restaurant
Heatheryford, Kinross, KY13 0NQ
Tel: 01577 864212 Fax: 01577 864920

Rooms	Facilities	Prices	Open
3 Double	All En Suite	B&B per person from £34.50 Single from £29.50 Dbl/Twn	Open Jan-Dec excl middle 2wks Jan. B&B + Eve.Meal from £55.00

Restaurant featuring fresh local Scottish produce with a hint of oriental flavours. Separate accommodation, all overlooking the trout lochans to the Ochil Hills beyond. Conveniently situated off junction 6 on the M90 motorway. Edinburgh, St Andrews, Perth, Stirling and Glasgow all within an hour's drive.

B&B

Mrs Mary Sneddon, St Serf's B&B
35 The Muirs, Kinross, KY13 7AS
Tel: 01577 862183/864340

Rooms	Facilities	Prices	Open
3 Family	2 En Suite fac 1 Priv.NOT ensuite	B&B per person £25.00-£30.00 Single £18.00-£22.00 Double	Open Easter-Xmas

Comfortable family home centrally situated in Kinross. Off road parking available. Local fishing available. Close to local golf courses. Within walking distance of Express bus service for Edinburgh.

by Kinross, Perthshire — Map Ref: 2B3

B&B

Caplawhead B&B
Caplawhead, Rumbling Bridge, by Yetts o'Muckhart, Kinross, KY13 0QD
Tel: 01259 781556
E-mail: Hamish-Frances@caplawhead.freeserve.co.uk

Rooms	Facilities	Prices	Open
1 Twin 1 Double	All En Suite	B&B per person from £25.00 Single from £22.50 Dbl/Twn	Open Jan-Dec excl Xmas

Welcome to Caplawhead. A beautifully restored farmhouse with wonderful views, set in the peaceful countryside by Glendevon. Secluded, yet within easy reach of all main tourist routes. Perfect for golfing, fishing, walking and sightseeing. Good wholesome Scottish breakfasts with a wide range of delicious alternatives. Local country inns provide excellent evening meals.

Important: Prices stated are estimates and may be subject to amendments

Kirkcaldy, Fife — Map Ref: 2C4

★★★ B&B

Arborteum
20 Southerton Road, Kirkcaldy, Fife, KY2 5NB
Tel: 01592 643673

1 Twin, 2 Double | 2 En Suite fac, 1 Priv.NOT ensuite | B&B per person from £22.00 Single, from £19.00 Dbl/Twn | Open Jan-Dec excl Xmas/New Year

Quietly located adjacent to Beveridge Park and close to the centre of Kirkcaldy. Walking distance from shops and railway station.

★★★ GUEST HOUSE

Bennochy Bank Guest House
26 Carlyle Road, Kirkcaldy, Fife
Tel: 01592 200733

2 Twin, 2 Family | 1 En Suite fac, 1 Pub Bath/Show | B&B per person £18.00-£25.00 Single, £18.00-£25.00 Twin | Open Jan-Dec

Comfortable accommodation on upper floors of large Victorian house in residential area, close to town centre and railway station. Private parking.

★★★ B&B

'Cherrydene'
44 Bennochy Road, Kirkcaldy, Fife, KY2 5RB
Tel: 01592 202147
E-mail: cherrydene@beeb.net

1 Single, 1 Double, 1 Family | 2 En Suite fac, 1 Priv.NOT ensuite | B&B per person from £18.00 Single, from £18.00 Double | Open Jan-Dec, B&B + Eve.Meal from £28.00

Victorian, end terraced house in quiet residential area, yet within easy reach of all amenities. Private parking. Easy access to A92 (Kirkcaldy West). Ideal base for golfing and touring.

★★ B&B

Mrs C Ketchion
Wemysshof, 69 Lady Nairn Avenue, Kirkcaldy, Fife, KY1 2AR
Tel: 01592 652806

1 Single, 1 Double, 1 Family | 1 Pub Bath/Show | B&B per person £16.00 Single, £16.00 Double | Open Jan-Dec, B&B + Eve.Meal £21.00

Situated in a quiet residential area on the east side of Kirkcaldy. Come and enjoy our chat and stories in our friendly home. Evening meal by request.

★★★★ B&B

North Hall
143 Victoria Road, Kirkcaldy, Fife, KY1 1DQ
Tel: 01592 268864 Mobile: 07887 731785
E-mail: cairns@northhall.freeserve.co.uk
Web: www.SmoothHound.co.uk/hotels/northhall.html

1 Twin, 2 Double | 2 En Suite fac, 1 Priv.NOT ensuite | B&B per person from £22.50 Dbl/Twn | Open Jan-Dec

Former manse with original oak stairs and doors. Close to town centre. Ideal for touring Fife villages. Edinburgh 26 miles (42kms), 30minutes by train.

VAT is shown at 17.5%: changes in this rate may affect prices.

Key to symbols is on back flap.

Kirkcaldy, Fife

Map Ref: 2C4

B&B

Norview

59 Normand Road, Dysart, Kirkcaldy, Fife, KY1 2XP
Tel: 01592 652804 Fax: 01592 650801
Mobile: 07901 861289

2 Twin, 1 Double — 2 Pub Bath/Show

B&B per person from £14.00 Single, from £14.00 Dbl/Twn. Room only per person from £14.00

Open Jan-Dec

Personally run bed and breakfast on main tourist route. Ideal for touring Fife. Golf courses and other amenities close by.

Kirkmichael, Perthshire

Map Ref: 4D12

B&B

Cruachan

Kirkmichael, Perthshire, PH10 7NZ
Tel/Fax: 01250 881226
E-mail: wsg@kirkmichael.net
Web: www.kirkmichael.net

1 Double, 1 Family, 1 Twin — 2 En Suite fac, 1 Priv.NOT ensuite

B&B per person from £28.00 Single, from £23.00 Dbl/Twn

Open Jan-Dec. B&B + Eve.Meal from £35.00

Traditional Victorian country cottage overlooking River Ardle, quiet location close to village amenities. Rooms with ensuite & TVs. Personally run by Alan & Daphne we offer a varied a la carte dinner menu using fresh produce - WINNERS of the 1999 Glenturret & Perthshire Tourist Board most enjoyable meal award. An ideal base for touring, with fishing, shooting, walking & many visitor attractions nearby. Pets welcome.

Kirriemuir, Angus

Map Ref: 2C1

B&B

Crepto

1 Kinnordy Place, Kirriemuir, Angus, DD8 4JW
Tel: 01575 572746
E-mail: davendjessma@bun.com

1 Single, 1 Twin, 1 Double — 2 Pub Bath/Show

B&B per person from £22.00 Single, from £22.00 Dbl/Twn

Open Jan-Dec

A friendly welcome at this modern house in quiet cul-de-sac. 10 minutes walk from centre of town. Gateway to Angus Glens.

B&B

Purgavie Farm

Lintrathen, Kirriemuir, Angus , DD8 5HZ
Tel/Fax: 01575 560213
E-mail: purgavie@aol.com

1 Twin, 1 Double, 1 Family — All En Suite

B&B per person from £25.00 Single, from £21.00 Dbl/Twn. Room only per person from £15.00

Open Jan-Dec. B&B + Eve.Meal from £32.00

19c house on working farm, with views over Strathmore Valley. Glamis Castle, 7 miles (13kms), Kirriemuir 6 miles (11kms). Natural Cooking of Scotland using local produce. Dinners by arrangement.

Ladybank, Fife

Map Ref: 2C3

GUEST HOUSE

Redlands Country Lodge

Pitlessie Road, Ladybank, Cupar, Fife, KY15 7SH
Tel/Fax: 01337 831091

2 Twin, 2 Double — All En Suite

B&B per person from £24.00 Dbl/Twn

Open Feb-Nov

Redlands is an attractive country cottage, with an adjacent Norwegian pine lodge, set in attractive gardens, with acres of woodland and fields all around. Good home cooking and baking. Only 14 miles from St Andrews and an ideal base for golfing and touring.

Important: Prices stated are estimates and may be subject to amendments

Letham, by Forfar, Angus — Map Ref: 2D1

B&B

Woodville
Heathercroft, Guthrie Street, Letham, by Forfar, Angus, DD8 2PS
Tel: 01307 818090

2 Twin — 2 Pub Bath/Show

B&B per person
from £20.00 Single
from £18.00 Twin
Room only per person
from £10.00

Open Jan-Dec
B&B + Eve.Meal
from £28.00

A warm traditional scottish welcome awaits in modern new house on the edge of the historic village of Letham. Ideal location for golf, fishing, walking, glens, castles (Glamis nearby) & birdwatching. Within easy distance of Dundee, Aberdeen, Edinburgh, Royal Deeside & St Andrews.

C V

by Leuchars, Fife — Map Ref: 2D2

B&B

Mrs Dale
Greenacres Lodge, Fordhill, St Michaels, by St Andrews, Fife, KY16 0BT
Tel: 01334 838242

1 Twin — En suite
1 Double — En suite
1 Twin/Dbl — En suite

B&B per person
£28.00-£35.00 Single
£18.00-£27.50 Dbl/Twn

Open Mar-Dec

Traditional Scottish country cottage with panoramic views over Eden Estuary. Open fire in the comfortable lounge. Dine by candlelight in the evening. Excellent location for golf or touring.

C W V

Leven, Fife — Map Ref: 2C3

★★★

GUEST HOUSE

Dunclutha Guest House
16 Victoria Road, Leven, Fife, KY8 4EX
Tel: 01333 425515 Fax: 01333 422311
E-mail: pam.leven@dunclutha-accomm.demon.co.uk

1 Twin — 3 En Suite fac
1 Double — 1 Priv.NOT ensuite
2 Family

B&B per person
from £25.00 Single
from £23.00 Dbl/Twn

Open Jan-Dec

Victorian former manse. 2 minutes level walk from centre of Leven. Good base for golfing enthusiasts and New Fife Coastal Walk. 50 minutes drive from Edinburgh and 40 minutes from the airport. 7 miles to the nearest railway station. All bedrooms with either ensuite or private facilities.

C W V

VAT is shown at 17.5%: changes in this rate may affect prices.

Key to symbols is on back flap.

Leven, Fife

Map Ref: 2C3

★★★★

B&B

Lorne House

Largo Road, Leven, Fife, KY8 4TB
Tel/Fax: 01333 423255
E-mail: accomm@lornehouse.co.uk
Web: www.lornehouse.co.uk

Situated on the A915 tourist route overlooking one of many superb golf courses. Ideal for the discerning person who enjoys dining at its best. We are renound in food circles and commended for service and hospitality. Historical St Andrews is only a short drive. Special off season breaks. Non-smoking.

1 Twn/Sgl 2 En Suite fac
2 Double 1 Priv.NOT ensuite

B&B per person
from £25.00 Single
from £20.00 Dbl/Twn

Open Jan-Dec excl Xmas/New Year
B&B + Eve.Meal from £35.00

Limekilns, Fife

Map Ref: 2B4

★★

B&B

Breck House

8 Red Row, Limekilns, Fife, KY11 3HU
Tel: 01383 872513

Ancient, listed building with beach front location. Former customs house featured in Robert Louis Stevenson's Kidnapped. 4 miles west of M90 (Junction 2) situated in quiet seafront village. Strictly non smoking.

1 Twin 1 Pub Bath/Show
1 Double

B&B per person
£20.00-£22.00 Single
from £20.00 Dbl/Twn

Open Jan-Dec

Lundin Links, Fife

Map Ref: 2C3

★★★

B&B

Sandilands Bed & Breakfast

20 Leven Road, Lundin Links, Fife, KY8 6AH
Tel/Fax: 01333 329881
Web: www.smoothhound.co.uk/hotels/sandilan.html

Victorian sandstone villa centrally located in the village of Lundin Links, gateway to the East Neuk of Fife. Several good hotels and pubs nearby. Largo Bay within walking distance. Fife coastal path provides excellent low-level walking. Prime golfing area.

1 Twin 2 En Suite fac
1 Double 1 Priv.NOT ensuite
1 Family

B&B per person
from £23.00 Single
from £20.00 Dbl/Twn

Open Jan-Dec

Markinch, Fife

Map Ref: 2C3

★★

B&B

Mrs C Craig

Shythrum Farm, Markinch, Fife, KY7 6HB
Tel: 01592 758372

Arable farm adjacent to coaching route used by Mary Queen of Scots. Balgonie Castle 0.5 mile (1km), Falkland Palace 5 miles (8kms). Ideal base for touring the scenic East Neuk of Fife. Easy access to St Andrews, Perth and Dunfermline the birth place of Andrew Carnegie.

1 Family En Suite fac
1 Twin Private fac

B&B per person
from £18.00 Single
from £18.00 Twin
Room only per person
from £12.00

Open Mar-Nov

Markinch, Fife | Map Ref: 2C3

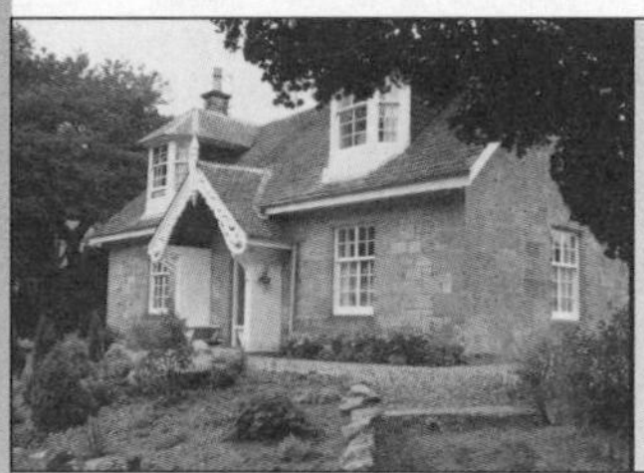

★★★ B&B

Gamekeeper's Cottage
Balbirnie Park, Markinch, Fife, KY7 6JU
Tel/Fax: 01592 612742

1 Double, 1 Family | All En Suite | B&B per person from £20.00 Double | Open Jan-Dec excl Xmas/New Year; B&B + Eve.Meal from £30.00

Nestling in peaceful woodland, this original gamekeeper's cottage ('c' listed) awaits you with a warm welcome and Lesley's delicious home cooking. All we ask is that you 'drive carefully, get here safely and we'll do the rest'. P.S. Don't blame us if you don't want to leave.

C V

★★★ RESTAURANT WITH ROOMS

Town House Hotel
1 High Street, Markinch, Fife, KY7 6DQ
Tel: 01592 758459 Fax: 01592 755039

2 Single, 2 Double | 3 Ensuite fac, 1 Priv.NOT ensuite | B&B per person from £30.00 Single, from £25.00 Double | Open Jan-Dec excl Xmas/New Year

Former coaching Inn, in centre of small village, Chef Proprietor offering food using local produce, served in pleasant surroundings. Ideal location for exploring the countryside and the numerous famous golf courses.

C £ V

Milnathort, by Kinross, Kinross-shire | Map Ref: 2B3

★★ B&B

Warroch Lodge Bed & Breakfast
Milnathort, Kinross-shire, KY13 0RS
Tel: 01577 863779

2 Twin | 1 En Suite fac, 1 Priv.NOT ensuite | B&B per person from £25.00 Single, from £20.00 Twin | Open Jan-Dec

Period lodge house set in attractive countryside with large cottage garden. Located 4 miles (6 kms) from Junction 6 of M90, with easy access to major towns. Evening meal by arrangement. Bird watching, golfing, fishing, hillwalking, gliding all nearby also Knockhill racing circuit.

C V

Montrose, Angus | Map Ref: 4F12

★★★ GUEST HOUSE

Cranes Meadow Guest House
28 The Mall, Montrose, Angus, DD10 8NW
Tel: 01674 672296 Fax: 01671 672296

1 Single, 2 Twin, 2 Double, 2 Family | 4 En Suite fac, 3 Pub Bath/Show | B&B per person from £20.00 Single, from £18.00 Dbl/Twn | Open Jan-Dec

A warm welcome in this family run guest house in quiet residential area with off street parking. Near to town centre, swimming pool and fitness centre. Closest guest house to Fire Training Centre.

TV C V

Montrose, Angus — Map Ref: 4F12

B&B

Fairfield Bed & Breakfast
24 The Mall, Montrose, Angus, DD10 8NW
Tel/Fax: 01674 676386
E-mail: Marlene.Scott@tesco.net

2 Twin, 1 Double — All En Suite — B&B per person from £23.00 Single, £20.00-£25.00 Dbl/Twn — Open Jan-Dec

Detached Georgian house, centrally situated in residential area, with ample street parking. Secure cycle parking. All rooms with en-suite facilities, TV, Sky TV and tea-making facilities. Near to Montrose basin, nature reserve. Ideal location for visiting plenty of golf courses. All rooms have full-size refrigerator.

HOTEL

George Hotel Montrose
22 George Street, Montrose, Angus, DD10 8EW
Tel: 01674 675050 Fax: 01674 671153
E-mail: thegeorge@talk21.com

10 Single, 4 Twin, 9 Double, 1 Family — All En Suite — B&B per person from £30.00 Single, from £25.00 Dbl/Twn — Open Jan-Dec

A privately owned stone-built hotel located in the centre of Montrose providing a central base for exploring this interesting part of Eastern Scotland with its championship golf courses sandy beaches and beautiful glens. There are some bedrooms on the third floor and no lift available.

GUEST HOUSE

The Limes Guest House
15 King Street, Montrose, Angus, DD10 8NL
Tel/Fax: 01674 677236
E-mail: thelimes@easynet.co.uk
Web: http://easyweb.easynet.co.uk/thelimes/

2 Single, 4 Twin, 4 Double, 2 Family — 4 En-suite fac, 2 Priv.NOT ensuite, 3 Pub Bath/Show, 4 Limited ensuite — B&B per person from £21.00 Single, from £18.00 Dbl/Twn; Room only per person from £16.00 — Open Jan-Dec

Family run, centrally situated in quiet, residential part of town. A few minutes walk from the centre, railway station, beach and two golf courses. Private parking.

B&B

Lunan Lodge
Lunan, by Montrose, Angus, DD10 9TG
Tel: 01241 830267 Fax: 01241 830435

2 Twin, 1 Family — 2 Pub Bath/Show — B&B per person to £20.00 Single, to £18.00 Twin — Open Apr-Oct

Warm welcome at modernised 18c manse, in quiet countryside overlooking Lunan Bay. 15 mins walk from sea. 4 miles (5kms) Montrose and Bird Sanctuary.

Montrose, Angus

Map Ref: 4F12

★★★

GUEST HOUSE

Oaklands Guest House

10 Rossie Island Road, Montrose, Angus, DD10 9NN
Tel/Fax: 01674 672018
E-mail: oaklands@altavista.net
Web: www.nebsnow.com/oaklands

All rooms ensuite at this comfortable family house, within walking distance of Montrose town centre. Parking. Secure parking for motorcycles and bikes.

1 Single
3 Twin
2 Double
1 Family

All En Suite

B&B per person
from £20.00 Single
from £18.00 Dbl/Twn

Open Jan-Dec

Newburgh, Fife

Map Ref: 2C2

★★★

B&B

Hillview

46 Scotland Terrace, Newburgh, Fife, KY14 6AR
Tel: 01337 840570

Family home in quiet residential area of Fife village. Ideal centre for touring. In the Tay Valley between Perth and St Andrews. Come and enjoy our warm Scottish welcome. On street parking.

1 Twin
1 Double

1 En Suite fac
1 Pub Bath/Show

B&B per person
from £18.00 Single
from £16.00 Dbl/Twn

Open Mar-Oct

★★★★

B&B

Ninewells Farmhouse

Woodriffe Road, Newburgh, Fife, KY14 6EY
Tel/Fax: 01337 840307
E-mail: nwfarm@globalnet.co.uk

Traditional farmhouse on operational arable/stock farm. Elevated position with glorious panoramic views over the Tay Valley towards the Perthshire hills. Convenient for Edinburgh, Perth and many golf courses. The lounge is a large conservatory type room with all round views. Visitors are welcomed with tea/coffee and homebaked biscuits or scones. Member of Scotland's Best.

1 Twin
1 Double
1 Family

1 En Suite fac
2 Priv.NOT ensuite

B&B per person
from £22.00 Single
from £18.00 Dbl/Twn

Open Apr-Oct

North Queensferry, Fife

Map Ref: 2B4

★★★

B&B

Battery House

3 East Bay, North Queensferry, KY11 1JX
Tel: 01383 410163 Fax: 01383 417850
E-mail: laura.malcolm@tesco.net
Web: www.stayhere.uk.com

Family run Victorian villa on the shores of the Forth with views of Forth Rail Bridge. 12 miles to Edinburgh city centre and 8 miles to airport with a half hourly train service to Waverley Station. Ideal base for touring Central Scotland. Non-smoking.

1 Family
1 Twin

1 Priv.NOT ensuite
1 Pub Bath/Show

B&B per person
from £19.00 Single
from £18.00 Double

Open Jan-Dec excl Xmas/New Year
B&B + Eve.Meal from £22.00

Peat Inn, Fife — Map Ref: 2D3

★★★★ B&B

Andrew & Ann Small
Mill House, Falfield, Peat Inn, Cupar, Fife, KY15 5LJ
Tel: 01334 840609

1 Twin, 2 Double — All En Suite, 1 Pub Bath — B&B per person: £26.00 Single; £20.00-£22.00 Dbl/Twn — Open Mar-Nov — B&B + Eve.Meal £30.00-£34.00

A converted steading in country location in Kingdom of Fife, seven miles (13km) from St Andrews. An ideal base for golf and touring the fishing villages of the East Neuk.

W V

by Peat Inn, Fife — Map Ref: 2D3

★★ B&B

Farmhouse
West Mains, Peat Inn, Cupar, Fife, KY15 5LF
Tel: 01334 840313

1 Twin, 1 Double — 1 Pub Bath/Show — B&B per person from £16.00 Single — Open Apr-Oct

Mixed farm with open views of countryside. Good base for touring, golfing and visiting the East Neuk of Fife. 7 miles (11kms) from St Andrews. Tea, coffee and home baking served in front of an open fire in the evening.

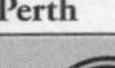

W V

Perth — Map Ref: 2B2

★★★★ GUEST HOUSE

Abercrombie
85 Glasgow Road, Perth, PH2 0PQ
Tel/Fax: 01738 444728

2 Single, 1 Twin, 1 Double — 3 En Suite fac, 1 Priv.NOT ensuite — B&B per person: £19.00-£30.00 Single; £20.00-£30.00 Dbl/Twn — Open Jan-Dec

Family run, Victorian town house, a few minutes from town centre. Ample parking. Ideal for all outdoor activities.

£ W V

★★★★ B&B

Aberdeen Guest House
Pitcullen Crescent, Perth, PH2 7HT
Tel/Fax: 01738 633183
E-mail: buchan@aberdeenguesthouse.fsnet.co.uk

1 Double — Ensuite; 1 Double — Pub Bath/Show; 1 Twn/Trpl — Pub Bath/Show — B&B per person: £18.00-£30.00 Single; £17.00-£22.00 Dbl/Twn — Open Jan-Dec

Delightful, comfortable Victorian terrace house, close to town centre. Renowned for its charm, hospitality and exceptional breakfast. Own private parking. French and German spoken.

C V

Important: Prices stated are estimates and may be subject to amendments

Perth — **Map Ref: 2B2**

★★★★ GUEST HOUSE

Ackinnoull Guest House
5 Pitcullen Crescent, Perth, PH2 7HT
Tel: 01738 634165

1 Twin
2 Double
1 Family

All En Suite

B&B per person
from £20.00 Single
from £18.00 Dbl/Twn

Open Jan-Dec

Beautifully decorated Victorian semi-villa on the outskirts of town. Private parking on premises. 'Perth in Bloom' winners, as picturesque outside as in. Special rates for bookings of 3 days or more.

ALBERT VILLA GUEST HOUSE

63 Dunkeld Road, Perth PH1 5RP
Tel: 01738 622730 Fax: 01738 451182
e.mail: albertvilla@tinyworld.co.uk
Web: www.visitscotland.com/albertvilla

Spacious and comfortable accommodation on 2 levels operating with 10 letting bedrooms, 7 having ensuite facilities. Our 3 ground floor rooms are self-contained offering separate external access. All rooms are attractively decorated and equipped with hospitality trays, colour television and central heating. Ample private parking at front and rear.

Albert Villa Guest House
63 Dunkeld Road, Perth, PH1 5RP
Tel: 01738 622730 Fax: 01738 451182
E-mail: albertvilla@tinyworld.co.uk
Web: www.visitscotland.com/albertvilla

4 Single
2 Twin
2 Double
2 Family

7 Ensuite
3 Standard
1 Pub Bath/Show

B&B per person
£22.00-£28.00 Single
£22.00-£28.00 Dbl/Twn

Open Jan-Dec

Family guest house with ample car parking, close to sports centre and swimming pool. Ground floor bedrooms each have their own entrance.

Almond Villa Guest House
51 Dunkeld Road, Perth, PH1 5RP
Tel: 01738 629356 Fax: 01738 446606
E-mail: almondvilla@compuserve.com

1 Single
2 Twin
1 Double
1 Family

4 En Suite fac
1 Priv.NOT En Suite

B&B per person
from £23.00 Single
from £23.00 Double
Room only per person
£23.00

Open Jan-Dec
B&B + Eve.Meal
from £35.00

Semi-detached Victorian villa, close to town centre, Gannochy Trust Sports Complex, the North Inch and River Tay. Non smoking house.

Alpine Guest House
7 Strathview Terrace, Perth, PH2 7HY
Tel: 01738 637687

1 Twin
2 Double

All En Suite

B&B per person
from £20.00 Single
from £18.00 Dbl/Twn

Open Jan-Dec

Personally run, situated on main A94 tourist route with easy access to town centre and surrounding area. Large private car park.

Perth — Map Ref: 2B2

Ardfern Guest House
15 Pitcullen Crescent, Perth, PH2 7HT
Tel: 01738 637031

1 Twin, 1 Double, 1 Family | 2 En Suite fac, 1 Priv Bathroom | B&B per person 20s20x from £18.00 Dbl/Twn | Open Jan-Dec excl Xmas/New Year

Victorian semi-villa on outskirts of city within easy access to all amenities. Non-smoking throughout. Off road parking. Many original features of the house sympathetically restored and retained.

GUEST HOUSE ★★★★

Arisaig Guest House
4 Pitcullen Crescent, Perth, PH2 7HT
Tel/Fax: 01738 628240
E-mail: reservations@arisaig.demon.co.uk

1 Single, 1 Twin, 2 Double, 1 Family | All En Suite | B&B per person from £22.50 Single from £21.00 Dbl/Twn | Open Jan-Dec

Comfortable family run guest house, with off street parking. Close to city's many facilities. Local touring base. Ground floor bedroom.

GUEST HOUSE ★★★★

Ballabeg Guest House
14 Keir Street, Bridgend, Perth, PH2 7HJ
Tel/Fax: 01738 620434

2 Single, 1 Twin, 1 Double | 2 En Suite fac, 1 Pub Bath/Show | B&B per person from £20.00 Single from £22.00 Dbl/Twn | Open Jan-Dec

Friendly family run house in quiet street off A94. 10 minutes from the city centre. Easy access to golf courses, walks, leisure centre. Nearby to Perth racecource and Scone Palace.

B&B ★★★

Beeches
2 Comely Bank, Perth, PH2 7HU
Tel: 01738 624486
E-mail: enquiries@beeches-guest-house.co.uk

2 Single, 1 Twin, 1 Double | All En Suite, 1 Pub Bath/Show | B&B per person from £20.00 Single from £20.00 Dbl/Twn | Open Jan-Dec

Semi-detached villa with ample car parking, conveniently situated on A94 tourist route. Single rooms available.

B&B ★★★

Beechgrove Guest House
Dundee Road, Perth, PH2 7AQ
Tel/Fax: 01738 636147
E-mail: beechgroveg.h@sol.co.uk
Web: www.beechgrove.uk.com

1 Single, 2 Twin, 2 Double, 1 Family | All En Suite | B&B per person from £25.00 Single from £25.00 Dbl/Twn | Open Jan-Dec

Listed building, former manse (Rectory) set in extensive grounds. Peaceful, yet only a few minutes walk from the city centre. Non-smoking establishment.

GUEST HOUSE ★★★★

Important: Prices stated are estimates and may be subject to amendments

Perth

Map Ref: 2B2

★★★★
B&B

Clifton House
36 Glasgow Road, Perth, PH2 0PB
Tel: 01738 621997 Fax: 01738 622678
E-mail: Moreland@clifton-house.fsnet.co.uk

1 Single	3 En Suite fac	B&B per person	Open Jan-Dec excl
2 Twin	1 Priv.NOT ensuite	£20.00-£23.00 Single	Xmas/New Year
1 Double		£20.00-£23.00 Dbl/Twn	

Delightful Victorian house, within easy walking distance of town centre. Ample private parking. Ideal location for all leisure facilities.

★★★
GUEST HOUSE

Clunie Guest House
12 Pitcullen Crescent, Perth, PH2 7HT
Tel/Fax: 01738 623625
E-mail: ann@clunieperth.freeserve.co.uk

1 Single	All En Suite	B&B per person	Open Jan-Dec
1 Twin		£19.00-£25.00 Single	B&B + Eve.Meal
2 Double		£19.00-£23.00 Dbl/Twn	£30.00-£34.00
3 Family			

A warm welcome awaits you at Clunie Guest House which is situated on the A94 Coupar Angus road. There is easy access to the city centre with all its amenities including a variety of eating establishments. Alternatively, an evening meal can be provided if it is booked in advance.

★★
B&B

Creswick
86 Dundee Road, Perth, PH2 7BA
Tel: 01738 625896

1 Twin	2 En Suite fac	B&B per person	Open Jan-Dec excl
2 Double	1 Priv.NOT ensuite	from £20.00 Single	Xmas/New Year
		from £18.00 Dbl/Twn	B&B + Eve.Meal
			from £26.00

Edwardian house on main Dundee road out of Perth but only about 10 minutes walk by riverside from city centre. Off road parking.

★★
GUEST HOUSE

The Darroch Guest House
9 Pitcullen Crescent, Perth, PH2 7HT
Tel/Fax: 01738 636893

2 Single	3 En Suite fac	B&B per person	Open Jan-Dec
3 Twin	1 Pub Bath/Show	from £16.00 Single	B&B + Eve.Meal
3 Double		from £18.00 Dbl/Twn	from £24.50
3 Family			

The Darroch is awarded "Highly Commendable" by Perth & Kinross Council Environmental Health Dept., giving a high standard of hygiene. We are easily found on the main A94 within walking distance of the town centre. Extensive breakfast menu. Off-street parking.

Perth | Map Ref: 2B2

B&B

Easter Clunie Farmhouse
Easter Clunie, Newburgh, Fife, KY14 6EJ
Tel: 01337 840218 Fax: 01337 842226
E-mail: cluniefarm@aol.com

2 Twin, 1 Family | 1 En Suite fac, 2 Priv.NOT ensuite | B&B per person from £18.00 Dbl/Twn | Open Apr-Nov

19c farmhouse on working farm. Quiet setting. Splendid Victorian walled garden. Convenient for main routes to Edinburgh and the Highlands. Panoramic views over beautiful countryside to the River Tay.

B&B

Mrs M Fair
Homerton, 54 Balhousie Street, Perth, PH1 5HW
Tel/Fax: 01738 624923

1 Twin, 1 Double | 1 Pub Bath/Show | B&B per person from £18.00 Single, from £16.50 Dbl/Twn | Open Jan-Dec

Family run bed and breakfast conveniently situated 10 minutes level walk from Perth City Centre. Balhousie Castle, North Inch Golf Course and Bells Sports Centre nearby. Pleasant river walks.

GUEST HOUSE

Kinnaird Guest House
5 Marshall Place, Perth, PH2 8AH
Tel: 01738 628021/630685 Fax: 01738 444056

1 Single, 3 Twin, 3 Double | All En Suite | B&B per person from £28.00 Single, from £23.00 Dbl/Twn | Open Jan-Dec

Georgian house, centrally situated overlooking park. Private parking. Short walk to town centre and convenient for railway and bus stations. Personally run attentive owners.

GUEST HOUSE

Park Lane Guest House
17 Marshall Place, Perth, PH2 8AG
Tel: 01738 637218 Fax: 01738 643519
E-mail: stay@parklane-uk.com

1 Single, 2 Twin, 2 Double, 1 Family | All En Suite | B&B per person from £23.00 Single, from £23.00 Dbl/Twn | Open Jan-Nov excl New Year

Georgian house overlooking park next to city centre. All ensuite rooms, private car park. Walking distance to golf course, restaurants and all amenities, including bus and railway stations.

GUEST HOUSE

Rowanlea Guest House
87 Glasgow Road, Perth, PH2 0PQ
Tel/Fax: 01738 621922
E-mail: kate.craik@faxvia.net

1 Single, 2 Twin, 3 Double | All En Suite | B&B per person £25.00-£28.00 Single, £21.00-£25.00 Dbl/Twn; Room only per person £19.00-£20.00 | Open Jan-Dec excl Xmas

Victorian semi-detached family run home, recently refurbished. Off street parking. Friendly personal attention. Non smoking house.

Important: Prices stated are estimates and may be subject to amendments

Perth — Map Ref: 2B2

★★★★ B&B

Westview Bed & Breakfast
49 Dunkeld Road, Perth, PH1 5RP
Tel/Fax: 01738 627787

1 Twin, 2 Double | All En Suite, 1 Pub Bath/Show | B&B per person from £20.00 Dbl/Twn | Open Jan-Dec, B&B + Eve.Meal from £28.00

Town house in easy walking distance of town centre, on A9 with private parking. All rooms with colour TV, twin let as single.

by Perth — Map Ref: 2B2

BLACKCRAIGS FARMHOUSE

Blackcraigs, Scone, Perthshire PH2 7PJ
Tel/Fax: 01821 640254

18th century farmhouse where a warm welcome awaits you. Good touring area. Ideally situated for persuing a wide range of activities including golf, fishing, horseriding, hill-walking. Also many interesting castles to visit. Fine restaurants and pubs locally. You will find us on the A94 four miles from Perth.

★★★ B&B

Blackcraigs Farmhouse
Scone, by Perth, Perthshire, PH2 7PJ
Tel/Fax: 01821 640254

1 Twin, 2 Double | 2 En Suite fac, 1 Pub Bath/Show | B&B per person from £20.00 Single, from £19.00 Dbl/Twn | Open Jan-Dec excl Xmas/New Year

A warm welcome at this comfortable farmhouse peacefully situated on 260 acre mixed farm, 4 miles (6kms) from Perth.

★★★★ B&B

Braeknowe Bed & Breakfast
Braeknowe, Tibbermore, Perthshire, PH1 1QJ
Tel: 01738 840295

1 Twin, 1 Double | 1 Pub Bath/Show | B&B per person from £18.00 Single, from £18.00 Dbl/Twn | Open May-Oct

Modern bungalow with conservatory in quiet setting, yet with easy access to major roads. 5 miles (8kms) west of Perth city centre.

★★★★ B&B

Fingask Farm
Rhynd, by Perth, Perthshire, PH2 8QF
Tel: 01738 812220 Fax: 01738 813325
E-mail: libby@agstirrat.sol.co.uk

1 Single, 1 Twin, 1 Double | 1 Priv.NOT ensuite, 1 Pub Bath/Show | B&B per person from £19.00 Single, from £19.00 Dbl/Twn | Open Apr-Nov

Enjoy the lovely garden and home cooking on this traditional farmhouse on a mixed working farm, approximately 5 miles (8kms) south east of Perth on an elevated site overlooking the Rivers Tay and Earn and the Ochil Hills.

by Perth

Map Ref: 2B2

HUNTINGTOWER HOUSE

Crieff Road, Perth PH1 3JJ

Tel: 01738 624681 Fax: 01738 639770 e.mail: Dlindsay@btinternet.com

This is a charming country house with a large secluded garden, near Perth. There is easy access to main routes throughout Scotland, and so is an excellent stop for touring holidays or business. There is ample parking for cars and a friendly welcome is assured.

★★★ B&B

B&B

Mrs H Lindsay

Huntingtower House, Crieff Road, by Perth, Perthshire, PH1 3JJ
Tel: 01738 624681 Fax: 01738 639770
E.mail: Dlindsay@btinternet.com

Detached Victorian house with 0.75 acre secluded garden. Convenient for touring with easy access to the A85, A9 and other main routes. Private bathrooms available. Tea and home baking on arrival.

2 Twin
1 Double

2 Priv.NOT ensuite
2 Pub Bath/Show

B&B per person
£18.00-£21.00 Single
£18.00-£21.00 Dbl/Twn

Open Jan-Dec

V

B&B

The Linn

3 Duchess Street, Stanley, by Perth, Perthshire PH1 4NG
Tel/Fax: 01738 828293

Situated beside the lovely village green in a country fishing village. Mouth watering breakfasts. Walking, golfing and two minutes walk to River Tay.

3 Twin
2 Double
2 Family

2 En Suite fac
1 Priv.NOT ensuite

B&B per person
from £20.00 Dbl/Twn

Open Jan-Dec excl Xmas/New Year

TV

C V

B&B

Lismore

1 Rorrie Terrace, Methven, by Perth, Perthshire, PH1 3PL
Tel/Fax: 01738 840441

Comfortable home in quiet residential area of village, 5 miles (10kms) from Perth. Good base for touring. Traditional scottish hospitality - a true home from home.

1 Twin
1 Double

1 Pub Bath/Show

B&B per person
from £17.50 Single
from £13.50 Dbl/Twn

Open Jan-Dec

P

C £ V

Important: Prices stated are estimates and may be subject to amendments

by Perth | Map Ref: 2B2

TOPHEAD FARM

TULLYBELTON, STANLEY, BY PERTH PH1 4PT
Telephone and Fax: 01738 828259
e.mail: dowtophead@bosinternet.com
Web: www.tophead-bandb.fsnet.co.uk

Enjoy the panoramic views from the veranda of this welcoming farmhouse which has a relaxing atmosphere and is tastefully furnished. The comfortable spacious bedrooms are bright and airy with SUPERKING BEDS!!

Guests can relax in the comfortable lounge and enjoy interesting breakfasts with home made preserves and local produce in the handsome dining room.

Tophead is an ideal centre for touring Central Scotland, hillwalking, golf, fishing, bird watching, or local sight seeing being situated only 4 miles north of Perth just off the A9 Inverness road. Edinburgh, St Andrews and Glasgow one hour away, while Crieff, Dundee and Pitlochry only 30 minutes away.

Prices £18-£24 plus £10 single supplement.

COME ON SPOIL YOURSELVES!! **SORRY NO SMOKING.**

★★★★

B&B

Tophead Farm

Tullybelton, Stanley, Perthshire, PH1 4PT
Tel/Fax: 01738 828259
E-mail: dowtophead@bosinternet.com
Web: www.tophead-bandb.fsnet.co.uk

A very warm Scottish welcome in this traditional farmhouse on 200 acre dairy farm. Perth 4 miles (6kms). Extensive views over rural Perthshire.

1 Twin
2 Double

1 En Suite fac
1 Pub Bath/Show
1 Priv.NOT ensuite

B&B per person
£18,00-£24.00 Dbl/Twn

Open mid Mar - mid Oct

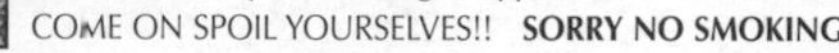

C W V

Pitlochry, Perthshire | Map Ref: 2A1

ANNSLEA

164 ATHOLL ROAD, PITLOCHRY, PERTHSHIRE PH16 5AR
Telephone: 01796 472430 Fax: 01224 495020
e.mail: annslea@artech.co.uk Web: www.pitlochryguesthouse.com

This elegant Victorian house offers an exceptionally high standard of bed and breakfast in an ideal location for the festival theatre. Touring, walking, golfing, fishing and all outdoor pursuits. All rooms have colour TV and welcome tray and most have private facilities. Off-season reductions for 3 nights.

★★★

GUEST HOUSE

Annslea Guest House

164 Atholl Road, Pitlochry, Perthshire, PH16 5AR
Tel: 01796 472430 Fax: 01224 495020
E-mail: annslea@artech.co.uk
Web: www.pitlochryguesthouse.com

Victorian house situated within easy walking of town centre. Large garden and private parking. Ideally located for restaurants, Festival Theatre and all other amenities. Some accommodation in annexe cottage in garden and grounds.

2 Twin
4 Double

4 En Suite fac
2 Pub Bath/Show

B&B per person
from £20.00 Dbl/Twn

Open Apr-Nov

V

Pitlochry, Perthshire **Map Ref: 2A1**

ATHOLL VILLA

29 Atholl Road, Pitlochry, Perthshire PH16 5BX
Tel: 01796 473820
e.mail: athollvilla@aol.com

Atholl Villa is a family run guesthouse where we offer our guests warm hospitality and friendly service. All our rooms have ensuite facilities, colour television and tea/coffee trays. We have secure off-street parking. There is also a lovely guests conservatory and garden where tea and coffee can be taken. Our high standards and home comforts help make your stay special.

This 10-bedroom Victorian detached stone built house of typical highland construction, built approximately 150 years ago is situated right at the edge of town, close to both rail and bus stations. This area is proud of its tourism traditions, and no thoroughfare sums up these traditions better than Pitlochry's Atholl Road. Here can be found an abundance of restaurants and shops, all offering a wide choice of goods to suit any buyer. Atholl Villa is situated just metres away.

★★★ GUEST HOUSE

Atholl Villa

29 Atholl Road, Pitlochry, Perthshire, PH16 5BX
Tel: 01796 473820
E-mail: athollvilla@aol.com

Lovely refurbished Victorian stone house set in an acre of landscaped garden on Atholl Road just metres from the main shopping centre, and a few minutes walk to the Theatre and the river. All rooms ensuite and a conservatory lounge to enjoy coffee and tea. Private off-street parking to rear. Vegetarian & special diets catered for. Evening meal available off season. Cyclists & walkers most welcome. Secure storage for cycles & motorbikes. Current winner – Best Guest House Garden in Pitlochry.

1 Twin
3 Double
1 Family
2 Triple

All En Suite

B&B per person
from £17.50

Open Jan-Dec

★★★ GUEST HOUSE

Bendarroch Guest House

Strathtay, Pitlochry, Perthshire, PH9 0PG
Tel: 01887 840420 Fax: 01887 840438
Web: www.bendarroch-house.demon.co.uk

Fully refurbished Victorian house set in landscaped grounds, panoramic views with the River Tay running past the estate. Situated between Aberfeldy and Pitlochry. Golfing, fishing and canoeing only 2 minutes away, other sports available in the vicinity. Dinner, freshly cooked daily using local produce. Coffee and liqueurs found in the conservatory lounge.

1 Single
3 Twin
1 Family

All En Suite

B&B per person
from £28.00 Single
from £25.00 Dbl/Twn

Open Jan-Dec
B&B + Eve.Meal
from £37.00

★★ B&B

Briar Cottage

Well Brae, Pitlochry, Perthshire, PH16 5HH
Tel: 01796 473678
E-mail: bredon@abbendon.demon.co.uk

Family B and B in elevated position, quiet residential area yet only 5 minutes walk from town centre. Ground floor bedrooms. En-suite facilities and parking available.

2 Twin
1 Double

1 En Suite fac
1 Pub Bath/Show

B&B per person
from £15.00 Dbl/Twn
Room only per person
from £12.50

Open Apr-Oct

Important: Prices stated are estimates and may be subject to amendments

Pitlochry, Perthshire — Map Ref: 2A1

★★ B&B

Bridge House B&B
53 Atholl Road, Pitlochry, Perthshire, PH16 5BL
Tel: 01796 474062

2 Family | All En Suite | B&B per person from £18.00 Single from £18.00 Family | Open Jan-Dec

Comfortable family home with accommodation on first and second floors overlooking Pitlochry town centre. Easy access to railway station, 5 minutes walk and close to other amenities.

TV C V

BUTTONBOSS LODGE

25 ATHOLL ROAD, PITLOCHRY, PERTHSHIRE PH16 5BX

Tel/Fax: 01796 472065 Evening Tel: 473000

Friendly and relaxed atmosphere guaranteed by Colin – P.G.A. golf professional, and Marleen – former KLM stewardess. This detached villa is centrally located. French, German and Dutch spoken. Ensuite bedrooms with TV and hospitality tray. Guest lounge with satellite TV. Ground floor rooms available. Private parking. Garage for motorbikes and cycles. Prices from £18 B&B.

★★★ GUEST HOUSE

Buttonboss Lodge
25 Atholl Road, Pitlochry, Perthshire, PH16 5BX
Tel: 01796 472065/473000 (eve)
Fax: 01796 472065

1 Single, 3 Twin, 4 Double | 7 En Suite fac, 1 Priv Show | B&B per person £18.00-£22.00 Single £18.00-£22.00 Dbl/Twn | Open Jan-Dec

Traditional Victorian house in centre of Pitlochry. Within walking distance of all facilities. Private parking. Nederlands, Deutch and Francais spoken.

TV P C V

Carra Beag Guest House

16 Toberargan Road, Pitlochry, Perthshire PH16 5HG
Tel/Fax: 01796 472835
e.mail: visitus@carrabeag.oik.co.uk
Web: www.s-h-systems.co.uk/hotels/carrabe.html

We pride ourselves on offering first rate service, value for money and warm hospitality in a stress-free relaxing atmosphere. Boasting a central location with excellent views you can enjoy period features, cosy fire in residents lounge and a sumptous breakfast of your choice.

Brian and Helen look forward to welcoming you.

★★★ GUEST HOUSE

Carra Beag Guest House
16 Toberargan Road, Pitlochry, Perthshire, PH16 5HG
Tel/Fax: 01796 472835
E-mail: visitus@carrabeag.oik.co.uk
Web: www.s-h-systems.co.uk/hotels/carrabe.html

2 Single, 3 Twin, 3 Double, 2 Family | 9 En Suite fac, 1 Pub Bath/Show | B&B per person from £15.00 Single from £15.00 Dbl/Twn | Open Feb-Dec incl New Year

Whatever your pursuits a friendly enjoyable stay is assured at Carra Beag. Enjoy magnificent uninterrupted views of the surrounding hills or stroll through our garden directly to Pitlochry's main street. We offer full facilities for walkers and cyclists, excellent food and wine. Private car park, and value for money.

TV P C W V

Pitlochry, Perthshire

Map Ref: 2A1

Craigroyston House

2 Lower Oakfield, Pitlochry PH16 5HQ
Telephone/Fax: 01796 472053
e.mail: craigroyston@ukonline.co.uk
Web: web.ukonline.co.uk/craigroyston

A Victorian country house set in own grounds with views of the surrounding hills. Centrally situated, there is direct pedestrian access to the town centre.

★ All rooms have private facilities, some with 4-posters and are equipped to a high standard.
★ Residents' lounge with real log fire.
★ Safe private parking.
★ Dining room with separate tables.
★ Colour TV, welcome tray, central heating.

AA SELECTED ♦♦♦♦

Bed & Breakfast from £20 per person.

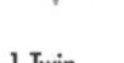

★★★★
GUEST HOUSE

Craigroyston House
2 Lower Oakfield, Pitlochry, Perthshire, PH16 5HQ
Tel/Fax: 01796 472053
E.mail: craigroyston@ukonline.co.uk
Web: http://web.ukonline.co.uk/craigroyston

Quietly situated in its own grounds with views of the surrounding hills. Offering safe off street parking and direct access to the town centre. The spacious bedrooms are well equipped with attention to detail and tastefully decorated with period furniture.

1 Twin
5 Double
2 Family

All En Suite

B&B per person
from £20.00 Dbl/Twn

Open Jan-Dec

W V

BRONZE

Important: Prices stated are estimates and may be subject to amendments

Pitlochry, Perthshire Map Ref: 2A1

Derrybeg Guest House

18 Lower Oakfield, Pitlochry PH16 5DS ★★★★ GUEST HOUSE
Tel: 01796 472070 Fax: 01796 472070

Both of DERRYBEG's adjoining buildings are set in a quiet location only a few minutes' walk from the town centre, enjoying magnificent views of the Vale of Atholl. The resident proprietors, Derek and Marion Stephenson, ensure only the finest hospitality, comfort, and good home cooking.

- All bedrooms with private facilities.
- Colour television and welcome tea/coffee tray in all bedrooms.
- Open all year for B&B or D,B&B. Unlicensed, but guests welcome to supply own table wine.
- Full central heating throughout.
- Comfortable lounge and dining room.
- Food Hygiene Excellent Award.
- Ample parking in the grounds.
- Leisure activities can easily be arranged, i.e. theatre bockings, golf, fishing, pony-trekking, etc.

Colour brochure/tariff and details of weekly reductions available on request.

★★★★ GUEST HOUSE

Derrybeg
18 Lower Oakfield, Pitlochry, Perthshire, PH16 5DS
Tel/Fax: 01796 472070

2 Single	All En Suite	B&B per person	Opne Jan-Nov plus
2 Twin		from £18.00 Single	Xmas/New Year
6 Double		from £18.00 Dbl/Twn	B&B + Eve.Meal
1 Family			from £33.00

Privately owned detached house, with large south facing garden, in quiet but central location. Elevated position with uninterupted views across Tummel Valley and surrounding hill sides. Three annexe rooms. Ample off road parking. Four course evening meal available and guests welcome to supply their own table wine.

C W V

★★ B&B

Donavourd Farmhouse
Donavourd, Pitlochry, Perthshire, PH16 5JS
Tel: 01796 472254
E-mail: donavourd@compuserve.com

1 Twin	2 En Suite fac	B&B per person	Open Feb-Dec
1 Double		£18.00-£22.00 Dbl/Twn	B&B + Eve.Meal
			£26.00-£30.00

200 year-old farmhouse with wonderful views down Strathtummel. Fresh farm foods with home baking. Quiet, rural position.

C V

★★★ HOTEL

Dundarach Hotel
Perth Road, Pitlochry, Perthshire, PH16 5DJ
Tel: 01796 472862 Fax: 01796 473024

4 Single	All En Suite	B&B per person	Open 9 Feb-14 Jan
13 Twin		£25.00-£54.00 Single	
8 Double		£25.00-£40.00 Dbl/Twn	
2 Family			

This hotel on the edge of the village is architecturally interesting, inside and out and stands in its own secluded garden but still close to town centre. A warm friendly welcome is assured by the resident owners the Smail family. The hotel offers both traditional and new bedrooms. All are well equipped. The airy, well seated public rooms are attractively decorated in warm colours and give many fine views over the surrounding valley.

C W V

Pitlochry, Perthshire

Map Ref: 2A1

★★★
GUEST HOUSE

Dundarave House

Strathview Terrace, Pitlochry, Perthshire, PH16 5AT
Tel/Fax: 01796 473109
E.mail: dundarave.guesthouse@virgin.net

2 Single
2 Twin
2 Double
1 Family

5 En Suite fac
2 Pub Bath/Show

B&B per person
from £18.00 Single
from £18.00 Dbl/Twn

Open Jan-Dec

Victorian built, late nineteenth century by local craftsmen, and set in it's own half acre of formal grounds. Dundarave is a house of great charm, character and serene atmosphere.

★★★★
B&B

Dun-Donnachaidh

9 Knockard Road, Pitlochry, Perthshire, PH16 5HJ
Tel: 01796 474018 Fax: 01796 474218

1 Twin
2 Double

All En Suite

B&B per person
£24.50-£27.50 Dbl/Twn

Open Feb-Nov

Situated in an elevated position with superb views over the town, down the Glen & across to the surrounding hills. A substantial stonebuilt house with a very high standard of accommodation. Lovely cornices original ceiling roses, and wood doors all lovingly restored. Generous size rooms, all rooms have en suite facilities.

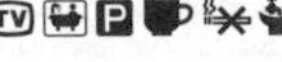

Pitlochry, Perthshire — Map Ref: 2A1

EASTER DUNFALLANDY COUNTRY HOUSE B&B

PITLOCHRY, PERTHSHIRE PH16 5NA ★★★★ B&B

Tel: 01796 474128 Fax: 01796 473994

e.mail: sue@dunfallandy.co.uk Web: www.dunfallandy.co.uk

Quietly situated country house enjoying wonderful views just 2 miles from Pitlochry and within easy reach of the areas many attractions. All 3 bedrooms are ensuite with complimentary toiletries. Decor and furnishing are high quality throughout. Gourmet breakfast.

★★★★ B&B

Easter Dunfallandy Country House B&B

Pitlochry, Perthshire, PH16 5NA
Tel: 01796 474128 Fax: 01796 473994
E-mail: sue@dunfallandy.co.uk
Web: www.dunfallandy.co.uk

2 Twin, 1 Double — All En Suite — B&B per person from £28.00 Dbl/Twn — Open Jan-Dec excl Xmas/New Year

A large Victorian country house retaining many original features regaining it's period charm. Situated in elevated position with panoramic views over the Vale of Atholl. 1.5 miles south of Pitlochry on quiet country road. Large country garden. Non-smoking house.

TV P W V

★★★ B&B

Ferryman's Cottage

Port-na-Craig, Pitlochry, Perthshire, PH16 5ND
Tel: 01796 473681

1 Dbl/Twn, 1 Family — 1 En Suite fac, 1 Priv.NOT ensuite — B&B per person from £19.50 Double — Open Mar-Dec excl Xmas/New Year

Our cosy home was once the Ferryman's Cottage serving the quiet, picturesque hamlet of Port-na-Craig, on the banks of the River Tummel. Perfectly situated for the theatre, dam, and fish ladder , yet only a five minute walk into town.

TV P C W V

★★★★ GUEST HOUSE

Kinnaird House

Kirkmichael Road, Pitlochry, Perthshire, PH16 5JL
Tel/Fax: 01796 472843
Web: www.kinnaird-house.co.uk

1 Single, 1 Twin, 4 Double — 4 En Suite fac, 1 Pub Bath/Show — B&B per person £20.00-£26.00 Single, £20.00-£28.00 Dbl/Twn — Open Jan-Dec

Enjoying an elevated position 1.5 miles above the delightful small town of Pitlochry this stone built Victorian villa has magnificent views of the surrounding hills, and glen. Very comfortable accommodation, a super breakfast and Mrs Burrows offers hospitality to match.

TV P C £ V

★★★ GUEST HOUSE

Number 10

10 Atholl Road, Pitlochry, Perthshire, PH16 5BX
Tel: 01796 472346
E-mail: num10pit@tinyonline.co.uk

2 Single, 3 Twin, 4 Double, 2 Family — 9 En Suite fac, 1 Pub Bath/Show — B&B per person £20.00-£30.00 Single, £20.00-£30.00 Dbl/Twn; Room only per person £15.00-£25.00 — Open Jan-Dec excl Xmas/New Year

The relaxed warm atmosphere, and friendly hospitality of experienced hosts Fran and Alan will make you want to return regularly to this cosy retreat. The hotel has comfortable bedrooms,a snug bar, quiet lounge and a dining room serving only fresh food based on Scottish produce.In easy walking distance of the town centre, with a lovely ten minute walk over the river to Pitlochry Theatre.

TV P £ W V

Pitlochry, Perthshire

Map Ref: 2A1

B&B

Pooltiel

Lettoch Road, Pitlochry, Perthshire, PH16 5AZ
Tel: 01796 472184
E-mail: ajs@pooltiel.freeserve.co.uk
Web: www.pooltiel.freeserve.co.uk

Located in an elevated position overlooking Pitlochry, with views of the surrounding hills this is an excellent base from which to enjoy numerous outdoor activities and explore Perthshire and the Southern Highlands.

1 Twin, 1 Family, 1 Double — 1 Pub Bath/Show

B&B per person
from £16.50 Single
from £16.50 Dbl/Twn

Open Apr-Oct

INN

Port-na-Craig Inn

Port-na-Craig, Pitlochry, Perthshire, PH16 5ND
Tel: 01796 472777 Fax: 01796 472931
E-mail: portnacraig@talk21.com

Nestling on the spectacular banks of the River Tummel in one of the oldest buildings in Pitlochry dating back over 300 years, the Portnacraig Inn and Restaurant has been lovingly restored. Directly below the Pitlochry Festival Theatre and only 200 yards from the famous salmon ladder. Taste of Scotland. 5 minute walk from town centre.

1 Double, 1 Family — All En Suite

B&B per person
from £30.00 Single
from £22.00 Double
Room only per person
from £18.00

Open Feb-Dec
B&B + Eve.Meal
from £40.00

B&B

Mrs Robertson

Lavalette, Manse Road, Moulin, Pitlochry, Perthshire, PH16 5EP
Tel: 01796 472364

Friendly family run B&B in bungalow on edge of village of Moulin. Within walking distance of Pitlochry town centre.

1 Single, 1 Double, 1 Family — 2 En Suite fac

B&B per person
from £16.00 Single
from £15.00 Double

Open Mar-Oct

B&B

Lt.Cmdr & Mrs Roemmele

'Holzhafen', 5 Windsor Gardens, Pitlochry, Perthshire, PH16 5BE
Tel: 01796 473562 Fax: 01796 470054
E-mail: croemmele@aol.com
Web: www.highland-gateway.com

Family run B&B within walking distance of town centre. Ideal base for touring this beautiful part of Perthshire. Great walking, fishing and theatre. Families and pets most welcome.

1 Single, 1 Twin, 1 Double — 1 En Suite fac, 1 Pub Bath/Show

B&B per person
from £16.00 Single
from £15.00 Dbl/Twn

Open Easter-Oct

Pitlochry, Perthshire

Map Ref: 2A1

★★★

GUEST HOUSE

Rosehill

47 Atholl Road, Pitlochry, Perthshire, PH16 5BX
Tel/Fax: 01796 472958

5 Double | 6 En Suite fac | B&B per person | Open Apr-Oct
2 Family | 1 Pub Bath/Show | £18.00-£21.00 Double

Very neat guest house at the centre of this popular Highland town. Peaceful situation just off the high street in easy walking distance of shops, bars and restaurants. Off-road parking. Colourful small garden - 5 times winner of 'Pitlochry in Bloom'.

★★★

HOTEL

Scotland's Hotel

40 Bonnethill Road, Pitlochry, PH16 5BT
Tel: 01796 472292 Fax: 01796 473284
E-mail: stay@scotlandshotel.co.uk
Web: www.scotlandshotel.co.uk

8 Single | 75 En Suite fac | B&B per person | Open Jan-Dec
23 Twin | | from £28.00 Single | B&B + Eve.Meal
30 Double | | from £20.00 Dbl/Twn | from £35.00
10 Family

Traditionally run Scottish Hotel with garden and views of the countryside, close to the centre of Pitlochry. Health and Leisure Club.

★★★★

B&B

Silver Howe

Perth Road, Pitlochry, Perthshire, PH16 5LY
Tel: 01796 472181

2 Twin | All En Suite | B&B per person | Open Apr-Oct
2 Double | | £20.00-£22.50 Dbl/Twn

Detached modern bungalow on town outskirts, with large south facing garden and outlook to Tummel Valley. Winner of 1999 and 2000 Glenturret Award for Most Enjoyable B&B in Perthshire.

★★

B&B

Wellwood House

West Moulin Road, Pitlochry, Perthshire, PH16 5EA
Tel: 01796 474288/ Fax: 01796 474299
Web: www.aboutscotland.co.uk/pitlochry/wellwood.html

4 Twin | 8 En Suite fac | B&B per person | Open Mar-Nov
5 Double | 2 Priv.NOT ensuite | from £25.00 Single
1 Family | 1 Pub Bath/Show | from £25.00 Dbl/Twn

Victorian villa with fine views over town yet only 200 yards to town centre. Ideal location for touring Perthshire.

Pitlochry, Perthshire

Map Ref: 2A1

★★★★

B&B

Wester Knockfarrie

Knockfarrie Road, Pitlochry, Perthshire, PH16 5DN
Tel: 01796 472020 Fax: 01796 474407

Wester Knockfarrie, a Victorian home quietly situated in woodlands on the outskirts of Pitlochry, yet only a few minutes walk from the town. Beautiful views over the Tummel Valley and the hills beyond, a peaceful garden to relax in with woodland strolls and forest trails close by. Individually designed non smoking bedrooms with fully fitted private facilities. A full Scottish breakfast is served in the elegant dining room. Private parking.

1 Twin — All En Suite
1 Double

B&B per person
from £20.00 Dbl/Twn

Open Mar-Oct

TV P W V

by Pitlochry, Perthshire

Map Ref: 2A1

★★

B&B

Gardeners Cottage

Faskally, Pitlochry, Perthshire, PH16 5LA
Tel: 01796 472450

Original gardeners cottage dating from mid 19th century. Adjoining Faskally wood and overlooking the Loch. Ground floor bedroom available.

1 Twin
2 Double

B&B per person
from £22.00 Single
from £17.00 Dbl/Twn

Open Jan-Dec

TV P V

St Andrews, Fife

Map Ref: 2D2

★★

B&B

Abbey Cottage

Abbey Walk, St Andrews, Fife, KY16 9LB
Tel: 01334 473727
E.mail: coull@lineone.net

Listed property dating from 18c with walled cottage garden. Close to centre of St. Andrews. Fantail doves and pet hens. Parking.

1 Twin — Private fac
1 Double — 1 Priv.NOT ensuite
1 Dbl/Twn — En Suite fac

B&B per person
from £20.00 Dbl/Twn

Open Jan-Dec

TV P V

St Andrews, Fife | Map Ref: 2D2

★★

B&B

Ardmore
1 Drumcarrow Raod, St Andrews, Fife, KY16 8SE
Tel: 01334 474574

2 Twin | 1 Pub Bath/Show | B&B per person £16.00-£18.00 Twin | Open Jan-Dec excl Xmas/New Year

Family house in quiet residential area, within walking distance of town centre. Convenient for all amenities. Tea and coffee in owner's lounge each evening. Your are welcome to borrow the use of our hairdryer and ironing facilities.

TV P

C V

★★★★

GUEST HOUSE

Aslar Guest House
120 North Street, St Andrews, Fife, KY16 9AF
Tel: 01334 473460 Fax: 01334 477540
E-mail: enquiries@aslar.com
Web: www.aslar.com

1 Single, 2 Twin, 2 Double | All En Suite | B&B per person from £28.00 Single, from £28.00 Dbl/Twn; Room only from £50.00 | Open Jan-Dec

Victorian family run terraced house furnished to a high standard with period features. Centrally situated for shops, golf courses, restaurants and cultural pursuits.

TV

£ W V

★★★★

B&B

Braeside House
25 Nelson Street, St Andrews, Fife, KY16 8AJ
Tel/Fax: 01334 472698
E-mail: sheila@braesidehouse.fsnet.co.uk

1 Twin, 1 Double | All En Suite | B&B per person from £25.00 Single, from £21.00 Dbl/Twn | Open Jan-Dec excl Xmas/New Year

A relaxed friendly atmosphere, comfortable ensuite rooms and the personal touch await. Private parking. Five minutes walk from town centre. Ten minutes from golf course/university. Non-smoking.

TV P

V

★★

GUEST HOUSE

Brownlees Guest House
7 Murray Place, St Andrews, KY16 9AP
Tel/Fax: 01334 473868

2 Single, 2 Twin, 2 Double | 4 En Suite fac, 1 Pub Bath/Show | B&B per person £18.00-£22.00 Single, £18.00-£25.00 Dbl/Twn | Open Jan-Dec

Centrally located, personally run Victorian terraced house. Ideal base for golf, beach and touring.

TV

C V

★★★

GUEST HOUSE

Burness House
Murray Park, St Andrews, Fife, KY16 9AW
Tel/Fax: 01334 474314
E-mail: burness.house@virgin.net
Web: www.burnesshouse.co.uk

1 Twin, 2 Double, 2 Family | All En Suite | B&B per person from £28.00 Single, from £20.00 Dbl/Twn | Open Jan-Dec

Comfortable family run guest house located near the centre of St Andrews with easy access to historic monuments and golf courses. Expect a very warm welcome.

TV

C £ V

St Andrews, Fife | Map Ref: 2D2

Cairnsden Bed & Breakfast
2 King Street, St Andrews, Fife, KY16 8JQ
Tel: 01334 476326 Fax: 01334 840355

1 Twin, 1 Double | 1 Priv.NOT ensuite | B&B per person from £20.00 Single, from £16.00 Dbl/Twn | Open Jan-Dec excl Xmas/New Year

★★ B&B

A friendly welcome awaits you at this home from home, just a short walking distance from the town centre. Ideally situated for all the great Golf courses of St Andrews. Early breakfasts provided to suit your needs. Well behaved dogs accepted. Beaches of East Neuk easily accessible.

---

38 Chamberlain Street
38 Chamberlain Street, St Andrews, Fife, KY16 8JF
Tel: 01334 473749

1 Twin | 1 Pub Bath/Show | B&B per person £18.00-£20.00 Single, £16.00-£20.00 Twin | Open Jan-Dec excl Xmas/New Year

★★ B&B

Quietly located 10 minutes walk from town centre. Local bus route to all amenities.

Doune House
5 Murray Place, St Andrews, Fife, KY16 2AP
Tel/Fax: 01334 475195
E-mail: dounehouse@aol.com

1 Single, 4 Twin, 4 Double | All En Suite | B&B per person from £20.00 Single, from £20.00 Dbl/Twn | Open Feb-Dec excl Xmas/New Year

★★★★ GUEST HOUSE

A warm welcome awaits you at this Victorian Town House recently modernised and beautifully refurbished. Close to town centre, golf courses and historical sites.

Dykes End
5 Kinburn Place, Double Dykes Road, St Andrews, Fife, KY16 9DT
Tel/Fax: 01334 474711
E-mail: seygolf@aol.com

1 Twin, 1 Double, 1 Family | 1 En Suite fac, 2 Priv.Bathrooms | B&B per person from £25.00 Single, from £22.00 Dbl/Twn | Open Mar-Oct

★★★★ B&B

A friendly welcome awaits you in superior quality home in prime residential area only 5 minutes walk from town centre, golf courses, beach and bus station. All bedrooms are non-smoking and have full ensuite or private facilities. Private parking is available and golf can be arranged.

Important: Prices stated are estimates and may be subject to amendments

St Andrews, Fife

Map Ref: 2D2

FOSSIL HOUSE AND COTTAGE B&B

12-14 Main Street, Strathkinness, St Andrews KY16 9RU
Tel/Fax: 01334 850639 *e.mail: the.fossil@virgin.net*
Web: www.fossil-guest-house.co.uk

'Arrive as guests, depart as friends'. Courtyard development two miles from St Andrews. Deluxe accommodation all ensuite and AA award winning breakfasts. 1998 booker prize for excellence. Guest lounge, conservatory, walled garden, guest parking. Ideal for touring. Peace and tranquillity with hotel facilities at B&B prices. *(AA ◆◆◆◆◆).*

★★★★

B&B

Fossil House & Cottage Bed & Breakfast

12-14 Main Street, Strathkinness, by St Andrews, Fife, KY16 9RU
Tel/Fax: 01334 850639
E-mail: the.fossil@virgin.net
Web: www.fossil-guest-house.co.uk

2 Twin / 1 Double / 1 Family — All En Suite — B&B per person £25.00-£30.00 Single, £22.00-£25.00 Dbl/Twn — Open Jan-Dec

Tasteful conversion of house and cottage, in pleasant mature courtyard setting, in peaceful village 2 miles from St Andrews. A warm welcome awaits.

C £ W V

Mrs M. Gourlay

13 Cairnsden Gardens, St. Andrews KY16 8SQ
Telephone/Fax: 01334 475303
e.mail: mgtgourlayb-b@13cg.fsbusiness.co.uk

The beautiful historic town of St. Andrews, the home of golf, is the perfect location to explore the East Neuk of Fife and well beyond. We offer you comfortable, friendly accommodation with central heating, TV, tea/coffee and biscuit facilities in all rooms to make your stay as enjoyable as possible.

★★★

B&B

Mrs M Gourlay

13 Cairnsden Gardens, St Andrews, Fife, KY16 8SQ
Tel/Fax: 01334 475303
E-mail: mgtgourlayb-b@13cg-fsbusiness.co.uk

1 Twin / 2 Double — 2 Pub Bath/Show — B&B per person £18.00-£22.00 Dbl/Twn — Open Jan-Nov

Be assured of a very warm welcome at this attractive bungalow where you'll find comfortable, ground floor accommodation with a home from home atmosphere. Situated in a quiet residential area. The town centre is only three minutes by car or easily accessible by a scenic stroll along the Lade Braes.

C W V

★★★

B&B

Mrs Muriel Gray

11 Queens Gardens, St Andrews, Fife, KY16 9TA
Tel/Fax: 01334 475536
E-mail: mgraybnb@aol.com

1 Single / 1 Twin / 1 Double — 2 En Suite fac — B&B per person from £20.00 Single, from £20.00 Dbl/Twn; Room only per person from £18.00 — Open Jan-Dec excl Xmas/New Year

Come and enjoy a break in our elegant Victorian family home right in the heart of historic St Andrews. We offer well appointed rooms, a good choice of breakfasts, and a warm welcome. Shops, beaches, golf courses, university and all other attractions are within very easy walking distance. Non smoking throughout. Ground floor bedroom available.

C W V

St Andrews, Fife — Map Ref: 2D2

HOTEL

Hazelbank Hotel
28 The Scores, St Andrews, Fife, KY16 9AS
Tel/Fax: 01334 472466

2 Single, 8 Twin, 8 Double, 3 Family — All En Suite

B&B per person from £45.00 Single, from £30.00 Dbl/Twn

Open Jan-Dec excl Xmas/New Year. B&B + Eve.Meal from £45.00

Refurbished elegant Victorian townhouse. Overlooking St Andrews Bay and golf courses. A drive and a wedge from the 18th on the Old Course. 3 minutes walk to University and historic town centre.

Fairnie House

Kate Pattullo, 10 Abbey Street, St Andrews, Fife KY16 9LA
Tel: 01334 474094 e.mail: kate@fairniehouse.freeserve.co.uk
Web: www.fairniehouse.freeserve.co.uk

Fairnie House is a lovely Georgian town house in a very central location. The Castle, Abbey, beaches, coastal walks, shops and restaurants are all within easy walking distance. Golf courses 15 minutes walk. Comfortable relaxed family run B&B. Rooms have colour TV and tea/coffee making facilities. Open all year.

B&B

Mrs Kate Pattullo
10 Abbey Street, St Andrews, Fife, KY16 9LA
Tel: 01334 474094
E-mail: kate@fairniehouse.freeserve.co.uk
Web: www.fairniehouse.freeserve.co.uk

2 Twin, 1 Double — 1 En Suite fac, 2 Priv.NOT ensuite, 2 Pub Bath/Show

B&B per person £18.00-£30.00 Single, £16.00-£25.00 Dbl/Twn. Room only per person £15.00-£23.00

Open Jan-Dec

Listed Georgian house built in 1750. Centrally situated just off South Street. Ideal position for everything St Andrews has to offer. Our style is cheerful, relaxed and informal. Breakfast is served in a large airy room on first floor. Ground floor bedrooms. Free on-street parking at frontage.

Pinewood Country House

Tayport Road, St Michaels, by St Andrews, Fife KY16 0DU
Tel: 01334 839860 e.mail: accommodation@pinewoodhouse.com
Fax: 01334 839868 Web: www.pinewoodhouse.com

A country guest house near Tentsmuir Forest in the heart of Scotland's premier golfing area and just ten minutes drive from St Andrews. Pinewood offers a homely and relaxing atmosphere with good food using fresh local produce. The five comfortably furnished bedrooms all have private facilities with TVs and welcome tray.

GUEST HOUSE

Pinewood Country House
Tayport Road, St Michaels, by St Andrews, Fife, KY16 0DU
Tel: 01334 839860 Fax: 01334 839868
E-mail: accommodation@pinewoodhouse.com
Web: www.pinewoodhouse.com

2 Twin, 3 Double — 4 En Suite fac, 1 Priv.NOT ensuite

B&B per person from £22.00 Dbl/Twn

Open Jan-Dec excl Xmas/New Year. B&B + Eve.Meal from £34.00

A country guest house near Tentsmuir Forest, close to three golf courses and just ten minutes drive from St Andrews. Recently refurbished and offers a homely and relaxing atmosphere with good food using fresh, local produce. Scotland's Best Award.

Important: Prices stated are estimates and may be subject to amendments

St Andrews, Fife

Map Ref: 2D2

B&B

Spinkstown Farmhouse
St Andrews, Fife, KY16 8PN
Tel/Fax: 01334 473475
E-mail: anne-duncan@lineone.net

Only 2 miles (1km) east of St Andrews this uniquely designed farm house with views of the sea and surrounding countryside. Bright and spacious.

1 Twin
2 Double

All En Suite

B&B per person
from £25.00 Single
from £22.00 Dbl/Twn

Open Jan-Dec excl Xmas/New Year

GUEST HOUSE

West Park House
5 St Marys Place, St Andrews, Fife, KY16 9UY
Tel: 01334 475933 Fax: 01334 476634
E-mail: rosemary@westparksta.freeserve.co.uk

Beautiful Listed Georgian house c1830 in heart of historic town. Close to Old Course and all amenities.

1 Twin
2 Double
1 Family

3 En Suite fac
1 Priv.NOT ensuite

B&B per person
from £30.00 Single
from £23.00 Dbl/Twn

Open Jan-Dec excl Xmas/New Year

by St Andrews, Fife

Map Ref: 2D2

B&B

Hawthorne House B&B
33 Main Street, Strathkinnes, by St Andrews, Fife, KY16 9RY
Tel/Fax: 01334 850855
E-mail: 106425.3361@compuserve.com

Friendly family run bed and breakfast in attractive village only five minutes drive from the world famous 'Old Course' and the 'Old Grey Town' of St Andrews.

1 Twin
2 Double

All En Suite

B&B per person
from £20.00 Dbl/Twn

Open Jan-Dec

B&B

Hillpark House
96 Main Street, Leuchars, by St Andrews, Fife, KY16 0HF
Tel/Fax: 01334 839280
E-mail: enquiries@hillparkhouse.com
Web: www.hillparkhouse.com

Elegant Victorian house refurbished to a high standard. Stylish decor incorporating many original features including a unique canopy bath/shower. Cosy and warm with open fire in season. Halfway between St Andrews and Dundee with golf and beaches nearby. Evening meals by prior arrangement.

1 Twn/Fam
2 Double

2 En Suite fac
1 Priv.NOT ensuite

B&B per person
from £27.00 Single
from £21.00 Dbl/Twn

Open Jan-Dec

by St Andrews, Fife — Map Ref: 2D2

B&B

Kingsbarns Bed & Breakfast
3 Main Street, St Andrews, Fife, KY16 8SL
Tel: 01334 880234
E-mail: hay@itek-uk.com
Web: www.east-neuk.co.uk/kingsbarns-bb

1 Twin, 2 Double — All En Suite — B&B per person from £22.00 Dbl/Twn — Open Apr-Oct

Very comfortable, friendly, family run B&B in picturesque coastal East Neuk village. Ten minutes walking distance to award winning beach. Lovely, peaceful woodland walks around village. Wide choice of golf courses in the vicinity. Ideal base to enjoy leisurely pace of countryside and only 6 miles to St Andrews.

V

B&B

Rockmount Cottage
Dura Den Road, Pitscottie, St Andrews, KY15 5TG
Tel: 01334 828164
E-mail: annmreid@rockmount1.freeserve.co.uk

1 Single, 1 Double, 1 Family — 1 Priv.NOT ensuite, 1 Pub Bath/Show — B&B per person £18.00-£25.00 Single, £18.00-£25.00 Double — Open Jan-Dec

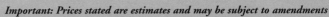

Easy to find in the centre of Pitscottie and well placed for touring the Kingdom of Fife and beyond. Modernised traditional Scottish cottage with south facing garden and car parking area. Bath and shower rooms fully equipped for ambulant disabled.

C V

by St Andrews, Fife — Map Ref: 2D2

Stravithie Country Estate

STRAVITHIE, ST ANDREWS, FIFE KY16 8LT
Tel: 01334 880251 Fax: 01334 880297

Bed and Breakfast on a beautiful old Scottish Country Estate with 30 acres of wooded grounds and gardens. Rooms within east wing of Castle. Facilities within the grounds include trout-fishing, open-air badminton, table-tennis, golf practice (9-holes), nature trail, launderette and telephone.

HOW TO FIND US
3 miles from St Andrews on the Anstruther road (B9131).
B&B FROM £32 per person per night.

★★★ B&B

Stravithie Country Estate
Stravithie, St Andrews, Fife, KY16 8LT
Tel: 01334 880251 Fax: 01334 880297

1 Twin, 1 Double, 1 Family — All En Suite — B&B per person from £32.00 Dbl/Twn — Open Apr-Oct

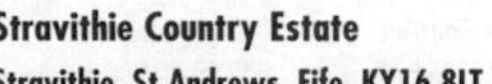

Bed & breakfast within 19c castle set in 30 acres of peaceful grounds, with nature walks, golf practice (9 holes), trout stream, riding, badminton. St Andrews 3 miles (5kms). Come and experience the atmosphere of a fine old Scottish country estate. Large sitting room style bedrooms with own kitchen. Continental breakfasts only available.

TODHALL HOUSE

DAIRSIE, BY ST ANDREWS, FIFE KY15 4RQ
Tel: 01334 656344 Fax: 01334 650791
e.mail: todhallhouse@ukgateway.net
Web: www.scotland2000.com/todhall

At Todhall our aim is to provide quality accommodation, traditional fare and warm, personal service. Come! Explore historic St Andrews (7 miles) and the many varied attractions in the Kingdom of Fife and beyond, or simply relax in peaceful surroundings. Excellent train service to Edinburgh – 1 hour.

AA ◆◆◆◆◆

★★★★★ B&B

Todhall House B&B
Dairsie, by St Andrews, KY15 4RQ
Tel: 01334 656344 Fax: 01334 650791
E-mail: todhallhouse@ukgateway.net
Web: www.scotland2000.com/todhall

1 Twin, 2 Double — All En Suite — B&B per person from £33.00 Single, from £27.00-£34.00 Dbl/Twn — Open Mar-Nov, B&B + Eve.Meal from £45.00

Refurbished to a high standard this traditional Scottish country house is peacefully located amidst extensive lawns and rosebeds, with panoramic view across the Eden valley. Tastefully appointed bedrooms, one with 4 poster bed. You can be assured of a warm welcome from Gill and John Donald. Please note this is a non-smoking house.

BRONZE

St Monans, Fife | Map Ref: 2D3

Inverforth
20 Braehead, St Monans, Fife, KY10 2AN
Tel: 01333 730205

2 Twin
1 Double

1 Pub Bath/Show

B&B per person
from £18.00 Single
from £18.00 Dbl/Twn

Open mid May-mid Oct

In an elevated position overlooking the harbour in this attractive small fishing village in the East Neuk of Fife. Victorian house with spacious bedrooms. Homebaking. 12 miles from St Andrews. Easy access to many golf courses.

NEWARK HOUSE

St Monans, Fife KY10 2DB Tel: 01333 730027

Newark House is a traditional Fife farmhouse in a secluded coastal location enjoying splendid sea views. It is ideally situated for the golfer with St Andrews only 20 minutes drive, and for the non-golfer with an abundance of local heritage, walks, bird-watching and local amenities.

Mrs Carol Thomson
Newark House, St Monans, Fife, KY10 2DB
Tel: 01333 730027

1 Double
2 Family

2 En Suite fac
1 Pub Bath/Show

B&B per person
£22.00-£24.00 Single
£17.00-£19.00 Double

Open Apr-Oct
B&B + Eve.Meal
£25.00-£33.50

Traditional Fife farmhouse in secluded location beside the sea and ruins of Newark Castle. Golf, walks, bird-watching and an abundance of local heritage. Evening meals by arrangement.

C W V

Stanley, Perthshire | Map Ref: 2B2

Beech-Lea Bed & Breakfast

Beech-Lea House, Strathord, by Stanley, Perth PH1 4PS
Tel: 01738 828715 e.mail: chaslizlin@aol.com
Web: http://members.aol.com/chaslizlin/Index.html

A warm welcome awaits guests at our new luxury comfortable B&B in beautiful quiet countryside. Enjoy an excellent breakfast from our menu overlooking large garden with 9-hole fun putting and wildlife pond situated just off A9 ten minutes from Perth. Excellent location – ½ hour Edinburgh, one hour Glasgow, two hours Inverness. Host of local attractions.

Beech-Lea Bed & Breakfast
Beech-Lea House, Strathord, by Stanley, Perth, Perthshire, PH1 4PS
Tel: 01738 828715 (mobile 07775 803842)
E-mail: chaslizlin@aol.com
Web: http://members.aol.com/chaslizlin/Index.html

1 Twin
1 Double
1 Family

All En Suite

B&B per person
from £25.00 Single
from £20.00 Dbl/Twn

Open Jan-Dec

A friendly welcome at this family B&B. Situated 6 miles from Perth city centre. 5 mins drive to fishing on the Tay. Fishing permits can be arranged. Many golf courses nearby.

TV

C £ V

Important: Prices stated are estimates and may be subject to amendments

Stanley, Perthshire — Map Ref: 2B2

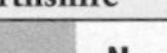

★★★

B&B

Newmill Farm

Stanley, Perthshire, PH1 4QD
Tel/Fax: 01738 828281
E-mail: guthrienewmill@sol.co.uk

1 Twin All En Suite
2 Double

B&B per person
from £25.00 Single
from £19.00 Dbl/Twn

Open Feb-Nov

Traditional farmhouse on 330 acre arable farm. Convenient for the A9, 6 miles (10kms) from Perth. Suitable for fishing and other outdoor pursuits. Evening meal by prior arrangement.

Strathkinness by St Andrews, Fife — Map Ref: 2D3

★★★★

B&B

The Paddock

Sunnyside, Strathkinness, by St Andrews, Fife, KY16 9XP
Tel: 01334 850888 Fax: 01334 850870
E-mail: thepaddock@btinternet.com
Web: www.colsbrij.freeserve.co.uk/paddock/paddock.htm

1 Twin All En Suite
2 Double

B&B per person
from £20.00 Dbl/Twn

Open Mar-Nov

Modern bungalow furnished to a high standard , in a semi-rural location on the edge of Strathkinness village, having open outlook to farmland to the rear. St Andrews is three miles away, with easy access to golf courses, beach , shops and cultural buildings. Craigtoun Country Park is within one and a half miles.

BETWEEN THE GRANITE OF THE HIGH CAIRNGORMS AND A DRAMATIC UNSPOILT COASTLINE, LIE HILLS, MOORS AND WOODED FARMLANDS, RIVER VALLEYS AND CHARACTERFUL TOWNS, AS WELL AS ABERDEEN, SCOTLAND'S THIRD CITY, NOTED FOR ITS UNIQUE SILVER GRANITE ARCHITECTURE AND ITS FLORAL DISPLAYS.

Telford's Bridge over River Spey at Craigellachie

ABERDEEN OFFERS PLENTY for visitors: museums, art gallery, great shopping plus an expanding range of leisure attractions along its extensive promenade. The city is also the gateway to Royal Deeside, noted not just for Balmoral Castle and royal family connections, but beautiful scenery with plenty of walking, climbing and castles to visit nearby, plus Royal Lochnagar Distillery.

MALT WHISKY IS MOST strongly associated with Moray and its unique Malt Whisky Trail, offering a wide choice of distilleries to visit many of which are located along the beautiful birchwood setting of the River Spey. The third major river in this area, the River Don, is associated with the Castle Trail, where some of the finest castles in Scotland are linked in a signposted trail, which range from the medieval fortress of Kildrummy to the Adam revival grandeur of Haddo House.

THE COASTLINE OFFERS yet more delights, not just in the coastal links golf courses, endless beaches and spectacular cliffs and coves, but also in a further range of visitor attractions, including the unique Museum of Scottish Lighthouses at Fraserburgh, the site of Scotland's first lighthouse, and also the equally unique displays at Macduff Marine Aquarium, where a natural kelp reef – seen through one of the largest viewing windows in any British aquarium – shelters a community of fish and other sea creatures usually only seen by divers.

Cardhu Distillery, Knockando, Aberlour

Grathes Castle, Banchory

GRAMPIAN IS CERTAINLY full of surprises – including the chance to see Britain's largest resident colony of bottle-nose dolphins, which turn up close to land anywhere on the coast between Findhorn and Banff.

EVENTS GRAMPIAN HIGHLANDS, ABERDEEN AND THE NORTH EAST COAST

4-7 APRIL
Sprit of Speyside Whisky Festival
Various venues, Speyside
Enjoy tastings, distillery visits, music and other themed activities during the celebration of whisky in it's spiritual home.
Contact: Elgin Tourist Information Centre
TEL: **01343 542666**
www.spiritofspeyside.com

7-8 JULY
Scottish Traditional Boat Festival
Portsoy, Banffshire
Traditional boats, craft and trade demonstrations, live music, street theatre, and food fayre.
TEL: **01261 842951**
www.sixvillages.org.uk/boatfest

1-11 AUGUST
Aberdeen International Youth Festival
Various venues, North East
An international multi-arts festival featuring some if the world's finest orchestras, bands, choirs, dance and theatre groups.
Contact: Ms N Wallis
TEL: **020 8946 2995**
TICKET LINE: **01224 641122**

3-6 AUGUST
Speyfest
Various venues, Fochabers
Pan-Celtic festival of traditional music and crafts.
Contact: Mr P Devine
TEL: **01343 820951**
www.speyfest.com

1 SEPTEMBER
Braemar Highland Gathering
The Princess Royal and Duke of Fife Memorial Park, Braemar
The first gathering in Braemar was nine hundred years ago making it the longest running gathering. The event is very popular and tickets need to be booked in advance. Attractions include heavy and track events, piping & highland dancing. The patron of the gathering is Her Majesty the Queen.
Contact: WM Meston
TEL: **01399 755377**

8-17 SEPTEMBER
Techfest
Various venues, Aberdeenshire
Aberdeen and the North East of Scotland's festival of technology and science, involving industry, schools and the community in an effort to promote science and technology.
TEL: **01224 274195**

*12-20 OCTOBER
Aberdeen Alternative Festival
Various venues, Aberdeen
Arts festival featuring music, drama, comedy, dance & children's events.
Contact: Aberdeen Alternative Festival
TEL: **01224 635822**
www.abfest.dial.pipex.com

31 DECEMBER
Stonehaven Fireball Festival
High Street, Stonehaven
Traditional fireball festival parade through the streets of Stonehaven.
Contact: Leisure & Recreation Department, South Aberdeenshire Council
TEL: **01569 762001**

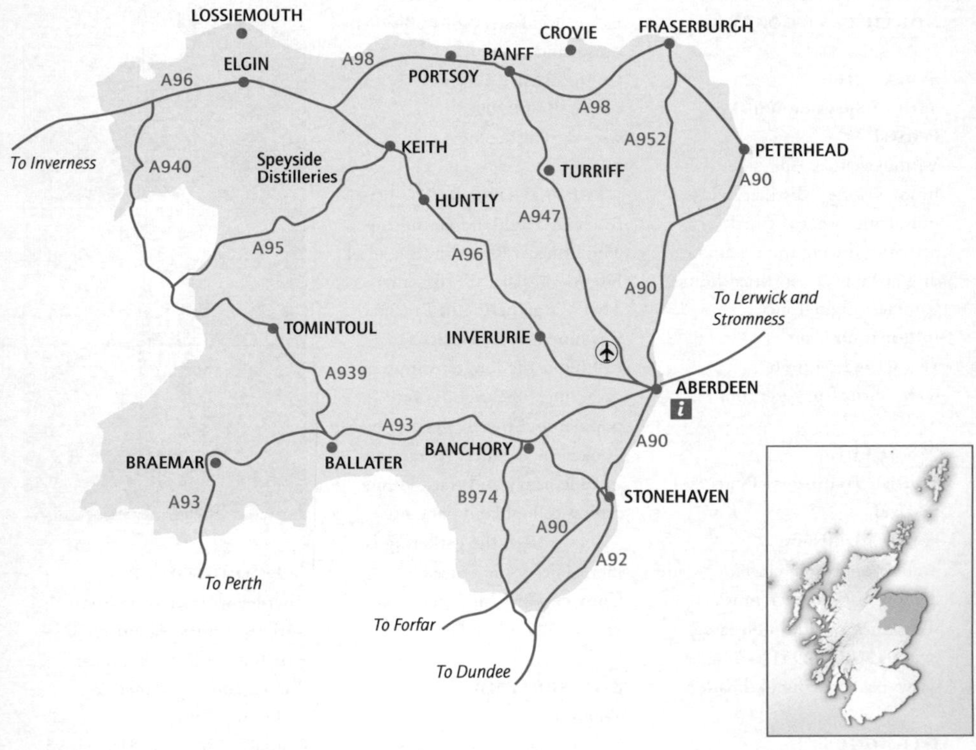

ABERDEEN AND GRAMPIAN TOURIST BOARD
27 Albyn Place
Aberdeen
AB10 1YL

TEL: **01224 632727**
FAX: **01224 581367**
www.agtb.org

ABERDEEN AND GRAMPIAN TOURIST BOARD

ABERDEEN
St Nicholas House
Broad Street
TEL: **(01224) 632727**
Jan-Dec

ALFORD
Railway Museum
Station Yard
TEL: **(019755) 62052**
Easter-Sept

BALLATER
Station Square
TEL: **(013397) 55306**
Easter-end Oct

BANCHORY
Bridge Street
TEL: **(01330) 822000**
Easter-Oct

BANFF
Collie Lodge
TEL: **(01261) 812419**
Easter-Sept

BRAEMAR
The Mews
Mar Road
TEL: **(013397) 41600**
April-Oct

CRATHIE
Car Park
Balmoral Castle
TEL: **(013397) 42414**
Easter-Oct

DUFFTOWN
Clock Tower
The Square
TEL: **(01340) 820501**
Easter-Oct

ELGIN
17 High Street
TEL: **(01343) 542666/543388**
Jan-Dec

FORRES
116 High Street
TEL: **(01309) 672938**
Easter-Oct

FRASERBURGH
Saltoun Square
TEL: **(01346) 518315**
Easter-Sept

HUNTLY
The Square
TEL: **(01466) 792255**
Easter-Oct

INVERURIE
18 High Street
TEL: **(01467) 625800**
Jan-Dec

STONEHAVEN
66 Allardice Street
TEL: **(01569) 762806**
Easter-Oct

TOMINTOUL
The Square
TEL: **(01807) 580285**
Easter-Oct

Aberdeen — **Map Ref: 4G10**

GUEST HOUSE

Abbian Guest House
148 Crown Street, Aberdeen, AB11 6HS
Tel/Fax: 01224 575826

1 Single	7 En Suite fac	B&B per person	Open Jan-Dec
1 Twin		£28.00-£35.00 Single	
3 Double		£22.00-£25.00 Dbl/Twn	
2 Family			

Victorian mid-terraced family run house, in central location convenient for bus, rail, sea ferry and city centre entertainments. Completely modernised, fantastic power showers.

ABERDEEN NICOLL'S GUEST HOUSE

63 SPRINGBANK TERRACE, FERRYHILL, ABERDEEN AB11 6JZ
Tel: 01224 572867 Fax: 01224 572867
e.mail: aberdeennicollsguesthouse@btinternet.com
Web: www.aberdeennicollsguesthouse.com

Family run, friendly, tastefully decorated, comfortable accommodation in city centre. Convenient for bus/rail stations, Duthie Park Winter Garden, the beautiful river Dee, beach, carnival, swimming pools, shops, theatre and restaurants. Within 5 miles radius of 6 golf courses. Ideal base for touring the Highlands and whisky trails. Private parking.

GUEST HOUSE

Aberdeen Nicoll's Guest House
63 Springbank Terrace, Ferryhill, Aberdeen, AB11 6JZ
Tel/Fax: 01224 572867
E-mail: aberdeennicollsguesthouse@btinternet.com
Web: www.btinternet.com/~aberdeennicollsguesthouse

2 Twn/Dbl	En Suite fac	B&B per person	Open Jan-Dec excl
1 Triple	En Suite fac	from £22.50 Single	Xmas/New Year
2 Family	Standard	from £17.00 Twin	
1 Twn/Dbl	Standard		

Family run, 6 bedroom guest house situated in Aberdeen's city centre, part of a 'listed' Victorian granite terraced street. Each room is tastefully decorated and very comfortable. Convenient for bus/rail stations, shops, theatre and restaurants. Within walking distance of beach, harbour and Winter Garden. Ideal base for touring the 'Highlands', 'Whisky Trails' etc. Within a 5-mile radius of 6 golf courses. Limited private off-street parking.

GUEST HOUSE

Aberdeen Springdale Guest House
404 Great Western Road, Aberdeen, AB10 6NR
Tel: 01224 316561 Fax: 01224 316561
E-mail: jamesestirling@msn.com
Web: www.aberdeenguesthouse.co.uk

1 Single	2 En Suite fac	B&B per person	Open Jan-Dec
1 Twin	1 Limited ensuite	£22.00-£25.00 Single	
2 Double	2 Pub Bath/Show	£19.00-£24.00 Dbl/Twn	
2 Family			

Attractive granite house 2 miles (3kms) from city centre. On main bus routes, 5 miles (8kms) from the airport and on route to Royal Deeside.

GUEST HOUSE

Balvenie Guest House
9 St Swithin Street, Aberdeen, AB10 6XB
Tel: 01224 322559 Fax: 01224 322773
E-mail: balveniegh@aol.com

2 Single	2 Pub Bath/Show	B&B per person	Open Jan-Dec
2 Twin		£18.00-£22.00 Single	
1 Double		£16.00-£18.00 Dbl/Twn	

Late Victorian granite built house in residential area in West End, close to city centre. Parking. Convenient for local and airport buses.

Important: Prices stated are estimates and may be subject to amendments

Aberdeen

Map Ref: 4G10

B&B

Mrs K Bevan
4 Brodiach Court, Westhill, Aberdeenshire, AB32 6QY
Tel: 01224 742749

2 Twin	1 En Suite fac 1 Priv.NOT ensuite 1 Pub Bath/Show	B&B per person to £25.00 Single to £25.00 Twin	Open Jan-Dec

Modern detached house in quiet residential cul-de-sac, in rural suburb on outskirts of Aberdeen. Convenient for Castle Trail and Royal Deeside. 7 miles to Dyce airport and centre of town.

C

GUEST HOUSE

Butler's Islander Guest House
122 Crown Street, Aberdeen, AB11 6HJ
Tel: 01224 212411 Fax: 01224 212411/586448
E-mail: islander@butlerigh.demon.co.uk
Web: www.butlerigh.demon.co.uk/index.htm

1 Single 3 Twin 3 Double	3 En Suite fac 2 Pub Bath/Show	B&B per person from £25.00 Single from £18.00 Dbl/Twn Room only from £20.00 Single from £13.50 Double	Open Jan-Dec

A Georgian terraced house in a central situation close to the city centre with all its amenities. A family run establishment with owners keen to maintain high standards throughout. Bus and railways stations nearby.

C W V

GUEST HOUSE

Campbells Guest House
444 King Street, Aberdeen, AB24 3BS
Tel: 01224 625444 Fax: 01224 624556
E-mail: cam444@zetnet.co.uk

1 Single 3 Twin 2 Family	4 En Suite fac 1 Pub Bath/Show	B&B per person from £25.00 Single from £20.00 Twin	Open Jan-Dec

Semi detached house, own car park and on main bus route. City centre 1 mile (2kms). Close to golf links, sandy beach, leisure centre and University. Residents bar/lounge with cable TV. Popular base for golfing parties and close to AECC. About 1 mile to beach and leisure attractions.

C V

Scottish Agricultural College
CRAIBSTONE ESTATE, BUCKSBURN, ABERDEEN AB21 9TR
Tel: 01224 711195 Fax: 01224 711298
Web: www.craibstone.sac.ac.uk

Situated in quiet rural location within large woodland estate only 5 miles from Aberdeen with own 18-hole golf course, it is the ideal venue for touring the north east of Scotland, playing the many golf courses or just relaxing. Whatever your needs we will give you a warm welcome.

CAMPUS ACCOMMODATION

Craibstone Estate
Scottish Agricultural College, Bucksburn, Aberdeen AB21 9YA
Tel: 01224 711195 Fax: 01224 711298
Web: www.craibstone.com

38 Single 20 Twin 1 Double	64 En Suite fac 13 Pub Bath/Show 4 Priv.NOT ensuite	B&B per person from £20.00 Single from £26.00 Twin	Open mid March-mid April, July-Sept B&B + Eve.Meal from £27.00

Halls of Residence, set in extensive country park on outskirts of Aberdeen, with easy access to all amenities.

W V

Aberdeen | Map Ref: 4G10

GUEST HOUSE

Dunrovin Guest House
168 Bon-Accord Street, Aberdeen, AB11 6TX
Tel: 01224 586081/572104 Fax: 01224 586081
E-mail: dellanzo@hotmail.com
Web: www.dunrovin.freeservers.com

Family run Victorian guest house situated in quiet tree-lined street mid-way between town centre and park on the river. A selection of cosmopolitan restaurants within walking distance.

3 Single, 3 Twin, 1 Double, 1 Family
1 Twin ensuite, 1 Family ensuite
B&B per person from £20.00 Single, from £17.50 Dbl/Twn
Open Jan-Dec excl Xmas/New Year

FURAIN GUEST HOUSE

North Deeside Road, Peterculter, Aberdeen AB14 0QN
Telephone: 01224 732189 Fax: 01224 739070

FURAIN GUEST HOUSE, on the A93, 8 miles west of Aberdeen centre, close to several historic castles and convenient for touring some of the most beautiful countryside in the UK. We give a full Scottish breakfast with choice, special diets catered for.

GUEST HOUSE

Furain Guest House
92 North Deeside Road, Peterculter, Aberdeen, AB14 0QN
Tel: 01224 732189 Fax: 01224 739070

Late Victorian house built of red granite. Family run. Convenient for town, Royal Deeside and the Castle Trail. Private car parking. Dinner available on Wednesday, Friday and Saturday.

1 Single, 3 Twin, 2 Double, 2 Family
All En Suite
B&B per person from £30.00 Single, from £20.00 Dbl/Twn
Room only per person from £28.00
Open Jan-Dec excl Xmas/New Year
B&B + Eve.Meal from £35.00

GUEST HOUSE

Greyholme
35 Springbank Terrace, Aberdeen, AB11 6LR
Tel: 01224 587081 Fax: 01224 212287
E-mail: nicki@greyholme-guesthouse.freeserve.co.uk

Personally run guest house close to city centre and all amenities. Near to main bus routes. Off street parking available.

2 Single, 1 Twin, 2 Double
2 Pub Bath/Show
B&B per person £20.00-£22.00 Single, £17.00-£19.00 Dbl/Twn
Open Jan-Dec

B&B

Mr and Mrs J A G McHardy
33 Carden Place, Aberdeen, AB10 1UN
Tel: 01224 645191

Victorian terraced house in west end of city. Within easy walking distance of city centre. Garden breakfast room. Non smoking house.

1 Single, 2 Twin
1 Pub Bath/Show, 1 Priv.NOT ensuite
B&B per person £20.00-£25.00 Single, £20.00-£25.00 Twin
Open Jan-Dec excl Xmas/New Year

Aberdeen Map Ref: 4G10

Maclean Bed & Breakfast
8 Boyd Orr Avenue, Aberdeen, AB12 5RG
Tel/Fax: 01224 248726
E-mail: j.maclean@abdn.ac.uk

2 Twin, 1 Double | 1 Pub bath/Show, 2 Twn with Showers | B&B per person £17.00-£20.00 Single, £15.00-£19.00 Double | Open Jan-Dec, B&B + Eve.Meal from £25.00

Family run B&B with conservatory dining area, set in quiet residential area just south of the River Dee. Very handy for easy access to routes going south. Off street parking.

Norwood Hall Hotel
Garthdee Road, Cults, Aberdeen, AB15 9FX
Tel: 01224 868951 Fax: 01224 869868
Web: www.norwood-hall.co.uk

2 F.poster, 2 Suites, 2 Family, 1 Twin, 14 Double | All En Suite | B&B per person from £40.00 Single, from £30.00 Dbl/Twn | Open Jan-Dec, B&B + Eve.Meal from £45.00

21 Bedroom Victorian Mansion within 7 acres of Wooded Gardens. Situated 3 miles of City Centre en route to Royal Deeside. Choice of dining in Tapestry Restaurant or Georgian Bar. A favourite choice for conferences, weddings and family gatherings.

★★
B&B

Regency Rooms
89 Crown Street, Aberdeen, AB11 6HH
Tel: 01224 211600 Fax: 01224 211884

5 Single, 3 Twin, 1 Double | All En Suite, 1 Pub Bath/Show | B&B per room £30.00 Single Ens, £35.00 Twn/Dbl Ens | Open Jan-Dec

Beautifully appointed rooms with first class facilities. City centre location. Complimentary continental breakfast tray.

St Elmo
64 Hilton Drive, Aberdeen, AB24 4NP
Tel: 01224 483065
E-mail: StElmoBandB@aol.com
Web: http://home.aol.com/StElmoBandB/

1 Triple, 1 Double, 1 Twin | 1 Pub Bath/Show | B&B per person from £20.00 Single, from £16.00 Dbl/Twn | Open Jan-Dec

A detached bungalow in residential area with off road parking. Totally non-smoking, with additional mini-fridges, microwaves, crockery and cutlery for restricted self-catering in evenings. Scottish breakfast provided. City centre 2 miles. Situated on main bus route. Off-street parking.

VAT is shown at 17.5%: changes in this rate may affect prices.

Key to symbols is on back flap.

Aberdeen — **Map Ref: 4G10**

HOTEL

University of Aberdeen
King's College, Aberdeen, AB24 3FX
Tel: 01224 273444 Fax: 01224 276246
E-mail: adgo26@abdn.ac.uk

Modern accommodation on university campus all ensuite with access to all facilities.

500+ Rooms (all singles)	76 Ensuite fac Pub Bath/Showers	B&B per person from £15.00 Single	Open Jun-Mar and Sep-Apr B&B + Eve.Meal from £30.50

CAMPUS ACCOMMODATION

University of Aberdeen Conference Office
Kings College, Aberdeen, AB24 3FX
Tel: 01224 273444 (res) Fax: 01224 276246
E-mail: mary.duncan@abdn.ac.uk

Student accommodation in heart of Aberdeen University's old town campus.

362 Single 22 Twin 43 Single	76 En Suite fac Ensuite Ensuite 45 Pub Bath/Show	B&B per person £15.00-£27.50 Single £39.50 Twin	Open 26Mar-12Apr 11Jun-18Sep from £9.50-£15.50

by Aberdeen — **Map Ref: 4G10**

B&B

Pat & John Allen
3 Greystone Place, Newtonhill, nr Stonehaven, AB39 3UL
Tel/Fax: 01569 730391
E-mail: patsbb@talk21.com

A friendly welcome awaits at this comfortable semi-detached house, set in coastal village 10 miles from Aberdeen. Evening meals by arrangement , including a range of vegetarian. Home made bread daily.

1 Twin 1 Double/Family	2 Priv.NOT ensuite	B&B per person from £16.00 Single from £16.00 Twin	Open Jan-Dec B&B + Eve.Meal from £22.50

Aberlour, Banffshire — **Map Ref: 4D8**

B&B

Roys Croft
Aberlour, Banffshire, AB38 9NR
Tel/Fax: 01340 871408

Small working croft in the heart of the Whisky Trail near the delightful village of Charlestown of Aberlour in Speyside.

1 Double 1 Twin	1 En Suite fac	B&B per person from £19.50 Single from £16.50 Dbl/Twn Room only per person from £13.00	Open Apr-Oct

Important: Prices stated are estimates and may be subject to amendments

Aboyne, Aberdeenshire

Map Ref: 4F11

★★★★ B&B

Mrs Eileen Barton

Alltdinnie, Birse, Aboyne, Aberdeenshire, AB34 5ES
Tel: 013398 86323 Fax: 013398 86211

1 Twin/Fam 2 Priv.NOT ensuite
1 Double

B&B per person
from £32.00 Single
from £26.00 Dbl/Twn

Open Apr-Oct
B&B + Eve.Meal
£40.00-£45.00

Historic, Victorian country house, peacefully located with large attractive gardens. Owners can arrange a variety of 2/3 night packages. Ideal situation for 'Castle and Whisky Trails '. Mrs Barton offers good 'home cooking' for those guests wanting an evening meal by prior arrangement.

C V

★★★ B&B

Birse Lodge House

Charleston Road, Aboyne, Aberdeenshire, AB34 5EL
Tel: 013398 86253 Fax: 013398 87796

1 Twin All En Suite
2 Double

B&B per person
from £33.00 Single
from £26.00 Dbl/Twn

Open Jan-Dec

Once the Dowar House of the Marchioness of Huntly, Birse Lodge House is a superb granite Victorian Country house in the heart of Royal Deeside. The house is situated in a large garden and is adjacent to the village green where, every August, the famous Aboyne Higland Games are held. A short stroll from the house takes you along the bank of the River Dee.

TV P

C W

★★★★★ B&B

Struan Hall

Ballater Road, Aboyne, Aberdeenshire, AB34 5HY
Tel/Fax: 013398 87241
E.mail: struanhall@zetnet.co.uk
Web: www.struanhall.zetnet.co.uk

2 Twin All En Suite
1 Double

B&B per person
from £26.00 Single
from £26.00 Dbl/Twn

Open Mar-end Oct

Peacefully situated in the two acres of mature gardens, this substantial family home has been sensitively restored to provide a traditional and very comfortable holiday base. Royal Deeside offers a vast range of outdoor and heritage attractions.

TV P

C £ V

Alford, Aberdeenshire

Map Ref: 4F10

★★★ B&B

Bydand Bed & Breakfast

18 Balfour Road, Alford, Aberdeenshire, AB33 8NF
Tel: 019755 63613

1 Twin All En Suite
1 Double

B&B per person
from £19.00 Single
from £19.00 Dbl/Twn
Room only per person
from £17.00

Open Jan-Dec

A warm welcome in this family B&B set in quiet residential area yet only 5 minutes walk from village centre. Ideal location for Castle and Whisky trails. Plenty of outdoor activities within village including dry ski slope and 18 hole golf course.

C

Alford, Aberdeenshire

Map Ref: 4F10

B&B

Lethenty Farm House

Tullynessle, Alford
Tel/Fax: 019755 63402
E-mail: lethentyout@freenet.co.uk

1 Twin	2 En Suite fac	B&B per person	Open Jan-Dec
2 Double	1 Priv.NOT ensuite	from £21.50 Single	
		from £19.50 Dbl/Twn	

Enjoy the unique atmosphere of the beautiful part of the Vale of Alford, with glorious views of the hills. Lethenty Farm House is set on a working farm of 400 acres of farmland. It is an ideal base for wildlife, walking, climbing or just relaxing yet only 3 miles from Alford. Ground floor accommodation.

C V

Ballater, Aberdeenshire

Map Ref: 4E11

GUEST HOUSE

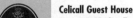

Celicall Guest House

3 Braemar Road, Ballater, Aberdeenshire, AB35 5RL
Tel: 013397 55699

2 Twin	All En Suite	B&B per person	Open Apr-Oct
2 Double		from £17.00 Dbl/Twn	

Completely refurbished comfortable accomodation, all en-suite and with private parking. At centre of this Royal Deeside village with shops and Restaurants all within strolling distance.

V

GUEST HOUSE

Coyles Hotel

43 Golf Road, Ballater, Aberdeenshire, AB35 5RS
Tel: 013397 55064 Fax: 013397 55212
E-mail: coyleshotel@sol.co.uk

1 Single	5 En Suite fac	B&B per person	Open Jan-Dec excl
3 Twin	2 Pub Bath/Show	£22.00-£26.00 Single	Xmas/New Year
4 Double		£18.00-£22.00 Dbl/Twn	
1 Family			

Quiet relaxed family run house with accommodation of a high standard. Peaceful location close to village shops and the golf course. Wide range of sporting activities and renowned royal connections with this beautiful area.

C V

B&B

Dee Valley Guest House

26 Viewfield Road, Ballater, Aberdeen-shire, AB35 5RD
Tel/Fax: 013397 55408

1 Twin	1 En Suite	B&B per person	Open Easter-Oct
1 Double		from £22.00 Single	
2 Family		from £17.00 Dbl/Twn	

Detached house in quiet residential area, close to village centre, bus station and golf course. Ideal for the older / infirm guest with a stair-lift to all bedrooms. Excellent base for touring.

W V

Ballater, Aberdeenshire

Map Ref: 4E11

EASTBANK

50 Albert Road, Ballater, Royal Deeside AB35 5QU
Tel: 013397 55742 Fax: 013397 55795
e.mail: eastbank.ballater@virgin.net Web: www.strathdee.com

Warm and comfortable B&B with a friendly atmosphere.
Ideal for golfers, hillwalkers, fishing and touring.
Close proximity to village amenities.
Contact Charlie or Isabel Michie.

B&B

Eastbank B&B

50 Albert Road, Ballater, Aberdeenshire, AB35 5QU
Tel: 013397 55742 Fax: 013397 55795
E-mail: eastbank.ballater@virgin.net
Web: www.strathdee.com

Warm and comfortable B&B with a friendly atmosphere. Ideal for golfers, hillwalkers, fishing and touring. Close proximity to village amenities. Contact Charlie or Isabel Michie.

1 Twin 2 Double	2 En Suite fac 1 Priv.NOT ensuite	B&B per person from £25.00 Single from £20.00 Dbl/Twn	Open Mar-Dec

TV P

C

INVERDEEN HOUSE B&B

11 BRIDGE SQUARE, BALLATER, ROYAL DEESIDE AB35 5QJ
From Overseas tel: 44 13397 55759 From UK tel: 013397 55759
e.mail: Inverdeen@aol.com Web: www.inverdeen.com
Web: www.royal-deeside.org.uk/inverdeen.htm

You will experience a warm welcome, excellent beds and superb, generous breakfasts in our stone-built listed building (1820). Next to River Dee and eight miles from Balmoral Castle. Positively no smoking. Inverdeen is lovely, super clean and really snug with excellent central heating. Drying facilities. Special Offer: Double Accommodation, 7 nights B&B for the price of 6, subject to availability.

B&B

Inverdeen House B&B

11 Bridge Square, Ballater, Royal Deeside, AB35 5QJ
Tel: 013397 55759
E-mail: inverdeen@aol.com
Web: www.inverdeen.com

We offer a splendid selection of great breakfasts featuring pancakes with Genuine Canadian maple Syrup, Venison sausage, home-baked muffins and home-made jam. Inverdeen House faces the A93 (at the Dee Bridge). There is easy access to such attractions as hillwalking, mountain climbing, orienteering, cycling, skiing, pony trekking, fishing, gliding, 4x4 driving, bird watching, SST's, Archaeolink and the Whisky, Castle and Stone Circle trails.

2 Double 1 Family	1 Priv.NOT ensuite 1 Pub Bath/Show	B&B per person from £40.00 Single £22.50-£25.00 Double	Open Jan-Dec

TV

C £ V

Ballater, Aberdeenshire **Map Ref: 4E11**

Monaltrie Lodge

Bridge Square, Ballater AB35 5QJ
Tel/Fax: 013397 55296 e.mail: bhepburn@talk21.com

Monaltrie Lodge is a traditional Victorian villa standing in its own grounds overlooking the river Dee. Very quiet, yet central, with mountain views. Off-street parking. Dinner is by arrangement, and the food enjoys an excellent STB rating. Full central heating. Ensuite bathrooms with power showers. Open all year.

B&B

Monaltrie Lodge
Bridge Square, Ballater, Aberdeenshire, AB35 5QJ
Tel/Fax: 013397 55296
E-mail: bhepburn@talk21.com

1 Twin
2 Double

All En Suite

B&B per person
from £25.00 Dbl/Twn

Open Jan-Dec excl Xmas/New Year
B&B + Eve.Meal from £40.00

A charming Victorian villa within its own grounds overlooking the River Dee in a quiet yet central location. Off-street parking. There are many historic places to visit nearby such as Balmoral and Crathie Kirk with many National Trust Castles in the area. Evening meal available by arrangement using only fresh local produce.

£ V

Moorside Guest House

BRAEMAR ROAD, BALLATER AB35 5RL
TEL/FAX: 013397 55492
E.MAIL: moorside.house@virgin.net

A warm welcome awaits you at Moorside House which offers quality accommodation at an affordable price, in the heart of Royal Deeside. All rooms have ensuite, TV, courtesy tray, hair dryer and electric blankets. Excellent breakfasts with home-made bread and preserves. Parking. Ideal for hill-walking, golf and touring.

GUEST HOUSE

Moorside Guest House
Braemar Road, Ballater, Aberdeenshire, AB35 5RL
Tel/Fax: 013397 55492
E-mail: moorside.house@virgin.net

2 Twin
4 Double
3 Family

All En Suite

B&B per person
from £20.00 Dbl/Twn

Open Apr-Oct

Friendly, personally run guest house in beautiful village in heart of Royal Deeside. All rooms ensuite, TVs, hairdryers and courtesy trays. Excellent breakfasts with homemade bread and preserves. Large garden and car park. Excellent restaurants nearby.

TV P

C £ V

Ballater, Aberdeenshire — Map Ref: 4E11

Morvada House

28 Braemar Road, Ballater AB35 5RL
Tel/Fax: 013397 56334
e.mail: morvada@aol.com

Allan and Thea Campbell welcome you to the beautiful village of Ballater. This peaceful village is well situated for walking (Lochnagar and Glen Muick), visiting castles (Balmoral and Braemar), or distilleries (Royal Lochnagar and Glenlivet). Warmth, personal service, absolute cleanliness, trust, a laugh, and acknowledgement are assured during your stay.

★★★ GUEST HOUSE

Morvada Guest House
28 Braemar Road, Ballater, Deeside, AB35 5RL
Tel/Fax: 013397 56334
E-mail: morvada@aol.com

1 Twin, 5 Double — All En Suite — B&B per person From £20.00 Single, from £20.00 Dbl/Twn — Open Jan-Dec excl Xmas/New Year

A friendly family run Victorian house offering traditional highland hospitality with modern en-suite facilities and a guests lounge. Furnished to a high standard with sky tv, tea and coffee including herbal tea and hot chocolate in the bedrooms. A quiet location close to the village centre and golf course with shops and wide choice of restaurants nearby.

★★ B&B

Morven Lodge
29 Braemar Road, Ballater, Aberdeenshire, AB35 5RQ
Tel: 013397 55373

1 Twin, 2 Double — 2 Priv.NOT ensuite, 2 Pub Bath/Show — B&B per person from £18.00 Dbl/Twn — Open May-Sep

A large granite block house of the Victorian period. Convenient base for touring Deeside. A former rectory retaining much of the period character and features. Situated close to the village centre with nearby restaurants and golf course. Ideal holiday base for enjoying Royal Deeside.

by Ballater, Aberdeenshire — Map Ref: 4E11

★★★ HOTEL

Loch Kinord Hotel
Ballater Road, Dinnet, Aberdeenshire, AB34 5JY
Tel: 013398 85229 Fax: 013398 87007
Web: www.loch-kinord-hotel.com

1 Single, 1 Twin, 10 Double, 3 Family — 9 En Suite fac, 6 Pub Bath/Show — B&B per person from £30.00 Single, from £20.00 Dbl/Twn — Open Jan-Dec, B&B + Eve.Meal from £45.00

Under the enthusiastic new ownership of Jenny and Andrew Cox the hotel has undergone some refurbishment. Situated in the centre of this small village it makes a great base for exploring Royal Deeside, skiing, walking, and playing golf. Non-residents very welcome and popular in the area for excellent food.

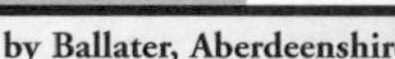

by Ballater, Aberdeenshire — Map Ref: 4E11

MIGVIE HOUSE

By Logie Coldstone, Aboyne, Aberdeenshire AB34 4XL
Telephone: 013398 81313 Fax: 013398 81635
Web: www.b-and-b-scotland.co.uk/migvie.htm

Migvie House nestles in the secluded upper reaches of Royal Deeside, with its romantic castles, famous distilleries and numerous sporting pursuits. The culmination of a perfect day could end at our peaceful old farmhouse. Lovingly restored, with antiques, country furnishings, wood fires and mountain views. Amidst small highland estate.

B&B

Carole Luffman
Migvie House, by Logie Coldstone, Aboyne, Aberdeenshire, AB34 4XL
Tel: 013398 81313 Fax: 013398 81635
Web: www.b-and-b-scotland.co.uk/migvie.htm

2 Twin | All En Suite | B&B per person | Open Mar-Oct
1 Double | | from £33.00 Single | Evening meals some
| | from £25.00 Dbl/Twn | times available.

Nestling in the secluded upper reaches of Royal Deeside this traditional stone farmhouse has been lovingly restored with a tremendous attention to detail accentuating its charm and character. Fully en-suite with a no-smoking policy. Glorious views across the fields and woods to hills and mountains beyond. Evening meals occasionally available.

V

Banchory, Aberdeenshire — Map Ref: 4F11

B&B

Ardconnel
6 Kinneskie Road, Banchory, Kincardineshire, AB31 5TA
Tel: 01330 822478

1 Twin | 1 En Suite fac | B&B per person | Open Mar-Oct
1 Double | 1 Priv.NOT ensuite | from £26.00 Single |
| | from £20.00 Dbl/Twn |

Very comfortable modern bungalow in quiet spot overlooking local golf course. Town centre and all amenities within 3 minute walking distance.

V

B&B

D Mutch
Dorena, Strachan, By Banchory, Kincardineshire, AB31 6NL
Tel/Fax: 01330 822540

1 Twin | All En Suite | B&B per person | Open Jan-Dec
2 Double | | from £20.00 Dbl/Twn |

Modern bungalow on edge of quiet village, with views across the fields and woods. Private parking. Only 3 miles from Banchory. Excellent hospitality assured.

V

Important: Prices stated are estimates and may be subject to amendments

Banchory, Aberdeenshire **Map Ref: 4F11**

★★★★★ B&B

The Old West Manse

71 Station Road, Banchory
Aberdeenshire, AB31 5UD
Tel/Fax: 01330 822202

A substantial house this former manse enjoys a quiet situation looking over the main west bound route into Banchory, with fine views towards the River Dee and hills beyond. With decor, furnishings and hospitality of the highest standard Jayne and John offer a real home from home experience in a relaxed and informal atmosphere. Jayne's substantial three course dinners and a table licence complete what is sure to be a very enjoyable experience.

2 Twin, 1 Double | 2 En Suite fac, 1 Priv.NOT ensuite | B&B per person £35.00 Single, from £27.50 Dbl/Twn | Open Feb-Dec, B&B + Eve.Meal from £46.00, Dinner £18.50

TV P C W V

★★★ B&B

Barbara J Robertson

Struan, Echt, AB32 6UL
Tel: 01330 860799

Modern house of a high standard in quiet residential village approximately 12 miles from Aberdeen. Rolling hills and farmland dominate the scenery in this lovely part of Grampian. Popular Inns within a couple of miles.

1 Single, 2 Double | 1 En Suite fac, 2 Priv.NOT ensuite, 2 Pub Bath/Show | B&B per person to £18.00 Single, to £18.00 Double | Open Apr-Sep

TV P C

★★★★ B&B

Towerbank House

93 High Street, Banchory, Kincardineshire, AB31 5XT
Tel/Fax: 01330 824798
E-mail: diane.john@dawps.fsnet.co.uk

Centrally situated Victorian house, south facing with splendid views towards the Deeside hills. Short stroll to all amenities.

1 Single, 2 Twin | All En Suite | B&B per person from £25.00 Single, from £20.00 Twin | Open Jan-Dec

TV P W V

Banchory, Aberdeenshire

Map Ref: 4F11

GUEST HOUSE

Village Guest House
83 High Street, Banchory, Kincardineshire, AB31 5PJ
Tel/Fax: 01330 823307

2 Twin, 2 Double | 2 En Suite fac, 1 Priv.NOT ensuite | B&B per person from £30.00 Single, from £25.00 Dbl/Twn; Room only per person from £28.00 | Open Jan-Dec; B&B + Eve.Meal from £40.00

Charming Victorian house in centre of Royal Deeside village. Warm Scottish welcome, finished with a taste of tartan. Stepped access from rear car park. Short stroll to village centre, restaurants and all amenities. Bus stop nearby.

C W V

by Banchory, Aberdeenshire

Map Ref: 4F11

B&B

Lochton House
Lochton of Durris, by Banchory, Aberdeenshire, AB31 6DB
Tel/Fax: 01330 844543
E-mail: crofters-inn@fsbdial.co.uk

2 Twin, 1 Double | All En Suite | B&B per person from £25.00 Single, from £22.00 Dbl/Twn; Room only per person from £16.00 | Open Jan-Dec excl Xmas/New Year; B&B + Eve.Meal from £34.00

Set 6 miles outside Banchory on A957 road to Stonehaven an Inn with regular local and tourist trade offering three comfortable en-suite bedrooms. Stonehaven and beaches 9 miles.

C V

B&B

Monthammock Farm
Durris, by Banchory, Kincardineshire, AB31 6DX
Tel/Fax: 01330 811421

1 Twin, 1 Double | 1 En Suite fac, 1 Priv.NOT ensuite, 1 Pub Bath/Show | B&B per person from £25.00 Single, from £20.00 Dbl/Twn | Open Jan-Dec excl Xmas/New Year; B&B + Eve.Meal £35.00-£40.00

Tranquility and a warm welcome at this sympathetically converted steading, with spectacular views over Deeside.

C V

Banff

Map Ref: 4F7

GUEST HOUSE

Bryvard Guest House
Seafield Street, Banff, AB45 1EB
Tel/Fax: 01261 818090
E-mail: bryvard@hotmail.com

2 Double, 1 Family | 1 Ensuite fac, 1 Private fac | B&B per person from £22.50 Single, from £22.50 Dbl/Twn | Open Jan-Dec

Edwardian town house, modernised to a high standard but retains much of its original character. Former market town with golf, sandy beaches and historic Duff House nearby. Fishing trips available and arranged.
Under 5's Free, Under 11's Half price.

C V

Important: Prices stated are estimates and may be subject to amendments

Banff

Map Ref: 4F7

★★★

B&B

Dorothy & Alec Clark

Montcoffer House, Montcoffer, Banff, AB45 3LJ
Tel: 01261 812979 Freephone: 0800 2985831
E-mail: montcoffer@aol.com

1 Single	2 En Suite fac	B&B per person	Open Jan-Dec excl
1 Double	1 Priv.NOT ensuite	£18.00 Single	Xmas/New Year
1 Family		£18.00 Double	B&B + Eve.Meal
			£27.00

Listed 17c mansion, overlooking Deveron Valley. Ideal centre for walking, golf, fishing, Castle and Whisky trails. Home cooked evening meals using mostly organically grown home produce. Packed lunches available on request. Set in two-and-a-half acres of walled garden. Members of Pride of Scotland, Best Banffshire & Buchan.

★★★★

B&B

Links Cottage B&B

Inverboyndie, Banff, Aberdeenshire, AB45 2JJ
Tel/Fax: 01261 812223

1 Twin	All En Suite fac	B&B per person	Open Mar-Nov
2 Double		from £25.00 Dbl/Twn	

Nestling by a sandy beach on Banff Links, picturesque Links Cottage with its attractive seaside garden offers tranquility to weary travellers. Relax in spacious, comfortable ensuite rooms, enjoy a wide selection of tasty breakfasts and explore the spectacular coastal scenery. Include visits to castles, Distilleries and charming fishing villages. Experience the magic of

★★★

B&B

Mrs Monica Mackay

13 Fife Street, Banff, AB45 1JB
Tel: 01261 812509
E-mail: william.mackay@btinternet.com
Web: www.btinternet.com/~real.mackay

1 Single	2 En Suite fac	B&B per person	Open Jan-Dec excl
1 Twin	1 Priv.NOT ensuite	from £20.00 Single	Xmas/New Year
1 Family		from £18.00 Twin	

Quality accommodation, food and service in this Georgian town house situated in a quiet street near picturesque harbour and close to town centre. Sandy beach in walking distance. Golf courses, castles and Duff House all nearby. Ample on street parking. Laundry services available. Fridge in every bedroom.

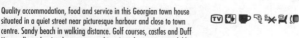

Banff Map Ref: 4F7

B&B

Morayhill
Bellevue Road, Banff, AB45 1BJ
Tel: 01261 815956 Fax: 01261 818717
E-mail: morayhill@cs.com
Web: www.coolbean.co.uk/morayhill/index.html

2 Twin	2 En Suite fac	B&B per person	Open Jan-Dec
1 Double	1 Priv.NOT ensuite	from £18.00 Single	

Large Victorian house, centrally situated for town, golf, and fishing. Warm and friendly welcome assured. Private Parking. Many places of interest locally including Duff House and The Sculpture Garden.

B&B

The Orchard
Duff House, Banff, Aberdeenshire, AB45 3TA
Tel/Fax: 01261 812146
E.mail: jma6914291@aol.com
Web: www.strathdee.com/orchard.html

1 Single	All En Suite	B&B per person	Open Feb-Nov
2 Twin		from £22.00 Single	
1 Double		from £22.00 Dbl/Twn	

Recently refurbished traditional house sitting in own grounds. Quiet location yet only 0.8 miles walk to town centre. On popular walk, near golf course close proximity to River Deveron and within easy reach of many surrounding golf courses.

Important: Prices stated are estimates and may be subject to amendments

Braemar, Aberdeenshire

Map Ref: 4D11

★★★

GUEST HOUSE

Clunie Lodge Guest House

Cluniebank Road, Braemar, Royal Deeside, AB35 5ZP
Tel: 013397 41330 Fax: 013397 41938
E-mail: ClunieLodge@msn.com
Web: www.clunielodge.co.uk

1 Single
1 Twin
1 Double
2 Family

2 En Suite fac
1 Priv.NOT ensuite
2 Pub Bath/Show

B&B per person
from £25.00 Single
from £23.00 Dbl/Twn

Open Jan-Dec excl Xmas

Victorian former manse house peacefully located close to village centre and short drive to golf course. Ideal base for walking, touring and golfing.

★★★

B&B

Craiglea

Hillside Drive, Braemar, Aberdeenshire, AB35 5YQ
Tel: 013397 41641 Fax: 013397 41252

1 Twin
1 Double

1 En Suite fac
1 Priv.NOT ensuite

B&B per person
from £20.00 Single
from £18.00 Dbl/Twn
Room only per person
from £15.00

Open Jan-Dec

Cosy, warm and roomy family home centrally situated in this quiet peaceful village renowned for its royal heritage. Short stroll to restaurants, pubs and shops.

★★★

GUEST HOUSE

Cranford Guest House

15 Glenshee Road, Braemar, Aberdeenshire, AB35 5YQ
Tel: 013397 41675
Web: www.braemarcranford.co.uk

3 Twin
3 Double

5 En suite fac
1 Pub Bath/Show
1 Private

B&B per person
£18.50-£20.00 Dbl/Twn

Open Jan-Dec excl Xmas

Attractive white painted Victorian guest house offering traditional Scottish hospitality. Fully modernised comfortable accommodation with en suite bedrooms, guest lounge and central heating throughout. Short stroll to village centre with views of surrounding mountains. Large private car park and garden.

Braemar, Aberdeenshire

Map Ref: 4D11

★★★

B&B

Mayfield House

11 Chapel Brae, Braemar, Aberdeenshire. AB35 5YT
Tel: 01397 41238
Web: www.mayhouse.co.uk

1 Single
1 Twn/Fam
2 Double

2 Pub Bath/Show

B&B per person
from £17.00 Single
from £17.00 Dbl/Twn

Open Jan-Dec excl
Xmas/New Year

Situated in a quiet, peaceful situation with views over the site of the Royal Highland gathering to the mountains beyond. A guest house since Victorian times the present owners continue the family tradition with highland hospitality and all modern comforts.

C V

★★★

GUEST HOUSE

Schiehallion House

10 Glenshee Road, Braemar, Aberdeenshire, AB35 5YQ
Tel: 013397 41679

1 Single
3 Twin
3 Double
2 Family

5 En Suite fac
1 Pub Bath/Show

B&B per person
from £20.00 Single
from £18.00 Dbl/Twn

Open Jan-Oct excl
New Year

Comfortable, tastefully decorated, Victorian house with attractive garden at gateway to Royal Deeside. Offering personal service and log fires. One ground floor annexe room. All nationalities welcome.

Buckie, Banffshire

Map Ref: 4E7

★★★★

B&B

Mrs Catherine Crawford

Glenelg, 26 Richmond Terrace, Portgordon, Buckie, Banffshire, AB56 2RA
Tel: 01542 833221

1 Single
1 Double
1 Family

2 Pub Bath/Show

B&B per person
from £16.00 Single
from £16.00 Double
Room only per person
from £10.00

Open Jan-Dec

Detached Victorian house in quiet residential area, with fine views overlooking the Moray Firth. Short walk to beaches. Home baking always available.

TV

C V

★★★★

B&B

Rosemount B&B

62 East Church Street, Buckie, Banffshire, AB56 1ER
Tel/Fax: 01542 833434

2 Twin
1 Double

2 En Suite fac
1 Priv.NOT ensuite

B&B per person
from £25.00 Single
from £22.00 Dbl/Twn

Open Jan-Dec excl
Xmas/New Year

Modernised Victorian detached house, centrally situated overlooking Moray Firth. Ideal for fishing, golf, Malt Whisky Trail, and at the start of the Spey Way Walk.

TV P

W V

Important: Prices stated are estimates and may be subject to amendments

Craigellachie, Banffshire

Map Ref: 4D8

★★★ B&B

Bridge View
Leslie Terrace, Craigellachie, Banffshire, AB38 9SX
Tel: 01340 881376
E-mail: bridgeview@talk21.com

Family home overlooking River Spey on Speyside Way, with transport collection available. Ideal base for touring, walking and Whisky trail.

1 Double, 1 Family — 1 En Suite fac, 1 Priv.NOT ensuite — B&B per person from £20.00 Single, from £17.00 Double — Open Apr-Oct

C V

Cullen, Banffshire

Map Ref: 4E7

★★★ B&B

Lily Cottage
1 Cathay Terrace, Cullen, Banffshire, AB56 4RX

Family run B&B in seaside town. All rooms ensuite. Ideal location for golf, walking and touring NE Scotland.

2 Double — All En Suite — B&B per person from £18.00 Single, from £18.00 Double — Open Jan-Dec excl Xmas/New Year

C V

★★★ B&B

Mrs M C Phimister
Alesund, 13 Ogilvie Park, Cullen, Buckie, Banffshire, AB56 4XZ
Tel: 01542 840017

Modern detached bungalow with garden, overlooking Cullen and the Moray Firth. Short walk to all amenities.

1 Twin, 1 Double — 1 Pub Bath/Show — B&B per person from £17.00 Single, from £16.00 Dbl/Twn — Open May-Sep

C

Dufftown, Banffshire

Map Ref: 4E9

★★★ B&B

Davaar B&B
Church Street, Dufftown, Keith, Banffshire, AB55 4AR
Tel: 01340 820464

Comfortable and personally run accommodation. Close to Whisky and Castle Trails.

1 Twin, 2 Double — 2 En Suite fac, 1 Pub Bath/Show — B&B per person from £16.00 Single, from £18.00 Dbl/Twn — Open Jan-Dec excl Xmas/New Year

C W V

★★★ B&B

Gowanbrae
19 Church Street, Dufftown, Keith, Banffshire, AB55 4AR
Tel/Fax: 01340 820461
E-mail: bedbreakfast@gowanbrae-dufftown.co.uk
Web: www.gowanbrae-dufftown.co.uk

Family run bed & breakfast in small Speyside town. Ideal location for touring the whisky trail, touring and walking.

1 Twin, 2 Double, 1 Family — All En Suite — B&B per person £18.00-£24.00 Single, £16.00-£20.00 Dbl/Twn — Open Jan-Dec excl Xmas/New Year

C V

Dufftown, Banffshire

Map Ref: 4E9

B&B

Nashville
8a Balvenie Street, Dufftown, Keith, Banffshire, AB55 4AB
Tel/Fax: 01340 820553
Mobile: 07703 984634
E-mail: nashville@dufftown72.freeserve.co.uk

Family run home in town centre. Convenient for Whisky Trail. A warm welcome awaits you. All rooms have many accessories including video recorder.

1 Twin
1 Double
1 Family

B&B per person
from £20.00 Single
from £15.00 Dbl/Twn
Room only per person
from £15.00

Open Jan-Dec

B&B

Mrs Mary M Robertson
11 Conval Street, Dufftown, Keith, Banffshire, AB55 4AE
Tel: 01340 820818

Warm welcome at quiet modern bungalow, off main street 18 miles (29 kms) south of Elgin. On Whisky Trail.

1 Twin
1 Double

1 Pub Bath/Show

B&B per person
from £18.00 Single
from £16.00 Dbl/Twn

Open Jan-Dec excl Xmas/New Year

Elgin, Moray

Map Ref: 4D8

ARDGYE HOUSE

Elgin, Moray IV30 8UP
Tel/Fax: 01343 850618 e.mail: ardgyehouse@hotmail.com

ARDGYE HOUSE is a gracious Edwardian mansion in its own extensive grounds situated close to main Aberdeen to Inverness road (3.5 miles west of Elgin). Superb accommodation in quiet surroundings. Central position ideal for beaches, golf, riding, fishing, castles and distilleries.
For full details contact Carol and Alistair McInnes.

GUEST HOUSE

Ardgye House
Elgin, Moray, IV30 3UP
Tel/Fax: 01343 850618
E-mail: ardgyehouse@hotmail.com
Web: www.scottishholidays.net

Gracious Edwardian mansion in own extensive grounds easily accessible from A96. 3 miles (5kms) from Elgin. Private facilities available.

1 Single
2 Twin
3 Double
4 Family

7 En Suite fac
3 Priv.NOT ensuite

B&B per person
£15.00-£20.00 Single
£15.00-£20.00 Dbl/Twn

Open Jan-Dec

GUEST HOUSE

Auchmillan
12 Reidhaven Street, Elgin, Moray, IV30 1QG
Tel: 01343 549077
Fax: 01343 569164
E-mail: auchmillan.guesthouse.elgin@virgin.net

Victorian villa with garden in conservation area of Elgin, quietly situated yet close to town centre and all amenities. Great breakfast.

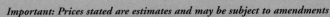

2 Single
5 Twin
2 Double
1 Family

5 En Suite fac

B&B per person
£17.00-£25.00 Single
£16.00-£24.00 Dbl/Twn

Elgin, Moray | **Map Ref: 4D8**

★★★ B&B

Belleville
14 South College Street, Elgin, Moray, IV30 1EP
Tel/Fax: 01343 541515
E-mail: belleville@talk21.com

Rooms	Facilities	Prices	Open
2 Double	All En Suite	B&B per person from £20.00 Single from £15.00 Double	Open Jan-Dec excl Xmas/New Year

Detached villa with off street parking, a few minutes walk from the town centre and Cathedral. A warm welcome with many extras at this no smoking house.

★★ B&B

Carronvale
18 South Guildry Street, Elgin, Moray, IV30 1QN
Tel/Fax: 01343 546864

Rooms	Facilities	Prices	Open
1 Twin 2 Double	1 Pub Bath/Show 1 WC	B&B per person from £20.00 Single from £16.00 Dbl/Twn	Open Jan-Dec excl Xmas/New Year B&B + Eve.Meal from £28.00

Victorian townhouse partly given over to form an art gallery. Non-smokers only. Close to town centre. No pets.

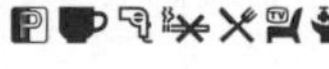

★★★★ B&B

The Croft
10 Institution Road, Elgin, Moray, IV30 1QX
Tel/Fax: 01343 546004
E-mail: thecroft_elgin@etn.org

Rooms	Facilities	Prices	Open
1 Single 1 Double 1 Family	2 En Suite fac 1 Priv.NOT ensuite	B&B per person from £23.00 Single from £24.00 Double	Open Jan-Dec

Friendly family run Victorian home built 1848 in quiet residential area. Easy walking distance of town centre and local amenities. Off-street parking.

★★★★ GUEST HOUSE

The Pines Guest House
East Road, Elgin, Moray, IV30 1XG
Tel/Fax: 01343 542766
Web: www.thepinesguesthouse.com

Rooms	Facilities	Prices	Open
2 Twin 2 Double 1 Family	All En Suite fac	B&B per person £26.00-£40.00 Single £18.00-£28.00 Dbl/Twn	Open Jan-Dec

Victorian elegance with modern comforts. Friendly atmosphere, freshly prepared food. Convenient for golf, fishing, Whisky and Castle Trails.

★★★ B&B

'Richmond' Bed & Breakfast
48 Moss Street, Elgin, Moray, IV30 1LT
Tel: 01343 542561
E-mail: richmond@clara.co.uk

Rooms	Facilities	Prices	Open
1 Single 2 Twin 2 Double 1 Family	2 En Suite fac 2 Limited En Suite Pub Bath/Show	B&B per person £16.00-£22.00 Single £18.00-£20.00 Dbl/Twn	Open Jan-Dec excl Xmas/New Year

Friendly, family home with garden close to town centre and all amenities. Ensuite rooms available.

Elgin, Moray

Map Ref: 4D8

★★ B&B

Rosemount

5 Mayne Road, Elgin, Moray, IV30 1NY
Tel: 01343 542907 Fax: 01343 551220

1 Twin. 1 Family — All En Suite

B&B per person from £35.00 Single, from £28.00 Twin; Room only per person from £35.00

Open Jan-Dec excl Xmas/New Year. B&B + Eve.Meal from £48.00

Large house in quiet area on edge of town centre. Private parking. Emphasis on fresh food and home cooking.

★★ GUEST HOUSE

West End Guest House

282 High Street, Elgin, Moray, IV30 1AQ
Tel: 01343 549629
E-mail: westend.house@virgin.net

3 Twin, 1 Double, 2 Family — 5 En Suite fac, 1 Priv.NOT ensuite

B&B per person from £20.00 Single, from £19.50 Dbl/Twn

Open Jan-Dec

Traditional Victorian villa with garden, close to A96. 10 minute walk from city centre and all amenities.

★★ B&B

Morag Whyte

5 Forestry Cottages, Newton, by Elgin, Moray
Tel: 01343 546702

1 Twin, 1 Double

B&B per person £14.00 Single, £14.00 Dbl/Twn

Open Jan-Nov excl New Year. B&B + Eve.Meal from £22.00

Modern semi-detached family home with garden , 3 miles (5 km) from Elgin. Both bedrooms on ground floor. Dinner available by prior arrangement. Home-baking normally available.

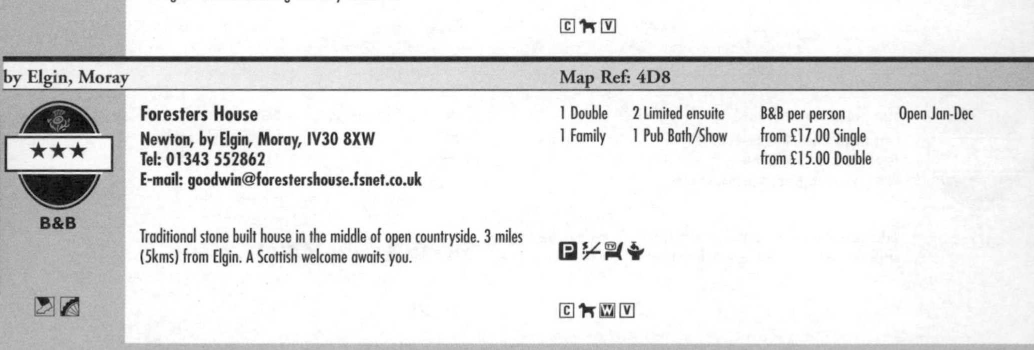

by Elgin, Moray

Map Ref: 4D8

★★★ B&B

Foresters House

Newton, by Elgin, Moray, IV30 8XW
Tel: 01343 552862
E-mail: goodwin@forestershouse.fsnet.co.uk

1 Double, 1 Family — 2 Limited ensuite, 1 Pub Bath/Show

B&B per person from £17.00 Single, from £15.00 Double

Open Jan-Dec

Traditional stone built house in the middle of open countryside. 3 miles (5kms) from Elgin. A Scottish welcome awaits you.

by Elgin, Moray | Map Ref: 4D8

B&B

'Parrandier', The Old Church of Urquhart

Meft Road, Urquhart, by Elgin, Moray, IV30 8NH
Tel/Fax: 01343 843063
Web: www.scottishholidays.net/parrandier

1 Twin, 1 Double, 1 Family | 2 En Suite fac, 1 Priv.NOT ensuite | B&B per person from £25.00 Single, from £18.00 Dbl/Twn; Room only per person from £16.00 | Open Jan-Dec; B&B + Eve.Meal from £28.00

Perched on a hill top this beautiful rural setting offers uninterrupted views across surrounding farmland. Built in 1843 the church is recently converted into a unique family home. The character of the church has been retained encompassing arched windows and beamed ceilings. Guest lounges and open fire. Dinner available.

Findhorn, Moray | Map Ref: 4C7

B&B

Heath House

Findhorn, Moray, IV36 3WN
Tel/Fax: 01309 691082
E-mail: elizabeth-tony.cowie@talk21.com

1 Twin, 1 Double | 1 En Suite fac, 1 Pub Bath/Show | B&B per person from £18.00 Dbl/Twn | Open Feb-Nov

Modern bungalow in secluded cul-de-sac on outskirts of Findhorn close to beach. 4 miles (7km) to Forres.

by Fochabers, Moray | Map Ref: 4E8

B&B

Mrs Mary Shand

Castlehill Cottage, Fochabers, Morayshire, IV32 7LJ
Tel: 01343 820761

1 Twin, 1 Family | 2 Pub Bath/Show | B&B per person from £17.00 Single, from £15.00 Twin; Room only per person from £11.00 | Open Jan-Dec excl Xmas/New Year

Family cottage set back from A96, with own flower garden and ample parking. 6 miles (10kms) east of Elgin.

Forres, Moray — Map Ref: 4C8

★★★ B&B

Mrs Jacqui Banks

April Rise, 16 Forbes Road, Forres, Moray, IV36 0HP
Tel: 01309 674066

1 Single 1 Twin 1 Family	2 En Suite fac 1 Pub Bath/Show	B&B per person to £20.00 Single £16.50-£18.00 Twin	Open Jan-Dec B&B + Eve.Meal £22.00-£25.00

Traditional Scottish hospitality in friendly family home. 2 rooms ensuite. Short walk to town and all amenities. Dinner by arrangement.

C W V

Caranrahd

Sanquhar Road, Forres, Moray, IV36 1DG
Tel: 01309 672581

2 Double 1 Family	2 Pub Bath/Show	B&B per person from £16.00 Single from £16.00 Double	Open Jan-Dec excl Xmas/New Year

Traditional Scottish hospitality in friendly family home, within quiet residential area. Ideal touring base.

C V

Mrs S Ferbrache

Cobo, 33 Manachie Road, Forres, Moray, IV36 2JT
Tel: 01309 673016

1 Single 1 Twin	1 Pub Bath/Show	B&B per person £18.00 Single £18.00 Twin	Open Jun-Aug

Modern family bungalow situated on edge of Forres and with secluded gardens. 10 minutes walk to town centre.

V

Milton of Grange Farmhouse

Milton-of-Grange Farm, by Forres, Moray, IV36 0TR
Tel/Fax: 01309 676360
E-mail: hildamassie@aol.com

2 Twin 3 Double 2 Family	3 Ensuite fac	B&B per person £18.00-£25.00 Single £18.00-£22.00 Dbl/Twn	Open 15Jan-15Dec

Beautifully appointed farmhouse on working farm, with all rooms ensuite with Forres 2 miles away, an ideal base for touring the whisky & castle trails or play golf. Nearby is the historic village of Findhorn, popular with birdwatchers & boating enthusiasts. A warm welcome is assured here.

C W V

Morven

Caroline Street, Forres, Moray, IV36 1AN
Tel/Fax: 01309 673788
E-mail: morven2@globalnet.co.uk

3 Twin	1 Priv.NOT ensuite 2 Pub Bath/Show	B&B per person from £18.00 Single from £18.00 Twin Room only per person from £16.00	Open Jan-Dec

Victorian house offering bed and breakfast in a warm friendly family atmosphere, with all conveniences. Short stroll into town centre.

C W V

Important: Prices stated are estimates and may be subject to amendments

Forres, Moray

Map Ref: 4C8

★★★★ B&B

Sherston House
Hillhead, Forres, Moray, IV36 2QT
Tel: 01309 671087

2 Double	Ensuite fac	B&B per person	Open Jan-Dec
1 Twin	Priv.NOT ensuite	from £20.00 Single	B&B + Eve.Meal
1 Family	Priv.NOT ensuite	from £17.50 Dbl/Twn	from £30.00

Tastefully restored stone built house, 1 mile (2km) from Forres and beside main A96. Garden area available. Dinner by prior arrangement.

Springfield B&B
Croft Road, Forres, Moray, IV36 3JS
Tel: 01309 676965 Fax: 01309 673376
E-mail: catherinebain@tinyworld.co.uk

1 Double	All En Suite	B&B per person	Open Jan-Dec
1 Family		from £20.00 Single	
		£17.50-£20.00 Double	
		Room only per person	
		from £15.00	

Large, comfortable, modern home, set in own grounds. Short stroll to town centre, restaurants and all amenities. From Elgin on A96, left at roundabout first right (Findhorn Rd) first left to the bottom. From Inverness A96 over the first roundabout to next, take the right into Forres then as above.

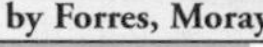

by Forres, Moray

Map Ref: 4C8

Mrs Flora Barclay
Moss-Side Farm, Rafford, Forres, Moray, IV36 0SL
Tel: 01309 672954

1 Twin	B&B per person	Open Apr-Sep
1 Double	from £15.00 Single	
1 Family	from £15.00 Dbl/Twn	
	Room only per person	
	from £10.00	

Traditional farmhouse with modern extension set in 28 acres on the outskirts of Forres. Ideal for golf, fishing and walking. On the Whisky and Castle Trails. Home cooking and baking. A quiet place for a relaxing holiday.

Invercairn House
Brodie, Forres, Moray, IV36 2TD
Tel/Fax: 01309 641261

2 Single	2 Pub Bath/Show	B&B per person	Open Jan-Dec excl
2 Twin		from £17.00 Single	Xmas/New Year
1 Dbl/Fam		from £17.00 Dbl/Twn	B&B + Eve.Meal
			from £26.50

Visit our comfortable home by the gates of Brodie Castle, a fascinating stone building built in 1856 as Brodie Castle Railway Station. Excellent centre for exploring Castles, Distilleries or seek out the Moray Firth Dolphins. Drive through the Highlands to the West Coast; Golf, Fish, Ride, Birdwatch or Walk. Enjoy Angela's delicious cooking with Scottish dishes then relax with a Malt! On Aberdeen to Inverness bus route & Sustran Cycle Route 1.

Fraserburgh, Aberdeenshire

Map Ref: 4G7

Clifton House
131 Charlotte Street, Fraserburgh, Aberdeenshire, AB43 9LS
Tel: 01346 518365

2 Single	2 En Suite fac	B&B per person	Open Jan-Dec excl
1 Double	1 Pub Bath/Show	from £18.00 Single	Xmas/New Year
1 Family		from £17.00 Double	

Family run guest house in centre of Fraserburgh. Near shopping facilities and all amenities. On main bus routes. Five minutes walk from lighthouse museum, heritage museum, new Esplanade complex. Aden Park, Maggie's Hoosie all nearby. Fishing heritage museum in Peterhead gives an insight in to this busy fishing port.

VAT is shown at 17.5%: changes in this rate may affect prices.

Key to symbols is on back flap.

Fyvie, Aberdeenshire

Map Ref: 4G9

B&B

Mrs Marjory Wyness

Meikle Camaloun, Fyvie, Aberdeenshire, AB53 8JY
Tel/Fax: 01651 891319

1 Twin	1 En Suite fac	B&B per person	Open Jan-Dec excl
1 Double	1 Priv.NOT ensuite	from £26.00 Single	Xmas/New Year
		£20.00-£25.00 Dbl/Twn	

Large comfortable farmhouse, with inviting garden and superb views over rolling farmland. Ideal for Whisky and Castle Trails. Close to Fyvie Castle.

TV P V

Gardenstown, Banffshire

Map Ref: 4G7

B&B

Bankhead Croft

Gamrie, by Banff, Banffshire, AB45 3HN
Tel/Fax: 01261 851584
E-mail: Lucinda@bankheadcroft.freeserve.co.uk
Web: www.bankheadcroft.freeserve.co.uk

1 Twin	All En Suite	B&B per person	Open Jan-Dec
1 Double		from £18.00 Single	B&B + Eve.Meal
1 Family		from £18.00 Dbl/Twn	from £28.00
		Room only per person	
		from £12.00	

Enjoy friendly welcoming hospitality in our modern country cottage in peaceful surroundings. 2 miles (3 kms) from coast. 6 miles (10 kms) East of Banff. Evening meals available using home produce. Special diets catered for and packed lunches available. Ideal for all outdoor pursuits. Large caravan available.

P C W V

B&B

The Palace Farm

Gamrie, Gardenstown, Banff, Banffshire, AB45 3HS
Tel: 01261 851261 Fax: 01261 851401
E-mail: robbie@palace-farm.freeserve.co.uk

1 Twin	2 En Suite fac	B&B per person	Open Jan-Dec excl
1 Double	1 Private fac	from £19.00 Single	Xmas/New Year
1 Family		from £19.00 Dbl/Twn	B&B + Eve.Meal
		Room only per person	from £26.00
		from £16.00	

A warm welcome awaits you at Palace farm a 18th century farmhouse, on a mixed arable farm. Excellent home cooking from a qualified cook using fresh farm produce and local fish just a few miles away from Gardenstown built virtually on a cliff face. Crovie reach by a narrow foot path, and of course Pennan, all with breathtaking views. Certificate of excellence and member of Scotlands Best.

TV P C W V

Glenlivet, Banffshire — Map Ref: 4D9

Roadside Cottage

Tomnavoulin, Glenlivet, Ballindalloch, Banffshire AB37 9JL
Telephone: 01807 590486 Fax: 01807 590486

Awake to bird-song, the aroma of a traditional breakfast, a stunning view from your window. Every guest is a VIP in this land of moor and hills, rivers and ski-slopes, birds and wildlife – and whisky! This is the good life! Scotvec Certificate of Excellence. **Member of Pride of Moray.**

★★★ B&B

Roadside Cottage Bed & Breakfast

Tomnavoulin, Ballindalloch, Banffshire, AB37 9JL
Tel/Fax: 01807 590486

Rooms	Facilities	Prices	Open
1 Single 1 Double 1 Family	2 Pub Bath/Show	B&B per person from £16.00 Single from £16.00 Double Room only per person from £10.00	Open 6Jan-19Dec B&B + Eve.Meal from £26.00

Traditional stone built cottage situated in this beautiful Highland glen in the heart of malt whisky country. Warm and friendly welcome, a relaxed atmosphere, real fires. Home cooking with fresh local produce. Children and pets welcome. Excellent base for walking the Speyside Way; lots of local waks and cycling trails on the Crown Estate.

Hopeman, Moray — Map Ref: 4D7

★★★ B&B

Millseat

Inverugie Road, Hopeman, Moray, IV30 5SX
Tel: 01343 830097
E-mail: millseat@amserve.net Web: www.millseat.cjb.net

Rooms	Facilities	Prices	Open
1 Single 1 Double 1 Family	All En Suite	B&B per person from £16.00 Single from £14.00 Double Room only per person from £11.00	Open Jan-Dec

Comfortably furnished self-contained suite suitable for ambulent disabled. 5 mins walk from lovely sandy beaches and harbour. Quiet fishing village with shops, cafe and hotel. Watersports, golf, bowls, horseriding. Castle and whisky trails all nearby. Wildlife in abundance including dolphins. 7 miles from Elgin with all its amenities. Lovely garden for guests to relax and watch resident rabbits, ducks and hens.

Huntly, Aberdeenshire — Map Ref: 4F9

★★★ B&B

Mrs Beryl Florence

Hillview, Provost Street, Huntly, Aberdeenshire, AB54 8BB
Tel: 01466 794870

Rooms	Facilities	Prices	Open
1 Twin 2 Double	1 En Suite fac 1 Pub Bath/Show	B&B per person £16.00-£18.00 single from £15.00 Dbl/Twn from £16.00 Dbl ens	Open Jan-Dec

Family run, modern house in quiet residential area. Centrally situated with easy access to all local amenities. Ideal touring base. Private parking.

★★★ GUEST HOUSE

Greenmount Guest House

43 Gordon Street, Huntly, Aberdeenshire, AB54 8EQ
Tel: 01466 792482

Rooms	Facilities	Prices	Open
2 Single 4 Twin 2 Family	4 En Suite fac 1 Priv.NOT ensuite 1 Pub.Bath/Show/Wc 1 Toilet	B&B per person from £16.00 Single	Open Jan-Dec excl Xmas/New Year

c1854 town house with annexe. Friendly personal attention. Private parking. In town centre but quiet. On Castle and Whisky Trails, ideal touring base. Popular area for salmon and sea trout.

VAT is shown at 17.5%: changes in this rate may affect prices.

Key to symbols is on back flap.

Huntly, Aberdeenshire

Map Ref: 4F9

★★★

B&B

Mrs Doreen Ingram
Strathlene, MacDonald Street, Huntly, Aberdeenshire, AB54 5EW
Tel: 01466 792664

1 Single, 1 Twin, 1 Double — 1 En Suite fac, 1 Pub Bath/Show

B&B per person from £16.00 Single, £15.00-£18.00 Dbl/Twn

Open Jan-Dec excl Xmas/New Year

Traditional granite built house, near the centre of this market town and convenient for the railway station. Warm welcome and traditional Scottish hospitality assured. Excellent base for exploring the Whisky and Castle Trails, and the Moray coastline with its historic harbours and picturesque villages.

TV C

★★★

B&B

Mrs Renetta Shand
'New Marnoch', 48 King Street, Huntly, Aberdeenshire, AB54 8HP
Tel: 01466 792018

1 Double, 1 Twin — En Suite fac, Shared fac

B&B per person from £16.00 Double, from £15.00 Twin, from £17.00 Single

Open Apr-Nov

Modern bungalow in quiet situation, yet near to town centre. Private off road parking. Many attractions and activities available in the area, including the Whisky and Castle Trails, the historic harbour on the coast, fishing, walking and more.

TV P V

★★

B&B

Southview Guest House
Victoria Road, Huntly, Aberdeenshire, AB54 8AH
Tel: 01466 792456

1 Twin, 2 Double, 1 Family — 2 Pub Bath/Show

B&B per person from £16.00 Single, from £15.00 Dbl/Twn

Open Jan-Dec

Detached Victorian house in quiet residential area close to town centre. Overlooking the bowling green. Good value accommodation, open all year. Excellent base for exploring this area, with its wide variety of attractions and activities.

TV P C V

by Huntly, Aberdeenshire

Map Ref: 4F9

★★

B&B

Boghead House
Cairnie, by Huntly, Aberdeenshire
Tel: 01466 760200 Fax: 01466 760394
E-mail: boghead@tesco.net
Web: www.scottishholiday.net/boghead

1 Twin, 1 Double, 1 Family — All En Suite

B&B per person from £18.50 Single, from £16.50 Dbl/Twn

Open Jan-Dec excl Xmas/New Year

Converted rural post office, built in 1883, and now providing comfortable bed and breakfast accommodation; spacious guests lounge, all bedrooms ensuite. Located just off the A96, 5 miles from both Keith and Huntly. Excellent base for exploring the coastline with its historic harbours, the Castle and Whisky Trails, and much more.

TV P C V

★★★

B&B

Mrs A J Morrison
Haddoch Farm, Huntly, Aberdeenshire, AB54 4SL
Tel: 01466 711217
E-mail: alice.morrison@tinyworld.co.uk

1 Single, 1 Double, 1 Family — 2 Pub Bath/Show

B&B per person from £16.00 Single, from £15.00 Double

Open Apr-Oct, B&B + Eve.Meal from £25.00

Mixed stock/arable farm near River Deveron, on B9022, 3 miles (5kms) from Huntly and 15 miles (24kms) from coast. Fine views of countryside. Home cooking.

P V

by Huntly, Aberdeenshire

Map Ref: 4F9

B&B

Mrs Paula Ross
'Bandora', Yonder Bognie, Forgue, by Huntly, Aberdeenshire, AB54 6BR
Tel: 01466 730375

2 Double | All En Suite, 1 Pub Bath/Show | B&B per person from £18.00 Single, from £16.00 Double | Open Jan-Dec

Newly built modern bungalow. 7 miles (11 kms) from Huntly, 12 miles (19 kms) from Banff on A97. French and Italian spoken. Warm welcome assured. Quiet rural base for exploring the surrounding countryside, with its castles, walks and distilleries or for trips to the coast and its historic villages and harbours.

C V

by Insch, Aberdeenshire

Map Ref: 4F9

B&B

Mrs Fiona Grant
Earlsfield Bed & Breakfast, Earlsfield, Kennethmont, Insch, Aberdeenshire, AB52 6YQ
Tel/Fax: 01464 831473
E-mail: grant@earls-field.freeserve.co.uk

1 Double, 1 Family | En Suite fac, Priv. NOT Ensuite | B&B per person from £25.00 Single, from £14.00 Double | Open Jan-Dec excl Xmas/New Year, B&B + Eve.Meal from £22.00

Arable farm within 1 mile (2kms) of Leith Hall (NTS) and close to Castle and Whisky Trails. Beautiful countryside, ideal hillwalking.

V

Inverurie, Aberdeenshire

Map Ref: 4G9

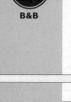

B&B

Earlsmohr Bed & Breakfast
85 High Street, Inverurie, Aberdeenshire, AB51 3QJ
Tel: 01467 620606

3 Twin | All En Suite | B&B per person from £20.00 Single | Open Jan-Dec excl Xmas/New Year

C V

B&B

Fridayhill
Kinmuck, by Inverurie, Aberdeenshire, AB51 0LY
Tel/Fax: 01651 882252
E.mail: fergusmcgh@aol.com
Web: www.b-and-b-scotland.co.uk/fridayhill.htm

2 Double | 1 En Suite fac, 1 Priv.NOT ensuite | B&B per person from £25.00 Double | Open Jan-Dec

High standard of accommodation, with ensuite/private facilities. In rural surroundings, with fine views, yet within easy access to all amenities. Only 7 miles from Dyce airport. Roam in the beautiful garden with rockeries and fish pond, and watch the interesting variety of wild birds.

£ V

Inverurie, Aberdeenshire

Map Ref: 4G9

B&B

Mrs E Harper

Broadsea, Burnhervie, Inverurie, Aberdeenshire, AB51 5LB
Tel/Fax: 01467 681386
E-mail: elizharper@broadsea99.freeserve.co.uk

1 Double | All En Suite | B&B per person from £22.00 Single £19.00-£22.00 Double | Open Jan-Dec

Accommodation of a high standard on this family farm of 200 acres. Inverurie 5 miles. Aberdeen 20 miles. Bennachie is very close by. Ideally situated for Archaeolink, Castle and Whisky Trails.

by Inverurie, Aberdeenshire

Map Ref: 4G9

B&B

The Steading

Old Westhall, Oyne, Insch, Aberdeenshire, AB52 6QU
Tel: 01464 851554 Fax: 01464 851641
E-mail: marr@thesteading.com
Web: www.thesteading.com

1 Twin, 1 Double | All En Suite | B&B per person from £25.00 Single from £20.00 Dbl/Twn | Open Jan-Dec

Modern conversion of traditional farm steading. All guest rooms on ground floor with full en-suite facilities. South facing garden with uninterrupted panoramic views of nearby hill and castle (well within easy walking distance).

Johnshaven, Kincardineshire

Map Ref: 4G12

B&B

Ellington

Station Place, Johnshaven, Kincardineshire, DD10 0JD
Tel: 01561 362756
E-mail: ellington13@supanet.com

1 Twin, 1 Double | All En Suite | B&B per person from £20.00 Single from £20.00 Dbl/Twn | Open Jan-Dec excl Xmas/New Year

New family home, quietly situated in fishing village of Johnshaven. Bedrooms ensuite. One ground floor bedroom. Off road parking.

Keith, Banffshire

Map Ref: 4E8

GUEST HOUSE

The Haughs Farm Guest House

The Haughs, Keith, Grampian, AB55 6QN
Tel/Fax: 01542 882238

2 Twin, 1 Double, 2 Family | 3 En Suite fac, 2 Priv.NOT ensuite | Open Apr-Oct

Traditional farmhouse on 165 acre farm. Just off main road and near the town. On Whisky Trail. Many local sports including golf available at numerous courses.

B&B

Mr T Smith

65 Mid Street, Keith, Banffshire, AB55 3AF
Tel: 01542 882156

1 Twin, 3 Double | 1 Pub Bath/Show | B&B per person from £15.00 Single from £15.00 Dbl/Twn | Open Jan-Dec

Town centre house situated at centre of Whisky Trail, close to all amenities, ideal base for touring.

Important: Prices stated are estimates and may be subject to amendments

by Keith, Banffshire | **Map Ref: 4E8**

B&B

Chapelhill Croft
Crossroads, Keith, Banffshire, AB55 6LQ
Tel: 01542 870302
E-mail: chapelhill@btinternet.com
Web: www.scottishholidays.net/chapelhill

Warm, friendly welcome on working croft. Guests welcome to participate in running of the croft. Home cooking.

1 Twin, 1 Double — 1 En Suite fac, 1 Pub Bath/Show

B&B per person from £17.00 Single, from £14.00 Dbl/Twn

Open Jan-Dec excl Xmas/New Year. B&B + Eve.Meal from £25.00

C W V

Lossiemouth, Moray | **Map Ref: 4D7**

B&B

Carmania
45 St Gerardines Road, Lossiemouth, Moray, IV31 6JX
Tel: 01343 812276

Modern detached bungalow with large garden. In residential area on south side of town centre. Within walking distance of beach, golf and bowling.

1 Twin, 1 Double — 1 En Suite fac, 1 Priv.NOT ensuite

B&B per person from £21.00 Single, from £18.00 Dbl/Twn

Open Apr-Oct

TV P

W V

B&B

Letchworth Lodge
Dunbar Street, Lossiemouth, Moray, IV31 6AN
Tel: 01343 812132
E-mail: letchworthlodge@tinyworld.co.uk

Spacious excellent quality accommodation in elegant Victorian house. Walking distance from championship golf course, bowling green and beach. Private parking.

1 Family, 1 Twin, 1 Double — 1 Pub Bath/Show

B&B per person £20.00 single, £17.50-£20.00 Dbl/Twn

Open Jan-Dec

TV P

C W V

B&B

Mrs Jean R McPherson
Skerry Lodge, Stotfield Road, Lossiemouth, Moray, IV31 6QR
Tel/Fax: 01343 814981
E-mail: skerrylodge@connectfree.co.uk
Web: www.skerrylodge.connectfree.co.uk

Traditional family-run establishment, with friendly atmosphere. Situated on sea front with views of Moray Firth. No Smoking.

1 Twin, 2 Double — 1 En Suite fac, 1 Pub Bath/Show

B&B per person £17.00 Single, £16.00-£17.50 Dbl/Twn

Open Apr-Sep

TV

C W V

B&B

Moray View
1 Seatown Road, Lossiemouth, Moray, IV31 6JL
Tel: 01343 813915

350 year old house of character immediately on sea front, overlooking harbour and beach. Convenient for town centre and all amenities.

1 Twin, 2 Double — 2 Pub Bath/Show

B&B per person from £21.00 Single, from £17.00 Dbl/Twn

Open Jan-Dec excl Xmas/New Year

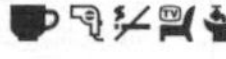

C V

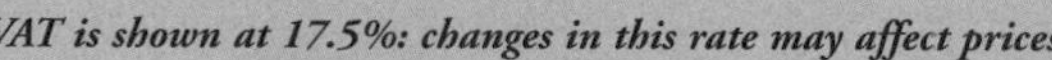

VAT is shown at 17.5%: changes in this rate may affect prices.

Key to symbols is on back flap.

Lossiemouth, Moray — Map Ref: 4D7

★★★★ B&B

Mormond
Prospect Terrace, Lossiemouth, Moray, IV31 6JS
Tel: 01343 813143

Rooms	Facilities	B&B per person	Open
1 Double 1 Twin	1 En Suite fac 1 Priv.NOT ensuite	from £17.00 Single from £17.00 Twn from £22.00 Dbl	Open Jan-Dec excl Xmas/New Year

Traditional villa in quiet residential area of Lossiemouth, with outstanding view across Moray Firth. Close to all amenities. Friendly, happy atmosphere.

C W V

Methlick, Aberdeenshire — Map Ref: 4G9

★★ B&B

Sunnybrae Farm
Gight, Methlick, Ellon, Aberdeenshire, AB41 7JA
Tel: 01651 806456

Rooms	Facilities	B&B per person	Open
1 Single 1 Twin 1 Double	2 En Suite fac	from £18.00 Single from £18.00 Dbl/Twn	Open Jan-Dec

Comfortable accommodation on a working farm, in a quiet peaceful location with superb views. Close to Castle and Whisky Trails. Dogs welcome.

P

Old Deer, by Peterhead, Aberdeenshire — Map Ref: 4G8

★★★ B&B

The Old Bank House
6 Abbey Street, Old Deer, Peterhead, Aberdeenshire, AB42 5LN
Tel: 01771 623463

Rooms	Facilities	B&B per person	Open
1 Twin 1 Double	All En Suite	£20.00-£25.00 Single £19.00-£22.00 Dbl/Twn	Open Mar-Nov

Originally village Bank, now comfortable family home, tastefully refurbished. In centre of quiet historic village, close to Aden Country Park. Non-smoking. Peterhead 9 miles.

W

Oldmeldrum, Aberdeenshire — Map Ref: 4G9

CROMLET HILL

SOUTH ROAD, OLDMELDRUM, ABERDEENSHIRE AB51 0AB
Telephone: 01651 872315 Fax: 01651 872164

A superb listed building overlooking *Bennachie* and the *Grampian Hills* beyond. Recently restored, the original features are retained inside and out and the house is furnished in sympathetic and luxurious style. Set in beautiful secluded gardens including a large Victorian conservatory. Private parking. Aberdeen city centre 30 minutes.

★★★★ B&B

Cromlet Hill Guest House
South Road, Oldmeldrum, Aberdeenshire, AB51 0AB
Tel: 01651 872315 Fax: 01651 872164

Rooms	Facilities	B&B per person	Open
1 Twin 1 Double 1 Family	All En Suite	from £28.00 Single from £22.00 Dbl/Twn	Open Jan-Dec

Spacious, elegant, Listed Georgian mansion, in large secluded gardens within conservation area. Airport 20 minutes. On the castle trail and close to many well known National Trust properties.

TV P

C V

Important: Prices stated are estimates and may be subject to amendments

eldrum, Aberdeenshire Map Ref: 4G9

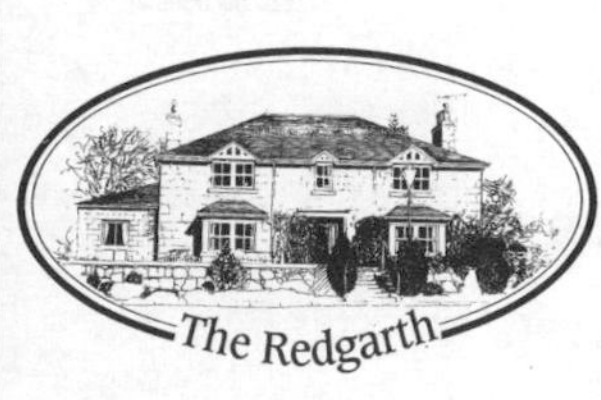

THE REDGARTH

Kirkbrae, Oldmeldrum AB51 0DJ
Tel: 01651 872353 e.mail: redgarth1@aol.com

Family run inn providing varied choice of home-cooked dishes including vegetarian and range of cask conditioned ales.
Luxury ensuite rooms wih breathtaking views over surrounding countryside. Beer garden well-placed for hill-walking, golf, fishing, castle, whisky and coastal trails.

★★★★ INN

The Redgarth
Kirk Brae, Oldmeldrum, AB51 0DJ
Tel: 01651 872353
E-mail: redgarth1@aol.com

1 Twin, 2 Double | All En Suite, 3 Pub Bath/Show | B&B per person from £40.00 Single, from £25.00 Dbl/Twn | Open Jan-Dec excl Xmas/New Year

Detached, granite-built house with large gardens & car park, with fine views towards Bennachie. Non-smoking bedrooms. Home-cooking, including vegetarian choice. Selection of ales (cask conditioned).

Peterhead, Aberdeenshire Map Ref: 4H8

★★ GUEST HOUSE

Carrick Guest House
16 Merchant Street, Peterhead, Aberdeenshire, AB42 1DU
Tel/Fax: 01779 470610
E-mail: carrickhouse@ukonline.co.uk

1 Single, 3 Twin, 2 Family | All En Suite fac | B&B per person from £20.00 Single, from £20.00 Twn/Fam | Open Jan-Dec excl Xmas/New Year

Comfortable accommodation, centrally situated for all amenities. Two minutes walk from main shopping centre, harbour and beach. Convenient for maritime museum, lighthouse museum and several nearby golf courses.

St Cyrus, Angus Map Ref: 4G12

★★ GUEST HOUSE

Burnmouth House
St Cyrus, nr Montrose, Angus, DD10 0DL
Tel: 01674 850430

1 Single, 1 Twin, 2 Double, 1 Family | 2 Public shower, 1 Priv En Suite, 1 Pub Bath/Show, 1 En Suite | B&B per person from £18.00 Single, from £17.00 Dbl/Twn | Open Mar-Nov

In small hamlet overlooking the sea, 7 miles (11 kms) North of Montrose. Fishing can be arranged. Good base for touring.

★★★ B&B

Kirkton
St Cyrus, by Montrose, Angus, DD10 0BW
Tel: 01674 850650

2 Twin | 1 En Suite fac, 1 Priv.NOT ensuite | B&B per person from £20.00 Single, from £18.00 Twin | Open Jan-Dec

Comfortable and spacious family home, near nature reserve and beach. Ideal for touring, golfing and fishing. Downstairs bedroom and private parking. Warm welcome.

Spey Bay, Moray

Map Ref: 4E7

B&B

Brackla

27 Nether Dallachy, Spey Bay, Moray, IV32 7PL
Tel: 01343 821070

1 Double | Ensuite Shower | B&B per person £20.00 Double | Open Feb-Nov

Modern friendly family home with open views to rear. 1 miles (2km) to Spey Bay. Dinner available by prior arrangement.

Stonehaven, Kincardineshire

Map Ref: 4G11

GUEST HOUSE

Arduthie House

Ann Street, Stonehaven, Kincardineshire, AB39 2DA
Tel: 01569 762381 Fax: 01569 766366
E-mail: arduthie@talk21.com

1 Single, 2 Twin, 2 Double, 1 Family | 5 En Suite fac | B&B per person from £18.00 Single, from £24.00 Dbl/Twn | Open Jan-Dec, Evening Meal from £12.00

Centrally located elegant detached Victorian house with attractive garden. Spacious guests lounge, sun lounge and 4 poster bedroom available. Evening meals by arrangement.

C W V

★★★★

B&B

Beachgate House

Beachgate Lane, Stonehaven, Aberdeenshire, AB39 2BD
Tel/Fax: 01569 763155
Web: www.beachgate13.freeserve.co.uk

1 Twin, 2 Double | 2 En Suite fac, 1 Priv.NOT ensuite | B&B per person £18.00-£20.00 Dbl/Twn | Open Jan-Dec excl Xmas/New Year

A warm welcome at this centrally located beach B & B. Private parking. Ideal for touring Royal Deeside.

V

B&B

Car-Lyn-Vale

Rickarton, Stonehaven, Kincardineshire, AB39 3TD
Tel: 01569 762406

1 Twin, 2 Double | All En Suite | B&B per person from £20.00 Dbl/Twn | Open Apr-Oct

In a peaceful rural setting, this non-smoking B&B with all bedrooms ensuite. Safe parking and a large garden full of colour. High standards of cleanliness and warm hospitality will combine to make your stay as special as possible. Much advice and information on the area is available.

V

Stonehaven, Kincardineshire — Map Ref: 4G11

Dunnottar Mains Farm
Stonehaven, Kincardineshire, AB39 2TL
Tel/Fax: 01569 762621
E-mail: dunnottar@ecosse.net

★★★★ B&B

1 Double — Ensuite fac
2 Double — Priv.NOT ensuite

B&B per person
from £25.00 Single
from £20.00 Double

Open Apr-Oct

Traditional farmhouse welcome at this working farm, overlooking Dunnottar Castle on the coast.

Ms C Ling
4 Urie Crescent, Stonehaven, Kincardineshire, AB39 2DY
Tel: 01569 762220

★★ B&B

1 Single — 1 Pub Bath/Show
1 Double
1 Family

B&B per person
from £18.00 Single
from £18.00 Double
Room only per person
from £15.00

Open Jan-Dec excl Xmas/New Year

Victorian semi-detached house in a quiet residential area at the top of the town. Easy walking distance of town centre and eating places. Stonehaven is well known for its picturesque harbour, and the magnificent site of Dunnottar Castle.

Sirdhana
11 Urie Crescent, Stonehaven, AB39 2DY
Tel: 01569 763011 Fax: 01569 760294
E-mail: sirdhana.stonehaven@virgin.net

★★★★ B&B

1 Twin — All En Suite
1 Double

B&B per person
from £20.00 Dbl/Twn

Open Easter-Sep

Traditional victorian house built of local granite offering very comfortable accommodation. Stylish decor yet retaining many original period features. Two fully en-suite bedrooms (one four poster) with tea and coffee, colour tv's and full central heating - sorry no smoking, no pets and no singles.

Woodside of Glasslaw Guest House
Stonehaven, Kincardineshire, AB39 3XQ
Tel/Fax: 01569 763799
E-mail: douton@globalnet.co.uk

★★★ GUEST HOUSE

2 Twin — All En Suite
2 Double
1 Family

B&B per person
from £22.00 Single
from £20.00 Dbl/Twn

Open Jan-Dec

Modern bungalow in rural setting, yet within easy access of main routes and Deeside. Ample parking. All rooms ensuite. Warm welcome assured.

by Stonehaven, Kincardineshire

Map Ref: 4G11

★★★

B&B

Bankhead of Glenbervie

Bankhead, Glenbervie, Stonehaven, Kincardineshire, AB39 3YD
Tel: 01569 740329

1 Twin, 1 Double | 1 En Suite fac, 1 Priv.NOT ensuite | B&B per person from £20.00 Single, from £17.00 Dbl/Twn | Open Jan-Dec excl Xmas/New Year

A modernised bungalow with a large colourful garden and lovely views across the surrounding countryside. Warm and friendly hosts offering very comfortable accommodation in a peaceful setting.

TV P V

★★

B&B

Tewel Farmhouse

Tewel Farm, Stonehaven, Kincardineshire, AB39 3UU
Tel: 01569 762306 Fax: 01569 760386

1 Twin, 1 Fam/Dbl | All En Suite | B&B per person from £21.00 Single, from £17.00 Twin, from £18.00 Double | Open Jan-Dec

Traditional farmhouse in quiet location in the outskirts of Stonehaven. With lovely views of surrounding countryside, on Auchenblae Road.

P C V

Strachan, by Banchory, Kincardineshire

Map Ref: 4F11

★★★

B&B

Templeton Farm

Strachan, Banchory, Kincardineshire, AB31 6LN
Tel: 01330 850657
E-mail: harry@fiddes98.freeserve.co.uk
Web: www.fiddes98.freeserve.co.uk

1 Single, 1 Twin, 1 Double, 1 Family | 2 En Suite fac, 1 Priv.NOT ensuite, 1 Pub Bath/Show | B&B per person from £22.00 Single, £18.00-£22.00 Dbl/Twn | Open Feb-Dec excl Xmas/New Year

Recently converted former farm steading with open views over Feugh Valley and westwards to the Deeside hills. One ground floor room available. 3 miles (5 KM) from Banchory with shops, restaurants, pubs, etc.

TV P C V

Strathdon, Aberdeenshire

Map Ref: 4E10

★★★

B&B

Buchaam Holiday Properties

Buchaam Farm, Strathdon, Aberdeenshire, AB36 8TN
Tel/Fax: 01975 651238
E-mail: e.ogg@talk21.com

1 Twin, 1 Double, 1 Family | 2 Pub Bath/Show | B&B per person from £16.00 Single, from £16.00 Dbl/Twn | Open May-Oct

Large farmhouse on 600 acre mixed farm with sporting facilities, including badminton, table tennis and putting green. Free river fishing.

P C V

Strathdon, Aberdeenshire

Map Ref: 4E10

★★★

B&B

House of Newe
Strathdon, Aberdeenshire, AB36 8TG
Tel: 01975 651247

1 Twin, 2 Double | 1 En Suite fac, 2 Priv.NOT ensuite | B&B per person from £18.00 Single, from £18.00 Dbl/Twn | Open Jan-Dec excl Xmas/New Year, B&B + Eve.Meal from £24.00

Early 17C house, set in own grounds, in unspoilt Scottish Glen; sympathetically modernised house with memorabilia from demolished Castle Newe. Good food a speciality, using home grown vegetables and fresh eggs.

The Smiddy House
Glenkindie, Aberdeenshire, AB33 8SS
Tel: 01975 641216

1 Twin, 1 Double | All En Suite | B&B per person from £17.00 Single, from £17.00 Dbl/Twn | Open Jan-Dec excl Xmas/New Year, B&B + Eve.Meal from £24.00

Friendly bed and breakfast on Highland Route and Castle Trail. Set in pleasant surroundings. A good variety of wild birds to be seen in the garden.

Tarland, Aberdeenshire

Map Ref: 4D10

★★

B&B

Kirklands of Cromar
Tarland, Aberdeenshire, AB34 4YN
Tel: 013398 81082
E-mail: morna@kirklandsofcromar.co.uk
Web: www.kirklandsofcromar.co.uk

1 Twin, 1 Double | 2 Priv.NOT ensuite | B&B per person from £18.00 Single, from £15.00 Dbl/Twn | Open Jan-Dec excl Xmas/New Year

Traditional former manse in large secluded garden built by same architect as Balmoral Castle. Beautiful views all around, especially southwards to Tomnaverie Stone Circle. Pubs and shops in village square 1 minutes walk away. Peaceful and relaxed. Golf course behind.

Tomintoul, Banffshire

Map Ref: 4D10

Bracam House B&B
32 Main Street, Tomintoul, AB37 9EX
Tel/Fax: 01807 580278
E-mail: camerontomintoul@compuserve.com

1 Single, 1 Twin, 1 Double | 1 En Suite fac, 1 Shared bathroom | B&B per person £15.00 Single, £15.00 Twin, £16.00 Double | Open Jan-Dec

Detached house in central location within Highland village. All amenities with in walking distance. Ensuite room available.

Findron Farm
Braemar Road, Tomintoul, Ballindalloch, Banffshire, AB37 9ER
Tel/Fax: 01807 580382

1 Twin, 1 Double, 1 Family | 2 En Suite fac, 1 Priv.NOT ensuite | B&B per person from £15.00 Single, from £15.00 Dbl/Twn | Open Jan-Dec excl Xmas/New Year, B&B + Eve.Meal from £23.00

Comfortable farmhouse on working farm with new conservatory dining area and offering a warm and friendly welcome, situated 1 mile (2 kms) from Tomintoul. 4 miles (7 km) from the Lecht ski-slopes.

VAT is shown at 17.5%: changes in this rate may affect prices.

Key to symbols is on back flap.

Tomintoul, Banffshire

Map Ref: 4D10

★
SMALL HOTEL

Glenavon Hotel

The Square, Tomintoul, Ballindalloch, Banffshire, AB37 9ET
Tel: 01807 580218 Fax: 01807 580733
E-mail: glenavon@globalnet.co.uk
Web: www.users.globalnet.co.uk/~glenavon

Small family run hotel with relaxed atmosphere. Home cooking, open fire. Families and pets always welcome. Close to the Lecht ski slopes. Popular venue for fishing holidays.

2 Single
1 Twin
2 Double
1 Family

B&B per person
from £20.00 Single
from £15.00 Dbl/Twn
Room only per person
from £15.00

Open Jan-Dec
B&B + Eve.Meal
from £24.00

C V

by Tomintoul, Banffshire

Map Ref: 4D10

★★★
B&B

Auchriachan Farmhouse

Mains of Auchriachan, Tomintoul, Ballindalloch, Banffshire, AB37 9EQ
Tel: 01807 580416
E-mail: iduffus@hotmail.com

Traditional farmhouse 1 mile (2kms), from Tomintoul village. Ideal for outdoor activities, including skiing, Whisky and Castle Trails. One ground floor bedroom.

1 Twin
1 Double
1 Family

2 En Suite fac
1 Pub Bath/Show

B&B per person
£15.00-£17.00 Dbl/Twn

Open Jan-Dec excl Xmas/New Year

C W V

Turriff, Aberdeenshire

Map Ref: 4F8

★★★
B&B

W & M Stewart

The Gables, Station Road, Turriff, AB53 4ER
Tel: 01888 568715

A friendly welcome at this red sandstone family home situated on the outskirts of Turriff, yet only 5 minutes walk to town centre. Overlooking the park. Private car parking.

2 Twin
1 Double

2 En Suite fac
1 Priv.NOT ensuite

B&B per person
from £20.00 Single
£18.00 Dbl/Twn

Open Jan-Dec

C V

Important: Prices stated are estimates and may be subject to amendments

SCENIC VARIETY IS THE KEYNOTE IN THIS AREA – FROM THE SOARING CRAGGY HEIGHTS OF GLENCOE TO THE WIDE-SKIES AND GLITTERING LOCHANS OF THE FLOW COUNTRY OF CAITHNESS IN THE NORTH. EAST-WEST CONTRASTS ARE JUST AS SPECTACULAR. THIS AREA TAKES IN BOTH THE SUNNY, SANDY SHORES OF THE INNER MORAY FIRTH AROUND NAIRN, WITH ITS COASTAL LINKS GOLF COURSES, AND THE DAZZLING WHITE BEACHES AROUND MORAR IN THE WEST, WITH THE SMALL ISLES FILLING THE HORIZON.

Trotternish Peninsula, Isle of Skye

WITH THE TORRIDON MOUNTAINS, Kintail and the peaks of Sutherland all adding to the spectacle, this area has more than simply scenic grandeur. There are substantial towns with everything for the visitor. Inverness, sometimes called 'the capital of the Highlands' is a natural gateway to the northlands. At the western end of the Great Glen is Fort William, in the shadow of Britain's highest mountain, Ben Nevis. This town is another busy location, a natural route centre and meeting place with a whole range of facilities and attractions. The eastern seaboard also has plenty of interesting towns: picturesque Cromarty, with the air of an old-time Scottish burgh, Dornoch with its cathedral and famous championship golf course. Tain with Glenmorangie Distillery on its outskirts. Helmsdale with its evocation of Highland life in the Timespan Heritage Centre and Art Gallery. Further north, Wick and Thurso are major centres.

Dunrobin Castle, Golspie

Plockton

THE ISLE OF SKYE is famed for the spectacle of the Cuillin Hills with their craggy ridges offering a serious climbing challenge. However, there are plenty of less active pursuits. Armadale Castle and the Museum of the Isles, Dunvegan Castle and the Aros Experience all tell the fascinating story of the island.

EVENTS THE HIGHLANDS AND SKYE

27-28 JANUARY
Sled Dog Rally
Aviemore, Highlands
Sled dog racing and timed trials taking place over two days attracting many teams.
Contact: John & Penny Evans
TEL: **01604 686281**

14 FEBRUARY-3 MARCH
Inverness Music Festival
Various venues, Inverness
Annual music festival and gala
Contact: Mr R Grant, Inverness Music Festival
TEL: 01463 716616

5-7 MAY
Feis Rois
Wester Ross, Highlands
Feis Rios is a 3-day traditional music, song and dance tuition festival that is now a celebrated national event.
Contact: Rita Hunter, Feis Rois Inbhich
TEL: **01349 862600**
EMAIL:
rita@feisrois.freeserve.co.uk

25 MAY-9 JUNE
The Highland Festival
Various venues over the Highlands.
Music, theatre, dance, visual art and street events to celebrate Highland culture.
Contact: Balnain House
TEL: **01463 711112**
EMAIL:
info@highlandfestival.org.uk
www.highlandfestival.demon.co.uk

8 AUGUST
Skye Highland Games
Portree, Isle of Skye
Traditional Highland games plus a three day piping competition commencing on Monday 6th August.
Contact: Allan Stewart
TEL: **01478 612540**

4-7 OCTOBER
Highland Food Festival
Various venues, Highlands
Exhibitions, cookery demonstrations, wine and food tastings, competitions, music and entertainment.
Contact: Pauline Munro
TEL: **01463 713504**

13-28 OCTOBER
Highland Archaeology Week
Various venues, Highlands and Skye
Many events throughout the Highlands with an archaeology theme including walks, talks, children's activities, exhibitions, concerts and films.
Contact: Archaeology Unit, Highland Council
TEL: **01463 702502**
EMAIL:
archaeology@highland.gov.uk

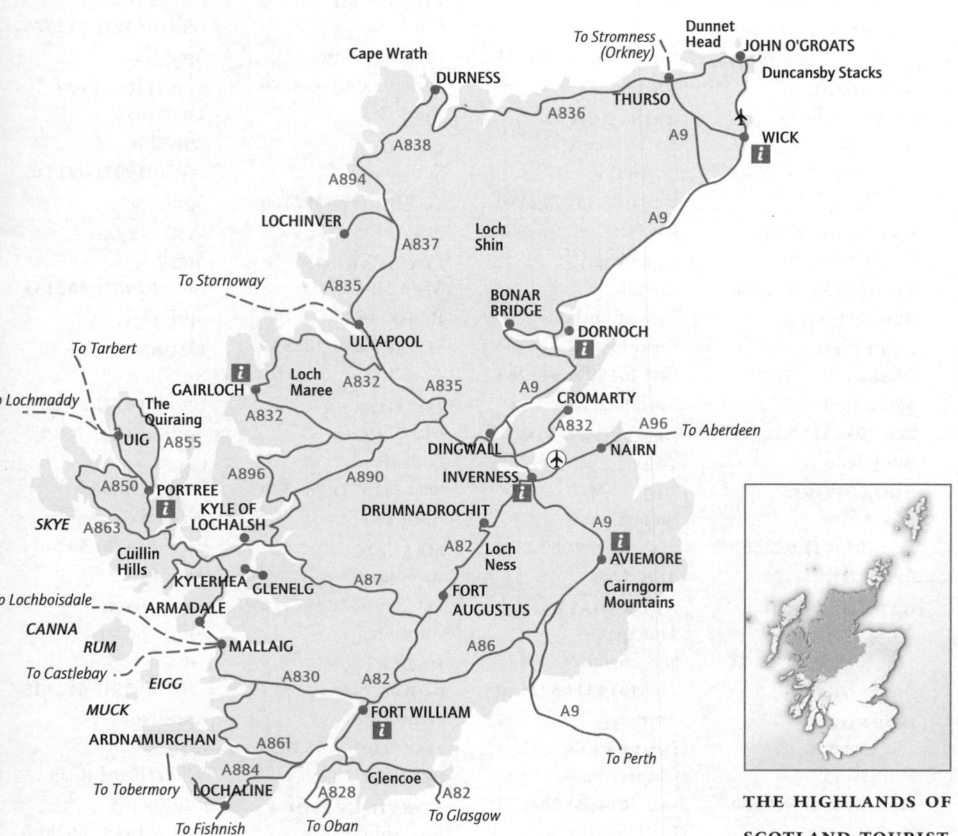

THE HIGHLANDS OF SCOTLAND TOURIST BOARD
Peffery House
Strathpeffer
Ross-shire
IV14 9HA

TEL: **0870 5143070**
FAX: **01997 421168**
www.highlandfreedom.com

THE HIGHLANDS OF SCOTLAND TOURIST BOARD

AVIEMORE
Grampian Road
Inverness-shire
TEL: **(01479) 810363**
Jan-Dec

BALLACHULISH
Argyll
TEL: **(01855) 811296**
April-Oc

BETTYHILL
Clachan
Sutherland
TEL: **(01641) 521342**
April-Sept

BROADFORD
Isle of Skye
TEL: **(01471) 822361**
April-Oct

DAVIOT WOOD
A9 by Inverness
TEL: **(01463) 772203**
April-Oct

DORNOCH
The Square
Sutherland
TEL: **(01862) 810400**
Jan-Dec

DUNVEGAN
2 Lochside
Isle of Skye
TEL: **(01470) 521581**
April-Sept

DURNESS
Sango
Sutherland
TEL: **(01971) 511259**
April-Oct

FORT AUGUSTUS
Car Park
Inverness-shire
TEL: **(01320) 366367**
April-Oct

FORT WILLIAM
Cameron Square
Inverness-shire
TEL: **(01397) 703781**
Jan-Dec

GAIRLOCH
Auchtercairn
Ross-shire
TEL: **(01445) 712130**
Jan-Dec

GLENSHIEL
Kintail
Kyle of Lochalsh
Ross-shire
TEL: **(01599) 511264**
April-Oct

GRANTOWN ON SPEY
High Street
Morayshire
TEL: **(01479) 872773**
April-Oct

HELMSDALE
Timespan
Sutherland
TEL: **(01431) 821640**
April-Sept

INVERNESS
Castle Wynd
TEL: **(01463) 234353**
Jan-Dec

JOHN O'GROATS
County Road
Caithness
TEL: **(01955) 611373**
April-Oct

KILCHOAN
Pier Road
Argyll
TEL: **(01972) 510222**
Easter-Oct

KINGUSSIE
King Street
Inverness-shire
TEL: **(01540) 661297**
May-Sept

KYLE OF LOCHALSH
Car Park
Inverness-shire
TEL: **(01599) 534276**
April-Oct

LAIRG
Sutherland
TEL: **(01549) 402160**
April-Oct

LOCHCARRON
Main Street
Ross-shire
TEL: **(01520) 722357**
April-Oct

LOCHINVER
Main Street
Sutherland
TEL: **(01571) 844330**
April-Oct

MALLAIG
Inverness-shire
TEL: **(01687) 462170**
April-Oct

NAIRN
62 King Street
Nairnshire
TEL: **(01667) 452753**
April-Oct

NORTH KESSOCK
Ross-shire
TEL: **(01463) 731505**
Jan-Dec

PORTREE
Bayfield House
Bayfield Road
Isle of Skye
TEL: **(01478) 612137**
Jan-Dec

RALIA
A9 North
by Newtonmore
Inverness-shire
TEL: **(01540) 673253**
April-Oct

SPEAN BRIDGE
Inverness-shire
TEL: **(01397) 712576**
April-Oct

STRATHPEFFER
The Square
Ross-shire
TEL: **(01997) 421415**
April-Nov

STRONTIAN
Argyll
TEL: **(01967) 402131**
April-Oct

THURSO
Riverside
TEL: **(01847) 892371**
April-Oct

UIG
Ferry Terminal
Isle of Skye
TEL: **(01470) 542404**
April-Oct

ULLAPOOL
Argyle Street
Ross-shire
TEL: **(01854) 612135**
April-Nov

WICK
Whitechapel Road
Caithness
TEL: **(01955) 602596**
Jan-Dec

Acharacle, Argyll

Map Ref: 3F12

B&B

Mrs Elaine Kershaw

Cala Darach, Glenmore, by Glenborrodale, Acharacle, Argyll, PH36 4JG
Tel: 01972 500204

1 Double	Shower En Suite	B&B per person	Open Apr-Oct
1 Double	Bath En Suite	£28.00 Single	
1 Twin	Ensuite cloakroom & Private Bathroom	£20.00-£24.00 Dbl/Twn	

Beautiful house situated in countryside 3 miles west of Glenborrodale. Set against a background of ancient oak woods. All bedrooms have uninterrupted views over Loch Sunart and are tastefully decorated and furnished. Private, comfortable guest lounge with TV and video. Evening supper by prior arrangement. Ample private parking.

TV P C

by Achmore, Ross-shire

Map Ref: 3F9

B&B

Maple Lodge

Braeintra, by Achmore, by Strome Ferry, Ross-shire, IV53 8UP
Tel: 01599 577276
E-mail: geraldine@maple-lodge.co.uk

1 Twin	1 En Suite fac	B&B per person	Open Jan-Dec excl Xmas/New Year
1 Family	1 Priv.NOT ensuite	from £16.50 Twin	B&B + Eve.Meal from £25.00

Detached house in elevated location with splendid views over quiet crofting glen. 15 minutes from Plockton Skye Bridge. Friendly welcome. Evening meal by arrangement. Licensed amateur radio room (GM4NTL) available for use by licensed amateurs.

TV P C V

Alness, Ross-shire

Map Ref: 4B7

B&B

Averon Bank Cottages

Ardross Road, Alness, Ross-shire, IV17 0QA
Tel: 01349 882392

3 Twin	All En Suite	B&B per person	Open Jan-Dec
		from £23.00 Single	
		£20.00-£23.00 Twin	

Detached cottage with a private garden area, on the edge of Alness. It provides comfortable accommodation, whether for just a short stay or for a longer break, and is an ideal base for day trips to the North and West Highlands, as well as the coastal towns and villages of the area. This is a no smoking house.

TV P

Ardgay, Sutherland

Map Ref: 4A6

B&B

Corvost

Ardgay, Sutherland, IV24 3BP
Tel/Fax: 01863 755317

1 Single	2 Pub Bath/Show	B&B per person	Open Jan-Dec excl Xmas/New Year
1 Twin		£14.00-£16.00 Single	B&B + Eve.Meal
1 Double		£14.00-£16.00 Dbl/Twn	£23.00-£25.00

Set in a beautiful and historical Highland Strath, this modern bungalow on working croft is the ideal place to relax. Golfing, fishing, hillwalking and birdwatching all available in area.

P C V

Ardnamurchan, Argyll

Map Ref: 3E12

B&B

Doirlinn House

Kilchoan, Acharacle, Argyll, PH36 4LH
Tel/Fax: 01972 510209

1 Twin	1 En Suite fac	B&B per person	Open Mar-Nov
1 Double	1 Priv.NOT ensuite	from £24.00 Single	
1 Family		from £20.00 Dbl/Twn	

In the heart of this quiet village, overlooking Kilchoan Bay with the island of Mull beyond. Originally the village inn this victorian house has spacious, airy rooms. Pleasant garden where you can sit and watch seals basking on the rocks. A hearty breakfast served until late morning if required. Good quality accommodation at affordable prices.

TV P C V

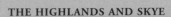

Ardnamurchan, Argyll — Map Ref: 3E12

GUEST HOUSE

Feorag House

Glenborrodale, Acharacle, Argyll, PH36 4JP
Tel: 01972 500248 Fax: 01972 500285
E-mail: admin@feorag.demon.co.uk
Web: www.feorag.demon.co.uk

1 Twin 2 Double	All En Suite	B&B per person from £47.50 Single from £35.00 Dbl/Twn	Open Jan-Dec B&B + Eve.Meal from £55.00

Delightful country house on the shores of Loch Sunart. Peace and tranquility, warm and friendly atmosphere with imaginative cuisine. Ideal central location for exploring Ardnamurchan. Unlicensed, but you are welcome to bring your own wine.

Arisaig, Inverness-shire — Map Ref: 3F11

B&B

Leven House B&B

Borrodale, Arisaig, Inverness-shire, PH39 4NR
Tel: 01687 450238
E-mail: ejmacmillan@aol.com

2 Dbl/Fam	Both En Suite	B&B per person £30.00 Single £22.00 Double	Open Jan-Dec excl Xmas/New Year

Recently built modern, family home offering two comfortable ensuite bedrooms with TV's and tea-trays. Situated in peaceful setting just off the A830 road to the isles. Lovely beaches within a short stroll, ideal for relaxing break or as a base for walking, driving or sailing to the small isles of Eigg, Muck, Rhum. Scenic 9-hole golf-course only 6 miles.

Aultbea, Ross-shire — Map Ref: 3F6

MELLONDALE GUEST HOUSE

47 MELLON CHARLES, AULTBEA, ROSS-SHIRE IV22 2JL

Tel: 01445 731326 Fax: 01445 731326

Enjoy the personal touch at Mellondale. From the warm welcome to the home cooking in a peaceful setting overlooking Lochewe, Mellondale is the perfect place to relax and take in the spectacular scenery. Ideal for walking, climbing and birdwatching. Inverewe Gardens 9 miles.

GUEST HOUSE

Mellondale Guest House

47 Mellon Charles, Aultbea, Ross-shire, IV22 2JL
Tel/Fax: 01445 731326

2 Twin, 2 Double — All En Suite, 2 Pub Bath/Show

B&B per person from £21.00 Single, from £21.00 Dbl/Twn

Open Mar-Nov. B&B + Eve.Meal from £34.00

Comfortable family guest house set in 4 acres, with open views of Loch Ewe. 9 miles (14.4 Kms) from Inverewe Gardens. Ideal walking centre.

B&B

Sandale

5 Pier Road, Aultbea, Ross-shire, IV22 2JQ
Tel: 01445 731336
Fax: 01445 731076

1 Twin, 1 Double, 1 Family — All En Suite

B&B per person from £18.00 Dbl/Twn. Room only per person from £15.00

Open Mar-Oct

House with sun lounge and views over Loch Ewe, set in a colourful garden. Traditional Scottish hospitality. 6 miles to Inverewe Gardens. Convenient for all outdoor activities.

B&B

Tranquility

21 Mellon Charles, Aultbea, Ross-shire, IV22 2JN
Tel/Fax: 01445 731241

1 Single, 1 Double, 1 Family — 2 En Suite fac, 1 Priv.NOT ensuite

B&B per person from £20.00 Single, from £20.00 Double

Open Jan-Dec excl Xmas. B&B + Eve.Meal from £32.50

Small comfortable family home surrounded by open croftland and with superb views over the Torridons and The Minches. Tea and biscuits on arrival. Evening meals available. Private parking. Birdwatching, walking, fishing all close by. Peace and quiet on the spot. Close to Inverewe gardens .

Aviemore, Inverness-shire — Map Ref: 4C10

B&B

Ardenlea

13 Craig-na-Gower Avenue, Aviemore, Inverness-shire, PH22 1RW
Tel: 01479 811738
E-mail: burgon@ardenlea13.freeserve.co.uk

1 Twin, 1 Double — All En Suite

B&B per person from £18.00 Single, from £15.00 Dbl/Twn

Open Jan-Dec

Traditional Scottish hospitality in friendly family home. Ideal base for touring beautiful Strathspey.

VAT is shown at 17.5%: changes in this rate may affect prices.

Key to symbols is on back flap.

Aviemore, Inverness-shire Map Ref: 4C10

B&B

Avalon

Coylumbridge, Aviemore, Inverness-shire, PH22 1RD
Tel: 01479 810158

1 Twin, 1 Double — All En Suite
B&B per person: from £20.00 Single; from £19.00 Dbl/Twn
Open Jan-Dec

Modern house with comfortable en-suite rooms ideally placed 2 miles (3kms) from Aviemore, just by the ski road and 6 miles (10kms) from the ospreys.

B&B

Cairn Eilrig

Glenmore, Aviemore, Inverness-shire, PH22 1QU
Tel: 01479 861223

1 Twin, 1 Family — 1 Pub Bath/Show
B&B per person: £16.00-£18.00 Twin
Open Jan-Dec

Bungalow situated in Glenmore Forest Park with superb open views of the Cairngorms. Warm Highland hospitality guaranteed. Ski lifts 2 miles (3 kms).

GUEST HOUSE

Cairngorm Guest House

Main Road, Aviemore, Invernes-shire, PH22 1RP
Tel/Fax: 01479 810630
Web: www.aviemore.co.uk/cairngormguesthouse

3 Twin, 5 Double, 1 Family — All En Suite
B&B per person: £20.00-£40.00 Single; £18.00-£25.00 Dbl/Twn
Open Jan-Dec

Detached stone house, within 5 minutes walk of the centre, bus and rail stations. Private parking.

Important: Prices stated are estimates and may be subject to amendments

Aviemore, Inverness-shire — Map Ref: 4C10

ERISKAY

Craig-na-Gower, Aviemore PH22 1RW
Tel: 01479 810717 Fax: 01479 812312
e.mail: eriskay@cali.co.uk

Eriskay is situated within the village of Aviemore and offers quiet comfortable ensuite accommodation. Ideal for walking, bird-watching, cycling, pony trekking and touring. With its friendly and relaxed atmosphere Eriskay is the perfect base for Winter and Summer pursuits.

B&B

Eriskay
Craig-na-Gower Avenue, Aviemore, Inverness-shire, PH22 1RW
Tel: 01479 810717 Fax: 01479 812312
E-mail: eriskay@cali.co.uk

Rooms	Facilities	Prices	Open
1 Twin 2 Double	All En Suite	B&B per person from £22.00 Single from £17.00 Dbl/Twn	Open Jan-Dec

B&B

Mrs M Fraser
Waverley, 35 Strathspey Avenue, Aviemore, Inverness-shire, PH22 1SN
Tel: 01479 811226
E-mail: maggie.fraser@talk21.com

Rooms	Facilities	Prices	Open
1 Twin 1 Double	Private fac Ensuite fac	B&B per person £20.00-£25.00 Single £17.00-£20.00 Dbl/Twn	Open Jan-Dec

Bungalow situated in quiet cul-de-sac within easy access to all of towns amenities. Accommodation all on one level.

B&B

Junipers
5 Dell Mhor, Aviemore, Inverness-shire, PH22 1QW
Tel: 01479 810405 Fax: 01479 812850

Rooms	Facilities	Prices	Open
1 Single 1 Double 2 Family	1 En Suite fac 1 Pub Bath/Show 1 Priv.NOT ensuite	B&B per person from £18.00 Single from £16.00 Dbl/Twn	Open Jan-Dec

Comfortable home with large sun room and Alpine garden, midway between Aviemore and Coylumbridge.

GUEST HOUSE

Kinapol Guest House
Dalfaber Road, Aviemore, Inverness-shire, PH22 1PY
Tel/Fax: 01479 810513
E-mail: kinapol@aol.com
Web: www.aviemore.co.uk/kinapol

Rooms	Facilities	Prices	Open
1 Double 1 Family 1 Twin	2 Pub Bath/Show	B&B per person from £16.00 Single from £16.00 Double Room only per person from £10.00	Open Jan-Dec

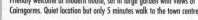

Friendly welcome at modern house, set in large garden with views of Cairngorms. Quiet location but only 5 minutes walk to the town centre.

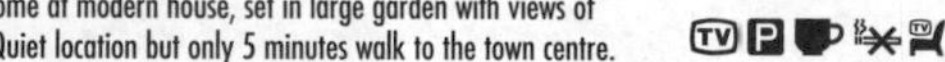

VAT is shown at 17.5%: changes in this rate may affect prices.

Key to symbols is on back flap.

Aviemore, Inverness-shire Map Ref: 4C10

THE TEMPERANCE HOUSE

2 Dalfaber Road, Aviemore PH22 1PU
Tel: 07767 687237 e.mail: gnl@greatnorthlodges.co.uk

Period decorated Edwardian fishing/shooting lodge backing onto the River Spey. Comfortable accommodation enhanced by modern luxuries. Enchanting bedrooms, welcoming log fires and excellent breakfasts using fresh local produce.

The Temperance House
2 Dalfaber Road, Aviemore, Inverness-shire, PH22 1PU
Tel: 07767 687237 Fax: 01479 841 400
E-mail: gnl@greatnorthlodges.co.uk

3 Dbl/Twn | All Ensuite fac | 1 Pub Bath | B&B per person | from £38.50 Single | from £38.50 Dbl/Twn | Open Jan-Dec

VERMONT GUEST HOUSE

Grampian Road, Aviemore, Inverness-shire PH22 1RP
Tel: 01479 810470

Located in the heart of Aviemore the ideal base to tour The Highlands. All rooms have en-suite, TV and hospitality tray. A warm welcome awaits you and a full Scottish breakfast and friendly atmosphere. Car parking at rear of house. Payphone in hallway.

B&B

Vermont Guest House
Grampian Road, Aviemore, Inverness-shire, PH22 1RP
Tel: 01479 810470

1 Twin | 1 Double | 1 Family | All En Suite | B&B per person | from £16.00 Dbl/Twn | Room only per person | from £14.00 | Open Jan-Dec

Situated in centre of Aviemore, all bedrooms with en suite facilities. Ideally placed for touring Spey Valley, and access to Cairngorm ski area.

V

Ballachulish, Argyll — Map Ref: 1F1

Ballachulish Home Farm

★★★★ B&B

BALLACHULISH, ARGYLL PH49 4JX

A warm welcome awaits you at our modern farmhouse, situated on an elevated site amid naturally wooded parkland, giving a sense of peace and quietness. Accommodation includes three double rooms, all ensuite, bright spacious lounge, separate dining room and drying facilities. Very central for touring West Highlands.

For details contact Mrs J McLauchlan. Tel/Fax: 01855 811792.

★★★★ B&B

Ballachulish Home Farm
Ballachulish, Argyll, PH49 4JX
Tel/Fax: 01855 811792
Web: www.host.co.uk

1 Twin, 2 Double — All En Suite — B&B per person from £25.00 Single, from £22.50 Dbl/Twn — Open Apr-Oct

New, traditional style farmhouse, situated on an elevated site amid naturally wooded parkland, giving a sense of peace and quietness. Open view across Loch Leven. Non-smoking house with large spacious bedrooms.

★★★ GUEST HOUSE

Craiglinnhe House
Lettermore, Ballachulish, Argyll, PH49 4JD
Tel/Fax: 01855 811270
web: www.milford.co.uk/go/craiglinnhe.html

3 Twin, 3 Double — All En Suite — B&B per person from £22.00 Dbl/Twn — Open Feb-Dec, B&B + Eve.Meal from £37.00

Lochside victorian villa a mid spectacular mountain scenery offering period charm with modern comfort warm friendly atmosphere good food and wine ideal base for exploring the western highlands.

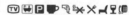

★★ B&B

Cuildaff
West Laroch, Ballachulish, Argyll, PH49 4JQ
Tel: 01855 811436
E-mail: cuildaff@talk21.com

1 Twin, 2 Double — 2 Ensuite fac — B&B per person from £15.00 Single, from £16.00 Dbl/Twn, Room only per person from £14.00 — Open Jan-Dec

Modern house situated in its own garden in a secluded position in the village of Ballachulish, with mountain views and Loch Leven nearby. Laundry and drying facilities - advice on hill walking and climbing. Beautician aromatherpy, reflexology and reiki healing in house by appointment. Private parking. Vegetarians catered for and organic produce used where possible. Evening meals, available in winter for groups.

★★ B&B

Mrs Dow
Tigh-ard, Brecklet, Ballachulish, Argyll, PH49 4JG
Tel: 01855 811328

1 Twin, 1 Double — 2 Pub Bath/Show — B&B per person £16.00 Dbl/Twn — Open Apr-Oct

Family home on edge of village, with magnificent views across Loch Leven to hills beyond. 12 miles (19 kms) from Fort William. Relax in our sun lounge and watch the sun set over the loch. All rooms with hospitality tray. Guests bathroom conveniently situated adjacent to the 2 bedrooms. Ample private parking.

Ballachulish, Argyll — Map Ref: 1F1

GUEST HOUSE

Fern Villa Guest House

Loanfern, Ballachulish, Argyll, PH49 4JE
Tel: 01855 811393 Fax: 01855 811727
E.mail: BB@fernvilla.com
Web: www.fernvilla.com

2 Twin
3 Double

All En Suite

B&B per person
from £20.00 Dbl/Twn

Open Jan-Dec
B&B + Eve.Meal
from £33.00

A warm welcome awaits you in this fine Victorian granite built house in the lochside village amidst spectacular scenery. One mile from Glencoe, convenient for Fort William. Home baking and Natural Cook of Scotland features on our dinner menu. Table licence. The perfect base for walking, climbing or touring in the West Highlands. Private parking.

GUEST HOUSE

Lyn-Leven Guest House

Ballachulish, Argyll, PH49 4JP
Tel: 01855 811392 Fax: 01855 811600
E.mail: lynleven@amserve.net

1 Single
2 Twin
3 Double
2 Family

All En Suite

B&B per person
from £25.00 Single
from £21.00 Dbl/Twn

Open Jan-Dec excl Xmas
B&B + Eve.Meal
from £30.00

A very warm Highland welcome awaits you at the RAC small hotel of the year 1996. Situated within attractive, well cared for gardens overlooking Loch Leven in the heart of some of Scotlands most spectacular scenery. Traditional home cooking. Ample parking. Glencoe only 1 mile. Ideal base for skiing, walking, climbing and fishing.

B&B

Parkview

18 Park Road, Ballachulish, Argyll, PH49 4JS
Tel: 01855 811560
E-mail: db.macaskill@talk21.com

1 Twin
2 Double

2 Pub Bath/Show

B&B per person
from £15.00 Dbl/Twn

Open Jan-Dec excl Xmas

A traditional Highland welcome awaits you at this family run B&B, situated in the centre of Ballachulish village overlooking Meall Mhor and The Pap of Glencoe. Ideal base for walkers and climbers in the Glencoe area. Fort William 14 miles to north. Glencoe 3 miles. In wet weather relax in our cosy TV lounge or read from our selection of local interest books. Drying facilities available.

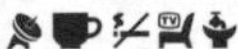

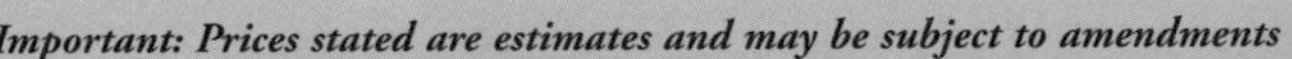

Important: Prices stated are estimates and may be subject to amendments

Ballachulish, Argyll — Map Ref: 1F1

★★★ GUEST HOUSE

Strathassynt Guest House
Loan Fern, Ballachulish, Argyll, PH49 4JB
Tel: 01855 811261 Fax: 0870 0569202
Web: www.strathassynt.com

2 Twin, 3 Double, 1 Family — All En Suite
B&B per person: from £20.00 Single; from £18.00 Dbl/Twn
Open Jan-Dec; B&B + Eve.Meal from £27.00

Comfortable family run licenced guest house in a small village amidst superb loch & mountain scenery. Excellent facilities for walkers and cyclists including skiing, canoeing and bike hire. Home baking and cooking using fresh local produce. Family room available. French/German spoken. Evening meal by prior arrangement.

★★★★ B&B

Mrs Pamela Weir
Ardno House, Lettermore, Ballachulish, Argyll, PH49 4JD
Tel: 01855 811830
E.mail: pamweir@globalnet.co.uk

2 Double, 1 Family — All En Suite
B&B per person: £19.00-£25.00 Single
Open March-October

High quality accommodation providing every comfort and warmest hospitality. A passion for quality and unrivalled customer satisfaction is evident from the moment you arrive. Wonderful walks and drives amidst the most magnificent scenery. Numerous eating places within five minutes drive.

Banavie, by Fort William, Inverness-shire — Map Ref: 3H12

★★★ B&B

Braeburn
Badabrie, Fort William, Inverness-shire, PH33 7LX
Tel: 01397 772047
E-mail: chris@badabrie.co.uk

1 Twin, 2 Double, 2 Family — 3 Ensuite fac
B&B per person: from £18.00 Single; from £18.00 Dbl/Twn
Open Jan-Dec excl Xmas/New Year

Modern detached house adjoining owners accommodation with lovely views of Ben Nevis and Loch Linnhe. All rooms recently refurbished. Relax in our spacious guest lounge with patio doors leading out to our garden with seating in the summer. The Caledonian Canal is nearby where there is a walkway and places to eat and enjoy a drink. Jacuzzi available to guests.

Banavie, by Fort William, Inverness-shire

Map Ref: 3H12

B&B

Mrs G King

Glenshian, Banavie, by Fort William, Inverness-shire, PH33 7LX
Tel: 01397 772174 Fax: 01397 773031
E-mail: glenshian@aol.com
Web: www.host.co.uk

Glenshian, situated alongside the Caledonian Canal, offers spectacular panoramic views of Ben Nevis and surrounding mountains. Ideal location to enjoy ski-ing, walking, climbing etc. Tour the beautiful west coast or simply relax in peaceful and comfortable surroundings. Expect a warm welcome and hospitality in a friendly informal atmosphere.

1 Twin
2 Double
1 Family

All En Suite

B&B per person
£16.00-£25.00 Dbl/Twn

Open Jan-Dec

B&B

Seangan Bridge

Banavie, Fort William, Inverness-shire, PH33 7PB
Tel: 01397 772228

Modern crofthouse on 20 acre croft. Excellent views of Ben Nevis. 5 miles from Fort William. Ideal for touring, walking, ski-ing.

1 Twin
1 Double

All En Suite

B&B per person
from £18.00 Single

Open Mar-Nov
B&B + Eve.Meal
from £30.00

Beauly, Inverness-shire

Map Ref: 4A8

B&B

Ellengowan

Croyard Road, Beauly, IV4 7DJ
Tel: 01463 782273

Comfortable, centrally heated home near Priory. Ideal base for touring. A short walk to Beauly's shops, banks and restaurants. Off road parking.

1 Twin

All En Suite
2 Priv.NOT ensuite

B&B per person
£14.00-£16.00 Twin

Open Apr-Oct

B&B

Rheindown Farm Holidays

Rheindown Farm, Beauly, Inverness-shire, IV4 7AB
Tel: 01463 782461

Farmhouse on working farm, in elevated position overlooking Beauly and the Firth beyond.

1 Double
1 Family

1 Pub Bath/Show

B&B per person
from £15.50 Double

Open Mar-Nov

B&B

Wester Moniack Farmhouse

Kirkhill, Inverness, Inverness-shire, IV5 7PQ
Tel: 01463 831237
E-mail: Wester.Moniack@tesco.net
Web: http://www.SmoothHound.co.uk/hotels/wester.html

For Highland hospitality at its best come and be spoilt at this comfortable friendly farmhouse where we aim to please all our guests and give excellent value for money. Situated 8 miles north of Inverness just off the A862 follow signs to Moniack Castle Wineries and we are right next door.

1 Double
1 Family

1 Pub Bath/Show

B&B per person
from £15.00 Single
from £15.00 Double

Open Jan-Dec
B&B + Eve.Meal
from £22.00

by Beauly, Inverness-shire — Map Ref: 4A8

★★★ B&B

Mrs E Ramsden

Broomhill, Kiltarlity, Beauly, Inverness-shire, IV4 7JH
Tel/Fax: 01463 741447
Web: cali.co.uk/freeway/broomhill

1 Twin, 1 Double | 1 Pub Bath/Show | B&B per person from £13.50 Single, from £13.50 Dbl/Twn | Open Jan-Dec excl Xmas/New Year. B&B + Eve.Meal from £20.50

Edwardian country house set in own grounds amongst open countryside approx 1/2 mile from Kiltarlity and (18kms) from Inverness. Totally non smoking. Packed lunches and evening meals available. Prices remain the same throughout the year, good touring base for the Highlands.

TV P V

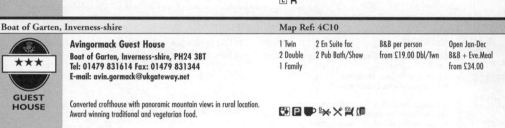

Bettyhill, Sutherland — Map Ref: 4B3

★★ GUEST HOUSE

Dunveaden House

Bettyhill, by Thurso, Sutherland, KW14 7SP
Tel: 01641 521273

1 Single, 3 Twin, 2 Double | 2 Pub Bath/Show | B&B per person from £16.00 Single, from £16.00 Dbl/Twn | Open Apr-Oct

Traditional guest house situated in the village of Bettyhill, on the north coast. Sandy beaches close by; fishing available; walking; birdwatching and much more all in the area.

P TV C

Boat of Garten, Inverness-shire — Map Ref: 4C10

★★★ GUEST HOUSE

Avingormack Guest House

Boat of Garten, Inverness-shire, PH24 3BT
Tel: 01479 831614 Fax: 01479 831344
E-mail: avin.gormack@ukgateway.net

1 Twin, 2 Double, 1 Family | 2 En Suite fac, 2 Pub Bath/Show | B&B per person from £19.00 Dbl/Twn | Open Jan-Dec. B&B + Eve.Meal from £34.00

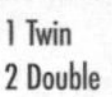

Converted crofthouse with panoramic mountain views in rural location. Award winning traditional and vegetarian food.

P TV C £ V

★★★ B&B

Burnside

Drumullie, by Boat of Garten, Invernessshire, PH24 3BX
Tel/Fax: 01479 831396

1 Single, 1 Twin | 1 Pub Bath/Show | B&B per person from £14.50 Single, from £14.50 Twin. Room only per person from £10.00 | Open Jan-Dec

Comfortable, modern detached house, set back from A95, 5 miles (8kms)from Aviemore. Ideal for touring Spey Valley. Magnificent open views to front.

TV P W V

★★★★ B&B

Chapelton Steading B&B

Chapelton Steading, Boat of Garten, Inverness-shire, PH24 3BU
Tel: 01479 831327
E-mail: chapelton@btinternet.com
Web: www.boatofgarten.com/chapelton

2 Twin, 1 Double | All En Suite | B&B per person from £24.00 Single, from £21.00 Dbl/Twn | Open Mar-Oct

This converted and extended barn comfortably accommodates 6 guests and features privacy and independence. Handcrafted furnishings, a log fire, home-baking, interesting collections of books and paintings all add to the friendly atmosphere of this family home. The rural setting and traditional country garden are enhanced by the views to the Cairngorm mountains.

TV P

Boat of Garten, Inverness-shire — **Map Ref: 4C10**

★★★ GUEST HOUSE

Granlea Guest House
Deshar Road, Boat of Garten, Inverness-shire, PH24 3BN
Tel/Fax: 01479 831601
E-mail: dixons@granlea.freeserve.co.uk
Web: www.granlea.freeserve.co.uk

Stone built Edwardian house, in village centre, close to Osprey reserve and golf course. Ideal touring base.

1 Twin
2 Double
1 Family

2 En Suite fac
1 Pub Bath/Show

B&B per person
from £19.00 Single
from £19.00 Dbl/Twn

Open Jan-Dec excl Xmas/New Year
B&B + Eve.Meal from £32.00

C V

★★★★ GUEST HOUSE

Moorfield House
Deshar Road, Boat of Garten, Inverness-shire, PH24 3BN
Tel: 01479 831646
E-mail: moorfieldhouse@msn.com
Web: www.moorfieldhouse.com

Informality is the key to this luxuriously furnished Victorian house. Ideally suited to those seeking relaxed and peaceful surroundings. A friendly welcome, comfortable beds and a hearty breakfast await. Fully non smoking. Evening meal by arrangement.

2 Twin
3 Double

All En Suite

B&B per person
from £31.00 Single
from £26.00 Dbl/Twn

Open Mar-Oct
B&B + Eve.Meal from £45.00

★★★ B&B

Steornabhagh
Deshar Road, Boat of Garten, Inverness-shire, PH24 3BN
Tel: 01479 831371

Attractive, comfortable bungalow just off main street, in peaceful garden setting. Ideal touring base. Bedrooms ensuite.

1 Twin
2 Double

All En Suite

B&B per person
from £20.00 Single
from £20.00 Dbl/Twn

Open Jan-Dec

V

Brora, Sutherland Map Ref: 4C6

AR DACHAIDH

BADNELLAN, BRORA, SUTHERLAND KW9 6NQ

Tel/Fax: 01408 621658 e.mail: badnellan@madasafish.com
Web: http://www.robbins-associates.co.uk/brora/

THE TASTE OF SCOTLAND

Traditional croft house in quiet crofting area. Ideal stop for touring the whole of the north. Good for walking, birdwatching, golf, fishing, cycling, motorcycling or just sitting on the miles of quiet beaches. Home cooked meals a speciality. Treat yourself to a romantic stay in a four poster bed.

B&B

Ar Dachaidh
Badnellan, Brora, Sutherland, KW9 6NQ
Tel/Fax: 01408 621658
E-mail: badnellan@madasafish.com
Web: http://www.robbins-associates.co.uk/brora/

1 Single	1 Pub Bath/Show	B&B per person	Open Mar-Nov
1 Twin		from £17.00 Single	B&B + Eve.Meal
1 Double		from £17.00 Dbl/Twn	from £23.00

Traditional 19C croft house, very quietly situated behind the village of Brora. Friendly welcome, home cooked evening meals, B&B certificate of excellence. Motorcycle friendly.

B&B

Mrs J Ballantyne
Clynelish Farm, Brora, Sutherland, KW9 6LR
Tel/Fax: 01408 621265
E-mail: murdoch@clynelish.fs.co.uk

1 Twin	2 En Suite fac	B&B per person	Open mid Mar-mid Oct
2 Double	1 Priv.NOT ensuite	£20.00-£25.00 Single	
		£20.00-£22.50 Dbl/Twn	
		Room only	
		from £15.00	

Listed house circa 1865 on family run working livestock farm in quiet location about a mile (2kms) from Brora and beaches. Golfing and fishing available locally. Open March to October or by arrangement.

GLENAVERON

Golf Road, Brora, Sutherland KW9 6QS

Tel/Fax: 01408 621601 e.mail: glenaveron@hotmail.com

Glenaveron is a luxurious Edwardian house with extensive mature gardens. Only a short walk to Brora golf club and lovely beaches. A 25 minute drive to the Royal Dornoch golf club. An ideal base for touring The Northern Highlands and Orkney. All rooms are en-suite. Non smoking.

B&B

Alistair Fortune
Glenaveron, Golf Road, Brora, Sutherland, KW9 6QS
Tel/Fax: 01408 621601
E-mail: glenaveron@hotmail.com

1 Twin	All En Suite	B&B per person	Open Jan-Dec excl
1 Double		from £28.00 Single	Xmas/New Year
1 Family		from £25.00 Dbl/Twn	

Spacious stone built family home, set in mature gardens, in a peaceful area of Brora. A few minutes walk from the golf course; several others, including Royal Dornoch in the area. Other sporting and leisure facilities nearby, as are sandy beaches, historic sites, eating establishments. Excellent base for exploring the far north of Scotland; ideal stopover en route to Orkney.

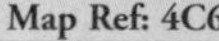

Brora, Sutherland

Map Ref: 4C6

B&B

Elizabeth & Geoffrey Smyth
'Seaforth', Achrimsdale, Brora, Sutherland, KW9 6LT
Tel: 01408 621793
E-mail: seaforth_1@brora1.freeserve.co.uk

1 Twin 1 Double	1 Pub Bath/Show	B&B per person £16.00-£18.00 Single £16.00-£18.00 Dbl/Twn	Open Jan-Dec excl Xmas/New Year

Traditional farmhouse set on working croft. South-facing outlook towards the sea. 1.5 miles from Brora village. Cosy atmosphere and a warm welcome. Ground floor bedrooms. Hot snacks and packed lunches available. Open all year.

B&B

Tigh Fada, Non-Smokers' Haven
18 Golf Road, Brora, Sutherland, KW9 6QS
Tel/Fax: 01408 621332
E.mail: clarkson@tighfada.fsnet.co.uk

2 Twin 1 Double	1 En Suite fac 2 Priv.NOT ensuite	B&B per person £20.00-£25.00 Dbl/Twn	Open Jan-Dec excl Xmas/New Year

Fine sea views and open peat fires, home baking and a real Highland welcome. Ideal half way house between Inverness and John O'Groats, or if catching a ferry to Orkney. Why not stay longer and visit Dunrobin Castle, the Timespan Heritage Centre, or go fishing or golfing. Explore beautiful Sutherland, or take a day trip to the rugged West Coast.

Cannich, Inverness-shire

Map Ref: 3H9

B&B

Kerrow House
Cannich, by Beauly, Inverness-shire, IV4 7NA
Tel: 01456 415243 Fax: 01456 415425
E-mail: stephen@kerrow-house.demon.co.uk
Web: www.kerrow-house.demon.co.uk

1 Twin 1 Double 1 Family	2 En Suite fac 1 Priv.NOT ensuite	B&B per person from £22.00 Single from £22.00 Dbl/Twn	Open Jan-Dec

Large country house, 250 years old with many period features. Set in wooded grounds on banks of River Glass with 3.5 miles of private trout fishing free to guests. Recognised Investors in People.

Important: Prices stated are estimates and may be subject to amendments

Carrbridge, Inverness-shire — Map Ref: 4C9

★★★
B&B

An Sealgair
Station Road, Carrbridge, Inverness-shire, PH23 3AN
Tel/Fax: 01479 841331
E-mail: shalger@aol.com

1 Twin 2 Double	All En Suite 1 Pub Bathroom	B&B per person from £20.00 Single from £18.00 Dbl/Twn Room only per person from £12.00	Open Jan-Dec

A modern, purpose built bungalow in residential area 800m from main street. All ensuite facilities. Ideally situated for touring Scotland, birdwatching, walking and cycling.

C W V

★★★
B&B

Birchwood
12 Rowan Park, Carrbridge, Inverness-shire, PH23 3BE
Tel/Fax: 01479 841393
E.mail: normanwhitehall@lineone.net

1 Double 1 Twin	En suite use of Show/Toilet	B&B per person from £18.00 Double from £16.00 Twin	Open Jan-Dec excl Xmas/New Year

Modern bungalow in quiet cul-de-sac, on edge of this highland village. Warm welcome assured. Ideal base for touring, bird watching and walking. Enjoy breakfast in conservatory with full view of garden.

TV P

V

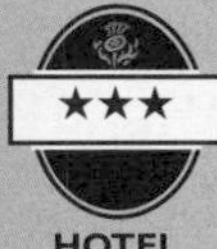
★★★
HOTEL

The Cairn Hotel
Main Road, Carrbridge, Inverness-shire, PH23 3AS
Tel: 01479 841212 Fax: 01479 841362

2 Single 1 Twin 2 Double 2 Family	4 En Suite fac 1 Pub Bath/Show	B&B per person from £19.00 Single from £19.00 Dbl/Twn	Open Jan-Dec

Family run hotel with cosy bar and friendly atmosphere, situated in the centre of small Highland village. A good base for touring and skiing.

TV P

C W V

Carrbridge, Inverness-shire

Map Ref: 4C9

GUEST HOUSE

Craigellachie House

Main Street, Carrbridge, Inverness-shire, PH23 3AS
Tel/Fax: 01479 841641
E-mail: e.pedersen@talk21.com

Warm comfortable hospitality assured. Ample parking. Centre of village. Ideal base for holiday activities. Dinners available using fresh Scottish produce.

1 Single, 2 Twin, 2 Double, 2 Family
3 En Suite fac, 2 Pub Bath/Show
B&B per person from £17.00 Single, from £17.00 Dbl/Twn
Open Jan-Nov
B&B + Eve.Meal from £30.00

GUEST HOUSE

Feith Mhor Country House

Station Road, Carrbridge, Inverness-shire, PH23 3AP
Tel: 01479 841621
E-mail: feith.mhor@btinternet.com

Elegant 19c house set in beautiful open countryside. Family run with accent on local fresh produce. 1 mile (2 kms) from Carrbridge. Pets welcome at owners discretion.

3 Twin, 2 Double, 1 Family
All En Suite
B&B per person £22.00-£25.00 Single, £22.00-£25.00 Dbl/Twn
Open Jan-Dec

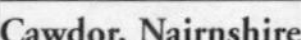

Cawdor, Nairnshire

Map Ref: 4C8

B&B

Dallaschyle

Cawdor, by Nairn, IV12 5XS
Tel: 01667 493422 Fax: 01667 493638
E-mail: bookings@dallaschyle.fsnet.co.uk

Enjoy the peace and tranquility of our modern home set in 2 acres of colourful garden and woodland. Ideal base for exploring local historical attractions including Cawdor Castle, Culloden Battlefield. Home baking and preserves a speciality.

1 Double, 1 Family
1 Pub Bath/Show
B&B per person £24.00 Single, £18.00 Double
Open Apr-Oct

B&B

Fairview

Culcharry, Cawdor, Nairnshire, IV12 5QY
Tel: 01667 404459 Fax: 01667 454382
E-mail: irislapham@aol.com

Attractive detached bungalow situated in quiet spot overlooking open countryside. Close to Cawdor Castle, Culloden Moor and Fort George. Woodland walks, bowling, fishing and golf within easy reach.

1 Family – Ensuite fac
1 Twin – Private fac
B&B per person from £17.00 Single, from £17.00 Twin
Room only per person from £14.00
Open Mar-Oct

Conon Bridge, Ross-shire

Map Ref: 4A8

B&B

Mrs C Morrison

Dun Eistein, Alcaig, Conon Bridge, Ross-shire, IV7 8HS
Tel: 01349 862210

Highland cottage on country road with views of Ben Wyvis from garden. 11 miles (18kms) north of Inverness. Non-smoking.

1 Double – 1 En Suite fac
1 Family – 1 Priv.NOT ensuite
B&B per person from £24.00 Single, from £18.50 Double
Open May-Sep

Important: Prices stated are estimates and may be subject to amendments

Contin, Ross-shire Map Ref: 4A8

B&B

Hideaway B&B
Craigdarroch Drive, Contin, by Strathpeffer,
Ross-shire, IV14 9EL
Tel/Fax: 01997 421127
Web: www.SmoothHound.co.uk/hotels/hideaway.html

Modern bungalow in quiet setting, one mile from Contin village. Near to Falls of Rogie. Centrally situated for touring the Northern Highlands. Good base for bird watching, walking or just relaxing.

1 Twin 2 Double	All En Suite	B&B per person from £16.00 Single from £15.00 Dbl/Twn	Open Jan-Dec excl Xmas/New Year

C V

B&B

Nayrendah
Craigdarroch Drive, Contin, by Strathpeffer,
Ross-shire, IV14 9EL
Tel/Fax: 01997 421408 mobile 07720 720431

Comfortable, en-suite accommodation in modern detached bungalow in an attractive woodland setting. Close to Contin and the Victorian spa town of Strathpeffer incorporating the museum of childhood. Plenty to see and do. Inverness only 18 miles distant.

2 Double	All En Suite	B&B per person £18.00-£20.00 Single £16.00-£18.00 Double	Open Jan-Dec

Contin, Ross-shire

Map Ref: 4A8

TAIGH-AN-EILEIN

TAIGH-AN-EILEIN, CONTIN, ROSS-SHIRE IV14 9ES
Telephone/Fax: 01997 421009 e.mail: lorna.mac@talk21.com

A charming and tastefully restored 18th-century former manse set in the tranquility of Contin Island. Large comfortable rooms, and log fires, overlooking magnificent Highland scenery make this the ideal spot for relaxation. Contin is the perfect base to visit the West Highlands, with excellent opportunities for fishing and walking.

B&B

Taigh-an-Eilein
Contin, Ross-shire, IV14 9ES
Tel/Fax: 01997 421009
E.mail: lorna.mac@talk21.com

2 Double | All En Suite | B&B per person from £22.00 Double | Open Apr-Sep

Late 18th Century former manse set in spacious and well maintained grounds, including a walled garden. Comfortable accommodation, a relaxing atmosphere and a warm friendly welcome make this an ideal base from which to explore the Highlands. The far North, Wester Ross and even the islands are all within reach, as are Loch Ness and the Moray coast.

C V

Corpach, by Fort William, Inverness-shire

Map Ref: 3G12

B&B

Heston
Corpach, Fort William, Inverness-shire, PH33 7LT
Tel: 01397 772425

1 Twin | All En Suite | B&B per person | Open Mar-Oct
1 Double | 1 Pub Bath/Show | £20.00-£22.00 Single
£18.00-£20.00 Dbl/Twn

Modern family home with magnificent views across Loch Linnhe. 4 miles (6kms) from Fort William. Ideal base for touring the Highlands - skiers, walkers, climbers welcome. Family room - all en-suite. Traditional home-cooked Scottish breakfast.

TV P

C

★★

GUEST HOUSE

The Neuk
Corpach, by Fort William, Inverness-shire, PH33 7LR
Tel: 01397 772244

1 Twin | All En Suite | B&B per person | Open Jan-Dec excl
1 Double | from £27.00 Single | Xmas/New Year
2 Family | from £18.00 Dbl/Twn | B&B + Eve.Meal from £29.00

A warm friendly welcome awaits you at this detached villa on Mallaig road (A830) with panoramic views over the Mamore Mountains, Ben Nevis and Loch Linnhe. Within few mins walk of Canal Bank and Neptunes Staircase. Evening meals by arrangement. Ideal base for touring surrounding area or walking, cycling and skiing. Featured in Scotland's essential guide to the high roads.

TV P

C W V

B&B

Margaret Watson, Albyn House
Albyn Drive, Corpach, by Fort William,
Inverness-shire, PH33 7LW
Tel: 01397 772821

2 Family/Dbl/Twin | All En Suite | B&B per person £16.00-£20.00 Double | Open Jan-Dec

Modern family home in quiet cul-de-sac 4 miles (6.5 kms) from Fort William town centre. Within walking distance of well known local restaurants. Views of Ben Nevis and surrounding area. Families welcome. Ideal base for walking, skiing and climbing. Close by Corpach and Banavie railway stations. Private parking. Extensive breakfast menu.

TV P

C V

Important: Prices stated are estimates and may be subject to amendments

Cromarty, Ross-shire Map Ref: 4B7

BEECHFIELD HOUSE

4 URQUHART COURT, CROMARTY, ROSS-SHIRE IV11 8YD

Tel: 01381 600308 Fax: 01381 600826 e.mail: beechfield@cali.co.uk

Beechfield House situated at the edge of Cromarty is friendly, warm, comfortable and modern with traditional features. Enjoy peace and tranquility. Delicious breakfasts served in our large conservatory. Excellent evening meals available nearby. Dolphin trips, walks, golf. Inverness 30 minutes. Brochure available. Special Short Breaks – 3 nights. One double room with ensuite, one twin with ensuite, one twin with private facilities. Totally non-smoking.

B&B

Beechfield House

4 Urquhart Court, Cromarty, Ross-shire, IV11 8YD
Tel: 01381 600308 Fax: 01381 600826
E-mail: beechfield@cali.co.uk

1 Twin	Ensuite fac	B&B per person	Open Mar-Oct
1 Double	Ensuite fac	from £22.00 Single	
1 Twin	Private fac	from £20.00 Dbl/Twn	

Built with guests comfort in mind, this large modern house with a conservatory and garden is situated on the outskirts of the lovely 18C town of Cromarty. Off street parking, non smoking house, credit cards accepted. Activities available in the area include golfing, walking and dolphin watching trips.

by Cromarty, Ross-shire Map Ref: 4B7

★★★★

B&B

Newfield

Newhall Bridge, Poyntzfield, IV7 8LQ
Tel: 01381 610325
Web: www.newfeild-bb.co.uk

1 Single	1 En Suite fac	B&B per person	Open Jan-Dec
1 Double	1 Priv.NOT ensuite	from £18.00 Single	
1 Family		from £18.00 Double	

Comfortable bed & breakfast in a traditional cottage set amidst peaceful farming country on the Black Isle. 18 miles from Inverness and 6 miles to Cromarty. An ideal location for touring the east, North and West Coast of the Highlands. Udale Bay Bird Sanctuary 1 mile away. Dolphin trips available at Cromarty and Avoch.

by Cromarty, Ross-shire | Map Ref: 4B7

Braelangwell House

Balblair, Ross-shire IV7 8LQ
Tel: 01381 610353 Fax: 01381 610467
e.mail: Braelangwell@btinternet.com
web: www.btinternet.com/~braelangwell

A fine Georgian house of the late 18th-century situated in fifty acres of beech woodland and gardens including the original walled garden where you can play croquet on the lawn. Choose from three bedrooms –The Garden Room, a double room with a four poster bed; The Chinese Room, another double bed; The Henrietta Room with twin beds. All rooms have an ensuite or private bathroom, television, radio and tea/coffee making facilities. Enjoy breakfast in the elegant diningroom and relax in the library, conservatory or upstairs hall with lovely views over the garden to the Cromarty Firth.

★★★

B&B

Mrs L E Strange

Braelangwell House, Balblair, Ross-shire, IV7 8LQ
Tel: 01381 610353 Fax: 01381 610467
E-mail: braelangwell@btinternet.com
Web: www.btinternet.com/~braelangwell

1 Twin | 1 En Suite fac
2 Double | 2 Priv.NOT ensuite

B&B per person
£25.00-£35.00 Single
£25.00-£30.00 Dbl/Twn

Open Apr-Oct

Fine Georgian house dating from the late 18th Century, situated in 5 acres of garden and 50 acres of woodland. 7 miles from Cromarty. Convenient for road and air links from the south. Ideal base for exploring the northern Highlands.

C V

Culloden Moor, Inverness-shire | Map Ref: 4B8

★★★

B&B

'Bay View'

West Hill, Culloden Moor, Inverness-shire, IV2 5BP
Tel/Fax: 01463 790386

1 Twin | 1 En Suite fac
2 Double | 1 Priv.NOT ensuite

B&B per person
from £25.00 Single
from £20.00 Double

Open Apr-Oct

Quiet, comfortable house in pleasant country surroundings with magnificent views over the Moray Firth. Evening meals by arrangement, home cooking.

★★★

B&B

Culdoich Farm

Culloden Moor, Inverness-shire, IV2 5EL
Tel: 01463 790268

1 Twin | 1 Pub Bath/Show
1 Dbl/Fam

B&B per person
from £18.00 Single
from £18.00 Dbl/Twn

Open May-Oct

18c farmhouse built the year after the Battle of Culloden on mixed arable and livestock farm. On hillside near Culloden Battlefield and Clava Stones. Home baking always available.

C V

Culloden Moor, Inverness-shire

Map Ref: 4B8

★★★★ B&B

Leanach Farm

Culloden Moor, Inverness-shire, IV2 5EJ
Tel/Fax: 01463 791027
E-mail: RosanneMacKay@compuserve.com
Web: www.leanachfarm.co.uk

Modern large family farmhouse on 400 acre sheep and cattle farm. 5 miles (9kms) from Inverness, near Culloden Battlefield. Home cooked evening meals by arrangement.

2 Twin
1 Double

All En Suite

B&B per person
from £22.00 Single
from £22.00 Dbl/Twn
Room only per person
from £17.00

Open Jan-Dec
B&B + Eve.Meal
from £33.00

★★★ B&B

'Strathmore'

Viewhill Farm Road, Culloden Moor, Inverness, IV2 5EA
Tel: 01463 791607

Spacious self-contained apartment with own sitting room and bathroom. 1 mile from Culloden Battlefield. Inverness 4 miles.

1 Family

En Suite

B&B per person
£18.00-£20.00 Single
£18.00-£20.00 Double

Open Jan-Dec
B&B + Eve.Meal
£45.00-£53.00 Dbl

★★ B&B

Westhill House

Westhill, by Inverness, IV1 2BP
Tel: 01463 793225 Fax: 01463 792503
Web: www.scotland-info.co.uk/westhill

Set in lovely rural surroundings, this modern family home rests within its own grounds and pretty garden. 1 mile from historic Culloden Battlefield and a central base to explore Inverness, Loch Ness and the Highlands. 3 miles from Inverness station and 5 miles from the airport.

1 Twin
1 Family

All En Suite

B&B per person
from £18.00 Twin

Open late Mar-Oct

★★★★ B&B

Woodside Farmhouse

Woodside of Culloden, Westhill, Inverness, IV2 5BP
Tel/Fax: 01463 790242
E-mail: margaret.maclean@ukgateway.net

Modern farmhouse on working farm, opportunity to see Border Collie Sheepdogs in action. Open outlook over the countryside and panoramic views to the Moray Firth, Inverness and hills of Ross-shire. Friendly welcome with home bakes a speciality. Ideal base for touring the Highlands and close to historic Culloden Battlefield. Credit cards taken.

2 Twin
1 Double

All En Suite

B&B per person
from £21.00 Single
from £21.00 Dbl/Twn

Open Feb-Nov
B&B + Eve.Meal
from £33.00

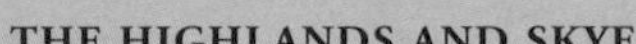

Dalcross, by Inverness, Inverness-shire — **Map Ref: 4B8**

★★★★ B&B

Easter Dalziel Farmhouse
Easter Dalziel Farm, Dalcross, Inverness-shire, IV2 7JL
Tel/Fax: 01667 462213

1 Twin 2 Double	2 Pub Bath/Show	B&B per person £20.00-£26.00 Single £17.00-£20.00 Dbl/Twn	Open Jan-Dec excl Xmas/New Year B&B + Eve.Meal from £29.00

Victorian farmhouse with beautiful gardens on stock/arable farm. Panoramic views to open countryside, friendly atmosphere, log fire in lounge and home baking. Inverness 7 miles (11 kms). Culloden 5 miles (8 kms). Evening meals by prior arrangement.

Daviot, Inverness-shire — **Map Ref: 4B9**

★★ B&B

M MacLeod
Chalna, Daviot East, Inverness-shire, IV2 5XQ
Tel/Fax: 01463 772239

1 Twin 1 Double 1 Family	1 En Suite fac 1 Pub Bath/Show	B&B per person £17.70-£20.00 Dbl/Twn	Open Mar-Oct

Modern, detached, stone built villa, in extensive grounds in rural setting. 7 miles (11kms) South of Inverness. Fishing available.

Diabaig, Ross-shire — **Map Ref: 3F8**

★★★★ B&B

Upper Diabaig Farm
Upper Diabaig, Torridon, Achnasheen, Ross-shire, IV22 2HE
Tel: 01445 790227

2 Twin 1 Double	1 En Suite fac 1 Pub Bath/Show	B&B per person from £18.00 Dbl/Twn	Open Apr-Sep

Dramatic drive by Torridon Hills to modern house on working croft. Traditional Scottish hospitality. Warm and comfortable. Good home cooking with evening meals availalbe by prior arrangement.

Important: Prices stated are estimates and may be subject to amendments

Dornie, by Kyle of Lochalsh, Ross-shire Map Ref: 3G9

Tigh Tasgaidh

Dornie, Kyle of Lochalsh, Ross-shire IV40 8EH
Tel: 01599 555242 e.mail: lgordoncan@aol.com

Historic Highland house 1/4 mile from romantic Eilean Donan castle. Luxurious accommodation, an outstanding location and spectacular views combine to make this a special experience. Excellent breakfasts and packed lunches. A great base for touring the Isle of Skye and Western Highlands. Guided walks and climbing arranged. Warm welcome.

★★★

B&B

Mrs Gordon Canning
Tigh Tasgaidh, Dornie, by Kyle of Lochalsh, Ross-shire, IV40 8EH
Tel: 01599 555242
E-mail: lgordoncan@aol.com

1 Twin	All En Suite	B&B per person	Open Feb-Nov
2 Double	1 Pub Bath/Show	£24.00 Dbl/Twn	

Historic house standing in its own grounds overlooking Loch Long. Spectacular views, restaurants within walking distance. Reduced tariff for longer breaks. Friendly, relaxing base to explore this beautiful area. All needs catered for, organic and local produce widely used.

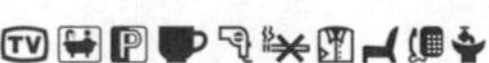

★★★

B&B

Fasgadale
2 Sallachy, Dornie, by Kyle of Lochalsh, Ross-shire, IV40 8DZ
Tel: 01599 588238

1 Twin	B&B per person	Open Apr-Oct
1 Double	from £15.00 Dbl/Twn	
	Room only per person	
	from £15.00	

Modern bungalow on working croft. An elevated position with views across Loch Long. Gaelic spoken.

Castle View

Upper Ardelve, By Dornie, Kyle of Lochalsh IV40 8EY
Telephone and Fax: 01599 555453
e.mail: rosemary@castleview-scotland.co.uk
Web: www.castleview-scotland.co.uk

The countryside surrounding Eilean Donan Castle is of exceptional beauty and grandeur with magnificent mountain, loch and forest scenery. Rich in wildlife, the area offers fascinating rewards for observant nature lovers. There are otters, seals, wild goats and deer, whilst overhead may be seen buzzards, falcons and the magnificent golden eagle.

★★★

B&B

Rosemary McClelland
Castle View, Upper Ardelve, Dornie,
By Kyle of Lochalsh, Ross-shire, IV40 8EY
Tel/Fax: 01599 555453
E-mail: rosemary@castleview-scotland.co.uk
Web: www.castleview-scotland.co.uk

1 Twin	All En Suite	B&B per person	Open Jan-Dec excl
2 Double		£20.00-£22.00 Dbl/Twn	Xmas/New Year
			B&B + Eve.Meal
			£30.00-£32.00

Warm welcome assured in new croft house with breathtaking views to Eilean Donan Castle, Loch Duich and the Sisters of Kintail. Evening meal available by arrangement. Reserved for total non-smokers only.

Dornie, by Kyle of Lochalsh, Ross-shire

Map Ref: 3G9

★★★ B&B

Sealladh Mara

Dornie, by Kyle of Lochlash, Ross-shire, IV40 8EY
Tel: 01599 555296 Fax: 01599 555250

Modern family home, looking over Loch Duich and Eilean Donan Castle towards Kintail mountains. Handy for touring to Skye and Wester Ross. Ideal for walking.

1 Twin | 1 En Suite fac | B&B per person | Open Jan-Dec
2 Double | | £15.00-£19.00 Single |

TV P V

Dornoch, Sutherland

Map Ref: 4B6

Auchlea

Mrs F Garvie, Auchlea, Dornoch IV25 3HY
Tel: 01862 811524 e.mail: fionamgarvie@yahoo.com
Web: http://hometown.aol.com/johngarvie/BandB.html

Luxury bungalow with beautiful views of mountains and sea. Accommodation 3 ensuite bedrooms, one with jacuzzi. Excellent evening meals served in a warm friendly atmosphere. Cosy log fire in comfortable lounge. One mile from historic cathedral town of Dornoch. Miles of sandy beaches and Royal Dornoch golf course.

★★★ B&B

Auchlea

Balnapolaig Muir, Dornoch, Sutherland, IV25 3HY
Tel: 01862 811524
E.mail: fionamgarvie@yahoo.com
Web: http://hometown.aol.com/johngarvie/BandB.html

Purpose built bungalow set in a large garden with ample parking and beautiful views of mountains and sea. Built in 1998, having accommodation comprising 3 en-suite bedrooms, one of which has a jacuzzi. Excellent evening meals cooked on an Aga cooker in a warm and friendly atmosphere. Cosy log fire in comfortable lounge. 1 mile out of the historic Cathedral town of Dornoch with miles of sandy beaches as well as Royal Dornoch Golf Course.

3 Twin | All En Suite | B&B per person from £20.00 Single from £18.00 Twin Room only per person from £15.00 | Open Jan-Dec excl Xmas/New Year B&B + Eve.Meal from £28.00

TV P C V

★★★ B&B

Fearn House

High Street, Dornoch, IV25 3SH
Tel: 01862 810249

A friendly welcome from the new owners at this stone built house on quiet street in centre of Dornoch, overlooking Cathedral.

1 Twin | 2 En Suite fac | B&B per person | Open Mar-Oct
3 Family | 2 Priv.NOT ensuite | from £21.00 Single |
| | from £18.00 Double |

TV C

Important: Prices stated are estimates and may be subject to amendments

Dornoch, Sutherland

Map Ref: 4B6

HIGHFIELD HOUSE

Evelix Road, Dornoch, Sutherland IV25 3HR

Telephone: 01862 810909 Fax: 01862 811605
e.mail: enquiries@highfieldhouse.co.uk
Web: www.highfieldhouse.co.uk

Enjoy the informality and comfort of our spacious non-smoking home. Highfield stands in an acre of woodland garden with beautiful southerly views over the Dornoch Firth. The centre of the lovely cathedral town of Dornoch, Royal Dornoch Golf Club and beach are a short stroll away. Our guest bedrooms are ensuite with full facilities and we have ample parking, conservatory lounge and elegant dining room with individual tables for delicious hearty and/or healthy breakfasts. This is the ideal location for touring the wonderful Northern Highlands. A very warm welcome is assured. Please call or write for our brochure.

AA ◆◆◆◆◆

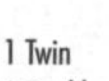

B&B

Highfield House

Evelix Road, Dornoch, Sutherland, IV25 3HR
Tel: 01862 810909 Fax: 01862 811605
E-mail: enquiries@highfieldhouse.co.uk
Web: www.highfieldhouse.co.uk

A modern house at edge of this picturesque golfing town – a warm welcome assured in this very comfortable family home.

1 Twin
2 Double

All En Suite

B&B per person
from £35.00 Single
from £26.00 Dbl/Twn

Open Jan-Dec

B&B

Hillview

Evelix Road, Dornoch, Sutherland, IV25 3RD
Tel: 01862 810151

Hillview is a double fronted bungalow situated in rural woodland setting. 3 mins from Dornoch, double room with private bathroom & lounge. Private parking. Dornoch boasts breathtaking walks & views nearby. Award wining beach. Two golf courses one of which is a championship course.

1 Double

1 Priv.NOT ensuite

B&B per person
from £16.00 Double

Open Jan-Dec

B&B

Khuzistan

9 Poles Road, Dornoch, Sutherland, IV25 3HP
Tel: 01862 810552

Friendly, family run modern home (incl a ground floor room) with excellent garden area. Off road parking available.

1 Twin
2 Double

1 En Suite fac
2 Priv.NOT ensuite

B&B per person
from £20.00 Dbl/Twn

Open Apr-Oct

Dornoch, Sutherland

Map Ref: 4B6

B&B

Mrs R Matheson

Tordarroch, Castle Street, Dornoch, Sutherland, IV25 3SN
Tel: 01862 810855

1 Single	Limited ensuite	B&B per person	Open Apr-Oct
1 Twin	Ensuite fac	£18.00-£20.00 Single	
1 Double	1 Priv.Bathroom	£19.50-£22.00 Dbl/Twn	

18th century town House, full of character, set in large enclosed gardens in the centre of the historic Royal Burgh of Dornoch. Close to the Cathedral, founded in the 13th Century. Royal Dornoch Golf Club and sandy beaches nearby.

B&B

Parfour

Hilton of Embo, Embo Street, Dornoch,
Sutherland, IV25 3PW
Tel/Fax: 01862 810955
E-mail: parfourdornoch@talk21.com
Web: http://freespace.virgin.net/parfour.dornoch

2 Twin	All En Suite	B&B per person	Open Jan-Dec
		£28.00-£40.00 Single	
		£23.00-£25.00 Twin	

Parfour, which has been very recently built offers guests a very comfortable stay in a well appointed house. Your hosts will provide a wide range of breakfast choice. The house commands panoramic views to the Dornoch Firth and the 14th hole of the Royal Dornoch Golf Course.

Drumnadrochit, Inverness-shire

Map Ref: 4A9

B&B

Allanmore Farm Bed & Breakfast

Drumnadrochit, Inverness-shire, IV3 6XE
Tel: 01456 450247

1 Twin	1 Pub Bath/Show	B&B per person	Open Apr-Oct
2 Double		£16.00-£17.00 Dbl/Twn	

16th Century farmhouse on stock and arable farm in peaceful setting. 10 minutes walk to village.

Drumnadrochit, Inverness-shire Map Ref: 4A9

DRUMBUIE FARM

DRUMBUIE FARM, LOCH NESS, DRUMNADROCHIT IV3 6XP
Telephone: 01456 450634 Fax: 01456 450595
e.mail: drumbuie@amserve.net

Custom built luxury farmhouse on working farm. Drumbuie sits on an elevated site overlooking Loch Ness and surrounding hills with spectacular views. The farm boasts a herd of "hairy" Highland cattle as well as sheep, lambs, other cattle breeds and also grows its own animal feeds. All rooms ensuite. Four poster bed. No smoking.

★★★★

B&B

Drumbuie Farm

Loch Ness, Drumnadrochit, Inverness-shire, IV3 6XP
Tel: 01456 450634 Fax: 01456 450595
E-mail: drumbuie@amserve.net

1 Twin
2 Double

All En Suite

B&B per person
from £19.00 Dbl/Twn
Room only per person
from £18.00

Open Jan-Dec excl
Xmas/New Year

Modern farmhouse, with all rooms ensuite, on an elevated site overlooking Loch Ness and surrounding farmland. Own herd of Highland cattle. Non-smoking household.

TV P C £ W V

WOODLANDS

East Lewiston, Drumnadrochit, Inverness-shire IV63 6UJ
Tel: 01456 450356 Fax: 01456 450199 Web: www.host.co.uk
e.mail: Drysdale@woodlandsbandb.fsnet.co.uk

Relax in our modern, comfortable family home set in the quiet Highland village of Lewiston, Drumnadrochit. Close to Loch Ness, an ideal centre for touring the Highlands and only 15 miles from Inverness. No evening meals.

Jim and Janette await to give you a warm Scottish welcome.

★★★★

B&B

J & J Drysdale

Woodlands, East Lewiston, Drumnadrochit, Inverness-shire, IV63 6UJ
Tel: 01456 450356 Fax: 01456 450199
E-mail: Drysdale@woodlandsbandb.fsnet.co.uk
Web: www.host.co.uk

1 Twin
2 Double

All En Suite

B&B per person
£17.00-£20.00 Dbl/Twn

Open Jan-Dec

Modern family-run house with an acre of garden in quiet situation on the edge of Drumnadrochit, close to Loch Ness. Inverness 15 miles (24kms).

TV P C £ W V

Drumnadrochit, Inverness-shire | Map Ref: 4A9

B&B

Ferness Cottage
Lewiston, Drumnadrochit, Inverness-shire, IV63 6UW
Tel: 01456 450564

1 Twin, 2 Double — All En Suite
B&B per person: from £16.00 Single, from £16.00 Dbl/Twn
Open Jan-Dec incl Xmas/New Year

Friendly family run B&B in 200 year old traditional modernised cottage close to Drumnadrochit and Loch Ness. Ideal base for touring the Highlands.

B&B

Gillyflowers Bed & Breakfast
Drumnadrochit, Inverness-shire, IV63 6UJ
Tel/Fax: 01456 450641
E-mail: gillyflowers@cali.co.uk

1 Twin, 2 Double — 1 En Suite fac
B&B per person: from £17.00 Single, from £14.50 Dbl/Twn
Open Jan-Dec

Renovated farmhouse of character and charm. Countryside location close to Loch Ness. Hospitality assured.

B&B

Glen Rowan House
West Lewiston, Drumnadrochit, Inverness-shire, IV63 6UW
Tel: 01456 450235 Fax: 01456 450817
E.mail: glenrowan@loch-ness.demon.co.uk
Web: www.loch-ness.demon.co.uk

2 Twin, 1 Double — All En Suite
B&B per person: from £25.00 Single, from £17.00 Dbl/Twn
Open Jan-Dec excl Xmas/New Year

Comfortable house with large garden running down to river in a quiet village by Loch Ness between Drumnadrochit and Urquhart Castle. Boat trips and horse riding close by. Non-smoking establishment. Ample off road parking. All rooms tastefully furnished with bedrooms on ground floor.

Drumnadrochit, Inverness-shire Map Ref: 4A9

B&B

Kilmore Farmhouse
Drumnadrochit, Inverness-shire, IV63 6UF
Tel: 01456 450524
E-mail: kilmorefarm@supanet.com
Web: www.ibmpcug.co.uk/~ecs/guest/kilmore/

2 Double, 1 Family — All En Suite

B&B per person £15.00-£18.00 Double

Open Jan-Dec. B&B + Eve.Meal £25.00-£28.00

Modern farmhouse peacefully situated with splendid views of surrounding hills. Site of Special Scientific Interest. Highland Cattle.

C V

B&B

Maes Howe Bed & Breakfast
Maes Howe, Walled Garden, Balmacaan, Drumnadrochit, Inverness-shire, IV63 6UP
Tel: 01456 450382

1 Single, 1 Twin, 1 Double — 2 Pub Bath/Show

B&B per person £16.00-£17.00 Single, £16.00-£17.00 Dbl/twn

Open Apr-Oct

Modern house quietly located in old walled garden, with panoramic views of hills. 2 miles (3kms) from Loch Ness and 14 miles (22kms) from Inverness.

P

V

B&B

Monearn
Drumnadrochit, Inverness-shire, IV63 6XD
Tel: 01456 450396

1 Twin, 1 Double — All En Suite

B&B per person from £16.00 Single

Open Mar-Oct

Comfortable and beautiful home furnished to a high standard, in quiet location close to Drumnadrochit, with south facing views of surrounding hills. Sole occupany of upstairs flat containing a double and a twin bedded room with private bathroom, suitable for a party of up to four people. Substantial continental breakfast only.

P

B&B

Riverbank
West Lewiston, Drumnadrochit, Inverness-shire, IV63 6UW
Tel: 01456 450274
E-mail: jennydru@breathemail.net

1 Single, 1 Twin, 2 Double — 1 En Suite fac, 3 Priv.NOT ensuite

B&B per person from £15.00 Single, from £17.00 Dbl/Twn

Open Jan-Dec

Modern chalet style house with ground floor accommodation peacefully situated. Ample parking. Riverside and woodland walks nearby.

TV P

C W V

Key to symbols is on back flap.

Drumnadrochit, Inverness-shire
Map Ref: 4A9

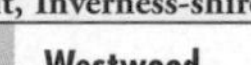

B&B

Westwood
Lower Balmacaan, Drumnadrochit, Inverness-shire, IV63 6WU
Tel/Fax: 01456 450826
E-mail: sandra@westwoodbb.freeserve.co.uk

1 Single	2 Ensuite fac	B&B per person	Open Jan-Dec
1 Twin	1 Pub Bath/Show	from £17.00 Single	B&B + Eve.Meal
1 Double		from £17.00 Dbl/Twn	from £30.00

Comfortable modern bungalow with beautiful views of the surrounding hills. Quiet location in popular highland village. Loch Ness, Urquhart Castle and the 'Nessie' exhibitions are close by. Westwood is the ideal centre for exploring the highlands, high and low level hiking, or just relaxing and enjoying our wonderful highland air.

Duirinish, by Plockton, Ross-shire
Map Ref: 3F9

B&B

Seann Bhruthach
Duirinish, by Plockton, Ross-shire, IV40 8BE
Tel: 01599 544204
E-mail: ian-morag@mackenzie29.fsnet.co.uk

1 Twin	Private fac	B&B per person	Open Jan-Dec excl
2 Double	Ensuite fac	from £20.00 Single	Xmas Eve/Day
		from £20.00 Dbl/Twn	B&B + Eve.Meal
			from £30.00

A very warm welcome in our comfortable modern home in picturesque crofting township with outstanding views over the Inner Hebrides. Home cooked evening meal available, must be pre-booked.

Dunbeath, Caithness
Map Ref: 4D4

B&B

Tormore Farm, Mrs M MacDonald
Dunbeath, Caithness, KW6 6EH
Tel/Fax: 01593 731240

1 Twin	1 Pub Bath/Show	B&B per person	Open May-Oct
1 Double		from £15.00 Single	B&B + Eve.Meal
1 Family		from £14.00 Dbl/Twn	£21.00-£23.00

Warm Highland hospitality on this traditional working farm. Dinner available on request. One ground floor bedroom. Extensive sea view from the farm, clifftop walks, including varied bird species & especially puffins.

Duncanston, Ross-shire Map Ref: 4B8

'GRIANAN' BED & BREAKFAST

Brae Dunvournie, Duncanston, Black Isle, Ross-shire IV7 8JB
Tel: 01349 877758 e.mail: kite@grianan.freeserve.co.uk

'Grianan' is situated 1 mile from the A9 and is an ideal touring base to castles, dolphins, mountains, sandy beaches and RSPB reserves. Rural location in a 1 acre garden, open mountain views, woodlands and resident kites. Organic and vegetarians catered for. Packed lunches available. Walkers, cyclists and bird-watchers welcome.

B&B

'Grianan', Mrs P Jayes,

Brae Dunvournie, Duncanston, Dingwall, Ross-shire, IV7 8JB
Tel: 01349 877758 Mobile: 07866 642014
E-mail: Kite@grianan.freeserve.co.uk

A stay at Grianan will leave you rested and relaxed. A comfortable house set in gardens that will please both the keen gardener and those who just enjoy looking. The garden attracts a wide range of birds both large and small that will entertain you while at dinner and breakfast. Dinner is provided by your hosts using their own organic produce from the garden according to season. Grianan is popular with birders, walkers and for enjoying the Highlands.

Double | All Ensuite fac | B&B per person £19.00-£20.00 Single £19.00-£20.00 Double | Open Jan-Dec excl Xmas/New Year B&B + Eve.Meal £29.00-£35.00

Dundonnell, Ross-shire Map Ref: 3G7

B&B

Mrs A Ross

4 Camusnagaul, Dundonnell, Ross-shire, IV23 2QT
Tel: 01854 633237 Fax: 01854 633382

Ideal for walkers and climbers, being close to the An Teallach Mountain Range. Warm welcome assured on working croft.

1 Twin, 1 Double, 1 Family | 1 Ensuite fac, 2 Pub Bath/Show | B&B per person from £16.50 Single from £16.50 Dbl/Twn | Open Jan-Dec

Dunnet Head, Caithness Map Ref: 3D2

B&B

Dunnet Head Tearoom

Brough Village, Dunnet Head, Thurso, Caithness, KW14 8YE
Tel: 01847 851774
E-mail: briansparks@dunnethead.co.uk
Web: www.dunnethead.co.uk

Mainland Britains' most northerly cafe, providing a selection of traditional and vegetarian menus. Bed and breakfast accommodation and evening meal available. Extensive views of the countryside, and of the rocks and stacks, out to the Pentland Firth. Cliff-top walks, with a steep path down to the shore; 3 miles to the Dunnet Head Lighthouse.

2 Double, 1 Family | 1 Ensuite fac, 2 Limited ensuite | B&B per person from £17.00 Single from £17.00 Double Room only per person from £15.00 | Open Mar-Oct B&B + Eve.Meal from £21.00

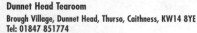

Durness, Sutherland

Map Ref: 4A3

B&B

Orcadia

Lerin, Durness, Sutherland, IV27 4QB
Tel: 01971 511336 Fax: 01971 511382

2 Double
1 Family

B&B per person
£17.00-£20.00 Single
£15.00-£17.00 Double

Open Jan-Dec

Bungalow offering comfortable accomodation with open views, and very close to famous Smoo caves. Ideal base for exploring the rugged North of scotland, with its glorious beaches.

B&B

Puffin Cottage

Durness, Sutherland, IV27 4PN
Tel/Fax: 01971 511208
E-mail: puffincottage@aol.com

2 Double

1 En Suite fac
1 Pub Bath/Show

B&B per person
from £17.00 Double

Open Apr-Sep

A friendly welcome awaits you at this comfortable cottage. En-suite room has sea views. Close to the village, yet in a quiet location. Golf course and beaches only a short distance away. Smoo cave 2 miles away. Hillwalking, bird and wildlife in abundance.

B&B

Smoo Falls

Durness, Sutherland, IV27 4QA
Tel/Fax: 01971 511228
E-mail: mackay@bosinternet.com

2 Twin
1 Double
1 Family

3 Ensuite fac
1 Pub Bath/Show

B&B per person
from £22.00 Single
from £20.00 Dbl/Twn

Open Mar-Oct

Extended croft house situated near to Smoo Cave. Ideal touring base for Northern coast, its beaches, and its other attractions.

Fort Augustus, Inverness-shire

Map Ref: 4A10

B&B

'Sonas'

Inverness Road, Fort Augustus, Inverness-shire, PH32 4DH
Tel: 01320 366291/366797

1 Twin
1 Double
1 Family

All En Suite

B&B per person
from £20.00 Single
from £15.00 Dbl/Twn
Room only per person
from £13.00

Open Jan-Dec

Comfortable modern house in elevated position on the northern edge of the village, with excellent views of surrounding hills. Attractive garden available for guests. Good parking.

B&B

Thistle Dubh

Auchterawe Road, Fort Augustus, Inverness-shire PH32 4BN
Tel: 01320 366380
E.mail: thistledubh@supanet.com

1 Twin
2 Double

All En Suite

B&B per person
from £20.00 Single
£20.00 Dbl/Twn

Open Mar-Nov

Very comfortable rooms in large modern home set in peaceful surroundings on edge of natural woodlands. 10 minutes walk to village, shops, restaurants and canal side.

Important: Prices stated are estimates and may be subject to amendments

Fort Augustus, Inverness-shire — **Map Ref: 4A10**

B&B

Tigh na Mairi

Canalside, Fort Augustus, Inverness-shire, PH32 4BA
Tel/Fax: 01320 366766
Mobile: 07714 337089

1 Twin
2 Double

1 Pub Bath/Show

B&B per person
from £11.00 Single
from £16.00 Double
Room only per person
from £10.00

Open Jan-Dec excl Xmas/NewYear

Detached traditional cottage with outstanding views on the banks of the Caledonian Canal. On the Great Glen cycle route, horseriding, canoeing and boat trips available locally. Vegetarians catered for.

TV P V

Fort William, Inverness-shire — **Map Ref: 3H12**

★★★

B&B

Abrach House

4 Caithness Place, Fort William, Inverness-shire, PH33 6JP
Tel: 01397 702535 Fax: 01397 705629
E-mail: cmoore3050@aol.com

1 Single
1 Double
1 Family

2 En Suite fac
1 Priv.NOT ensuite

B&B per person
from £20.00 Single
from £17.50 Dbl/Twn

Open Jan-Dec excl Xmas

Modern house in elevated position with excellent views over Fort William and surrounding hills and loch. Situated in a quiet cul-de-sac with its own private car park and large garden. There is a good drying room and laundry facilities. On local bus route.

TV P V

B&B

Alt-An Lodge

Achintore Road, Fort William, Inverness-shire, PH33 6RN
Tel: 01397 704546

1 Twin
2 Double

2 En Suite fac
1 Priv.NOT ensuite

B&B per person
£15.00-£22.00 Dbl/Twn

Open Jan-Dec

Comfortable en-suite / private accommodation in friendly B&B overlooking Loch Linnhe. Private parking. Traditional Scottish breakfast and hospitality awaits you.

TV P V

Fort William, Inverness-shire

Map Ref: 3H12

Bardnaclavan
17 Sutherland Avenue, Fort William, Inverness-shire, PH33 6JS
Tel: 01397 704678

1 Single, 1 Twin, 1 Family | 1 En Suite fac, 1 Pub Bath/Show | B&B per person from £18.00 Single, from £17.00 Double | Open Jan-Dec excl Xmas

Family home affording splendid views over Loch Linnhe. 1 mile (2kms) from Fort William town centre with regular bus service. Non smoking. Unrestricted on street parking. A warm welcome and Scottish hospitality awaits you.

Ben Nevis View
Station Road, Corpach, by Fort William, Inverness-shire, PH33 7JH
Tel: 01397 772131

1 Double, 1 Family | All En Suite | B&B per person from £16.00 Double | Open Feb-Oct

Modern house situated on the road to The Isles near the beginning of the Caledonian Canal. Only 3 miles from the centre of Fort William. Beautiful view of Ben Nevis and surrounding hills. Ample private parking, local restaurants/pubs within walking distance. Comfortable guests lounge with sky tv and video.

Mrs E Brady
24 Henderson Row, Fort William, Inverness-shire, PH33 6HT
Tel: 01397 702711

2 Twin | 1 Pub Bath/Show | B&B per person £14.00-£16.00 Single | Open Jan-Dec

In quiet cul-de-sac, ten minutes from town. Both rooms with colour TV and tea-making facilities. Good Scottish hospitality.

Important: Prices stated are estimates and may be subject to amendments

Fort William, Inverness-shire **Map Ref: 3H12**

B&B

Burnlea, Mrs Mairi MacKenzie
Achintore Road, Fort William, Inverness-shire PH33 6RN
Tel: 01397 705063

1 Twin 1 Double 1 Family	All Ensuite	B&B per person £17.50-£25.00 Single	Open Jan-Dec

Burnlea is situated on an elevated site on main road into Fort William with lovely views over Loch Linnhe to hills beyond. Full traditional Scottish breakfast, comfortable rooms all with TV's and tea making facilities. Ideal base for touring the West Highlands. Reduced rates for over winter months. Ample private parking. Families welcome. Friendly, relaxed atmosphere.

TV P C V

B&B

Mrs Fiona Campbell
Leasona, Torlundy, by Fort William, Inverness-shire, PH33 6SN
Tel: 01397 704661
Web: www.host.co.uk

1 Twin 2 Double	2 En Suite fac 1 Priv.NOT ensuite	B&B per person £20.00-£25.00 Single £15.00-£18.00 Dbl/Twn	Open Jan-Dec

Friendly, highland welcome awaits you in our modern family home. Situated in a beautiful Glen setting with outstanding views of Ben Nevis and Aonach Mor ski area. Only 2 1/2 miles from Fort William town centre. Excellent base for hill-walking, skiing, pony trekking and touring. Private parking.

TV P C V

B&B

K C Chisholm
5 Grange Road, Fort William, Inverness-shire, PH33 6JH
Tel: 01397 705548

1 Twin 1 Double	1 Pub Bath/Show	B&B per person from £22.50 Single from £14.00 Dbl/Twn	Open Jan-Dec

Comfortable bed and breakfast accommodation, a few minutes walk from the town centre. Good outlook across Loch Linnhe to the hills beyond. Excellent base for exploring this area; many tips and tours can be planned; other activities include walking, climbing, cycling and much more.

Fort William, Inverness-shire | Map Ref: 3H12

Corrieview

Corrieview, Lochyside
Fort William PH33 7NX
Telephone: 01397 703608

Traditional detached house in quiet residential area close to all amenities. All rooms with private facilities. Open views of Ben Nevis range and Mamore mountains. Well appointed and comfortable rooms and residents lounge. Ample private parking.

B&B

Corrieview

Lochyside, Fort William, Inverness-shire, PH33 7NX
Tel: 01397 703608

1 Twin
2 Double

2 En Suite fac
1 Priv.NOT ensuite

B&B per person
from £17.50 Dbl/Twn

Open Jan-Dec excl
Xmas/New Year

Detached family home in quiet residential area 2 miles (3kms) from Fort William. Convenient for touring West Coast. Ideal base for walkers/skiers and tourers. Ample off-street parking. Drying facilities available.

Fort William, Inverness-shire Map Ref: 3H12

"CROLINNHE"

"Crolinnhe", Grange Road, Fort William PH33 6JF
Telephone: 01397 702709 Fax: 01397 700506
e.mail: crolinnhe@yahoo.com

Spoil yourself with the elegance of Crolinnhe where this grand Victorian house stands proudly overlooking Loch Linnhe. Relax in the tastefully furnished rooms where the attention to detail is clearly visible. Start the day with a varied menu for breakfast in the charming dining room overlooking the loch and the hills beyond. Relax on cooler evenings by log fire with complementary sherry. The town of Fort William is only a 10 minute walk away where you may shop, take a boat trip on Loch Linnhe and more. Ben Nevis, Scotland's highest peak, invites you to a challenging but attainable climb.

Prices from £37.50-£60.00 per person per night.

B&B

'Crolinnhe'

Grange Road, Fort William, Inverness-shire, PH33 6JF
Tel: 01397 702709 Fax: 01397 700506
E-mail: crolinnhe@yahoo.com

1 Twin
2 Double

All En Suite

B&B per person
£37.50-£60.00 Dbl/Twn

Open Mar-Oct

Family run detached Victorian villa c1880, refurbished to a high standard. Friendly and welcoming atmosphere. Large colourful garden. Superb views. Short walk from town centre and all amenities.

V

B&B

Dailanna House

Kinlocheil, Fort William, Inverness-shire, PH33 7NP
Tel/Fax: 01397 722253
E-mail: flo@dailanna.co.uk
Web: www.dailanna.co.uk

2 Twin
1 Family

All En Suite

B&B per person
from £22.00 Single
from £19.50 Twin

Open Feb-Nov
B&B + Eve.Meal
from £32.00

Detached bungalow with large garden in elevated, peaceful position with fine views southwards over Loch Eil to the hills of Ardgour. Enjoy the coulourful sunset skies from out spacious lounge. The Isle of Skye, Morvan and Moidart are all easily accessible along the 'Road to the Isles'.

V

Fort William, Inverness-shire

Map Ref: 3H12

★★★ GUEST HOUSE

Glenlochy Guest House and Apartments

Nevis Bridge, North Road, Fort William, Inverness-shire, PH33 6PF
Tel: 01397 702909

Rooms	Facilities	B&B per person	Open
3 Twin	8 En Suite fac	from £20.00 Single	Open Jan-Dec
5 Double	2 Pub Bath/Show	from £18.00 Dbl/Twn	
2 Family			

Detached house with garden situated at Nevis Bridge, midway between Ben Nevis and the town centre. 0.5 miles (1km) to railway station. 2 annexe rooms.

TV P C £

★★ GUEST HOUSE

Glen Shiel

Achintore Road, Fort William, Inverness-shire, PH33 6RW
Tel/Fax: 01397 702271

Rooms	Facilities	B&B per person	Open
1 Twin	3 En Suite fac	£17.00-£21.00 Dbl/Twn	Open Easter-Oct
3 Double	1 Priv.NOT ensuite		
1 Family			

Modern house on the outskirts of the town with excellent views over Loch Linnhe. All rooms have tea makers and colour TV. Only 1.5 miles from centre of Fort William. Large private car park and garden. Non smoking.

TV P C V

Fort William, Inverness-shire Map Ref: 3H12

THE GRANGE

Grange Road, Fort William, Inverness-shire PH33 6JF
Tel: 01397 705516 Fax: 01397 701595
Web: www.grangefortwilliam.com

Tucked away in its own grounds, The Grange sits quietly overlooking Loch Linnhe yet on y 10 minutes walk from Fort William centre and restaurants. Fresh flowers, log fires and fine food all add to the charm of this special place to stay in the beautiful scenery of the West Highlands.

★★★★★ B&B

The Grange
Grange Road, Fort William, Inverness-shire, PH33 6JF
Tel: 01397 705516 Fax: 01397 701595
Web: www.grangefortwilliam.com

4 Double | All En Suite | B&B per person from £38.00 Double | Open Mar-Oct

Late Victorian house sympathetically renovated within easy walking distance of Fort William (10 minutes). Views over Loch Linnhe. Private parking.

★★★ GUEST HOUSE

Guisachan House
Alma Road, Fort William, Inverness-shire, PH33 6HA
Tel/Fax: 01397 703797
E-mail: info@stablesrooms.fsnet.co.uk

2 Single, 4 Twin, 8 Double, 1 Family | 14 En Suite fac, 1 Priv.NOT ensuite | B&B per person from £18.00 Single, from £18.00 Dbl/Twn | Open Jan-Dec excl Xmas/New Year

Family run establishment situated in its own grounds within easy walking distance of town centre, rail and bus stations. There is a comfortable lounge and well-stocked private bar. Open all year round.

★★★ B&B

'Kamas'
Lower Banavie, Fort William, Inverness-shire, PH33 7LX
Tel: 01397 705911
E-mail: kamas@supanet.com

1 Double, 1 Family | All En Suite | B&B per person £18.00-£20.00 Double | Open Feb-Nov

Modern detached villa 3 miles from centre of Fort William. 2 minutes walk from Banavie in quiet location near Neptunes Staircase with views of Ben Nevis and Aonach Mor. Family room available. Full Scottish breakfast and Highland hospitality.

C V

★★ B&B

Keirlee
36 Grange Road, Fort William, Inverness-shire, PH33 6JF
Tel: 01397 702803
E.mail: keirlee@hotmail.com

1 Family, 1 Double, 1 Twin | 1 Pub Shower | B&B per person from £14.00 Double | Open Jan-Dec

Semi-detached house is in a quiet street close to the centre of Fort William. Plenty to see and do in the area, an excellent base for exploring further afield.

C V

VAT is shown at 17.5%: changes in this rate may affect prices.

Key to symbols is on back flap.

Fort William, Inverness-shire | Map Ref: 3H12

B&B

Mrs E Kennedy
4 Perth Place, Fort William, Inverness-shire, PH33 6UL
Tel: 01397 706118

2 Double | 1 Pub Bath/Show | B&B per person £20.00-£22.00 Single £16.00-£18.00 Double Room only per person from £12.00 | Open Jan-Dec excl Xmas/New Year

Detached house in quiet residential area with picturesque views over Loch Linnhe to the Ardgour Hills.

B&B

Mrs R Kennedy
18 Mamore Crescent, Fort William, Inverness-shire, PH33 6HE
Tel: 01397 703767

2 Single 1 Double | B&B per person from £18.00 Single from £16.00 Double | Open Mar-Oct

Family run B&B located in a quiet residential area within easy walking distance of the town centre, several good restaurants and pubs, and the swimming pool and leisure centre. Convenient also for bus and rail stations. Ideal base for touring Lochaber area.

B&B

Kismet Villa Guest House
Heathercroft, off Argyll Terrace, Fort William, Inverness-shire, PH33 6RS
Tel: 01397 703654

1 Single 2 Twin 1 Double | 2 Pub Bath/Show | B&B per person from £15.00 Single from £15.00 Dbl/Twn | Open Jan-Dec B&B + Eve.Meal from £22.00

A warm welcome awaits you at our bed & breakfast 10 minutes walk from town centre. Comfortable bedrooms with tea trays and TV's. Walkers, skiers and tourers welcome. Ideal base for touring Fort William and Lochaber area. Ample private parking.

Important: Prices stated are estimates and may be subject to amendments

Fort William, Inverness-shire　　Map Ref: 3H12

LAWRIESTONE GUEST HOUSE

Achintore Road, Fort William,
Inverness-shire PH33 6RQ
Tel/Fax: 01397 700777
e.mail: lawriestone@btinternet.com
Web: www.btinternet.com/~lawriestone

Treat yourself to a break in this beautifully maintained fully refurbished elegant Victorian townhouse built in 1885. Situated in its own grounds only 5 minutes walk from the town centre, this family run guest house offers a high standard of accommodation, a friendly Scottish welcome and excellent Scottish breakfasts. Fort William is an ideal touring base with Oban, Mallaig, Isle of Skye, Inverness and Speyside all within easy reach for a day's outing. Non-smoking. Private car park. Sorry no pets.

B&B

Lawriestone Guest House

Achintore Road, Fort William, Inverness-shire, PH33 6RQ
Tel/Fax: 01397 700777
E-mail: lawriestone@btinternet.com
Web: www.btinternet.com/~lawriestone

A warm welcome awaits you at Lawriestone. Our main concern is your comfort and well being. The beautifully furnished rooms are all en-suite with colour TV and tea/coffee making etc. At breakfast a varied selection, including Scottish or vegetarian breakfasts, is available. Come and experience our hospitality and our beautiful location by Loch Linnhe and surrounding hills. Walking, fishing, golf, skiing etc are available locally.

1 Twin
2 Double

All En Suite

B&B per person
from £20.00 Dbl/Twn

Open Jan-Dec

GUEST HOUSE

Lochan Cottage Guest House

Lochyside, Fort William, Inverness-shire, PH33 7NX
Tel/Fax: 01397 702695
E-mail: lochanco@supanet.com

Lochan Cottage Guest House is situated in 1 acre of gardens with panoramic views over Ben Nevis, the highest mountain in Great Britian, and Aonach Mor. Traditional Scottish, vegetarian or continental breakfast. Home cooked 3 course evening meal available using fresh ingredients. Vegetarians catered for. Relax over a bottle of wine in our comfortable conservatory dining room or enjoy a fine Scottish malt in our cosy lounge.

1 Twin
5 Double

All En Suite

B&B per person
from £22.00 Dbl/Twn

Open Jan-Dec
B&B + Eve.Meal
from £34.00

VAT is shown at 17.5%: changes in this rate may affect prices.

Key to symbols is on back flap.

Fort William, Inverness-shire — Map Ref: 3H12

LOCHVIEW HOUSE

Heathercroft Road, Fort William PH33 6RE
Telephone/Fax: 01397 703149
e-mail: info@lochview.co.uk Web: www.lochview.co.uk

Lochview is situated on the hillside above the town in a quiet location with panoramic views over Loch Linnhe and the Ardgour Hills. All bedrooms are tastefully decorated and have private facilities, colour TV and tea/coffee facilities. There is a large garden and private parking.

GUEST HOUSE

Lochview House

Heathercroft, off Argyll Terrace, Fort William, Inverness-shire, PH33 6RE
Tel/Fax: 01397 703149
E-mail: info@lochview.co.uk
Web: www.lochview.co.uk

Situated in a quiet, hillside location above the town giving panoramic views over Loch Linnhe and the Ardgour Hills. Non-smoking house. Only 10 minutes walk from town centre. Ample private parking. Self catering apartment also available.

1 Single, 2 Twin, 5 Double — All En Suite

B&B per person: £25.00-£33.00 Single; £20.00-£26.00 Dbl/Twn

Open May-Sep

Mrs Mary MacLean,
Innishfree, Lochyside,
Fort William PH33 7NX

Innishfree

Telephone: 01397 705471

Modern detached house with attractive landscaped garden in quiet residential area. Breakfast served in conservatory with panoramic views towards Ben Nevis and Aonach Mhor. One family room ensuite and one double room ensuite, both with colour T.V., tea/coffee facilities. Private car parking. A warm Highland welcome awaits you.

B&B

Mrs Mary MacLean

Innishfree, Lochyside, by Fort William, Inverness-shire, PH33 7NX
Tel: 01397 705471

A warm highland welcome awaits you at this modern detached house with attractive landscaped garden located in quiet residential area. Breakfast served in conservatory with panoramic views towards Ben Nevis and Aonach Mhor. All rooms ensuite with colour TV. Private parking. Ideal base to explore the areas glens and lochs.

1 Double, 1 Family — All En Suite

B&B per person: £20.00-£24.00 Double

Open Jan-Dec

GUEST HOUSE

Mansefield House

Corpach, Fort William, Inverness-shire, PH33 7LT
Tel/Fax: 01397 772262
E-mail: mansefield@aol.com

This traditional Scottish Guest House is situated on the 'Road to the Isles' and set in mature gardens with views of the surrounding mountains. We specialise in relaxation, comfort and home cuisine. Being small and select the ambience is special and attention personal and friendly.

1 Twin, 2 Double, 2 Family — All En Suite

B&B per person: from £20.00 Dbl/Twn

Open Jan-Dec excl Xmas; B&B + Eve.Meal from £30.50

Important: Prices stated are estimates and may be subject to amendments

Fort William, Inverness-shire | Map Ref: 3H12

MELANTEE

ACHINTORE ROAD, FORT WILLIAM, INVERNESS-SHIRE PH33 6RW
TEL: 01397 705329 FAX: 01397 700453

Melantee is a comfortable bungalow with picturesque views of Loch Linnhe and the Ardgour Hills. Situated only 1.5 miles south of Fort William town centre, it is near all local amenities, and makes an ideal base for touring the lochs, glens and surrounding highland area.

B&B

Melantee
Achintore Road, Fort William, Inverness-shire, PH33 6RW
Tel: 01397 705329 Fax: 01397 700453

1 Single, 1 Twin, 1 Double, 1 Family | 2 Pub Toilet/Show | B&B per person from £15.50 Single, from £15.50 Dbl/Twn; Room only per person from £12.00 | Open Apr-Mar excl Xmas

Bungalow 1.5 miles (3kms) from town centre, overlooking the shores of Loch Linnhe and the Ardgour hills and on the main A82 road.

W V

B&B

Mrs Vera Moreland
Dalbreac, Mallaig Road, Corpach, by Fort William, Inverness-shire, PH33 7JR
Tel: 01397 772309
E-mail: scottish@globalnet.co.uk

1 Twin, 2 Double | 2 En Suite fac, 1 Priv.NOT ensuite | B&B per person from £18.00 Dbl/Twn | Open Apr-Oct

Receive a warm Scottish welcome in our family bungalow on the road to the Isles. Relax in our comfortable lounge with a cup of tea and homebakes. Homely atmosphere. Ample parking.

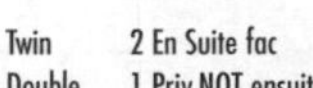

B&B

'Murphy'
2 Blar Mhor Road, Caol, Fort William, PH33 7HT
Tel: 01397 703582
E-mail: Jessie.Murphy@talk21.com

1 Family, 1 Dbl/Twn | B&B per person from £20.00 Single, from £16.50 Dbl/Twn; Room only per person from £10.00 | Open Jan-Dec; B&B + Eve.Meal from £20.00

Terraced house in residential area of Caol, approximately 3 miles from the centre of Fort William. Caledonian Canal and Neptunes staircase just a short walk away. Lochy Bar and Moorings Hotel both offer excellent food and are within easy walkingdistance. Pet friendly.

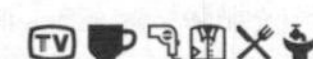

C V

B&B

Nevis View
14 Farrow Drive, Corpach, Fort William, Inverness-shire, PH33 7JW
Tel: 01397 772447 Fax: 01397 772800
E-mail: nevisview@tesconet.com

1 Single, 1 Double, 1 Family | 3 Pub Bath/Show | B&B per person from £18.50 Single, from £14.50 Double | Open Jan-Dec; B&B + Eve.Meal £23.50-£27.50

Friendly family home in quiet residential estate with good views. Home cooking. Vegetarian and vegan diets catered for. Small family room available . Non-smoking house. Excellent touring base.

C W V

Fort William, Inverness-shire

Map Ref: 3H12

Orchy Villa Guest House

Alma Road, Fort William, Inverness-shire PH33 6HA
Tel/Fax: 01397 702445 e.mail: orchyvilla@talk21.com

Comfortable, family run guest house, with panoramic views of the surrounding hills and the Great Glen. Conveniently situated for the town centre, rail and bus stations and leisure centres. Short distance from end of West Highland Way. All rooms have private facilities, colour TV and tea/coffee making facilities. Private parking.

★★

GUEST HOUSE

Orchy Villa Guest House

Alma Road, Fort William, Inverness-shire, PH33 6HA
Tel/Fax: 01397 702445
E-mail: orchyvilla@talk21.com

3 Double All En Suite
1 Family

B&B per person
from £15.00 Single
from £15.00 Double

Open Jan-Dec excl Xmas

Personally run family house in an elevated position conveniently situated for bus and railway stations. Short distance from town centre, swimming pool and leisure centre. Ample private parking. Panoramic views of surrounding hills and the Great Glen.

TV P

C £ W V

QUAICH COTTAGE

Upper Banavie, Fort William PH33 7PB
Tel & Fax: 01397 772799

Our modern detached home on an elevated rural site offers spacious accommodation and a warm friendly welcome. All rooms have uninterrupted views across the Great Glen and Caledonian Canal to Ben Nevis and ski area. The peaceful atmosphere will recharge the batteries. A Taste of Scotland restaurant within walking distance.

★★★

B&B

Quaich Cottage

Upper Banavie, Fort William, Inverness-shire, PH33 7PB
Tel/Fax: 01397 772799
Web: www.host.co.uk

1 Twin All En Suite
1 Double
1 Family

B&B per person
from £18.00 Single
from £18.00 Dbl/Twn

Open Jan-Dec

Modern villa nestling in the hills with spectacular views towards Ben Nevis and Nevis Range. Ideal base for skiers, walkers and climbers and touring North West Highlands. All rooms ensuite. Ample parking. Wide choice for breakfast - both traditional and continental. Easy access to Caledonian Canal. Fort William 4 miles. Banavie 1.5 miles. Drying facilities available.

TV P

V

★★★

B&B

'Rhiw Goch'

Top Locks, Banavie, by Fort William, Inverness-shire, PH33 7LX
Tel/Fax: 01397 772373
E-mail: kay@rhiwgoch.prestel.co.uk

3 Twin All En Suite

B&B per person
£18.00-£25.00 Twin

Open Jan-Dec

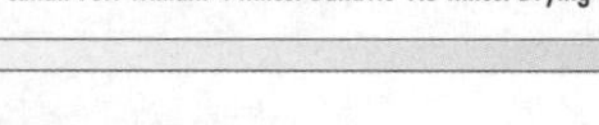

Situated at the top of Neptune's Staircase, 3 miles from Fort William, our ensuite bedrooms have superb views overlooking the Caledonian Canal and beyond to Ben Nevis. We will happily share our knowledge of the area with you. Enjoy the outdoor actvities on offer or simply take in the magnificent scenery. We also hire out mountain bikes and canadian canoes.

V

Important: Prices stated are estimates and may be subject to amendments

Fort William, Inverness-shire | **Map Ref: 3H12**

★★
GUEST HOUSE

Rhu Mhor Guest House

Alma Road, Fort William, Inverness-shire, PH33 6BP
Tel: 01397 702213
E-mail: ian@rhumhor.co.uk

1 Single
2 Twin
2 Double
2 Family

Ensuite fac
Pub Bath/Show

B&B per person
from £17.00 Single
from £16.00 Dbl/Twn

Open Apr-Oct

Large family house with extensive wild garden in quiet area above town. Short distance from town centre and all amenities.

RUSHFIELD HOUSE

Tomonie, Banavie, Fort William PH33 7LX
Tel: 01397 772063 Fax: 01397 772125
e.mail: rushbb0063@aol.com
Web: members.aol.com/rushbb0063/index.html

Modern house with excellent views of Ben Nevis situated within 3 miles of Fort William. All rooms ensuite. TVs, hospitality trays and ample parking. Non-smoking residence. Amenities close by include "Neptunes Staircase" on the Caledonian Canal, "Treasures of the Earth" Museum. Ten minute drive will find you Aonach Mor ski resort and restaurant with some excellent views also in the summer months. The "Jacobite Steam Train" enthusiasts will be able to view the train on its journey to Mallaig from bridge nearby. Fort William centre has many bars/restaurants or within walking distance we also have various bars/restaurants.

★★★
B&B

Rushfield House

Tomonie, Banavie, by Fort William,
Inverness-shire, PH33 7LX
Tel: 01397 772063 Fax: 01397 772125
E-mail: rushbb0063@aol.com
Web: members.aol.com/rushbb0063/index.html

1 Double
2 Family

All En Suite

B&B per person
from £18.00 Dbl/Twn

Open Apr-Oct

Modern bungalow with ground floor bedroom in quiet residential area, close to the canal and Neptune's staircase. Open views of Ben Nevis and Glen Nevis. Good selection of hotels and restaurants within a short distance. Excellent base for exploring the Western Highlands.

★★★
GUEST HOUSE

Stronchreggan View Guest House

Achintore Road, Fort William, Inverness-shire, PH33 6RW
Tel/Fax: 01397 704644
E-mail: patricia@apmac.freeserve.co.uk
Web: www.stronchreggan.co.uk

1 Twin
4 Double

All En Suite

B&B per person
from £20.00 Dbl/Twn

Open Apr-Oct
B&B + Eve.Meal
from £30.00

Stronchreggan View is family run by Archie and Pat McQueen. Modern double glazed house overlooking Loch Linnhe with views of the Ardgour Hills and surrounding countryside. Excellent centre for visiting Oban, Mull, Skye, Aviemore and many other spots.

Fort William, Inverness-shire | Map Ref: 3H12

B&B

Thistle Cottage
Torlundy, Fort William, Inverness-shire. PH33 6SN
Tel: 01397 702428

1 Twin	All En Suite	B&B per person	Open Jan-Dec
2 Double	1 Pub Bath/Show	from £15.00 Dbl/Twn	

A warm highland welcome awaits you in our modern bungalow in quiet location close to Nevis Range. Good base for touring all west coast attractions ski-ing, climbing and walking. Close to golf course. Ample parking. 3 miles from Fort William.

B&B

Torlinnhe
Achintore Road, Fort William, Inverness-shire, PH33 6RN
Tel/Fax: 01397 702583

1 Single	5 En Suite fac	B&B per person	Open Jan-Dec
1 Twin	1 Priv.NOT ensuite	£18.00-£22.00 Single	
2 Double		£18.00-£22,00 Dbl/Twn	
2 Family			

Friendly family run guest house with ample car parking situated 1 mile south of the town centre,on main A82 road. Views of Loch Linnhe and the hills beyond. All rooms en suite or with private bathrooms. Ideal base for touring, walking, climbing and ski-ing.

B&B

Voringfoss
5 Stirling Place, Fort William, Inverness-shire, PH33 6UW
Tel: 01397 704062 Fax: 01397 706151
E-mail: voringfoss@lineone.net

1 Twin	All En Suite	B&B per person	Open Jan-Dec
2 Double		from £20.00 Single	
		from £20.00 Dbl/Twn	

Highland hospitality at its best for those who prefer a quiet situation within one mile of the town centre. Landscaped garden affords panoramic views to surrounding hills. An ideal centre from which to explore the West Highlands. Special diets catered for.

Fort William, Inverness-shire Map Ref: 3H12

Westhaven

Achintore Road, Fort William PH33 6RW
Tel: 01397 705500

Magnificent situation overlooking Loch Linnhe and surrounding hills. Spacious ensuite rooms are furnished to highest standards with colour TV and hospitality tray and each has its own stunning loch view. There is a comfortable residents' lounge, pleasant garden and ample parking. *Perfect base for touring.*

Open March-October ★★★★ **B&B** NO SMOKING

B&B

'Westhaven'

Achintore Road, Fort William, Inverness-shire, PH33 6RW
Tel: 01397 705500

1 Twin 2 Double	All En Suite	B&B per person £19.00-£26.00 Dbl/Twn	Open Mar-Oct

Magnificent situation overlooking Loch Linnhe and surrounding hills. All spacious bedrooms have en-suite facilities, hospitality tray and colour TV complemented by a loch view. Comfortable lounge, ample parking and pleasant garden. Traditional scottish breakfast fayre. Sorry no smoking.

V

WOODLAND HOUSE

Torlundy, Fort William PH33 6SN
Tel: 01397 701698/700250 Fax: 01397 700433

A modern house situated in a beautiful quiet residential area 3 miles north of Fort William on A82. Ensuite rooms available. TV, tea/coffee facilities in all rooms. Central for touring the Highlands. Warm and friendly welcome. Designed for the disabled. Pets welcome by arrangement. Ample parking. Children welcome.

B&B

Woodland House

Torlundy, Fort William, Inverness-shire, PH33 6SN
Tel: 01397 701698/700250 Fax: 01397 700433
E-mail jmatheson@talk21.com

1 Double 1 Family	All En Suite 1 Pub Bath/Show	B&B per person from £18.00 Single from £15.00 Double	Open Jan-Dec excl Xmas/New Year

Modern family home in detached home set in its own grounds, in a semi rural location 10 minutes drive from Fort Willaim town.

TV P

C V

by Fort William, Inverness-shire Map Ref: 3H12

GUEST HOUSE

Carinbrook Guest House
Banavie, by Fort William, Inverness-shire, PH33 7LX
Tel/Fax: 01397 772318

1 Single, 1 Twin, 3 Double | 4 En Suite fac, 1 Priv.NOT ensuite | B&B per person £20.00-£25.00 Single, from £20.00 Dbl/Twn | Open Mar-Oct, B&B + Eve.Meal £30.00-£35.00

Large family house with panoramic views of Ben Nevis and Fort William. Excellent walking area. Ample parking. All home cooking. Evening meals by arrangement. Sorry no pets. No smoking.

B&B

Mrs MacLeod
Clintwood, 23 Hillview Drive, Corpach,
by Fort William, Inverness-shire, PH33 7LS
Tel: 01397 772680 Fax: 01397 772476

1 Twin, 2 Double | All En Suite | B&B per person £22.50-£25.00 Dbl/Twn | Open Mar-Oct

Clintwood is situated within a residential area of the village of Corpach. 4 miles (6 kms) from Fort William, off the road to the Isles. You can be sure of a warm, Highland welcome from your hosts Christine and Ian. Relax in our spacious lounge with fine views of Ben Nevis and surrounding mountains. Ideal base for walks, cruises, golf, fishing and pony trekking or touring the Highlands. We wish to make your stay with us truly memorable.

B&B

Tangusdale
Corpach, by Fort William, Inverness-shire, PH33 7LT
Tel: 01397 772591

1 Double, 1 Family | Ensuite fac, Private bathroom | B&B per person from £15.00 Single, from £18.00 Double, from £15.00 Family | Open Jan-Dec

Modern bungalow with all rooms on the ground floor, close to the canal and Neptune's staircase.Ensuite available. Private car park. TV lounge and tv in bedrooms. All beds have electric blankets. Tea and coffee making facilities. 5 to 6 mins from Fort William.

Important: Prices stated are estimates and may be subject to amendments

by Fort William, Inverness-shire   Map Ref: 3H12

Taormina

Banavie, Fort William PH33 7LY

Telephone: 01397 772217

Taormina is in a quiet situation in Banavie village close to Neptune's Staircase on the Caledonian Canal. From the large garden can be seen Ben Nevis and Aonach Mhor. Banavie Scotrail station and bus halt are five minutes' walk away.

Above all is our aim to make guests feel welcome.

B&B

Taormina

Banavie, Fort William, Inverness-shire, PH33 7LY
Tel: 01397 772217

1 Single
1 Twin
1 Double

1 Pub Bath/Show
1 Pub Toilet

B&B per person
from £15.00 Single
from £15.00 Dbl/Twn

Open Mar-Oct

Taormina is in a quiet situation in Banavie Village close to Neptune's Staircase on the Caledonian Canal. Ben Nevis and Aonach Mor can be seen from the large garden. Banavie Scotrail station and bus halt are five minute's walk away. Several good hotels and pubs locally.

Foyers, Inverness-shire   Map Ref: 4A10

Foyers Bay House

Foyers, Loch Ness, Inverness IV2 6YB

Tel: 01456 486624 Fax: 01456 486337

e.mail: panciroli@foyersbay.freeserve.co.uk Web: www.foyersbay.freeserve.co.uk

Splendid Victorian villa overlooking Loch Ness. Lovely grounds adjoining famous falls of Foyers. Conservatory cafe-restaurant with breathtaking views of Loch Ness. Ideal base for touring the many historical and tourist attractions in this beautiful region. Also six self-catering units within grounds.

GUEST HOUSE

Foyers Bay House

Lower Foyers, Inverness-shire, IV2 6YB
Tel: 01456 486624 Fax: 01456 486337
E.mail: panciroli@foyersbay.freeserve.co.uk
Web: www.foyersbay.freeserve.co.uk

2 Twin
3 Double

All En Suite

B&B per person
from £29.00 Single
from £24.00 Dbl/Twn

Open Jan-Dec
B&B + Eve.Meal
from £33.00

Set in its own 4 acres of wooded pine slopes, rhodedendrons and apple orchard, Foyers Bay House offers 5 rooms all with ensuite facilities. Just 500 yards from the famous Falls of Foyers and situated just by Loch Ness, home of the famous monster.

Gairloch, Ross-shire — Map Ref: 3F7

BRUACH RANNOCH

Pier Road, Gairloch, Ross-shire IV21 2BQ
Tel: 01445 712379

Friendly family home surrounded by acre of natural woodland and garden overlooking Flowerdale Bay. Local access to golf course, sea-angling, walking and many other activities. Hotels and restaurants within walking distance.

★★ B&B

Bruach Rannoch
Pier Road, Gairloch, Ross-shire, IV21 2BQ
Tel: 01445 712379

1 Twin — 1 En Suite fac
1 Double — 1 Priv.NOT ensuite

B&B per person
from £21.00 Single
from £18.00 Dbl/Twn

Open Apr-Oct

A warm and friendly welcome from Joan and Harry at this B&B overlooking Flowerdale Bay, Gairloch. Ideal location for walking, golfing, pony trekking, boat trips (fishing and nature watching) in beautiful Highland scenery.

TV P V

★★★ B&B

Croit Mo Sheanair
29 Strath, Gairloch, Ross-shire, IV21 2DA
Tel: 01445 712389

1 Twin — 1 En Suite fac
1 Double — 1 Pub Bath/Show

B&B per person
from £16.00 Dbl/Twn

Open Mar-Oct

Modern bungalow on a small working croft on outskirts of village. Furnished in an artistic style with original paintings, throughout. Open fire in lounge. Dining room and lounge boast paroramic views of Gairloch Bay and the Isle of Skye. Breakfast includes home-made bread and jams and free-range eggs. Vegetarians welcome. Cosy family atmosphere, where you can relax and feel at home. Various hotels in the area for evening meals.

P C

DUISARY

Strath, Gairloch, Ross-shire IV21 2DA
Tel/Fax: 01445 712252 e.mail: isabel@duisary.freeserve.co.uk

Comfortable accommodation and a true Highland welcome awaits you in modernised crofthouse on the outskirts of village where Gaelic is spoken and a little French and German. Superb views of sea and Torridon Hills. TV and central heating in bedrooms. Close to famous Inverewe Gardens. Idyllic setting with beaches, golf course, swimming and leisure centre nearby. Ideal for hill-walking, bird-watching, fishing or just relaxing.

★★★ B&B

Duisary
Strath, Gairloch, Ross-shire, IV21 2DA
Tel/Fax: 01445 712252
E-mail: isabel@duisary.freeserve.co.uk

1 Twin — 1 En Suite fac
1 Double — 1 Priv.NOT ensuite
1 Family — 2 Pub Bath/Show

B&B per person
from £16.00 Single
from £16.00 Dbl/Twn
from £18.00 Ensuite

Open Apr-Oct

Traditional stone built croft house on edge of village, with fine views across Gairloch to the hills of Torridon. 6 miles from Inverewe Gardens, safe sandy beaches within easy reach. Ideal spot for hill walking, bird watching, fishing or just relaxing.

TV P C W V

Gairloch, Ross-shire Map Ref: 3F7

B&B

Dunedin
42 Strath, Gairloch, Ross-shire, IV21 2DB
Tel: 01445 712050
E-mail: kendunedin@aol.com

A true Highland welcome awaits you at our peaceful home, which enjoys an elevated position in a secluded area on the edge of the village. Our lounge offers a panoramic view over the sea, ranging from Skye to the Torridon mountains. 8 miles from Inverewe Gardens. Many opportunities for fishing and walking, and the attractive 9-hole Golf Course and golden sands are only 2 miles away.

1 Double, 1 Twin | 1 Ensuite fac, 1 Priv.NOT ensuite | B&B per person from £20.00 Single, from £18.00 Dbl/Twn | Open May-Sep

HEATHERDALE
Charleston, Gairloch IV21 2AH
Tel: 01445 712388

A warm welcome awaits at Heatherdale, situated on the outskirts of Gairloch, overlooking the harbour and bay beyond. Within easy walking distance of golf course and sandy beaches. Ideal base for hill-walking. All rooms en-suite facilities, some with seaview. Excellent eating out facilities nearby. Ample parking. Residents lounge with open fire.

B&B

Heatherdale
Charleston, Gairloch, Ross-shire, IV21 2AH
Tel: 01445 712388

Modern detached house on hill on outskirts of Gairloch and overlooking the harbour. Ideal base for a relaxing holiday. Ample space for parking. All bedrooms now ensuite. A warm welcome assured.

1 Twin, 2 Double | All En Suite, 1 Pub Bath/Show | B&B per person from £25.00 Single, from £20.00 Dbl/Twn | Open Feb-Nov

B&B

Kerrysdale House
Gairloch, Ross-shire, IV21 2AL
Tel/Fax: 01445 712292
E-mail: Mac.Kerr@btinternet.com

18c farmhouse recently refurbished and tastefully decorated. Modern comforts in a peaceful setting. 1 mile (2kms) south of Gairloch.

1 Twin, 2 Double | 2 En Suite fac, 1 Priv.NOT ensuite | B&B per person from £20.00 Single, from £20.00 Dbl/Twn | Open Feb-Nov

B&B

Mrs Maclean
Strathlene, 45 Strath, Gairloch, Ross-shire, IV21 2DB
Tel: 01445 712170
E-mail: michael.maclean@virgin.net

Cosy bedrooms in this modern family home with views over Gairloch Bay to the Torridon Hills and Skye. No smoking house. Private parking. Tea tray and TV in bedrooms.

1 Double, 1 Family | All En Suite | B&B per person from £16.00 Dbl/Twn | Open Mar-Nov

Gairloch, Ross-shire

Map Ref: 3F7

B&B

Slioch

Lonemore, Gairloch, Ross-shire, IV21 2DB
Tel: 01445 712110
E-mail: Sylviamackay@eggconnect.net

2 Double | 1 Pub Bath/Show | B&B per person from £16.00 Double | Open May-Sep

Small and friendly, situated in an elevated position approx 1.5 miles from Gairloch. Superb views to the Golf Course and Hills beyond. Non-smoking house.

GUEST HOUSE

Whindley Guest House

Auchtercairn Brae, Gairloch, Ross-shire, IV21 2BN
Tel/Fax: 01445 712340

1 Twin, 1 Double, 1 Family | All En Suite | B&B per person from £25.00 Single, from £19.00 Dbl/Twn | Open Jan-Dec excl Xmas/New Year, B&B + Eve.Meal from £33.00

Modern bungalow with large garden in elevated position, with fine views overlooking Gairloch Bay, and across to Skye. Beach and golf course nearby. Evening meals by arrangement. Non smoking house.

Garve, Ross-shire

Map Ref: 4A8

B&B

'Birch Cottage'

Station Road, Garve, Ross-shire, IV23 2PS
Tel/Fax: 01997 414237
Web: www.SmoothHound.co.uk/hotels/birchcot.html

1 Twin, 2 Double | All En Suite, 1 Pub Bath/Show | B&B per person from £17.00 Single, from £15.00 Double, Room only from £24.00 per room | Open Feb-Nov

Traditional Highland cottage en route to Gairloch/Ullapool. Refurbished to a high standard. Garve railway station 50 metres. Two annexe bedrooms.

Important: Prices stated are estimates and may be subject to amendments

Gairloch, Ross-shire | Map Ref: 3F7

B&B

Mr & Mrs S Doyle

4 Mossford Cottages, Loch Luichart, Garve, Ross-shire, IV23 2QA
Tel: 01997 414334

A warm welcome awaits you at Mossford cottages, formerly 2 workers cottages, with panoramic views across Loch Luichart. Close to Loch Luichart railway station and 29 miles from Inverness or 36 miles to Ullapool. An ideal base for walking holidays and exploring Ross-shire. Evening meal available by prior arrangement.

1 Double	Ensuite fac	B&B per person	Open Jan-Dec excl
1 Family	Ensuite fac	from £18.00 Single	Xmas/New Year
1 Twin	Private fac	from £18.00 Dbl/Twn	B&B + Eve.Meal
1 Single	Private fac	Room only per person	from £24.00
		from £15.00	

V

Glencoe, Argyll | Map Ref: 1F1

B&B

Dorrington Lodge

Tighphuirst, Glencoe, Argyll, PH49 4HN
Tel: 01855 811653 Fax: 01855 811995
E-mail: hiltons@clara.co.uk

Comfortable, modern house just off main road, with excellent views over Loch Leven. Home cooked meals using quality local produce. Restricted smoking.

1 Twin	All En Suite	B&B per person	Open Apr-Oct
2 Double		from £17.50 Dbl/Twn	B&B + Eve.Meal
			from £28.00

V

B&B

Gleann Leac Na Muidhe

Glencoe, Argyll, PH49 4LA
Tel/Fax: 01855 811598
E-mail: jeffanna@namuidhe.freeserve.co.uk
Web: www.namuidhe.freeserve.co.uk

Experience the mountains from the doorstep. A warm welcome awaits you at this peaceful highland retreat situated 1 mile along a private road in the heart of the glen with stunning views all around. Feel the history, being a short distance from the remains of Maclains summer house where the chief of the MacDonald Clan met his death in the Glencoe Massacre of 1692. An ideal base for tourists, walkers and climbers alike. Vegetarians catered for.

2 Double	1 En Suite fac	B&B per person	Open Jan-Dec excl
	1 Priv.NOT ensuite	from £25.00 Single	Xmas/New Year
		from £20.00 Double	

V

Glencoe, Argyll

Map Ref: 1F1

B&B

Mrs K Rodger
An Darag, Upper Carnoch, Glencoe, Argyll, PH49 4HU
Tel: 01855 811643

1 Twin, 2 Double — All En Suite — B&B per person £17.00-£21.00 Dbl/Twn — Open Jan-Oct

Modern bungalow set on edge of Glencoe village with panoramic views of mountains all around. Comfortable ensuite bedrooms with TV's and tea trays. Outdoor enthusiasts welcome and advice available on local climbs/walks from our resident member of mountain rescue team. Packed lunches available. Enjoy outstanding mountain views from our breakfast room. Non smoking house.

C

GUEST HOUSE

Scorrybreac Guest House
Glencoe, Argyll, PH49 4HT
Tel/Fax: 01855 811354
E-mail: john@scorrybreac.freeserve.co.uk

3 Twin, 3 Double — 5 En Suite fac, 1 Priv.NOT ensuite — B&B per person £18.00-£40.00 Single, £16.00-£22.00 Dbl/Twn — Open 27Dec-Oct

Scorrybreac is a comfortable single storey guest house in beautiful woodland surroundings, overlooking Loch Leven, in a quiet secluded location on the edge of village, near local forest walks. Ideal base for exploring Glencoe and Ben Nevis area or for a shorter stay on a more extended tour of the Highlands. Colourful garden. Ample parking.

V

GUEST HOUSE

Strathlachlan, The Glencoe Guest House
Upper Carnoch, Glencoe, Argyll, PH49 4HU
Tel: 01855 811244 Fax: 01855 811873
E-mail: gh@glencoe-scotland.co.uk

1 Single, 2 Twin, 3 Double, 2 Family — 6 Ensuite fac, 2 Priv.NOT ensuite — B&B per person from £17.00 Single, from £17.00 Dbl/Twn — Open Jan-Dec

Strathlachlan is a modern, whitewashed bungalow standing on former croft land in a quiet, peaceful setting overlooking the River Coe. The guest house lies at the end of a cul-de-sac on the edge of Glencoe Village and only two minutes walk from the monument marking the site of the infamous massacre. Spectacular views in all directions. Popular with walkers, climbers and skiers who tell interesting stories round the fireside at the end of the day.

V

Golspie, Sutherland

Map Ref: 4B6

B&B

Mrs Barabra Melville
'Sgeir-An-Or', Station Road, Golspie, Sutherland, KW10 6SN
Tel: 01408 633231

2 Double, 1 Twin — Ensuite, Private facilities — B&B per person £20.00-£25.00 Single, £17.50-£20.00 Dbl/Twn — Open Jan-Dec

Modern detached bungalow in the coastal village of Golspie. Excellent ensuite rooms with the warmest of Highland welcomes. An ideal base for all outdoor pursuits. Dunrobin Castle and Timespan Centre all nearby.

C V

Grantown-on-Spey, Moray   Map Ref: 4C9

Bank House

1 The Square, Grantown-on-Spey, Moray PH26 3HG
Telephone: 01479 873256

Centrally situated. A few minutes walk from the renowned River Spey and golf course. Ideal for the whisky trail, bird watching fishing, golfing, walking and horse riding. The Bank House offers very spacious family rooms, comfortably heated with TV, tea/coffee facilities and armchairs. Cot and high chair provided. Children welcome. Full Scottish breakfast.

★★★
B&B

Bank House
1 The Square, Grantown-on-Spey, Moray, PH26 3HG
Tel: 01479 873256

1 Twin	1 Priv.NOT ensuite	B&B per person	Open Mar-Dec
1 Double	1 Pub Bath/Show	from £20.00 Single	
1 Family		from £17.00 Dbl/Twn	

Former Bank Manager's flat offering very spacious comfortable heated accommodation. Ideal touring base. Warm and friendly welcome assured. Centrally situated for whisky trail, golfing, fishing and bird watching.

C V

★★★
B&B

Crann-Tara Guest House
High Street, Grantown-on-Spey, Moray, PH26 3EN
Tel: 01479 872197

1 Single	2 Pub Bath/Show	B&B per person	Open Jan-Dec excl Xmas
1 Twin		from £17.00 Single	B&B + Eve.Meal
3 Family		from £17.00 Twin	from £27.00
		Room only per person	
		from £15.00	

19c town house, recently modernised and personally run. Near River Spey, with rod storage and drying room. Cycle hire and repair. Off-street car parking. Dinner available.

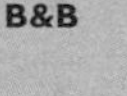

VAT is shown at 17.5%: changes in this rate may affect prices.

Key to symbols is on back flap.

Grantown-on-Spey, Moray | Map Ref: 4C9

Culdearn House

WOODLANDS TERRACE
GRANTOWN-ON-SPEY PH26 3JU
Tel: 01479 872106 Fax: 01479 873641
e.mail: culdearn@globalnet.co.uk
Web: www.culdearn.com

AA ★★

Elegant Country House offering a warm welcome from the Scottish hosts Isobel and Alasdair Little who provide freshly prepared food and modestly priced wines. All guest rooms have ensuite private facilities with colour TV, radio, hairdryer and welcome tray. Culdearn House has been modernised and decorated with sympathy to offer a high standard of comfort. Ideal location for fishing, golf, riding, walking, bird-watching and visiting castles and historic sites. Log fires in season. Three and seven day breaks available; all rates include dinner.

AA/RAC ★★

"RAC Hotel of the Year" 1996

Please contact Isobel and Alasdair Little for reservations.

GOLD

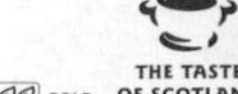

HOTEL

Culdearn House Hotel

Woodlands Terrace, Grantown-on-Spey, Moray-shire, PH26 3JU
Tel: 01479 872106 Fax: 01479 873641
E.mail: culdearn@globalnet.co.uk
Web: www.culdearn.com

1 Single
3 Twin
5 Double

All En Suite

Open Mar-Oct
B&B + Eve.Meal
£49.00-£75.00 pppn

Elegant Victorian house, retaining many original features and caringly restored to include all modern comforts. Warm and friendly atmosphere. All rooms ensuite facilities. Taste of Scotland member. Award winning kitchen. Interesting wine list and unique collection of malt whisky.

GUEST HOUSE

Dunallan House

Woodside Avenue, Grantown-on-Spey, PH26 3PA
Tel/Fax: 01479 872140
Web: www.dunallan.mcmail.com

1 Single
3 Twin
3 Double

6 En Suite fac
1 Priv.NOT ensuite

B&B per person
from £30.00 Single
from £22.00 Dbl/Twn

Open Jan-Dec
B&B + Eve.Meal
from £30.00

Dunallan is a splendid example of Victorian elegance oozing with the charm of a bygone era. Original period fireplaces are in the residents lounge and dining room, giving extra warmth to cheer you on those cooler evenings. Home cooking, featuring fresh local produce.

Important: Prices stated are estimates and may be subject to amendments

Grantown-on-Spey, Moray — Map Ref: 4C9

FIRHALL GUEST HOUSE

Grant Road, Grantown-on-Spey, Morayshire PH26 3LD
Tel/Fax: 01479 873097 e.mail: firhall@cs.com
Web: www.SmoothHound.co.uk/hotels/firhall.html

A warm friendly welcome awaits you at Firhall. Situated in the heart of the Highlands, Grantown is ideally placed for the malt whisky trail, historic castles, golf, fishing and the breathtaking local scenery. The town centre, golf course, forest trails and River Spey are just a short walk away.

GUEST HOUSE

Firhall Guest House

Grant Road, Grantown-on-Spey, Moray, PH26 3LD
Tel/Fax: 01479 873097
E-mail: firhall@cs.com
Web: www.SmoothHound.co.uk/hotels/firhall.html

Firhall is a fine example of victorian elegance, retaining much of the original character of this period. Particular features include the beautifully preserved pitched pine woodwork, ornate cornices and marble fireplaces. Home cooking. Family run.

Rooms	Facilities	B&B per person	Open
1 Single	3 En Suite fac	£17.00-£25.00 Single	Open Jan-Dec excl Xmas
1 Twin	1 Priv.NOT ensuite	£17.00-£25.00 Dbl/Twn	B&B + Eve.Meal
1 Double	1 Pub Bath/Show		£27.00-£35.00
3 Family			

GUEST HOUSE

Garden Park Guest House

Woodside Avenue, Grantown-on-Spey, Moray, PH26 3JN
Tel: 01479 873235

Victorian, stone built house set in own colourful garden, quietly located a short walk from the centre of Grantown on Spey. Guests' lounge with log-burning stove; home cooked meals made with fresh produce served in the dining room with its individual tables. A short selection of wines is available. Five ensuite rooms, one of which is on the ground floor. Dispense bar. French spoken.

Rooms	Facilities	B&B per person	Open
3 Twin	All En Suite	from £22.00 Single	Open Mar-Oct
2 Double		from £22.00 Dbl/Twn	B&B + Eve.Meal
			from £32.00

GUEST HOUSE

Parkburn Guest House

High Street, Grantown-on-Spey, Moray, PH26 3EN
Tel: 01479 873116

Semi detached Victorian villa standing back from main road with ample parking available. Fishing and fishing tuition can be arranged.

Rooms	Facilities	B&B per person	Open
2 Single	3 En Suite fac	from £20.00 Single	Open Jan-Dec
2 Twin	1 Limited ensuite	from £20.00 Dbl/Twn	
1 Double	1 Pub Bath/Show		

Grantown-on-Spey, Moray

Map Ref: 4C9

Rossmor Guest House

WOODLANDS TERRACE, GRANTOWN-ON-SPEY PH26 3JU
Tel/Fax: 01479 872201 e.mail: dennis.day@virgin.net
Web: http://freespace.virgin.net/dennis.day/rossmor.html

Splendid Victorian villa, with many original features, where a warm welcome with personal friendly service awaits you. Spacious and comfortable guest rooms, all ensuite. A non-smoking house. Ideal location for touring the many distilleries, castles, Moray Firth coast, Cairngorms and RSPB reserves.

★★★★ GUEST HOUSE

Rossmor Guest House
Woodlands Terrace, Grantown-on-Spey, Moray, PH26 3JU
Tel/Fax: 01479 872201
E-mail: dennis.day@virgin.net
http://freespace.virgin.net/dennis.day/rossmor.html

2 Twin, 4 Double — All En Suite

B&B per person: from £25.00 Single; from £21.00 Dbl/Twn

Open Mar-Nov

Spacious Victorian detached house with original features and large garden. A warm welcome. Parking. Panoramic views. No smoking throughout.

★★★ GUEST HOUSE

Strathallan House
Grant Road, Grantown-on-Spey, Morayshire, PH26 3LD
Tel/Fax: 01479 872165

1 Single, 1 Twin, 2 Double, 1 Family — 4 En Suite fac, 1 Priv.NOT ensuite

B&B per person: from £20.00 Single; from £20.00 Dbl/Twn

Open Mar-Oct. B&B + Eve.Meal from £33.00

Victorian house, retaining original features and offering a high standard of comfort. On quiet side road, yet within easy walking distance to all local amenities. Ideal touring base.

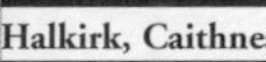

Halkirk, Caithness

Map Ref: 4D3

★★ B&B

Mrs Margaret G Banks
Glenlivet, Fairview, Halkirk, Caithness, KW12 6XF
Tel: 01847 831302

2 Twin, 1 Double — All En Suite

B&B per person: from £16.00 Dbl/Twn

Open Jan-Dec excl Xmas/New Year

Modern house on outskirts of the village, close to river and 6 miles (10kms) South of Thurso.

★★★★ B&B

The Bungalow Bannochmore
Harpsdale, Halkirk, Caithness, KW12 6UN
Tel: 01847 841216

1 Twin, 2 Double — All En Suite

B&B per person: from £21.00 Single; from £19.00 Dbl/Twn

Open Apr-Oct

Modern detached house on a working farm in a quiet rural setting, 0.75 mile (1.5kms) from salmon fishing on River Thurso. All rooms ensuite.

Important: Prices stated are estimates and may be subject to amendments

Halkirk, Caithness

Map Ref: 4D3

★★★
B&B

Sordale House

Sordale (on A9), nr Halkirk, Caithness, KW12 6XB
Tel: 01847 831270 Fax: 01847 831971
E-mail: peter.p.j.rodgers@talk21.com

1 Twin 2 Double	2 Pub Bath/Show	B&B per person from £18.00 Single from £17.00 Dbl/Twn	Open Jan-Dec excl Xmas/New Year B&B + Eve.Meal from £26.00

19th Century farmhouse, modernised yet retaining its character, located 4 miles from the town of Thurso. Very convenient for the Orkney ferry at Scrabster; good base for exploring the coastline and inland areas of Caithness and north Sutherland; fishing, birdwatching, walking, plus much more.

C V

B&B

Varrich

Sordale, Halkirk, Caithness, KW12 6UU
Tel: 01847 831481

1 Twin 1 Double 1 Family	2 En Suite fac 1 Pub Bath/Show	B&B per person £18.00-£20.00 Dbl/Twn	Open Apr-Sep

Spacious modern house situated 6 miles south of Thurso, and 2 miles from the village of Halkirk. Excellent base for exploring the far north coast and the flow country. Walking, fishing, birdwatching all available in the area. Good stopover point for the Orkney Ferry.

C V

Helmsdale, Sutherland

Map Ref: 4C5

★★★
B&B

Broomhill House

Navidale Road, Helmsdale, Sutherland, KW8 6JS
Tel/Fax: 01431 821259

1 Twin 1 Double	All En Suite	B&B per person from £18.00 Dbl/Twn	Open Mar-Oct B&B + Eve.Meal from £29.00

Victorian stone built house with turret. Magnificent panoramic view over Helmsdale to the sea. Local heritage centre and art gallery in the village. Harbour nearby. Ideal base for exploring the far north, or for stopping off en-route to Orkney. Golf, tennis, squash, indoor bowls, sea and river angling available nearby.

C W V

B&B

Torbuie

Navidale, Helmsdale, Sutherland, KW8 6JS
Tel: 01431 821424

1 Twin 1 Double	All En Suite	B&B per person from £20.00 Single from £18.00 Dbl/Twn	Open Apr-Oct

Well appointed modernised croft house, with spacious bedrooms. Situated on the edge of Helmsdale, with superb views over the Moray Firth. Good stopping off point en route to Orkney; excellent base for exploring the far north and west Highlands.

C V

B&B

Toshlair

Strathnaver Street, Helmsdale, Sutherland, KW8 6JH
Tel/Fax: 01431 821485

1 Single 1 Twin 1 Family	1 Pub Bath/Show	B&B per person from £15.00 Single from £15.00 Twin Room only per person from £10.00	Open Mar-Oct

Comfortable bed and breakfast accommodation in the centre of the village of Helmsdale. Harbour and local heritage centre nearby. Fishing available locally. Collection from the railway station can be arranged.

C V

Insh, Inverness-shire

Map Ref: 4C10

★★★ B&B

Greenfield Croft

Insh, by Kingussie, Inverness-shire, PH21 1NT
Tel: 01540 661010 Fax: 01540 662377
E-mail: farmhouse@kincraig.com

1 Twin | All En Suite | B&B per person | Open Jan-Dec
2 Double | | from £20.00 Single | B&B + Eve.Meal
| | from £17.00 Dbl/Twn | from £30.00

Recently built bungalow on a working croft in quiet Highland village with superb views. Home cooking, log fire, all rooms with ensuite facilities. Evening meal available by arrangement.

Invergarry, Inverness-shire

Map Ref: 3H11

FOREST LODGE

South Laggan, Invergarry, by Spean Bridge, Inverness-shire PH34 4EA
Tel: 01809 501219 Fax: 01809 501476
e.mail: info@flgh.co.uk Web: www.flgh.co.uk

Staying one night or more, Ian and Janet Shearer's comfortable home offers pleasant ensuite accommodation, relaxed surroundings and home cooking served with friendly attention. Forest Lodge is conveniently situated in the centre of the Great Glen and is ideal for touring or participating in outdoor pursuits.

★★★ GUEST HOUSE

Forest Lodge

South Laggan, by Spean Bridge, Inverness-shire, PH34 4EA
Tel: 01809 501219 Fax: 01809 501476
E-mail: info@flgh.co.uk
Web: www.flgh.co.uk

2 Twin | 6 En Suite fac | B&B per person | Open Jan-Dec excl
3 Double | 1 Priv.NOT ensuite | £17.00-£21.00 Dbl/Twn | Xmas/New Year
2 Family | | | B&B + Eve.Meal
| | | £29.00-£33.00

Staying in the Great Glen for one night or more? Situated where the Caledonian Canal joins Loch Lochy and Oich. We offer pleasant, ensuite accommodation and home cooking in our relaxed and friendly home. Open all year for touring, walking or just to relax. Please call for a brochure.

★★★ B&B

Mrs H Fraser

Ardfriseal, Mandally Road, Invergarry, Inverness-shire, PH35 4HP
Tel: 01809 501281

1 Twin | 1 Pub Bath/Show | B&B per person | Open May-Oct
1 Double | | from £18-£20.00 Single |
| | £16.00 Dbl/Twn |

Modern family home in secluded area with magnificent views of surrounding hills. 1 mile (2kms) from Invergarry. Close to the Great Glen cycle route. Walkers and cyclists welcome. Ample private parking.

★★★ B&B

Lilac Cottage

South Laggan, by Spean Bridge, Inverness-shire, PH34 4EA
Tel: 01809 501410
E-mail: lilac.cottage@virgin.net

1 Twin | 1 Pub Bath/Show | B&B per person | Open Jan-Dec
1 Double | | from £16.00 Single |
| | from £16.00 Dbl/Twn |

Modernised 100 year old croft. Tour our beautiful area. Visit Loch Ness, climb Ben Nevis. Forest walks nearby. Go hill walking and come home to a warm welcome in comfortable accommodation. Lounge with colour TV and video. Only 3 miles from Invergarry.

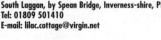

Important: Prices stated are estimates and may be subject to amendments

Invergordon, Ross-shire

Map Ref: 4B7

★★ B&B

Tigh-na-Coille
10 Ross Crescent, Milton, Kildary, Invergordon, Ross-shire, IV18 0PS

1 Twin, 1 Double | 1 Shower | B&B per person from £20.00 Single, from £22.00 Dbl/Twn; Room only per person from £12.00 | Open May-Oct

Modern family home in historic village of Milton only 5 miles north of Invergordon and 28 miles north of Inverness. Good base for touring the area.

Inverness

Map Ref: 4B8

★★★ GUEST HOUSE

Aberfeldy Lodge Guest House
11 Southside Road, Inverness, IV2 3BG
Tel: 01463 231120 Fax: 01463 234741
E-mail: class@algh.freeserve.co.uk
Web: www.SmoothHound.co.uk/hotels/aberfeld.html

2 Twin, 3 Double, 4 Family | All En Suite | Open Jan-Dec

Comfortable Guest House close to city centre. All rooms ensuite. Hearty breakfast, vegetarians catered for and children welcome. Private car park.

C V

★★★ B&B

Advie Lodge
31 Crown Drive, Inverness, IV2 3QQ
Tel: 01463 237247
E-mail: juneinverness@talk21.com

1 Single, 1 Twin, 1 Double | 2 En Suite fac, 1 Priv.NOT ensuite | Open Jan-Dec

Traditional town house in quiet residential area of Inverness, offering ensuite rooms and private parking. Within walking distance of the town centre and River Ness.

C V

★★ B&B

'An Airidh'
65 Fairfield Road, Inverness, IV3 5LH
Tel: 01463 240673 Fax: 01463 234447

1 Twin, 1 Double, 1 Family | 1 En Suite fac, 1 Pub Bath/Show | B&B per person from £15.00 Single, from £14.00 Dbl/Twn | Open Nov-Sep excl Xmas/New Year

Family home in quiet residential area. Short walking distance from town centre, restaurants, railway station, Eden Court Theatre. 7 miles to Loch Ness.

C V

Inverness — Map Ref: 4B8

B&B

Ardgowan
45 Fairfield Road, Inverness, IV3 5QP
Tel: 01463 236489
E-mail: margaret.shields@ukonline.co.uk

1 Twin, 1 Double, 1 Family — All En Suite — B&B per person from £17.00 Dbl/Twn — Open Jan-Dec

A large semi-detached house with spacious rooms within ten minutes walk of the town centre.

Ardgowan Lodge

Wester Phoineas, by Beauly, Inverness-shire IV4 7BA
Tel: 01463 741745 Fax: 01463 741745
Web: www.ardgowanlodge.co.uk

Ardgowan Lodge part of a former Victorian coach-house and stables, sits peacefully in two acres of secluded gardens. Beauly with its historic priory is an ideal base for exploring The Highlands. Enjoy comfort and hospitality at its very best and *'Bide a While'* in this glorious part of Scotland.

B&B

Ardgowan Lodge
Wester Phoineas, by Beauly, Inverness-shire, IV4 7BA
Tel/Fax: 01463 741745
Web: www.ardgowanlodge.co.uk

1 Twin, 2 Double — 2 En Suite fac, 1 Priv.NOT ensuite — B&B per person from £20.00 Dbl/Twn — Open Mar-Oct, B&B + Eve.Meal from £35.00

Converted Victorian Coach House and Stables set in 2 acres, secluded gardens, large residents lounge with exposed beams and wood burning stove, bedrooms have colour TV and tea and coffee making facilities.

GUEST HOUSE

Ardmuir House Hotel
16 Ness Bank, Inverness, IV2 4SF
Tel/Fax: 01463 231151
E-mail: hotel@ardmuir.com
Web: www.ardmuir.com

1 Single, 2 Twin, 5 Double, 2 Family — All En Suite — B&B per person from £34.50 Single, from £28.50 Dbl/Twn — Open Jan-Dec excl Xmas/New Year

Family run hotel on the bank of the River Ness close to town centre and Ness Islands. Conveniently situated for exploring the Highlands.

B&B

'Aros'
5 Abertarff Road, Inverness, IV2 3NW
Tel: 01463 235674

1 Double, 2 Family — All En Suite — B&B per person from £20.00 Double — Open Jan-Dec excl Xmas/New Year

Situated only 5 minutes walk from town centre, train and bus stations. A cheerful Highland welcome awaits you at this comfortable Victorian home. Ground floor room available.

Inverness Map Ref: 4B8

★★★
B&B

Atherstone Guest House
42 Fairfield Road, Inverness, IV3 5QD
Tel: 01463 240240

2 Single
2 Double

All En Suite

B&B per person
£18.00-£20.00 Single
£18.00-£20.00 Double

Open Jan-Dec

Attractively decorated and comfortably furnished with a homely atmosphere. All rooms ensuite. Private parking.

★
B&B

Avish B&B
80 Telford Road, Inverness, IV3 8HN
Tel: 01463 240502

2 Single
1 Twin
1 Double

2 Pub Bath/Show
1 Priv.NOT ensuite

B&B per person
from £12.00 Single
from £12.00 Dbl/Twn
Room only per person
from £10.00

Open Jan-Dec excl Xmas/New Year

Family home in quiet residential area. Short walk from town centre and all facilities. Smoking restricted.

★★
B&B

Balcroydon
6 Broadstone Park, Inverness, IV2 3LA
Tel: 01463 221506

1 Single
1 Twin
1 Family

All private fac

B&B per person
£21.00-£25.00 Single
£20.00-£24.00 Fam/Twn

Open Jan-Dec excl Xmas/New Year

Semi-detached house in quiet residential road, 5 minutes walk from town centre, bus and railway station. Off road parking.

Inverness Map Ref: 4B8

B&B

Balthangie B&B

37 Ballifeary Lane, Inverness, IV3 5PH
Tel: 01463 237637 Fax: 01463 224780
E-mail: les.d@zetnet.co.uk

1 Twin	All En Suite	B&B per person	Open Jan-Dec
2 Double		from £22.00 Dbl/Twn	

Modern family home in quiet residential area, within walking distance of town centre and all amenities. All the rooms are ensuite. Close to Eden Court Theatre, Sports Centre and Aquadome.

B&B

'Bonnieview'

Tower Brae (North), Westhill, Inverness, IV2 5FE
Tel: 01463 792468

1 Single	All En Suite	B&B per person	Open Jan-Dec
1 Twin	1 Pub Bath/Show	from £22.00 Single	B&B + Eve.Meal
1 Double		from £22.00 Dbl/Twn	from £34.00

Friendly welcome at this modern house quietly located overlooking the Moray Firth. 2 miles (3kms) from Culloden Moor, 4 miles (6kms) from Inverness. Evening meal on request.

Inverness — Map Ref: 4B8

B&B

Braehead
5 Crown Circus, Inverness, IV2 3NH
Tel: 01463 224222
E-mail: Ian.Mackenzie@tinyworld.co.uk

1 Single, 1 Double, 1 Family | 1 En Suite fac, 1 Pub Bath/Show | B&B per person from £20.00 Single, from £18.00 Double | Open Jan-Dec excl Xmas/New Year

Traditional stone built Victorian villa in residential area of Inverness with easy access to town centre and all amenities. Non-smoking.

B&B

Bridge House B&B
Bridge House, 19 Harris Road, Inverness, IV2 3LS
Tel: 01463 714770
E-mail: r.stewart@easynet.co.uk

2 Single, 1 Twin | 1 Pub Bath/Show | B&B per person from £18.00 Single | Open Jan-Dec

Family home in modern bungalow situated in quiet residential area.

B&B

Broadstone Lodge
1 Broadstone Park, Inverness, IV2 3JZ
Tel: 01463 231822

1 Single, 3 Twin, 1 Double, 1 Family | 2 Pub Bath/Show | B&B per person from £16.00 Single, from £16.00 Dbl/Twn | Open Jan-Dec excl Xmas/New Year

Detached villa in quiet residential area but near the centre of town. Scots Pine is a feature of the house.

B&B

Bunillidh Bed & Breakfast
47 Montague Row, Inverness, IV3 5DX
Tel: 01463 225079

1 Single, 1 Double, 1 Family | 1 Ensuite fac, 1 Pub Bath/Show | B&B per person from £16.00 Single, from £16.00 Dbl/Twn | Open Jan-Dec

Family home in quiet residential area, 5 minutes walk from Eden Court Theatre. Dinner by prior arrangement. One ensuite bedroom. 10 minutes to town centre and Railway and Bus Station.

B&B

Cambeth Lodge
49 Fairfield Road, Inverness, IV3 5QP
Tel: 01463 231764
E-mail: duffcambeth@tinyworld.co.uk

1 Twin, 2 Double | 1 En Suite fac, 1 Pub Bath/Show, 1 Priv.NOT ensuite | B&B per person from £16.00 Dbl/Twn | Open Jan-Dec excl Xmas/New Year

Victorian stone building with private parking in quiet residential area. 10 minutes walk to town centre. A warm Scottish welcome assured.

Inverness — **Map Ref: 4B8**

★★★

B&B

Mrs L Cameron

Tay Villa, 40 Harrowden Road, Inverness, IV3 5QN
Tel: 01463 232984

1 Twin 1 Double	All En Suite 1 Pub Bath	B&B per person from £18.00 Dbl/Twn	Open Mar-Nov

Stone built house, in quiet residential area, yet within easy walking distance to town centre. Ideal base for exploring Loch Ness, Moray Coast and Whisky Trail.

V

Carbisdale

43 Charles Street, Inverness, IV2 3AH
Tel/Fax: 01463 225689
E-mail: bettycarbisdale@hotmail.com

1 Twin 2 Double	2 Pub Bath/Show	B&B per person from £18.00 Dbl/Twn	Open Jan-Dec

Terraced family home furnished to high standard. Warm welcome. Close to town centre, and easy walk from rail station.

W V

Clach Mhuilinn

7 Harris Road, Inverness, IV2 3LS
Tel: 01463 237059 Fax: 01463 242092
E-mail: JACQI@ness.co.uk
Web: www.ness.co.uk

1 Twin Suite 1 Double	Both en suite	B&B per person from £45.00 Single £26.00-£31.00 Dbl/Twn	Open Mar-Nov

Excellent, welcoming B&B hospitality, non-smokers only, in Inverness residential area. Two charming bedrooms: one double, one twin suite, each with en-suite shower room, TV, hairdryer, tea/coffee tray and many extra touches to make your stay special.

£ W V

The Cottage

6a Bruce Gardens, Inverness, IV3 5EN
Tel/Fax: 01463 240253
E-mail: cottage@dircon.co.uk

1 Twin 1 Double	All En Suite	B&B per person from £50.00 Single £26.00-£30.00 Dbl/Twn	Open Apr-mid Oct

Modern cottage in traditional style, close to town centre, river walks and theatre. Tastefully decorated throughout, with both bedrooms having bath and shower ensuite. A warm welcome awaits you, with many guests returning each year.

£ V

Important: Prices stated are estimates and may be subject to amendments

Inverness — Map Ref: 4B8

★★★

GUEST HOUSE

Craigside Lodge

**4 Gordon Terrace, Inverness, IV2 3HD
Tel: 01463 231576 Fax: 01463 713409**

3 Twin
3 Double

All En Suite

B&B per person
from £22.00 Single
from £20.00 Dbl/Twn

Open Jan-Dec excl Xmas/New Year

Delightfully situated Georgian house overlooking the River Ness, and enjoying panoramic views from the lounge towards the cathedral, castle and the town, with distant hills beyond. Within a few minutes walk of all the amenities of the highland capital.

★★★

B&B

Craigwood

**23 Old Edinburgh Road, Inverness, IV2 3HJ
Tel: 01463 225629 Fax: 01463 231387
E.mail: Mark@craigwood.fsbusiness.co.uk**

1 Twin
2 Double

1 Pub Bath/Show
1 Limited ensuite

B&B per person
£22.00-£25.00 Dbl/Twn

Open Jan-Dec

This is an excellent opportunity to experience the capital of the Highlands, in a family run business which will guarantee you a warm and friendly Scottish welcome. Craigwood is of special architectural interest, being built in 1886, it is one of the best examples of a Victorian styled house of it's kind. It stands in a large garden, situated in a quiet residential area only 10 minutes walk from the town centre.

★★★

SMALL HOTEL

Crown Court Hotel

**25 Southside Road, Inverness, IV2 3BG
Tel: 01463 234816 Fax: 01463 714900
E-mail: reception@crowncourt.co.uk**

1 Single
3 Twin
5 Double

All En Suite

B&B per person
from £59.00 Single
from £39.50 Dbl/Twn

Open Jan-Dec

Lying in a quiet residential area close to Inverness town centre, the Crown Court Hotel has the ambience of a country house hotel in the town.

Inverness — Map Ref: 4B8

★★ GUEST HOUSE

Dalmore Guest House

101 Kenneth Street, Inverness, IV3 5QQ
Tel: 01463 237224 Fax: 01463 712249
E-mail: dalmoreguesthouse@hotmail.com

2 Single 1 Twin 2 Double 2 Family	1 Ensuite fac 1 Priv.NOT ensuite	B&B per person from £20.00 Single from £18.00 Dbl/Twn	Open Jan-Dec

Comfortable family run guest house close to the centre of Inverness and all facilities. Private parking. Ground floor room available. Credit cards accepted.

★★★ B&B

Dionard

39 Old Edinburgh Road, Inverness, IV2 3HJ
Tel: 01463 233557 Fax: 01463 710526

1 Twin 2 Double	All En Suite	B&B per person from £20.00 Dbl/Twn Room only from £30.00	Open Jan-Dec

Traditional Victorian stone built house in central location. Ideal base for visiting local attractions including Culloden Moor, Fort George and Loch Ness, and exploring the beautiful Scottish Highlands. Ground floor accommodation available.

★★★★ B&B

Druidh's Burn House

by Castle Heather, Old Edinburgh Road South, Inverness, IV2 6AR
Tel: 01463 226499 Fax: 01463 710745
E-mail: db@cozzee-nessie-bed.co.uk
Web: www.cozzee-nessie-bed.co.uk/intro.html

1 Twin 2 Double	All En Suite	B&B per person £49.00-£55.00 Single £29.00-£36.00 Dbl/Twn	Open Jan-Dec excl Xmas/New Year

Modern house on outskirts of Inverness but just a short drive from Raigmore Hospital and centre of city. A strict no smoking policy. Private parking. Looking out over Inverness to Moray Firth.

★★★★ B&B

Drumossie Park Cottage

Inverness, IV2 5BB
Tel/Fax: 01463 224127
E-mail: J.Naismith@talk21.com

2 Double	All En Suite	B&B per person from £20.00 Double	Open Jan-Dec

A warm welcome assured in our friendly family home on the outskirts of town. Close to Culloden Battlefield. Dinner by arrangement. Come as a guest leave as a friend.

Important: Prices stated are estimates and may be subject to amendments

Inverness

Map Ref: 4B8

★★★ GUEST HOUSE

East Dene
6 Ballifeary Road, Inverness, IV3 5PJ
Tel/Fax: 01463 232976
E-mail: dgreig@nildram.co.uk
Web: www.smoothhound.co.uk/hotels/eastd.html

1 Twin, 3 Double | 3 En Suite fac, 1 Priv.NOT ensuite | B&B per person £22.00-£28.00 Dbl/Twn | Open Feb-Nov

Semi-detached house in quiet residential area, 3 minutes from Eden Court Theatre and riverside walks. 10 minutes from town centre. Private parking.

TV P W V

★★ B&B

Furan Cottage
100 Old Edinburgh Road, Inverness, IV2 3HT
Tel: 01463 712094
E-mail: furancottage@talk21.com

2 Single, 1 Double, 1 Family | B&B per person from £16.00 Single, from £16.00 Double | Open Jan-Dec, B&B + Eve.Meal from £26.00

Family home on main road, 1 mile (2kms) from town centre. Private parking. No smoking house. Evening meals by prior arrangement.

TV P C V

★★★ B&B

'Handa'
Lochalsh Road, Inverness, IV3 8HW
Tel: 01463 236530
E-mail: handa@bun.com

1 Single, 1 Twin, 2 Double | B&B per person from £18.00 Single, from £18.00 Dbl/Twn | Open Jan-Dec

Family home in residential area with all rooms on ground floor. 15 minute walk to city centre and all amenities. Transport to/from Rail and Bus stations and airport available by prior arrangement.

TV P C V

★★★★ B&B

'Hebrides'
120a Glenurquhart Road, Inverness, IV3 5TD
Tel: 01463 220062
Web: www.hebrides-guesthouse.co.uk

1 Twin, 2 Double | 2 Ensuite fac, 1 Priv.NOT ensuite | B&B per person £18.00-£25.00 Dbl/Twn | Open Jan-Dec

Family home situated beside the Caledonian Canal on the A82 (Inverness to Loch Ness). Near to all leisure facilities. Town centre 1 mile (2kms).

TV P W V

VAT is shown at 17.5%: changes in this rate may affect prices.

Key to symbols is on back flap.

Inverness Map Ref: 4B8

B&B

Mrs Helen Kennedy
Kendon, 9 Old Mill Lane, Inverness, IV2 3XP
Tel: 01463 238215

1 Twin, 2 Double — All En Suite — B&B per person £21.00-£25.00 Dbl/Twn — Open Mar-Nov

Enjoy a warm welcome and a restful break in our family bungalow situated in a peaceful location within walking distance of town centre. Ideal base for touring Highlands, Speyside and Whisky trail. All rooms ensuite. Totally non-smoking.

B&B

Gillian & Bill Lee
Millwood House, 36 Old Mill Road, Inverness, IV2 3HR
Tel: 01463 237254 Fax: 01463 719400

1 Twin, 2 Double — 2 En Suite fac, 1 Priv.NOT ensuite, 1 Pub Bath/Show — B&B per person from £30.00 Single, from £30.00 Dbl/Twn — Open Mar-Nov

A warm friendly welcome in comfortable family home with cosy traditional cottage style bedrooms. Large secluded garden, in pleasant residential area close to town centre.

B&B

Lorne House
40 Crown Drive, Inverness, IV2 3QG
Tel: 01463 236271

1 Double, 1 Twin/Family — 1 En Suite fac, 1 Priv.NOT Ensuite — B&B per person from £22.00 double, from £18 twin/family — Open Jan-Dec excl Xmas/New Year

Victorian detached house in quiet residential area, close to town centre and railway station. Guest car parking. Private and ensuite facilities.

B&B

Lyndon Guest House
50 Telford Street, Inverness, IV3 5LE
Tel: 01463 232551
E-mail: donnas@tesco.net
Web: www.lyndon-guest-house.co.uk

1 Twin, 1 Double, 4 Family — All En Suite — B&B per person from £16.00 Single, from £16.00 Dbl/Twn — Open Jan-Dec excl Xmas/New Year

Comfortable home, a short distance from the town centre and all its amenities. Two rooms on ground floor. Ample parking.

Inverness | Map Ref: 4B8

B&B

Lynver
30 Southside Road, Inverness, IV2 3BG
Tel: 01463 242906

1 Twin
2 Double

All En Suite

B&B per person
from £25.00 Single
from £19.00 Dbl/Twn
Room only per person
from £17.00

Open Mar-Nov

Extremely comfortable modern detached villa in quiet residential area within five minutes walk of town centre and easy strolling distance of a wide range of cafes, bars and restaurants, yet within easy access of all major road networks to and from Inverness. An excellent base for exploring the beauty of the Highlands. Private parking available on site.

B&B

Lynwood
13 Ross Avenue, Inverness, IV3 5QJ
Tel: 01463 224758

1 Twin
1 Family

1 Pub Bath/Show

B&B per person
from £15.00 Single
from £15.00 Twin

Open Jan-Dec

Traditional Scottish hospitalit in friendly family home. Ten minutes walk from town centre. Close to Eden Court Theatre, Sports Centre and Aquadome.

C V

B&B

Mrs MacCuish
1 Caulfield Park, Inverness, IV2 5GB
Tel: 01463 792882

1 Twin
1 Double

1 En Suite fac
1 Pub Bath/Show

B&B per person
from £19.00 Dbl/Twn

Open May-Sep

Modern detached house with large garden on eastern outskirts of Inverness. 3 miles (5kms) from Culloden Battlefield. Private parking. Non-smoking throughout.

V

Highfield House

62 Old Edinburgh Road, Inverness IV2 3PG

Telephone/Fax: 01463 238892

Highfield House is a family home offering quality accommodation and warm Scottish hospitality. We are situated in a quiet residential area with off-road private parking yet only 10 minutes walk from the town centre. One double room with ensuite shower room, one family/double/twin room with private shower room. Price for 2001 – £20 per person family/double/twin with private shower, £22 en-suite double room.

B&B

Mrs Margaret MacGruer
62 Old Edinburgh Road, Inverness, IV2 3PG
Tel/Fax: 01463 238892

1 Double
1 Family

Ensuite Shower
Private Shower

B&B per person
from £20.00 Private
from £22.00 Ensuite

Open Feb-Nov

Warm friendly welcome in spacious detached house standing in its own grounds in a quiet residential area but only 0.5 miles (1km) from the town centre.

C V

Inverness Map Ref: 4B8

B&B

Mrs M Macrae
White Lodge, 15 Bishops Road, Inverness, IV3 5SB
Tel/Fax: 01463 230693

1 Twin 2 Double 1 F.Poster	All En Suite	B&B per person £25.00-£35.00 Single £20.00-£24.00 Dbl/Twn £30.00-£33.00 pp	Open Jan-Dec

Traditional Victorian sandstone home, offering central accommodation and warm hospitality. A short walk to town centre and local places of interest including the Cathedral, Eden Court Theatre, Aquadome, Castle, Bught Park and the Ness Islands. Ideal base for visiting Loch Ness and the magnificent Scottish Highlands.

TV P

C V

GUEST HOUSE

Macrae House
24 Ness Bank, Inverness, IV2 4SF

2 Twin 1 Double 1 Family	2 En Suite fac 1 Pub Bath/Show	B&B per person from £35.00 Single from £22.00 Dbl/Twn Room only per person from £19.00	Open Jan-Dec

A friendly atmosphere awaits you in this Victorian House set on the Ness Bank. Ideally situated for all the Town Centre amenities. Peaceful garden for guests to relax in. Private parking. Close to Eden Court Theatre.

TV P

C V

GUEST HOUSE

Malvern Guest House
54 Kenneth Street, Inverness, IV3 5PZ
Tel/Fax: 01463 242251
E-mail: malvern.guesthouse@virgin.net
Web: http://freespace.virgin.net/raymond.mackenzie

1 Twin 2 Double 3 Family	All En Suite	B&B per person from £20.00 Dbl/Twn	Open Jan-Dec

Victorian detached house in central location in Inverness. Off-street parking. All rooms are ensuite.

TV P

C £ V

GUEST HOUSE

Old Royal Guest House
10 Union Street, Inverness, IV1 1PL
Tel: 01463 230551 Fax: 01463 711916
Web: www.old-royal.co.uk

2 Single 3 Twin 3 Double 2 Family	5 En Suite fac 2 Pub Bath/Show	B&B per person from £22.00 Single from £20.00 Dbl/Twn	Open Jan-Dec

Four storey terraced guest house in the heart of the town centre and approximately 100yds from the railway station. Friendly personal attention of owners.

TV

£ V

Important: Prices stated are estimates and may be subject to amendments

Inverness — Map Ref: 4B8

'Pitfaranne'
57 Crown Street, Inverness, IV2 3AY
Tel: 01463 239338

B&B ★★★

4 Twin 2 Double 1 Family	1 En Suite fac 2 Priv.NOT ensuite 4 limited ensuite	B&B per person from £16.00 Single from £16.00 Dbl/Twn Room only per person from £16.00	Open Jan-Dec

End terraced house in quiet residential area within 10 minutes walk from town centre. Some private parking.

Rotherwood Guest House
7 Midmills Road, Inverness, IV2 3NZ
Tel: 01463 225732

GUEST HOUSE ★★★

1 Twin 2 Double	All En Suite	B&B per person from £25.00 Single from £20.00 Dbl/Twn	Open Jan-Dec

Traditional red sandstone house with a warm relaxing environment. In a quiet residential area yet only a few minutes walk from town centre and station. All rooms ensuite. Non-smoking house. 30 minutes by car to the famous Loch Ness.

Ryeford
21 Ardconnel Terrace, Inverness, IV2 3AE
Tel/Fax: 01463 242871
E.mail: ryeford@btinternet.com

GUEST HOUSE ★★★

1 Single 1 Twin 2 Double 2 Family	4 En Suite fac	B&B per person from £20.00 Single from £20.00 Dbl/Twn	Open Jan-Dec

Terraced house overlooking town centre and near Eastgate Shopping Centre, railway and bus stations.Non-smoking bedrooms. Early breakfasts available.

St Ann's House
37 Harrowden Road, Inverness, IV3 5QN
Tel/Fax: 01463 236157
E-mail: stannshous@aol.com

GUEST HOUSE ★★★

1 Single 2 Twin 2 Double 1 Family	5 En Suite fac 1 Priv.NOT ensuite	B&B per person from £20.00 Single from £24.00 Dbl/Twn	Open Mar-Oct

19c traditional stone built house in quiet residential area. Small comfortable family run, assuring a friendly welcome. Tranquil well planted garden available for guests enjoyment.

Inverness Map Ref: 4B8

B&B

St Kilda
28 Rangemore Road, Inverness, IV3 5EA
Tel: 01463 235200

1 Single	1 Pub Bath/Show	B&B per person	Open Jan-Nov excl
1 Double		from £16.00 Single	New Year
1 Family		from £15.00 Dbl/Twn	

Victorian house in quiet residential area. Easy walk to city centre and all amenities. Central base for exploring the Highlands and Loch Ness. Owner has special interest in needlework and craftwork.

Sealladh Sona

3 Whinpark, Canal Road, Muirtown, Inverness IV3 8NQ
Tel/Fax: 01463 239209 e.mail: cooksona@aol.com
Web: http://members.aol.com/cooksona

Relax as you watch the boats and hear the ducks on the canal, Marjory and Peter Cook invite you to spoil yourself in the comfort of their home – a smoke-free environment. Enjoy a wonderful choice of fresh local produce for breakfast. Highly recommended by *Which? B&B and Hotel Guides.*

B&B

Sealladh Sona
3 Whinpark, Canal Road, Muirtown, Inverness, IV3 8NQ
Tel/Fax: 01463 239209
E-mail: cooksona@aol.com
Web: http://members.aol.com/cooksona

2 Twin	All En Suite	B&B per person	Open Jan-Dec excl
1 Double		£26.00-£30.00 Dbl/Twn	Xmas/New Year

A Scottish couple welcome you to their modernised but traditional-style 120 year old home, peacefully situated overlooking the Caledonian Canal, but only 10 minutes from the town centre. Vegetarian breakfasts available. Homemade biscuits on the hospitality tray. Private parking.

STONEA

3A RESAURIE, SMITHTON, BY INVERNESS IV2 7NH
Telephone: 01463 791714
e.mail: mbmansfield@uk2.net

3 miles east of Inverness. We are in a small residential area adjacent to farmland overlooking Moray Firth, Ross-shire Hills, Ben Wyvis. Ground floor double and twin sharing bathroom. Double ensuite. High tea, dinner by arrangement. Ample parking. Great Britain Cycle Route 7 passes us. Non-smoking. Public transport nearby.

B&B

Stonea
3a Resaurie, Smithton, by Inverness,
Inverness-shire, IV2 7NH
Tel: 01463 791714
E.mail: mbmansfield@uk2.net

1 Twin	1 En Suite fac	B&B per person	Open Jan-Dec
2 Double	1 Pub Bath/Show	from £17.00 Single	B&B + Eve.Meal
		from £17.00 Dbl/Twn	from £29.00

Modern house set in quiet residential area 4 miles (6kms) from Inverness with panoramic views across the Moray Firth. Warm and friendly stay assured. Non-smoking. Home-cooked evening meals by arrangement.

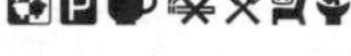

Inverness | Map Ref: 4B8

★★★ B&B

Strathisla
42 Charles Street, Inverness, IV2 3AH
Tel/Fax: 01463 235657
Web: http://website.lineone.net/~lewthwaite

2 Single	1 Pub Shower	B&B per person	Open Jan-Dec
1 Twin		from £17.00 Single	B&B + Eve.Meal
1 Double		from £15.00 Dbl/Twn	from £24.00

Comfortable B&B built in 1860, now with modern facilities. 3 minutes walk to town centre, off street parking. Evening meal by arrangement, Chinese spoken. Non smoking throughout.

W V

★★ GUEST HOUSE

Strathmhor Guest House
99 Kenneth Street, Inverness, IV3 5QQ
Tel: 01463 235397

1 Single	Priv toilet/shower	£20.00-£25.00 pp	Open Jan-Dec
2 Family	En suite	£18.00-£20.00 pp	
2 Double	En suite	£18.00-£22.00 pp	

Scottish hospitality in friendly family home. 10 minutes walk from town centre.

C W V

★★★ B&B

Sunnyholm
12 Mayfield Road, Inverness, IV2 4AE
Tel: 01463 231336 Fax: 01463 715788
Web: www.milford.co.uk/go/sunnyholm.html

2 Twin	All En Suite	B&B per person	Open Jan-Dec
2 Double		from £28.00 Single	
		from £20.00 Dbl/Twn	

Bungalow situated in quiet residential area close to town centre and castle. All bedrooms ensuite and on ground floor. Private car park.

V

★★ B&B

Tamarue
70a Ballifeary Road, Inverness, IV3 5PF
Tel: 01463 239724

1 Twin	1 Ensuite fac	B&B per person	Open Jan-Dec excl
2 Double	1 Pub Bath/Show	£15.00-£25.00 Single	Xmas/New Year
		£14.00-£20.00 Dbl/Twn	
		Room only per person	
		£14.00-£18.00	

Situated in quiet residential area, close to town centre, River Ness, golf course, Eden Court Theatre, Aquadome and Sports Centre. Off street parking.

V

VAT is shown at 17.5%: changes in this rate may affect prices.

Key to symbols is on back flap.

Inverness **Map Ref: 4B8**

B&B

Tigh na Teile

6 Island Bank Road, Inverness, IV2 4SY
Tel: 01463 222842 Fax: 01463 226844
E-mail: jenny@islandbank.co.uk

2 Twin
1 Double

All En Suite

B&B per person
£20.00-£30.00 Single
from £20.00 Dbl/Twn

Open Jan-Dec excl Xmas/New Year

Bed and Breakfast in a comfortable home. Situated in a quiet location with views over River Ness yet only a short walk to town centre and all its amenities. Eden Court Theatre close by.

B&B

The Tilt

26 Old Perth Road, Inverness, IV2 3UT
Tel/Fax: 01463 225352

1 Single
1 Twin
1 Family

1 Pub Bath/Show

B&B per person
from £17.00 Single
from £15.00 Twin

Open Jan-Dec excl Xmas/New Year

Family home within short distance of A9, town centre and all amenities. Convenient for Raigmore Hospital. Strictly non-smoking. Vegetarian menus and packed lunches available.

B&B

Mrs J Wilson

Cairnsmore, 41 Charles Street, Inverness, IV2 3AH
Tel: 01463 233485
E-mail: cairnsmore@tinyworld.co.uk
Web: www.scotland-inverness.co.uk/cairnsmore

1 Twin
2 Double

1 Pub Bath/Show

B&B per person
from £18.50 Dbl/Twn

Open Jan-Dec excl Xmas

Terraced house in quiet residential area, renovated to a high standard, close to shops, town centre, rail and bus station.

by Inverness **Map Ref: 4B8**

B&B

Sky House

Upper Cullernie, Balloch, by Inverness, Inverness-shire, IV2 7HU
Tel/Fax: 01463 792582
E-mail: skyhouse@talk21.com

1 Twin
1 Double

All En Suite

B&B per person
from £27.00 Single
from £18.00 Dbl/Twn

Open Jan-Dec excl Xmas/New Year

A friendly and relaxed welcome at this modern house with superb views over Moray Firth to the Black Isle. 10 minutes drive from Inverness airport or town. Non-smoking throughout.

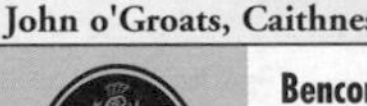

John o'Groats, Caithness

Map Ref: 4E2

★★★ B&B

Bencorragh House

Upper Gills, Canisbay, by John o'Groats, Caithness KW1 4YB
Tel/Fax: 01955 611449
E-mail: bartonsandy@hotmail.com
Web: www.BencorraghHouse.com

1 Twin 1 Double 1 Family	All En Suite	B&B per person from £24.00 Single from £20.00 Dbl/Twn	Open Mar-Oct B&B + Eve.Meal from £32.00

A working croft with Jacobs sheep, Highland cattle and Jersey cows, horses, chickens and other animals. Excellent outlook over the Pentland Firth towards the island of Stroma. Comfortable and spacious accommodation; a warm welcome and relaxing atmosphere. Excellent base for unwinding, while you explore this fascinating coastline and beyond.

★★ GUEST HOUSE

Caber-feidh Guest House

John O'Groats, Caithness, KW1 4YR
Tel: 01955 611219

2 Single 4 Twin 4 Double 4 Family	7 En Suite fac 3 Pub Bath/Show	B&B per person from £18.00 Single from £17.00 Dbl/Twn	Open Jan-Dec excl Xmas/New Year B&B + Eve.Meal from £24.00

Centrally situated in John O' Groats and 2 miles (3kms) from Duncansby Head. It is well situated for exploring the north east, including the north coast of Sutherland, the inland Flow Country, and more. Day trips to Orkney are a popular choice.

★★ B&B

Mill House

John o'Groats, Caithness, KW1 4YR
Tel: 01955 611239

1 Twin 2 Double	1 Pub Shower 1 Priv.NOT ensuite	B&B per person £20,00-£25.00 Single £16.50-£17.50 Dbl/Twn	Open May-Oct

Traditional farmhouse, with all rooms on the ground floor; situated on working mixed stock farm, 0.5 mile from John O' Groats and the Orkney passenger ferry. Views over the Pentland Firth towards Stroma and Orkney. Duncansby Head, famous for its cliffs, Stacks and seabirds, is a short distance away. Much more to see and do in the area.

★ HOTEL

Seaview Hotel

John o'Groats, Caithness, KW1 4YR
Tel/Fax: 01955 611220

1 Single 4 Twin 7 Double 4 Family	5 En Suite fac 4 Priv.NOT ensuite 2 Pub Bath/Show	B&B per person from £20.00 Single from £14.50 Dbl/Twn Room only per person from £14.00	Open Jan-Dec excl Xmas/New Year B&B + Eve.Meal from £25.00

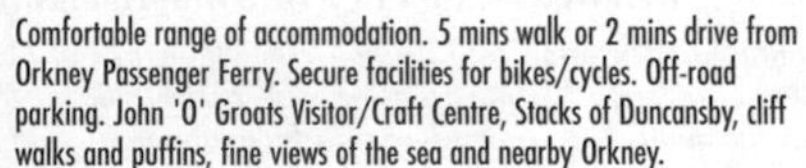

Comfortable range of accommodation. 5 mins walk or 2 mins drive from Orkney Passenger Ferry. Secure facilities for bikes/cycles. Off-road parking. John 'O' Groats Visitor/Craft Centre, Stacks of Duncansby, cliff walks and puffins, fine views of the sea and nearby Orkney.

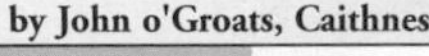

by John o'Groats, Caithness

Map Ref: 4E2

★★ B&B

Charnwood B&B

Main Street, Keiss, by Wick, Caithness, KW1 4UY
Tel: 01955 631258

1 Double 1 Family	1 Pub.bathroom	B&B per person £18.00-£20.00 Double	Open Mar-Oct

Charnwood is located in the peaceful village of Keiss which overlooks Sinclair Bay with its miles of sandy beach and harbour both within walking distance. Keiss is just 15 minutes drive from John O'Groats and the Orkney Passenger Ferry.

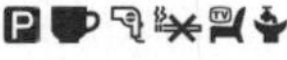

VAT is shown at 17.5%: changes in this rate may affect prices.

Key to symbols is on back flap.

by John o'Groats, Caithness — Map Ref: 4E2

B&B

The Hawthorns
Mey, by Thurso, Caithness, KW14 8XH
Tel/Fax: 01847 851710
E-mail: hawthorns-support@btinternet.com
Web: www.btinternet.com/~hawthorns-support

Spacious modern house, situated in the quiet village of Mey, on the north coast of Scotland. Open outlook towards Dunnet Head and across the Pentland Firth. Excellent base for exploring this fascinating corner of Scotland.

1 Twin, 2 Double — All En Suite

B&B per person from £18.00 Single, from £18.00 Dbl/Twn. Room only per person from £15.00

Open Jan-Dec. B&B + Eve.Meal from £30.00

★★ B&B

Post Office House
Canisbay, nr John o'Groats, Caithness, Scotland, KW1 4YH
Tel/Fax: 01955 611213
Web: www.john-o-groats.ukf.net

100 year old Post Office house. Panoramic views of Pentland Firth, close to John O'Groats and Orkney Ferries. Personally run. Extensive breakfast menu.

1 Twin, 2 Double — 1 Ensuite fac

prices on application

Open Easter-Sep

Kentallen, by Appin, Argyll — Map Ref: 1F1

★★★★ SMALL HOTEL

Ardsheal House
Kentallen of Appin, Kentallen,by Appin, Argyll, PA38 4BX
Tel: 01631 740227 Fax: 01631 74342
E-mail: info@ardsheal.co.uk
Web: www.ardsheal.co.uk

Historic Manor House, dating from the 18th Century. A former home of the Stewarts of Appin, situated in 800 quiet secluded acres, including 11 acres of garden and parkland, with walks down to the shoreline.
A comfortable family home, with a welcoming and relaxing atmosphere.

1 Single, 1 Twin, 4 Double — All En Suite

B&B per person from £45.00 Single, from £45.00 Dbl/Twn

Open Feb-Nov. B&B + Eve.Meal from £70.00

Kincraig, by Kingussie, Inverness-shire — Map Ref: 4C10

Braeriach Guest House

Braeriach Road, Kincraig, By Kingussie, Inverness-shire PH21 1QA
Telephone: 01540 651369
Web: www.kincraig.com/braeriach.htm

A handsome Victorian country house on the banks of the River Spey, enjoying a peaceful secluded setting with spectacular views across to the Cairngorm mountains. Furnished to a high standard, rooms are warm and spacious, beds comfortable and views memorable. Emphasis on good food using the best fresh local produce.

GUEST HOUSE

Braeriach Guest House
Braeriach Road, Kincraig, by Kingussie, Inverness-shire, PH21 1QA
Tel: 01540 651369
Web: www.kincraig.com/braeriach.htm

Former manse situated on the banks of the River Spey with picturesque garden extending to private jetty. Dinners available using home grown vegetables and free range eggs.

1 Twin, 2 Double — 2 En Suite fac, 1 Priv.NOT ensuite

B&B per person from £22.00 Single, from £20.00 Double. Room only per person from £18.00

Open Jan-Dec. B&B + Eve.Meal from £38.00

Important: Prices stated are estimates and may be subject to amendments

Kincraig, by Kingussie, Inverness-shire | Map Ref: 4C10

GUEST HOUSE

Insh Hall Lodge

Kincraig, Kingussie, Inverness-shire, PH21 1NU
Tel: 01540 651272 Fax: 01540 651208
E-mail: office@lochinsh.com
Web: www.lochinsh.com

Comfortable ensuite accommodation just 150m from the beach of scenic Loch Insh. Licensed Boathouse restaurant overlooking the activities on the water. Free watersports (set times) for guests staying 2 nights. Sauna, minigym, laundry, TV lounges. Dry ski slope, archery, mountain bikes, interpretation trail, children's adventure area. Dec - April downhill ski hire/instruction.

2 Single, 6 Twin, 5 Double, 6 Family — All En Suite

B&B per person: from £23.50 Single; from £18.50 Dbl/Twn

Open Jan-Dec. B&B + Eve.Meal from £29.50

C W V

GUEST HOUSE

Insh House Guesthouse

Kincraig, by Kingussie, Inverness-shire, PH21 1NU
Tel: 01540 651377
Web: www.kincraig.com/inshhouse.htm

Set in spacious grounds, this C listed Telford designed Manse, c1827, has all the original charm of a traditional Highland home. In good walking country, it is close to Glenfeshie & Loch Insh and equidistant from Kingussie & Aviemore. Birdwatching, watersports and skiing nearby.

2 Single, 1 Twin, 1 Double, 1 Family — 2 En Suite fac, 1 Pub Bath/Show

B&B per person: from £18.00 Single; from £20.00 Dbl/Twn

Open Boxing Day-mid Nov. B&B + Eve.Meal from £28.00

C V

B&B

Kirkbeag Bed & Breakfast

Kincraig, Kingussie, Inverness-shire, PH21 1ND
Tel/Fax: 01540 651298
E-mail: kirkbeag@kincraig.com

19c church, in quiet location converted to family home. Spiral staircase and craft workshop. Craft courses available. Aviemore 5 Miles (8 kms). Smokers welcome.

1 Twin, 1 Double — 2 Pub Bath/Show

B&B per person: from £17.00 Single; from £17.00 Dbl/Twn

Open Jan-Dec. B&B + Eve.Meal from £27.00

C W V

Kingussie, Inverness-shire **Map Ref: 4B11**

ARDEN HOUSE

Newtonmore Road, Kingussie, Inverness-shire PH21 1HE
Tel/Fax: 01540 661369
e.mail: ardenhouse@compuserve.com Web: www.kingussie.co.uk/ardenhouse/

Arden House, a Victorian villa with many period features offers real home comforts, log fire in season. Delicious home cooked food and owners in residence who pride themselves on caring for their guests. Ample off road parking. An ideal base for touring, golf, fishing, walking or just relaxing.

GUEST HOUSE

Arden House

Newtonmore Road, Kingussie, Inverness-shire, PH21 1HE
Tel/Fax: 01540 661369
E-mail: ardenhouse@compuserve.com
Web: www.kingussie.co.uk/ardenhouse/

1 Single	3 En Suite fac	B&B per person	Open Jan-Dec
1 Twin		from £18.00 Single	B&B + Eve.Meal
3 Double		from £18.00 Dbl/Twn	from £28.00
1 Family			

Conveniently sited for visiting the beautiful Spey Valley and Cairngorms, Arden House is family run to a high standard. Attractively decorated bedrooms with hospitality trays. Open log fire in comfortable lounge. A personal service and warm welcome assured. Ample parking. Perfect base for touring, golfing, fishing, walking and watersports.

GUEST HOUSE

Avondale Guest House

Newtonmore Road, Kingussie, Inverness-shire, PH21 1HF
Tel/Fax: 01540 661731
E-mail: walsh.lorraine@talk21.com

1 Single	5 En Suite fac	B&B per person	Open Jan-Dec
2 Twin	1 Pub Bath/Show	£19.00-£22.00 Single	B&B + Eve.Meal
4 Double		£19.00-£22.00 Dbl/Twn	£29.00-£32.00

A splendid example of an Edwardian Home nr. centre of village, this family run Guest House is attractively furnished and equipped with all we hope you could need for a comfortable, relaxing stay. Excellent home cooking. A beautiful part of Scotland with plenty to see & do. Lots of info to help you plan your days.

GLENGARRY

Bed & Breakfast ★★★★

East Terrace, Kingussie, Inverness-shire PH21 1JS
Telephone/Fax: 01540 661386
e.mail: glengarry@scot89.freeserve.co.uk Web: www.scot89.freeserve.co.uk

Traditional Victorian villa situated in its own tranquil grounds with private off-road parking. Glengarry has an enviable reputation for comfort and quality, provides the perfect base for all year round pursuits and is ideally suited to the discerning visitor. A warm welcome is assured.

B&B

Janet & Roger Crawford

Glengarry, East Terrace, Kingussie, Inverness-shire, PH21 1JS
Tel/Fax: 01540 661386
E-mail: glengarry@scot89.freeserve.co.uk
Web: www.scot89.freeserve.co.uk

1 Single	2 En Suite fac	B&B per person	Open Jan-Dec
1 Twin	1 Priv.NOT ensuite	from £19.00 Single	B&B + Eve.Meal
2 Double	1 Pub Bath/Show	£19.00-£21.00 Dbl/Twn	£29.00-£31.00

Stone built house c1900 with large garden and summer house, in quiet residential area, only a few minutes walk from centre of Kingussie. No smoking throughout.

Important: Prices stated are estimates and may be subject to amendments

Kingussie, Inverness-shire — Map Ref: 4B11

B&B

Greystones B&B

Acres Road, Kingussie, Inverness-shire, PH21 1LA
Tel: 01540 661052 Fax: 01540 662162
Web: http://surf.to/greystones

1 Single — 1 Priv.NOT ensuite
1 Double
1 Family

B&B per person
from £19.50 Single
from £19.50 Dbl/Twn
Room only per person
from £14.00

Open Jan-Dec excl Xmas/New Year
B&B + Eve.Meal
from £35.00

Friendly welcome in informal family home. A short walk from Kingussie. Evening meal available. The ideal place for adventurers to bring imagination and energy.

★★★★

GUEST HOUSE

The Hermitage

Spey Street, Kingussie, PH21 1HN
Tel: 01540 662137 Fax: 01540 662177
E-mail: thehermitage@clara.net
Web: www.thehermitage-scotland.com

2 Twin — All En Suite
2 Double
1 Family

B&B per person
from £21.00 Single
from £21.00 Dbl/Twn

Open Jan-Dec excl Xmas
B&B + Eve.Meal
from £32.00

Enjoy the splendour of the Highlands and make Kingussie your base. Let us help you plan your daily itinerary. Wonderful walking and mountain bike trails. In easy reach of skiing, fishing, birdwatching, heritage centres and whisky trail. A warm welcome awaits you at the Hermitage.

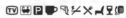

GUEST HOUSE

Homewood Lodge

Newtonmore Road, Kingussie, Inverness-shire, PH21 1HD
Tel/fax: 01540 661507
E.mail: homewood-lodge@bigfoot.com
Web: http://www.homewood-lodge-kingussie.co.uk

1 Twin — All En Suite
2 Double
1 Family

B&B per person
from £15.00 Single
from £15.00 Dbl/Twn

Open Jan-Dec
B&B + Eve.Meal
from £25.00

Detached Victorian stone villa, situated on elevated position at the southern end of the the village. Enjoying outstanding vistas towards the River Spey and the Cairngorms.

HOTEL

The Osprey Hotel

Ruthven Road, Kingussie, Inverness-shire, PH21 1EN
Tel/Fax: 01540 661510

1 Single — All En Suite
3 Twin
4 Double

B&B per person
from £25.00 Single
from £25.00 Dbl/Twn

Open Jan-Dec

Personally run hotel in centre of village, imaginative cuisine including vegetarian meals using fresh produce. Taste of Scotland member.

Kingussie, Inverness-shire | Map Ref: 4B11

★★★★ B&B

Rowan House
Homewood, Newtonmore Road, Kingussie, PH21 1HD
Tel: 01540 662153

1 Twin	1 En Suite fac	B&B per person	Open Jan-Dec excl Xmas
2 Double	2 Priv.NOT ensuite	from £17.00 Single	
		from £17.00 Dbl/Twn	

Enjoys outstanding views of the Spey Valley and Cairngorms. Situated in a quiet hillside position at the southern end of Kingussie. On National Cycle Route 7.

★★★★ B&B

St Helens
Ardbroilach Road, Kingussie, Inverness-shire, PH21 1JX
Tel: 01540 661430
E.mail: sthelens@talk21.com
Web: www.anotherworldminatures.com/bandb.htm

1 Twin	1 En Suite fac	B&B per person	Open Jan-Dec
1 Double	1 Priv.NOT ensuite	from £20.00 Dbl/Twn	

Elegant stone built house c1895 in elevated position with large secluded gardens and excellent views over village and Cairngorm mountains beyond.

Kinlochewe, Ross-shire | Map Ref: 3G8

★★ B&B

Cromasaig
Torridon Road, Kinlochewe, Ross-shire, IV22 2PE
Tel: 01445 760234 Fax: 01445 760333
Web: www.torridon-mountains.com/cromasaig/index.htm

1 Twin	1 Pub Bath/Show	B&B per person	Open Jan-Dec
1 Double		from £17.00 Single	B&B + Eve.Meal
1 Family		from £17.00 Dbl/Twn	from £30.00

Warm hospitality from climbing hosts in refurbished croft house, with drying room, at foot of Beinn Eighe. Non-smoking throughout. Dogs welcome indoors. Evening meals available using home grown produce.

Kinlochleven, Argyll | Map Ref: 3H12

★★★ B&B

Edencoille Guest House
Garbhien Road, Kinlochleven, Argyll, PA40 4SE
Tel/Fax: 01855 831358

2 Twin	2 Ensuite fac	B&B per person	Open Jan-Dec
1 Double	2 Pub Bath/Show	£18.00-£22.00 Dbl/Twn	B&B + Eve.Meal
1 Family			£28.00-£36.00

A warm, friendly welcome and excellent home cooking at our family-run B&B. Perfect base for touring, fishing, skiing, climbing, walking or just relaxing. We are situated opposite the Mamores, famous for their 12 Munroes which are within 5 mins walking distance from Edencoille.

Kishorn, Ross-shire — **Map Ref: 3F9**

★★★
B&B

Mrs M Moyes
1 Achintraid, Kishorn, Ross-shire, IV54 8XB
Tel: 01520 733224 Fax: 01520 733232
E-mail: vitalspark@btclick.com

1 Twin 1 Double	All En Suite	B&B per person from £25.00 Single from £20.00 Dbl/Twn	Open Jan-Dec excl Xmas/New Year

Friendly, comfortable, ensuite accommodation. Large upstairs lounge with patio, looking towards Bealach Na Ba and the Isle of Skye. Ideal base for walks and touring.

Kyle of Lochalsh, Ross-shire — **Map Ref: 3F9**

A'Chomraich

Mrs F Murchison, Main Street, Kyle of Lochalsh IV40 8DA
Telephone: 01599 534210

A warm welcome awaits you in our christian family home. Ideal for walkers and climbers. Walking distance from station and village. Ideal base for touring Skye and Wester Ross. Closed Saturday and Sunday.

'A'Chomraich', Mrs F Murchison
Main Street, Kyle of Lochalsh, Ross-shire, IV40 8DA
Tel: 01599 534210

1 Twin 2 Double	1 Pub Bath/Show 1 Toilet	B&B per person from £15.00 Single from £15.00 Dbl/Twn	Open Apr-Oct

Traditional Scottish hospitality in friendly family home. Ideal base for touring Skye and Wester Ross. Walking distance from station.

Caladh Solas, Mrs H Knowles
Lochalsh View, Auchtertyre, by Kyle of Lochalsh, IV40 8EG
Tel: 01599 566317
E-mail: knowles@caladhsolas.freeserve.co.uk
Web: www.caladhsolas.freeserve.co.uk/home

1 Single 1 Twin 1 Double	1 En Suite fac 1 Pub Bath/Show	B&B per person from £16.00 Single from £16.00 Dbl/Twn	Open Jan-Dec B&B + Eve.Meal from £26.00

A warm welcome assured in our comfortable family run Christian B&B. Children particularly welcome. Ideal base for touring west coast and Skye. Evening meal available by prior arrangement.

Glomach House
Alt-na-Chruivne, Glenshiel, by Kyle, IV40 8HN
Tel: 01599 511222 Fax: 01599 511382

1 Twin 2 Double	All En Suite	B&B per person from £17.50 Dbl/Twn	Open Jan-Dec

Modern house overlooking Loch Duich, near Junction to Glenelg ferry road and on main route to Skye, on National Trust for Scotland estate.

VAT is shown at 17.5%: changes in this rate may affect prices.

Key to symbols is on back flap.

Kyle of Lochalsh, Ross-shire | Map Ref: 3F9

B&B

Old Bank House
Main Street, Kyle of Lochalsh, Ross-shire, IV40 8AB
Tel: 01599 534283

1 Twin | 1 Pub Shower | B&B per person | Open Jan-Dec excl
1 Double | 1 add Toilet | £18.00-£22.00 Single | Xmas/New Year
1 Family | | £14.00-£18.00 Dbl/Twn

A warm welcome in spacious 100 year old former bank manager's house in the heart of Kyle of Lochalsh. Ideally situated for touring Skye and Wester Ross. Quiet rooms but only 2 minutes walk to local pubs and restaurants.

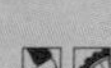

TV P C V

RESTAURANT WITH ROOMS

The Old Schoolhouse
Tigh Fasgaidh, Erbusaig, Kyle, IV40 8BB
Tel/Fax: 01599 534369
E-mail: cuminecandj@lineone.net

1 Twin | All En Suite | B&B per person | Open Apr-Oct
2 Double | | from £40.00 Single
| | from £27.00 Dbl/Twn

Restaurant with very comfortable ensuite accommodation, 3 miles (5kms) from Skye bridge at Kyle of Lochalsh, 4 miles (6kms) from Plockton.

TV P C W V

GUEST HOUSE

Soluis Guest House
Braeintra, by Achmore, Lochalsh, Wester Ross, IV53 8UP
Tel/Fax: 01599 577219
E.mail: soluisbraeintra@aol.com
Web: www.freenetpages.co.uk/hp/soluis

3 Twin | All En Suite | B&B per person | Open Jan-Dec excl
1 Double | | from £21.00 Single | Xmas/New Year
1 Family

Set amidst open countryside with big open views. Excellent centre for North West of Scotland including Skye, Applecross and Torridon. No smoking. Evening meal available. Disabled accommodation also available.

TV P V

Laide, Ross-shire Map Ref: 3F6

'CUL NA MARA'

Catalina Slipway, Sand Passage, Laide, Ross-shire IV22 2ND
Tel: 01445 731295 Fax: 01445 731570
e.mail: billhart@dircon.co.uk or billhart@deathsdoor.com
Web: www.culnamara-guesthouse.co.uk

A stay at "Cul Na Mara" (Gaelic – Song of the sea) is an enjoyable experience. Superior bed and breakfast accommodation. Guest rooms fully ensuite and fitted with colour television. Private dining room. Scottish high tea – an available option. Fully laid out garden overlooking the Minch. Private parking. Early booking advisable.

★★★ B&B

'Cul na Mara'
Catalina Slipway, Sand Passage, Laide, Ross-shire, IV22 2ND
Tel: 01445 731295 Fax: 01445 731570
E-mail: billhart@dircon.co.uk or billhart@deathsdoor.com
Web: www.culnamara-guesthouse.co.uk

Modern Highland home in quiet crofting area. Excellent sandy beaches nearby. Home cooking, with emphasis on fresh produce. Evening high tea available and evening meals by prior arrangement.

1 Double, 1 Family — All En Suite
B&B per person from £31.00 Single, from £21.00 Double
Open Jan-Dec excl Xmas/New Year. B&B + Eve.Meal from £31.00

★★★★ B&B

Mrs Annabell MacIver
The Sheiling, Achgarve, Laide, Ross-shire, IV22 2NS
Tel/Fax: 01445 731487
E-mail: annabell.maciver@talk21.com

Recently built bungalow finished to a high standard in small crofting community near Gruinard Bay. Fine views to Beinn Ghobhlach and Sail Mhor. Ideal base for touring Wester Ross. Totally non-smoking.

1 Twin, 1 Double — All En Suite
B&B per person from £23.00 Dbl/Twn
Open Mar-Nov

Lairg, Sutherland Map Ref: 4A6

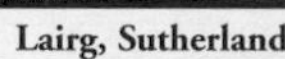

★★★ B&B

Carnbren
Station Road, Lairg, Sutherland, IV27 4AY
Tel: 01549 402259

Comfortable modern house overlooking Loch Shin, on the edge of the village of Lairg; situated on A836. Good central base for exploring the northern Highlands.

1 Double — En Suite fac; 1 Twin — Private fac; 1 Twin — Washbasin
B&B per person from £16.50 Dbl/Twn
Open Apr-Oct

★★★ B&B

Mrs Susan Hayhurst
Lochview, Lochside, Lairg, IV27 4EH
Tel/Fax: 01549 402578

Recently modernised and refurbished house. Located in position on edge of Loch Shin, all amenities closeby. Ideal location for touring the Highlands. Boat available for guests for fishing or rowing on Loch Shin. Ideal spot for birdwatching in both Lairg and N.W. Sutherland.

2 Twin, 1 Double — All En Suite
B&B per person from £18.00 Single, from £17.00 Dbl/Twn
Open Jan-Dec excl Xmas/New Year. B&B + Eve.Meal from £23.00

Lairg, Sutherland

Map Ref: 4A6

B&B

Park House

Station Road, Lairg, Sutherland, IV27 4AU
Tel: 01549 402208 Fax: 01549 402693
E-mail: dwalkerparkhouse@tinyworld.co.uk

2 Twin
1 Double

All En Suite

B&B per person
£23.00-£38.00 Single
£23.00-£26.00 Dbl/Twn

Open Jan-Dec excl Xmas/New Year
B&B + Eve.Meal
£36.00-£54.00

A warm welcome awaits you in this Victorian style house overlooking Loch Shin. Friendly and relaxed atmosphere. Emphasis on home cooking. Stalking, rough shooting, salmon and trout fishing available for guests by arrangement.

B&B

Mrs B M Paterson

Strathwin, Lairg, Sutherland, IV27 4AZ
Tel: 01549 402487

1 Double
1 Family

1 Pub Bath/Show

B&B per person
£17.00 Single
£15.00 Double

Open Apr-Sep

Modern bungalow in quiet location overlooking Little Loch Shin. Parking adjacent.

C

Lochcarron, Ross-shire

Map Ref: 3G9

B&B

Bank House

Main Street, Lochcarron, Ross-shire, IV54 8YD
Tel: 01520 722332 Fax: 01520 722780
E-mail: kenina_bankhouse@hotmail.com

1 Twin
1 Double
1 Family

1 Ensuite fac
1 Priv.NOT ensuite
1 Pub Bath/Show

B&B per person
from £23.00 Single
from £16.00 Dbl/Twn

Open Jan-Dec excl Xmas/New Year

Friendly welcome to Victorian House set in own gardens with river walk and close to the shores of Loch Carron. Ideally situated for touring. Guest lounge. Breakfast served in garden conservatory.

C W V

B&B

Castle Cottage

Main Street, Lochcarron, Ross-shire, IV54 8YB
Tel: 01520 722564

1 Twin
2 Double

1 En Suite fac
2 Pub Bath/Show

B&B per person
£17.00-£25.00 Single
£17.00-£21.00 Dbl/Twn

Open Jan-Dec excl Xmas/New Year

Modernised detached house in village centre with fine views across Loch Carron from all rooms.

C

Lochinver, Sutherland

Map Ref: 3G5

GUEST HOUSE

Ardglas Guest House

Inver, Lochinver, Sutherland, IV27 4LJ
Tel: 01571 844257 Fax: 01571 844632
Web: www.ardglas.co.uk

1 Single
1 Twin
4 Double
2 Family

8 Pub Bath/Show

B&B per person
from £16.00 Single
from £16.00 Dbl/Twn
Room only per person
from £14.00

Open Jan-Dec excl Xmas

Set above this popular fishing village with spectacular harbour, sea and mountain views. Homely atmosphere. Private parking.

C W V

Important: Prices stated are estimates and may be subject to amendments

Lochinver, Sutherland — **Map Ref: 3G5**

★★★★
B&B

Ardmore
80 Torbreck, Lochinver, Sutherland, IV27 4JB
Tel: 01571 844310

1 Twin
1 Double

B&B per person
from £18.00 Dbl/Twn

Open 22May-30Sep

Set just off the Stoer Road out of Lochinver (1.5 miles) Mrs MacLeod offers warm, comfortable accommodation. Ardmore is an ideal B&B to use as a base for touring the Northern Highlands. Many excellent walks in the area and plenty of wildlife and sandy beaches.

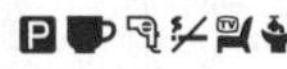

Davar
Inver, Lochinver, Sutherland. IV27 4LJ
Tel: 01571 844501
E-mail: am.gordon@talk21.com

1 Twin
1 Double
1 Family

All En Suite

B&B per person
from £20.00 Dbl/Twn

Open Apr-Nov

Modern family run house overlooking Lochinver Bay, with range of comfortable facilities. Private parking on site.

C W V

Tigh-na-Sith B&B
Cruamer, Lochinver, Sutherland, IV27 4LD
Tel: 01571 844740
E-mail: julie@tigh-na-sith.freeuk.com

1 Twin
1 Double

All En Suite

B&B per person
from £21.00 Dbl/Twn

Open Mar-Nov

Comfortable family run Bed & Breakfast. Panoramic views across Lochinver Harbour from lounge. Close to village centre, for restaurants and shops. Both rooms are ensuite. Sky TV available in the lounge.

W V

Veyatie Lochinver
66 Baddidarroch, Lochinver, Lairg, Sutherland, IV27 4LP
Tel: 01571 844424
E-mail: veyatie@baddid.freeserve.co.uk

1 Twin
2 Double

2 En Suite fac
1 Priv.NOT ensuite

B&B per person
£20.00-£25.00 Dbl/Twn

Open Jan-Dec

Spacious modern bungalow in secluded situation. Facing south with magnificent views across the harbour to Suilven. Private parking on site.

W V

Loch Ness (South), Inverness-shire — Map Ref: 4A10

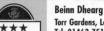

★★★ B&B

Beinn Dhearg
Torr Gardens, Lochness-side, Dores, Inverness, IV2 6TS
Tel: 01463 751336 Fax: 01463 751362

1 Twin, 1 Double, 1 Family — All En Suite — B&B per person from £20.00 Dbl/Twn — Open Jan-Dec

Modern, spacious house, in quiet setting 100yds from Loch Ness, 8 miles (13kms) south of Inverness. Wonderful views across the Loch. All ensuite. Private parking. Local Inn serving traditional Scottish Fayre. Nature walks close by. Popular walking and cycling area.

W V

Mallaig, Inverness-shire — Map Ref: 3F11

★★ B&B

Anchorage
Gillies Park, Mallaig, Inverness-shire, PH41 4QU
Tel/Fax: 01687 462454
E-mail: anchoragemallaig@talk21.com

1 Twin, 1 Double, 1 Family — All En Suite — B&B per person from £18.00 Single, from £18.00 Dbl/Twn — Open Jan-Dec excl Xmas/New Year

Family run guest house centrally situated in Mallaig village and only a few minutes walk from ferry terminal and railway station. Two bedrooms with excellent views over harbour and bay. All bedrooms with TV's, tea-trays and ensuite bathrooms. Early breakfasts available for those catching first Skye ferry. Ideal base for walking, visiting the small isles and touring.

TV

C V

★★ B&B

Glencairn
East Bay, Mallaig, Inverness-shire, PH41 4QT
Tel: 01687 462412

1 Twin, 2 Double — 1 En Suite fac — B&B per person £18.00-£20.00 Dbl/Twn — Open Apr-Sep

Modern detached house on the seafront overlooking the fishing harbour. Short walk to village centre. Ideal base for visiting the Isles of Skye, Eigg and Rhum. Local sea trips available. All rooms en suite with hospitality trays.

★ GUEST HOUSE

Springbank Guest House
East Bay, Mallaig, Inverness-shire, PH41 4QF
Tel/Fax: 01687 462459

1 Single, 1 Twin, 1 Double, 1 Family — 2 Pub Bath/Show — B&B per person from £16.00 Single, from £16.00 Dbl/Twn — Open Jan-Dec excl Xmas; B&B + Eve.Meal from £24.50

Situated overlooking the busy little harbour with unobstructed views of Skye and just a few minutes walk from the village. Warm, frienldy atmosphere. Evening meals by arrangement. All bedrooms comfortably furnished with wash-hand basins and tea/coffee facilities. Large visitors lounge with TV.

C W V

★★★ GUEST HOUSE

Western Isles
East Bay, Mallaig, Inverness-shire, PH41 4QG
Tel/Fax: 01687 462320
E-mail: westernisles@aol.com

1 Single, 1 Twin, 1 Double, 1 Family — 3 Pub Bath/Show — B&B per person from £19.00 Single, from £17.00 Dbl/Twn — Open Feb-Oct

Modern house overlooking the harbour and fishing boats, well situated for ferries to the islands. 4 miles (6kms) from renowned Morar sands.

TV

C V

Important: Prices stated are estimates and may be subject to amendments

Melvich, Sutherland — Map Ref: 4C3

GUEST HOUSE

The Sheiling Guest House
Melvich, Sutherland, KW14 7YJ
Tel/Fax: 01641 531256
E.mail: thesheiling@btinternet.com
Web: www.b-and-b-scotland.co.uk/sheiling.htm

Peaceful and spacious accommodation in the village of Melvich, with spectacular views over the bay. Two guests' lounges. Extensive breakfast selection. Genuine Highland hospitality. 17 miles to Orkney ferry, 16 miles to Forsinard RSPB reserve.

1 Twin, 2 Double — All En Suite, 1 Pub Bath/Show — B&B per person from £23.00 Dbl/Twn — Open Apr-Oct

GUEST HOUSE

Tigh-na-Clash Guest House
(Mrs Joan Ritchie), Melvich, Sutherland, KW14 7YJ
Tel/Fax: 01641 531262
E-mail: tighnaclash@mywebpage.net
Web: www.mywebpage.net/tighnaclash

Personally run guest house in attractive garden. Seven en-suite rooms, and one with private bathroom. Single rooms available. Choice of eating establishments nearby. Situated on the edge of the village of Melvich. 18 miles from Thurso, and a short inland drive to the Flow Country. Beaches, birdwatching, walking, golf, fishing, all available in the area.

2 Single, 2 Twin, 3 Double, 1 Family — 7 En Suite fac, 1 Priv.NOT ensuite — B&B per person from £21.50 Single, from £21.50 Dbl/Twn — Open Apr-Oct

Morar, Inverness-shire — Map Ref: 3F11

B&B

Loch Morar House
Morar, by Mallaig, Inverness-shire, PH40 4PB
Tel: 01687 462823

Recently built modern villa in peaceful location near Loch Morar yet only mins from the main A830 Mallaig road. Comfortable, ensuite bedrooms with hospitality trays and TV's. Cosy guests lounge where you can relax with a book from our small library. Extensive breakfast menu - traditional Scottish or continental selection.

2 Twin, 1 Double — All En Suite — B&B per person from £20.00 Single, from £20.00 Dbl/Twn — Open Apr-Nov

Nairn

Map Ref: 4C8

The Braighe
Albert Street, Nairn, IV12 4HQ
Tel/Fax: 01667 453285
Web: www.hometown.aol.com/braighe

★★★★ B&B

1 Single	2 En Suite fac	B&B per person	Open Jan-Dec excl
1 Twin	1 Priv.NOT ensuite	£20.00-£25.00 Single	Xmas/New Year
2 Double		£20.00-£25.00 Dbl/Twn	

Cosy, decorated in 'Laura Ashley' style. Considerable attention to detail to make guests as comfortable as possible. Guests spoilt with freshly squeezed orange juice, ground coffee and home made jams. Breakfast a serious affair, haggis, kippers, kedgeree. We take pride in our hospitality. 3 night packages. French and some German spoken.

Ceol-Mara
Links Place, Nairn, IV12 4NH
Tel: 01667 452495 Fax: 01667 451531
E-mail: ceolmara15@aol.com
Web: www.ceolmara.co.uk

★★★★ B&B

1 Single	All En Suite	B&B per person	Open Jan-Dec excl
1 Double		from £19.50 Single	Xmas/New Year
1 Family		from £19.50 Double	

A warm Scottish welcome assured in this seaside cottage situated in the fishertown conservation area with panoramic views over Moray Firth to the Black Isle. A stones throw to the beach and close to Championship Golf Courses. Welcome tray with home baking on arrival. Interesting breakfast menu, vegetarian, vegan and gluten free diets catered for. A member of Scotlands Best.

Durham House
4 Academy Street, Nairn, IV12 4RJ
Tel/Fax: 01667 452345
E-mail: durhamhouse@nairn34.freeserve.co.uk

★★★ B&B

1 Twin	2 En Suite fac	B&B per person	Open Jan-Dec
1 Double	1 Priv.NOT ensuite	from £18.00 Single	B&B + Eve.Meal
1 Family		from £18.00 Dbl/Twn	from £30.00

A warm welcome awaits you at Durham House, an elegant 19th century house sitting centrally in Nairn and lying 16 miles east of Inverness on the glorious Moray Firth coast. There are beautiful sandy beaches, two championship golf courses and many places of interest nearby making it an ideal holiday choice for all the family. Dinner by arrangement.

Glen Lyon Lodge
Waverley Road, Nairn, IV12 4RH
Tel: 01667 452780
E-mail: GLENLYON@bosinternet.com
Web: www.bandbnairn.com

GUEST HOUSE

1 Single	All En Suite	B&B per person	Open Jan-Dec
2 Double		from £20.00 Single	
2 Twin		from £20.00 Dbl/Twn	
1 Family		Room only per person	
		from £20.00	

GLEN LYON LODGE is an attractive. Victorian Villa set in its own grounds and pleasantly situated in Nairn's West End, 5 minutes walk from Town Centre and within 10 minutes of Harbour, Nairn's three golf courses and all amenities. The Lodge provides Bed & Breakfast accommodation with en suite facilities in all rooms, and private parking. Credit Cards Accepted: Visa.

Important: Prices stated are estimates and may be subject to amendments

Nairn

Map Ref: 4C8

★★★★ B&B

Inveran
Seabank Road, Nairn, IV12 4HG
Tel: 01667 453731 Fax: 01667 455290 – 24 hr booking service
E-mail: ClaymoreNairnScotland@compuserve.com
Web: www.inveran-highlands.co.uk

Elegant Victorian house, fully refurbished in traditional style with period antique furnishings and original features. Very comfortable spacious rooms and a traditional highland welcome with many personal touches.

3 Dbl/Twn | All En Suite | B&B per person from £60.00 Dbl/Twn | Open Jan-Dec

Lothian House Hotel

10 Crescent Road, Nairn IV12 4NB
Tel: 01667 453555 Fax: 01667 455454
Web: www.users.globalnet.co.uk/~lothot/

Enjoy your stay at this elegant family run Victorian hotel, convenient for all local amenities including beach, town and both championship golf courses. Licensed restaurant offering home cooked daily 'specials'. Ensuite rooms with sea views. Off-road parking. Negotiable rates. Special diets catered for. Open all year excluding Christmas.

★★★ SMALL HOTEL

Lothian House Hotel
10 Crescent Road, Nairn, Nairnshire, IV12 4NB
Tel: 01667 453555 Fax: 01667 455454
Web: www.users.globalnet.co.uk/~lothot/

Stone built house, c1850 in quiet residential area of town. Personally run by proprietors and within easy reach of town centre, beach and 2 championship golf courses. Sea views.

1 Single, 2 Twin, 2 Double, 1 Family | All En Suite | B&B per person from £25.00 Single, from £20.00 Dbl/Twn; Room only per person from £16.00 | Open Jan-Dec excl Xmas/New Year; B&B + Eve.Meal from £33.00

★★★★ B&B

Strathaden
Thurlow Road, Nairn, IV12 4EZ
Tel: 01667 454370

Comfortable family run bed and breakfast in recently re-furbished late Victorian villa. Quietly, yet conveniently situated within walking distance of the town centre, golf course, swimming pool and beach.

2 Twin, 1 Double | 2 Pub Bath/Show | B&B per person from £18.00 Single, from £18.00 Dbl/Twn | Open Jan-Dec excl Xmas/New Year

Nethy Bridge, Inverness-shire

Map Ref: 4C10

★★★ B&B

Aspen Lodge
Nethy Bridge, Inverness-shire, PH25 3DA
Tel: 01479 821042 Fax: 01479 821131
Web: www.nethybridge.com/aspenlodge.htm

A traditional stone built house set in the heart of this picturesque Highland village, which is an ideal base for touring Strathspey. A warm welcome, splendid breakfasts and well appointed rooms assure an enjoyable stay.

1 Double, 1 Twin | 1 En Suite fac, 1 Priv.NOT ensuite | B&B per person £25.00 Single, £19.50 Dbl/Twn | Open Jan-Dec excl Xmas/New Year

Nethy Bridge, Inverness-shire — Map Ref: 4C10

AWAITING INSPECTION

Aultmore House

Nethybridge, Inverness-shire, PH25 3EE
Tel: 01479 821473 Fax: 01479 821750
E-mail: taylor@aultmorehouse.co.uk

1 Twin, 2 Double — All En Suite
B&B per person from £35.00 Single, from £25.00 Dbl/Twn
Open Jan-Dec

Impressive Edwardian Manor House enjoying fine views of Cairngorms. From a setting of 25 acres of secluded wooded and landscaped grounds. Relaxed country house atmosphere in heart of Spey Valley.

Newtonmore, Inverness-shire — Map Ref: 4B11

★★★★ B&B

The Aspens

Spey Bridge, Newtonmore, Inverness-shire, PH20 1BD
Tel: 01540 673264

2 Twin, 1 Double — All En Suite
B&B per person from £20.00 Dbl/Twn
Open Apr-Oct
B&B + Eve.Meal from £35.00

Substantial modern house, offering high standard of facility and comfort. Set in magnificent scenery, yet easy access all main routes.

TV P C V

North Kessock, Ross-shire — Map Ref: 4B8

★★★★ B&B

Craigiewood

North Kessock, Inverness, IV1 3XG
Tel/Fax: 01463 731628
Web: www.high-lights.co.uk/accom/craigiewood

2 Twin — 1 En Suite fac, 1 Priv.NOT ensuite
B&B per person from £25.00 Single, from £20.00 Twin
Open Mar-Nov

Situated in superb countryside, Craigiewood is only 4 miles from Inverness on the Black Isle . The house is ideally situated for short trips to Inverness, Loch Ness, and the castles of Brodie and Cawdor. The famous Moray Firth dolphins are nearby. Craigiewood is an excellent starting point for journeys to the West Coast. Inverewe Gardens, Loch Maree, Torridon and Skye are an easy day trip away. Come and spoil yourself!

P £

Onich, by Fort William, Inverness-shire — Map Ref: 3G12

★★★ GUEST HOUSE

Camus House

Lochside Lodge, Onich, Inverness-shire, PH33 6RY
Tel/Fax: 01855 821200
E-mail: Young@CamusHouse.freeserve.co.uk
Web: www.SmoothHound.co.uk/hotels/camushouse.html

2 Twin, 3 Double, 2 Family — 6 En Suite fac, 1 Priv.NOT ensuite, 1 Pub Bath/Show
B&B per person from £25.50 Single, from £23.50 Dbl/Twn
Open Feb-Nov
B&B + Eve.Meal from £36.00

Large Victorian house in spectacular lochside location with unsurpassed views over Onich Bay to the mountains – midway between Ben Nevis and Glencoe – an ideal base for touring, walking, biking, climbing and skiing. Comfortable, tastefully furnished bedrooms with TV and hospitality tray. Excellent cuisine – restricted licence – and warm welcome awaits you.

TV P C £ V

Onich, by Fort William, Inverness-shire — Map Ref: 3G12

B&B

Foresters Bungalow
Inchree, Onich, Inverness-shire, PH33 6SE
Tel: 01855 821285

2 Twin, 1 Family | 1 Pub Bath/Show, 3 Priv.NOT ensuite | B&B per person from £16.00 Twin | Open Apr-Oct; B&B + Eve.Meal from £24.00

A warm welcome awaits you at our Swedish design home at the entrance to Glen Righ Forest. Wholesome meals with own garden produce. Forest walks and trails and hill climbing nearby. Well positioned between Fort William and Oban. A perfect place to relax and enjoy our Scottish hospitality. Evening meals by arrangment.

C

B&B

Tom-na-Creige
Nth Ballachulish, Onich, Inverness-shire, PH33 6RY
Tel/Fax: 01855 821405

1 Twin, 1 Double | All En Suite | B&B per person from £17.00 Single, from £17.50 Dbl/Twn | Open Jan-Oct excl New Year

Comfortable modern accommodation with spectacular views over Loch Linnhe to the Glencoe and Morvern Hills. An ideal centre for hillwalking, climbing, skiing, canoeing and touring the West Highlands or just relaxing through the four seasons. Family room available with outstanding loch views.

C W V

Plockton, Ross-shire — Map Ref: 3F9

B&B

Aisling
2 Bank Street, Plockton, Ross-shire, IV52 8TP
Tel: 01599 544208

1 Twin, 1 Double | All En Suite | B&B per person from £25.00 Single, from £18.00 Dbl/Twn | Open Jan-Dec excl Xmas/New Year

Very comfortable traditional home featuring original pine lining. Overlooking sheltered beaches of Loch Carron with garden area to the waters edge.

TV

C V

B&B

Bed & Breakast
Hill View, 2 Frithard Road, Plockton, Ross-shire, IV52 8TQ
Tel: 01599 544226

1 Twin, 2 Double | 2 En Suite fac, 1 Priv.NOT ensuite | B&B per person £16.00-£20.00 Dbl/Twn | Open Jan-Dec excl Xmas/New Year

Semi-detached house, comfortable warm and quiet. Ideal for all ages. Situated near village and loch. Ground floor rooms.

TV

W V

B&B

Heron's Flight
Dolan and Ann MacKenzie, Plockton, Ross-shire, IV52 8TL
Tel/Fax: 01599 544220
E-mail: ann@heronsflight.free-online.co.uk
Web: www.usq.edu.au/users/huntera/heronsflight

3 Double | 2 En Suite fac, 1 Priv.NOT ensuite | B&B per person from £18.50 Double | Open Jan-Dec excl Xmas/New Year

Traditional Highland hospitality in friendly family home in very quiet location on shores of Loch Carron. Ample private car parking. 5 minutes walk to village centre.

V

VAT is shown at 17.5%: changes in this rate may affect prices.

Key to symbols is on back flap.

Plockton, Ross-shire | **Map Ref: 3F9**

B&B

Mrs Janet Mackenzie Jones
Tomacs, Frithard, Plockton, Ross-shire, IV52 8TQ
Tel: 01599 544321

1 Twin	1 En Suite fac	B&B per person	Open Jan-Dec
2 Double	1 Priv.NOT ensuite	£16.00-£20.00 Dbl/Twn	
	1 Pub Bath/Show		

A warm welcome in very comfortable family home in quiet location in village of Plockton. Lovely views of Lochcarron and Applecross hills from bedrooms.

TV C W V

B&B

Minvaugh
2 Railway Cottages, Plockton, Ross-shire, IV52 8TT
Tel: 01599 544333

1 Single	1 Pub Bath/Show	B&B per person	Open Jan-Dec excl
1 Double		from £16.00 Single	Xmas/New Year
1 Family		from £16.00 Double	

The warmest of Highland welcomes in traditional 100 year old cottage with elevated position and splendid views over Plockton. 5 minutes walk to village centre, shops, pubs and restaurants.

P C V

★★★

B&B

'Seabank'
6 Bank Street, Plockton, Ross-shire, IV52 8TP
Tel/Fax: 01599 544221
Web: http://seabank-plockton.co.uk

1 Single	1 En Suite fac	B&B per person	Open Jan-Dec excl
2 Double	2 Priv.NOT ensuite	from £18.00 Single	Xmas/New Year
		from £18.00 Double	

Very friendly welcome in our traditional home situated in very quiet waterside location. Only 2 minutes walk to Plockton village centre and hotels.

TV P W V

Poolewe, Ross-shire | **Map Ref: 3F7**

★★★

B&B

Benlair
Near Cove, Poolewe, Ross-shire, IV22 2LS
Tel: 01445 781354

2 Twin	All En Suite	B&B per person
		from £20.00 Dbl/Twn

Comfortable family run cottage in tranquil setting with superb views over the sea, 200 yards from sandy beach, near village of Cove. 7 miles from Inverewe Gardens.

TV P V

Poolewe, Ross-shire

Map Ref: 3F7

B&B

Creagard B&B
2 Naast, Poolewe, Ross-shire
Tel: 01445 781389

1 Twin 1 Double	1 Pub Bath/Show	B&B per person from £14.00 Single from £15.00 Dbl/Twn	Open Apr-Oct B&B + Eve.Meal from £24.00

Modern croft house with outstanding views across Loch Ewe to the Munros beyond. Dinner and lounge available. 3.5 miles from Inverewe Gardens. Evening tea and home baking served in the lounge.

Rogart, Sutherland

Map Ref: 4B6

B&B

Tigh na Fuaran
Rogart, Sutherland, IV28 3UA
Tel/Fax: 01408 641224

1 Twin 1 Double	1 Pub Bath/Show	B&B per person from £16.00 Single from £16.00 Dbl/Twn	Open May-Sep

Modern bungalow, quiet location with ample parking and terraced gardens.

Scourie, Sutherland

Map Ref: 3H4

B&B

An-Sean-Dachaich
55 Scourie, Scourie, Sutherland, IV27 4TE
Tel: 01971 502001
E-mail: margaret.elder@btinternet.com

1 Twin 2 Double	All En Suite	B&B per person from £20.00 Single from £17.00 Dbl/Twn	Open Apr -Oct

Comfortable Bed and Breakfast in former Crofter's house. Views across Scourie Bay. Private parking. All en-suite rooms. Ideal base for touring North West Scotland. Within walking distance of hotel and restaurant. Quiet yet central location within the village.

B&B

Fasgadh
Scouriemore, Scourie, Sutherland, IV27 4TG
Tel: 01971 502402
E-mail: sandra@scouriemore.co.uk

1 Twin 1 Double	1 Priv.NOT ensuite 1 Ensuite fac	B&B per person £16.00-£18.00 Dbl/Twn	Open Mar-Oct Oct-Mar by arrangement

Modern purpose built bungalow, situated above village of Scourie, with views across village and bay. A short walk to village will take you to the villlage amenities, Hotel and restaurant, also the beach.

B&B

Greenhill
Scourie, by Lairg, Sutherland, IV27 4SV
Tel/Fax: 01971 502351
E-mail: evfraser@aol.com

1 Twin 2 Double	All En Suite	B&B per person from £21.00 Dbl/Twn	Open Apr-Oct

Comfortable family run Bed and Breakfast, located on the edge of Scourie. Restaurants within walking distance. Trips to Handa Island available within easy reach. All bedrooms en-suite. Full breakfast menu.

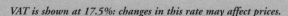

Scourie, Sutherland — Map Ref: 3H4

B&B

Scourie Lodge
Scourie, via Lairg, Sutherland, IV27 4TE
Tel: 01971 502248

1 Twin, 2 Double | 2 En Suite fac, 1 Priv.NOT ensuite, 1 Pub Bath/Show | B&B per person £25.00-£35.00 Single, £22.50-£30.00 Dbl/Twn | Open Mar-Nov, B&B + Eve.Meal £37.50-£45.00

Beautifully situated on Scourie Bay on the west coast of Sutherland. Near its picturesque harbour. Location for visiting the many local beauty spots. The beautiful gardens can be accessed by guests at their leisure.

Shieldaig, Ross-shire — Map Ref: 3F8

MRS M. C. CALCOTT

TIGH FADA, 117 DOIRE-AONAR, NR SHIELDAIG, BY STRATHCARRON IV54 8XH

Telephone: 01520 755248 Fax: 01520 755248

Quiet accommodation in comfortable modern crofthouse set in isolated crofting village with access to seashore and woodlands. Situated off the A896 on Kenmor Road, approximately 2 miles from Shieldaig. Good centre for walking, nature watching, photography, painting, home produced wools and knitwear available from croft shop.

B&B

Mrs M C Calcott
Tigh Fada, 117 Doireaonar, nr Shieldaig,
by Strathcarron, Ross-shire, IV54 8XH
Tel/Fax: 01520 755248

1 Twin, 1 Double, 1 Family | 2 Pub Bath/Show | B&B per person from £14.50 Dbl/Twn | Open Jan-Nov, B&B + Eve.Meal from £23.00

Quiet accommodation in comfortable modern crofthouse set in isolated crofting village with access to seashore and woodlands. Situated off A896 Kenmore Road, approximately 2 miles from Shieldaig. Good centre for walking, nature watching, photography, painting. Home produced wools and knitwear available from Croft Shop.

Bernisdale, by Portree, Isle of Skye, Inverness-shire — Map Ref: 3D8

★★★★ B&B

Lochview
45 Park, Bernisdale, Isle of Skye, IV51 9NT
Tel: 01470 532736

1 Family, 1 Double | 1 Priv.NOT ensuite, En Suite fac | B&B per person £19.00-£28.00 Single, £19.00-£24.00 Fam/Dbl | Open Mar-Nov

Very comfortable modern family home in quiet elevated position enjoying splendid views over croftland and Loch Snizort. Ideal base for relaxing and touring the North end of Skye.

Breakish, Isle of Skye, Inverness-shire — Map Ref: 3F10

B&B

Ashfield
14 Upper Breakish, Isle of Skye, Inverness-shire, IV42 8PY
Tel: 01471 822301

2 Double | 1 En Suite fac | B&B per person from £16.00 Double | Open Mar-Oct

A warm Highland welcome in our very comfortable bungalow set in croftland. Open views to Scalpay, Pabbay and the Applecross Mountains on the Mainland. Gaelic spoken. Four miles from Skye bridge.

Breakish, Isle of Skye, Inverness-shire — Map Ref: 3F10

B&B

Nethallan
12 Lower Breakish, Breakish, Isle of Skye, Inverness-shire, IV42 8QA
Tel: 01471 822771

2 Double, 1 Family — All En Suite — B&B per person from £25.00 Single, from £18.00 Double — Open Jan-Dec excl Xmas/New Year

Warm friendly welcome in spacious traditional Skye house. Set in a quiet waters edge location with stunning views over islands to The Cuillins and Rasaay. Secluded sandy beach nearby. Abundant local wildlife including otters, seals and many birds.

B&B

Moidart
Lower Breakish, Isle of Skye, IV42 8QA
Tel: 01471 822857 Fax: 01471 820176
E.mail: chia857@netscapeonline.co.uk

1 Twin, 1 Double — All En Suite — B&B per person from £25.00 Single, from £18.00 Dbl/Twn — Open Mar-Nov

A friendly welcome at this family B&B magnificent views over Broadford Bay and the Red Cuillins. Comfortable accommodation all ensuite. Colour TV and tea tray.

B&B

Tir Alainn
8 Upper Breakish, Isle of Skye, IV42 8PY
Tel: 01471 822366 Fax: 01471 822462
E-mail: ttmkn@tiralainn.demon.co.uk
Web: www.visitskye.com

2 Double — All En Suite — B&B per person from £30.00 Single, from £22.00 Double — Open Mar-Oct

Modern bungalow with magnificent views to Cuillin and Torridon hills and often enjoying splendid sunsets over the sea. Friendly welcome and comfortable warm rooms.

Broadford, Isle of Skye, Inverness-shire | Map Ref: 3E10

ASHGROVE

11 Black Park, Broadford, Isle of Skye IV49 9DE
Telephone and Fax: 01471 822327

Comfortable accommodation in three-bedroomed bungalow. Colour TV lounge, tea-making facilities. Two bedrooms with WHB, shower and toilet ensuite, one bedroom with private bathroom. Seven miles from Skye Bridge. Turn off main road at Lime Park/Black Park junction.

From £18 to £20 per person. ★★★ B&B

B&B

Ashgrove
11 Black Park, Broadford, Isle of Skye, IV49 9DE
Tel/Fax: 01471 822327

1 Twin, 2 Double | 2 En Suite fac, 1 Priv.NOT ensuite | B&B per person from £18.00 Dbl/Twn | Open Jan-Dec

Modern bungalow with fine views of sea and mountains.

B&B

'Caberfeidh'
1 Lower Harrapool, Broadford, Isle of Skye, Inverness-shire, IV49 9AQ
Tel: 01471 822664

2 Double | All En Suite | B&B per person from £20.00 Double | Open Jan-Nov excl New Year

Modern bungalow situated at waters edge. Minutes walk from Broadford. A warm welcome, very comfortable rooms and a substantial home cooked breakfast.

B&B

Cluaidh
Bayview Crescent, Broadford, Isle of Skye, IV49 9BD
Tel: 01471 822604

1 Twin, 1 Double | All En Suite | B&B per person from £18.00 Dbl/Twn | Open Apr-Oct

Situated in a quiet residential area, this family run B&B offers comfortable ensuite rooms. Plenty to do and see in the area and a wide variety of birdlife and wildlife about. Plenty eating places nearby. Private Parking.

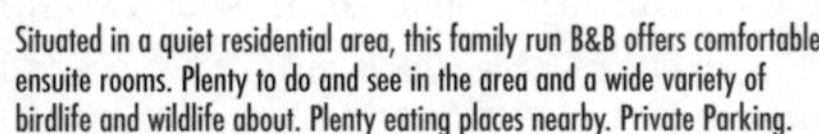

B&B

Corry Lodge
Broadford, Isle of Skye, IV49 9AA
Tel: 01471 822235 Fax: 01471 822318
Web: www.corrylodge.co.uk

1 Twin, 3 Double | All En Suite | B&B per person from £25.00 Dbl/Twn | Open 31Mar-Oct, B&B + Eve.Meal from £42.50

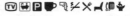

Late 18c shooting lodge, totally restored to its former splendour on 80 acre estate stretching to the shoreline. Traditional evening meal available using fresh local produce.

Important: Prices stated are estimates and may be subject to amendments

Broadford, Isle of Skye, Inverness-shire

Map Ref: 3E10

B&B

Earsary
7-8 Harrapool, Broadford, Isle of Skye, Inverness-shire, IV49 9AQ
Tel: 01471 822697 Fax: 01471 822781
E-mail: earsary@isleofskye.net
Web: www.isleofskye.net

Modern house with high standard of accommodation on working croft with pedigree Highland Cattle. Panoramic views over Broadford Bay. Special Xmas & New Year breaks. Property on working farm/croft. Gaelic spoken.

1 Twin
1 Double
1 Family

All En Suite
1 Pub bath/Show

B&B per person
from £20.00 Single
from £18.00 Dbl/Twn

Open Jan-Dec

V

B&B

Fairwinds
Elgol Road, Broadford, Isle of Skye, Inverness-shire, IV49 9AB
Tel/Fax: 01471 822270
E-mail: janet.donaldson@talk21.com

Peacefully situated bungalow in extensive garden overlooking Broadford River and the mountains. Bicycles for hire. Ideal base for walking, touring and birdwatching.

1 Twin
2 Double

All En Suite

B&B per person
from £20.00 Dbl/Twn

Open Mar-Oct

W V

B&B

Hillcrest
Black Park, Broadford, Isle of Skye, Inverness-shire, IV49 9AE
Tel: 01471 822375

Family run bed and breakfast with off road parking. Eating places within 0.5 mile (1km) distance. Children welcome.

1 Twin
1 Family

All En Suite

B&B per person
from £16.00 Twin

Open Jan-Nov

B&B

'Hillview'
Black Park, Broadford, Isle of Skye, IV49 9DE
Tel: 01471 822083

Very comfortable modern home in elevated position with views over to Applecross and Torridon Hills. Good location for Cuillin Hills and Skye Touring.

1 Double
1 Family

1 En Suite
1 Priv facilities

B&B per person
from £17.00 Double

Open Jan-Dec excl Xmas/New Year

C

Broadford, Isle of Skye, Inverness-shire — Map Ref: 3E10

LIME STONE COTTAGE

KATHIE M McLOUGHLIN, 4 LIME PARK, BROADFORD, SKYE IV49 9AG

Telephone: 01471 822142

Welcome to Lime Stone Cottage. A charming turn of the century crofters cottage originally built for workers at the local lime kiln now fully restored offering highest standards of modern comfort whilst retaining all its original character. Add to this a truly romantic atmosphere combined with panoramic views over Broadford Bay and the mainland beyond. Experience the real delight of a living fire in the comfortable quiet surrounding of the sitting/dining room or take the air in the floral garden and feel the rolling sea breezes with scent of heather. All this within easy walking distance of local amenities.

B&B

Kathie M McLoughlin

Lime Stone Cottage, 4 Lime Park, Broadford, Isle of Skye, Inverness-shire, IV49 9AG
Tel: 01471 822142

1 Twin
2 Double

All En Suite

B&B per person
from £30.00 Single
£18.00-£25.00 Dbl/Twn

Open Jan-Dec

Traditional detached, tastefully refurbished limestone workers cottage. Situated in Broadford.

Ptarmigan

Broadford, Isle of Skye IV49 9AQ

Telephone: 01471 822744 Fax: 01471 822745

e.mail: info@ptarmigan-cottage.com Web: www.ptarmigan-cottage.com

15 metres from seashore, all bedrooms are on the ground floor and enjoy truly outstanding views over Broadford Bay and beyond. Ideal otter/bird watching - binoculars and tide clock supplied. Superb central location for touring with the spectacular world famous Cuillins nearby and the mountainous mainland within 10 minutes drive.

B&B

Ptarmigan

Broadford, Isle of Skye, Inverness-shire, IV49 9AQ
Tel: 01471 822744 Fax: 01471 822745
E.mail: info@ptarmigan-cottage.com
Web: www.ptarmigan-cottage.com

1 Twin
2 Double

All En Suite
1 Pub Bath/Show

B&B per person
from £24.00 Dbl/Twn

Open Jan-Dec

Attractive, friendly family home on Broadford Bay. Panoramic views across islands to mainland. 15 metres over lawns to seashore. All rooms on ground floor and with views over water.

Important: Prices stated are estimates and may be subject to amendments

Broadford, Isle of Skye, Inverness-shire

Map Ref: 3E10

B&B

Mrs Dolina Robertson
Westside, Elgol Road, Broadford, Isle of Skye, Inverness-shire, IV49 9AB
Tel/Fax: 01471 822320
E-mail: dolly.skye@talk21.com

A warm welcome and good food at this modern bungalow in a quiet lane, with views across to Beinn Na Cailleach. Full central heating. Convenient for all local facilities and touring Skye. Gaelic Spoken.

1 Single, 1 Twin, 1 Double — All En Suite

B&B per person from £22.00 Single, from £22.00 Dbl/Twn

Open Feb-Nov

W V

B&B

Mrs Scott
Tigh-na-Mara, Lower Harrapool, Broadford, Isle of Skye, Inverness-shire, IV49 9AQ
Tel/Fax: 01471 822475
E-mail: jackieconder@yahoo.co.uk

Family room in 150 year old cottage on the sea shore. 8 miles from Skye Bridge. Own sitting room. French and Italian spoken, children welcome.

1 Family — 1 Priv.NOT ensuite, 1 Pub Bath/Show

B&B per person £17.00-£18.00 Double

Open Apr-Oct

C V

by Broadford, Isle of Skye, Inverness-shire

Map Ref: 3E10

B&B

Mrs Flora A MacLeod
Hazelwood Cottage, Heaste, by Broadford, Isle of Skye, Inverness-shire, IV49 9BN
Tel: 01471 822294 Fax: 01471 822161

Modern bungalow in peaceful setting on working croft, with panoramic views over Loch Eishort towards the hills of Knoydart.

1 Twin, 1 Double — All En Suite

B&B per person £18.00-£21.00 Dbl/Twn

Open Apr-Nov

C V

GUEST HOUSE

The Skye Picture House
Ard Dorch, Broadford, Isle of Skye, Inverness-shire, IV49 9AJ
Tel: 01471 822531 Fax: 01471 822305
E-mail: gill@skyepicturehouse.co.uk
Web: www.skyepicturehouse.co.uk

Spacious modern home in stunning waterside location looking over to Scalpay. Very friendly welcome. Home cooking. Professionally run photographic courses and holidays available. Proprietors both RPS distinction holders.

2 Single, 1 Twin, 2 Double, 1 Family — 4 En Suite fac, 1 Pub Bath/Show, 1 Priv.NOT ensuite

B&B per person £18.00-£26.00 Single, £18.00-£26.00 Dbl/Twn

Open Jan-Dec; B&B + Eve.Meal £29.00-£37.00

C W V

Carbost, Isle of Skye, Inverness-shire — Map Ref: 3D9

B&B

Blue Lobster
Forester's House, Grula, Glen Eynort, Isle of Skye IV47 8SG
Tel: 01478 640320
E-mail: bluelobster_grula@yahoo.com

2 Twin, 1 Double | 1 Pub Bath/Show, 2 Limited ensuite | B&B per person from £24.00 Single, from £18.00 Dbl/Twn | Open Mar-Jan excl Xmas/New Year, B&B + Eve.Meal from £26.00

Simple informal and friendly accomadation in early 1950's tradtional wooden house. Peaceful and remote area amidst hills and forest. Close to sea loch.

Dunvegan, Isle of Skye, Inverness-shire — Map Ref: 3D9

B&B

Catriona Allan
4 Harlosh, Dunvegan, Isle of Skye, Inverness-shire, IV55 8ZG
Tel: 01470 521248
E-mail: Wallan8333@aol.com

1 Double, 1 Family | All En Suite | B&B per person from £18.00 Single, from £18.00 Double | Open Mar-Oct

A warm highland welcome in comfortable modern family home in quiet crofting community. Splendid sea and mountain views. 4 miles from Dunvegan. Families with children most welcome.

KILMUIR PARK

Dunvegan, Isle of Skye IV55 8GU
Tel/Fax: 01470 521586 e.mail: gmmilne@aol.com

George and Mairi extend a warm welcome to their recently built home. Situated close to Dunvegan Castle and enjoying panoramic views of MacLeods tables. Quality accommodation is complimented by freshly prepared traditional meals. Ideal base for touring Skye.

B&B

Kilmuir Park
Dunvegan, Isle of Skye, IV55 8GU
Tel/Fax: 01470 521586
E-mail: gmmilne@aol.com

2 Twin, 1 Double | All En Suite | B&B per person from £25.00 Single, from £25.00 Dbl/Twn | Open Jan-Dec, B&B + Eve.Meal from £40.00

Modern family home with panoramic views to Macleods' Tables. 2 kms from the centre of Dunvegan village also ideal for touring the northern part of the island. Evening meals available. Fishing and other field sports can be arranged on request.

GUEST HOUSE

Roskhill House
Roskhill, Dunvegan, Isle of Skye, Inverness-shire, IV55 8ZD
Tel: 01470 521317 Fax: 01470 521761
E-mail: stay@roskhill.demon.co.uk
Web: www.roskhill.demon.co.uk

1 Twin, 3 Double | 3 En Suite fac, 1 Priv.NOT ensuite | B&B per person from £32.00 Single, from £27.00 Dbl/Twn | Open Jan-Dec excl Xmas/New Year, B&B + Eve.Meal from £41.50

This cosy crofthouse is beautifully situated 3 miles south of Dunvegan Castle, ideal for touring this historic & romantic island, walking, climbing, bird watching, etc. Delicious old fashioned home cooking prepared fresh each day and served in the stone walled dining room with log fire & resident's bar. High standards, peaceful surroundings and personal attention assured. Your 'home away from home', stay a while.

Dunvegan, Isle of Skye, Inverness-shire
Map Ref: 3D9

★★★
B&B

Uiginish Farmhouse
Dunvegan, Isle of Skye, IV55 8ZR
Tel: 01470 521431

1 Twin
2 Double

All En Suite

B&B per person
£18.00-£22.00 Single
£18.00-£22.00 Dbl/Twn

Open May-Oct

Modern farmhouse on working farm. Scenic lochside location looking towards Dunvegan Castle. Quiet rural area only 4 miles from village with all its amenities.

by Dunvegan, Isle of Skye, Inverness-shire
Map Ref: 3D9

★★★
B&B

5 Harlosh
Dunvegan, Isle of Skye, Inverness-shire, IV55 8ZG
Tel: 01470 521483

1 Twin
1 Double

All En Suite
1 Pub Bath/Show

B&B per person
from £18.00 Single
from £18.00 Dbl/Twn

Open Mar-Oct

Very comfortable modern croft in elevated rural location with magnificent views over Loch Bracadale and to Cuillin Hills. Very friendly warm welcome. Good base for touring Skye, hill walking and other outdoor pursuits. Gaelic spoken.

Elgol, Isle of Skye, Inverness-shire
Map Ref: 3E10

ROWAN COTTAGE

9 Glasnakille, by Elgol, Isle of Skye IV49 9BQ
Tel: 01471 866287 Fax: 01471 866287
Web: www.rowancott.demon.co.uk

Situated in a beautiful quiet location with panoramic views. Specialising in fresh local seafood dinners. The perfect base for boat trips to famous Loch Coruisk in the heart of the Cuillin Mountains. Send for a brochure or visit our web site.

★★★★
B&B

Rowan Cottage
9 Glasnakille, by Elgol, Isle of Skye,
Inverness-shire, IV49 9BQ
Tel/Fax: 01471 866287
E-mail: rowan@rowancott.demon.co.uk
Web: www.rowancott.demon.co.uk

2 Double
1 Twin

1 En Suite fac

B&B per person
£20.00-£25.00 Dbl/Twn

Open Mar-Nov
B&B + Eve.Meal
from £36.00

Traditional croft house with log fire. Magnificent views to Sleat and Rhum. Very cosy, comfortable rooms, warm welcome local seafood dinners – All fresh home cooking available.

Glenhinnisdale, Isle of Skye, Inverness-shire
Map Ref: 3D8

★★★
B&B

Mrs I Nicolson
Cnoc Preasach, Glenhinnisdale, Snizort,
Isle of Skye, Inverness-shire, IV51
Tel: 01470 542406

1 Twin
1 Double
1 Family

1 Pub Bath/Show
1 En Suite fac

B&B per person
from £15.50 Single
from £15.50 Dbl/Twn
£17.00 En Suite

Open Mar-Oct
B&B + Eve.Meal
from £25.00

Farmhouse in quiet elevated position overlooking Glenhinisdale. 6 miles (9.6Kms) from Uig Ferry. 100 acre croft. Home cooking.

Kilmuir, Isle of Skye, Inverness-shire | Map Ref: 3D7

Kilmuir House
Kilmuir
Near Uig
Isle of Skye
IV51 9YN
Tel: 01470 542262
Fax: 01470 542461

Lovely old manse in large walled garden overlooking Loch Snizort and Outer Hebrides. Furnished with antiques and centrally heated throughout, we offer excellent home cooking using local produce and our own free-range eggs. Kilmuir is steeped in history and Gaelic culture and tradition is still much in evidence here.

e.mail: phelpskilmuirhouseskye@btinternet.com

★★★
B&B

Kilmuir House
Kilmuir, nr Uig, Isle of Skye, IV51 9YN
Tel: 01470 542262 Fax: 01470 542461
E-mail: phelpskilmuirhouseskye@btinternet.com

1 Twin
2 Double

1 En suite fac
2 Pub Bath/Show

B&B per person
from £20.00 Single
from £20.00 Dbl/Twn

Open Jan-Dec
B&B + Eve.Meal
from £30.00

Former manse in superb situation overlooking Loch Snizort to Outer Isles. Warm hospitality and high standard of home cooking using fresh local produce.

Kyleakin, Isle of Skye, Inverness-shire | Map Ref: 3F10

Blairdhu House
Old Kyle Farm Road, Kyleakin, Isle of Skye IV41 8PR
Tel: 01599 534760 Fax: 01599 534623
e.mail: blairdhuskye@compuserve.com
Web: ourworld.compuserve.com/homepages/blairdhuskye

Beautifully situated house with the most spectacular scenery. All rooms ensuite with TV, radio, tea/coffee making facilities, hairdryers. Ideal for bird-watching – binoculars supplied. Cruises available around the sheltered water to see seals and a variety of birds on our cruising boat *The Seacruise*.

★★★★
B&B

Blairdhu House
Old Kyle Farm Road, Kyleakin, Isle of Skye, IV41 8PR
Tel: 01599 534760 Fax: 01599 534623
E.mail: blairdhuskye@compuserve.com
Web: http://ourworld.compuserve.com/homepages/blairdhuskye

1 Twin
1 Double
1 Family

All En Suite

B&B per person
from £20.00 Dbl/Twn

Open Jan-Dec excl
Xmas/New Year

A friendly welcome at this family run B&b, a modern home just over the Skye Bridge. Excellent views and comfortable ensuite rooms. Non smoking house.

★★★
HOTEL

Dunringell Hotel
Kyleakin, Isle of Skye, Inverness-shire, IV41 8PQ
Tel: 01599 534180 Fax: 01599 534460
E-mail: holiday@dunringell-hotel.co.uk
Web: www.dunringell-hotel.co.uk

4 Single
1 Twin
6 Double
7 Family

11 En Suite fac
7 Pub Bath/Show

B&B per person
£18.00-£30.00 Single
£18.00-£30.00 Dbl/Twn

Open Mar-Nov
B&B + Eve.Meal
£32.00-£44.00

Country house hotel outside this attractive island village. Tranquil setting, fine mature garden. Close to bridge. Some annexe accommodation. Unlicensed.

Kyleakin, Isle of Skye, Inverness-shire

Map Ref: 3F10

★★★ B&B

Mrs A MacRae
17 Kyleside, Kyleakin, Isle of Skye, IV41 8PW
Tel: 01599 534197
e.mail: adjmacrae@talk21.com

1 Single 1 Pub Bath/Show
1 Double 1 Priv.NOT ensuite

B&B per person
£16.00-£17.00 Single
£16.00-£18.00 Double

Open Jan-Dec

Semi-detached home with splendid views over the water to Kyle of Lochalsh. Very comfortable rooms and a warm friendly welcome. Convenient for all village amenities. Gaelic spoken.

TV

C V

★★★ B&B

Morrison B&B
4 Olaf Road, Kyleakin, Isle of Skye, Inverness-shire, IV41 8PJ

1 Single 1 Pub Bath/Show
2 Double

B&B per person
from £15.50 Single
from £15.50 Double

Open Apr-Nov

Very comfortable rooms and a warm welcome in cosy B&B in quiet residential area of Kyleakin. Convenient for bus route, 2 mins walk to village pubs and restaurants.

TV

V

Ord, Sleat, Isle of Skye, Inverness-shire

Map Ref: 3E10

★★★ B&B

Fiordhem
Ord, Sleat, Isle of Skye, Inverness-shire, IV44 8RN
Tel: 01471 855226
E-mail: sales@fiordhem.co.uk
Web: www.fiordhem.co.uk

1 Twin All En Suite
2 Double

B&B per person
£25.00-£27.00 Dbl/Twn

Open Apr-Sep
B&B + Eve.Meal
from £40.00-£45.00

Unique stone cottage, 20 feet from lochside. Breathtaking views of Cuillins and the Small Isles. Location of distinction.

TV

W

Penifiler, by Portree, Isle of Skye, Inverness-shire

Map Ref: 3E9

★★★ B&B

Caberfeidh
2 Heatherfield, Portree, Isle of Skye, Inverness-shire, IV51 9NE
Tel: 01478 612820
E-mail: msmmack@aol.com

1 Twin 1 En Suite fac
2 Double 2 Pub Bath/Show

B&B per person
£17.00-£20.00 Dbl/Twn

Open Apr-Oct

Traditional cottage in beautiful waters edge location with views to Portree and Quirang. A warm Highland welcome and very comfortable rooms.

P

C

Portree, Isle of Skye, Inverness-shire

Map Ref: 3E9

★★★★ B&B

Almond Bank
Viewfield Road, Portree, Isle of Skye, Inverness-shire, IV51 9EU
Tel: 01478 612696 Fax: 01478 613114
E-mail: jansvans@aol.com

2 Twin 3 En Suite fac
2 Double 1 Priv.NOT ensuite

B&B per person
£24.50-£35.00 Single
£25.00-£30.00 Dbl/Twn

Open Jan-Dec

Modern house on the outskirts of Portree. Well appointed lounge and dining room with panoramic views of Portree Bay.

TV P

C £ W V

Portree, Isle of Skye, Inverness-shire | **Map Ref: 3E9**

B&B

An Traigh
3 Heatherfield, Penifiler, Portree, Isle of Skye IV51 9NE
Tel: 01478 613236
E-mail: an_traigh@yahoo.co.uk

1 Single, 1 Twin, 1 Double — 2 En Suite fac, 1 Priv.NOT ensuite — B&B per person £18.00-£20.00 Single, £18.00-£20.00 Dbl/Twn — Open Apr-Oct

Very comfortable modern home in outstanding shoreside location overlooking Portree Bay to the village and the Storr beyond. 5 mins drive to Portree, shops, restaurants and attractions.

B&B

'Balloch'
Viewfield Road, Portree, Isle of Skye, Inverness-shire, IV51 9ES
Tel: 01478 612093

1 Twin, 3 Double — All En Suite — B&B per person from £23.00 Dbl/Twn — Open Mar-Nov

Large comfortable villa in own garden. 5 minutes walk to Portree town centre and a good range of restaurants and other local amenities.

W V

B&B

Mrs E Brown
'Feochan', 11 Fisherfield, Portree, Isle of Skye, IV51 9EU
Tel/Fax: 01478 613508
E-mail: feochan@lineone.net

1 Twin, 2 Double — All En Suite — B&B per person from £18.00 Dbl/Twn — Open Apr-Oct

Family home with spendid views over Portree, a warm welcome and very comfortable rooms. Ideal base for touring the island and exploring the Cuillins and Trotternish Ridge.

V

B&B

Sandra Campbell B&B
9 Stormyhill Road, Portree, Isle of Skye, IV51 9DY
Tel: 01478 613332
E-mail: sandra_campbell_b_b@yahoo.co.uk

3 Double — All En Suite — B&B per person from £18.00 Double — Open Jan-Dec

A very warm welcome in comfortable family home. 5 minutes walk from Portree village centre, open all year.

B&B

Easdale Bed & Breakfast
Bridge Road, Portree, Isle of Skye, IV51 9ER
Tel: 01478 613244
Mobile: 07769 922261

1 Single, 2 Double — 2 Ensuite fac, 1 Pub Bath/Show — Open Jan-Dec

Overlooking Portree Bay and the Cuillin mountain range. Secluded bungalow situated in the centre of Portree. Central location for touring the island. Friendly welcome.

C

Portree, Isle of Skye, Inverness-shire — **Map Ref: 3E9**

B&B

Glendale
2 Carn Dearg Place, Portree, Isle of Skye, Inverness-shire, IV51 9PZ
Tel/Fax: 01478 613149

1 Single 2 Twin 1 Double	2 En Suite fac 2 Pub Bathrooms	B&B per person from £23.00 Single from £20.00 Dbl/Twn	Open Jan-Dec

Detached bungalow within easy walking distance of the centre of Portree.Very friendly warm welcome. Families particularly welcome. Singles welcome.

C W V

B&B

Grenitote
9 Martin Crescent, Portree, Isle of Skye, Inverness-shire, IV51 9DW
Tel: 01478 612808

1 Twin 1 Double	All En Suite	B&B per person from £17.00 Dbl/Twn	Open Jan-Dec excl Xmas/New Year

A warm welcome and comfortable rooms in our friendly home in quiet residential area 5 minutes walk from Portree village centre. Gaelic spoken.

V

B&B

Highfield Bed & Breakfast
Viewfield Road, Portree, Isle of Skye, IV51 9ES
Tel: 01478 612781

1 Twin 2 Double	All En Suite	B&B per person £20.00-£24.00 Dbl/Twn	Open Mar-Oct

Bungalow property 5 minutes walk from Portree. Quiet location overlooking Portree Bay. Private parking and large garden.

V

B&B

Elizabeth MacDonald
25 Urquhart Place, Portree, Isle of Skye Inverness-shire, IV51 9HJ
Tel: 01478 612374
E-mail: elizabeth.macdonald@talk21.com

1 Single 1 Twn/Trpl 1 Double	1 En Suite fac 1 Pub Bath/Show	B&B per person from £18.00 Single from £20.00 Dbl/Twn from £15.00 Triple	Open Jan-Dec

Traditional Highland hospitality in friendly family home. 1 mile from town centre. Gaelic spoken.

C W V

B&B

D A MacKinnon
22 Kitson Crescent, Portree, Isle of Skye, Inverness-shire
Tel: 01478 612068

1 Double 1 Family	1 Pub Bath/Show	B&B per person from £22.00 Single from £16.00 Double	Open Jan-Dec

A friendly welcome in comfortable home with good views over Portree Bay. In elevated quiet residential area only 5 mins walk from village centre. Gaelic spoken.

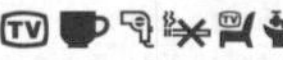

Portree, Isle of Skye, Inverness-shire — **Map Ref: 3E9**

B&B ★★★

Mrs M MacLeod
The Sheiling, Stormyhill, Portree, Isle of Skye, Inverness-shire, IV51 9DL
Tel: 01478 612278

1 Single, 1 Double, 1 Family — 1 Pub Bath/Show — B&B per person from £18.00 Single, from £17.00 Double — Open Mar-Nov

Traditional family home 2 mins walk from Portree village centre. Warm friendly welcome, gaelic spoken.

B&B ★★★

Mrs A MacSween
Cnoc Iain, 3 Sluggans, Portree, Isle of Skye, Inverness-shire, IV51 9LY
Tel: 01478 612143
E-mail: cnociain@tinyworld.co.uk
Web: www.cnociain.com

1 Twin, 2 Double — All En Suite — B&B per person £19.00-£25.00 Dbl/Twn; Room only per person £15.00-£20.00 — Open Mar-Oct

Large modern house in elevated position overlooking Portree and out to Rasaay. Warm friendly welcome and comfortable rooms.

B&B ★★★★

Mardon
Achachork, Portree, Isle of Skye, IV51 9HT
Tel: 01478 612330
Web: http://mardon.b.breakfast.achnachork.porteee

2 Double — All En Suite — B&B per person from £20.00 Double — Open Apr-Oct

Beautifully furnished and welcoming home with many personal touches. In quiet location with splendid views over Portree to Cuillin Hills. 3 minutes drive north of the village

---

B&B ★★★★

Ms Catriona Matheson
'Drumorell', 15 Fraser Crescent, Portree, Isle of Skye, IV51 9DS
Tel: 01478 613058/612414

1 Double, 1 Family — 1 Pub Bath/Show, 1 Priv.NOT ensuite — B&B per person from £20.00 Single, from £18.00 Double — Open Jan-Dec excl Xmas/New Year

A very friendly welcome in comfortable home with an elevated corner position of quiet residential area, garden and patio area for guest use. Views to Portree Bay and Cuillins mountain range. 5 minutes walk to village square, shops and restaurants. Full Scottish and seafood breakfast available in new conservatory . House decorated to a very high standard. Limited parking. Family room with washbasin.

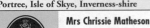

Portree, Isle of Skye, Inverness-shire — **Map Ref: 3E9**

★★★
B&B

Mrs Chrissie Matheson
No. 8 Storr Terrace, Portree, Isle of Skye, IV51 9LT
Tel: 01478 613174

2 Family | 1 Priv.NOT ensuite, 1 Pub Bath/Show | B&B per person £16.00-£20.00 Double; Room only per person £13.00-£16.00 | Open Apr-Nov

Very friendly and warm Bed & Breakfast in quiet area 10 minutes from the village. Families welcome.

C

★★★
B&B

Morray
Stormyhill Road, Portree, Isle of Skye
Inverness-shire, IV51 9DY
Tel: 01478 612462

1 Twin, 1 Double | 1 Pub Bath/Show | B&B per person £16.00-£17.00 Dbl/Twn | Open Apr-Oct

Modern Bungalow in quiet elevated position 10 mins walk from Portree Village centre. A warm welcome and very comfortable rooms.

V

★★★
B&B

Oronsay
1 Marsco Place, Portree, Isle of Skye,
Inverness-shire, IV51 9PH
Tel/Fax: 01478 612192 (home) Work: 01478 612873

1 Twin, 1 Double | 2 Priv.NOT ensuite | B&B per person from £20.00 Single; from £18.00 Dbl/Twn | Open Mar-Oct

Modern bungalow in elevated, quiet residential area, 2 minutes walk from Portree centre, shops and restaurants. Warm friendly welcome and views to Cuillins.

V

RICHARD & CLARE'S PLACE

5 Penifiler, By Portree, Isle of Skye, Inverness-shire IV51 9NF
Telephone: 01478 612476 Web: www.gael.net/rsmith

Off the beaten track. Traditional croft house. Close to Portree and central for touring Skye, offering comfortable friendly accommodation, all rooms with ensuite facilities, hospitality tray and central heating. Two double and one twin/double. Totally non-smoking. A warm welcome awaits. Details from Richard and Clare Smith.

★★★
B&B

'Richard and Clares Place'
5 Penifiler, by Portree, Isle of Skye,
Inverness-shire, IV51 9NF
Tel: 01478 612476
Web: www.gael.net/rsmith

1 Twin, 2 Double | All En Suite | B&B per person from £15.00 Single; from £15.00 Dbl/Twn; Room only per person from £15.00 | Open Jan-Dec excl Xmas

Traditional rural Skye crofthouse with fabulous panoramic views over Portree Bay. Very comfortable rooms and a warm family welcome.

C W V

Portree, Isle of Skye, Inverness-shire

Map Ref: 3E9

B&B

'Sgiathan Mara'
Hill Place, Portree, Isle of Skye, IV51 9GS.
Tel: 01478 612927

1 Twin
1 Double

All En Suite

B&B per person
from £22.00 Dbl/Twn

Open Apr-Oct

A very warm and comfortable welcome in modern home in elevated position on outskirts of Portree. Good views to Cullins. Ideal base for relaxing holidays. Fifteen to twenty minutes walk to village centre.

B&B

Woodlands
Viewfield Road, Portree, Isle of Skye, Inverness-shire
Tel/Fax: 01478 612980

1 Twin
1 Double

All En Suite fac

B&B per person
from £20.00 Dbl/Twn

Open Apr-Oct

Modern family home in elevated position overlooking Portree Bay. Quiet location but only 10mins walk from Portree town centre.

by Portree, Isle of Skye, Inverness-shire

Map Ref: 3E9

GUEST HOUSE

Corran House
Kensaleyre, Portree, Isle of Skye, IV51 9XE
Tel: 01470 532311

1 Single
1 Double
2 Family

1 En Suite fac
3 Priv.NOT ensuite

B&B per person
£22.00-£24.00 Single
£22.00-£24.00 Double

Open Jan-Nov

In a small country village overlooking Loch Snizort, 8 miles (10kms) from Portree and from Uig ferry terminal. Extensive gardens with lovely views.

★★★★

B&B

Moorside
20 Borve, by Portree, Isle of Skye, IV51 9PE
Tel/Fax: 01470 532301

2 Double

All En Suite

B&B per person
from £20.00 Double

Open Apr-Oct

Modern house situated on a working croft, within 3 miles of Portree. Ideally suited for touring the island. A warm welcome awaits you.

B&B

'Rubislaw' B&B
34 Bernisdale, Portree, Isle of Skye, IV51 9NS
Tel/Fax: 01470 532212

1 Twin
2 Double

2 Ensuite fac
1 Pub Bath/Show

B&B per person
from £16.00 Dbl/Twn

Open May-Sep
B&B + Eve.Meal
from £26.00

Extended croft house situated in the quiet, peaceful crofting community of Bernisdale . Just 7 miles from Portree and 15 miles from Dunvegan. Central for touring the north end of Skye. Gaelic spoken .

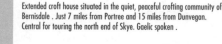

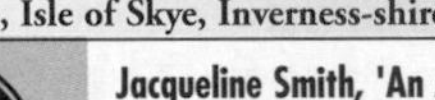

by Portree, Isle of Skye, Inverness-shire

Map Ref: 3E9

★★★★ B&B

Jacqueline Smith, 'An Airadh Shamhradh'

8 Camustianavaig, by Portree, Isle of Skye, IV51 9LQ
Tel: 01478 650224/613787
Fax: 01478 650224

1 Twin | All En Suite | B&B per person | Open Easter-Sep
1 Double | | from £20.00 Dbl/Twn

A warm welcome and very comfortable rooms in beautiful home with outstanding views over Camstianauaig Bay (where seals are often to be seen) to the Cuillin Hills. Extensive continental breakfast or traditional Scottish.

★★★ B&B

Tianavaig Bed & Breakfast

1/7 Camastianavaig, Braes, by Portree, Isle of Skye, Inverness-shire, IV51 9LQ
Tel: 01478 650325

1 Twin | 2 En Suite fac | B&B per person | Open Jan-Dec
2 Double | 1 Priv.NOT ensuite | £17.50-£20.00 Single
| | £17.50-£20.00 Dbl/Twn

A pretty rural location by the seashore, magnificent sea and mountain views. Guest lounge with log fire. Portree 5 miles (8kms).

C W V

Sleat, Isle of Skye, Inverness-shire

Map Ref: 3F10

★★★ B&B

Coille Challtainn

6 Duisdale Beag, Isleornsay, Sleat, Isle of Skye, Inverness-shire, IV43 8QU
Tel: 01471 833230
E-mail: macdonald@coillechalltainn.idps.co.uk

1 Twin | All En Suite | B&B per person | Open Mar-Nov
2 Double | | from £20.00 Single
| | from £19.00 Dbl/Twn

Modern bungalow in elevated position in small country village overlooking the sea. Gaelic spoken. Non-smoking house.

C V

Staffin, Isle of Skye, Inverness-shire

Map Ref: 3E8

★★ SMALL HOTEL

Glenview Inn & Restaurant

Culnacnoc, Staffin, Isle of Skye, Inverness-shire, IV51 9JH
Tel: 01470 562248 Fax: 01470 562211
E-mail: valtos@lineone.net
Web: www.SmoothHound.co.uk

1 Twin | 4 En Suite fac | B&B per person | Open Easter-Oct
3 Double | 1 Priv.NOT ensuite | from £20.00 Dbl/Twn | B&B + Eve.Meal
1 Family | | | from £37.50

Tastefully converted traditional island house, ideally situated for exploring Northern Skye. Friendly atmosphere, good food. Taste of Scotland. Adequate parking available. The restaurant specialises in local fish and seafood and a choice of traditional vegetarian and ethnic delicacies are offered.

C £ V

Struan, by Dunvegan, Isle of Skye, Inverness-shire

Map Ref: 3D9

★★★
B&B

'Glenside'
4 Totarder, Struan, Isle of Skye, Inverness-shire, IV56 8FW
Tel: 01470 572253

1 Twin	1 En Suite fac	B&B per person	Open Apr-Oct
1 Double	1 Priv.NOT ensuite	from £17.00 Dbl/Twn	

Traditional Highland hospitality on working 40 acre croft. Centrally situated for touring all areas of Skye.

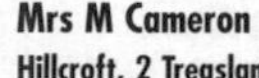

Treaslane, Isle of Skye, Inverness-shire

Map Ref: 3D8

★★★★
B&B

Mrs M Cameron
Hillcroft, 2 Treaslane, by Portree, Isle of Skye, Inverness-shire, IV51 9NX
Tel: 01470 582304

2 Double	All En Suite	B&B per person	Open Mar-Nov
		£18.00-£25.00 Double	

Friendly welcome at modernised house on working croft overlooking Loch Snizort. On A850 9 miles (14 kms) north of Portree.

Uig, Isle of Skye, Inverness-shire

Map Ref: 3D8

★★★
B&B

Ard-na-Mara
11 Idrigill, Uig, Isle of Skye, IV51 9XU
Tel: 01470 542281 Fax: 01470 542289
E-mail: accomadation.on.skye@talk21.com

2 Double	All En Suite	B&B per person	Open Jan-Dec
1 Twin/4		from £18.00 Dbl/Twn	

Warm welcome assured in this friendly home. 100yds from ferry terminal for Outer Hebrides.

★★★
B&B

Idrigill House
1 Idrigill, Uig, Isle of Skye, Inverness-shire, IV51 9XU
Tel: 01470 542398 Fax: 01470 542447
E.mail: s.watkins@lineone.net
Web: www.idrigill.co.uk

1 Single	1 En Suite fac	B&B per person	Open Jan-Dec excl
1 Twin	2 Priv.NOT ensuite	from £17.00 Single	Xmas/New Year
2 Double		from £17.00 Dbl/Twn	

A very warm and friendly welcome, quiet location with magnificent views. Convenient for ferry to Western Isles.

Uig, Isle of Skye, Inverness-shire — Map Ref: 3D8

★ B&B

Mrs A MacKinnon

Harris Cottage, Uig, Portree, Isle of Skye, IV51 9XU
Tel: 01470 542268
E-mail: harriscottage@altavista.net

1 Twin 1 Double 1 Family	2 Pub Bath/Show	B&B per person from £16.00 Single from £16.00 Dbl/Twn	Open Apr-Oct B&B + Eve.Meal from £28.00

A warm welcome in comfortable home with elevated position enjoys splendid open views over Uig Bay. 15 mins walk to ferry terminal.

★★★ B&B

Mrs M MacLeod

11 Earlish, Uig, Isle of Skye, IV51 9XL
Tel: 01470 542319

1 Twin 1 Double 1 Family	2 Pub Bath/Show	B&B per person from £16.50 Single from £16.50 Dbl/Twn	Open Mar-Nov

Crofthouse on a working croft about 2 miles (3kms) from Uig Ferry Terminal. Complimentary tea and cakes served at 9pm. Emphasis on friendly welcome and a hearty breakfast. Quiet location.

Waternish, Isle of Skye, Inverness-shire — Map Ref: 3D8

★★★ B&B

Hazelbank

16 Lochbay, Waternish, nr Dunvegan, Isle of Skye, IV55 8GD
Tel: 01470 592301

1 Twin 1 Double	All Ensuite fac	B&B per person from £26.00 Single from £22.00 Dbl/Twn Room only per person from £18.00	Open Easter-Nov

Modern bungalow in peaceful rural area with magnificent loch and sea views.

Spean Bridge, Inverness-shire — Map Ref: 3H12

The Braes Guest House

Spean Bridge PH34 4EU
Tel: 01397 712437 Fax: 01397 712108

This is a family run guest house, situated in its own grounds, overlooking Ben Nevis mountain range on outskirts of Spean Bridge. Ideal base for touring, climbing, ski-ing and fishing. Central heating, tea/coffee facilities, (6 rooms ensuite, 1 private facilities). Comfortable lounge with TV. Home cooking. Parking. **Open all year.**

★★★ GUEST HOUSE

The Braes Guest House

Tirindrish, Spean Bridge, Inverness-shire, PH34 4EU
Tel: 01397 712437 Fax: 01397 712108

1 Single 1 Twin 5 Double	6 En Suite fac 1 Priv.NOT ensuite	B&B per person from £22.00 Single from £20.00 Dbl/Twn	Open Jan-Dec B&B + Eve.Meal from £34.00

Family run guest house in elevated position with outstanding views of Ben Nevis Mountain Range. Set in own grounds with small terraced garden. Relax in our comfortable lounge and enjoy the magnificent view. Friendly welcome, tasty home-cooking, personal attention. Ample parking. Ideal base for touring and walking. Drying facilities available.

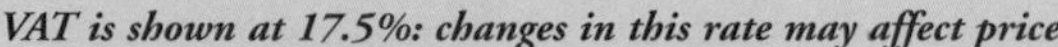

Spean Bridge, Inverness-shire — Map Ref: 3H12

★★★★ B&B

Coinachan Guest House

Gairlochy Road, Spean Bridge, Inverness-shire, PH34 4EG
Tel/Fax: 01397 712417
E-mail: coinachan@supernet

1 Twin, 3 Double — All En Suite — B&B per person from £20.00 Dbl/Twn — Open Jan-Dec

Tastefully modernised 17c Highland home privately situated overlooking mountains and moorland. En suite bedrooms, cosy guest lounge (available all day), books, flowers and local information. Carefully prepared four-course evening meal. Relaxed informal atmosphere where nothing is too much trouble for the resident hosts. Ideal base for touring the Highlands.

V

★★★★ GUEST HOUSE

Corriechoille Lodge

Spean Bridge, Inverness-shire, PH34 4EY
Tel: 01397 712002
E-mail: enquiry@corriechoille.com
Web: www.corriechoille.com

1 Twin, 2 Double, 2 Family — All En Suite — B&B per person £29.00-£34.00 Single, £22.00-£27.00 Double — Open Mar-Oct, B&B + Eve.Meal £38.00-£43.00

A recently renovated historic building of great character in a secluded situation with breathtaking mountain views. This family run guest house is ideal for walking, fishing or simply relaxing. Ground floor bedroom wtih disabled facilities available. Evening meals available by prior arrangement.

TV P V

★★★ B&B

Druim Fada B&B

Station Road, Spean Bridge, Inverness-shire, PH34 4EP
Tel/Fax: 01397 712018
E-mail: druim.fada@tinyworld.co.uk

2 Double — 1 En Suite fac, 1 Priv.NOT ensuite — B&B per person from £22.00 Single, from £22.00 Double, Room only per person from £15.00 — Open Jan-Dec excl Christmas, B&B + Eve.Meal from £37.00

Quietly located close to A82, station and golf course. Modern house with emphasis on comfort, hospitality and cuisine. Relax in the quiet spacious ambience of the 27ft pine-lined guest's lounge. Wide range of games and videos available. Wholesome Scottish cusine imaginatively cooked. Fresh local produce used where possible. Suppers provided. Parking. Highly Commended Healthy Choice award.

TV P C W V

Spean Bridge, Inverness-shire Map Ref: 3H12

B&B

Faegour House
Tirindrish, Spean Bridge, Inverness-shire, PH34 4EU
Tel/Fax: 01397 712903
E-mail: mocio@aol.com
Web: www.fort-william.net

2 Double | All En Suite | B&B per person from £19.00 Double | Open Jan-Dec excl Xmas/New Year

Expect to receive a very warm welcome at this modern family bungalow. Located by the village of Spean Bridge it has an open outlook with mountain views. Spacious, and comfortable with ample private parking.

B&B

C Fyfe
Springburn Farm , Stronaba, Spean Bridge, Inverness-shire, PH34 4DX
Tel/Fax: 01397 712707
E-mail: info@springburn.freewire.co.uk
Web: www.stronaba.co.uk

1 Twin, 2 Double | All En Suite | B&B per person £22.50-£27.50 Single, £17.50-£22.50 Dbl/Twn | Open Jan-Dec

Family home in own grounds with panoramic views of Ben-Nevis and surrounding hills. Bedrooms with all facilities and comfortable lounge for relaxing after a days sightseeing. Why not spend the evening feeding the Highland Cows?

C V

B&B

Highbridge
Spean Bridge, Inverness-shire, PH34 4EX
Tel: 01397 712493

1 Twin, 1 Double | Limited ensuite, Ensuite fac | B&B per person £14.00-£20.00 Dbl/Twn | Open Easter-Sep

Secluded cedar wood, family home. Excellent views of Ben Nevis and Aonach Mor. Fort William 9 Miles (14kms), Spean Bridge 1.5 miles (2kms).

Spean Bridge, Inverness-shire

Map Ref: 3H12

★★★ GUEST HOUSE

Inverour Guest House

Roybridge Road, Spean Bridge, Inverness-shire, PH34 4EU
Tel/Fax: 01397 712218
E-mail: alex@inverour.freeserve.co.uk
Web: www.fort-william.net/inverour

Charming welcoming Victorian Guest House offering comfortable bedrooms, hearty breakfasts and friendly courteous service. Cosy lounge with log fire and conservatory. Ideally situated in the village and close to local amenities and restaurants. Excellent base for exploring the West Highlands. Nevis Ski Resort 4 miles. Parking, laundry and drying facilities. Evening meals by prior arrangement.

2 Single
3 Twin
3 Double

4 En Suite fac
4 Pub Bath/Show

B&B per person
from £18.00 Single
from £20.00 Dbl/Twn

Open Jan-Dec excl Xmas
B&B + Eve.Meal
from £30.00

★★ B&B

Mahaar B&B

Corriechoille Road, Spean Bridge, Inverness-shire, PH34 4EP
Tel/Fax: 01397 712365
E-mail: mahaar.bnb@btinternet.com

Detached modern bungalow in centre of Spean Bridge. Private parking, TV's, tea and coffee making facilities in all rooms. Convenient for Fort William (only 9 miles) 2mins from golf course and railway station. Excellent walking and climbing area. Ideal base for skiers (Aonach Mor 4 miles) 1 mile from Commando Monument. 2 miles from Caledonian Canal. Lockable bike shed. Pets welcome. Credit cards accepted.

2 Single
1 Twin
1 Double
1 Family

2 Pub Bath/Show
2 Priv.NOT ensuite

B&B per person
from £16.50 Single
from £15.50 Dbl/Twn

Open Jan-Dec

★★★★ B&B

Mehalah Riverside House

Lower Tirindrish, Spean Bridge, Inverness-shire, PH34 4EU
Tel: 01397 712893

A delightful home in quiet location on banks of River Spean with views of Aonach Mor and Grey Corries. Home cooking and fresh local produce, organically grown, where possible. Taste of Scotland accredited.

1 Twin
1 Double

All En Suite

B&B per person
from £20.00 Dbl/Twn

Open Jan-Dec excl Xmas/New Year
B&B + Eve.Meal
from £40.00

★★ B&B

Tirindrish House

Spean Bridge, Inverness-shire, PH34 4EU
Tel: 01397 712398 Fax: 01397 712595
E-mail: wpeterwilson@cs.com

Tirindrish House is a lovely historic Highland house dating from Jacobite times. Set in 15 acre grounds with outstanding views of Nevis Range mountains. It is an ideal base for exploring the Highlands and Islands. Warm welcome assured in this comfortable family home. Pets welcome. Tennis available. Evening meal by arrangement.

1 Twin
1 Double
1 Family

1 En Suite fac
2 Priv.NOT ensuite

B&B per person
£18.00-£28.00 Single
£18.00-£20.00 Dbl/Twn

Open Jan-Dec
B&B + Eve.Meal
£30.00-£32.00

Important: Prices stated are estimates and may be subject to amendments

by Spean Bridge, Inverness-shire

Map Ref: 3H12

★★ B&B

Dreamweavers

Earendil, Mucomir, by Spean Bridge, PH34 4EQ
Tel: 01397 712548
E-mail: helen@dreamweavers.co.uk
Web: www.dreamweavers.co.uk

Traditional Scottish hospitality and cuisine in quiet rural area near to Caledonian Canal. Special services available for disabled travellers. Indoor and outdoor activities for children, baby sitting service. Complementary therapies available.

1 Twin	1 Priv.NOT ensuite	B&B per person	Open Jan-Dec
1 Double	1 Priv.NOT ensuite	£15.00-£20.00	B&B + Eve.Meal
1 Family	En Suite fac		£30.00

C V

★★★★ B&B

Invergloy House

Invergloy, Spean Bridge, Inverness-shir, PH34 4DY
Tel/Fax: 01397 712681
E-mail: cairns@invergloy-house.co.uk

A warm welcome is offered in our beautifully secluded 130 year old coach-house, set in 50 acres of woodland estate overlooking Loch Lochy. Tastefully furnished bedrooms with hospitality trays. Our guest lounge has magnificent views over the loch towards the mountains. Access to private shingle beach, fishing, woodland walks. SAE for details. Non-smoking. Children over 8 years old very welcome.

3 Twin	All En Suite	B&B per person	Open Jan-Dec excl
		from £23.00 Twin	Xmas/New Year

W

Stoer, Sutherland

Map Ref: 3G5

★★★ B&B

Elderbank

Stoer, nr Lochinver, Sutherland, IV27 4JE
Tel: 01571 855207

A warm friendly welcome awaits you at this Bed & Breakfast. Situated in a peaceful location with views to the surrounding area. Lochinver 7 miles away with a choice of eating places. Ideal location for birdwatching, wildlife, hill-walking and touring the west of Sutherland.

1 Twin	1 Pub Bath/Show	B&B per person	Open May-Sep
1 Double		from £20.00 Single	
		from £16.50 Dbl/Twn	

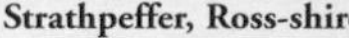

Strathpeffer, Ross-shire

Map Ref: 4A8

★★★★ B&B

Mrs S Fleming

White Lodge, Strathpeffer, Ross-shire, IV14 9AL
Tel: 01997 421730
E-mail: whitelodge@vacations-scotland.co.uk
Web: www.vacations-scotland.co.uk/whitelodge.html

Charming B Listed 18th century former farmhouse, one of the oldest buildings in Strathpeffer. Situated behind the square in this delightful Victorian Spa Village. Off street parking. All rooms with ensuite. Sorry no pets. Non Smoking.

1 Twin	All En Suite	B&B per person	Open Jan-Dec
1 Double		£27.00-£30.00 Single	
		£20.00-£25.00 Dbl/Twn	

V

VAT is shown at 17.5%: changes in this rate may affect prices.

Key to symbols is on back flap.

Strathpeffer, Ross-shire — Map Ref: 4A8

THE GARDEN HOUSE GUEST HOUSE

STRATHPEFFER, ROSS-SHIRE IV14 9BJ

Tel/Fax: 01997 421242
e.mail: garden.house@virgin.net
Web: freespace.virgin.net/garden.house

Set in the Victorian spa village of Strathpeffer it provides an ideal central touring base for Ross and Cromarty and other parts of the Northern Highlands. The guest house is located on the southwest side of the village surrounded by woodland and fields. The house is set well back from the main road through the village, about 250 metres from the village square. A lounge is available for guests at all times. Dinner is served each evening for guests wishing to sample home cooking. A table licence permits the sale of wine with meals.

NON-SMOKING ESTABLISHMENT

GUEST HOUSE

The Garden House Guest House

Garden House Brae, Strathpeffer, Ross-shire, IV14 9BJ
Tel/Fax: 01997 421242
E-mail: garden.house@virgin.net
Web: freespace.virgin.net/garden.house

1 Twin — All En Suite
3 Double
1 Family

B&B per person
from £20.00 Dbl/Twn

Open Mar-Nov
B&B + Eve.Meal
from £30.00

Friendly welcome at family run guest house in Spa village. Good walking country and touring base. 21 miles (32kms) from Inverness. Open March-October. Telephone/Fax bookings all year. Non-smoking establishment.

C £ W V

B&B

Inver Lodge

Strathpeffer, Ross-shire, IV14 9DL
Tel: 01997 421392

1 Twin — 2 Pub Bath/Show
1 Family

B&B per person
from £20.00 Single
from £16.00 Twin

Open Mar-mid Dec
B&B + Eve.Meal
from £27.00

Stone-built family home in lovely Highland spa town. Dinner available using quality local produce. Open wood fire. Walkers and cyclists very welcome and well catered for.

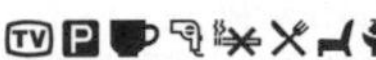

C £ V

Important: Prices stated are estimates and may be subject to amendments

Strathpeffer, Ross-shire | **Map Ref: 4A8**

B&B

Scoraig Bed & Breakfast

8 Kinnettas Square, Strathpeffer, Ross-shire, IV14 9BD
Tel: 01997 421847
E-mail: macdonald@kinnettas.freeserve.co.uk

1 Single	1 En Suite fac	B&B per person	Open Jan-Dec
1 Twin	2 Pub Bath/Show	from £15.00 Single	B&B + Eve.Meal
1 Double		from £15.00 Dbl/Twn	from £23.50
1 Family			

Comfortable, personally run B & B, situated in quiet residential area close to the centre of this Victorian spa village. Home cooking with dinner by arrangement. Private parking. Ideal base for day trips to Skye, the far North and West Highlands. Walkers and cyclists welcome.

C V

B&B

Margaret S L Scott

Craigvar, The Square, Strathpeffer, Ross-shire, IV14 9DL
Tel: 01997 421622 Fax: 01997 421796
E-mail: ms@gilsmith.demon.co.uk

1 Single	All En Suite	B&B per person	Open Jan-Dec exc
1 Twin		£27.00-£30.00 Single	Xmas/New Year
1 Double		£20.00-£27.00 Dbl/Twn	

Elegant residence in unique Highland village. Splendid breakfast menu, personal touches, and a wonderful Highland welcome.

C W V

Strathy Point, Sutherland | **Map Ref: 4B3**

B&B

Mrs P MacAskill

Sharvedda, Strathy Point, by Thurso, Sutherland, KW14 7RY
Tel: 01641 541 311

2 Twin	2 En Suite fac	B&B per person	Open Jan-Dec
1 Double	1 Priv.NOT ensuite	from £20.00 Single	B&B + Eve.Meal
		from£18.00 Dbl/Twn	£30.00-£32.00

Modern family home with views to sea and open croft land. Evening meals available. Home baking. Lots of advice available on day trips and tours, both in the area and further afield, including Orkney. Wildlife, birdwatching, hillwalking and sandy beaches.

C W V

Strontian, Argyll

Map Ref: 1E1

B&B

Craig-na-Shee

Anaheilt, Strontian, Argyll, PH36 4JA
Tel: 01967 402051 Fax: 01967 402178
E-mail: jacamelli@aol.com

1 Twin, 1 Double | 1 Guest bathrm | B&B per person from £15.00 Single, from £15.00 Dbl/Twn | Open Jan-Dec | B&B + Eve.Meal from £24.50

Modern bungalow in peaceful glen, about 1 mile from the village. Open views to the surrounding hills. Full Scottish breakfast and vegetarian alternative. Ironing/drying facilities. Home baking and packed lunches. Evening meal by arrangement. Guests lounge with colour TV. Pets welcome. Reduced rates for stays of (a) more than 3 days and (b) a week.

C W V

B&B

Kinloch House B&B

Strontian, Argyll, PH36 4HZ
Tel: 01967 402138 Fax: 01967 402261
E-mail: mikefrith@compuserve.com

1 Twin, 2 Double | All En Suite | B&B per person from £20.00 Single, from £20.00 Dbl/Twn | Open Jan-Dec excl Xmas/New Year

New bungalow set in 13 acres. Magnificient position overlooking Loch Sunart and surrounding mountains. 10 minutes walk from the centre of village of Strontian. Ideal centre for exploring an area of outstanding natural beauty with abundant wildlife. On a wet day relax in our comfortable lounge overlooking the Loch. All rooms en-suite. Special rates for 3 nights or longer.

W V

B&B

Struan

19 Anaheilt, Strontian, Argyll, PH36 4JA
Tel: 01967 402057

1 Single, 1 Twin, 1 Double | All En Suite | B&B per person £20.00 Single, £20.00 Dbl/Twn | Open Apr-Oct

A warm comfortable Highland welcome awaits you at 'Struan'. The B & B enjoys magnificent views of Ariundle Glen and Sgurr Dhomhnuill. Ariundle Nature Trail is within easy walking distance as is the compact village of Strontian set on the beautiful banks of Loch Sunart. Ideal base for walking, fishing and exploring the beautiful Ardnamurchan Peninsula.

V

Tain, Ross-shire

Map Ref: 4B7

B&B

Carrington's B&B

Morangie Road, Tain, Ross-shire, IV19 1PY
Tel/Fax: 01862 892635

1 Double, 2 Family | 2 En Suite fac | B&B per person from £17.00 Single, from £15.00 Double | Open Jan-Dec excl Xmas/New Year

Detached family home on the outskirts of Tain overlooking the sea. Close to town centre and golf course. Excellent base for exploring - John O'Groats, Ullapool and Inverness all within easy reach. Good stopover point enroute to Orkney, being just off the A9.

C W V

Important: Prices stated are estimates and may be subject to amendments

Tain, Ross-shire

Map Ref: 4B7

GUEST HOUSE

Golf View Guesthouse
13 Knockbreck Road, Tain, Ross-shire
Tel: 01862 892856 Fax: 01862 892172
E-mail: golfview@btinternet.com
Web: www.golf-view.co.uk

Secluded Victorian house with panoramic views over golf course and across the Dornoch Firth. Centrally situated in Scotland's oldest Royal Burgh.

3 Twin	3 En Suite fac	B&B per person	Open Feb-Nov
1 Double	2 Pub Bath/Show	from £25.00 Single	
1 Family		from £20.00 Dbl/Twn	

B&B

Northfield Bed & Breakfast
23 Moss Road, Tain, Ross-shire, IV19 1HH
Tel: 01862 894087
E-mail: may-mclean@northfield23.fsnet.co.uk

Comfortable family-run home in quiet location. Log burning stove in lounge and a warm welcome assured. Tea, coffee and home baking on arrival. Golfing can be arranged locally. A wide choice of day trips available, perhaps to the far north or over to the rugged west coast.One twin ensuite, one double ensuite, one single private facilities.

1 Single	Private fac	B&B per person	Open Jan-Dec excl Xmas/New Year
1 Twin	Ensuite fac	from £15.00-£17.00 Single	
1 Double	Ensuite fac	from £16.00-£19.00 Dbl/Twn	

B&B

Rosslyn
4 Hartfield Gardens, Tain, Ross-shire, IV19 1DL
Tel: 01862 892697

Comfortable, personally run B&B quietly situated a short distance from the centre of Scotland's oldest Royal Burgh. Private parking. Near to several golf courses, good base for exploring the far North and the West Highlands.

1 Twin	All En Suite	B&B per person	Open Feb-Nov
1 Family		from £16.00 Single	
		from £16.00 Twin	

Talmine, Sutherland

Map Ref: 4A3

B&B

R M & G A Morrison
Cloisters, Church Holme, Talmine, Sutherland, IV27 4YP
Tel/Fax: 01847 601286
Web: www.cloistertal.demon.co.uk

Located four miles north of Tongue off the A838, Cloisters, built in traditional style alongside our home, a converted 19th century church, offers superb B&B accommodation with stunning sea views. Enjoy birdwatching, fishing, climb majestic Ben Loyal or Ben Hope. Pack lunches are available and an excellent licensed retaurant is within easy walking distance. Why not escape to the peace and tranquility of Scotland's outback.

3 Twin	All En Suite	B&B per person	Open Jan-Dec
		£25.00 Single	
		£20.00 Twin	

Thurso, Caithness — **Map Ref: 4D3**

★★★★ B&B

Annandale, (Mrs D Thomson)
2 Rendel Govan Road, Thurso, Caithness, KW14 7EP
Tel: 01847 893942
E-mail: thomson@annandale2.freeserve.co.uk

2 Twin, 1 Double | 2 Pub Bath/Show | B&B per person £17.00-£18.00 Dbl/Twn | Open Jan-Dec excl Xmas/New Year

Comfortable B & B situated in quiet residential area. Ideal base for touring north coast and convenient for Orkney ferry.

TV C

★★★★ B&B

'Carlingwark'
5 Mears Place, Thurso, Caithness, KW14 7EW
Tel: 01847 894124
E-mail: EdgarMF@aol.com

1 Single, 1 Twin, 1 Double | 2 Pub Bath/Show | B&B per person from £17.00 Single, from £17.00 Dbl/Twn | Open Easter-Oct

Modern detached bungalow with enclosed landscaped garden in quiet cul-de-sac. Well furnished and comfortable, friendly family home. Evening cup of tea and home baking. Excellent base for exploring Caithness and north Sutherland, or for trips to Orkney.

TV C V

★★★★ B&B

Mrs J D Falconer
Murray House, 1 Campbell Street, Thurso, Caithness, KW14 7HD
Tel: 01847 895759
E-mail: murrayhouse.thurso@bigfoot.com

1 Single, 1 Twin, 2 Double | 2 En Suite fac, 2 Priv.NOT ensuite | B&B per person from £25.00 Single, from £16.00 Dbl/Twn | Open Jan-Dec excl Xmas/New Year

Set in the centre of the town, a warm welcome and comfortable stay are assured in this refurbished 19c town house. Private parking. Ideal for visiting Dunnet Head, Britains most northerly point, John O'Groats and Orkney. Within easy walking distance of restaurants.

TV P W V

B&B

Mrs Catherine Murray
1 Granville Crescent, Thurso, Caithness, KW14 7NP
Tel/Fax: 01847 892993

2 Twin | 1 En Suite fac, 1 Priv.NOT ensuite | B&B per person £20.00-£25.00 Single, £18.00-£20.00 Twin | Open Jan-Dec excl Xmas/New Year

Quietly situated, yet within easy reach of station and all facilities. All ground floor rooms, one ensuite, one with private bathroom. 5 minutes drive to Scrabster for Orkney Ferry.

TV P V

B&B

Shinval Bed & Breakfast
Glengolly, Thurso, Caithness, KW14 7XN
Tel: 01847 894306 Fax: 01847 890711
E-mail: mary@shinval.swinternet.co.uk

1 Twin, 1 Double, 1 Family | 1 En Suite fac, 1 Pub Bath/Show, 1 Priv.NOT ensuite | B&B per person from £17.00 Single, from £17.00 Dbl/Twn; Room only per person from £13.00 | Open Jan-Dec

Family home in quiet rural setting. 2 miles (3kms) from Thurso. Extensive countryside views. Convenient for Orkney ferry, touring Caithness and Sutherland, birdwatching, walking, and much more.

TV P C W V

Important: Prices stated are estimates and may be subject to amendments

Thurso, Caithness

Map Ref: 4D3

GUEST HOUSE

Waterside House

3 Janet Street, Thurso, Caithness, KW14 7AR
Tel: 01847 894751
E-mail: waterside.house@tinyonline.co.uk
Web: http://come.to/waterside.house

Traditional stone-built Georgian family town house close to town centre and all amenities free on-street parking. Open outlook across River Thurso.

Rooms	Facilities	Prices	Open
2 Twin 3 Double 2 Family	3 En Suite fac 1 Priv.NOT ensuite 3 Pub Bath/Show	B&B per person from £18.00 Single from £18.00 Dbl/Twn Room only per person from £15.00	Open Jan-Dec

Tongue, Sutherland

Map Ref: 4A3

B&B

Dalcharn

77 Dalcharn, Tongue, Lairg, Sutherland, IV27 4XU
Tel: 01847 611251

Modernised croft house, situated in peaceful rural location. Idyllic sandy beaches within walking distance. Gaelic spoken. Hairdryer and iron supplied. Cheaper rates applicable to children upto 12 years.

Rooms	Facilities	Prices	Open
1 Double 1 Family	1 Pub Bath/Show 1 Limited ensuite	B&B per person from £15.00 Single from £13.00 Double Room only per person from £10.00	Open Jan-Dec excl Xmas/New Year B&B + Eve.Meal £20.00-£22.00

B&B

Rhian Guest House

Rhian Cottage, Tongue, Sutherland, IV27 4XJ
Tel: 01847 611257
E-mail: jenny.anderson@tesco.net

Charming modernised gamekeeper's cottage, 0.5 miles (1km) outside village. Dramatic views of Ben Loyal. Ideal base for fishing, bird watching, walking and touring. Annexe outwith scheme.

Rooms	Facilities	Prices	Open
1 Twin 1 Double 1 Family	2 En Suite fac 1 Priv.NOT ensuite	B&B per person £27.00-£30.00 Single £20.00-£22.00 Dbl/Twn	Open Jan-Dec excl Xmas/New Year B&B + Eve.Meal from £35.00

Tore, by Muir of Ord, Ross-shire

Map Ref: 4A8

B&B

Shieldaig

Tore, Muir-of-Ord, Ross-shire, IV6 7RY
Tel: 01463 811410 Fax: 01463 811725
Web: www.shieldaig55.freeserve.co.uk

Modern, comfortably furnished bungalow, close to A9 7 miles N of Inverness. Warm, friendly welcome. Suggestions on sightseeing throughout the area. Ideal base for exploring the far North.

Rooms	Facilities	Prices	Open
2 Twin	2 Priv.NOT ensuite	B&B per person from £18.00 Single from £15.00 Twin	Open Feb-Nov

Torridon, Ross-shire

Map Ref: 3G8

B&B

'Tigh Suas'

Wester Alligin, Torridon, Achasheen, IV22 2HD
Tel: 01445 791220

A modern house on 20 acre croft with sheep, cows, hens and ducks. Peacefully situated on the hillside with magnificent views across Loch Torridon to the hills beyond. Very comfortable accommodation, almost separate within the owners house, offering en-suite facilities and combined dining-living room. Evening meal available on request by prior arrangement.

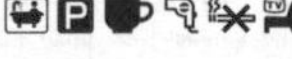

Rooms	Facilities	Prices	Open
1 Family	All En Suite	B&B per person from £25.00 Single £18.00-£19.00 Dbl	Open Jan-Dec

VAT is shown at 17.5%: changes in this rate may affect prices.

Key to symbols is on back flap.

Ullapool, Ross-shire — Map Ref: 3G6

★★★ B&B

ARDLAIR

MOREFIELD BRAE, ULLAPOOL IV26 2TH

Telephone: 01854 612087

Ardlair is situated on an elevated site overlooking Loch Broom and Ullapool. Ideal for walking, climbing, sailing, touring, bird-watching. New 9-hole golf course three minutes drive. Ferry terminal to Western Isles. One hour to the sub-tropical gardens at Inverewe. Ample parking. Follow the A835 for approx 1½ miles North of Ullapool. Third house on right.

B&B

Ardlair
Morefield Brae, Ullapool, Ross-shire, IV26 2TH
Tel: 01854 612087

2 Family — both Ensuite fac
2 Double — 1 Priv.NOT ensuite; 1 Pub Bath/Show

B&B per person from £18.00 Double

Open Apr-Oct

Modern house in elevated position, with large garden giving excellent views over Loch Broom. Under 2 miles (3kms) north of Ullapool. Leisure centre and golf course close by.

C V

Ardvreck Guest House

Morefield Brae, Ullapool IV26 2TH
Tel: 01854 612028 e.mail: Ardvreck.Guesthouse@btinternet.com
Fax: 01854 613000 Web: www.SmoothHound.co.uk/hotels/ardvreck.html

Spacious and well-appointed accommodation. All rooms ensuite with television and tea/coffee facilities, rural setting with spectacular views of sea, mountains, and Ullapool. Durness on the North Coast (75 miles) can be reached in a day as can the famous Inverewe Gardens (55 miles south).

B&B from £23–£28 *Contact Mrs Stockall* **★★★★ GUEST HOUSE**

GUEST HOUSE

Ardvreck Guest House
Morefield Brae, Ullapool, Ross-shire, IV26 2TH
Tel: 01854 612028 Fax: 01854 613000
E.mail: Ardvreck.Guesthouse@btinternet.com
Web: www.SmoothHound.co.uk/hotels/ardvreck.html

2 Single, 2 Twin, 4 Double, 2 Family — All En Suite

B&B per person from £23.00 Single; from £23.00 Dbl/Twn; Room only per person from £20.00

Open Mar-Oct

Guest house set amidst some of the best hillwalking country and breathtaking scenery in Scotland. Elevated country position overlooking Ullapool and Lochbroom. Spacious, well appointed rooms most with spectacular sea view, all with ensuite shower room, T.V and tea/coffee facility. Residents lounge available at all times. Local facilities include a leisure centre, swimming pool, sauna, golf course, fishing and museum.

£ W V

B&B

Broombank
4 Castle Terrace, Ullapool, Ross-shire, IV26 2XD
Tel: 01854 612247
E-mail: Shirley.Couper@tesco.net

1 Twin, 2 Double — All En Suite

B&B per person £16.00-£20.00 Dbl/Twn

Open Jan-Dec excl Xmas/New Year

A warm welcome awaits in our modern comfortable bunglaow with open views to hills and down the Loch to the Summer Isles. Quiet area but only 5 minutes walk to village centre.

Important: Prices stated are estimates and may be subject to amendments

Ullapool, Ross-shire | Map Ref: 3G6

BROOMVALE

26 Market Street, Ullapool, Ross-shire IV26 2XE
Tel: 01854 612559

A warm welcome awaits you in our new modernised house with private parking. Excellent base for exploring North West of Scotland. Tea and coffee in all rooms. TV lounge available all day. 9-hole golf course. One hour's drive from famous Inverewe Gardens. Five minutes walk from ferry terminal.

B&B

Broomvale
26 Market Street, Ullapool, Ross-shire, IV26 2XE
Tel: 01854 612559

1 Twin, 1 Double | 2 Pub Bath/Show | B&B per person £17.00-£18.00 Dbl/Twn | Open Mar-Oct

Comfortable accommodation in quiet location in fishing port of Ullapool. Excellent touring base, and handy for ferry to Stornoway.

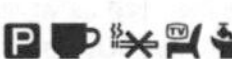

W V

B&B

Mrs Penny Browne
3 Castle Terrace, Ullapool, Ross-shire, IV26 2XD
Tel: 01854 612409

1 Single, 1 Twin, 1 Double | 1 Ensuite fac, 2 Pub Bath/Show | B&B per person from £17.00 Single, from £18.00 Double, from £16.00 Twin | Open Apr-Oct

Bed and Breakfast in family home, with ensuite available. Quiet residential location within walking distance of town amenities. House has views to Summer Isles.

V

B&B

Clisham
Rhue, Ullapool, Ross-shire, IV26 2TJ
Tel/Fax: 01854 612498

2 Family | 2 Limited ensuite | B&B per person from £16.00 Double | Open May-Sep

Small working croft peacefully situated in elevated position, giving superb views over Loch Broom. 3 miles (5kms) north of Ullapool.

C W V

B&B

Creagan House
18 Pulteney Street, Ullapool, Ross-shire, IV26 2UP
Tel: 01854 612397 Fax: 01854 613396
E-mail: kmullapool@aol.com

2 Twin, 2 Double, 1 Family | 3 En Suite fac, 1 Pub Bath/Show | B&B per person £14.00-£25.00 Dbl/Twn | Open Jan-Dec

Traditional stone built cottage dating back to 1840. Situated in centre of village, close to all amenities, leisure centre and golf course. Ideal base for hillwalking, cycling and touring the west coast. Travel cots available. Pets by arrangement.

C V

Ullapool, Ross-shire **Map Ref: 3G6**

GUEST HOUSE

Dromnan Guest House

Garve Road, Ullapool, Ross-shire, IV26 2SX
Tel: 01854 612333 Fax: 01854 613364
E-mail: dromnan@msn.com
Web: www.destinationscotland.com/dromnan

Rooms	Facilities	Prices	Open
2 Twin 3 Double 2 Family	All En Suite	B&B per person £30.00-£36.00 Single £23.00-£26.00 Dbl/Twn	Open Jan-Dec

Family run guest house on outskirts of the west coast fishing village of Ullapool, overlooking Loch Broom. 5 minutes from ferry to the Outer Isles.

B&B

Essex Cottage

West Terrace, Ullapool, Ross-shire, IV26 2UU
Tel: 01854 612663

Rooms	Facilities	Prices	Open
1 Twin 1 Double	All En Suite	B&B per person from £18.00 Dbl/Twn	Open Apr-Nov

Traditional stone built house with views over Loch Broom. A short walk to the restaurant, shops, ferry terminal and leisure cenre and golf course. Ideal location for hillwalkers.

B&B

Hillview, Mrs R Urquhart

1 Vyner Place, Ullapool, Ross-shire, IV26 2XR
Tel: 01854 612700

Rooms	Facilities	Prices	Open
1 Single 1 Twin		B&B per person from £16.00 Single from £16.00 Twin	Open Mar-Nov

B&B

Loch Dubh House

Strathkanaird, Ullapool, Ross-shire, IV26 2TW
Tel: 01854 666224 Fax: 0870 0569379
E-mail: stay@lochdubhhouse.co.uk

Rooms	Facilities	Prices	Open
1 Twin 1 Double	1 Pub Bath/Show 1 Priv.NOT ensuite	B&B per person from £23.00 Single from £18.00 Dbl/Twn	Open Jan-Dec

Seven miles north of Ullapool and one mile from the sea - close to the Inverpolly Nature Reserve and a short distance from Assynt. An ideal base for walking, fishing, bird - watching, painting, touring - whatever your interest in the North West Highlands we offer excellent accommodation in the heart of the hills.

Important: Prices stated are estimates and may be subject to amendments

Ullapool, Ross-shire

Map Ref: 3G6

★★★★ B&B

Mrs J MacRae
3 Vyner Place, Morefield, Ullapool, Ross-shire
Tel/Fax: 01854 612023

1 Dbl/Fam En Suite fac
1 Twn/Fam Priv.NOT ensuite

B&B per person
£16.00-£18.00 Single
£16.00-£18.00 Dbl/Twn
Room only per person
£15.00

Open Jan-Dec excl Xmas Day.

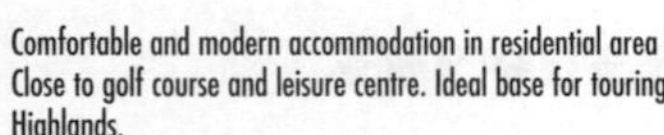

Comfortable and modern accommodation in residential area of Ullapool. Close to golf course and leisure centre. Ideal base for touring Western Highlands.

C V

★★★★ B&B

Northbank
11 Moss Road, Ullapool, Ross-shire
Tel: 01854 612093

1 Twin
1 Double

B&B per person
from £15.00 Dbl/Twn

Open Apr-Oct

Comfortable family home near centre of Ullapool set in quiet residential area. Ferry terminal just a few minutes. Close to North West Highlands Tourist Route.

V

★★★★ GUEST HOUSE

Point Cottage Guest House
22 West Shore Street, Ullapool, Ross-shire
Tel: 01854 612494 Fax: 01854 613464
E-mail: stay@pointcottage.co.uk
Web: www.pointcottage.co.uk

1 Twin All En Suite
2 Double

B&B per person
£25.00-£45.00 Single
£20.00-£26.00 Dbl/Twn

Open Feb-Oct

Tastefully converted 18c fisherman's cottage where a warm welcome and a high level of local knowledge are assured. Marvellous lochside views to mountains beyond. Very quiet location but only 2 minutes walk to village centre. Vegetarian cooked breakfast available.

V

The Sheiling

GARVE ROAD
ULLAPOOL IV26 2SX
Tel/Fax: 01854 612947

A warm welcome is assured at the MacKenzies comfortable house which stands in its own one acre landscaped garden beside the picturesque shore of Loch Broom. Facilities include guests laundry, sauna, drying room and a rod room to complement the 40sq. miles of trout loch fishing exclusive to guests.

★★★★ GUEST HOUSE

The Sheiling Guest House
Garve Road, Ullapool, Ross-shire, IV26 2SX
Tel/Fax: 01854 612947

2 Twin All En Suite
4 Double

B&B per person
from £23.00 Dbl/Twn

Open Jan-Dec excl Xmas/New Year

Modern house with large loch facing garden in peaceful location on shore of Loch Broom. $^1/_2$ mile from the village. Free trout fishing on many local lochs, partly exclusive. Use of local produce features highly with homemade sausages and local smoked fish. Sauna in grounds for use of guests.

C V

Ullapool, Ross-shire — Map Ref: 3G6

★★★ B&B

Spindrift

West Terrace, Ullapool, Ross-shire, IV26 2UU
Tel: 01854 612526 Fax: 01854 612099
E-mail: k.ross@btclick.com

1 Twin	All En Suite	B&B per person	Open Easter-Oct
1 Double		£20.00-£23.00 Dbl/Twn	

Comfortable ensuite accommodation and generous breakfasts are provided in family home with magnificent outlook yet convenient to all local facilities. Two spoilt cats also in residence!

B&B

Torran

Loggie, Lochbroom, Ullapool, Ross-shire, IV23 2SG
Tel: 01854 655227 Fax: 01854 655344
E-mail: macktorran@tesco.net

1 Single	1 Pub Bath/Show	B&B per person	Open Jan-Nov
1 Twin		from £17.00 Single	
1 Double		from £17.00 Dbl/Twn	

Family home on working croft in peaceful setting over looking the beautiful Loch Broom. Enjoy a Scottish breakfast using our own free range eggs. Iron age brochs & salmon farm close by. A relaxing and peaceful holiday location.

Wick, Caithness — Map Ref: 4E3

B&B

Bilbster House

by Wick, Caithness, KW1 5TB
Tel/Fax: 01955 621212
E.mail: ianstewart@bilbster.freeserve.co.uk

1 Twin	2 En Suite fac	B&B per person	Open Jan-Dec excl
2 Double	1 Pub Bath/Show.	£17.50-£18.50 Single	Xmas/New Year
		£17.50-£18.50 Dbl/Twn	Oct-Easter prior
			arrangement only

Listed country house dating from late 1700's set in 5 acres of grounds. Traditionally furnished.

Important: Prices stated are estimates and may be subject to amendments

Wick, Caithness — Map Ref: 4E3

B&B

'The Clachan' Bed & Breakfast
13 Randolph Place, South Road, Wick, Caithness, KW1 5NJ
Tel: 01955 605384
Web: www.theclachan.co.uk

1 Twin, 2 Double — All En Suite — B&B per person from £25.00 Single, from £20.00 Dbl/Twn — Open Jan-Dec excl Xmas/New Year

Family run detached house dating back to 1938. Purpose built accommodation to the back of the house, with all rooms ensuite, ensuring a peaceful and relaxing stay. A wide variety of interests with John O' Groats on the doorstep, where there are daily trips to Orkney in the summer. Wick has many sites of historical interest. Meals available within walking distance. Totally non-smoking house.

B&B

Mrs I Leask
14 Port Dunbar, Wick, Caithness, KW1 4JJ
Tel: 01955 604054

1 Twin, 2 Double — 2 Pub Bath/Show — B&B per person £16.00 Single, £16.00 Dbl/Twn — Open Jan-Dec

Bungalow with fine views of Wick harbour. Quiet residential area a short walk from the town centre.

B&B

MacMillar House
1 Tolbooth Lane, Wick, Caithness, KW1 4ND
Tel: 01955 602120 Fax: 01955 605667
E-mail: sammy.777@btinternet.com

1 Single, 1 Double, 1 Family — All En Suite — B&B per person from £22.00 Single, from £20.00 Double — Open Jan-Dec

Modernised 18th Century town house now providing comfortable accommodation for visitors to Wick. Centrally situated within easy walking distance of several eating establishments. Good base for the business or leisure traveller.

THE OUTER ISLES ARE FOR VISITORS SEEKING ADVENTURE, A SENSE OF BEING OUTSIDE BRITAIN – YET STILL A PART OF IT – AND SEEING A DIFFERENT CULTURE. ALL THREE ISLAND GROUPINGS – THE WESTERN ISLES, ORKNEY AND SHETLAND – CONTRAST WITH EACH OTHER. ORKNEY AND SHETLAND SHARE A NORSE HERITAGE, WHILE THE WESTERN ISLES ARE THE STRONGHOLD OF THE GAEL. EXCELLENT FERRY AND AIR LINKS MEAN GETTING TO ANY OF THESE GROUPS OF ISLANDS IS STRAIGHT FORWARD.

Old Man of Hoy, Isle of Hoy, Orkney

THE WESTERN ISLES offer some of Scotland's finest seascapes and beaches, as well as the springtime flowers of the machair – the shell-sand coastal pasture. Ancient monuments such as the spectacular Callanais Standing Stones are a reminder of the heritage of prehistory on the islands. The preserved Black House at Arnol is a reminder of the more recent life of the crofters on these islands, and is one of many heritage museums on the islands.

ORKNEY'S GREEN ISLANDS, like the Western Isles, have a strong sense of continuity stretching back to ancient times. The past is all around at places like Skara Brae, a magnificently preserved Stone Age village, and Maes Howe, a unique burial chamber already more than a millennium old when pillaged by Vikings. Kirkwall is the setting for St Magnus Cathedral, the most magnificent Norman work in Scotland. Another theme to explore is the seagoing tradition, including the recent history of Scapa Flow as a naval anchorage, portrayed at the fascinating museum at Lyness on Hoy. Orkney's wildlife includes spectacular seabird colonies along its dramatic coastline.

Voe, Shetland Mainland

Traditional crofters' cottages, Western Isles

SHETLAND HAS THE STRONGEST SENSE of somewhere different. Here the Scandinavian influence is apparent – in dialect, music, even architecture and traditions. The sea pervades the way of life, with nowhere more than three miles from salt water. Like Orkney, there is an abundance of wildlife – seals, otters and seabirds – from Sumburgh Head in the south of the islands past the national nature reserve at Herrmaness on Unst to Muckle Flugga at the most northerly point of Britain. Shetland is for adventurers, with long summer daylight hours in 'the land of the simmer dim' leaving even more time to enjoy the unique island ambience.

EVENTS OUTER ISLANDS: WESTERN ISLES, ORKNEY &SHETLAND

1 JANUARY
Men & Boy's "Ba"
Kirkwall Town Centre, Orkney
Traditional street football game where there can be up to 400 players in teams of "Uppies" and "Doonies". Also played on Christmas day.
Contact: J.D.M Robertson
TEL: **01856 872961**

30 JANUARY
Up Helly Aa
Lerwick Town Centre, Shetland
Traditional Viking fire festival culminating in the burning of a replica galley.
Contact: Shetland Islands Tourism
TEL: **01595 693434**

***3-6 MAY**
Shetland Folk Festival
Various venues, Shetland
Traditional Scottish music festival.
Contact: Festival Office
TEL: **01595 694757**

24-27 MAY
Orkney Folk Festival
Various venues, Orkney
Four day folk festival, featuring a wide range of traditional music in and around Stromness.
Contact: Johnny Mowat, Folk Festival Office
TEL: **01856 851331**

22-27 JUNE
St Magnus Festival
Various venues, Orkney
Annual festival of music, drama, dance and visual art.
Contact: Glynis Hughes
TEL: **01856 871445**

31 AUG-3 SEPTEMBER
Walk Shetland 2001
Various venues, Shetland
A 5 day celebration of the Islands on foot.
Contact: Shetland Islands Tourism
TEL: **01595 693434**

12–19 OCTOBER
Royal National Mod
Various venues, Stornoway
Scotland's premier festival of Gaelic music, song, drama, dance and literature.
Contact: Donald John McSween
TEL: **01851 703487**

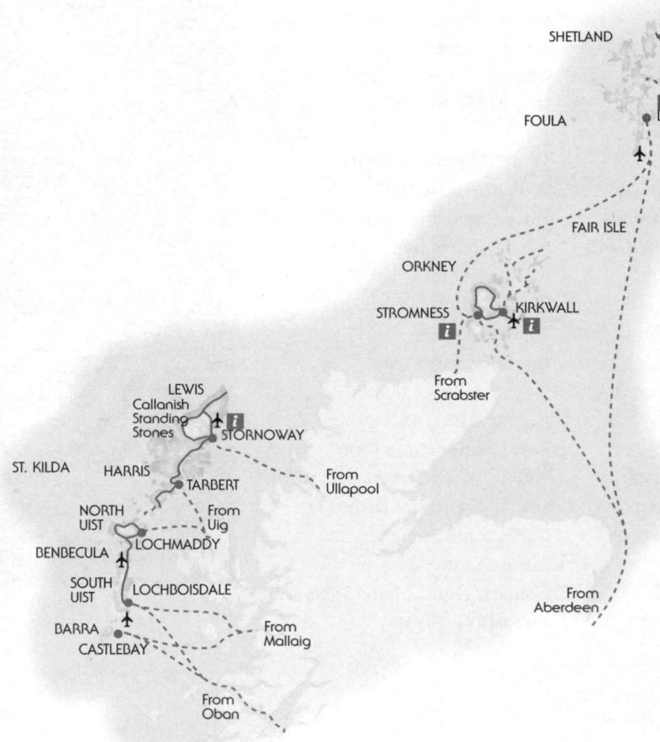

WESTERN ISLES TOURIST BOARD
26 Cromwell Street
Stornoway
Isle of Lewis
HS1 2DD

TEL: **01851 703088**
FAX: **01851 705244**
www.witb.co.uk

ORKNEY TOURIST BOARD
6 Broad Street
Kirkwall
Orkney
KW15 1NX

TEL: **01856 872856**
FAX: **01856 875056**
www.visitorkney.com

SHETLAND SCANDS TOURISM
Market Cross
Lerwick
Shetland
ZE1 0LU

TEL: **01595 693434**
FAX: **01595 695807**
www.shetland-tourism.co.uk

WESTERN ISLES TOURIST BOARD

CASTLEBAY
Main Street
Isle of Barra
TEL: **(01871) 810336**
Easter-Oct

LOCHBOISDALE
Pier Road
Isle of South Uist
TEL: **(01878) 700286**
Easter-Oct

LOCHMADDY
Isle of North Uist
TEL: **(01876) 500321**
Easter-Oct

STORNOWAY
26 Cromwell Street
Isle of Lewis
TEL: **(01851) 703088**
Jan-Dec

TARBERT
Pier Road
Isle of Harris
TEL: **(01859) 502011**
Easter-Oct

ORKNEY TOURIST BOARD

KIRKWALL
6 Broad Street
Orkney
TEL: **(01856) 872856**
Jan-Dec

STROMNESS
Ferry Terminal Building
The Pier Head
Orkney
TEL: **(01856) 850716**
Jan-Dec

SHETLAND TOURIST BOARD

LERWICK
The Market Cross
Shetland
TEL: **(01595) 693434**
Jan-Dec

Scaristavore, Isle of Harris, Western Isles — Map Ref: 3C6

B&B

Sandview House
6 Scaristavore, Isle of Harris, Western Isles, HS3 3HX
Tel/Fax: 01859 550212

1 Single 1 Twin 1 Family	2 En Suite fac 1 Priv.NOT ensuite	B&B per person from £25.00 Single from £20.00 Double Room only per person from £14.00	Open Jan-Dec B&B + Eve.Meal £30.00-£35.00

Friendly, comfortable bed & breakfast superbly situated overlooking one of the most beautiful beaches in Harris. Adjacent to the local golf course. 5 miles from the Leverburgh Ferry to North Uist. Evening meals; rooms with private facilites.

C V

Tarbert, Isle of Harris, Western Isles — Map Ref: 3C6

B&B

Mrs J M Morrison
Avalon, 12 Westside, Tarbert, Harris, Western Isles, HS3 3BG
Tel: 01859 502334/502570
E-mail: info@avalonguesthouse.co.uk

2 Twin 1 Double	2 En Suite fac 1 Priv.NOT ensuite	B&B per person from £18.00 Dbl/Twn	Open Jan-Dec B&B + Eve.Meal from £28.00

New house on working croft with magnificent view over West Loch Tarbert. Ideal for hill walking,fishing and bird watching. 0.5 mile to ferry terminal.

C V

B&B

Mrs A Morrison
Hillcrest, West Tarbert, Harris, Western Isles, HS3 3AH
Tel: 01859 502119

1 Twin 1 Double 1 Family	2 En Suite fac 1 Priv.NOT ensuite	B&B per person from £18.00 Single from £18.00 Dbl/Twn	Open Apr-Nov B&B + Eve.Meal from £29.00

Modern croft in an elevated position overlooking West Loch Tarbet with fine views of mounains and islands. This is an excellent base for exploring all of Harris and Lewis. Miles of unspoilt beaches and an abundance of wildlife, with a variety of plantlife practically on our doorstep. Wonderful walking, country fishing trips and scenic cruises available. 1 mile from ferry terminal.

C W V

Aignish, Point, Isle of Lewis, Western Isles — Map Ref: 3E4

B&B

Ceol-na-Mara
1a Aignish, Isle of Lewis, HS2 0PB
Tel/Fax: 01851 870339
E-mail: sarah@lesmacdonald.freeserve.co.uk
Web: www.lesmacdonald.freeserve.co.uk

1 Twin 1 Double 1 Family	1 Pub Bath/Show 1 Priv.NOT ensuite	B&B per person £19.00-£21.00 Single £17.00-£19.00 Dbl/Twn	Open Jan-Dec B&B + Eve.Meal £27.00-£31.00

Comfortable modern home in pleasant rural area near Stornoway, on the Eye Peninsula. Friendly and welcoming. Home cooking. Evening meals by arrangement. Ample off street parking.

C V

Back, Isle of Lewis, Western Isles — Map Ref: 3E4

B&B

Mrs M Fraser
Seaside Villa, Back, Lewis, Western Isles, HS2 0LQ
Tel: 01851 820208

1 Twin 2 Double	All En Suite	B&B per person from £20.00 Dbl/Twn	Open Jan-Dec B&B + Eve.Meal from £32.00

Beautiful views overlooking picturesque bay with miles of unspoilt sandy beaches and Sutherland Hills in the distance. Home cooking and baking using all local fayre – vegetarians welcome. Special highland hospitality. Abundant wildlife with unique corncrake an added attraction.

C V

Breasclete, Isle of Lewis, Western Isles

Map Ref: 3D4

GUEST HOUSE

Loch Roag Guest House
22a Breasclete, Isle of Lewis, HS2 9EF
Tel/Fax: 01851 621357
Web: www.lochroag.com

Lochroag Guest House offers a perfect blend of comfort, the best of local cuisine, spectacular scenery and easy access to all attractions.

2 Single 1 Twin 1 Family	All En Suite	B&B per person £23.50-£29.50 Single £23.50-£29.50 Twin	Open Jan-Dec B&B + Eve.Meal £41.50-£47.50

C V

Callanish, Isle of Lewis, Western Isles

Map Ref: 3D4

GUEST HOUSE

Eshcol Guest House
21 Breasclete, Callanish, Lewis, Western Isles HS2 9ED
Tel/Fax: 01851 621357

Modern detached house quietly situated in the crofting village of Breasclete, with an open outlook over Loch Roag towards the Uig hills. Good base to explore Lewis, or just to relax. Only 2 miles to the Callanish standing stones. All bedrooms non-smoking. Local produce used where possible in our highly recommended evening meals. B.Y.O.B.

2 Twin 1 Double	2 En Suite fac 1 Priv.NOT ensuite	B&B per person from £29.00 Single from £29.00 Dbl/Twn	Open Jan-Dec excl Xmas/New Year B&B + Eve.Meal from £47.00

C W V

B&B

Catherine Morrison
27 Callanish, Callanish, Lewis, Western Isles, HS2 9DY
Tel: 01851 621392

Comfortable accommodation, with attractive garden, set on working croft; overlooking Loch Roag to the mountains beyond. Closest bed and breakfast to the famous standing stones, some 150 yds away, with their nearby interpretation and visitor centre.

1 Twin 1 Double	1 Priv.NOT ensuite 1 Pub Bath/Show	B&B per person to £20.00 Dbl/Twn	Open Mar-Sep

Gress, Stornoway, Isle of Lewis, Western Isles

Map Ref: 3D4

B&B

Caladh
44 Gress, Isle of Lewis, HS2 0NB
Tel: 01851 820743
E-mail: EVE@caladh.fsbusiness.co.uk

Modernised croft house situated in quiet crofting village, 9 miles north of Stornoway. Open outlook over Gress river and saltings, and to the nearby sandy beach. Good area for birdwatching trips. African grey parrot lovers especially welcome!

2 Twin	All En Suite	B&B per person from £18.00 Single from £17.00 Twin Room only per person from £10.00	Open Jan-Dec B&B + Eve.Meal from £27.00

C V

Stornoway, Isle of Lewis, Western Isles

Map Ref: 3D4

★★★★
B&B

Mrs J MacKenzie
Hebron, 14 MacLean Terrace, Stornoway, Lewis, Western Isles, HS1 2QZ
Tel: 01851 702890

Friendly, traditional island welcome at our modern house in quiet location overlooking golf course and castle grounds. All rooms decorated to a high standard complete with N.S, tea-trays with home bakes. Lounge for guests use. Extensive breakfast menu including home baked bread and oatcakes. Vegetarians catered for. Ample private parking.

1 Single 1 Twin 1 Double	All En Suite	B&B per person from £20.00 Single from £20.00 Dbl/Twn Room only per person from £16.00	Open Jan-Dec excl Xmas/New Year

C V

Tolsta Chaolais, Isle of Lewis, Western Isles — Map Ref: 3C4

B&B

Aros
18a Tolsta Chaolais, Isle of Lewis, Western Isles, HS2 9DW
Tel: 01851 621266
E-mail: katekblue@yahoo.com

1 Twin, 1 Double — 1 Pub Bath/Show

B&B per person from £20.00 Single, from £18.00 Dbl/Twn

Open May-Sep. B&B + Eve.Meal from £30.00

Comfortable, spacious house in peaceful village between Calanais & Carloway. Good for walking. Home cooking & baking.

Berneray, Isle of North Uist, Western Isles — Map Ref: 3B7

B&B

Burnside Croft
Berneray, North Uist, Western Isles
Tel/Fax: 01876 540235
E-mail: splashmackillop@burnsidecroft.fsnet.co.uk

1 Twin, 2 Double — 2 En Suite fac, 1 Priv.NOT ensuite

B&B per person from £20.00 Single, from £20.00 Dbl/Twn. Room only per person from £18.00

Open Feb-Nov. B&B + Eve.Meal from £38.00

A fine example of traditional Highland hospitality. You quickly become one of the family enjoying Gloria's good food and Don Alick's wide ranging conversation.

Grimsay, Isle of North Uist, Western Isles — Map Ref: 3B8

B&B

Mrs C MacLeod
Glendale, 7 Kallin, Grimsay, North Uist, Western Isles, HS6 5HY
Tel: 01870 602029
E-mail: glendale@ecosse.net

2 Twin, 1 Double — 2 En Suite fac, 1 Priv.NOT ensuite

B&B per person from £20.00 Single, £16.00-£19.00 Dbl/Twn. Room only per person from £11.00

Open Jan-Dec. B&B + Eve.Meal £28.00-£31.00

Modern house in quiet position overlooking the harbour. Views over the Minch and to the hills of South Uist. All rooms with private facilities. Home cooked evening meals available by arrangement.

Birsay, Orkney — Map Ref: 5B11

B&B

Primrose Cottage
Birsay, Kirkwall, Orkney, KW17 2NB
Tel/Fax: 01856 721384
E-mail: i.clouston@talk21.com

1 Single, 1 Twin, 1 Double — 2 En Suite fac, 1 Pub Bath/Show

B&B per person from £15.00 Single, from £19.00 Dbl/Twn

Open Jan-Dec excl Xmas. B&B + Eve.Meal from £27.00

In quiet location overlooking Marwick Bay, close to RSPB reserves. Ideal for bird watching, trout fishing and quiet cliff top walks. Local produce used whenever possible, fresh fish and shellfish. Reduced rates for longer stays.

Harray, Orkney — Map Ref: 5B11

B&B

Rickla
Harray, Orkney, KW17 2JT
Tel: 01856 761575 Fax: 01856 761880
E-mail: jacky@rickla.com
Web: www.rickla.com

1 Twin, 1 Double — All En Suite

B&B per person £25.00-£30.00 Dbl/Twn

Open Jan-Dec excl Xmas/New Year

Luxury en-suite accommodation in the Neolithic Heartland of Orkney. Guest rooms have panoramic views over lochs, hills and the World Heritage Site. Non-smoking, supremely quiet; far from the madding crowd yet centrally situated and close to several restaurants. Discrete hospitality, private dining tables, bedrooms with no shared walls. The ideal touring base. 10% discount for stays of more than 3 nights.

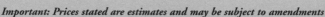

Kirkwall, Orkney — Map Ref: 5B12

★★★
B&B

Bellavista
Carness Road, Kirkwall, Orkney, KW15 1TB
Tel/Fax: 01856 872306

Rooms	Facilities	B&B per person	Open
2 Single 1 Twin 1 Double	2 En Suite fac	£18.00 Single £18.00 Dbl/Twn	Open Jan-Dec excl Xmas/New Year

Family home peacefully situated close to sea front 1.25 miles (2kms) from Kirkwall town centre.

SCORRALEE

Scorradale Road, Orphir, Orkney KW17 2RF
Tel/Fax: 01856 811268 e.mail: ebclouston@compuserve.com

An Orcadian family home within a peaceful quiet area near to Scapa Flow, famous in wartime now famous for diving on the wrecks, nine miles from Kirkwall and Stromness, our main towns. Lots of birdwatching and nice walks, plenty parking, small ferries services to outer islands. Just 200 yards from Scarrabrae Inn. All bedrooms ensuite.

★★★
B&B

Mr & Mrs E B Clouston
Scorralee, Scorradale Road, Orphir, Orkney, KW17 2RF
Tel/Fax: 01856 811268
E-mail: ebclouston@compuserve.com

Rooms	Facilities	B&B per person	Open
1 Twin 2 Double	All En Suite 1 Pub Bath/Show	£18.00-£25.00 Dbl/Twn	Open Jan-Dec

A warm welcome assured at this warm, comfortable, modern house on elevated site, looking out over Scapa Flow. Equal distance from Kirkwall and Stromness. Evening meals by arrangement.

BRONZE

★★★
B&B

Mrs J Hume
1 Papadale Close, Kirkwall, Orkney, KW15 1QP
Tel: 01856 874201

Rooms	Facilities	B&B per person	Open
2 Twin	1 Pub Bath/Show	from £18.00 Single from £15.00 Twin	Open Jan-Dec excl Xmas/New Year

Modern family home in quiet residential area within walking distance of Kirkwall town centre. Close to the swimming pool. Many local attractions nearby, such as the Cathedral, Tankerness Museum and the Highland Park distillery. Other historic monuments and sites within a short drive.

★★
GUEST HOUSE

Sanderlay Guest House
2 Viewfield Drive, Kirkwall, Orkney, KW15 1RB
Tel: 01856 875587 Fax: 01856 876350
E-mail: enquiries@sanderlay.co.uk
Web: www.sanderlay.co.uk

Rooms	Facilities	B&B per person	Open
1 Single 1 Twin 2 Double 2 Family	4 En Suite fac 1 Pub Bath/Show	£18.00-£22.00 Single £14.00-£20.00 Dbl/Twn Room only per person £11.00-£19.00	Open Jan-Dec

Comfortable modern house in quiet residential area on outskirts of town. Some ensuite and 3 self-contained family units. Private parking available. Credit cards accepted. Ideal base for exploring the Orkney mainland or for visiting the North Isles.

North Ronaldsay, Orkney — Map Ref: 5D10

★★ GUEST HOUSE

The Observatory Guest House
North Ronaldsay Bird Observatory, North Ronaldsay, Orkney, KW17 2BE
Tel: 01857 633200/633200 Fax: 01857 633207
E-mail: alison@nrbo.prestel.co.uk

Unique eco-friendly activity centre offering comfortable accommodation in a crofting environment. Resident specialists in ornithology.

2 Twin 2 Double	All En Suite	B&B per person from £23.00 Single from £18.00 Dbl/Twn	Open Jan-Dec excl Xmas/New Year B&B + Eve.Meal from £27.00

Rendall, Orkney — Map Ref: 5B11

★★ B&B

Ida Sinclair
Riff, Rendall, Orkney, KW17 2PB
Tel/Fax: 01856 761541
E-mail: Ida.Sinclair@farming.co.uk

Riff Farm is situated 4 miles from Rousay Ferry close to the shore of Puldrite Bay with expansive views across to the Northern Isles. A warm Orcadian welcome assured.

1 Twin 1 Double	All En Suite	B&B per person £15.00 Single £15.00 Dbl/Twn	Open Jan-Dec B&B + Eve.Meal from £23.00

Stenness, Orkney — Map Ref: 5B12

★★★ HOTEL

Standing Stones Hotel
Stenness, Orkney, KW16 3JX
Tel: 01856 850449 Fax: 01856 851262
E-mail: standingstones@sol.co.uk

Situated on the shores of the Loch of Stenness, just off the main Kirkwall to Stromness road. This is an excellent central base for exploring Orkney's many historical and archaeological attractions, or for fishing or birdwatching.

4 Single 6 Twin 4 Double 3 Family	All En Suite	B&B per person from £30.00 Single from £30.00 Dbl/Twn Room only per person from £25.00	Open Jan-Dec excl Xmas/New Year B&B + Eve.Meal from £45.00

Stromness, Orkney — Map Ref: 5B12

AWAITING INSPECTION

Ferry Bank
2 North End Road, Stromness, Orkney, KW16 3AG
Tel: 01856 850642

Ferry Bank traditionally built and situated with its own garden grounds. Superb site with panoramic views overlooking harbour and countryside. Idylic location for ferry terminal and all other amenities. Exceptional breakfast menu and many extras.

1 Family 1 Double	All En Suite	B&B per person £18.00-£20.00 Double	Open Jan-Dec excl Xmas/New Year

★★★★ B&B

Thira
Innertown, Stromness, Orkney, KW16 3JP
Tel: 01856 851181 Fax: 01856 851182

Situated in a quiet location 2 miles from Stromness, unrivalled views of Hoy Sound. Home cooking with fresh produce. All rooms ensuite. Private parking. Non smoking establishment.

2 Single 1 Twin 1 Double	All En Suite	B&B per person from £24.00 Single from £24.00 Dbl/Twn Room only per person from £22.00	Open Apr-Dec B&B + Eve.Meal from £34.00

Important: Prices stated are estimates and may be subject to amendments

Stromness, Orkney — Map Ref: 5B12

B&B

Mrs M Tulloch
Olnadale, Innertown, Stromness, Orkney, KW16 3JW
Tel: 01856 850418

1 Twin, 2 Double | 1 En Suite fac, 1 Pub Bath/Show | B&B per person from £18.00 Single, £17.00-£18.00 Dbl/Twn | Open Jan-Dec

Modern house with panoramic views of Hoy Sound. Quiet location on the edge of town, but only a short walk down to the main street. This fascinating and charming town, with its sea-faring associations, is best explored on foot - do allow time for this. Many of Orkney's historic sites are just a short drive away.

C W

Hillswick, North Mainland, Shetland — Map Ref: 5F4

B&B

Almara
Upper Urafirth, Hillswick, North Mainland, Shetland, ZE2 9RH
Tel/Fax: 01806 503261
E-mail: almara@zetnet.co.uk
Web: www.users.zetnet.co.uk/almara/

1 Single, 1 Twin, 1 Double | 2 En Suite fac, 1 Pub Bath/Show | B&B per person from £20.00 Single, from £20.00 Dbl/Twn | Open Jan-Dec excl Xmas/New Year, B&B + Eve.Meal from £30.00

Extremely hospitable family home with elevated views over Urafirth. Perfect area for walking, birdwatching, wildlife and fishing. Near Hillswick and Eshaness cliffs and Ronas Hill. Excellent home cooking.

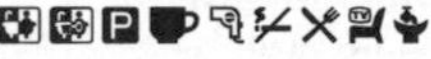

C W V

GOLD

Lerwick, Shetland — Map Ref: 5G6

B&B

Bonvista Guesthouse
26 Church Road, Lerwick, Shetland, ZE1 0AE
Tel: 01595 692269

2 Single, 1 Twin, 1 Double, 1 Family | B&B per person from £20.00 Single, from £18.00 Dbl/Twn, Room only per person from £14.00 | Open Jan-Dec excl Xmas/New Year, B&B + Eve.Meal from £25.00

Former Laird's Town House, now a 'B' Listed building, close to the hub of the town. A short walk from the Knab, the public golf course, the Bressay and Out Skerries ferries.

C V

Muckle Roe, North Mainland, Shetland — Map Ref: 5F4

B&B

Westayre B&B
Muckle Roe, Brae, Shetland, ZE2 9QW
Tel: 01806 522368

1 Twin, 1 Double, 1 Single | All En Suite | B&B per person from £20.00 Single, from £20.00 Dbl/Twn, Room only per person from £12.00 | Open Mar-Oct, B&B + Eve.Meal from £32.00

A warm welcome awaits you at our 110 acre working croft on the picturesque island of Muckle Roe where we have been breeding sheep, pet lambs, ducks and cats. Joined to the mainland by a small bridge and an ideal place for kids. High standards of home cooking and baking. In the evening sit by the open peat fire and enjoy the view over Swarbacks Minn. Spectacular cliff scenery and clean, safe sandy beaches. Bird watching. Central for touring.

C W V

Trondra, by Scalloway, Shetland — Map Ref: 5F6

B&B

Bed+Breakfast
South Burland, Trondra, Shetland, ZE1 0XL
Tel: 01595 880961 Fax: 01595 880962

1 Twin, 2 Double, 1 Family | 3 En Suite fac | B&B per person £25.00-£30.00 Single, £20.00-£23.00 Dbl/Twn | Open Jan-Dec excl Xmas/New Year

Panormic seaward views overlooking the island of Foula and the entrance to Scalloway Harbour. Spacious rooms all with luxury ensuite facilities. Residents lounge.

W

THE SCOTTISH TOURIST BOARD, in conjunction with the English Tourism Council and Wales Tourist Board operates a national accessible scheme that identifies, acknowledges and promotes those accommodation establishments that meet the needs of visitors with disabilities.

The three categories of accessibility, drawn up in close consultation with specialist organisations concerned with the needs of people with disabilities are:

CATEGORY 1

Unassisted wheelchair access for residents

CATEGORY 2

Assisted wheelchair access for residents

CATEGORY 3

Access for residents with mobility difficulties

CATEGORY 1

ABERDEEN PATIO HOTEL
Beach Boulevard
Aberdeen
AB24 5EF
TEL: 01224 633339

ACHILTY HOTEL
Contin
by Strathpeffer
Ross-shire
IV14 9EG
TEL: 01997 421355

AIRLIE MOUNT HOLIDAY SERVICES
2 Albert Street
Alyth
Perthshire
PH11 8AX
TEL: 01828 632986

AIRLIE HOUSE
Main Street
Strathyre
Stirling
FK18 8NA
TEL: 01877 384247

ARDGARTH GUEST HOUSE
1 St Mary's Place
Portobello
Edinburgh
EH15 2QF
TEL: 0131 669 3021

BATTLEDOWN BED & BREAKFAST
off Station Road
Forgandenny
by Perth
Perthshire
PH2 9EL
TEL: 01738 812471

BEARDMORE HOTEL & CONFERENCE CENTRE
Beardmore Street
Clydebank
Nr Glasgow
G81 4SA
TEL: 0141 951 6000

THE BEECHES GUEST HOUSE
112 Victoria Street
Dyce
Aberdeen
Aberdeenshire
AB21 7AU
TEL: 01224 722249

MRS S BOARD
Fourpenny Cottage
Skelbo
Dornoch
Sutherland
IV25 3QS
TEL: 01862 810727

BRAE LODGE GUEST HOUSE
30 Liberton Brae
Edinburgh
EH16 6AF
TEL: 0131 672 2876

MR J G BRISTOW
56 Dumbreck Road
Glasgow
G41 5NP
TEL: 0141 427 0129

BURRASTOW HOUSE HOTEL & RESTAURANT
Walls
Shetland
ZE2 9PD
TEL: 01595 809 307

CARLOGIE HOUSE HOTEL
Carlogie Road
Carnoustie
Angus
DD7 6LD
TEL: 01241 853185

CARLTON GEORGE HOTEL
44 West George Street
Glasgow
G2 1DH
TEL: 0141 353 6373

CLAYMORE HOUSE HOTEL
Seabank Road
Nairn
IV12 4EY
TEL: 01667 453731

COILLE-MHOR HOUSE
20 Houston Mains Holdings
Uphall
West Lothian
EH52 6PA
TEL: 01506 854044

COVENANTERS' INN
Auldearn
Nairn
IV12 5TG
TEL: 01667 452456

CREAG MHOR HOTEL
Onich
Inverness-shire
PH33 6RY
TEL: 01855 821379

CRUACHAN GUEST HOUSE
Monument Hill
Dalmally
Argyll
PA33 1AA
TEL: 01838 200496

CUIL-NA-SITHE
Lochyside
Fort William
Inverness-shire
PH33 7NX
TEL: 01397 702 267

DALHOUSIE COURTE HOTEL
Cockpen Road
Bonnyrigg
EH19 3HS
TEL: 0131 660 3200

DHAILLING LODGE
155 Alexandra Parade
Dunoon
Argyll
PA23 8AW
TEL: 01369 701253

DOLLY'S B&B
33 Aignish Point
Isle of Lewis
HS2 0PB
TEL: 01851 870755

DRUMOIG HOTEL & GOLF COURSE
Leuchars
by St Andrews
Fife
KY16 0BE
TEL: 01382 541800

DRYBURGH ABBEY HOTEL
St Boswells
Roxburghshire
TD6 0RQ
TEL: 01835 822261

DUNVALANREE HOUSE
Portrigh Bay
Carradale
Argyll
PA28 6SE
TEL: 01583 431226

EMPIRE TRAVEL LODGE
Union Street
Lochgilphead
Argyll
PA31 8JS
TEL: 01546 602381

EXPRESS BY HOLIDAY INN
Stoneyfield
Inverness
IV2 7PA
TEL: 01463 732700

FOREST HILLS HOTEL
Kinlochard,
by Aberfoyle
Perthshire
FK8 3TL
TEL: 01877 387277

GARDEN HOUSE HOTEL
Sarkfoot Road
Gretna
Dumfriesshire
DG16 5AJ
TEL: 01461 337621

GLASGOW HILTON
1 William Street
Glasgow
G3 8HT
TEL: 0141 204 5555

GLASGOW MARRIOTT HOTEL
500 Argyle Street
Glasgow
G3 8RR
TEL: 0141 226 5577

THE GLENEAGLES HOTEL
Auchterarder
Perthshire
PH3 1NF
TEL: 01764 662231

THE GLENHOLM CENTRE
Broughton
by Biggar
Lanarkshire
ML12 6JF
TEL: 01899 830408

GREENACRE
Aberfeldy Road
by Killin
Loch Tay
Perthshire
FK21 8TY
TEL: 01567 820466

HIGHLAND COTTAGE
Breadalbane Street
Tobermory
Isle of Mull
PA75 6PD
TEL: 01688 302407

HILDASAY GUEST HOUSE
Upper Scalloway,
Scalloway
Shetland
ZE1 0UP
TEL: 01595 880822

HOLIDAY INN EXPRESS LIVINGSTONE
Starlaw Road
Bathgate
West Lothian
EH48 1LQ
TEL: 01506 650650

HOLIDAY INN EXPRESS - STIRLING
Springkerse Business Park
Stirling
FK7 7XH
TEL: 01786 449922

HOLIDAY INN GLASGOW
161 West Nile Street
Glasgow
G1 2RL
TEL: 0141 352 0110

HOWARD JOHNSON HOTEL
Cartsburn
Greenock
PA15 4RT
TEL: 01475 786666

HUNTERS LODGE HOTEL
Annan Road
Gretna
Dumfriesshire
DG16 5DL
TEL: 01461 338214

INCHYRA GRANGE HOTEL
Grange Road
Polmont
Stirlingshire
FK2 0YB
TEL: 01324 711911

THE INVERCAULD ARMS HOTEL
Invercauld Road
Braemar
Aberdeenshire
AB35 5YR
TEL: 01339 741605

INVERNESS MARRIOTT HOTEL
Culcabock Road
Inverness
IV2 3LP
TEL: 01463 237166

INVERNETTIE GUEST HOUSE
South Road
Peterhead
Aberdeenshire
AB42 0YX
TEL: 01779 473530

ISLE OF SKYE HOTEL
Queensbridge
18 Dundee Road
Perth
Tayside
PH2 7AB
TEL: 01738 624471

ISLES OF GLENCOE HOTEL & LEISURE CENTRE
Ballachulish
nr Fort William
Argyll
PA39 4HL
TEL: 01855 821582

JAMES WATT COLLEGE
Waterfront Campus
Custom House Way
Greenock
Renfrewshire
PA15 1EN
TEL: 01475 731360

JARVIS INTERNATIONAL
Almondview
Livingston
West Lothian
EH54 6QB
TEL: 01506 431222

JURYS EDINBURGH INN
43 Jeffrey Street
Edinburgh
Lothian
EH1 1DH
TEL: 0131 500 3300

LAV'ROCKHA GUEST HOUSE
Inganess Road
St Ola
Kirkwall
Orkney
KW15 1SP
TEL: 01856 876107

LOCH TORRIDON HOTEL
Torridon
Achnasheen
Ross-shire
IV22 2EY
TEL: 01445 791242

MRS MACKENZIE DAWSON
Gattaway Farm
Abernethy
Perthshire
PH2 9LQ
TEL: 01738 850746

THE MARCLIFFE AT PITFODELS
North Deeside Road
Pitfodels
Aberdeen
AB15 9YA
TEL: 01224 861000

MELVILLE GUEST HOUSE
2 Duddingston Crescent
Edinburgh
Lothian
EH15 3AS
TEL: 0131 669 7856

MONCREIF
133 Alexandra Parade
Dunoon
Argyll
PA23 8AW
TEL: 01369 707945

NORTHBAY HOUSE
Balnabodach
Castlebay
Isle of Barra
HS9 5UT
TEL: (01871) 890 255

NORTH LODGE GUEST HOUSE
Canonbie
Dumfriesshire
DG14 0TF
TEL: 01387 371409

THE OLD STATION
Stravithie Bridge
St Andrews
Fife
KY16 8LR
TEL: 01334 880585

PANMURE HOTEL
Tay Street
Monifieth
Angus
DD5 4AX
TEL: 01382 532911

POSTHOUSE GLASGOW CITY
Bothwell Street
Glasgow
G2 7EN
TEL: 0870 400 9032

RATHCLUAN
Carslogie Road
Cupar
Fife,
KY15 4HY
TEL: 01334 650000

ROSSLEA HALL HOTEL
Ferry Road
Rhu
by Helensburgh
Dunbartonshire
G84 8NF
TEL: 01436 439955

ROWANTREE GUEST HOUSE
38 Main Street
Glenluce
Wigtownshire
DG8 0PS
TEL: 01581 300244

MRS E RYRIE
24 Lindsay Drive
Wick
Caithness,
KW1 4PG
TEL: 01955 603001

SHERATON GRAND HOTEL EDINBURGH
1 Festival Square
Edinburgh
EH3 9SR
TEL: 0131 229 9131

THE SHETLAND HOTEL
Holmsgarth Road
Lerwick
Shetland
ZE1 0PW
TEL: 01595 695515

SHOREFIELD
Edinbane
Isle of Skye
IV51 9PW
Tel: 01470 582444

SIMPSONS
79 Lauriston Place
Edinburgh
EH3 9HZ
TEL: 0131 622 7979

SPEEDBIRD INN
Argyll Road
Dyce
Aberdeen
AB21 0AF
TEL: 01224 772884

STEWART HALL OF RESIDENCE
Motherwell College
Dalzell Drive
Motherwell
Lanarkshire
ML1 2PP
TEL: 01698 261890

STIRLING MANAGEMENT CENTRE
University of Stirling
Stirling
FK9 4LA
TEL: 01786 451712

STRATHPEFFER HOTEL
Strathpeffer
Ross-shire
IV14 9DF
TEL: 01997 421200

STRONSAY HOTEL
Stronsay
Orkney
KW17 2AR
TEL: 01857 616213

THISTLE ABERDEEN AIRPORT
Aberdeen Airport
Argyll Road
Aberdeen
AB21 0AF
TEL: 01224 725252

THISTLE ABERDEEN ALTENS
Souterhead Road,
Altens
Aberdeen
AB12 3LF
TEL: 01224 877000

THISTLE EDINBURGH
107 Leith Street
Edinburgh
EH1 3SW
TEL: 0131 556 0111

THISTLE IRVINE
46 Annick Road
Irvine
Ayrshire
KA11 4LD
TEL: 01294 274272

THORNDALE
Manse Road
Stonehouse
Lanarkshire
ML9 3PQ
TEL: 01698 791133

TIGH-NA-CHEO
Garbhein Road
Kinlochleven
Argyll
PA40 4SE
TEL: 01855 831434

TRAVELODGE EDINBURGH SOUTH
46 Dreghorn Link
A720 City Bypass
Edinburgh
EH13 9QR
TEL: 07775 846074

THE TREFOIL CENTRE
Gogarbank
Edinburgh
EH12 9DA
TEL: 0131 339 3148

TURNBERRY HOTEL
Turnberry
Ayrshire
KA26 9LT
TEL: 01655 331000

UNIVERSITY OF DUNDEE
West Park Villas
West Park Road
Dundee
DD2 1NN
TEL: 01382 344039

UNIVERSITY OF ABERDEEN
King's College
Aberdeen
AB24 3FX
TEL: 01224 273444

VIEWFIELD HOUSE HOTEL
Portree
Isle of Skye
Inverness-shire
IV51 9EU
TEL: 01478 612217

WELCOME LODGE
M74 Motorway Junc 13
Abington
Biggar
Lanarkshire
ML12 6RG
TEL: 01864 502782

WELCOME LODGE
Welcome Break Service Area
M74
Gretna Green
Dumfriesshire
DG16 5HQ
TEL: 01461 337566

WESTWOOD GUEST HOUSE
Houndwood
by St Abbs
Berwickshire
TD14 5TP
TEL: 01361 850232

MRS WILLIAMS
Strathwhillan House
Brodick
Isle of Arran
KA27 8BQ
TEL: 01770 302331

THE WINDSOR HOTEL
18 Albert Street
Nairn
IV12 4HP
TEL: 01667 453108

CATEGORY 2

ABERDEEN MARRIOTT
Overton Circle
Dyce
Aberdeen
AB21 7AZ
TEL: 01224 770011

ARDENCAPLE HOTEL
Shore Road
Rhu
by Helensburgh
Dunbartonshire
G83 8LA
TEL: 01436 820200

ARDEN HOUSE
Newtonmore Road
Kingussie
Inverness-shire
PH21 1HE
TEL: 01540 661369

AUCHENDINNY GUEST HOUSE
Treaslane
Skeabost Bridge
Isle of Skye
Inverness-shire
IV51 9NX
TEL: 01470 532470

AUCHENSKEOCH LODGE
by Dalbeattie
Kirkcudbrightshire
DG5 4PG
TEL: 01387 780277

AUCHRANNIE COUNTRY HOUSE HOTEL
Brodick
Isle of Arran
KA27 8BZ
TEL: 01770 302234

BALBIRNIE HOUSE HOTEL
Balbirnie Park
Markinch
by Glenrothes
Fife
KY7 6NE
TEL: 01592 610066

THE BALLACHULISH HOTEL
Ballachulish
nr Fort William
Argyll
PH49 4JY
TEL: 01855 811606

THE BALTASOUND HOTEL
Baltasound
Unst
Shetland
ZE2 9DS
TEL: 01957 711334

BARNTON HOTEL
Queensferry Road
Edinburgh
EH4 6AS
TEL: 0131 339 1144

BARONY HOTEL
Birsay
Orkney
KW17 2LS
TEL: 01856 721327

THE CALEDONIAN
Princes Street
Edinburgh
EH1 2AB
TEL: 0131 459 9988

CLAN MACDUFF HOTEL
Achintore
Fort William
Inverness-shire
PH33 6RW
TEL: 01397 702341

CLONYARD HOUSE HOTEL
Colvend
Dalbeattie
Kirkcudbrightshire
DG5 4QW
TEL: 01556 630372

COMELY BANK
32 Burrell Street
Crieff
Perthshire
PH7 4DT
TEL: 01764 653409

DALL LODGE COUNTRY HOUSE HOTEL
Main Street
Killin
Perthshire
FK21 8TN
TEL: 01567 820217

DRYFESDALE HOTEL
Lockerbie
Dumfriesshire
DG11 2SF
TEL: 01576 202427

DYCE SKEAN DHU
Farburn Terrace
Dyce
Aberdeen
AB21 7DW
TEL: 01224 723101

EWOOD HOUSE
12 Kings Gate
Aberdeenshire
AB15 4EJ
TEL: 01224 648408

ALISTAIR FORTUNE
Glenaveron
Golf Road
Brora
Sutherland
KW9 6QS
TEL: 01408 621601

GARVOCK HOUSE HOTEL
St John's Drive
Transy
Dunfermline
KY12 7TU
TEL: 01383 621067

GLASGOW MOAT HOUSE
Congress Road
Glasgow
G3 8QT
TEL: 0141 306 9988

HILCROFT HOTEL
East Main Street
Whitburn
West Lothian
EH47 0JU
TEL: 01501 740818

HILTON EDINBURGH AIRPORT
Edinburgh International Airport
Edinburgh
EH28 8LL
TEL: 0131 519 4400

HILTON EDINBURGH GROSVENOR HOTEL
7-21 Grosvenor Street
Edinburgh
EH12 5EF
TEL: 0131 226 6001

HOLIDAY INN GARDEN COURT
Queensferry Road
Edinburgh
EH4 3HL
TEL: 0131 332 2442

HUNTINGTOWER HOTEL
Crieff Road
Perth
PH1 3JT
TEL: 01738 583771

IVORY HOUSE
14 Vogrie Road
Gorebridge
Midlothian
EH23 4HH
TEL: 01875 820755

JARVIS CALEDONIAN HOTEL
Church Street
Inverness
IV1 1DX
TEL: 01463 235181

KEAVIL HOUSE HOTEL
Crossford
Dunfermline
Fife
KY12 8QW
TEL: 01383 736258

KINLOCH HOUSE HOTEL
Kinloch
by Blairgowrie
Perthshire
PH10 6SG
TEL: 01250 884237

LOCH FYNE HOTEL
Newtown
Inveraray
Argyll
PA32 8XT
TEL: 01499 302148

LOG CABIN HOTEL
Glen Derby
Kirkmichael
Blairgowrie
Perthshire
PH10 7NB
TEL: 01250 881288

MRS F MEREDITH, CLUNEBEG LODGE
Clunebeg Estate
Drumnadrochit
Inverness-shire
IV3 6UU
TEL: 01456 450387

KYANACHAN LOCH TUMMEL HOTEL
Tummel Bridge
Perthshire
PH16 5SB
TEL: 01389 713713

THE MILL
Grahamshill
Kirkpatrick Fleming
by Lockerbie
Dumfriesshire
DG11 3BQ
TEL: 01461 800344

MOORINGS HOTEL
114 Hamilton Road
Motherwell
ML1 3DG
TEL: 01698 258131

CLOISTERS
Church Holme
Talmine
Sutherland
IV27 4YP
TEL: 01847 601286

MUCKRACH LODGE HOTEL
Dulnain Bridge
Inverness-shire
PH26 3LY
TEL: 01479 851257

MURRAYPARK HOTEL
Connaught Terrace
Crieff
Perthshire
PH7 3DJ
TEL: 01764 653731

NAVIDALE HOUSE HOTEL
Navidale
Helmsdale
Sutherland
KW8 6JS
TEL: 01431 821258

NETHYBRIDGE HOTEL
Nethy Bridge
Inverness-shire
PH25 3DP
TEL: 01479 821203

NEW LANARK MILL HOTEL
New Lanark
Lanarkshire
ML11 9DB
TEL: 01555 667200

THE NEW WEIGH INN HOTEL
Burnside
Thurso
Caithness
KW14 7UG
TEL: 01847 893722

THE OBSERVATORY GUEST HOUSE
North Ronaldsay
Orkney
KW17 2BE
TEL: 01857 633200

OLD PINES RESTAURANT WITH ROOMS
by Spean Bridge
Inverness-shire
PH34 4EG
TEL: 01397 712324

ORASAY INN
Lochcarnan
South Uist
Outer Hebrides
HS8 5PD
TEL: 01870 610298

PATIO HOTEL
1 South Avenue
Clydebank Business Park
Clydebank
Glasgow
Dunbartonshire
G81 2RW
TEL: 0141 951 1133

POSTHOUSE EDINBURGH
Corstorphine Road
Edinburgh
EH12 6UA
TEL: 0870 400 9026

TOR-NA-COILLE HOTEL
Inchmarlo Road
Banchory
Kincardineshire
AB31 4AB
TEL: 01330 822242

TRAVELODGE DUMBARTON
A82, Milton
Dumbarton
Strathclyde
G82 2TY
TEL: 01389 765202

KINGS HALL UNIVERSITY OF ABERDEEN
Aberdeen
AB24 3FX
TEL: 01224 273444

WHITCHESTER GUEST HOUSE
Hawick
Roxburghshire
TD9 7LN
TEL: 01450 377477

CATEGORY 3

AARON GLEN GUEST HOUSE
7 Nivensknowe Road
Loanhead
Midlothian
EH20 9AU
TEL: 0131 440 1293

ABBEY LODGE HOTEL
137 Drum Street
Gilmerton
Edinburgh
EH17 8RJ
TEL: 0131 664 9548

ABERDOUR HOTEL
38 High Street
Aberdour
Fife
KY3 0SW
TEL: 01383 860325

ABERFELDY LODGE GUEST HOUSE
11 Southside Road
Inverness
IV2 3BG
TEL: 01463 231120

ALCORN GUEST HOUSE
5 Hyndford Street
Dundee
Angus
DD2 3DY
TEL: 01382 668433

ANCHORAGE GUEST HOUSE
31 Balloch Road
Balloch
Dumbartonshire
G83 8SS
TEL: 01389 753336

THE ANCHORAGE HOTEL
Shore Road
Ardnadan
Dunoon
Argyll
PA23 8QD
TEL: 01369 705108

APPLEACRE
Birgham Main Street
by Coldstream
Berwickshire
TD12 4NF
TEL: 01890 830306

ARDBEG COTTAGE
19 Castle Street
Lochmaben
Dumfriesshire
DG11 1NY
TEL: 01387 811855

ARNABHAL
5 Gearraidh Bhailteas
Bornish
South Uist
HS8 5RY
TEL: 0178 710371

ASHBANK
105 Main Street
Redding
Falkirk
Stirlingshire
FK2 9UQ
TEL: 01324 716649

ATHOLL VILLA
29 Atholl Road
Pitlochry
Perthshire
PH16 5BX
TEL: 01796 473820

AVALON GUEST HOUSE
79 Glenurquhart Road
Inverness
Inverness-shire
IV3 5PB
TEL: 01463 239075

THE KNOWES
32 Riddrie Knowes
Glasgow
G33 2QH
TEL: 0141 770 5213

BALAVIL SPORT HOTEL
Main Street
Newtonmore
Inverness-shire
PH20 1DL
TEL: 01540 673220

BALLATHIE HOUSE HOTEL
Kinclaven
by Stanley
Perthshire
PH1 4QN
TEL: 01250 883268

BEEHIVE COTTAGE
12 Kingston
North Berwick
East Lothian
EH39 5JE
TEL: 01620 894785

BIRCHBANK ACTIVITY LODGE
Knockan
Elphin
by Lairg
Sutherland
IV27 4HH
TEL: 01854 666203

BRAEFIELD GUEST HOUSE
Braefield Road
Portpatrick
Wigtownshire
DG9 8TA
TEL: 01776 810255

BRIAR COTTAGE
Well Brae
Pitlochry
Perthshire
PH16 5HH
TEL: 01796 473678

BRITANNIA HOTEL
Malcolm Road
Aberdeen
AB21 9LN
TEL: 01224 409988

BROOMFIELD HOUSE
Thorn Street
Earlston
Berwickshire
TD4 6DR
TEL: 01896 848084

THE BUNGALOW
81 High Street
Buckie
Banffshire
AB56 1BB
TEL: 01542 832367

CHERRYBANK INN
210 Glasgow Road
Perth
PH2 ONA
TEL: 01738 624349

CHESTERTON HOUSE
Formaston Park
Aboyne
Aberdeenshire
AB34 5HF
TEL: 013398 86740

CLARKE COTTAGE GUEST HOUSE
139 Halbeath Road
Dunfermline
Fife
KY11 4LA
TEL: 01383 735935

CORMISTON COTTAGE
Cormiston Road
Biggar
Lanarkshire
ML12 6NS
TEL: 01899 220200

CORSEWALL LIGHTHOUSE HOTEL
Kirkcolm
by Stranraer
Wigtownshire
DG9 0QG
TEL: 01776 853220

COUL HOUSE HOTEL
Contin
by Strathpeffer
Ross-shire
IV14 9EY
TEL: 01997 421487

CRAIGATIN HOUSE
165 Atholl Road
Pitlochry
Perthshire
PH16 5QL
TEL: 01796 472478

CRAIGLYNNE HOTEL
Woodlands Terrace
Grantown-on-Spey
Moray
PH26 3SX
TEL: 01479 872597

CRAIGNETHAN HOUSE
Jedburgh Road
Kelso
Roxburghshire
TD5 8BZ
TEL: 01573 224818

CRAIGVRACK HOTEL
38 West Moulin Road
Pitlochry
Perthshire
PH16 5EQ
TEL: 01796 472399

CRANSHAWS SMIDDY
Cranshaws
Duns
Berwickshire
TD11 3SL
TEL: 01361 890277

CRIEFF HYDRO
Crieff
Perthshire
PH7 3LQ
TEL: 01764 655555

BARN LODGE
Croftside
Pirnhill
Stirling
Stirlingshire
FK7 8EX
TEL: 01786 813591

CROIT ANNA HOTEL
Achintore Road
Fort William
Inverness-shire
PH33 6RR
TEL: 01397 702268

CROMASAIG
Torridon Road
Kinlochewe
Ross-shire
IV22 2PE
TEL: 01445 760234

CROSS KEYS HOTEL
36-37 The Square
Kelso
Roxburghshire
TD5 7HL
TEL: 01573 223303

DARROCH LEARG HOTEL
Braemar Road
Ballater
Aberdeenshire
AB35 5UX
TEL: 013397 55443

DINWOODIE LODGE HOTEL
Johnstone Bridge
by Lockerbie
Dumfiesshire
DG11 2SL
TEL: 01576 470289

DREAMWEAVERS
Mucomir
by Spean Bridge
Inverness-shire
PH34 4EQ
TEL: 01397 712548

DROMNAN GUEST HOUSE
Garve Road
Ullapool
Ross-shire
IV26 2SX
TEL: 01854 612333

DRUMFORK FARM
Helensburgh
Dumbartonshire
G84 7JY
TEL: 01436 672 329

DRUMNADROCHIT HOTEL
Drumnadrochit
Inverness-shire
IV63 6TU
TEL: 01456 450218

DRUMOSSIE PARK COTTAGE
Drumossie Brae
Inverness
Inverness-shire
IV2 5BB
TEL: 01463 224127

DUNALLAN HOUSE
Woodside Avenue
Grantown-on-Spey
PH26 3JN
TEL: 01479 872140

DUNEDIN
42 Strath
Gairloch
Ross-shire
IV21 2DB
TEL: 01445 712050

DUNMORE
19 Newton Street
Blairgowrie
Perthshire
PH10 6HT
TEL: 01250 874451

DUNROAMIN
South Keiss
Wick
Caithness
KW1 4XG
TEL: 01955 631283

EAST HAUGH HOUSE COUNTRY HOTEL & RESTAURANT
East Haugh
by Pitlochry
Perthshire
PH16 5JS
TEL: 01796 47 3121

EDINBURGH FIRST
University of Edinburgh
Pollock Halls
Edinburgh
Lothian
EH16 5AY
TEL: 0131 667 0662

ETTRICKVALE
33 Abbotsford Road
Galashiels
Selkirkshire
TD1 3HW
TEL: 01896 755224

FAIRFIELD HOUSE HOTEL
12 Fairfield Road
Ayr
Ayrshire
KA7 2AR
TEL: 01292 267461

FALLS OF LORA HOTEL
Connel Ferry
by Oban
Argyll
PA37 1PB
TEL: 01631 710483

FENDOCH GUEST HOUSE
Sma' Glen
Crieff
Perthshire
PH7 3LW
TEL: 01764 653446

FENWICK HOTEL
Fenwick
by Kilmarnock
Ayrshire
KA3 6AU
TEL: 01560 600478

FERNHILL HOTEL
Heugh Road
Portpatrick
Wigtownshire
DG9 8TD
TEL: 01776 810220

FINDLAY, ROSS (IONA) LTD
Martyr's Bay
Isle of Iona
Argyll
PA76 6SP
TEL: 01681 700357

THE FISHERMANS TAVERN HOTEL
10-16 Fort Street
Broughty Ferry
Dundee
Angus
DD5 2AD
TEL: 01382 775941

FISHERS HOTEL
75-79 Atholl Road,
Pitlochry
Perthshire
PH16 5BN
TEL: 01796 472000

FORBES ARMS HOTEL
Milltown of Rothiemay
Huntly
Aberdeenshire
AB54 7LT
TEL: 01466 711248

FORSS HOUSE HOTEL
Forss
by Thurso
Caithness
KW14 7XY
TEL: 01847 861201

ERSKINE BRIDGE HOTEL
Erskine
Renfrewshire
PA8 6AN
TEL: 0141 812 0123

WAVERLEY
35 Strathspey Avenue
Aviemore
Inverness-shire
PH22 1SN
TEL: 01479 811226

FREEDOM INN
Aviemore Centre
Aviemore
Inverness-shire
PH22 1PF
TEL: 01479 810781

GAIRLOCH VIEW
3 Digg
Staffin
Isle of Skye
IV51 9LA
TEL: 01470 562718

THE GALLEY OF LORNE INN
Ardfern
by Lochgilphead
Argyll
PA31 8QN
TEL: 01852 500284

GLEN ORCHY HOUSE
20 Knab Road
Lerwick
Shetland
ZE1 OAX
TEL: 01595 692031

GLEN MHOR HOTEL
9-12 Ness Bank
Inverness
IV2 4SG
TEL: 01463 234308

ROADCHEF LODGE
Hamilton Roadchef Service
Area (M74N)
Hamilton
Lanarkshire
ML3 6JW
TEL: 01698 891904

THE GOLDENSTONES HOTEL
Queens Road
Dunbar
East Lothian
EH42 1LG
TEL: 01368 862356

GORDON HOTEL
Wellington Road
Nigg
Aberdeen
AB12 3GH
TEL: 01224 873012

EDENMOUTH FARM
Kelso
Roxburghshire
TD5 7QB
TEL: 01890 830391

GREENLAWNS
13 Seafield Street
Nairn
Inverness-shire
IV12 4HG
TEL: 01667 452738

GREEN PARK HOTEL
Clunie Bridge Road
Pitlochry
Perthshire
PH16 5JY
TEL: 01796 473248

HAZELDEAN HOUSE
4 Moffat Road
Dumfries
DG1 1NJ
TEL: 01387 266178

HEATHPETE
24 Balloch Road
Balloch
Dunbartonshire
G83 8LE
TEL: 01389 752195

HETLAND HALL HOTEL
Carrutherstown
Dumfriesshire
DG1 4JX
TEL: 01387 840201

HILTON EDINBURGH BELFORD
69 Belford Road
Edinburgh
EH4 3DG
TEL: 0131 332 2545

HILTON STRATHCLYDE
Phoenix Crescent
Bellshill
N. Lanarkshire
ML4 3JQ
TEL: 01698 395500

HILTON DUNDEE HOTEL
Earl Grey Place
Dundee, Angus
DD1 4DE
TEL: 01382 229271

HOLLAND HOUSE
18 Holyrood Park Road
Edinburgh
EH16 5AY
TEL: 0800 028 7118

HOLLY TREE HOTEL
Kentallen
Appin
Argyll
PA38 4BY
TEL: 01631 740292

HORIZON HOTEL
Esplanade
Ayr
Ayrshire
KA7 1DT
TEL: 01292 264384

INNISCHONAIN HOUSE
Tarbet
Arrochar
Argyll
G83 7DD
TEL: 01301 702 726

KELLY'S GUEST HOUSE
3 Hillhouse Road
Edinburgh
EH4 3QP
TEL: 0131 332 3894

KILDONAN HOTEL
27 Queens Terrace,
Ayr
Ayrshire
KA7 1DX
TEL: 01292 285122

KILSPINDIE HOUSE HOTEL
Aberlady
Longiddry
EH32 0RE
TEL: 01875 870682

THE KIMBERLEY HOTEL
Dalriach Road
Oban, Argyll
PA34 5EQ
TEL: 01631 571115

KINGSPARK LLAMA FARM
Berriedale
Caithness
KW7 6HA
TEL: 01593 751202

KINKELL HOUSE
Easter Kinkell
by Conon Bridge
Ross-shire
IV7 8HY
TEL: 01349 861270

KIRKLAND COUNTRY HOUSE HOTEL
Ruthwell
Dumfriesshire
DG1 4NP
TEL: 01387 870284

THE KIRKTON INN
1 Main Street
Dalrymple
Ayrshire
KA6 6DF
TEL: 01292 560241

THE KNOWE
Ancaster Road
Callande
Perthshire
FK17 8EL
TEL: 01877 330076

LILYBANK GUEST HOUSE
Shore Road
Lamlash
Isle of Arran,
KA27 8LS
TEL: 01770 600230

LINDSAY GUEST HOUSE
108 Polwarth Terrace
Edinburgh
EH11 1NN
TEL: 0131 337 1580

LINKS HOTEL
Mid Links
Montrose
Angus
DD10 8RL
TEL: 01674 671000

LOCH TUMMEL INN
Strathtummel
Pitlochry
Perthshire
PH16 5RP
TEL: 01882 634272

LOCHAN COTTAGE GUEST HOUSE
Lochyside
Fort William
Inverness-shire
PH33 7NX
TEL: 01397 702695

CROFTERS WAYSIDE INN
Lochton of Durris
by Banchory
Aberdeenshire
AB31 6DB
TEL: 01330 844543

LOMOND COUNTRY INN
Main Street
Kinnesswood
Kinross
KY13 9HN
TEL: 01592 840253

LYNDALE
Station Road
Beauly
Inverness-shire
IV4 7EH
TEL: 01463 782252

LYNEDOCH
7 Mayne Avenue
Bridge of Allan
Stirlinghsire
FK9 4QU
TEL: 01786 832178

MARDON
BED & BREAKFAST
37 Kenneth Street
Inverness
IV3 5DH
TEL: 01463 231005

2 MULINDRY COTTAGES
Bridgend
Isle of Islay
Argyll
PA44 7PZ
TEL: 01496 810397

MILLSEAT
Inverugie Road
Hopeman
Morayshire
IV30 5SX
TEL: 01343 830097

MILTON LEA
by Balmullo
St Andrews
Fife
KY16 0AB
TEL: 01334 839144

DUMFRIES & GALLOWAY
COLLEGE
Heathhall
Dumfries
DG1 3QZ
TEL: 01387 243840

MORAYDALE
276 High Street
Elgin
Morayshire
IV30 1AG
TEL: 01343 546381

AVALON
12 Westside
Tarbert
Harris
Western Isles
HS3 3BG
TEL: 01859 502334

MOYNESS HOUSE
6 Bruce Gardens
Inverness
IV3 5EN
TEL: 01463 233836

NEWBYRES COTTAGE
8 Hunterfield Road
Gorebridge
Midlothian
EH23 4TR
TEL: 01875 821268

THE NORTHERN HOTEL
1 Great Northern Road
Aberdeen
AB24 3PS
TEL: 01224 483342
FAX: 01224 276103

THE OLD MILL AND
RESTAURANT
Mill Lane
Pitlochry
Perthshire
PH16 5BH
TEL: 01796 474020

PIERSLAND HOUSE
HOTEL
15 Craigend Road
Troon
Ayrshire
KA10 6HD
TEL: 01292 314747

PITBAUCHLIE HOUSE
HOTEL
Aberdour Road
Dunfermline
Fife
KY11 4PB
TEL: 01383 722282

THE PRIORY
Bracklinn Road
Callander
Perthshire
FK17 8EH
TEL: 01877 330001

PRIORY LODGE
8 The Loan
South Queensferry
West Lothian
EH30 9NS
TEL: 0131 331 4345

QUALITY HOTEL STATION
PERTH
Leonard Street
Perth
PH2 8HE
TEL: 01738 624141

QUALITY HOTEL STATION
AYR
Burns Statue Square
Ayr
Ayrshire
KA7 3AT
TEL: 01292 263268

RED HOUSE HOTEL
Station Road
Coupar Angus
Perthshire
PH13 9AL
TEL: 01828 628500

THE REIVERS REST
81 High Street
Langholm
Dumfriesshire
DG13 0DJ
TEL: 013873 81343

RHUGARBH CROFT
Appin
Argyll
PA38 4BA
TEL: 01631 730309

RICHMOND PARK HOTEL
26 Linlithgow Road
Bo'ness
West Lothian
EH51 0DN
TEL: 01506 823213

ROB ROY MOTEL
Aberfoyle
Stirlingshire
FK8 3UX
TEL: 01877 382245

ROCKMOUNT COTTAGE
Dura Den Road
Pitscottie
Cupar
KY15 5TG
TEL: 01334 828164

ROMAN CAMP HOTEL
off Main Street
Callander
Perthshire
FK17 8BG
TEL: 01877 330003

ROSE COTTAGE GUEST HOUSE
Gelson
Castle Douglas
Kirkcudbrightshire
DG7 1SH
TEL: 01556 502513

RSR BRAEHOLM
31 East Montrose Street
Helensburgh
Argyll & Bute
G84 7HR
TEL: 01436 671880

RUFFLETS COUNTRY HOUSE HOTEL
Strathkinness Low Road
St Andrews
Fife
KY16 9TX
TEL: 01334 472594

SCOTTIES B&B
213 Nicol Street
Kirkcaldy
Fife
KY1 1PF
TEL: 01592 268596

SHAWLANDS HOTEL
Ayr Road
Canderside Toll
by Larkhall
Lanarkshire
ML9 2TZ
TEL: 01698 791111

SOLUIS MU THUATH GUEST HOUSE
Braeintra
by Achmore
Strome Ferry
Ross-shire
IV53 8UP
TEL: 01599 577219

SPINNAKER HOTEL
12 Albert Road
Gourock
Renfrewshire
PA19 1BU
TEL: 01475 633107

SPRINGVALE HOTEL
18 Lethame Road
Strathaven
Lanarkshire
ML10 6AD
TEL: 01357 521131

STAKIS EAST KILBRIDE
Stewartfield Way
East Kilbride
Lanarkshire
G74 5LA
TEL: 01355 236300

STRATHBURN HOTEL
Burghmuir Drive
Inverurie
Aberdeenshire
AB51 4GY
TEL: 01467 624422

SUNBANK HOUSE HOTEL
50 Dundee Road
Perth
PH2 7BA
TEL: 01738 624882
FAX: 01738 442515

SWALLOW HOTEL
Kingsway West
Invergowrie
Dundee
Angus
DD2 5JT
TEL: (01382) 641122

TOBERMORY HOTEL
53 Main Street
Tobermory
Isle of Mull
PA75 6NT
TEL: 01688 302091

THE TONTINE HOTEL
6 Ardgowan Square
Greenock
Renfrewshire
PA16 8NG
TEL: 01475 723316

TORBAY LODGE
31 Lovers Walk
Dumfries
DG1 1LR
TEL: 01387 253922

TRAVELODGE GLASGOW CENTRAL
5 Hill Street
Glasgow
G3 6RP
TEL: 0141 333 1515

THEATRE HOTEL LTD
25/27 Elmbank Street
Glasgow
G2 4PB
TEL: 0141 227 2772

WHINRIG
12 Burgh Road
Lerwick
Shetland
ZE1 0LB
TEL: 01595 693554

WOLSELEY PARK HOTEL
Stirling Road
Callander
Perthshire
FK17 8DA
TEL: 01877 330261

WOODLAND HOUSE
Torlundy
Fort William
Inverness-shire
PH33 6SN
TEL: 01397 701698

Area codes

A	SOUTH OF SCOTLAND: AYRSHIRE AND ARRAN, DUMFRIES AND GALLOWAY, SCOTTISH BORDERS	2
B	EDINBURGH AND LOTHIANS	58
C	GREATER GLASGOW AND CLYDE VALLEY	117
D	WEST HIGHLANDS & ISLANDS, LOCH LOMOND, STIRLING AND TROSSACHS	136
E	PERTHSHIRE, ANGUS AND DUNDEE AND THE KINGDOM OF FIFE	196
F	SCOTLAND'S CASTLE AND WHISKY COUNTRY ROYAL DEESIDE TO SPEYSIDE	264
G	THE HIGHLANDS AND SKYE	307
H	OUTER ISLANDS: WESTERN ISLES, ORKNEY, SHETLAND	442

The Scottish Tourist Board produces a series of four accommodation guides to help you choose your holiday accommodation. The most comprehensive guides on the market, they give details of facilities, price, location and every establishment in them carries a quality assurance award from the Scottish Tourist Board.

SCOTLAND: HOTELS & GUEST HOUSES 2001
£9.50 (INCL. P&P)

Over 1,400 entries, listing a variety of hotels and guest houses throughout Scotland. Also includes inns, lodges, restaurant with rooms, bed and breakfasts, campus accommodation, serviced apartments and international resort hotels. Comprehensive location maps. Completely revised each year. Full colour throughout.

SCOTLAND: BED & BREAKFAST 2001
£6.50 (INCL. P&P)

Over 1,700 entries, listing a variety of bed and breakfast establishments throughout Scotland. Also includes hotels, guest houses, inns, lodges, restaurant with rooms and campus accommodation. Comprehensive location maps. Completely revised each year.

SCOTLAND: CARAVAN & CAMPING 2001
£4.50 (INCL. P&P)

Over 200 entries, listing caravan parks and individual caravan holiday homes for hire. Includes self-catering properties. Comprehensive location maps. Completely revised each year.

SCOTLAND: SELF CATERING 2001
£7.00 (INCL. P&P)

Over 1,100 entries, listing cottages, flats, chalets, log cabins and serviced apartments to let. Many in scenic areas or bustling towns and cities. Caravan holiday homes included. Comprehensive location maps. Completely revised each year. Full colour throughout.

TOURING GUIDE TO SCOTLAND
£6.00 (INCL. P&P)

A new, fully revised edition of this popular guide which now lists over 1,500 things to do and places to visit in Scotland. Easy to use index and locator maps. Details of opening hours, admission charges, a general description and information on disabled access.

TOURING MAP OF SCOTLAND
£4.00 (INCL. P&P)

A new and up-to-date touring map of Scotland. Full colour with comprehensive motorway and road information, the map details over 20 categories of tourist information and names over 1,500 things to do and places to visit in Scotland

YOU CAN ORDER ANY OF THE ABOVE BY FILLING IN THE COUPON ON THE NEXT PAGE OR BY TELEPHONE.

Mail Order

Please tick the publications you would like, cut out this section and send it with your cheque, postal order (made payable to Scottish Tourist Board) or credit card details to:

Scottish Tourist Board, FREEPOST, dunoon, argyll PA23 8PQ

scotland: Hotels & Guest Houses 2001	£9.50 (incl. p&p)	☐
scotland: Bed & Breakfast 2001	£6.50 (incl. p&p)	☐
scotland: Caravan & Camping 2001	£4.50 (incl. p&p)	☐
scotland: Self Catering 2001	£7.00 (incl. p&p)	☐
Touring Guide to Scotland	£6.00 (incl. p&p)	☐
Touring Map of Scotland	£4.00 (incl. p&p)	☐

BLOCK CAPITALS PLEASE:

name (Mr/Mrs/Ms)

address

post code telephone No.

total remittance enclosed £

please charge my *visa/access account (*delete as appropriate)

card no. **expiry date**

Signature

Date

TELEPHONE ORDERS

To order BY PHONE: simply call free 08705 511511 (national call rate) quoting the books you would like and give your credit card details.

Mark Hill is a London-based full-time writer of novels and scripts. Formerly he was a journalist and a producer at BBC Radio 2 across a range of major daytime shows and projects. He has won two Sony Gold Awards.

TWO O'CLOCK BOY

MARK HILL

sphere

SPHERE

First published in Great Britain in ebook in 2016 by Sphere

This edition published in 2017 by Sphere

1 3 5 7 9 10 8 6 4 2

All characters and events in this publication, other than those clearly in the public domain, are fictitious and any resemblance to real persons, living or dead, is purely coincidental.

A CIP catalogue record for this book is available from the British Library.

ISBN 978-0-7515-6323-8

Typeset in Adobe Caslon Pro by Palimpsest Book Production Limited,
Falkirk, Stirlingshire
Printed and bound in Great Britain by Clays Ltd, St Ives plc

Papers used by Sphere are from well-managed forests
and other responsible sources.

Sphere
An imprint of
Little, Brown Book Group
Carmelite House
50 Victoria Embankment
London
EC4Y 0DZ

An Hachette UK Company
www.hachette.co.uk

www.littlebrown.co.uk

For Fiona & Archie

Time shall unfold what plighted cunning hides;
Who cover faults, at last shame them derides.

WILLIAM SHAKESPEARE

1

The English Channel, 1986

The boy loved his parents more than anything on this Earth. And so he had to kill them.

Perched on the edge of the bunk, he listened to them now. To the squeak of their soles on the deck above as they threw recriminations back and forth in voices as vicious as the screeching seagulls wheeling in the sky. He heard the crack of the sail in the wind, the smack of the water against the hull inches from his head, a soothing, hypnotic rhythm.

Slap . . . slap . . . slap . . .

Before everything went wrong, before the boy went away as one person and came back as someone different, they had been full of gentle caresses and soft words for each other. But they argued all the time now, his parents – too stridently, loud enough for him to hear – and the quarrel was always about the same thing: what could be done about their unhappy son?

He understood that they wanted him to know how remorseful they were about what had happened. But their misery only made him feel worse. He couldn't remember the last time he'd been able to speak to them, to utter a single word, and the longer he stayed silent the more his parents fought. The boy plugged his fingers into his ears, closed his eyes, and listened to the dull roar within him.

His love for them was untethering, drifting away on a fierce tide.

Slap . . . slap . . . slap . . .

A muffled voice. 'Darling.'

The boy's hands were pulled gently from his face. His mother crouched before him. Her eyes were rimmed red, and her hair was plastered to her face by sea spray, but she was still startlingly beautiful.

'Why don't you come up top?'

Her cold fingers tucked a loose strand of his hair behind his ear. For a brief moment he felt a familiar tenderness, wanted to clasp her to him and ignore the bitter thoughts that churned in his head. But he didn't, he couldn't. It had been weeks since he'd been able to speak.

A shadow fell across the hatch. His father's voice boomed, 'Is he coming up?'

'Please, let me handle this,' his mother barked over her shoulder, and after a moment of hesitation, the shadow disappeared.

'We're doing the best we can.' She waited for her son to speak. 'But you must tell us how you feel, so that we can help you.'

The boy managed a small nod, and hope flickered in his mother's gaze.

'Your father and I . . . we love you more than anything. If we argue it's because we can never forgive ourselves for what happened to you. You know that, don't you?'

Her eyes filled with tears, and he would do anything to stop her from crying. In a cracked voice, barely more than a whisper, he heard himself say, 'I love you.'

His mother's hand flew to her mouth. She stood, hunched in the cabin.

'We're about to eat sandwiches.' Moving to the steps, she spoke brightly, but her voice trembled. 'Why don't you come up when you're ready?'

He nodded. With a last, eager smile, his mother climbed to the hatch and her body was consumed by sunlight.

The boy's heel thudded against the clasp of the toolbox beneath his berth. He pulled out the metal box and tipped open the lid to reveal his father's tools. Rasps, pliers, a spirit level. Tacks and nails, a chisel slick with grease. Lifting the top tray, the heavier tools were revealed: a saw, a screwdriver, a peen hammer. The varnish on the handle of the hammer was worn away. The wood was rough, its mottled head pounded to a dull grey. He lifted it, felt its weight in his palm.

Clenching the hammer in his fist, he stooped beneath the bulkhead – in the last couple of years he'd grown so much taller – to listen to the clink of plastic plates, his parents' animated voices on the deck.

'Sandwiches are ready!' called his mother.

Every night he had the same dream, like a terrible premonition: his parents passed him on the street without a glance, as if they were total strangers. Sooner or later, he knew, this nightmare would become a reality. The resentment they felt that their child had gone for ever, replaced by somebody else, someone ugly inside, would chip away at their love for him. Until there was nothing left.

And he was afraid that his own fierce love for them was slowly rotting, corroded by blame and bitterness. One day, when it was gone completely, other emotions would fill the desolate space inside him. Fury, rage. A cold, implacable hatred. Already he felt anger swelling like a storm where his love had been. He couldn't bear to hate them, yearned to keep his love for his parents – and his memories of a happy time before he went to that place – uncorrupted, and to carry it with him into an uncertain future.

And so he had to act.

Gripping the hammer, the boy moved towards the hatch. His view filled with the blinding grey of the sky and the blur of the wheeling gulls, which screamed a warning to him that this world would always snatch from him the things he cherished, that life would always be this way.

He stepped onto the windblown deck in the middle of a sea that went on for ever.

Slap . . . slap . . . slap . . .

2

Present day

Everybody wanted a piece of Detective Inspector Ray Drake.

He circled the room, accepting handshakes and backslaps until there was no one left to congratulate him. Soon, he hoped, they'd all get too drunk to remember he was there and he'd be able to slip away.

He was being selfish, he knew that, but large social gatherings like this made him uncomfortable, particularly when he was in the spotlight. If she were here, Laura would tell him to leave right away, not to worry about what anybody else thought.

Detective Constable Eddie Upson was already well on the way to getting pissed. Waving his pint around, he cornered Drake to moan about missing out on promotion.

'It's not like I haven't delivered.' Lager slopped belligerently over the lip of his pint. 'You know what I can do.'

'Excuse me a moment, Eddie.'

At the back of the room, clinging to the wall beneath a curled poster of Jimmy Greaves, was Flick Crowley, the only person who looked like she wanted to be in this pub less than he did, and Drake pushed towards her. On his way, he elbowed Frank Wanderly.

'Sorry, Frank.'

'That's quite all right.' The duty sergeant clasped his hands together. Tall and gaunt, and with not a single hair on his head, everybody at the nick fondly called him Nosferatu. 'And congratulations once again, DI Drake, it's well deserved.'

A few hours earlier, Drake and his Murder Investigation Team had received a Commendation for outstanding service, commitment and teamwork, after the successful completion of a series of homicide investigations in Haringey. Cops and civilian staff had come from Tottenham Police Station to celebrate beneath a blizzard of Spurs memorabilia – shirts, scarves and photos – on the walls.

Drake smiled his thanks, and kept moving.

'You're looking smart tonight, guv,' Flick said.

Drake was wearing the same clothes he always did, a dark off-the-peg suit, white shirt and a frayed brown tie – which Laura had bought him many years ago and lately he'd taken to wearing again – so he guessed she was being mischievous. He was a restless, wiry man who found it impossible to stop moving for long, and no oil painting either. Drake's craggy face was all unexpected drops and sharp angles, as if carelessly hacked from stone.

'I spoke to Harris earlier.' He placed his glass of orange juice on the ledge against the wall, glad to be shot of it. 'Told him how glad I was that you got the promotion.'

Flick frowned. 'As if you had nothing to do with it.'

Detective Chief Inspector Harris had been adamant that they should bring an experienced pair of hands into the Murder Investigation Team, but Ray Drake had gone to war on Flick's behalf, and she'd been promoted from Detective Constable to Detective Sergeant. He had worked to build her confidence, to make her believe in herself a bit more. She was prone to hide behind procedures and systems, but fundamentally she was a fine copper. In time, when she'd learned more readily to trust her instincts, she'd be a very good detective indeed.

'If anyone deserves the chance, it's you.'

Flick glanced over at Upson, his arms draped over the shoulders of the two young PCs he'd clearly singled out to be his drinking comrades for the evening, regardless of their feelings on the matter. 'Eddie doesn't seem to think so.'

'He'll come round. I want you to lead the next investigation, whenever it comes in.'

'Really?' she asked, surprised.

'I think you're ready, DS Crowley.'

She took a gulp of wine, not knowing what to say. 'I meant to ask, how's April?'

'Good.' Drake stiffened at the mention of his daughter's name. Things hadn't been good between them, not since the funeral, and he hadn't the slightest idea how to make things better. 'She's good.'

'The offer still stands. If you'd like me to talk to her . . .'

'Thank you.' He nodded at Harris. 'The DCI has brought along a couple of suits from Scotland Yard.'

'I didn't mean to—'

'Come on,' he said quickly, 'I'll introduce you.'

'You know what? I think I'll give it a miss.' She drained her glass of red. 'Besides, it looks like Vix has got that area locked down.'

Detective Constable Vix Moore was working the guys from the Yard, nodding gravely, the tips of her long blonde bob bouncing, as they explained the latest Met reorganisation proposals.

'Besides,' said Flick, 'I'm shattered, and I want to get home.'

'Stay a while longer. We're celebrating your good news, as well.'

'To be honest, it's been a crazy couple of months – work's been non-stop – and I fancy an early night.' Drake wondered if there was something else on her mind. Flick's watchful almond eyes gave little away beneath a thick fringe of brown hair. A tall woman, a shade below six foot, she had a tendency to hunch, as if the weight of the world was bearing down on her shoulders. She had been a keen swimmer once upon a time, and a good one, she had told Drake. The top of her arms tapered into a strong, lean body, but her broad shoulders rolled forward apologetically. 'Sorry, guv, but I don't think I could bear it if someone *says a few words*.'

'Fair enough.' Having heard more than one of Harris's interminable speeches, he couldn't blame her. 'But just for the record, I'm proud of you.'

'Thank you.' A hesitant smile played across her face. 'I really appreciate everything you've done.'

Her last words were clipped by the sound of a pen ringing loudly against a glass.

'Attention, everybody!' DCI Harris's stomach strained against a tight Lycra top, and his shins were pale beneath lurid black and yellow cycling shorts.

'Too late,' Drake whispered as conversation died and a respectful space opened around him and Flick.

'I know everyone's having fun, however I really wanted to say a few words about the very deserved commendation given to DI Drake and his team,' said Harris. 'But first, we've a new detective sergeant in our midst, so I want you all to put your hands together for Flick Crowley.'

'Smile for the ladies and gentlemen, DS Crowley,' murmured Drake, behind the grin bolted to his face.

Hanging onto her empty glass, Flick shot him a look that suggested, on balance, she'd rather face a firing squad.

3

Kenny hated going straight. Loathed it.

He'd been a good boy for three years now – three years, eight months and fourteen days, to be exact – and every single minute of every single hour had been excruciating. A few years back, if you'd told him that he'd be strapped onto the dreary treadmill of so-called everyday life, he'd have laughed in your face. Now the joke was on him, having to work nights in a supermarket, stacking shelves and lugging pallets beneath pallid yellow lights that exaggerated every pimple and line on your face.

The night bus groaned away down Tottenham High Road, carrying off the motley collection of night owls who sat obscured like phantoms behind glass thick with condensation, and within minutes Kenny was striding down Scales Road, past the foxes nosing around the bins, to let himself into his little terraced house.

Tonight he'd had another row with his supervisor, a spotty kid with a business degree. He picked fights with Kenny every chance he got just to show who was in charge, stomping up and down the aisles, clip-on tie swinging like a limp dick. Stack those boxes, tidy that display!

On top of that, Kenny had lost his mobile. God knows where. He knew he'd had it when he left home, but when he'd gone to put it in his locker it had disappeared.

A floorboard creaked above him, and he spotted Phil's bag nudged beneath the stairs. That girlfriend of his had likely thrown him out again and he was sleeping in the spare room. Kenny loved his sons, honestly he did, but Phil's snore was as loud as a steam train.

He took a glass from a kitchen cabinet and poured a measure of Bell's. This was his nightly ritual, the one part of his day he looked forward to: a modest snifter before bed.

After the first sip the familiar debate began in his head.

He'd been given a second chance, and for that he was grateful. But he missed his old life. This was the truth that always returned in the early hours. He yearned for the thrill of living on the edge. Time was, every decision had consequences. Kenny woke in the morning not knowing how he'd get his hands on money to feed his family, or whether the cops would come knocking. He could be packing a bag for prison or heading out on a five-day bender. Each and every day was different; Kenny had felt *alive*.

Now he was a worker ant, toiling in the early hours alongside students and ethnics. The plan was to buy a cab. He worked nights, slept mornings and went out on his moped in the afternoons to learn The Knowledge. Babs was learning it, too. At weekends they tested each other about roads, cul-de-sacs and byways. In a couple of years they'd have enough in the bank to buy a Hackney Cab. They'd watched a documentary about a cabbie who'd earned so much money he'd bought himself a plot of land on the Costa, a little piece of paradise, complete with a pool and an orchard. That was their dream, their destination. All he had to do was keep turning up for work. It wouldn't be for ever.

Because for reasons he didn't want to examine too carefully, Kenny was desperate to move away.

As far as he could.

That old uneasiness settled on him. His thoughts drifted to those people from the home. It didn't seem possible they were all dead. But it was Jason's death that really got to him. Jason, who'd gone crazy with the stress and strain of it, so they said, and put a shooter to the heads of his nearest and dearest. Jason was a mad sod, everyone knew that, but nobody would convince Kenny that Jason killed his girl and kid and then blew his own brains out.

He drained the glass and placed it in the sink. Blobs of rain pattered across the window. The back door rattled. Checking the handle, he found it unlocked. That was Babs, in and out of the garden all night, smoking, littering the plant pots with fag butts. He turned the key in the door and wearily climbed the stairs.

Kenny took a piss, careful not to splash the seat, and shuffled down the hallway. Christ, it was pitch black. The door to the spare bedroom was open, the room empty. Phil must have changed his mind about staying – or more likely he was still out with mates.

A pungent stink hit him as soon as Kenny opened the door to his bedroom – Babs's muggy exhalations. Kenny loved that smell. He was seconds away from snuggling against her.

But there was another smell he couldn't place – chemical, plastic.

His wife cried out – a toneless, muffled sound.

'Sorry, love.' Kenny stumbled out of his trousers, trying not to disturb her. The stench in his nostrils was bitter, acrid. 'Bloody stinks in here.'

The soles of his socks felt damp. He dabbed anxiously against the wall to find the light switch.

And when he turned it on, when he *saw*, he knew he was lost.

His head was yanked back and a cold blade placed against the loose skin at his throat.

A voice hissed in his ear: 'Hello, Kenny. Long time no see.'

4

Ray Drake walked anxiously towards the crime scene. He was there within minutes; it was barely a few hundred yards from Tottenham Police Station.

Police vans and squad cars were parked along the street. Clots of people gathered in the sweep of the cherry lights to watch the proceedings from the outer cordon. An inner cordon sealed off the middle of the street to all but scene-of-crime officers and authorised personnel. Drake badged the uniform there, and took a pair of polythene shoe-covers from a bag dangling from his clipboard.

Eddie Upson stood on the pavement, making the bins look untidy. His eyes were bloodshot, and his shirt flapped open at the bottom to reveal a wiry tangle of stomach hair. When Drake left the pub last night – after that speech by Harris finally ended – Upson looked settled in for a long session.

'Upstairs, sir.'

Drake nodded up at the bedroom. 'What's it like?'

'Not pleasant.' Upson smothered a yawn. 'It's kind of . . . intense.'

'We keeping you up, Eddie?'

'Bit of a headache.' Upson stretched. 'Thought you'd leave all the crime-scene malarkey to Flick – uh, DS Crowley – now.'

Upson discreetly tucked in his shirt as they walked up the path to the house. Drake knew he shouldn't be there, Flick was the officer in charge and he should just let her get on with it, but Harris would be all over this investigation like a rash. A triple murder just around the corner from a police station – the media would have a field day.

That's what he told himself. But there was something else.

When he was given the name and address of the possible victims, an alarm, a warning signal buried deep inside of him, had gone off, spluttered into life like a candle, dormant for decades, igniting in the depths of a bottomless cave.

He had to be there. He *needed* to be there.

'Talk me through it,' he said.

At the door, they slipped the elasticated bootees onto their shoes, Eddie swaying dangerously as he lifted one leg and then the other.

'The house is rented by a middle-aged couple called Kenny and Barbara Overton.'

'We're sure it's them?'

'Neighbours ID'd their DVLA photos.'

'And the third victim?'

'Kenny and Barbara have two grown-up sons who're always popping in. Phillip and, uh . . .' He squinted at his notebook. 'Ryan.'

'Which one is it?'

'We don't know yet. They're twins – but not identical. Cars are on the way to both addresses.'

They stepped aside to let a pair of scene-of-crime officers carry tubs of equipment into the house. Drake took nitrile gloves from his pocket and shook them out, taking his time about it. There was a faint tremor in his hands when he snapped them over his wrists.

'Coming inside, guv?'

Upson had an expectant look on his face. Drake wondered how long he'd been standing there fiddling with the gloves, unconsciously putting off the moment when he had to step inside . . .

On the landing a large battery-powered arc light was stooped towards the doorway of the front bedroom, its white beam switched off. The bodies inside that room could stay there all day and long into the night, as the CSIs painstakingly recorded the crime scene and a pathologist studied them in situ.

From the room came the whir of a camera. Every detail of the crime scene would be photographed hundreds of times and the images added to an evidence database.

Drake ducked beneath the lamp, stepping carefully across the tread plates that allowed everyone to move around without contaminating evidence on the floor. A crime scene could become a crowded place, with crime scene examiners, coppers, pathologists and medical staff trampling everywhere. On the other side of the room, Flick Crowley frowned at the bodies.

'Who found them?'

'A neighbour gets up early every morning,' said Flick. 'He's out of the house by five thirty, works in the kitchen of a West End hotel. He walks past, sees the front door is wide open. Thinks it's a burglary, so he goes inside to take a look around. Seconds later, he comes out screaming. Runs into a pair of Specials scoffing burgers on the High Road. They come back, call the paramedics and close off the scene.'

'And nobody else saw or heard anything?'

'The neighbour on the left is a young mum. She was up at three a.m. breastfeeding. Said she heard a shout.'

'A shout?'

'A noise, a cry, she couldn't be sure.' Flick pressed against the wall to let the forensics guy leave. 'She didn't think anything of it. Mr and Mrs Overton love a good row, apparently.'

Turned inwards to face each other, the three victims were trussed to kitchen chairs by layer upon layer of plastic film, from toes to nostrils. Their arms were formless lumps pinned to their sides.

The wrapping glinted blue in the stark morning light, except across their torsos, which were slashed and shredded and dripping red. Serrated flesh and chunks of gristle poked from jagged holes in their chests and stomachs. Smooth piping and ruptured veins and organs glistened vividly against glimpses of white ribcage. The gouges were deep and wide and, Drake guessed, made by a long, flat blade. He leaned closer to get a better sense of depth. The fleshy bottom lips of the wounds were angled sharply downwards, like fish mouths.

Their killer had stood over them and brought the knife down again and again. Were they awake, these poor people, Drake wondered, and forced to watch the deaths of their loved ones, knowing they would be next? Were they killed one after the other, in a particular order? Or did the killer stab at them randomly, whirling wildly from one victim to another, until the slaughter was complete?

A sliced arterial vein could spurt blood a good few feet into the air. Spatters of it flecked the walls, the net curtains, the delicate china figurines on the window ledge. The duvet on the bed was soaked, the rug beneath the victims' chairs sodden black. Blood bubbled at the base of the tread plates as Drake stepped across them.

There was a riot of partial footprints in the sticky liquid, left by the special constables who discovered the grisly scene and the paramedics who searched futilely for any faint pulse. Maybe, just maybe, the perpetrator's prints would be among them.

There was no sign of a blade. The killer may have dropped it in panic, in the house or surrounding streets. It could even be lying on the steps of the station round the corner. That would go down well in the press.

'No weapon's been found,' said Flick, as if reading his mind. 'We're hoping to get enough bodies together for a search within twenty minutes. Millie Steiner's on it now.'

A systematic search was difficult at the best of times, let alone in the crowded inner-city streets. The surrounding area was a dense maze. Parts of the High Road would have to be closed off before the rush of Saturday-morning shoppers made the task of finding the weapon all but impossible.

'The King is dead,' intoned a voice behind Drake. 'Long live the King!' Peter Holloway, the crime scene manager, stood in the doorway. 'Just can't keep away, can you, DI Drake?'

'What else am I going to do on a weekend?'

'Practise that golf swing,' he said. 'Or take that lovely daughter of yours somewhere special.'

'I'd rather come and interfere with your crime scene, Peter,' said Drake. 'For old time's sake.'

‘My people need to get on,’ said Holloway.

‘We won’t be long,’ said Flick.

Holloway was right, of course. His team needed to go about their business. Logging and recording. Videoing, photographing, removing evidence for examination. As CSM, Holloway’s job was to coordinate the collection of evidence and protect the integrity of the forensic investigation. Ray Drake always liked to get to the crime scene as soon as possible. The first few hours of any investigation – the so-called Golden Hour – were the most critical, and he and Holloway often exchanged forthright views if the CSM felt he was getting in the way.

Drake had a grudging admiration for the bombastic know-all. A lean, middle-aged man, there was a vanity to his precise movements. When Holloway pulled down the hood of his coveralls, his face was taut and unblemished. Drake often wondered if he’d had some discreet work done.

‘You’ve very big boots to fill, DS Crowley.’ A pair of half-moon glasses tipped from his hair onto his nose with a jerk of his head.

‘If I didn’t know it already,’ said Flick, who was looking at the windowsill, ‘there’s a plenty of people to remind me.’

Holloway gestured with his clipboard. ‘You’ll never be the investigator that DI Drake is.’

‘Thanks,’ Flick said quietly. ‘I’ll try to remember that.’

‘No need to be so touchy, DS Crowley. What I mean is, be your own person, do things your own way. If you try to be a mere simulacrum of Ray Drake, you’ll fail.’

‘I’ve no idea what a simulacrum is, but thank you anyway.’

‘She’ll go far, this one,’ said Holloway, nodding at her.

Drake didn’t look up from the bodies. ‘Yes, she will.’

'One's missing,' said Flick.

'Excuse me?'

'The figurines.' She pointed at three porcelain eighteenth-century figures – a woman in a gown and bonnet, men in waistcoats and three-cornered hats – spaced irregularly on the sill. 'There's a space where one's missing.'

'Smashed, maybe,' said Drake.

'Guv . . .?' Vix Moore's head peeked from behind the banister on the landing, her gaze moving quickly from Drake to Flick. 'I mean, guv . . .'

'What is it, Vix?'

'Someone's just turned up at the cordon. Says he's Ryan Overton.'

'I'll come down.' Hesitating in the doorway, Flick looked at the cocooned victims one last time. 'They're like human flies ensnared by a giant spider.'

Holloway followed her to the door. 'I was thinking more along the lines of mouldy wrapped sandwiches at a seaside café.' He turned to Drake. 'Make it quick, please.'

Left alone in the room, Drake forced down the nausea he felt. The stench in the room, of plastic and plasma, was overpowering as he moved from one body to another.

The younger man – in all likelihood Phillip Overton – sat with his head thrown back like a schoolboy laughing at the back of the class, a tight ruffle of plastic shredded around his mouth. His blank eyes were open, and his scalp was sprayed with inky globules of blood.

Barbara Overton's head, partly concealed by the sheets of plastic cut away by the paramedics, lolled on her chest. Her hair, matted with blood and gristle, was pulled back in a lank ponytail, her slack face imprinted with traces of the terror of her final catastrophic moments on Earth.

Drake arrived at Kenny Overton. The tops of his thighs burned when he crouched to get an eye-level view of the dead man's face. Wisps of fine auburn hair congealed against Kenny's scalp. His jowls flopped over the moist plastic around his neck, and his gaping mouth revealed crooked teeth and withered gums stained by vomit and blood.

Horrific death aside, time had not been kind to Kenny Overton.

That sense of foreboding tightened in Drake's stomach. His hand shook when he lifted it. Something hidden, something dangerous and wrong, had been revealed.

A countdown, a slow, inexorable pulse in his gut.

'Kenny,' he whispered. 'It's you.'

5

1984

Ray Drake first met Connor Laird on the hot summer day when Sally Raynor found the new kid at Hackney Wick Police Station.

'Fucking hippy,' an officer muttered as he lifted the wooden counter to allow Sally into the warren of corridors behind the front desk. She swept past in a heavy poncho and long woollen skirt. A battered satchel, its straps curled and frayed, bumped on her hips.

Sergeant Harry Crowley's office was barely larger than a broom cupboard, just big enough to squeeze in Harry and a desk heaped with a mountain of paperwork. The heat hit Sally like a hammer when she walked in, the office was right above the station's boiler. Harry knew where all the bodies were buried in this place, and Sally suspected that someone was trying to sweat him out of the building.

A kid, no older than fourteen or fifteen, was perched on a stool in front of Harry's desk, and she asked, 'Who have you got here?'

Harry scratched his belly. 'A tough guy.'

A fan burred at the edge of his desk, lifting a coil of Brylcreemed hair from Harry's forehead. He looked like

Tommy Cooper, that funny magician on the telly, and some joker had given him a red fez, which was forced over the top of a framed photograph of his wife and children.

Harry reached into his tunic to take out a packet of cigarettes, stuck one in the corner of his mouth.

'What's your name?' Sally crouched in front of the boy. A thick helmet of dark hair framed the kid's dirty face, his mouth was an angry smear. 'Where have you come from?'

'Don't waste your breath. He ain't one for talking.' Harry blew out smoke. 'One of my lads found him wandering the streets this afternoon. Dennis knocked his helmet off.'

'Dennis? That's his name?'

'That's what I call him – Dennis the fucking Menace.' Harry poked about on the desk for an ashtray. 'Maybe a slap will loosen his tongue.'

'Don't you dare, Harry.'

The copper's throaty laugh disintegrated into a tangle of coughs. He grabbed his belt, yanked up his sagging trousers. 'That's a bit rich coming from Gordon's girl. Talking of which . . .'

When Harry wiggled his fat fingers, Sally took a battered envelope from her satchel. Inside was a wad of money. He brushed the edges of the notes and dropped the envelope into a drawer.

'I'm going to need a bigger cut from now on; upstairs is getting nervous about our arrangement and it'd be politic to sprinkle more goodwill around the place.'

'Gordon isn't going to like that,' said Sally.

'You tell Tallis he can like it or he can lump it.' The red tip of the cigarette crackled in his mouth.

'You people.' She shook her head. 'Always out for what you can take.'

'If Gordon wants to do business in my borough, he knows the rules.' Harry dabbed at his forehead with a hanky. 'A posh girl like you, maybe you want to pay me some other way.' He came so close she could smell the nicotine and stale sweat lifting from his pores. 'I hear you got a thing for us working-class fellas.'

Sally spoke in a fierce whisper: 'You're scaring the boy, Harry.'

'Scared? Does he look scared to you?' A laugh rattled in Harry's throat. 'Those eyes tell a different story. Go on. Take him away.'

'Take him where?'

He tugged at his belt again. The heavy handcuffs clipped at his waist were forever dragging down his trousers, so he snapped them off, threw them on the desk. 'Gordon runs a children's home, don't he? He can stay there.'

'He may have family, a home.'

'You got somewhere to go back to, Dennis?' Harry cupped an ear, but the boy just stared.

'And what if Gordon won't take him?'

'Drop him down a hole for all I care, but something tells me this one will be useful to him. Come on, get up.'

Grabbing his arm, the sergeant pulled the kid off the stool and swung him against the desk. He made a big show of wiping the vinyl seat with his handkerchief.

'Remember to tell Gordon about the money. And you . . .' Harry jabbed a finger at the kid. 'I don't want to see you again. I got a nose for wrong 'uns, and it tells me that no good is going to come of you.'

* * *

When she arrived in the car park with the boy, Sally saw Ray leaning against the bonnet of her Morris Marina, throwing pebbles at a drain.

She sighed. 'I told you to go home.'

'Thought I'd wait for you.' Ray lifted himself off the car. 'To discover what secret thing it was you had to do.'

'Go home, Ray,' said Sally. 'Myra will go spare.'

'She's at some committee meeting with my father, and they'll be there till the evening. So, you know, I've got all day. We can do something.'

'I'm going back to the Longacre.' Sally balanced the satchel on a knee to search for her car key. 'And you can't come.'

'Hi, I'm Ray Drake.' He nodded at the kid who had come out of the station with her – another teenager, roughly the same age as him – but the boy just stared. As soon as Sally opened the driver's door, he clambered into the front passenger seat. Ray frowned at Sally over the roof of the car. 'Not very friendly, is he? What's his name?'

'Don't know yet.'

'Huh. What's wrong with him?'

Sally leaned in, keeping her voice low. 'Not everyone grew up with a silver spoon in their mouth, Ray. Not everyone is taught impeccable manners at expensive public schools. Where do you want me to drop you?'

He grinned. 'The Longacre will do.'

'You know Gordon doesn't want you there.' She placed her hands on the baking metal of the roof. 'He doesn't like you hanging around.'

'And why would that be?'

'Go home, Ray,' she said, and started to climb in – but he made one of his funny faces. All he had to do was go bug-eyed or pucker his lips and she could deny him nothing. It had been the same since he'd been a toddler. When he wanted something, or when she got angry, all he had to do was grin like a maniac or pull his ears, and she would relent. Even now, when he was afraid that all the joy had gone out of her, when it seemed to him that she was a pale shadow of the funny and vivacious Sally he once knew, he could still get round her.

She shook her head. 'Stop it.'

'Stop what?'

'You know what.'

'Tell you what, I'll do you a deal.'

'No deals, Ray.'

'Drop me off outside. I won't come in; I'll make my own way home.'

And before she could reply he had come round the driver's side and lifted the seat to climb into the back.

Sitting behind the wheel in the baking-hot interior, Sally rolled a cigarette, slapped in the dashboard lighter. Ray shifted against the door behind her to make himself unobtrusive, so that he could listen. If there was one thing Ray Drake was good at, it was listening.

'You going to give me the silent treatment all day?' Sally asked the kid beside her.

In the rear-view mirror, Ray saw the make-up caked against her damp cheeks, the rash of angry spots racing down her jaw and neck. Her nails were almost as dirty as those of the mysterious boy next to her.

When the lighter popped, she applied the burning coil to the tip of the roll-up. The stink of tobacco filled the hot car. 'I want to help, but I'm going to need a name.'

'Connor,' said the boy, finally. 'Connor Laird.'

'Where do you live, Connor? Do you have family?'

The boy called Connor turned away to watch shimmering waves of heat slam into the concrete car park. 'Who's Gordon?'

'Now there's a question,' murmured Ray.

Sally's turned angrily. 'Shut up, Ray.'

Removing a fleck of tobacco from her lip, the poncho fell away from the crook of Sally's elbow to reveal livid scars. She quickly flipped it back but Ray saw them, had seen them before. He didn't know if it was the sight of those red tracks or the cloying smoke filling the sweltering compartment that made him feel sick.

'You'll find out soon enough,' Sally told Connor, and started the car.

The Longacre Children's Home butted up against a railway track at the end of a street where once-grand Victorian homes stood derelict. Some of the empty houses had become squats. Colourful banners hung from windows. Wall murals celebrated forgotten revolutions in far-flung places. The car bumped along the pitted road, past abandoned vehicles and dumped furniture.

'How long will I be here?' Connor asked when Sally swung the car to the kerb outside the double-fronted building.

'That depends,' she said. 'Tell me where you live and I'll take you home.'

Connor stabbed a thumb at Ray in the back. 'Isn't he coming in?'

'*He* doesn't live here,' said Sally. 'He's got a home of his own to go to, and he's going there now. Aren't you, Ray?'

'Whatever you say, sis.' Ray sat up, his sopping T-shirt peeling away from the hot plastic of the seat to cling against his spine.

'Why don't you go inside, Connor?' said Sally. 'I'll be a moment.'

The boy looked up the steps to where the door to the home was ajar. The dull roar of children came from somewhere behind the house.

'See you, Connor.' Ray waved, but the boy walked inside without looking back. 'Myra would have a thing or two to say about that boy's manners.'

'I'm not your sister, Ray.'

'You're my big sister.' He angled a foot on the bottom step to look up at the shoddy house, with its rotten window frames and peeling sills. 'And I don't like you hanging around here.'

'I'm your second cousin, the bad girl. Your parents would go crazy if they knew you were with me.' She glanced over her shoulder. 'Here.'

'My parents hate *everyone*.' He grinned. 'Me included, I think. But it's what I think that counts, and you'll always be my sister, the only one I'll ever have.'

'Go away and do something that normal kids do. Go to the pictures, climb a tree. Look up a girl's skirt.' A curtain in the window shivered, and Sally climbed the steps. 'Enjoy your childhood while you can.'

'Myra says I've got a talent for sticking my nose into other people's business. The kids at my school, I know all their secrets.'

'I'm not joking, Ray. I don't want you here.' She spoke quietly. 'And Gordon doesn't want you here.'

She jumped in surprise when the door creaked open. A plump kid with red hair stood there.

'Hello, Kenny,' said Ray.

The ginger boy nodded warily and stammered at Sally: 'Gordon says to come in.'

Sally turned back to Ray. 'You don't belong here. Shove off back to school, why don't you?'

'It's months before I go back, the whole summer. I promise you, you'll miss me when I've gone.' When Sally moved to the door, he called, 'I'm not going to let anything happen to my wicked second cousin. Just so she knows.'

'She doesn't need saving. Go and practise your missionary act somewhere else.'

Then she slammed the door behind her, leaving Ray Drake staring up at the house, the smile slipping from his face.

'Who said she needed saving?' he asked.

Inside the home, dust motes danced in the bright hallway. The walls were covered with smeared drawings and dirty fingerprints. Through an open doorway on the left Connor Laird glimpsed an enormous room dominated by two tables, each long enough to seat a dozen kids.

He would later discover there were only two doors left on their hinges in the entire house. One of them closed on a room on the right. When Sally finally came in, she led him through this door into an untidy office where a man with shoulder-length chestnut hair sat with his feet on a desk. His paisley shirt was crushed beneath a scruffy corduroy jacket the colour of strained tea. His forehead and cheeks were pockmarked, and his jaw was hidden behind a sculpted beard. When he saw Connor, the man broke out into a snaggle-toothed smile. Connor quickly pushed the handcuffs he had stolen from the sergeant's desk deeper into his pocket.

'And who's this?' Gordon asked, in a lilting Scottish accent.

'Harry gave him to me.' Sally dropped her satchel onto a sofa, absently scratching her elbow. 'Said he's got nowhere to go.'

'What's your name, son?' Gordon came round the desk to plant his hands on Connor's shoulders.

'Connor.'

'A good Celtic name.'

Sally inspected her nails. 'Connor's the strong, silent type.'

'Keep yourself to yourself, do you? I can understand that. My name is Mr Tallis, but I'd be grateful if you called me Gordon. You're welcome to stay, Connor. Sally will arrange the paperwork, but we needn't worry about that yet.' He smirked at her. 'He's scaring me with those eyes.'

'Harry wants more money.'

'A lad like you will make plenty of mates here, Connor, but I'd be honoured if you considered me your first friend.' When the boy glanced at Sally, Gordon smirked. 'She doesn't count. Sal's only your friend if you've something she wants.' His eyes slid to her. 'Did you give it to him?'

'He wants more, he said—'

Gordon held up a hand. 'Let's get the boy settled in. Then we'll discuss it.'

'The money isn't enough.'

His voice lifted irritably. 'I *said* let's get the boy settled in.' Gordon opened the door to shout into the corridor: 'Kenny!'

Returning to Connor, he said, 'Breakfast is at six thirty

a.m. You'll be expected to have showered and brushed your teeth – there are communal brushes in the bathrooms, we share everything here, Connor – and to have made your bed. Supper is at six. We all muck in with the daily chores. The Dents will add your duties to the rota on the wall. If you're unable to read, one of the other children will explain them to you.'

When Gordon's hand shot out to grab Connor's cheek, the boy snatched at his wrist.

'Ha! You're stronger than you look, and fast. A bit of spunk, too. We're going to be pals, I think, you and me.' Gordon removed his hand from Connor's grip as the red-haired kid reappeared in the doorway. 'Kenny here will show you around. Let's talk again soon, lad.'

The last thing Connor saw as the door closed behind him was Sally – eager, expectant – an arm stretching towards Gordon.

'My name's Kenny,' said the kid, as they walked towards the back of the house, the linoleum crackling beneath their feet. 'Kenny Overton.'

'Connor.'

'I've been here two years.' Kenny spoke like it was a badge of honour. 'But others have been here even longer.'

Every opening revealed more tatty rooms, and scruffy, listless kids. A girl scribbled feverishly in a book, barely looking up as they passed.

'Do you smoke?' asked Kenny, as they arrived in a massive kitchen, a gloomy room despite the midday sun high in the sky. 'You can have one of mine if you promise to be my friend.'

Connor said: 'I'm nobody's friend.'

Kenny blushed. 'Please don't tell Elliot I asked you.'

The room stank of boiled vegetables. Pots and pans hung over a pine table. Outside, a long garden inclined towards a copse of trees. When a train blipped past beyond them, the windows buzzed in their frames.

On the patio a man and a woman were wedged into deckchairs. A can of lager was balanced on the man's belly, which bulged like risen dough over the shiny fabric of his Speedos. The woman, grossly overweight, wore a bikini.

'That's the Dents, Ronnie and Geraldine. They run the place for Gordon. They're all right, as long as you stay out of their way.'

Children swarmed over the faded brown lawn. One boy saw Connor right away. He was tall and broad, a lumbering youth who towered over the other kids.

Connor guessed this was Elliot. His size, the sullen sneer on his face, and the way his mates fanned out on either side of him, marked him out as trouble. Within moments he was pounding up the garden, his gang falling into formation behind him like geese. Sensing the excitement, other kids fell into their slipstream.

Geraldine Dent, who'd seen it all before, called in a bored voice: '*Elliot*.'

Arms pumping like pistons, Elliot pushed Connor into the kitchen, his brow knotted in pantomime menace, shoving him against the table.

'Who's this, then?' He grabbed a fistful of Connor's T-shirt and twisted it. A forest of small heads bobbed in the doorway behind them.

'His name's Connor,' stammered Kenny.

'Shut your face; he can tell me himself!'

One of Elliot's mates pinched Kenny's arm, and he yelped.

'What's your name?' snarled Elliot, shaking the newcomer. 'You wanna live, tell me your name!'

'Connor.'

'Yeah? Well, Connor, around here you do what I say, got it?'

Elliot's mates giggled. One of them – Connor would later learn his name was Jason – jabbed his finger in Connor's ribs. It was typical pack bravado. All his mates crowded close. The tail of Connor's spine throbbed against the table's edge; the stolen handcuffs dug into his leg. Pots and pans bumped against the back of his head.

'I said, have you got it?'

Connor slowly stretched his hands above his head in a display of surrender, and Elliot grinned, sticking out his forefingers like they were six-shooters. 'Stick 'em up!' he said. 'Stick 'em up, pardner!'

All the kids laughed like drains, and they were still laughing when Connor pulled two saucepans from the hooks and swung them hard into either side of Elliot's head with a satisfying bong. The boy crumpled to the floor.

Then Connor stood over Elliot, bringing the pans down on his head, pounding them into his nose – whack, whack, whack – like he was hammering a nail into wood, before the Dents managed to drag him off.

6

'Gav, it's me, open up!'

Elliot Juniper banged on the door with the flat of his hand, still trying to convince himself that it was all a mistake, a big misunderstanding. Everything would straighten itself out soon enough. They'd laugh about it later down the Oak, him and Gavin.

When he cupped his hands against the frosted glass he was sure he could see a figure, barely a smudge at the end of the hallway, and lifted the flap of the letterbox.

'I can see you, Gav. Let me in!'

He didn't want to make a scene on a quiet street like this, all double-fronted homes, big cars in the driveways and trimmed hedges. First sign of trouble and a nervous neighbour, meerkat sticker in the window, would be on the phone to the Old Bill. Elliot hadn't been in trouble for years, but he shouldn't be driving after last night's morose drinking session, didn't want to take any chances.

Thanks to his hangover, the world moved behind a thick membrane. Every molecule above his neck was sore. His brain hurt; his skin and eye sockets too. His nose, bashed flat a long time ago and never right since, throbbed on his face.

Besides, getting breathalysed would be the least of his problems if Rhonda discovered he was driving over the limit.

And it would be even worse – catastrophic didn't seem a strong enough word – if she discovered *why* he was here. Whatever happened, she couldn't know.

Elliot still had his mouth to the flap when the door cracked open. Instinctively, he pushed his way in, expecting to find Gavin. Instead, he saw a small woman in a sweater and leggings.

'Where is he?' Elliot was surprised to discover Gavin had a wife. But when he thought about it – and the realisation made him wince – he hardly knew anything about him. 'Where's Gavin?'

'There's no one called Gavin here.' The woman held the front door open. 'Please leave.'

'Gav!' He grabbed the banister, called upstairs. 'Gavin!'

'This is my house and I'm asking you to—'

'I'm going to leave,' Elliot said, 'when I've spoken to Gavin.'

'And I've told you,' the woman's voice cracked, 'there's no one here with that name.'

Elliot marched into the lounge and saw post stacked on a dining table. He went over and rifled through the envelopes. The same name was on every one. 'Who's Jane McArthur?'

'I am.' The woman stood in the doorway, darting anxious looks up the stairs. 'And this is my house.'

Elliot eyed the photos on the wall: men and women and plenty of a smiling baby, but not a single one of Gavin. He felt the anger deflate inside him, leaving in its place a stinging bewilderment.

And the terrible certainty that his savings were gone.

'I don't understand.' He pulled a hand down his face. 'He said he lived here.'

The woman spoke low. 'Well, he doesn't.'

'I've picked him up here half a dozen times.'

'Not from here you haven't.' She edged towards a phone on a cabinet. 'I'm going to call the police.'

The woman's eyes were wide, her lips pressed tightly together. She was distraught. Any moment now she would burst into tears or scream. Upstairs, a baby began to wail.

For the first time it occurred to Elliot what he had done. A big, burly man – an intimidating sight with his shaved head, tattoo sleeve and smashed nose – and he'd barged into this poor woman's home, was stomping around like he was deranged. For all she knew he was going to rob her, strangle her, take her baby. Burning with shame, he held up his hands in apology, aware that it was too little, too late.

'I'm sorry,' he said. 'There's been a . . . I thought he . . .'

'Please go.' The woman's stricken whisper was almost drowned by the infant cries from upstairs.

Elliot stumbled past her, head down. As soon as he was outside, the door slammed behind him. He hurried down the path without looking back, fumbling in a pocket for his e-cigarette.

Back in the van, he sucked miserably on the vape. He knew it wasn't a good idea to hang around for too long – that poor woman would be calling the police already, he would do the same in her shoes – but Elliot couldn't help but take one last look at the house. It just didn't make sense to him. He'd been here more than once, to wait for Gavin and give him a lift down the pub, had parked in this very spot.

But now he thought about it . . .

He couldn't remember one time when he'd seen Gavin

actually inside the house or stepping outside, closing the door behind him. As far as Elliot could remember, he'd only ever seen Gavin waiting on the step, or bouncing down the path, waggling his fingers in greeting.

Two days ago Gavin had been down the Oak, scheming, planning, selling Elliot a dream of a glorious future in burgers, and now he had vanished with Elliot's money.

All his life's savings. Thirty grand gone, just like that.

Correction.

All of Rhonda's life's savings.

Because, let's face it, she was the only one who ever put money into the account. She was the one who made the effort to put by a little each month. Elliot couldn't save money if his life depended on it. Cash rocketed out of his pocket. Gavin may have run off with it but, unquestionably, it was Elliot's fault the money had gone. He had handed it to him – in cash! He had been an almighty fool, and not for the first time in his miserable life. Elliot was petrified that Rhonda would finally have had enough of his gullibility, his naivety. She might even come to the conclusion – and this made his stomach churn – that he was pulling a fast one and had taken the money himself. After all, people don't change. That's what they say.

She'd get shot of him, and who could blame her?

A little bit of bile slipped up his throat and he swallowed it. He drove home, puffing miserably on the electronic cigarette Rhonda had given him months ago – Elliot still hadn't got used to it, hated the taste, and desperately wanted a proper fag – thinking about how he had sat on the sofa last night phoning Gavin's pay-as-you-go again and again. Leaving hopeful messages, angry messages, pleading messages, and drowning his sorrows when what was called for was a clear head.

His gut told him he would never see Gavin again. All he had was a phone number. That address, the house where he had supposedly lived, was a lie. He didn't even know if Gavin was his real name.

Elliot was glad to get out of Harlow, the Essex town where Gavin had taken him to see the empty shop unit in which they were going to start their burger franchise, or so he had been led to believe. Leaving the sprawl behind, he felt a little better. Dozens of new estates were being built along the M11 corridor, tens of thousands of new homes were eating into this beautiful green space, but Elliot loved the increasing isolation as he drove deeper into the countryside, with its fields and trees, flat open spaces and blue sky. He wound down the window and let the breeze dry his clammy forehead.

He drove into the narrow lane where he lived, beneath the canopy of tree branches folding across the road like clasping hands, and swung the van up the steep, muddy drive, avoiding the crumbling holes, to park up against the dilapidated barn in the barren plot next to his cottage. Cranked the handbrake.

Rhonda would be at work this morning, thank God, and Dylan was God knows where with his mates. It would give Elliot time to work out the best way to tell her what he'd done.

I've lost your money. I gave it to a man down the pub. He's gone.

If it was only about the stolen money he could live with it, just about, but it was the latest in a long succession of dismal Elliot errors of judgement. The thought of losing Rhonda and Dylan made him sick.

The door of the cottage led straight into the living room, which was a mess from all the clothes, papers, bottles and plates that had accumulated during the week. It was his Saturday-morning routine to clean the house while Rhonda was at work. But Elliot couldn't face it this morning. Instead, he dropped onto the sofa without even bothering to clear a space and stared into the ashes of last night's fire.

He sat like that, an Xbox controller digging into a buttock, for several minutes. Despondent, tired, afraid. And then his phone chirruped in his pocket. A text had arrived.

Elliot experienced a brief moment of joy – an adrenalin rush of hope – when he saw it was from Gavin. He'd got worked up for nothing. It had all been a terrible mistake. Gavin was away on business, in some inaccessible place without a signal. He had told Elliot he was in the catering trade and travelled a lot, after all. Thanks to his hangover-addled brain, Elliot had gone to completely the wrong address. That was just like him, jumping to conclusions.

But although the message was simple enough, it took him a few moments to make sense of it:

TURN ON THE NEWS

The TV remote was somewhere on the sofa, beneath the slanket, the layers of cushions and women's mags, Dylan's discarded drink cartons and wrappers. Impatient, nerves shredded, Elliot tipped everything to the floor.

Finding the control wedged into the sofa lining, and pressing up and down the TV channels until he found the right one, or thought he had, he watched live footage of police cars and vans in a London street. Yellow tape snapped in the wind. The camera zoomed to an open door, men and women in white paper suits walking in and out.

The headline threaded across the bottom of the screen: THREE SLAUGHTERED IN NORTH LONDON HOME . . . THREE SLAUGHTERED IN . . .

A reporter's voice spoke of three bodies found inside the house, believed to be Kenneth and Barbara Overton and their son Phillip, although police had as yet made no official statement.

Elliot followed the comings and goings, confused about what he was meant to be looking at, then tried the number. The call rang and rang, and when he tried again, it dropped straight to voicemail. He didn't bother leaving a message. Gavin's voicemail was already full of his angry pleas.

Kenneth Overton, thought Elliot.

Little Kenny from *that* place?

Unease building inside him, he picked up his coat and left the cottage. Unable to face the terrible prospect of her telling him that she'd had enough of him, Elliot didn't want to be there when Rhonda got home.

7

Gripped by nerves, Flick Crowley lingered in her office printing and stapling, putting off the inevitable. But just before lunchtime, she conducted her first team briefing with the North London MIT.

The Incident Room, on the second floor of Tottenham Police Station, was filled with plain-clothed and uniformed officers. She knew many of the people in the room already, and others had been drafted in from the Specialist Crime Directorate.

Drake had appointed her as the lead investigator on the Overton murders, but when she went to the whiteboard where the location and victim details had been written she saw him sitting on the side of a desk, arms folded, deep in thought, and couldn't shake the feeling she was on probation.

'Hello, everybody.' She forced herself to look at the assembled team, not at the floor. 'Sorry to spoil your weekend.'

Most of the people present would hardly have had a chance to settle into their Saturday routines before they were obliged to drop everything – kids' football, shopping trips, lunch and dinner dates – and come into work.

She picked up a marker pen. 'You'll have had time, I hope, to familiarise yourselves with the details. We have three victims, all members of the same family, a stone's throw from here. I don't need to tell you we need to get this solved quickly, and we've been promised the resources to make that happen.'

Detective Sergeant Dudley Kendrick jotted something in the incident logbook. All the details of the case would be recorded in there, along with every development, so that lines of inquiry weren't duplicated.

'The victims have been identified as Kenneth and Barbara Overton, aged forty-eight and fifty-two, and their son Phillip Overton, aged twenty-seven,' said Flick. 'Kenneth and Barbara lived off Scales Road. Between the hours of eleven last night and four o'clock this morning they were bound to chairs and stabbed repeatedly in the chest and stomach. The forensic investigation is continuing, and I'm told we'll get those results in the next day or so, but if you've managed to look at the crime-scene photos you'll know that the attack was brutal and frenzied. It's important that we find the person, or people, responsible. As far as we can tell, no valuables were stolen from the house, and there's no sign of forced entry.'

DC Millie Steiner, a young black officer who had been born and raised in the area, lifted her slight frame in her chair. Flick liked Steiner. She was bright and tenacious and always put in a solid shift, despite attending a bewildering variety of night classes. 'A neighbour told me Barbara Overton used to smoke in the garden, and the door was always unlocked.'

'The perpetrator entered the house with enough plastic film to tightly bind three adults to chairs,' Flick continued, 'and sent texts – purporting to be from their father – to both of the Overtons' sons, Phillip and Ryan. The three victims were found by a neighbour who saw the door was open; this was at,' she checked her notes, 'a quarter to six this morning. The victims were dead by the time paramedics attended the scene.'

Kendrick held up a finger. A veteran of the MIT, he was the only man left this century, it seemed to Flick, who deemed it acceptable to shave his moustache to a thin strip above the lip. 'Three people would be a handful for one person to subdue; you think we're looking for more than one killer?'

'It's possible, but Kenny went to work at seven thirty that night, leaving Barbara alone in the house for a couple of hours at least. Phil Overton's text was sent at 9.39 p.m., and his brother Ryan's around eleven. Kenneth, or Kenny as he was known, didn't get home till after three. The family could have been subdued one at a time. The chairs were arranged in the bedroom to face each other, so perhaps the intention was for them to watch each other die.'

The noisy blast of a jackhammer in the street below disturbed the contemplative moment of silence. Upson fiddled with the height lever on his chair.

'So the sons were lured to the house?' asked Vix Moore sharply.

The young DC had only been on the team for a couple of months but made no bones about her desire to climb to the top of the Homicide and Serious Crime Command greasy pole. Vix wasn't to everyone's taste, but Flick wished she'd had a single ounce of her confidence when she had joined the MIT.

'Kenny Overton's mobile was used to text them both, so we're assuming the murders were premeditated.'

Flick pulled the cap off the marker pen with her teeth and wrote on the whiteboard:

COME HOME TONIGHT – V URGENT!!!
LOVE, DAD XXX

'Phil arrived,' said Flick. 'But Ryan didn't pick up the message. Kenny worked nights at the Co-op in Hornsey.'

'Have we run a check on the phone number?' someone asked.

'The messages were sent from Kenny's mobile.' Kendrick clicked his pen top. 'Phillip Overton's phone was found in his pocket when the plastic was cut away from his body. He'd received exactly the same text.'

Flick went on to allocate responsibilities to the team. Friends and family would be interviewed. Ryan was in the building already, along with Phil Overton's on-off girlfriend, and work colleagues from both Kenny's nightshift and Barbara's part-time job. Phil also had a record for minor drugs offences as a teenager, and had popped up on camera during the riots a few years back. They'd compile a list of his known associates.

CCTV footage from the surrounding roads and nearby traffic cameras would be sifted through – a painstaking process that could take days. License plates of vehicles parked nearby would be cross-checked; phone calls made by the family tracked; follow-up house-to-house interviews completed. The morning's sweep of the area had found nothing. No murder weapon, no blood trail or holdall or dumped roll of plastic. Uniformed officers would search again for the weapon and for Kenny's mobile, but with every hour that passed, the chances of finding them became more unlikely.

Flick concluded: 'Kenny Overton has spent his life in and out of prison. Handling stolen goods, shoplifting, dealing, you name it. So let's talk to his former criminal friends. A charge sheet like that, you pick up enemies along the way.'

When Drake nodded absently, Flick felt a delicious thrill of validation. After she'd taken more questions from the room, she tucked her clipboard beneath her arm. She didn't possess a flair for the dramatic, but she would never forget the agonised post-mortem expressions of the Overton family, and felt she had to say something.

'These victims need us to find whoever did this. Because if you've visited the crime scene, or have seen the photos, you'll know that this is an extraordinarily vicious crime, and it is inconceivable that the person, or persons, who committed it be allowed to remain free.'

After the meeting, everyone turned back to their monitors or headed to the coffee machine. Flick went into her new office and shut the door, her heart still clattering in her chest. The desk was bare except for a computer and a framed photo of her nieces and nephew, the shelves empty save for a couple of reference manuals. There was a rap on the door and Drake leaned in, smiling.

'You had them eating out of your hand.'

'You think? I'm not so sure.' Outside, Vix Moore was speaking behind her hand to Kendrick.

'People don't like change, Flick, especially when it upsets the dynamic of a team. But they're a good bunch, they'll get used to it.' He walked to the blinds. 'And you've got a nice view of the car park.'

'You're welcome to it,' she said, knowing full well he had the same depressing view in his office on the floor above. 'Thanks for being there this morning.'

Drake tapped the window with a finger. It was a wonder the panes didn't vibrate when he stood near them. He was a man who seemed to throw a crackling energy into the air around him, like a tuning fork.

She wondered whether something had happened with April. Relations were strained between Drake and his daughter, she knew that much. Flick had met April, along with Myra, Drake's odd, scary mother, at his wife's funeral several months back. The girl had clung to her boyfriend's arm and seemed to go out of her way to avoid her father. Drake was already grieving for his beloved wife. It had saddened Flick to see him so lost.

Now he turned, leaned against the sill. 'Because of the proximity of the murders to the station, and the subsequent media heat, Harris has asked me to keep an eye on the investigation.'

'Of course.' Flick swallowed. 'You're the Senior Investigating Officer.'

'But you're the lead on this. I'm here to help you to run things whichever way you see fit.'

She mustered a smile. 'I appreciate that, guv.'

If she had to pick somebody from upstairs to watch her back, it would be Ray Drake, and she appreciated being able to bounce ideas off him. He was an excellent detective with a wealth of experience, and she owed him her career, no question. In the four years she had worked in the MIT, still an overwhelmingly masculine environment, he'd carefully nurtured her confidence and drive, steadily given her more authority. Yet she couldn't help but be unnerved by the way he'd hung about in the office all morning, couldn't shake the feeling that he expected her to screw up. That he was having second thoughts about her promotion.

That was ridiculous, she told herself, she'd been in the job barely five seconds.

'The killer will be one of Kenny's criminal mates, I'd bet my life on it.' Chances were he was right, but it was an odd thing for Drake to state so early in the investigation. For years, he'd taught her to maintain an objective distance, even when one line of inquiry showed potential. 'I've come across plenty of Kenny Overtons, and they don't change.'

'We'll chase it down,' said Flick.

'He's got himself involved in some illegal enterprise and it's gone sour.' Drake sounded almost indignant. 'Find out what it is and you're home and dry. *That's* your line of inquiry.'

'Okay.' That thought again: *He doesn't trust me*. 'I'd better go see Ryan.'

To her surprise, he stood. 'I'll come with you.'

He thinks I'm going to mess it up.

The interview suite was where the traumatised relatives of the victims of crime were taken. It was decorated in sympathetic pastel colours and filled with soft furnishings. A watercolour hung on the wall. Plastic flowers were arranged on a low table.

Ryan Overton was pacing when they walked in. A family liaison officer, an eternally cheerful detective constable called Sandra Danson, stood at the door.

'Hello again, Ryan, sorry to keep you waiting,' said Flick.

His arms clapped his sides. 'Where am I gonna go on a day like this?'

'Would you like a coffee, Ryan?' Danson was a broad woman who was always experimenting with a new diet. Flick would often get caught behind her in the canteen queue as she interrogated bemused staff about the calories, saturated fats and carbs in each and every dish. She'd often see her again later, raiding the vending machine for chocolate.

'Me and the ex split up a few weeks back.' Ryan slumped in a chair. 'She was always good in situations like this.'

'Would you like us to contact her?' asked Danson.

'She's gone to Tyneside. The relationship didn't end well.'

'Ryan, this is Detective Inspector Drake,' said Flick, and Ryan nodded grimly. 'Can you tell him what you told me about the message you received from your father?'

'From his phone.' Ryan's eyes darted to Drake, leaning against the wall. 'He told me to come round – or someone did – said it was urgent.'

'Ryan was out last night,' Flick told Drake.

'Down the pub.'

'He left his mobile at home.'

'I don't know what I was thinking. I always have it with me. Always. But just this once I left it in the bog when I went out. I didn't see it till I got home at, I dunno, six?'

'Six this morning?' said Drake.

'My local has a lock-in. It can get messy.' Ryan rubbed his eyes with the heel of a hand. 'The landlord won't thank me for telling you.'

Ryan smothered a wince, his emotions still battened down. Sooner or later that anguish would have to come out. Flick had met close relatives of murder victims who buried their feelings in the aftermath. Many of them succumbed to heart attacks or strokes, depression, even suicide.

You had to let the grief out. Get it out, or it would kill you.

'It weren't from the old man. He never, ever texts, you get me?' Ryan's eyes flashed. 'Dad could barely use his phone to make a call, let alone send a message. Besides, he weren't the kind of bloke who'd put loads of kisses.' He grimaced. 'And he ain't going to start now, is he?'

'Is that why you didn't go to the house when you received the text?' asked Flick. 'Because you didn't believe it was your dad?'

'I was off my face; I just wanted some shut-eye. But I couldn't sleep. It was like that message was in my head.' Ryan snorted bitterly. 'And if I went round last night, I would have been dead, wouldn't I?'

'Ryan, I know this is difficult for you, but do you know of anyone who held a grudge towards your parents, bore them any ill will?'

'Ill will?' he snapped. 'I don't know anyone who'd want to slaughter my whole family! Look, the old man weren't no angel. He was into all sorts of dodgy stuff back in the day.'

Opening her notebook, Flick said, 'I've been looking through your father's record. I'm afraid it's a long one. He was convicted—'

'So he *deserves* to be dead, that what you're saying?'

Flick reddened. 'We were wondering if he became involved in any enterprise that could have led to his falling out with someone.'

'I told you earlier, he'd gone straight, he wanted to drive a taxi and live the good life in Spain. When we was kids the old man lied and lied, so I always knew when he was serving up bullshit. If he was involved in something, I'd have known.'

'And what about your brother?' asked Drake.

'Phil weren't no angel. But he didn't have those kind of mates.'

'What kind of mates?'

'The type that would break in and . . . and . . .' Ryan's voice became tiny. 'Butcher his family.' The room fell quiet save for the faint rasp of Ryan's palm scraping across the stubble on his jaw. 'And me neither, before you ask. Dad cleaned up his act after what happened to Jason.'

Drake folded his arms.

'Jason?' asked Flick.

'Dad's best mate, committed suicide years back.' He watched Flick write something. 'He was always round ours when we were kids. Him and Dad went way back. When Jason did himself in it knocked the old man for six.'

'How long ago was this?' asked Flick.

'Three or four years. He shot his girlfriend and their baby daughter, then turned the gun on himself.'

'What was his full name, Ryan?' asked Drake, one shoe tapping on the carpet.

'Burgess. Jason Burgess.'

Flick wrote down the name. She didn't know if it had any relevance, probably not, but she was, and always would be, a thorough note-taker.

'The fire just went out of Dad after that. Mum told him he had to give up the life or sling his hook, and she meant it. Dad didn't have any skills to speak of, so he got it into his head to write a misery memoir.'

'A what?' asked Danson.

'Mum loved those books. *Santa's Secret Kiss. Auntie's Sadistic Cellar.* You know, people cashing in on abusive childhoods. They make a mint, and the old man was always going on about his early days. It was his excuse for everything. *That's why my life's so fucked, Ryan, because my childhood was shit.* Trouble was, he could barely write his own name, let alone a whole book. Didn't stop him trying, though. He even started doing research.' Tears welled in his eyes. '*Ryan*, he says to me, *if you knew what happened at that place, it'd make your hair curl.* He got cold feet about the book. Fact was, he couldn't string a sentence together. He didn't know a comma from his colon. Asked me to stash the notes in my flat, just in case.'

Drake looked up sharply.

'In case of what?' Flick asked.

'I dunno.' Ryan shrugged. 'He seemed to think it was important.'

'We're drifting here,' said Drake.

Flick frowned. Ryan had just lost his mother, father and brother in a shocking act of violence, and Ray Drake was getting impatient.

'Maybe one day I'll write the book myself. As a tribute, like.' Ryan sighed. 'If I'm still alive.'

'You think somebody may still want to kill you?'

He shot her an incredulous look. 'I was meant to be there last night, wasn't I?'

Before Flick could reply, Drake cleared his throat. 'Ryan, you can help us enormously by thinking of all the people your father and brother knew who could do something like this.'

'How many times? He was out of it . . . Look, there's one or two names I can give you, but they're small fry, because that's what Dad was. He was a nobody, same as everybody else he knew.'

'Thank you.' Drake's phone rang. 'Sorry, I've got to take this.'

Flick watched him leave, wished he'd never come in the first place. Ryan's head was all over the place. A more gentle approach may have been more productive, certainly more humane. Ray Drake, of all people, should know that. When he'd gone, Ryan placed his head in his hands.

'Am I going to be all right?'

She felt an overwhelming sadness for him. 'You'll be safe, Ryan. You have my word on that.'

8

'Give me a ring, even if you're not coming back. Call when you get this message. I'm not kidding no more, Gav.'

'If that was me,' said Bren, watching Elliot cut the call, 'I would have turned the air blue, called him every name under the sun.'

'Been there, done that.' Elliot shrugged. 'Hasn't made him call back.'

They were sat in the beer garden of the Royal Oak, a stone's throw from Elliot's home. It used to be a sanctuary for him, a quaint little country pub with a thatched roof and whitewashed walls – there had been an inn on this spot since Queen Bess was in pigtails – but it was tainted for him now. Only days ago, he had huddled in one of the snugs with Gavin, who took him carefully through the process of buying a burger franchise. Romancing him, grooming him.

A biting breeze whipped in low across the fields, rattling the table canopies. Elliot was frozen: the landlord didn't turn on the outdoor heaters till evening. Bren shifted his numb buttocks on the narrow plank along the bench. He sat awkwardly, side on from Elliot, chubby legs crossed on the patio. He could probably squeeze his bulk into the narrow gap beneath the bench, just about, but they would need the fire brigade to cut him out again.

'So what are you going to do about it?'

'No idea.'

Elliot wasn't one of those people who coped well with stress, and he certainly wasn't one of life's problem-solvers. Where decisions were concerned he left all the heavy lifting to Rhonda. She always knew the right thing to do. But he wouldn't – he just couldn't – talk to her about this, not if he wanted to hang onto her.

'What did you make of him? Gavin, I mean.'

'He smiled a lot.' Bren, who was the closest thing Elliot had to a friend these days, stroked his cold thighs. 'And he never drank.'

'Yeah.' Bren had nailed it.

'Who sits in a pub and drinks fizzy water? That set off alarm bells.'

Elliot drained his pint. Three beers in, and his hangover was easing, that was something. 'Then why didn't you say so?'

'Ain't against the law not to drink. And, anyway, you were so wrapped up in his get-rich-quick scheme that you wouldn't have listened to me. If it makes you feel any better, I would have fallen for the same scam.' Bren patted his big belly. 'Probably best that I stay away from the burger business, though.'

Elliot appreciated Bren's attempt to cheer him up, but could barely muster a smile. He had fallen hook, line and sinker for Gavin's cheerful bullshit. Gavin had shown him glossy brochures and business plans and paperwork with embossed letterheads; he'd even gone to the trouble of taking him to that empty shop unit. Elliot of all people, who had wasted so much of his own life lying and cheating and stealing, should have known better. Takes one to know one, and all that.

It was karma, that's what it was. All he wanted was a quiet life. Elliot loved his routine, the pub, the long walks. But he had trusted somebody from the outside world. As soon as you let a stranger into your life everything went to shit, it happened every single time.

'She's not going to forgive me,' he said bitterly. 'Not this time.'

'You could always try Owen.'

'Ain't gonna happen,' Elliot said sharply. He had enough problems on his plate without adding Owen Veazey to them.

Bren looked hurt. 'Only trying to help, Ell.'

'Yeah, well . . .' He snatched up his phone and his ridiculous plastic fag, put them in his pocket. 'Keep your ideas to yourself.'

Bren watched him swing his legs from under the bench. 'You going?'

'Better get off.' Elliot felt ashamed of his outburst – Bren was only trying to help, after all – and he clapped him on the shoulder. 'Thanks for listening.'

'Don't dismiss it out of hand, Ell.' Bren's chins quivered against his collar. 'We're not talking a long-term loan. Just to tide you over till you can find this Gavin. You could pop the money back in the bank before Rhonda even notices it's gone. Owen knows you; he'll do you all right.'

'Sure,' said Elliot, who wasn't inclined to touch Owen with a bargepole. 'See you soon, Bren.'

But before he could leave, his phone rang. The screen flashed urgently: Gavin's number.

'You gonna answer it?' asked Bren, watching.

Elliot slowly lifted the mobile to his ear.

And heard a child weep. Juddering sobs. Angry tears.

'Hello?' Elliot asked. 'Gav?'

The sobbing became snivels, and then –

'She'll know the kind of man you are,' said an angry voice.

And it howled: an agonising cry of emotional pain that nearly burst Elliot's eardrum.

He yanked the phone away, cut the call. Stared at the mobile as if it could somehow explain what he'd just heard. Acid churned in his guts.

Elliot was gripped by an odd disconnect. He had the overwhelming feeling that there was something that he really needed to know, something important.

'You know what? I might stay for another pint, after all.' He started walking away. 'You go get them in.'

'Where you off to?' asked Bren.

'To buy some fags.'

9

Lines of inquiry opened up in the investigation by late afternoon.

Flick's team had compiled a list of Kenny's criminal associates, and Upson and Steiner were locating last-known addresses. The response from old mates of Kenny's had been uniform. *Ain't seen Kenny in years. Kenny dropped his old friends. Kenny don't come round here no more. His missus put his head in a noose.* And so on.

Fact was, Kenny's criminal acquaintances didn't have a bad word to say about him. He never grassed, never ripped off his mates, never made enemies.

'So basically . . .' Millie Steiner corrected her posture, as her Alexander Technique teacher had taught her, in a chair borrowed from the Incident Room. 'Kenny was a saint.'

They were sitting in Flick's office. Upson took the edge of Flick's desk, looking down. 'If it weren't for the fact that his record stretches back to flogging used arrows after the Battle of Hastings, I'd have to agree.'

'Ryan's right,' said Flick. 'Kenny was small potatoes, the same goes for Phil. I'm just not seeing it.'

She hadn't seen Ray Drake since he'd walked out of the interview suite earlier. According to Kendrick he'd spent the afternoon with Harris, coordinating a response to the press. The DCI loved his moments in the spotlight, and

Flick imagined him knotting and re-knotting his tie *just so,* and practising authoritative gestures that gave him gravitas in front of the TV people, as Drake advised him on what to say. Drake hated the cameras, hated speaking to the press, and would stay well out of it.

'What about Barbara? Have we missed a trick there?'

'She worked part time at Greggs,' said Steiner. 'Was a hard worker, a bit of a character by all accounts, and loved a chat. Customers liked her.'

'You don't do that to someone . . .' Flick leaned back to examine the ceiling tiles. 'You don't truss up an entire family and stab them to death unless you've a seriously massive grudge.'

'We're working on it, *guv*,' Upson said, picking up the framed photo of Flick's nieces and nephew from her desk. 'Everyone's moving as quickly as they can.'

Flick glared at Upson, but he was too busy frowning at the photo.

'What about the mobile? Someone sent Ryan a message.'

'Kenny complained to a work colleague last night that he'd lost his phone,' Steiner said. 'He swore blind he'd had it on the way to work.'

'Ryan said Kenny took the 41 to Hornsey every night and the night bus back. Someone could have nicked it then.'

Steiner jotted in her notebook. 'I'll get the CCTV footage from London Transport.'

'Wait up.' Upson waved the photo frame, and Flick anxiously expected it to slip from his fingers and shatter on the floor. 'If someone who had reason enough to kill him sat next to Kenny on the bus, wouldn't he recognise him?'

'Perhaps Kenny did recognise him. Perhaps they chatted.

Get someone to dust Kenny's locker at the supermarket. It'll be in a secure area, so get the CCTV as well.'

There was a rap on the window, and Sandra Danson stuck her head in. 'Ryan's finished, Ma'am.'

Flick snatched the frame from Upson and replaced it carefully on her desk. On the way to the interview suite she checked her voicemail messages. They were about work stuff, mostly. Holloway had a query about a departmental charge code. Kendrick wanted to know how far to widen door-to-door inquiries in the surrounding tangle of streets. A friend from college had texted about going for a drink.

It had been a long time since she'd let her hair down – Flick couldn't even remember the last time she'd been on a proper dress-up, cab-home night out. A few months back she'd signed up for one of those internet dating agencies for professionals, had received quite a lot of interest, too, but hadn't done anything about it. She just didn't have the time or, if she was honest, the inclination. She fancied splashing out on some new clothes, getting her hair done. She and Nina could make a day of it, lounging about at some fancy spa, but she worked long hours and weekends, and could never usually muster the energy. She would rather sit around her sister's house where she could relax and chat over a glass of wine while the children ran about making merry hell.

Her thoughts drifted uneasily to Nina and her husband Martin. Flick couldn't shake the feeling that there was something not quite right between them. The last few times she had stayed there she had picked up a tension, a definite atmosphere, but she couldn't put her finger on what it was. Nina and Martin were the happiest couple she knew, no question, and he was as close as a brother to Flick. The idea that their marriage was in trouble – they had three small children, who Flick loved dearly – was too painful to contemplate.

Ryan Overton had spent the afternoon working on a list of Kenny's criminal acquaintances and former friends, anybody who had bad blood with his family, and he'd worked with a furious intensity. Danson said he'd refused any food and drink except a packet of Monster Munch and a can of Red Bull. He looked wretched.

'We'll get you to a hotel, Ryan. Or a police safe house if you prefer.'

Ryan's voice was flat. 'I just wanna go home.'

A squad car was requisitioned to take him back to Finsbury Park where he lived on the twelfth floor of a tower block. Dismissing Danson, Flick climbed in the back of the car. Moving back and forth between the crime scene and the office, tasks multiplying every hour, she hadn't stopped all afternoon, and could do with a few minutes out of the building. Their route took them down the Seven Sisters Road, past the takeaways and convenience stores and the endless shop-to-lease signs. Ryan's head lolled against the headrest as he stared at the shutters rattling down on shops and businesses after a busy trading day.

'They were giving it a real go, you know? Dad had finally got his life on track. Thanks to Jason, in a weird way.'

Kenny and Jason: two lifelong friends who died violently with their families, Jason by his own hand, Kenny at the hands of a murderer. Flick had checked the suicide on the database and found no reason to question the coroner's verdict. Jason Burgess had killed his partner and their infant daughter. He'd had well-documented mental health issues, a history of violent crime. It had never been established where he'd purchased the firearm, but he'd have known plenty of people who'd supply one for the right price. There was just one nagging question: a gun would cost hundreds, perhaps thousands of pounds – how could Burgess, living from hand to mouth, afford something like that?

'At the station you said your dad didn't believe Jason killed himself,' Flick said.

'Stubborn old git wouldn't let it go, but Dad had a blind spot about Jason.'

'Do you think Jason did it?'

'Course. He was a nutcase, he had serious anger issues. Mum couldn't stand him.' Ryan eyed a couple of women emerging from a Turkish café. 'She hated the way he was in and out of our house, stinking up the sofa, drinking all the old man's booze, moaning about his life. Get Kenny and Jason together and they'd break your fucking heart. If anyone was going to turn a gun on himself it was Uncle Jase. One day, when I was about twelve, me, Phil and Mum came home to find him sitting in the kitchen, a bloody great knife on the table.' He spread his hands apart: *this* big. 'He wasn't allowed in the house for a while after that.'

He leaned forward to the driver to indicate a turning. 'Next left, mate. Anyway, when Jason died, Dad was cut up about it. Mum told him to get his act together or he'd be out on his arse. That was when he said he was going to write the book.' Ryan laughed bitterly. 'As if! My old man, the author – never going to happen, was it?'

'Why'd he change his mind about it, do you think?'

'Dad would come out in a cold sweat just holding a pencil.

Besides, in his heart of hearts I don't think he wanted to look back.' A muscle in his jaw ticked. 'He told me that he'd found some people from his past, from a children's home he was at called the Longacre, but you could see something about it had rattled him.'

Flick turned to face him. 'What?'

'He never said, kept it all bottled up. That's when he gave me his notes in a file.' Ryan tapped the side of his nose. '*Keep 'em safe, son.*'

'What was in the file?'

'Mouldy bits of paper, as far as I could tell, old newspapers. My eyes glazed over, to be honest.'

'Can you find it for me, Ryan?'

'I'll try, but don't hold your breath. Don't know if I've even got it any more.'

The car pulled up onto the forecourt of a tower block. A group of kids booted a football against a wall. They gestured at the car and made siren sounds. *Nee naw nee naw.*

'He was finally getting himself together.' Ryan watched the kids kicking the ball about. 'He was really trying, you know?'

'We can talk again tomorrow,' said Flick.

'What if they come for me?' He turned to her. 'What if whoever killed them wants to finish the job?'

'We're not going to leave you alone, Ryan. There'll be an armed officer outside your door round the clock, for as long as it takes.'

Ryan snorted, reaching for his seat belt release. 'No offence, but I've seen that movie, and it *never* works.'

10

At dusk, when Ray Drake arrived beneath the black mass of Ryan Overton's tower block, a few determined kids were still kicking a football.

Work had kept him from coming earlier. Drake wanted to keep an eye on Flick's investigation, but DCI Harris had insisted he coordinate the police response to the frenzied media coverage. A meeting with a Met communication officer had dragged on. The press office was inundated with inquiries, and a briefing was hastily organised, had gone reasonably well despite there being little to report. As usual, Drake positioned himself well away from the nest of cameras and microphones while Harris enjoyed the limelight.

He stared up at the tower, a rectangle against the night sky. Drake hadn't given a thought to Kenny Overton for many years. The idea that he had been living so close to the nick was disconcerting. It had been a long time since they'd last seen each other, decades, and they probably wouldn't have given each other a second glance if they'd passed on the street. But Drake's instinct was that Kenny's murder, so near to his place of work, wasn't just a coincidence. Ryan Overton's remark about Kenny's childhood, and *that* research, had nagged at him all afternoon.

He tried to concentrate on his wife's recital of a Prokofiev concerto – Laura had been a professional musician and

Drake played all her acclaimed cello recordings on repeat on the music system – but the music did nothing to temper his anxiety. Taking out his mobile, he scrolled again to that familiar number.

It rang and rang and rang, and then his daughter's voice said: 'Hi, this is April. I can't get to the phone right now, but you're clever, and know what to do!'

The tone beeped in his ear. She hadn't come home last night. He'd phoned her five, maybe six times already today, and hadn't left a message, but he was determined to say something this time, to ask how she was, and when he would see her. Staring at the parked cars ahead, Ray Drake took a deep breath, opened his mouth and—

A body plummeted out of the sky and smashed onto the roof of the car in front with an almighty bang and crack of glass.

The car's suspension bounced. The alarm screeched, wing lights flashed crazily. A broken arm flopped from the dented roof to hang across the shattered windscreen. The kids raced off across the forecourt screaming in terror, melting into the muddle of subways and passages.

Drake flung open his door and crunched across the glass towards the body. Ryan Overton's ragdoll limbs were flung every which way, the two ends of his torso at right angles. A woman screamed nearby. A dog barked at the pulsing wail of the alarm. Running to the tower block entrance, Drake stabbed random intercom buttons. When the door unlocked with a hornet buzz, he ran inside.

Two lifts, a fire door to a stairwell.

There was little chance the killer could have left the building in the scant seconds since Overton's body fell twelve storeys. An LED indicator showed a lift dropping towards the lobby: five . . . four . . . three . . . two . . . one . . .

The pneumatic machinery wheezed. The lift settled. The doors trundled open. Drake lurched forward, and a woman screamed, pulling her toddler close. He held up his hands, *don't be afraid*, and backed away. He flung open the door to the stairwell, and his soles slapped on the concrete as he took two steps at a time, sticking close to the banister, darting glances up the central shaft.

By the time he pulled open the door to the twelfth floor his knees were buckling. He could barely get his breath. Drake doubled over, heart pumping, shirt clinging to his back, propped his hands on his knees and waited for air to fill his lungs. Time was, momentum would have kept him moving, but he was a middle-aged man now. A few yards over, the lift clanked into life. Just as he reached it, the small square window in the door disappeared into the floor, obscuring whoever was inside.

A fire door dissected the long corridor and Drake ran through it. The copper outside Overton's flat was startled when he pulled out his badge. 'Open it up!'

The officer fumbled a door key beneath the sallow ceiling lights. The car alarm squealed faintly on the other side of the building. Curious residents emerged from flats. Drake shouted: 'Get back inside!'

They slipped into the flat, through a stubby hallway into the living room. Wild applause thundered from the television. The balcony window was open. Heavy curtains moved in the wind. Drake saw a small crowd gathering around Ryan Overton's broken body splayed across the roof of the car. The alarm screaming, lights flashing. A slim figure in a red hoodie peeled from the group, walking casually towards the entrance of the estate. Stepping onto the street, the figure paused to salute Drake, then disappeared into the dark.

'Oh my . . .' The officer stared down at the body, dumbfounded.

'With me.'

Slipping gloves from his pocket, Drake led the way back down the corridor and through the fire door. It was solid metal, another square of reinforced glass in the centre. When it was shut, the copper at Overton's door wouldn't have seen anything on the other side.

Drake pushed at the doors of the flats on the same side of the corridor as Ryan's. The third door swung open at his touch, the lock was broken. He stepped into the dark flat to find the balcony window open. Ryan's flat was four windows along. The balconies in between were placed evenly apart. With a bit of dexterity it would have been possible to jump from one to the other, and into Overton's flat.

'What's your name?'

'Gill.'

'Officer Gill, I need you to get downstairs,' said Drake. 'Move those people away from the body. Don't let anybody use the lifts, or enter or leave the building.'

Gill swallowed. 'I was outside . . . nobody came . . .'

'Did you leave the door at any time?' The uniform shook his head. 'Did you fall asleep?' Gill flinched, shocked. 'Then you did your job. Go downstairs.'

Back in the corridor, Drake watched Gill disappear into the stairwell. Sirens emerged faintly from the city din. He hadn't much time.

When he returned to Overton's flat, it was filled with explosions and gunfire – a movie on the television. The flat reeked of booze and stale smoke. An open pack of B&H lay on a low table, an ashtray cradled the ash skeleton of a cigarette. An empty Bacardi bottle lay on the floor beside an upturned chair. The intruder must have come in through the window as Overton faced the TV, clamped a hand over his mouth, or a knife to his throat, and dragged him to the balcony to tip him over.

Along the back wall was a shelf of storage boxes. Drake peered inside. There was a cupboard containing DVDs, a torn carton of cigarettes, a stash of mucky mags.

No box of research.

The bedroom off the hallway was tiny, barely big enough for a queen-sized bed and a pine wardrobe. Drake rifled through a chest of drawers and found underwear, balled-up T-shirts, belts.

The wardrobe door listed to the side when he pulled it open. A single suit hung inside, reeking of mothballs. Jeans, shirts, a denim jacket. Pristine white trainers were lined up at the bottom, a pair of leather shoes in a box. He ran his fingers along the duvet lining. There was nothing under the bed except for a lone sock, furred by lint and dust.

The sirens were louder now, converging. No box file, no notes.

The kitchen was barely more than an alcove. He flung open cupboards full of glasses and broken devices. A pair of scales, stacked plates and bowls, a toaster missing a plug shoved at the back.

Outside, the siren of an ambulance whooped as it entered the estate. The living-room walls pulsed blue. Drake heard raised voices in the corridor. He was running out of time.

Switching on the light in the bathroom, he saw a shower cubicle and toilet, a sink smeared with dried toothpaste. The space smelled of damp towels and talc.

High on a wall was a shelf for towels. Drake pressed his hand between the rough cotton – and felt paper, a couple of dumped tabloids. But underneath the bottom towel was a shoebox. Drake took the box into the living room and opened it, ignoring the shouts and clanging doors in the corridor. Inside was a pile of clear plastic folders containing newspaper cuttings. Headlines leapt out at him as he flicked quickly through the brown and curled cuttings: CRASH A TRAGIC . . . SUICIDE SAYS COURT . . . TWINS KILLED . . .

Footsteps, voices, outside the door of the flat.

His heart lurched when he saw the cutting, yellow with age, at the bottom.

The headline read: JUDGE VISITS LOCAL CHILDREN'S HOME.

Below it was a black-and-white photograph, the forced smiles of a grim line of adults and children.

Tallis, Kenny, Toby, Jason, the judge and his wife, Elliot, Amelia.

Connor Laird, slipping into the shadows at the edge of the photo.

Disappearing before his eyes.

Her hand, hot and clammy.

Fetid breath. Fingers clawing.

The crackle of flame.

Drake was about to slip the photo out and pocket it, when a voice said: 'Sir?'

Flick Crowley stood at the door. She stared at the upturned chair, the curtains swaying in the breeze. The clipping in his gloved hands. 'I don't understand.'

'Someone climbed over the balcony.' Drake eased the clipping back into the pile, replaced the lid on the box, as uniforms poured into the room. 'From a neighbouring flat.'

'Is that the file Ryan was talking about?' When Drake nodded, she said: 'I'll get it bagged up and taken away.' She stared, looking sick. 'I promised Ryan we'd keep him safe.'

'I can handle this if you—'

'*No.*' She shook her head. 'I'll be fine.' Then she gave him a curious look, as if it had only just occurred to her that he was already here in Ryan Overton's flat. 'Show me where they got in.'

Drake moved to the door, glancing back uneasily at the shoebox.

11

Spending all day down the pub probably wasn't the best way to get a grip on the situation, but it was the only way Elliot knew how to absorb the increasingly disconcerting turn of events.

It was bad enough that Gavin had taken his money, but to bring to his attention a triple murder and then to cry down the phone like a baby, to hurl angry insults . . . Perhaps Gavin was a headcase and was having some kind of breakdown. Or perhaps Elliot was.

Truth was, he was putting off for as long as possible having to explain to Rhonda about the money – how he had lost tens of thousands of pounds of her savings. The idea that she would throw him out gnawed at him. After umpteen pints, and too many fags, he badly needed forty winks. Maybe then he could muster up the courage to come clean.

I gave it away, all of it.

Gavin, that weird voice on the phone, had hit a nerve.

She'll know the kind of man you are.

And then there was that business with poor Kenny . . .

But when he walked up the lane, the sky thickening with dark, and heard raised voices, he knew he wouldn't be able to skulk upstairs for a nap.

Elliot lingered at the front door, getting his shit together. He pinched the metal tendrils of the wind chime hanging above the door so that they didn't jangle in his ear, threw the cigarette he had been smoking down the drive. Straightening his collar, he cupped his hand over his mouth to check his own stinking breath.

'We're in here,' called Rhonda from the kitchen, when he let himself inside. The living room was spotless, the surfaces dusted and the carpet vacuumed, and Elliot felt even worse. Rhonda had come home, after working all Saturday, and cleaned up.

He walked into the kitchen to see Dylan flinging his arms around, and saying: 'I ain't gonna do that!'

The kid stuffed his hands into the pockets of his leather jacket. He was tall and skinny with big eyes, olive skin and a swirl of curly hair gelled across his forehead into an enormous fringe. His mouth pouted in disgust as Rhonda, still dressed in her blue dental assistant's smock, moved around the room spraying cleaner on every surface.

'I'm not asking you.' She rubbed the kitchen table with a cloth. 'That's not how this works.'

'You mean,' Dylan made an incredulous face, 'this is a dictatorship.'

'If you like.' Rhonda blew a spiral of hair out of her eyes. 'You live in my house, you follow my rules.'

'Well, I'm sorry, Kim Jong-un, you don't have the right to tell me who I can and can't see.'

'I'm your mum, and the last time I looked, that gives me every right.'

Conscious of the stink of booze on him, Elliot loitered at the door. 'You're going to have to bring me up to speed.'

'He rules North Korea,' Dylan said, smirking.

'Very good, I see what you did there.'

Rhonda threw the cloth in the sink and regarded her son, hands on hips. She had the same olive skin, and the same curly hair, which was permed into tight, shivering corkscrews, but none of her son's height. She couldn't have been more than five foot five. 'A couple of Dylan's so-called mates have got done for shoplifting.'

Dylan shoved his hands into his pockets. 'What's that got to do with me? The answer, in case you're wondering, is nothing!'

'They were caught stealing sweets from the shop down the road, the one by the GP.' Rhonda shook her head as if she couldn't quite get her brain around it. 'Another boy – leather jacket, skinny jeans, ridiculous fringe – was seen legging it.'

Dylan slapped his forehead. 'Which could describe literally thousands of other kids. *Thousands*. All this goes to show is what a low opinion you have of me, your own son.'

Rhonda appealed to Elliot. 'Tell him.'

'It's a pretty silly fringe,' he said.

'Okay, we'll give you the benefit of the doubt.' Rhonda pulled kitchen towel off the holder to rub at the fridge handle. 'Let's just suppose, for the sake of a quiet life, it's not you. But you're not seeing those boys again for a while.'

'Yeah?' Dylan snorted. 'And how are you going to stop me?'

'By taking away your phone.'

'But you won't.' Dylan flashed a smile, a nasty, triumphant thing. 'Because then you'd have no idea where I was, I could be arrested or run over, I could be lying on the road dead, and then you'd be sorry.'

Dylan was a sweet kid most of the time. They used to

be good pals, Elliot and the boy. But these days, consumed by turbulent teenage hormones, he probed boundaries constantly, tested limits, flew off the handle at the slightest thing. His mother struggled to cope with his moods. Christ, they both did.

It didn't help that Rhonda worked every hour available to put food on the table and, he winced, put a little money aside each month. Or that Elliot, who worked cash-in-hand on building sites, never knew what hours he would be working from one day to the next – times being what they were, sometimes he didn't work at all. Dylan resented living at the end of a potholed lane in the country – the 'arse end of the arse end of nowhere', he called it – and spent a lot of time staring at his phone or cocooned in enormous headphones. That's when he wasn't off with his mates, getting up to who knows what.

The kid didn't know he was born. Elliot wanted to tell Dylan where he was at his age, in that shithole home, and what he did there. How he had nightmares, even now, about what went on at the Longacre. That place had made him the man he was. A ne'er-do-well, a jailbird. A failure.

And look what happened to Kenny.

When he thought of that TV footage, an unexpected feeling veered close. That information, the vital, connective fact he needed to make sense of what had been happening to him, bobbed tantalisingly near, like a piece of driftwood on the tide. For a moment he felt like a tremendous truth was about to be revealed to him . . .

But then Rhonda said to Elliot: 'Please, you have a go.'

'The last thing your mum needs is for you to get involved in any—'

'In any what?' The boy's eyes flashed.

'Just stay away from trouble. Once you get sucked into—'

'You're a fine one to talk. You being in prison for most of your life.'

'That's enough!' snapped Rhonda.

'Then you should listen to me,' Elliot said calmly. Getting into a shouting match wasn't going to help, he had learned that much. 'Because you don't want to end up like I did.'

'A burglar.' Dylan counted on his fingers. 'A thief, a *thug*.'

'Yeah.' Elliot swallowed. 'And a few more besides.'

Rhonda ripped off another square of kitchen towel and blew her nose.

'I got off to the wrong start in life,' continued Elliot, and Dylan played an imaginary violin. 'I didn't have your advantages. A home, a mum who loves me; I had to learn the hard way. But I did learn, eventually.' He reddened, thinking of the money he had lost. 'I learned from my mistakes.'

'Fell on your feet, didn't you?'

'I don't understand.'

'Mum took you in off the street, gave you a home.'

'I wasn't on the street. But, if you like, yeah, I owe everything to your mum. She believed in me.'

'*Believes*,' said Rhonda, squeezing his hand.

'And when are you going to pay her back what you owe?'

Elliot sucked in a breath. 'Excuse me?'

'When are you going to pay her back for all this beautiful trust by getting a proper job, one you can actually stick at for more than five minutes? When are *you* going to make something of yourself, instead of pissing off down the pub all day?'

'I like to think,' Elliot ploughed on, 'that we're a family, the three of us. We support each other, and trust—'

'But we're not, though, are we?' Dylan's voice cracked with emotion. 'Me and Mum are family, but you're not, you're some passing bloke.'

'Dylan!' Rhonda strode forward. 'Take that back.'

'You can't take back a *fact*.'

'Go to your room!'

'I'm not five years old! I'm going out.' He stormed past Elliot.

A moment later, they heard the front door slam. The old sash windows rattled.

'He makes me so angry.'

Elliot bunched kitchen towel and gave it to Rhonda. 'He can't help it. At his age, he's got all these hormones flying about. He doesn't know if he's coming or going half the time.'

'He shouldn't talk to you that way.'

'He'll calm down. And later he'll get into a state about something else. Look, he's left his phone.' Dylan's beloved android device sat on the table. 'So he won't have gone far.'

He pulled Rhonda to him. Her tears dampened his shirt.

'I just don't know what's going on in his head right now.' Her voice was muffled against his chest.

'He'll come good; he's not a bad kid.'

'Yeah.' She folded the tissue to dab at her eyes. 'You came good, after all. It was touch and go, but you're a good boy now.'

'I am.'

She'll know the kind of man you are.

He pressed her head to his chest so she couldn't see his bleary eyes. But she pushed away from him. 'I'd better get back to the cleaning. Somebody didn't do it this morning.'

'Sorry, I—'

'Went down the pub.'

'Bren had something he wanted to talk about.'

'And you stink of smoke.'

He held up his palms. 'I've had a couple.'

'Whatever it was, I'm sure it must have been important for you to spend all day there.' Rhonda sighed. 'Maybe what we need is a holiday.'

Elliot's chest tightened. 'We could go see your mum in the valleys.'

'I was thinking somewhere more exotic. Palm trees, cocktails, white sand. We could do with some sun. Mauritius, maybe. Let's splurge.'

'Sure,' he said. 'We can talk about it.'

'I'll look on the internet tonight.'

'There's no rush.'

Moments later she was dragging the vacuum cleaner up the stairs. He was about to take out his phone when the front door opened. Dylan came into the kitchen, snatched up his own mobile.

'I can't be sure,' said Elliot, 'but I think your mum is angry.'

'You think?' Dylan smirked. 'You're an idiot, Elliot.'

'That's me.' Elliot was glad he could still dredge a smile of sorts from the boy. Every week brought some painful change in Dylan's personality, some complicated new reaction to the world. Perhaps in a few months he wouldn't smile at all. But Elliot, like a prospector clinging to a mountainside, would continue to dig deep for them. 'Elliot the idiot.'

'I'm going out.' Dylan headed towards the door.

'So,' Elliot said, 'if you were going to steal from that shop, what would you have taken? Hypothetically, I mean.'

Dylan made a big show of taking a container of mints from his pocket, shaking one into his hand and popping it onto his tongue.

'Don't do it again,' said Elliot, serious.

And then the boy was gone. Elliot heard the thud of the hoover against the skirting upstairs. He took out his phone and called Bren.

'Ell, what gives?'

'I've been thinking about what you said this morning. Let's set up a meet with Owen. Just for a chat.'

'Sure thing. When do you want to see him?'

'Soon,' said Elliot hoarsely. 'As soon as possible.'

12

Convinced that he kept seeing the same vehicle hanging back in the distance, Drake pulled his car to the kerb and killed the engine. In the rear-view mirror, clubbers staggered down the Pentonville Road towards King's Cross and the Tube. At a bus stop, a man's head rested facedown on a briefcase hugged to his chest.

It had been a long night at the tower block. A tent had been erected around the shattered body of Ryan Overton, its white walls rippling and cracking in the wind whistling through the estate. Access to the block was restricted so that the lifts, stairwell and twelfth-floor corridor could be dusted for prints.

Flick Crowley, shell-shocked, had kept herself busy. The shoebox of cuttings was barcoded and removed by Holloway's team.

Drake had joined the MIT at the section house for a couple of hours, fielded an anxious call from Harris, and then left. Traffic was thin at this early hour – an occasional vehicle climbed the road – but he had a nagging sense, barely more than that, of the same car in the distance.

A silver open-top roared up the hill towards the Angel, a scream in the stillness. Drake was reaching for the ignition when his phone rang. His immediate hope was that it was April, but the caller's number was blocked. He touched the screen.

'DI Drake,' he said, listening to the purr of an engine at the other end.

Nobody spoke, so he cut the call. It rang again. With a fluttering sense of unease, he put it to his ear and listened. A long way behind, just beyond the junction at the Angel, a car slowed to a stop and killed its lights.

Down the phone he heard a handbrake crank, the jangle of keys.

'Who is this?' said Drake. 'You've got the wrong number.'

The seat belt whipped across his chest when he unclicked it. He had a vague idea about walking towards the car, was reaching for the driver's door when he heard a sound in his ear.

Faint, barely more than a breath . . .

The angry sobbing of a boy.

Drake snatched at the door release and stepped onto the road – just as a car blipped by inches from him, its horn blaring angrily. He threw himself against the Mercedes. When he returned the phone to his ear, the call had been cut.

Trotting towards the junction, picking up speed, he saw the full beams of the car flash on. An Audi, he thought, but couldn't be sure. The engine fired, and when Drake ran, the vehicle turned in a screeching swerve and accelerated away. Drake watched it disappear down the City Road. Then went back to his car to continue his journey home.

Ray Drake lived in a five-storey townhouse in an expensive Islington square. Technically, it was still Myra Drake's house; she'd been born there, and insisted she had every intention of dying in it. But she now lived in a flat in the basement with internal access to the main house. Myra sneered at the stair lift Laura had fitted to the basement stairs and refused to use it. She sourly observed all the improvements Ray's wife had made to the house down the years. For so long a musty Victorian pile, Laura had painstakingly modernised and refurbished it. Walls were knocked down, creating a sense of light and space, ancient wiring and fittings ripped out and much of Myra's dark and fusty furniture banished to her flat. The old woman had put up stiff resistance, but with velvet stubbornness Laura had got her way. A few short months ago all Drake's family had lived there, but his wife was gone now and April was barely there.

Water spattered noisily into the gleaming stainless-steel sink when Drake ran the cold tap in the kitchen. He drank a glass of water and pulled out a stool to scroll down his logged calls to April. So far she'd ignored every single one.

Drake squinted when the light went on. Myra shuffled into the kitchen, a clawed hand holding her dressing gown tight at the neck. The old woman had never been much of a sleeper, and often drifted around the house in the early hours. More than once she'd scared the wits out of them all by floating past in the dead of night, like a wraith.

'Why are you sitting in the dark?' she asked sharply.

'I just got in.'

'You look shattered, Raymond. Go to bed.'

'I will, in a minute.'

Waving dismissively, the old woman edged to the fridge to pour a glass of milk. Without her glasses she was long-sighted, and hooked a crooked forefinger over the top of the glass so that she didn't overfill it. When she returned the jug to the fridge, she stood with her aged, bony hands, as thin and sharp as the talons of a bird of prey, flat on the counter. At eighty-seven, age had evaporated the round lines of her face, leaving her gaunt and skeletal. High cheekbones curved into triangular shadow beneath her pallid eyes. Her hair, once fashioned into a muscular perm, was thinning against her skull. But she was still an imposing figure, despite a stoop, and her mind was as sharp as ever.

'Where's April?'

Myra looked at him grimly over the glass. 'She's gone, Raymond.'

'What are you talking about?'

The old woman's voice was brittle. 'She's packed her things and left.'

'When did this happen?' he asked, shocked.

'Yesterday.' He bit down on his annoyance. God forbid the old woman actually rang him to tell him. 'The boy came to pick her up.'

The *boy*. Myra could never bring herself to utter Jordan's name. Something like this had been on the cards for a while, but he hadn't wanted to admit it to himself.

'The girl has always had too little structure in her life. You have given her too much rope.'

'She's old enough to make her own choices.'

'She needs her father, now of all times. That boy is . . .' Myra's thin lips curled in distaste. 'What we used to call a Flash Harry.'

Jordan never stood a chance with Myra. His father was a self-made businessman, a cockney market trader made good. Myra's family was old money, as was her late husband's. Notions of class and entitlement gnawed at Myra.

'She'll come back; she just needs time.'

A thin band of milk glistened in the down of her top lip.

'She's a selfish child, always has been. You must bring her home.'

He sighed. 'Myra . . .'

'I don't like to see you unhappy, Raymond.' Those eyes, yellowed and spotted by broken blood vessels, studied him. 'You do not cope well. And there's something else, I can see it in your eyes. Something is troubling you. Is it that case I heard on the news? The triple murder.'

'There's been a fourth killing. A mother, a father and their two sons are dead. One of the victims . . . his name was Kenny Overton.'

'And what's the significance of this person?'

'He was at the home,' he said.

'*That* place.' She pushed away the glass. 'Well, these things happen.'

'There've been other deaths. People from the Longacre.'

Myra's long fingers absently rubbed the locket she always wore around her neck. 'You've been under enormous strain recently.'

'Something's *happening*, Myra.' Picking up on his anxiety, she waited for him to continue. 'There's a photograph . . . from a newspaper cutting.'

'And these murders, do they have anything to do with what . . . happened?'

'Yes,' he said, meeting her eyes. 'I think so.'

'I shall retire to bed. I'll wash up in the morning.' The rough towelling of her dressing gown brushed against his thigh as she passed him, stopping at the door. 'I'm sure you are perfectly capable of handling it. You must do whatever is necessary, as you always have, to protect your daughter.'

His eyes lifted to hers. 'Yes.'

'You're in charge of the investigation?'

'I'm SIO.'

'Well, then.' The old woman plucked a speck of lint from the arm of her gown and placed it in a pocket. 'It gives me no pleasure to say it, Raymond, but—'

'Not now, Myra.' He rinsed the glass at the sink, placed it on the draining board.

'She made you soft, that wife of yours.'

'Myra . . .'

'I know you don't like to hear these things, but you must act before it's too late. Before you lose your daughter for ever.'

'You've made your point.' He snatched up his keys.

'Where are you going?'

'There's something I've got to do.'

When he slammed out of the front door, she switched off the light and stood, absently rubbing the locket, thinking about her beloved son.

13

A heavy metal door stuttered beneath a harsh yellow light, the image frozen on a computer screen.

'The bad news is there's only one camera on the estate.' Eddie Upson pressed a button on the keypad and the image moved. 'Good news is it's just above the entrance.'

Numbers at the top of the screen – a time stamp – began to hurl forward, the milliseconds a blur of movement. The image showed the entrance to Ryan Overton's tower block taken from a high angle in the dank lobby. The light was gloomy, the exterior beyond the heavy metal doors pitch black.

'The video is low resolution so don't expect terrific quality.'

He moved the jogging mechanism on the player to reveal a family, a man and a woman, a small boy, moving into the frame from the direction of the elevator. The frame rate on the image was so poor that the figures jerked forward with every step, cheating time and space. With a final tug of his arm, the boy was pulled out the door, which snapped closed.

'We've yet to identify everyone who came in and out around the time of Ryan's death. That's fourteen people. I'd imagine most, if not all, live on the estate.'

The rooftops outside the window were swollen with the imminent dawn. A pile of printouts littered the desk, images of everybody who had entered and exited the building an hour each side of the murder. Men and women in winter coats, carrying shopping bags, pushing buggies, kids surging inside with bikes and skateboards.

'This guy looks like our best bet. He entered the building fifteen minutes before Ryan took the express elevator.'

'No jokes, please, Eddie.' Flick wasn't in the mood.

Cranking the jogging wheel on the playback equipment, Upson pointed at the screen. A dark shadow could be glimpsed on the window of the entrance. The image jumped. The door was ajar. A figure stepped inside – face buried in a red hoodie – to move at the extreme edge of the screen. Flick saw a shoulder and an elbow, the fingers of a gloved hand, the soft point of the hood.

'You'd have to be clinging to the wall to skirt the lens like that.' Millie Steiner leaned forward. 'They're avoiding the camera.'

Moments later the figure was gone.

'Show me again,' said Flick. She made Upson replay the image several times. He jogged the sequence back and forth. A dark figure. The door swung open. Tip of the hood. A gloved hand. Gone, repeat.

'How tall would you say?'

'Five foot eight or nine,' said Steiner.

'Man or woman?'

Upson sipped from a can of coke. 'It's difficult to say. That hooded top is baggy. Whoever it was had to be powerful enough to tip a strong lad like Ryan Overton over the balcony. A bloke, if I had to guess.'

Maybe not, thought Flick. They'd have to wait for the autopsy report, but if the empty Bacardi bottle in the flat was anything to go by, Ryan had been drowning his sorrows.

Taken by surprise, unsteady on his feet, and with the right momentum, it wouldn't have taken much effort to tip him over that balcony.

'Now run it on.'

Upson jogged the image forwards. The screen became an explosion of undulating lines. The time stamp went crazy. Slowing the image, he touched the screen.

'There's the guv.'

Drake crashed through the door and disappeared immediately. A moment later a mother and toddler left the building. Flick was gripped by the image of empty space. The numbers hurtled onwards. A couple of minutes later the hooded figure, face still hidden, ran from the elevator side of the frame to press the exit button and lunge through the entrance. It was barely onscreen for a second.

'The DI had a choice: take the stairs or stay in reception. Unfortunately, he chose wrong.'

'I probably would have done the same.' Steiner stifled a yawn.

'It's been a long day,' said Flick, looking with surprise at the time on her phone. 'Go home and sleep. Come back in refreshed tomorrow.'

Upson didn't need telling twice. 'Don't mind if I do.' Flick heard his bones pop when he stood and stretched, tugged his jacket from the back of the chair. 'You coming, Fli . . . boss?'

'I've a couple of things to finish up,' she said, but Upson had already left the glassed-in office, barely bigger than a cubicle, where they kept the video equipment.

Crushed cans were lined up on the desk. Millie Steiner picked up a bin and swept them into it. 'Whatever you're thinking, don't.' When Flick didn't respond, she added: 'He was protected.'

'Not well enough.'

Flick hadn't eaten anything since a sandwich at lunchtime, God knows how many hours ago. She was shattered, her blood sugar was bumping along the bottom, and she couldn't shake the feeling that she was responsible for Ryan Overton's death, despite everyone's reassurances. If she'd insisted he stayed in a Met safe house, he'd still be alive.

'I shouldn't have let him go home, it—'

A lump formed in her throat and she stopped. Steiner was a sweet and empathetic girl, and Flick knew she could speak in confidence, but she wasn't about to get emotional in front of her.

'Why don't you go home? It'll look better in the morning.'

'I will.'

When Millie had gone, Flick turned off the lights and walked through the empty Incident Room. Met Police badge screensavers bounced across computer screens. Her first day as lead officer on an investigation, and it had all been a bit of a mess. In her office, she collapsed into the chair.

It was a surprise to Flick that Ray Drake had seen fit to go to Ryan Overton's flat last night, almost stumbling upon Ryan's killer in the process. The DI said he'd decided on the spur of the moment to look in on Ryan, but the fact that he had even gone there without informing her didn't seem like a huge vote of confidence. Did he trust her to lead the investigation? The murder of a family was going to heap pressure on everyone to get a quick result, she understood that, but if he had concerns she wished he'd raised them with her directly.

'Bollocks to it,' she muttered. She logged out of the computer, picked up her bag.

In his office, the duty sergeant was sat among a nest of monitors showing various parts of the building.

'Heck of a day, DI Crowley.' Frank Wanderly grinned. 'I take a few days off and as soon as I get back all hell breaks loose.'

'Go anywhere nice?' asked Flick.

'Just pottered about in the garden.'

Most people would jet off somewhere warm to soak up some rays, but Flick could just imagine Nosferatu, who liked to work the late shift, walking around his garden in the dead of night with a watering can, moonlight gleaming off that shiny skull.

'You have a good morning, Frank,' she said, buzzing herself out to the car park.

After the heat blasting from the station radiators, the cold winter air made her shudder. Flick would get a couple of hours' sleep and take a shower, then grab breakfast on the way back in.

In the car, she slumped against the driver's seat, fatigue washing over her. Within moments she felt herself being dragged down towards sleep – and jerked out of her stupor. Forcing herself to sit up, limbs as heavy as lead, Flick vigorously rubbed a hand up and down her face, lifted the key to the ignition – just as the automatic gate to the car park rattled open, and Ray Drake's Mercedes swung in, its headlights sweeping across the concrete. Drake climbed out of the vehicle. Its lights winked as it locked.

If Flick had left five minutes earlier, she'd be on her way home. He couldn't see her, she could just slip away, but she was anxious about his close scrutiny of the investigation. At the tower block and in the office there'd been little time to talk. She felt a responsibility, felt compelled, to give him an update. Maybe, at the same time, she could fish for a few crumbs of reassurance about the job she was doing.

With a sigh, Flick slipped the key from the ignition, pulled her bag over her shoulder and slipped from the car.

14

Frank Wanderly peered at the clock above the door when he saw Ray Drake. 'Another early one, Detective Inspector?'

'Busy day ahead, Frank.'

The sergeant jammed paper from his desk into a recycling bin. 'You wait for one homicide and four come along at once.'

'DS Crowley has certainly got her hands full,' said Drake, impatient to get on.

'Got to give her credit, though, she's working flat out. She only left five minutes ago.'

The years Wanderly had spent working till dawn beneath electric light hung on his pale face like a shroud. But he was an amiable man, who never seemed to resent the endless parade of drunks and derelicts that washed up at the station in the early hours.

'How's your daughter, Ray?'

'Pretty good, thanks.'

The phone rang. The sergeant's hand hovered over it. Drake said quickly, 'By the way, Frank, I forgot to put something in the Property Room earlier, can I borrow the key?'

'Of course.' Wanderly lifted a finger, *one moment*, and answered the call, 'Sergeant Frank Wanderly. Who's speaking, please?' As he began his conversation, he spun his chair to a shallow metal cabinet on the wall. Inside were dozens of keys. He rifled through them, took one out and lobbed it at Drake. 'I'm afraid they need to speak to CID on that particular issue . . .'

His office was on the second floor, the MIT Incident Room was on the first, but Ray Drake took the stairs to the basement. Access to the Property Room was restricted. Once evidence had been logged, it was tagged and kept secure until it could be examined. Items from hundreds of investigations were kept there: seized drugs, stolen goods, weapons such as decommissioned firearms.

The black bulb of a CCTV camera squatted above the door, but there was nothing Drake could do about that. No one was likely to check the recording. If they did, he'd repeat his earlier lie to Wanderly.

The air conditioning chilled him as soon as he let himself through the heavy door. Fluorescents buzzed into noisy life to reveal a massive room with long freestanding steel shelves bolted to the concrete floor, every inch piled with evidence. Larger items were placed against the bare brick walls: a damaged safe, a fish tank, a cash register. A set of hub caps was wedged behind an acetylene cylinder.

Snapping on gloves, Drake headed to the first aisle where the most recent evidence was placed. His fingers brushed over the plastic wrapping and boxes as he checked dates and barcodes.

With a growing sense of unease, Drake moved methodically down the length of the shelving. Several minutes later he still hadn't found the shoebox. For all he knew, the cuttings were still in the office upstairs, strewn across a desk. He couldn't remain down here much longer – the camera would record the time he spent inside.

And then he saw it. The box had fallen behind a pile of boxes. The plastic wrapping wasn't sealed, which suggested not everything inside had been logged. Maybe no one had looked at it yet. Removing the lid, he saw the transparent plastic folders. Inside each of those, a cutting.

He scanned each one, flicking through the flopping plastic, skimming the headlines and first paragraphs: SUICIDE . . . BLAZE . . . JUDGE . . . CRASH . . .

What he saw of each article, piecing together names and dates and stories, only increased his disquiet. It was no wonder Kenny Overton had abandoned his research, no wonder he had yearned to go abroad, far away. And yet, Drake suspected, it wouldn't have made the slightest bit of difference. Moving to the ends of the Earth wouldn't have saved him. Familiar names, people he hadn't thought about in decades – now erased from the world, and long forgotten – detonated dread memories . . .

Of Tallis, of Sally – he hadn't thought about Sally in a long time, and felt a pang of guilt – and of all the doomed kids at that home.

Drake found what he was looking for, the oldest cutting in the file. Slipping it from the plastic, he eyed the photograph that could be enough to end his career and destroy his relationship with his daughter if Flick's investigation swung in the wrong direction. His eyes lingered on the kid on the edge of the dismal group of people who posed on that fateful day.

A boy from a lifetime ago.

Connor Laird, slipping into the shadows. Cringing from the camera's flash, half turned, one pale eye glaring.

There was a barcode at the top of the plastic sheet. The

clipping had been logged. He couldn't just walk away with it.

'Guv?'

The metal door boomed shut. Drake's heart leapt.

'Just a moment!' His voice was a throaty croak. 'Give me a second!'

'Guv? Where are you?'

A woman's voice. Footsteps approaching on the concrete. He stepped back to see Flick Crowley at the end of the aisle.

'Flick!' he said, in as cheery a voice as he could muster. 'Let me just put this back!'

Drake stepped close to the shelving, smothering her view of the clipping. He quickly folded the paper below the photograph and tore, coughing to cover the sound of the dry paper splitting apart along the crease.

'Just one . . .' Stuffing the photo inside his breast pocket, he replaced the rest of the cutting in the plastic and shoved it into the box. Pushed the box back into the wrapping. '. . . moment!'

When he looked up, Flick was at his side. He had no idea how much she had seen.

She frowned, looking at him, then down at the box.

'Frank told me you'd gone home,' he said, gulping down his agitation. 'I was just reading this stuff.'

She blinked at him. 'I thought you were at home, sir.'

'I've been in my office all night.'

She gazed at him curiously. Her eyes dropped to his gloves, and he peeled them off as casually as he could.

'That's the research Kenny gave Ryan.' She nodded at the box in his hands. 'Anything interesting?'

'Ancient history,' he said. 'Old newspaper cuttings, mainly.'

She reached out for it. 'I'll take a look.'

'Leave it till morning.' He struggled to keep the annoyance from his voice. 'You look done in, Flick, why are you still here?'

'To tell the truth, I don't think I'd be able to sleep.' She took the box off the shelf, shivering in the chill of the air conditioning.

'I'm not asking you. Go home and sleep. You're not going to get anything done by running yourself into the ground.'

He reached for the box, but Flick held it tightly. 'I'm here now, I'll just take a quick look.' When he stared, she said: 'Shall we go? It's freezing down here.'

The heavy door to the Property Room clanged shut.

'Do you think this is the end of it? Now the Overtons are dead?'

'It's a contract job,' Drake said. 'Kenny, Phil, maybe even Ryan, was involved in some criminal enterprise that backfired.' He dropped the gloves in a waste bin. 'So, yes, I think it's over. Don't over-complicate things, Flick.'

She hesitated, her fingers drumming a question on the wrapping around the box, but when he held open the door to the stairwell, she walked through. Drake wondered how much she'd seen in the Property Room. Flick Crowley was a copper who rarely deviated from well-trodden systems of investigation. That could buy him time to discover what was going on. But he also knew she was a clever and stubborn investigator, and it would be foolish to underestimate her.

His skin prickled with foreboding. Something was set in motion all those years ago. An evil from that home had been revived, he was certain of that. And if he didn't take measures, it would be the end of him.

On his way home he pulled the car to the kerb, and dropped the newspaper photograph down a drain. Watched the faces of the kids – Amelia, Connor, Elliot and the others – soak into the dank water and tear apart.

15

1984

Elliot listened to Gordon's heavy steps pound on the stairs.

Bang, bang, bang.

Hands trembling, he pulled the thin blanket over him. In the darkness, he could barely make out the silhouettes of the other kids. They lay unmoving in their beds, frozen with fear. Usually Elliot would sleep like a log. But this time he knew – his guts churned at the thought of it – that Gordon was coming for him.

His smashed nose hurt like hell. He wished it had been fixed properly, at a hospital. After Connor's attack, Gerry Dent had laughed and said he should get it seen by a doctor or it would look like an exploded tomato for the rest of his life. But Gordon refused point blank, so the Dents patched it up as best they could. For days, the dressings on Elliot's face were a sodden mess of mucus and snot. When the bandages finally came off, his nose didn't look right.

'We all get the face we deserve eventually, Elliot,' Gordon smirked. 'You just got yours early.'

Elliot clenched his jaw, determined not to cry. The one thing he wanted from life was a family, lots of kids, which he'd bring up right – not that he'd ever admit it, wild horses wouldn't make him tell anyone – but there was little chance of that happening now, not with this nose.

If the pain made his eyes water, the embarrassment was even worse. At least none of the kids had the nerve to laugh at him to his face.

Since Connor arrived, everything had gone wrong. Gordon had taken a shine to the new kid, chose him now to make his special deliveries, and Elliot was out of favour. And that meant he was fair game if Gordon was drunk or in a bad-tempered mood, which was nearly all the time, these days.

He gave Connor the evils at every opportunity, but Elliot's so-called mates, turncoats like Ricky and Jason, didn't have the stomach for a fight. They saw something in the new kid's eyes, a coldness, an unpredictability, that made them keep their distance.

If the business in the kitchen was anything to go by, Connor was sneaky. Elliot's left eyelid fluttered every time he heard the pots and pans jangle on their hooks. But the day would come when he would get his revenge, he just had to bide his time. Keeping his temper in check wasn't easy. He was a chip off the old block. His old man had been lightning quick with his fists, Elliot had learned that the hard way, right up to the moment his father dropped dead from a heart attack, leaving him to rot in this dump.

If Elliot had learned one thing from his dad, it was to use his size and strength to get what he wanted. As a result, it had always been him who had been Gordon's eyes and ears about the place, who got to lounge about the office, reading comics. That was where you wanted to be – at Gordon's side, not shoved in with the rest of the kids –

because it meant you didn't have to fear the heavy tread of his shoes on the stairs in the dead of night.

Bang, bang, bang.

'He gave you a bloody good hiding, Elliot,' Gordon said that morning, chuckling. 'He messed you up good, boy.'

'He took me by surprise.' Elliot glared at Connor. It still hurt when he spoke, and there was a persistent ringing in his ears.

The manager sat with his feet on his desk. The door to the small room behind him, with its dirty mattress and ribbed green radiator, was closed. Elliot guessed Sally was in there, asleep, or off her face. When she first arrived, Sally had acted as a kind of buffer between Gordon and the children, shielding them, taking the edge off his temper, but now she seemed to spend most of the time in that room, sleeping so deeply and for so long you'd think she was never going to wake up.

'Connor's got brains and balls.' Gordon tossed the desk paperweight. It made a smacking sound in his palm when he caught it. 'So you're going to show him where to make deliveries around town.'

All Elliot had to do was grab that paperweight, a glass globe speckled with bubbles, and swing it into the kid's face. Then they'd see who had the brains; then they'd see who had the balls.

Gordon jumped to his feet to spin the dial on the office safe. When the door chunked open, he took out packets of brown paper, sealed with shiny zigzags of sticky tape, and heaped them into an Adidas sports bag.

'I want you to show Connor the ropes,' he said. 'The addresses, the routes, introduce him to the customers. And then you're done.'

Elliot whined. 'Gordon—'

'And then you're done, boy.'

'I can find them myself,' Connor said.

'No. My customers don't talk to just anyone. Elliot will make the necessary introductions.'

A tornado of resentment twisted inside of Elliot. He would be the same as all the other kids now, and that was a bad place to be.

Bang, bang, bang.

The manager crouched in front of him. 'I understand what you're feeling. Your nose has been put out of joint in more ways than one. But look on the bright side, lad – no more walking to the ends of the earth. You'll be able to relax, get to know the other boys and girls.' He squeezed Elliot's shoulder. 'We'll always be mates. But Connor . . . he's got that little extra something.'

That afternoon, Elliot and Connor walked across the borough, sticking to the least populated byways. They passed abandoned factories and railway sidings, squeezing through fenced-off gaps on streets bombed forty years before. They looked like a couple of restless teenagers aimlessly roaming across the city, except that Connor carried the sports bag containing the brown packets. They made deliveries to houses and estates, underpasses, squats and even business premises. Elliot begrudgingly introduced Connor to twitching men and women who could barely look them in the eye. Connor studied them carefully, memorising faces, routes and meeting points, taking it all in.

The two boys barely said a word to each other all day. Elliot was sulking and Connor kept himself to himself, and anyway spent most of the time looking over his shoulder.

Because they were being followed.

Sure enough, there was a figure hanging back in the distance, hiding around corners. Elliot was terrified they were going to get arrested, slung in prison, and it was with relief he saw it was only that posh kid who was always hanging around the home waiting for Sally, the one called Ray.

'What does he want?' asked Elliot.

Connor didn't answer. He watched the kid carefully but kept moving, and by the end of the afternoon, nearing their last delivery at a snooker hall down by the marshes, it looked like the boy had drifted away. By then Elliot was hot and itchy and tired, and when his nose throbbed, which was basically *all the time*, it reminded him of what Connor had done to it. He'd had enough. He hurled himself onto a park bench beside the canal, unable to keep his mouth shut any longer.

'Why you hanging about here, anyway?'

Connor stared. 'You're the one who's stopped.'

'I mean, why are you at the home? You don't belong. Nobody knows you're there. You could piss off any time.'

Wasps buzzed around the rusted frame of a shopping trolley poking from the brown water. Connor dropped the bag and stood on the edge of the canal path. Elliot was gripped by the urge to shove him into the water, but something told him he'd live to regret it.

'I don't want to go anywhere else.'

'Why not?' Elliot couldn't believe his ears. No one in their right mind would want to be at that place, with the casual cruelty of the Dents and Gordon's beatings, and what happened late at night when he was drunk and his heavy steps echoed on the wooden stairs. 'It don't make no sense. I'd be off like a shot!'

'Because . . .' Staring at his own elongated reflection on the surface of the stagnant water, Connor's reply trailed off. He was a weird one, all right.

Perhaps it was the fact that he didn't even bother to answer that enraged Elliot, but all the frustration he felt – his busted nose, the ringing in his ears, the way Gordon treated the new kid – boiled up inside of him. He jumped off the bench and picked up the bag. He swung it high, meaning to lob it in the water – but at the last moment he came to his senses and dropped it to the ground.

'I could have got you in trouble,' he told Connor. 'I could have told Gordon you lost it.'

'I don't care what he thinks.'

The kid was full of it. 'Sure you do. He'd kill us!'

Connor picked up the bag by its strap and Elliot thought he was going to continue on his way, but instead he spun on his heels like an Olympic discus thrower, and let go of the bag. It flew over their heads and landed in the water. They watched it turn in a lazy circle on the surface and then sink, the last package of drugs inside. Elliot groaned in disbelief. This kid was a maniac.

'We don't tell him!' Elliot said in a panic 'We'll say we made the delivery.' Connor's lack of concern only made him more frantic. 'Say you won't tell him!'

But Connor just walked off.

When they got back to the home, one of the kids, a sullen girl called Amelia, was sitting outside. She watched them warily, ready to run.

'What you doing here?' snapped Elliot.

Amelia wore a pink T-shirt, a cracked silver star embossed on the front, and flared jeans. Her hair was tied back in a scruffy ponytail. Ignoring him, she hugged her notebook and tensely watched Connor. Elliot didn't usually pay much attention to this kid. Amelia was one of the quiet ones, the ones with dull eyes who stepped aside when he approached – there were loads of those in this place. But this one loved to draw. Meek as a lamb she was, but always getting in trouble for scrawling on the walls and furniture, on every smooth surface she could find. Gordon got angry about it, she'd been on the end of a series of slaps, but it didn't stop her. In the end, Gerry Dent had bought her a sketchbook, which she'd lovingly covered with stickers, glitter and crepe paper.

As soon as they stepped inside, they understood why she was hovering. Shouts and screams came from behind the closed office door. Usually, you walked into the house and heard the thrum of the kids in your head, like a swarm of bees. But on days like this, when Gordon had been drinking, everyone scattered to the bottom of the garden or the far corners of the house. They knew what was coming and they did their best to make themselves invisible. The manager drank every night, but some days he started drinking first thing in the morning and didn't stop – those were the days you feared.

'How long's it been going on?' Connor asked Amelia.

'What does it matter?' said Elliot. 'If they—'

'I'm not talking to you,' Connor snapped.

Elliot was getting sick of the way the new kid treated him.

'Hours,' Amelia said.

'Drinking,' said Elliot, who knew how the rows always started, and how they ended. 'And . . . other stuff.'

Connor stood at the office door and listened to Gordon and Sally screaming obscenities.

'She's crying,' he said.

Connor rattled the knob, and the thought of the door flying open to reveal Gordon terrified Elliot, who sloped away quickly, thinking about that last package slipping beneath the water in a foam of bubbles.

Maybe they'd get away with it – some of the people they delivered to couldn't tell you what day of the week it was, perhaps they wouldn't notice. But Elliot had no doubt that Connor would lie and say he had done it, that he would really drop him in the shit. He considered getting his attack in first and telling Gordon that Connor had lost the package. But he knew that wouldn't work, Gordon wouldn't believe him, not in a million years.

At dinner, Elliot's chest and stomach were knotted so tightly that he could barely breathe, let alone eat. The food tasted like ashes in his mouth. He didn't hear any of the conversation at the table, didn't even join in when Jason and Kenny and David started flinging food. For the first time since he'd been at the Longacre, he considered legging it. Nothing happened that evening, though. Gordon didn't emerge from his office, and Elliot dared to hope they'd got away with it.

But that night, tossing and turning in bed in the early hours, he heard the muffled ring of a phone downstairs, and knew his luck had run out.

Bang, bang, bang.

That small room behind Gordon's desk terrified him.

He'd never been inside, but the kids who had been taken there were never the same again. They lost something – he couldn't explain what it was, exactly: a spark, a fragment of themselves. You could see it in their eyes, in the way they looked at you but didn't see you.

There were six of them in the bedroom. Connor was below the bay window, with Amelia on a mattress beside him. Kenny was in the room, too, and Karen and Debs. Elliot's bed was nearest the door. Everyone was supposed to be asleep, but he could hear quick, panicked breaths. A train clattered along the track behind the house, sending patterns of light jerking across the ceiling. Elliot glimpsed Connor, turned away.

Minutes later, the office door opened. A whimper came from one of the other beds. Elliot's shattered nose throbbed, as if in warning.

Bang, bang, bang.

Gordon's footsteps, slow and heavy. The rasp of his palm on the banister.

Elliot pressed his eyes shut, pretending to sleep, but when Gordon reached the doorway, he couldn't resist looking. The manager stood so close to the end of his bed that he could smell his body odour, the alcohol lashing off him. Gordon dabbed at the wall, trying to find the light. He gave up – it didn't work anyway – and slapped at the crumbling plaster.

'Is there something you want to tell me, lad?' he slurred into the darkness. 'Because you've put me in a very awkward situation.'

Elliot shook. This wasn't how things were meant to be.

'I got a call,' Gordon continued. 'A friend of mine didn't receive his goods. To say he's not happy is an understatement.

And if he's not happy – well, you can imagine how unhappy I am.'

'Don't know what you're talking about,' said Elliot. 'Go away.'

'Let's go; we'll talk it through downstairs. Come along, boy.' The noise in Elliot's head was unbearable. Lurching forward, Gordon's knees bumped against the frame and the bed shuddered. Elliot forced himself not to cry out. 'I'll not tell you again.'

'Leave him alone,' said a voice, and Elliot tensed. He could just make out the silhouette of Connor standing in the middle of the room.

Gordon's neck craned forward. 'That you, Connor?'

'Go away.'

'Don't be like that, lad. I don't know what Elliot did with the produce, but it's very expensive, so it is, and either he gives it back or he accepts the consequences.'

'I lost it.' Connor's shadow darted across the floor so quickly that Gordon stumbled backwards in surprise. 'I threw the bag in the canal.'

Gordon swayed, his ragged breath catching in his throat.

'Well, you are a brave lad, I was right about you.' He wagged a finger. 'Perhaps you did it, perhaps you didn't. But tonight, I think, you have me at a disadvantage. I'll be honest, I'm not feeling hunky-dory. That Sally has sapped me dry. None of you appreciate what I have to put up with where that girl is concerned. So I'm going to let it go, just this one time.' Elliot heard the dry snap of his whiskers as the manager ran a hand down his beard. He shuffled to the door. 'You kids have a good night's sleep, and I'll see you in the morning.'

Then they heard his slow heavy steps on the stairs.

Bang, bang, bang.

Far below, the door to the office opened and closed.

Connor had slipped back into bed. Elliot could just about make him out, the pillow pressed over his head beneath a sliver of moonlight.

'Connor!' he whispered. 'Connor!'

But Connor never answered. Elliot lay down, his earlier terror turning to guilt and shame. Connor had stood up to Gordon – something that Elliot would never dare to do – when it would have been easier to make Elliot's life a living hell.

He had challenged him, embarrassed him in front of the other kids, and that was something Gordon would never – could never – forget. Connor was a nutcase. It was the only explanation.

And if they ever went to war, those two, Elliot didn't want to be there, because he had no idea how far they would go, the adult and the boy, to destroy the other.

16

Back at her desk, weary and starving, Flick considered taking Ray Drake's advice about going home. But she was there now, wedged into her chair with her coat on, the shoebox in front of her. The first grey threads of morning bloated the horizon. Delivery vans and lorries rumbled along the High Road below.

She didn't think she had the energy to return the box to the basement, let alone drive home, so she took out the cuttings that Ray Drake had found in Ryan Overton's flat. Articles from old newspapers and photocopies on curling paper. The clippings were torn and dog-eared, many were littered with Post-it notes covered in an illegible scrawl.

An A4 sheet of yellow lined paper had been slipped into one of the plastic sheaves. Flick could barely make out the scribbled blizzard of spidery writing and crossings-out. At first she thought it was a code, but then she realised that Kenny, a man who had spent much of his childhood institutionalised, could barely write. If necessary, there were graphologists they could employ, but she was reluctant. Cutbacks being what they were, the MIT was expected to justify the cost of everything.

The one thing she could read, because it was printed in clumsy block capitals, was a list of crossed-out names.

~~DAVID HORNER~~
~~KAREN SMITH~~
~~REGINA BERMAN~~
~~RICKY HANCOCK~~
~~JASON BURGESS~~

At the bottom were other names:

ELLIOT JUNIPER
AMELIA TROY
DEBORAH WILLETTS
CONNOR LAIRD???!!!

Flick laid the list to one side and picked up the clippings. The first was a single column, glued to a sheet of A4. It was taken from the *Sheffield Star*, and dated 20 October 1991.

Mother and Twins Killed in Fire

A single mother and her infant twins were last night killed in a blaze that ripped through a sheltered housing complex.

Firemen were unable to save Regina Berman (17) and her one-year-old daughters, Annabel and Darcey, who died from smoke inhalation in an upstairs bedroom of their flat.

Residents and staff were evacuated to a nearby leisure centre when the blaze ripped through Colney Court in the early hours of the morning.

Miss Berman had joined the Colney Assisted Housing scheme after being made homeless. Neighbours described her as a good mother who made an impression on everyone she met.

'Her little girls had so much to live for,' neighbour, Hilary Frost (43), said. 'They were poor, but always had a smile for everybody.'

The cause of the blaze, which is thought to have started in the family's flat, is still unknown.

Flapping her arms out of her coat, Flick picked up the next article. The *South London Guardian and Gazette*, 23 January 1998.

Local Couple Tragedy – Suicide Says Court

A local couple killed themselves in a suicide pact, a court heard.

Jeff Moore and Karen Smith, both 30, of Sweepers Road, Bermondsey, attached a rubber hose to the exhaust of their car on 12 November last year and died of carbon monoxide poisoning.

A neighbour alerted police when he spotted smoke coming from beneath a garage door. When police and ambulance crews gained access, they found Mr Moore and Miss Smith in the back seat of the vehicle.

The court heard Mr Moore, a refuse collector for Lambeth Council, and Miss Smith, who worked in the Clean 'N' Tidy Launderette in New Cross, had both been depressed about not being able to adopt because of Miss Smith's history of drink and drug dependency.

A friend of the couple, Benedict Donaldson, was ejected from the court when he interrupted proceedings. Speaking to the *South London Guardian*, he angrily refuted the Coroner's assertion that the couple had killed themselves.

'I spoke to Karen and Jeff nearly every day and they were happy, and looking forward to the future.'

The Coroner recorded a verdict of suicide.

Flick placed the article face down on top of the first. Her mouth was dry – a coke from the vending machine would give her a sugar kick – but she wanted to finish reading. The next cutting was printed on greasy paper that looked like it had curled through a fax machine. It was from the *Canberra Star*, dated 5 September 2001.

A stable mate at a local stud farm has died in a barn fire that also claimed the lives of six horses.

David Horner (27) was bedded down at the Appletree Stud Farm to nurse a sick mare when the blaze ripped through the barn during the night. A workmate who spotted the flames pulled Mr Horner from the blaze, but he later died in hospital.

Several horses were saved, but a number had to be put down as a result of their injuries.

English-born Mr Horner had worked at the ranch for several years.

Owner Wayne Garry told the Canberra Star that Mr Horner had a special bond with the animals. 'Davey was a shy guy, and awkward with people. Those horses meant everything to him. We're all sick here; it's a senseless waste of a life.'

Authorities suspect a dropped cigarette could have been

the cause of the fire, but stressed that they didn't want to preempt any inquiry.

Flick made a note to find out if David Horner had any family in the UK, and reached for the next clipping. From the *St Albans Examiner*, dated 14 March 2008:

Crash A Tragic Accident

A family of five were killed when their car left the road and sank in the River Ver.

Local man Ricky Hancock (38), unemployed —

Flick blinked. Another family. She took a breath, and read on.

Local man Ricky Hancock (38), unemployed, his wife Jennifer (34) and their three children, Nathan (12), Fleming (8) and Tiffany (4), all drowned.

Mr Justice Egan told St Albans Coroner's Court that Mr Hancock was four times over the limit when the Peugeot sank into the freezing river in a matter of seconds. The family had been returning from a party outside St Albans.

Partygoer Sheila Fisher told the court that she had seen another man climb into the car with the family. No one else at the party confirmed the sighting, and Mrs Fisher admitted she had consumed a lot of alcohol and could be mistaken.

Flick rubbed her eyes. She double-checked the articles against the list of crossed-out names. There weren't any clippings about the death of Jason Burgess, but Kenny knew those facts all too well. Jason shot dead his partner and daughter, then turned the gun on himself.

Another family dead.

Neither were there articles about the death of anyone called Elliot Juniper, Deborah Willetts, Amelia Troy – that last name was familiar to her somehow – or Connor Laird, whose name had been underlined. There was nothing to suggest that they'd died in a fire or drowned or committed suicide. Everyone else on the list, the ones with their names scored through by Kenny's uncertain hand, were dead. Their families, if they had families, were dead.

And now Kenny Overton and his own family had been murdered.

According to Ryan, all these people had been at the same children's home – the Longacre – a long time ago. If that were true, nobody would ever make a connection between the victims, who had scattered across the country, across continents, decades ago. And these were only the people Kenny had managed to locate.

What had become of all the others from the home?

Perhaps it was the tentative fingers of dawn light pressing into her eyes, or the fact that she'd hardly eaten a thing, but a wave of nausea washed over her. The implication of what she'd read still sinking in, she took out the last two clippings. Both were stiff with age. The first was taken from the *Hackney Express*. An edition dated 31 July 1984. The short article was headlined: JUDGE VISITS LOCAL CHILDREN'S HOME.

> Noted High Court judge Leonard Drake dropped in to meet the kids at the Longacre Children's Home this week.

Mr Drake and his wife Myra visited in his role as Chairman of the Hackney Children's Protection League to meet manager Gordon Tallis and his dedicated staff.

The eminent judge, who has presided over some of the country's biggest court cases, told the *Express* he was impressed with what he'd seen of the home, a refuge for many kids in the borough without a family.

'The children seem happy here. I've communicated my delight to Mr Tallis.'

Mr Tallis said the children in the home, who range in age from eight to sixteen years, were over the moon to have such an important person visit.

'Sometimes,' he told our reporter, 'the children can feel forgotten by the outside world, so it was a boost to everyone's morale that Mr and Mrs Drake took the time to visit us. We're all very grateful!'

There was a caption above the article, but the accompanying photo was missing. The top edge of the paper was serrated roughly where it had been torn. The caption said: *A happy visit: (From left to right) Mr Gordon Tallis, Kenny Overton, Toby Turrell, Jason Burgess, Mr Leonard Drake and Mrs Myra Drake, Elliot Juniper, Amelia Troy, Connor Laird.*

Flick blinked. Leonard and Myra Drake. Ray Drake's parents. His father, if she remembered correctly, had been a High Court judge, and Flick had seen his sour old mother at Laura Drake's funeral. If Ray had read these clippings earlier, why hadn't he mentioned it?

The door to her office swung open and a cleaner walked in with a sack. The Incident Room was filled with the drone of vacuum cleaners.

'I'm sorry.' Flick held up a finger. 'I'll get out of your way in a few moments.'

The last newspaper clipping was dated 6 August 1984. An entire page this time, folded in the middle. The *Hackney Express* masthead was at the top. The front-page headline, in large black capitals, read: LOCAL HERO KILLED IN CHILDREN'S HOME BLAZE.

> A children's home manager died a hero when a blaze ripped through the building to which he had devoted his life.
>
> Gordon Tallis (44) made the fatal decision to return one last time to the burning building and was overwhelmed by flames.
>
> Firefighters arrived at the scene late on Wednesday night and battled the blaze into the morning, but the building was gutted by fire.
>
> Sergeant Harry Crowley of Hackney Police told the *Express*: 'Gordon was a respected figure in the local community. He loved those kids, and it was absolutely typical that he went back inside – he was a man who cared too much.'

'Fuck!' Flick slapped the desktop angrily. When she looked up, the cleaner had returned and she blushed. 'I'm sorry. Just one more minute.'

Of all the people, it had to be *him*.

> Another body was discovered in the blaze, but has yet to be identified. Police are concerned for the safety of 14-year-old Connor Laird.
>
> 'Connor is a vulnerable lad,' said Sgt Crowley. 'He panicked during this awful tragedy, and we ask him to come

forward – if only to let us know he's safe and well.'

Hours earlier, Mr Tallis had welcomed High Court judge Leonard Drake and his wife Myra to the home on a special visit, as reported in the Hackney Express last week. The blaze destroyed the building in the early hours, as last week's *Express* went to press.

Him. She was still annoyed at seeing her father's name.

'Get a grip, Flick,' she muttered.

A photograph below the article showed the aftermath of the blaze. A double-fronted three-storey house was gutted, its windows blown out, the broken timber of its roof protruding into the sky like the ribcage of a vast animal. A fire engine was parked in the foreground of the photo and two police cars. Figures pointed up at the smoking husk.

It all seemed so long ago, so irrelevant. Except that it wasn't. Flick had never been one of those coppers who put her faith in instinct. She trusted the process, and liked to build cases slowly and methodically, accumulating layer upon layer of evidence. But she sensed that this photo, these clippings, held the key to the deaths of Kenny Overton and his family.

Flick called Eddie Upson's number. The clock on the wall said: 6.34 a.m. He'd only gone home a few short hours ago. She realised she was being selfish, and was about to hang up, when he answered.

'Yeah, guv.' His voice was groggy.

She picked up a pen and a scrap of paper. 'Sorry to wake you, Eddie.'

'It's all right.' He yawned. 'I like to take a freezing shower first thing, then read the Bible for an hour. What can I do you for?'

'Does the name Connor Laird ring any bells to you?'
'Connor what?'
'Connor Laird.' She spelled it. 'L–A–I–R–D.'
'Uh.' She heard the rustle of his duvet. 'Nope, should it?'
'What about Elliot Juniper?'
'Juniper?
'Like the berry.'
'Doesn't ring any bells.'
'Deborah Willetts.'
He grunted, *no*.
'What about Amelia Troy?'
'Like the artist, you mean?'
The penny dropped. 'Thanks, Eddie. Get back to sleep.'
'I'll be in as soon as I can, boss.'
She put down her pen. 'There's no hurry.'

Gathering up the cuttings – not noticing a Post-it note flutter to the floor – Flick rested the pile on her lap and closed her eyes. Another wave of tiredness washed over her and she felt her weight slide towards her feet, as if she were melting into the floor. A plinking noise next door jerked her awake.

The cleaners had gone. The lights in the Incident Room flickered on, and Dudley Kendrick walked in. He waved through the glass as he turned on his computer, taking out a coffee and a croissant from a paper bag. The smell of it made Flick's stomach rumble.

Looking at her phone, she remembered that her sister had rung a couple of times yesterday. In the chaos of events she hadn't had the chance to call her back. Flick had no business phoning anybody at this time on a Sunday morning, but Nina's kids would already be rampaging around the house, and her sister would be up with them, so no harm done. But when Flick rang the number it was Martin, her brother-in-law, who answered.

'Flick,' he said, in that Aussie drawl of his.

Hearing Angel and Hugo screaming in the background, the burble of the radio and the flatulent sizzle of something on the pan, Flick had half a mind to head straight there. Martin's fry-ups were legendary, and she could do with some cuddles from the kids, maybe grab some sleep. Flick was at their house so often she kept a change of clothes in the spare bedroom, her own toothbrush in the bathroom. Nobody could begrudge her a few hours after working through the night.

'I know it's early,' she said.

Usually, Martin would give her an earful of good-natured abuse for calling so early. But all he said this morning was an awkward, 'yeah', and she worried again that something was wrong between him and her sister.

'Nina's in bed. Coral was up half the night with a tummy bug.'

'Is she okay?' she asked, concerned.

'She's fine, but mother and child are sleeping off a shit night.'

'It's just, Nina called me. Do you know what about?'

'You know what?' She sensed that he was choosing his words carefully. 'I think she should probably talk to you herself.'

'Is everything okay there, Martin?'

'Do I need a lawyer, Flick?' He laughed. 'Look, we're all great here, but it's not a good time. Angel – don't hit your brother!'

'I'll speak to her later,' she said. 'If you think—'

'I've got to go. The eggs are burning and Angel's war with Hugo has just gone to Defcon One. It's just another day in paradise, Flick.'

'Yeah,' she said. 'Lucky you.'

She waited for a reply, but he'd already rung off. Flick dropped the phone onto her desk and stretched. A walk round the block and breakfast in a local café would be sensible.

But there was one more thing she wanted to do. Switching on her computer, Flick waited for it to boot up, then clicked on a search engine and typed in: *Amelia Troy*.

17

Elliot burned with guilt and shame when he saw Owen Veazey at his usual table in a tatty pub clinging to the edge of an estate in Harlow. Owen had been a regular for donkey's years. Elliot remembered seeing him there a decade ago, when he was still knocking about on the edges of the local criminal element, and the place had looked rundown even then.

Low and squat, and built with the same bleak functionality as the maisonettes that surrounded it, the pub was hunched at the end of a paved precinct where half a dozen anorexic trees were planted in squares of mud and dog shit. The pub's entrance and its windows were topped by half-closed shutters, like metal eyelids, which protected it from vandalism when it was shut, and its customers, a shabby swarm of derelicts and old fellas, from the attention of the local constabulary during its highly irregular opening hours.

If you were unfortunate enough to be wandering in this part of town before breakfast on a Sunday morning, you'd be hard pressed to know it was even a pub. The sign had fallen off years back, and it was in nobody's interest to put it back on again.

Wall lamps threw sour brown light over the scruffy interior, despite the hard winter glare outside, so that Elliot felt like he was trudging along the bottom of a muddy pond.

A few Sunday-morning diehards sat at the bar watching girls twerk and grind on a music video. A fruit machine burbled against a pillar, bursting occasionally into a noisy instrumental version of 'U Can't Touch This' as lights raced up and down its panels.

'Sit yourself down, Elliot.' Owen rose in greeting. 'It's good to see you.'

He was an older man, with a tanned, wrinkled face and neat short back and sides, pressed trousers, comfortable loafers, and a mustard golfing sweater. He owned a number of these jumpers, Elliot remembered, in a variety of colours. When Owen sat, he carefully lifted the creases of his trousers, a proper pair of slacks, between thumb and forefinger. He was an incongruous sight in this grubby pub, dressed in his Pro-Celebrity tournament clobber, while everyone else pitched up in shapeless grey joggers and football shirts.

'It's been too long, Elliot.' Owen's soft voice was often lost against the whirl of the fruit machine. 'You're looking well.'

'You too, Owen.'

A wiry, sharp-faced man with a harelip came to the table, four pints wedged between his stretched hands.

'This is Perry,' Owen gestured at the man, 'an associate of mine. We saw you coming and took the liberty of getting you a drink. It's cooking lager, I'm afraid, not much demand for microbreweries around here.'

'Cheers, Owen.' Bren slurped his pint.

Elliot didn't recognise Perry, and didn't care for the way the man barely acknowledged them. Instead, the newcomer licked a finger to turn the sports pages on a tabloid.

Owen sipped his pint. 'We don't see you around any more.'

The way he talked, it was like they were close friends who had drifted apart. But the truth was Elliot could count on one hand the number of occasions he had met Owen. The last time had been when he had just met Rhonda and was spending every moment he could with her, when it was a revelation to him that he might live an honest life. But everyone around here knew about Owen Veazey: his reputation, the kind of activities he was mixed up in. Lending money wasn't the half of it. Elliot had for once used some common sense and kept his distance.

In fact, now that he was here with Owen and his charming friend Perry, Elliot was fast coming to the conclusion that he was on the verge of making a terrible mistake and hardened his resolve. Owen's terms, he decided, would have to be bloody good. Elliot would take a lot of convincing about the loan. If he didn't like what he heard, he would get up and walk out.

'Life takes you in different directions,' he told Owen.

'Ain't that the truth?'

The old man clocked Elliot smearing his sweaty palms on his jeans. 'I appreciate how difficult it is for you to come to me. Nobody in their right mind, let's face it, would approach Owen Veazey for money. You'd have to be mad or desperate. Which are you, Elliott, mad or desperate?'

'A little bit of both, probably.'

Owen nodded. 'Tell me what it is you're after.'

The fruit machine whirled excitedly as a couple of blokes fed coins into its slot, and Bren turned to watch them play.

'A short-term loan.'

'How much are we talking?'

'Thirty grand.'

The old man raised his eyes to the ceiling, as if working out the numbers. 'That's a lot of money at short notice, even for me.'

There was still time for Elliot to go home and fall on Rhonda's mercy. Tell her how he'd lost the money. The only thing Elliot was guilty of was being a fool – if being a fool was a crime, Elliot would be serving life – but he clenched his fists, certain she would never believe him.

'I'm not going to ask why you need it.' Owen flicked a look at Bren, who was mesmerised by the machine's spinning reels. 'It's none of my business. But there would be consequences for you and for your family if you borrow money from me. Do you understand?'

'I do,' Elliot croaked.

'Have a drink.' Owen gestured to his glass. 'Bren tells me you've a wife and kid.'

'We're not married.' Elliot sipped the pint, but the lager didn't shift the frog in his throat. 'He's not my boy.'

'Do you love them?'

'Very much.' he said. 'They're . . .'

Truth was Elliot didn't want to diminish his devotion to Rhonda, and to Dylan, by describing it to Owen. The old man seemed to sense his reluctance, and smiled.

'I'm glad to hear it, Elliot. I've had three – no . . .' He frowned at Perry. 'How many wives have I had?'

'Four.' Perry's eyes never lifted from the paper. 'Last time I counted.'

'That's right, four.' Owen grinned. 'Lovely ladies, all, except the second one. She was a fucking nightmare, to be honest. But as you can imagine, I'm no angel either. Point is, I know how difficult it is to keep a relationship together.

So I'm going to put my cards on the table, Elliot, because I like you. We don't know each other very well, but Bren speaks very highly of you, and that's good enough for me.'

Steeling himself for the conditions of the loan, Elliot resolved again not to agree to Owen's terms straight away, not to make any rash decisions. He didn't want to be paying him back till the end of days.

'I could lend you money.' Owen clicked his fingers. 'I could lend it to you just like that. But you know how I operate. You've probably heard the horror stories. Because if I lend you money, Elliot, you'll be paying me back for years, decades even. There'd be so much interest on the loan you'd never get the monkey off your back. I'd be on you, and Perry would be all over you, like a second skin. Your relationship with . . .'

'Rhonda,' said Bren.

'Your relationship with Rhonda will deteriorate. I've seen how this goes, Elliot, many times, and it's not pretty. I don't want that to happen to you. Which is why I'm not going to lend you the money.'

Dumbfounded, Elliot gazed at the bubbles popping on his pint.

'Where most people are concerned, I don't give a toss,' continued Owen. 'I hope you understand my thinking on this.'

'It's just a short-term loan.' The machine behind him burst into song and coins clattered into its tray. 'Until I can find the man who—'

'There is no such thing as a short-term loan. Not in my world.'

'Bren said you—'

'Bren made a mistake. I appreciate his bringing you along, it's always good to catch up with old pals, but I'm not going to be able to help you.'

Elliot felt sick. He didn't want to be in this pub, with its nicotine-stained walls and creaking furniture and tired clientele, the noise from the fruit machine so loud that he could hardly hear himself think. But he couldn't go home empty handed.

'When Rhonda sees the money is gone, she's going to leave me.'

Owen raised the pint to his lips. 'But at least you won't be up to your neck in debt.'

Elliot scraped back his chair and dropped his head into his hands. He was out of options, and would have to fall on Rhonda's mercy.

He had no idea how long he was slumped like that when he heard Owen say: 'Bren, give us a moment.'

'Sure thing.'

Elliot heard Bren's grunt of effort as he climbed to his feet, felt a quick, reassuring squeeze on his shoulder. When Elliot sat up, the blood drained from his skull, making him light-headed.

'Tell you what,' said Owen, 'I've a suggestion. I'm a man down on a job I've got coming up. A little bit of breaking and entering.'

'No.' Elliot physically recoiled.

'Hear me out before you say no.' Owen moved his glass out of the way, to lean forward. 'It's at the house of a retired couple. In your neck of the woods, as a matter of fact. He was a banker, a broker, something like that.'

'No.' Elliot shook his head.

Perry threw down the paper. Started probing his gums with a finger.

'I know for a fact, and don't ask me how, that this couple keep a lot of cash at home,' continued Owen. 'We're talking thousands, tens of thousands. And they're away right now. So what I'm proposing is—'

'No,' Elliot said.

'Bren tells me you did some time for burglary back in the day. I need someone with experience, a bit of know-how, to accompany a friend of mine,' he nodded at Perry, 'into the house within forty-eight hours, before they come back from holiday.'

'I've got to go.' Elliot stood. 'That's not me; I haven't done that for—'

'I understand. Please, don't feel insulted.' Owen raised his palms. 'You've a problem and I saw an opportunity. It seemed a way to kill two birds with one stone, so to speak.'

Elliot just wanted out of there. 'Thanks for the offer, but—'

'Don't mention it.' The old man rose and clasped his hand tightly. Elliot felt a corner of card stab into the flesh of his thumb. 'A short-term loan. No interest, no hassle. Could be in your account by tomorrow.' When Elliot stared, Owen let go. 'Point taken.'

Perry nodded. 'Bye, then.'

Sunlight burned into Elliot's eyes when he got outside. He squinted at the business card with Owen's number on it. He didn't want it, would tear it up as soon as he got home, that's what he'd do. Striding across the estate, a flimsy supermarket bag dancing around his ankles, he lit a B&H. Halfway to the van he heard a voice behind him.

'Wait, Ell! Hold up!' Bren waddled towards him, wheezing.

In his agitation, Elliot had almost left him behind. He turned angrily. 'What else did you tell Owen about me?'

Bren caught his breath before he answered. 'What do you mean?'

'He knew I'd done time.'

'He asked about you.' Bren looked confused. 'He wanted to know the kind of man you are.'

The kind of man you are.

'He asked me to do a job.' Elliot's cheeks pinched as he sucked bitterly on the cigarette. 'A one-off, he said, and he'd lend me the money, interest free, in return.'

Bren didn't seem outraged by what Owen had suggested or, it seemed to Elliot, particularly surprised.

'That's Owen all over.' Bren shrugged. 'He don't mean anything by it. He's just trying to help.'

'Trying to help!' Elliot lurched forward. 'Hell will freeze over before I do that again, do you understand?'

'Okay, then.' Bren stepped back. 'We all know where we stand. No harm done.'

Elliot walked quickly to his van, wanting to be out of that dismal place. Didn't care, right at that moment, if Bren came with him or not.

18

'It's a waste of time and resources.' Ray Drake folded his arms. 'And I'm surprised we're even talking about it.'

First thing on Sunday morning, and Flick was struggling. She'd lined up the cuttings on her desk, but Drake barely gave them a glance.

'Kenny Overton researched these—'

'You're making basic mistakes.' He spoke over her. 'Concentrate on your gaps analysis – working out what we know and what we don't. The movements of the victims, compiling phone data, interviewing—'

'With respect, sir,' she said, 'we're doing all that.'

The Incident Room was full. Flick could see her team bashing the phones, chasing up reports. She held out the list of names, but Drake went to the window. It was as if he didn't want to look at it. Flick could understand his scepticism, but she had never seen him so agitated. She wondered how much grief Harris had given him in the aftermath of Ryan Overton's death. She couldn't get the memory of his prowling about in the Property Room out of her mind . . .

A cough – a sound – he stepped forward.

Now wasn't the time to mention it. She felt that the Sword of Damocles was poised above her head, and that her promotion would be rescinded before she'd even had time to get her feet under the desk. The irony wasn't lost on her. Flick had a reputation as a plodder; Drake himself had urged her to work more instinctively. Now she was, and he was slapping her down.

'Kenny researched all these people because they went to the children's home Ryan mentioned. Look.' She held up one of the clippings, but Drake made no move to take it. 'He tried to find the kids he'd known at the Longacre in the eighties and discovered many had died.'

'How many?' Drake asked.

'Five.'

'So, in actual fact, very few.'

'There could have been fifty kids at that home, or just nine.'

'Kids who have been institutionalised for any length of time can be damaged. Many become addicts, criminals. They form self-destructive habits and their lives spiral out of control. The death rate will naturally be higher.'

'Did you read the cuttings?' Last night he'd said he had, but now she wasn't so sure. If he'd read them, he'd understand what she was trying to say. 'Most of these people were killed in unexplained circumstances.'

'Jason Burgess committed suicide. As did Karen Smith and her partner.' Drake propped himself against the sill. 'There's nothing in there that has any significance to this investigation.'

She spaced all the cuttings apart on the desk. 'David Horner was burned—'

'Listen to me, Flick.' Drake's voice lifted irritably. 'Kenny Overton was a fantasist, a dreamer – Ryan admitted it himself – who spent his life trying to figure out where it all went wrong. Trying to find some kind of meaning to every bad choice he made.' He gestured at the plastic slips. 'What about all the other cuttings he threw away because they simply didn't fit with the idea he'd formed in his head that he was a victim? Besides, there's no evidence to suggest he knew any of these people. These could be articles torn randomly from old newspapers.'

'That'll be easy enough to check,' said Flick.

Drake looked away. 'I wouldn't be so sure.'

'Their families, sir.' She counted on her fingers. 'Karen Smith, Jason Burgess, Ricky Hancock – they all died with their loved ones, everyone except David Horner, who didn't have any. And now Kenny is murdered . . . along with *his* family.'

Drake watched all the activity in the Incident Room, as if there were far more important things that they should be doing. 'What did I tell you last night? Don't overcomplicate things. You know as well as I do that there's a tight window of opportunity in any investigation. Don't get dragged off on some ludicrous flight of fancy.'

He was closing her down in every direction. There was a good reason why Drake didn't want to follow this line of inquiry further, and they both knew what it was. She'd avoided mentioning it till now. She picked up the cutting with the photograph torn away.

'We know Kenny went to the Longacre. The photograph is missing.' She showed him the torn edge above the caption. 'But his name is here, along with some others, including . . .' She placed a finger beneath the names of Leonard and Myra Drake.

'I saw it.' Drake's left hand ticked impatiently against his leg. 'Leonard . . . my father was involved in a number of children's charities back then. It was a long time ago.'

'Perhaps your mother would remember something . . .'

'Myra can barely remember the day before yesterday.'

Flick's impression of the old woman was that she was still as sharp as a blade. 'That's not—'

'Flick.' Drake pinched the bridge of his nose. 'I'm going to be honest with you. Harris is spitting feathers. He wants to know why Ryan was allowed to go home.'

'Ryan insisted,' she said quickly. 'And we had an armed—'

'He knows all that,' said Drake, not unkindly. 'But he's thinking that right now this investigation, because of its profile, needs a more experienced lead officer.' He looked annoyed when her mobile buzzed. She placed it in her top drawer. 'I told him you deserve this chance because I have faith in your abilities. But the pressure to get motoring on this is intense. What we absolutely don't need right now is to waste time flying off on a fantastical tangent.'

She swallowed. 'Yes, guv.'

When he opened the door, the burble of the Incident Room, the chunter of printers and the ringing phones, poured into her office. For the first time he glanced at the cuttings. 'Let's talk later.'

The best thing Flick could have done right then was to knuckle down to work, God knows there was plenty piling up, but she was convinced she'd be replaced sooner or later, come what may. And besides, she'd already made the call . . .

'One more thing, guv.' She snatched a sheet off the printer. 'Those other names on the list – the ones that aren't crossed out – appear in the caption of the missing photograph. Elliot

Juniper has a criminal file. Theft, burglary, handling stolen goods; a list as long as your arm.' With a sigh, Drake closed the door. 'Someone called Connor Laird is mentioned, and Deborah Willetts, I can't find either of them in the system, but look.' She placed the printout on the edge of her desk, as if she was trying to tempt a feral cat with a treat.

Drake looked exasperated. 'Where's this going, Flick?'

'There's only a single mention of the Longacre children's home anywhere on the internet,' she said quickly. 'It burned down just hours after your mother and father visited it, in nineteen eighty-four. But Amelia Troy's name rang a bell. A few years ago she was the biggest thing to hit British Art. She won the Turner Prize, her paintings sold for tens of thousands. Troy and her husband Ned Binns were this golden couple of the art world.'

Drake reluctantly picked up the sheet.

'That's a newspaper interview she did years ago,' continued Flick. 'She mentions being in a children's home in Hackney called the Longacre.'

A photo below the interview showed Amelia Troy and Ned Binns on a sofa, dressed identically from head to toe in black denim and Doc Martens. Their legs were entwined so you couldn't tell where one of them ended and the other began, their heads leaned together in a single massive explosion of bird's-nest hair. They looked lazily at the camera from beneath heavy lids. Amelia wore thick make-up and blood-red lipstick. Ned's face was hidden behind a riotous red beard. Burning cigarettes drooped languidly in their fingers.

'And she's still alive,' said Drake.

'Yes, but about seven years ago she almost died in a

suspected overdose that killed her husband.' She waited for a moment while Ray Drake scanned the interview. 'It was all over the papers.'

Drake dropped the sheet. 'So what are you saying?'

'Point is, he died, she nearly died. Another kid from the Longacre, another accident. I just think it's worth talking to her.' When Drake laughed shortly, Flick gestured to the Incident Room. 'Everyone's hard at work. Amelia Troy still lives at the same address in Bethnal Green.'

Drake shook his head. 'You haven't been listening to me, Flick.'

She blurted out: 'I've already arranged to see her.'

Flick did her best not to shrink from his grim stare.

'We'll take my car,' he said finally.

19

A whipping cluster of colourful balloons taped to a battered steel door wasn't what Ray Drake was expecting.

He thought he knew all about Amelia Troy – had made it his business to know. There was a time when you couldn't turn on the TV or open a magazine without seeing her unfocused gaze, or hearing her throaty, self-regarding laugh as she ranted about life, politics, art. There wasn't a subject under the sun about which she didn't have an opinion. When the papers required outrageous state-of-the-nation analysis or a provocative quote to spice up a tired news story, Amelia was happy to oblige.

It was that period when Art was as big as rock 'n' roll and enormous amounts of money were being made by a new generation of hungry, media-savvy young artists. Amelia Troy was right at the vanguard of it. She was never slow to regale interviewers with her traumatic rags-to-riches story. Chain-smoking, sipping from a hip flask, she'd explain how she bounced from institution to institution as a child, hinting darkly of brutal abuse, a life of terror.

The only way to cope, she said, was to harness the creativity within her. She drew her bleak, dangerous world on walls and windows using crayons, felt tips, chalk or boot polish, whatever she could get her hands on. One day she shoplifted a 99p painting set from a corner shop. That set, she said, changed her life. With the help of a couple of well-heeled benefactors, and the vaguest suggestion of sexual favours along the way, Troy got into one of the country's top art colleges. From that moment, she proclaimed arrogantly, Art would never be the same.

Critics lapped it up. Troy's work, they said, was a 'tumorous clot of catastrophic energy, as treacherous and implacable as cancer'. She painted kinetic and intoxicating canvases of blood reds and sinister blacks, which almost, but not quite, obliterated the carefully detailed figures beneath. Instead of a signature, each painting was signed with a trademark Amelia kiss. A powerful clique of art dealers paid obscene amounts for it. Troy's shows sold out. And her nihilistic lifestyle added a more dangerous context to her anguished body of work.

When she married another *enfant terrible* of the art world, a self-proclaimed conceptual terrorist called Ned Binns, her work and appearance began to deteriorate. Her uniform of shapeless Clash T-shirts and jeans only accentuated her dramatic weight loss. Commentators drily noted the way her mass of hair was knotted and uncombed, and her thick make-up more sloppily applied.

When a whisper campaign implied a dependency to heroin, Troy's increasingly irrational behaviour did nothing to dispel the rumours. No society party was complete without the newly-weds hurling abuse at each other. Binns had his own demons, but despite his well-documented adultery and his controversial works, which involved sending threatening letters to politicians and celebrities and compiling a multimedia exhibition out of the tangled legal paper trail, Amelia Troy stood by her man.

But the moment she became forever known as a burnout – a totem of the wicked, hedonistic art scene – came when she showed up drunk for an awards ceremony and showered the attendees with a string of obscenities live on television.

Troy fell off the radar. She shuffled in and out of rehab, so they said, battling addiction and mental health problems. And by the time Troy and Binns were discovered naked and overdosed on the bed in their apartment, the fickle art world had moved on.

By all accounts Troy had a lucky escape. She was at death's door, and her body would have lain undiscovered for weeks, perhaps months, if her husband hadn't managed to rouse himself long enough from his terminal stupor to call 999. When the paramedics arrived, Binns was dead – and Amelia barely alive.

A comeback exhibition at a fringe gallery of work promising a more positive outlook on life was poorly received. The world, it appeared, only wanted to know Amelia Troy as an artistic fuck-up.

It had been a relief to Drake when she'd drifted back into obscurity. He couldn't even remember the last time he'd read anything about her, but he certainly remembered the precocious girl from the Longacre and her sketchbook filled with uncanny life drawings. There'd never been anything in her personality back then to suggest she'd become a gobby firebrand and, for a short while, the most famous artist in Britain. Amelia had been like the other children – quiet, anxious, someone who instinctively withdrew from the dangerous gaze of adults.

It was a risk to come to her warehouse. The danger was

that she'd remember him. But something, someone, was circling, and he needed all the information he could get. He clung to a quote from the single interview she'd given following her overdose. A reporter had asked her why she barely painted any more.

'Because I can't remember any of it,' she'd replied, 'it's gone.' Asked what it was she couldn't remember, she'd said: '*Everything*.'

Huddled against the wall.

Her hand hot and clammy in his.

Flecks of spittle arcing high.

Threats, obscenities.

Flick stared at the balloons whipping in the breeze. 'Looks like a party.'

The journey to Amelia's apartment had been tense. Flick had spent most of the time on the phone to the office, furiously scribbling notes, eager to show that she wasn't abandoning her other responsibilities. Approaching Bethnal Green, they drove down a winding road past industrial units – the prefab businesses, scrapyards and lock-ups shuttered this Sunday lunchtime – alongside a rail track. At the end was a hulking redbrick Victorian warehouse isolated on scrubland. The meshed windows on the ground floor were intact, but the building looked abandoned. There was a gravel area big enough to park a couple of cars. The steel entrance, with its jostling balloons, was wedged open.

'She said to go to the top floor.'

The small lobby was cold and damp, but the elevator was still an impressive piece of machinery. When Flick hit the button its gears detonated into life in the depths of the building. A box trundled down towards them, cables grinding.

The panelled elevator was lit by a bare bulb. Closing the cage, they ascended past sealed-off stumps of corridor. Halfway up, Drake and Flick heard something unexpected in that gloomy place: the sound of happy children.

When the elevator shunted to a halt, and Drake pulled back the lattice, they emerged into the centre of a vast space saturated with blinding light from the surrounding tall windows. The floor was spattered with speckled blobs of dried paint, which made the surface uneven. Sitting at a long trestle table were a dozen kids, painting and drawing and filling the enormous space with chat and laughter. Other children bolted like unstable atoms, paint dripping from the brushes in their hands, despite the best efforts of a small group of adults to get them under control.

Flick frowned at the sole of one of her shoes, and the sticky yellow splodge of paint smeared there, as a woman walked towards them.

'DS Flick Crowley.' Flick held out her hand. 'We're looking for—'

'Thank God.' The woman threw up her arms. 'I thought you didn't look like parents. The last thing we need is for one of the kids to walk off with a stranger!'

It took a moment for Ray Drake to realise that this amiable woman, casually dressed in a splattered T-shirt and jeans ripped at the knees, dark hair pulled back in a loose ponytail, was Amelia Troy. She looked healthy and tanned and happy. Younger than he remembered from newspaper cuttings ten, fifteen years back, when she had seemed prematurely aged. And happier, by far, than the miserable, timid child he remembered from the home.

'This is Detective Inspector Raymond Drake,' said Flick.

Amelia took his hand. Her shake was strong, and despite the chill in the vast space, warm. Drake held her look, searching for any hint of recognition, but sensed no response.

'You're having a party,' he said.

'I see why you're a policeman, absolutely nothing escapes your attention. I hold an open house for local kids every weekend, God help me. There aren't many places in this world where they can come and have creative fun and make a mess.' She gestured to a kid who was splashing orange paint on a roll of paper. 'Every week I think, Never again! But they love it so much.' She laughed. 'They can lark about, get themselves filthy and express themselves. This is a working space – or it was.'

'This is your studio?' asked Flick.

'This is my home.'

Drake turned to see that the other end of the massive warehouse, past the central elevator, was furnished as a living area, with sofas, lamps, a television on a stool; beyond that, separated by a long stretch of concrete, was an enormous double bed, a kitchen area. Everything was open plan, the areas separated by narrow paths of space like the floor of a department store.

'It must cost a fortune to warm up.'

'I may as well just chuck fifty-pound notes out the windows. Strategically placed heaters make it bearable, just about.' She smiled at Drake. 'And my beloved electric blanket, of course.'

'It's like something out of a movie,' said Flick, incredulous.

'I've lived here for nearly twenty years now and I'm too lazy to move.' A toddler crashed into Amelia's legs and fell over. 'Blooming heck, Darnell, you can run fast!' For a split second the boy looked like he was going to cry, but Amelia placed a hand against his cheek, and he calmed immediately. Plonked back on his feet, he ran off, screaming with delight. 'I can't hear myself think in here, why don't we go upstairs?'

Taking a packet of cigarettes and a lighter from a ribbed radiator hidden behind a painting, she led them to a fire door. Canvases were leaned beneath the windows. Chaotic patterns, which, if you looked closer, began to take on the outlines of people. Some appeared finished but most were abandoned, or ruined by obliterating brushstrokes. In the bottom right-hand corner of each, the red imprint of her lips.

'The kids look like they've been making their own improvements to your work.'

'A few years back those paintings would have cost you an arm and a leg.' Amelia shrugged. 'These days I can't give them away.'

Their feet clanged up the steps of an iron fire escape clinging to the outside of the building.

'You don't seem worried about it.'

'I still paint for pleasure, but these days I don't feel my entire life is ruined because my work isn't hanging in the reception of some scumbag corporation.'

The tarpaper on the roof of the building was covered with fag butts, which skittered like insects in the breeze. A deckchair, its canvas middle flapping, sat by a chimney mount, a mug filled with rainwater beside it. East London lay below them, squat and grey, beneath an armada of charging cloud.

'You're not what I was expecting,' said Flick, stepping onto the roof.

'You're wondering what I've done with the tragic druggie.' The tip of Amelia's cigarette fizzed when she lit it. 'Everyone's a bit surprised, but I suppose that's my own fault, you can never escape your past. Truth is, these days I live a dull and inconsequential life. Bog standard.'

'Nothing more bog standard than living in a warehouse,' said Drake.

She laughed. 'So why is it you're here?'

Flick handed her a photograph. Pressing the cigarette between her lips, Amelia studied it. 'And who is this?'

'His name is Kenny Overton,' said Flick. 'Do you recognise him?'

Amelia tucked a loose strand of hair behind her ear. Drake watched the way the tendons and veins bulged just beneath the skin of her hand, in sharp contrast to her face, which was smooth and angular and, even now in middle age, very striking. There were faint lines splaying from her eyes. Considering the life she had lived – an abusive childhood, years of drug dependency – she had aged extraordinarily well.

'This poor man's family was killed; it was in the papers,' she said. 'But what has it got to do with me?'

'We understand Mr Overton was at the Longacre children's home with you in the nineteen eighties,' said Flick.

Amelia blew out smoke thoughtfully. 'Was he now?'

'We're investigating a possible link between the home and the murder of Mr Overton and his family.'

Amelia gently fanned the photo, as if it were a Polaroid developing in her hand, then gave it back to Flick. 'I'm afraid I can't help you.'

'You don't remember him?'

'I'm sorry, I'm not trying to be difficult . . . I don't remember anything about that place.' Her eyes drifted to Drake. 'I've a bit of a block.'

'A block?' asked Flick.

'For many years I carried that home around in here.' She tapped her temple. 'I was obsessed, I never stopped going on about it, it nearly destroyed me – well, you only have to look at my work. The horror of that place poured onto the canvas, my demons fuelled my art. I would have given anything to rid myself of those memories, even though I made millions from them. But the amazing thing is they're gone.' She sighed. 'Something happened to me a few years back . . . I don't know if you know this, but my husband died.'

'Ned,' said Flick.

'The very one.' Her gaze drifted over Flick's shoulder to a phone mast glittering atop a tower block. 'And you probably know we overdosed. He died and I . . . I was in a coma for weeks. It was touch and go; the doctors thought I was a goner. And when I awoke all my memories of that place were gone, every detail.'

The sun began to poke through a tear in the clouds. Amelia shaded her eyes. It was the middle of winter but her tan was deep and even. She may have given up painting, Drake thought, but she still clearly had rich friends across the world, and more than enough money to travel whenever and wherever she desired.

'The anger I had for that place energised my work and made me very successful.' She puffed on her cigarette. 'When those memories went, so did my urge, my obsession, let's say, to create. I've tried, really I have, darling, but everything

I've painted since has been toss. *C'est la vie*. After Ned's death I was done with the business, really.'

'Can that just happen, losing your memory like that?'

'A couple of therapists told me I'm in a fugue state – do you know what that is? I don't, really. I've . . .' Her voice became an officious monotone. '*Escaped from reality, taken on a new persona*. They said it was only temporary. Well, it's been years now. They're still inside me, those memories, and I've been warned they'll emerge sooner or later, to mess up my life all over again, lucky old me.'

'Isn't that unhealthy?' asked Flick. 'Keeping all that stuff buried?'

Amelia pinched the smoking tip off the cigarette and flicked the dead butt across the roof. 'Oh, I imagine so! I should be a quivering jelly of neuroses. I have my moments. I miss Ned very much . . .' She watched a train click past on the track below. 'But not as much as I thought I would. We loved each other, but we also made each other very miserable. Ned wasn't a happy man, and sometimes he could be . . . difficult. These last seven years, though, I've been content. For the first time in my life I don't feel the awful pain of that place. One day it may come back, I can't do anything about that, but until it does, I'm going to enjoy life.' Her eyes widened. 'Christ, listen to me go on.'

'It's a far cry from the life you lived with your husband,' said Flick. 'The children's parties and everything.'

'Yes, it is.' Amelia kicked at a clump of gravel with her foot. 'Ned would have hated the life I have now, *hated* it, we both would have. Back then, we shared one ambition.'

'What was that?'

'We wanted to die.' She smiled ruefully. 'He managed to

achieve it. I didn't, and I'm glad I didn't. But the life I have now would have been a living hell to Ned.' She frowned at her watch. 'Look, a few years ago I would have loved nothing more than to discuss my problems until sundown; you'd get tears, smashed furniture, the lot. But there's ice cream to dish out, so maybe you could tell me why you're talking to me about a man I apparently knew a hundred years ago.' When Flick glanced at Drake, Amelia frowned. 'Am I in danger?'

'It's only one avenue of investigation,' Drake said, 'and not a very promising one; we don't want to alarm you.'

'That bloody place.' The colour drained from her face. 'For years it made me cut myself and pump my veins full of shit. It nearly finished me. And now you're telling me it's not done with me yet?'

'It's most likely nothing,' said Flick. 'But has anything unusual happened recently?'

'Such as?'

'Has anybody spoken to you about the Longacre? Have you received any odd calls?'

Amelia hugged her chest. A cloud raced across the sun, sending the temperature plummeting. 'You're making me very anxious.'

'As I say,' Drake shot Flick a warning look, 'it's only one line of investigation.'

'What did you say your name was again?'

'Detective Inspector Ray Drake.' He took out a card. Flick reached into her bag and found one of her own.

'There's absolutely no reason to be alarmed,' Flick touched Amelia's arm, 'but feel free to phone me any time you want.'

When they moved towards the fire escape, Amelia paused

to gaze sadly at the city stretched across the horizon. 'That place, I can't remember anything about it, but I still can't escape from it.'

When they arrived back in the car park, Drake pointed a fob at his car, which unlocked with a whoop. He leaned across the roof to Flick, who stood on the passenger side.

'It was a waste of time,' he said. 'All we've done is frighten a woman for no good reason. I want an update on the investigation on my desk by the end of the day.'

Flick nodded, a blush sizzling up her neck, and climbed inside.

Pulling his seat belt around him, Drake recalled that last, uncertain smile Amelia Troy had given him as the cage of the elevator slammed shut and he descended into the depths of the building, and realised how grateful he was to see her again after all these years.

20

1984

Ray was never much into sports at school. He was too slight for rugby, and didn't care for getting slammed face down into the mud by the bigger boys. Rowing, with its freezing early mornings, was a struggle.

But he had always been agile and never shied away from a challenge, attributes that came in handy when he decided, just for the fun of it, to climb up the side of the Longacre and into a first-floor window. Well, partly for the fun of it. He wouldn't be going to the trouble if Sally had phoned him, as she normally made the effort to do. If she wasn't going to let him know that she was okay, he would just have to bloody well find out for himself.

Part of him enjoyed all the cloak-and-dagger stuff. Perhaps, when he was older, he could become a spy rather than the boring barrister his parents expected him to be. You can be anything you want in life, Ray sensed that instinctively – whether he could convince Myra and Leonard of the fact was another story.

Sally's car was outside the home when he arrived, and he heard the children inside, but nobody was answering the door. So Ray jumped at the drainpipe, scrambling for a foothold on the brackets that fixed the pipe to the brick.

There was a tricky moment when bolts shifted and the pipe jerked away from the wall, and he hung on for dear life, but then he managed to get a hand to the nearest sash window and lift it. Heaving himself over the sill, swinging his legs inside, he collapsed on the worn carpet, laid staring up at a stain on a ceiling tile, getting his breath back.

Then a voice asked: 'Who are you?'

Ray sat up to see a young girl sitting on a mattress against the wall opposite. Her knees were bunched in front of her, pencil poised over a notebook covered in crepe and glitter.

'Me and Jason have got a game going on,' Ray said. 'Hide-and-seek.'

The key to getting by at school, he had discovered, was to walk about as if you owned it, as if you had the brazen right to be there as much as any of the house masters, captains or the senior boys who fancied themselves as judge, jury and executioner. Ray was quick-witted and personable, people liked him, and he had discovered that more often than not he could talk himself out of – and sometimes into – difficult situations.

But the girl said, 'You're not from here.'

'I am.' He climbed to his feet. 'You just don't see me because I'm really, *really* good at hide-and-seek.'

He could see she didn't believe a word of it. Most kids would have screamed the place down if they saw a stranger falling through an upstairs window. Instead, she went back to her book, totally absorbed. The top of her pencil twirled and danced over the page.

Ray's interest was piqued. 'What are you doing?'

'Drawing.'

'Oh, yeah?' He threaded his way through the clutter of

furniture, careful not to bang his shins on the corners of the beds that jutted into the room like an invading fleet. 'Can I have a look?'

She didn't say yes, but she didn't say no either, and Ray gently tugged the book from her grasp. He turned the pages, expecting to see the usual childish stick figures and bulging girlish hearts, and was surprised by the detailed, painfully intricate images. The girl had drawn various kids he vaguely recognised from the home – Kenny, Regina, Connor – and he found himself drawn ever deeper into the winding swirls and whorls curling around the page. The gentle strokes would crackle suddenly, like a surge of electricity, and the detail of a face emerged out of the disturbance. Some of the children were smiling, some of them were laughing, but they all had unbearably sad eyes, expressive beyond their years.

He was seriously impressed.

'Did you do these all by yourself?' The girl nodded, eyes clamped on the sketchbook in case he tried to run off with it. 'I'm Ray. What's your name?'

'Amelia Troy.'

He held out his hand, as he had been taught to do since he was barely able to walk. She stared, but he kept it there until her fingers tentatively reached out, and they shook.

'You're a real talent,' he said, and a smile ghosted across Amelia's face. 'Maybe you could draw me one day. Do you want to be an artist when you grow up?'

Her eyes widened, as if he had asked her if she was planning to travel to the moon. You can be anybody you want to be, that's what he told himself, but maybe not if you're a child like Amelia, living in a dump like this, with its damp and draughts and peeling wallpaper, and its festering atmosphere of dread.

'You know what?' he said. 'Myra – my mother – sits on the board of an art gallery, and it's quite a famous one. When you're older, if you do me some drawings, I can arrange for them to see them. Maybe they could recommend a college you could go to. Would you like that?'

The girl looked down, embarrassed. Ray realised Amelia had probably been made many promises in her short life, and not a single one of them had happened.

'I'll do it for you,' he said, and meant it. Ray never said anything without meaning it. 'Because I've a feeling we're going to be friends.'

The girl rolled her eyes. 'We've only just met.'

'Doesn't matter,' he said. 'I'm never wrong about stuff like that.'

He looked around the dismal room, with its clutter of beds and mattress and clothes strewn all over the floor, the windows smeared with a thousand and one fingerprints, and wondered what had led Sally to this place. How she could tolerate the stink of filth and unhappiness. She had grown up in a home where she had everything she could possibly want: a loving family life and a good education. She had come here originally because she wanted to make a difference to the lives of these kids. Now it seemed to him that something had gone terribly wrong. She had fallen under the spell of Gordon Tallis, that much was clear to Ray, and was as much as prisoner of this place as the children.

Ray wanted her out of there, and all the children, too. But there was nothing he could do – he was just a kid. One day, when he was older, people would listen to him. He would have the authority of an adult and would set about making a difference, a *real* difference, to the lives of people. One day, he knew, he would do some good in the world.

His parents expected him to become a barrister, not because of any sense of social justice on their part, but because it was what Leonard had done, and Leonard's father before him, and his father before that. Well, Ray would see about that. To defy his parents would be unthinkable. But Ray had inherited Myra Drake's iron will, her indestructible self-belief, and they knew it. One day he would force them to understand that what they demanded of him wasn't what he wanted for himself.

'Do you know Sally?' Ray asked Amelia. 'Do you know where I can find her?'

'She'll be in the office,' said the girl. 'Where she always is.'

He returned the book. 'It was lovely to meet you, Amelia. We're going to meet again.'

'Are we?'

'I made you a promise.' He stood. 'And I keep my promises.'

On the landing he heard the low thrum of the children's voices in the garden – Sally said they were encouraged to stay outside during the summer – and banging from the kitchen. Ray crept over the bare floorboards, and down the stairs.

The closed door of the office was on the left. When he yanked on the handle, it didn't budge, so he knocked.

'Sal! Are you in there?' He kept an eye on the long hallway and the kitchen, where the shadows of Gordon's staff, the Dents, lumbered across the black-and-white tiles.

'Sal!' When he put his ear to the office door, he heard the roar of air. 'Sally!'

'So this is a nice surprise,' said a voice, and Ray turned to see the manager sat on the bottom stair, hands flopping forward over his knees. 'Particularly as I don't remember anyone letting you in.'

Ray blurted out: 'One of the children.'

'If you say so, lad.' Gordon lifted a hand, unconvinced. 'Maybe next time you could let us know when you intend to drop in, so we can polish our best silver, perhaps dish up a few canapés.'

'Where's Sally?'

'She's asleep. She works very long hours, Raymond – that's your name, yes? – and she's all tired out.'

From the doorway opposite appeared the new kid, Connor, and another boy, a brute called Elliot. The last time Ray had seen him, he'd had a bandage around his face. But it was gone now, and his nose was misshapen and purple.

Ray felt uneasy. 'I'd like to see her.'

'Another time, perhaps. Let me give her a message for you.'

'Maybe we could wake her up.'

'Disturbing a young lady's beauty sleep, breaking and entering? And here's me thinking you were a young gentleman.'

'If you don't mind, I've come all this way.'

Gordon laughed. 'You are by far the most polite housebreaker I've ever met, but I'm afraid our children are unsettled by strangers, so I'm going to have to ask you to leave.'

'And I'm going to have to insist,' said Ray, praying that his voice didn't crack, 'that I see her.'

'Why don't we just call the police?'

Ray stood his ground when Gordon approached, but his hands trembled behind his back. 'I can't see you doing that.'

'You're a bright and clever boy. A credit, no doubt, to your very expensive education.' Gordon's smile vanished. 'But you're not welcome, lad. I cannot allow people to let themselves in and walk about the place.'

'My parents are very involved in children's charities.'

'Good for them,' said Gordon. 'Public-spirited people, so they are.'

'Maybe they could come and see the work you do here.' Ray swallowed. 'They would be very interested.'

'They're welcome,' Gordon spread his arms wide, 'any time.'

'I just want to see—'

'I'm not going to ask you again,' said Gordon.

But Ray didn't want to go. He wanted to see Sally, and he didn't understand why he wasn't allowed. When he was small, Ray had depended more than he liked to admit on her affection. Goodness knows he got little enough from his parents. They loved him, he was sure of that, but just weren't wired to show it. The environment he grew up in was stifling, prohibitive. From an early age he attended a series of expensive prep schools where he was taught to be – expected to behave as – a young adult. Sally had spent a lot of time with him. With her he could behave how he wanted, just be a small kid, she had no expectations of him. The thought of losing her to this place . . . sickened him.

But he had no choice, and he had to go.

Nodding at Connor, he said, 'How are you enjoying it here?'

But the boy didn't answer. There was a frightening intensity in his eyes. Ray had met lots of bullies, there were plenty of them at school – you learned quickly who to avoid, and

Ray had always been a good judge of character – but he didn't understand this kid at all. There was a truculence to Connor, a wilfulness. It was insecurity or malice . . . or maybe something worse.

Ray nodded at Amelia, who stood on the stairs, and was about to go when the office door opened.

'What are you doing here?' Sally asked sleepily. She was dressed, but her hair pressed against her cheeks, twisting around the sunglasses she wore.

'You never called me,' Ray said, with relief. 'I was worried!'

'This is a wonderful, heart-warming moment,' Gordon growled. 'But please, Sal, take the boy out of here. Now.'

Sally pushed Ray outside, and they sat on the steps, looking down on the street and the train track. Reggae music pumped lazily from one of the squats.

'I asked you not to come here,' she said.

'You didn't call.' All the tension of his encounter with Gordon whipping loose inside him, he struggled to keep a whine from his voice.

'Sometimes I don't get the chance,' she said. 'I've responsibilities, things to do.'

'I need to know that you're okay.'

'You don't have to worry about me.'

'But I do. This place . . .' He darted a look over his shoulder. 'It's wrong.'

'I asked you not to come here. I expressly asked you.'

'You're not the same person.'

'No, I'm not. Because I'm not a child any more, Ray, I'm an adult, and being an adult isn't a whole lot of fun sometimes, as you'll find out.'

'Not around here it isn't – or being a kid, for that matter.'

but not here. I promise to ring, but I don't want you to come here. I mean it this time, Ray.'

That was fine with him. He didn't want to come back anyway. There was stuff about this home that he didn't want to know about – those deliveries he saw Connor and Elliot making around the borough, for a start – and if he did ask her about it, she might well refuse to see him again, and he couldn't bear that. Sally was right: this was no place for him. He'd be going back to school in a couple of months, would be gone for the best part of the year, and schoolwork would consume all his time and energy. When he came back to the city, with a bit of luck she would have moved on, and they'd both be able to forget about this wretched place for good.

'I'll stay away, but you have to call me,' he said. 'Twice a week.'

'It's a deal.' She placed a finger beneath the glasses to rub an eye and when they lifted momentarily he thought he saw a tinge of yellow beneath an eyelid, which made him feel sick. 'Just because I'm here, with Gordon, doesn't mean I'm going to stop caring about you.'

Maybe that's what this was all about. He wasn't worried about Sally at all, just about himself. Maybe he couldn't face the fact that she was free to make her own mistakes, had

...d at the sunglasses. 'Take them off.'

'Don't tell me what to do.'

'Why not?' He couldn't help himself, and tried to grab at the glasses, but Sally jumped up, holding them to her face.

'Because I'm not going to be ordered around by you!' She went to lean on the railings, out of his reach, and they stayed there like that, both of them upset, until she said: 'If you want to meet we can do that, every couple of weeks or so, but not here. I promise to ring, but I don't want you to come here. I mean it this time, Ray.'

That was fine with him. He didn't want to come back anyway. There was stuff about this home that he didn't want to know about – those deliveries he saw Connor and Elliot making around the borough, for a start – and if he did ask her about it, she might well refuse to see him again, and he couldn't bear that. Sally was right: this was no place for him. He'd be going back to school in a couple of months, would be gone for the best part of the year, and schoolwork would consume all his time and energy. When he came back to the city, with a bit of luck she would have moved on, and they'd both be able to forget about this wretched place for good.

'I'll stay away, but you have to call me,' he said. 'Twice a week.'

'It's a deal.' She placed a finger beneath the glasses to rub an eye and when they lifted momentarily he thought he saw a tinge of yellow beneath an eyelid, which made him feel sick. 'Just because I'm here, with Gordon, doesn't mean I'm going to stop caring about you.'

Maybe that's what this was all about. He wasn't worried about Sally at all, just about himself. Maybe he couldn't face the fact that she was free to make her own mistakes, had her own life to live, her own life to ruin. She was able to go where she wanted, could drift to the ends of the earth and never come back if that's what she wanted. Myra and Leonard allowed him no such uncertainty. He would go back to school, and then to Oxford, and he would become a barrister, end of story. His whole life was mapped out for him, and there was nothing he could do about it, unless something drastic happened, unless something cataclysmic occurred to completely alter his destiny. That was why he felt so emotional – she was free and he was trapped.

Ray wondered whether, in the years to come, when they were both adults and he had his own life and family and responsibilities, they would still be friends. He prayed that they would.

'It's a deal,' he repeated under his breath.

Sensing his misery, Sally sat down, putting an arm around him. To his relief, she changed the subject. Reminded him of an afternoon in the park when he was small and fell in a pond – the look on Myra's face was a picture! He laughed at that, and they started talking about the days they spent together when he was barely taller than her knees – forgetting about Gordon and the Longacre – until dusk, a good three hours later, when she told him she had to go back in.

Ray stood and noticed his hands were covered in glitter from Amelia's notebook. He wiped his them down his legs as Sally opened the door to go back inside and when he looked up he saw, or thought he saw, Connor Laird standing in the gloom of the hallway, like a mirror image, his expression hidden in shadow.

When he trotted down the steps to go home, Ray was relieved he didn't have to go back to that place ever again.

21

Flick worked into the evening, only nipping out of the office to pick up a Happy Meal, which she devoured at her desk as she trawled through the automatic number plate recognition data Steiner had compiled. Chewing on the burger, her thoughts drifted back to those cuttings Kenny Overton had painstakingly collected. The people he believed had been at the same children's home decades ago, and who had since died.

Despite the fruitless meeting with Amelia Troy, and Ray Drake's displeasure at her wasting time on what he insisted was a dead end, something nagged at her about the cuttings, but she knew she'd be walking on thin ice if she diverted resources into looking into the deaths of those people. The fact that Drake's parents had visited the Longacre must have rattled him more than he was letting on, and she couldn't shake the memory of him in the Property Room. Flick would never be one of life's maverick coppers – she'd spent her whole career slavishly playing by the rules, not exploiting them as her dad had done – but she absolutely hated loose ends. She needed to be satisfied in her own mind about those articles, and it was a bitter irony that the one person who could probably provide details about the Longacre was the last person in the world she wanted to see: her father.

The fries made her feel queasy, so she threw the greasy

pocket in the bin and read interview reports. A couple of names kept cropping up in the investigation. According to one of his mates, Phillip Overton had owed money to a loan shark. He'd kept the debt quiet, hadn't even told his brother. The money, a couple of grand, was eventually paid back at the usual astronomic rate of interest, but not before a couple of nasty encounters with the street lender.

Flick called Eddie Upson into the office.

'How long ago are we talking?'

'About six months,' he said. 'Phil played football at a local leisure centre. A couple of his teammates saw him have beer chucked in his face by the guy in a pub.'

After grabbing a few hours' sleep, Upson was chipper this afternoon. It was Flick, who'd worked through the night, who felt – and probably looked – like something from a horror show.

'Got a name?'

'The Golden Eagle.'

'The loan shark, Eddie.'

'Dave Flynn,' said Upson. 'Sounds a dashing kind of guy. Vix is chasing up an address now.'

Door-to-door interviews at the two crime scenes hadn't turned up any new leads. At Ryan Overton's estate, where a distrust of the police was endemic, it was especially tough to get information. The pensioner who lived in the flat that had been used to gain access to Ryan's balcony was in Gdansk, and not due to return until the following week.

There was a stack of other interviews and evidence reports for Flick to plough through. Peter Holloway's scene-of-crime analysis was pending. Pathology results weren't due for another twenty-four hours, and she'd been warned not to expect any results that would smash the investigation wide open.

At the end of the day, Holloway sat in her office, legs crossed neatly at the knees. 'Nothing so far,' he said.

'You're telling me that the perpetrator went in and out of the Overton house, and in and out of Ryan's flat, without leaving any trace evidence?'

Holloway's glasses dropped to his chest. 'Don't shoot the messenger, DI Crowley. The intruder or intruders took considerable care.'

Flick was incredulous. 'No prints, no hairs or flakes of skin.'

'It'll all be in the report,' Holloway said. 'Our perpetrator was in Ryan Overton's flat for a matter of seconds rather than minutes, and knew what they were doing. This is a person who has prepared meticulously, and who, I suggest, has a more than passing knowledge of forensic procedure. That's not necessarily to say they have professional insight. Television crime dramas feature forensic techniques; texts are freely available on the internet and shared on social media. Pay attention to the basics and it's relatively simple to cover your tracks.'

She struggled to keep the disappointment from her voice. 'Thanks, Peter.'

Holloway stood. 'One day into the investigation and you look awful.'

'I have an underactive thyroid,' she said defensively.

'Remember to eat occasionally, DS Crowley.' He eyed the remains of her fast food in the bin. 'Something nutritious.'

'I will.' She cracked a window, conscious of the greasy burger smell. 'I think that's everything for now.'

In the evening, with the Incident Room emptying, Flick was shutting down her computer when she noticed a Post-it note curled beneath the wheel of her chair. Printed in Kenny Overton's clumsy capitals was the name RONNIE DENT, and an address in Euston. Curious, she typed in Dent's name and to her surprise found that a string of his previous convictions – assault, shoplifting, drink driving and drug offences – had been Back Record Converted, transferred from paper files to the Holmes 2 computer database, along with his employment history. There, right at the top, was a mention of the Longacre home.

With the investigation stalling and few leads showing promise, she'd put off going to see Drake for as long as possible. But when she finally mustered the courage to go upstairs, just before eight, his office was empty.

Tiredness washed over her as she drove home. Pulling up at traffic lights to turn left towards her flat, the indicator ticked heavily in her head. She really needed a good night's sleep. But Nina hadn't phoned and Flick couldn't rid herself of the suspicion that there was something her sister was keeping from her. Besides, the bed in Nina's spare room was much more comfortable than her own knackered futon. A horn blared behind her – the lights had turned green.

Flick cranked the indicator right, and swung the car in the opposite direction.

22

Something was approaching.

He felt it pulsing, no more than a fleeting movement at the corner of his eye, edging out of the shadows. This phantom, this reckoning, almost upon him.

The past was crashing into the present. Decades ago, something had been set in motion, a terrible force gaining momentum. Feeding, becoming stronger. All the while Ray Drake had been building something precious. He was a son, a father – and a husband who had been forced to watch his wife fade away before his eyes, her cells eviscerated by disease. And now he sensed a greater catastrophe – with the slaughter of a family just yards from his own police station.

A curtain had been lifted to reveal an evil design. He had to be ready.

Drake pulled up outside Jordan Bolsover's luxury Docklands apartment building and killed the engine, listened to the end of one of Laura's Bach suites, letting her music flood through him and calm his jangling nerves. When the last note faded, the distant burble of traffic and churning river barely penetrated the quiet of the car.

Nestled behind cubes of shrubbery, the building was bathed in a blue light, which danced and rippled across the surface of the Thames. It was typical of City-boy Jordan to have a swanky riverside pad. Drake made a point of doing his homework on every man who came into his daughter's orbit, and didn't like what he found in his credit rating. Jordan spent money hand over fist. There was the apartment, the sports car, the exotic holidays, the membership of the exclusive gym where celebrities pounded the treadmill safely removed from the Great Unwashed. Jordon's expensive bespoke suits were tailored to accentuate each of the muscle groups in the torso he'd sculpted with the aid of a personal trainer. Back when they still spoke, April told Drake that Jordan was buying into a syndicate to own a thoroughbred. The low six-digit salary that Jordan earned would barely cover all these outgoings.

The money wasn't an issue, but Drake didn't like Jordan, who was arrogant and narcissistic. It drove him crazy to think that his little girl could fall in love with such a man. But Drake also knew that was exactly *why* she'd fallen for Jordan – because it sent him nuts. The more April knew Drake despised her boyfriend, the more her bond with Jordan strengthened.

Laura hadn't liked Jordan either, but she'd told Drake to back off and let the relationship cool of its own accord. Laura knew how to let problems burn themselves out. Drake loved his wife and trusted her instincts absolutely, but she was gone now, and he needed to keep his daughter close.

His mobile rang. The screen flashed: CALLER UNKNOWN. This was the sixth call. Each time he picked it up he heard a child's weeping.

But the electronically altered voice was too low, too stylised for it to be a child, and this time when he connected the call – and said, 'Ray Drake' – it spoke.

'I don't want to speak to you, put the other one on.'

'You're talking to—'

'I said put him on!' barked the voice.

'Who is this?' Drake listened to the electronic squall, his heart racing. 'Tell me who—'

The line went dead. A moment later, Drake scrolled down his contacts list until he found the number he needed. After several rings, the call was answered.

'Lewis,' he said. 'How goes it?'

'Ray,' said Lewis Allen. 'This is out of the blue. What's the time?'

Drake could hear conversation in the background, the clink of cutlery. 'It's late, Lewis, I'm sorry.'

'You're doing me a favour,' said Allen, voice low. 'We've got neighbours round. Hold on a sec.' Drake heard the laughter fade as Allen moved into another room and closed the door. 'That's better, I can hear you now. It's been a long time, Ray, and you were never one for social calls.'

'Amelia Troy,' said Drake. 'Remember her?'

Lewis Allen whistled. 'How could I forget? It was a big deal at the time. Her husband was some big artist or something. Well,' he snorted, 'I say artist, but I use the term loosely.'

Drake and Allen went way back, had walked the beat together as young PCs, and joined CID at about the same time. Then Allen moved to the nick at Bethnal Green, where he'd investigated the circumstances of the overdose of Troy and Binns.

'Remind me how they were found, she and her husband,' said Drake.

'Why are you asking after all these years, Ray? Got new evidence or something?'

'It's April,' said Drake. 'She's doing an essay, some evening college thing. I said I'd ask you. It escaped my mind and she's got to have it done by tomorrow.'

'No problem,' said Allen, playing along with the lie. 'The emergency dispatcher got a call.'

'From who?'

'Binns. He and the wife took an overdose, and the last thing he did before he fell unconscious was to call 999. You listen to the call, he was incoherent, could barely speak. The signal was traced to a warehouse they lived in, him and Troy. The paramedics found 'em laying on a bed, surrounded by junkie paraphernalia, syringes everywhere.'

'And Binns was dead.'

'He was done for when they arrived. Troy was barely alive, and was raced to hospital. Just in time, by all accounts. She was one lucky lady.'

Ned Binns was a troubled soul who took vast quantities of drugs. His wealth and marriage to Troy had opened up whole new opportunities for self-destruction. Allen and the other coppers who attended the scene concluded it was just another tragic overdose, and their decision was subsequently supported by the coroner's verdict.

But Drake had to be sure.

'Was Amelia Troy ever charged?'

'A file was sent to the CPS. Binns was a loose cannon, a bipolar smackhead. The rumour was he used to knock her around.'

'I didn't know that,' said Drake.

'It was decided she needed psychiatric help, not prison. If he hadn't made that call, she'd be dead.'

'Binns was at death's door, but he managed to call 999?'

'I've seen druggies do some seriously unexpected things,' Allen said. 'Journalists tried to sniff out all the salacious details, but there was nothing fishy about it. They overdosed, Ray, simple as that.'

'Thanks, Lewis, I appreciate it.' The blast of a tugboat horn as it chugged up river penetrated the quiet of the car.

'Hell of an essay your daughter's writing. Things have moved on from Van Gogh's ear, I suppose. I was really sorry to hear about Laura, Ray. She was a lovely lady.'

'I owe you, Lewis.'

Drake killed the connection and walked to reception. A shimmering blue light gave the walls a poolside glimmer. The porter, an old guy frowning over a puzzle book, looked up as Drake strode to the elevator.

'Can I help you, sir?'

'I'll see myself up.' Drake pressed the button for the eighth floor.

'I have to buzz you—'

The porter moved around the side of his desk too quickly, clipping his knee. His exclamation was cut off as the lift door closed.

Don't come on strong, Ray. She's scared and confused. Drake's fingers curled as he imagined Laura's hand slipping into it. *Don't argue. Don't get angry. You'll lose her.*

'I'll try,' he said, out loud.

The eighth-floor corridor smelled of pine freshener. A vase of flowers decorated an alcove. Drake could hear the thud of music and muffled laughter coming from Jordan's apartment. He rang the doorbell, and when the laughter continued, put his thumb on it and kept it there.

The door finally swung open. 'I've turned it down already!'

Jordan's tracksuit bottoms were worn low to expose his taut stomach and jutting abs, a bottle of Japanese beer was tucked into the elastic waist like a holstered gun. An unbuttoned pale cream shirt revealed a fine gold chain across his hairless chest. Since Drake had seen him last, Jordan's cropped hair had turned platinum.

'Mr Drake! How's it going?'

Music and laughter continued behind the closed living-room door. Despite the young man's apparent surprise, Drake had a feeling he was expected.

'Can I come in?'

'Course!'

Jordan bowed gravely. Drake saw his pupils were large and round, and wondered what he'd discover on the other side of that closed door.

Stay calm.

He led Drake into a dark bedroom. 'We've some mates over. Why don't you wait here and I'll get April?'

The unmade duvet on the bed was coiled like a scoop of ice cream. There was a built-in wardrobe along the length of one wall, an en-suite bathroom. The walls were covered with arty monochromes of snaking naked torsos. April's trolley case stood at the end of a king-sized bed. He picked it up, easily: empty.

Balcony doors were flung open to the cold evening and the sparkling city lights at dusk. A boat puttered down the river, leaving a frothy wake. On the balcony was a metal table with two chairs. Drake prodded the mashed butts in an ashtray. Several were marked with lipstick.

'What are you doing here?'

The bedside lamp clicked on, and Drake barely recognised

his own daughter. Her blonde hair flamed red in the glow of the lamp, and her skin, so pale and porcelain in the sunlight, was almost translucent. There were shadows beneath her eyes. For the first time, Drake saw just how much weight she'd lost. Her feet were bare. Arcing across the top of her left foot was a tattoo he'd never seen before, an orchid.

His first instinct was to go to her, but he checked himself. These days, any attempt at affection antagonised her. Instead, he nodded to the balcony. 'You're smoking now?'

'I'm old enough.' Once it had been a joke between them, *when I'm old enough*, then a threat. Now it was a dismissal. 'I asked you why you're here.'

He nodded at the case. 'I don't know what you're trying to prove. Come home.'

'This is my home now.' She gestured around her. 'Mine and Jordan's.'

Drake enjoyed the battle of wills that often took place with suspects across a metal table in an interview room, and invariably got what he wanted. What was left unspoken, he knew, often screamed more loudly than any confession. Ray Drake had forgotten more secrets than most people had ever learned. But here, in this bedroom, the unspoken fact of their mutual grief – April for her mother, Drake for his wife – stood between them, and he couldn't find the words that would make everything good again.

Jordan slipped into the room to take her hand. April towered over him.

'I had to learn from Myra that you'd left home.'

'And I bet Gran loved telling you I'd gone. I bet she couldn't wait.' April snorted. 'You should be happy for me, Ray.'

To his irritation, she'd begun to address him by his first name, the same way he addressed the old woman.

'Please don't—'

'I didn't even think you'd notice. You're always so busy at work.'

'It wasn't my—'

She spat out the words: 'Mum was dying.'

And there it was, out loud. This was the conversation they should have had months ago, just the two of them, at home; their home, not in a strange room clinging to the cold river.

'We're engaged now.' She held up a hand, a ring glinting on a finger in the soft light. 'Aren't you going to congratulate us, Ray?'

'Don't call me that.' *Don't get angry.* 'I'm your dad.'

'Look, Mr Drake – Ray.' Jordan stepped forward. 'Thing is, I love April, and she loves me. You've got it into your head that I'm a bit down market, I accept that, but I have to pinch myself to believe that your daughter would honour someone like me with her love.' He took April's hand. 'I intend to make her happy.'

Drake didn't take his eyes of his daughter. 'Come home.'

'Fact is, Ray, you two ain't been getting on. Maybe you can both get a bit of distance now April lives with me, get things into perspective. It'd be heartbreaking if the two of you fell out – permanent, like.'

Ignoring him, Drake said: 'You don't know what you're doing.'

She laughed bitterly. 'Of course I don't – I'm in love. But then you wouldn't understand a little thing like *feelings*.'

She turned and ran from the room.

'Well.' Jordan made a face. 'That could have gone better.'

As Drake moved past, Jordan grabbed his arm. When Drake reeled angrily towards him, he held his hands up.

'Leave her be, Ray.' His voice was soft. 'She's upset.'

'I'm going to talk to my daughter.'

'I'd rather you didn't. We've got company.'

'What will I find next door?' asked Drake.

'It's a mess. There's drunk people, empty bottles and smelly takeaway food. You know how it is.'

'Drugs?'

'Of course not, Ray . . . Mr Drake.' Jordan made a big show of looking offended. 'What do you take me for?'

'Some spliff, maybe, or cocaine? Because you know how I'd react, don't you?'

Jordan grinned. 'You'd go mental.'

'As a police officer, I'd find myself in a very difficult position. There'd be shouting and recrimination, and April would have another reason to hate me. Is that what you're banking on, Jordan? That I'll barge my way in next door?'

'This anger you've got inside of you, Ray, it's not healthy. Get to the gym and onto a punchbag, let it all out.'

Drake rubbed the silk of Jordan's shirt collar between his fingers.

'Careful with that.' Jordan shifted uneasily. 'That's expensive.'

'If I discover my daughter is taking drugs, we're going to have a talk, you and me.'

Jordan forced a smile. 'Look forward to it, Mr Drake.'

Drake pushed past him and out the front door. He marched to the lift without looking back, stomach clenched like a fist.

'Tell you what,' Jordan called from the door, 'just to show there's no hard feelings, you're still invited to the wedding. Leave it with me, I'll talk April round.' Drake stabbed at the lift button and finally the doors trundled open. 'You take care, Ray!'

The porter was hovering by the lift when he arrived back in reception. 'If you're visiting, you're supposed to sign in!'

Drake stormed into the car park. The river lapped angrily against the embankment. In the car he fumbled with the music system. Shut his eyes and listened to Mozart's Requiem, let the music pour through him.

Laura had taught him how to let it soak the anger from every muscle and tendon, from the marrow in his bones, to cool the blood boiling in his veins. The engine purred below him, barely more than a soft vibration.

A faint trace of Laura's perfume lingered in the compartment. He imagined he heard, as the last mournful notes of the mass faded, the steady rhythm of her breath beside him.

Ray Drake missed his wife so much.

23

Nina and Martin lived in a big, comfortable house in Green Lanes, which smelled of pot-pourri. Giant sofas covered in exotic throws and cushions nestled against colourful walls. Lamps threw soft light through stained-glass doors. Objects d'art – mementoes they had brought home from their world travels – were placed on ever higher shelves so that they wouldn't end up in small hands and used as weapons.

It was a home from home for Flick, who hated her own cramped one-bedroom flat, and she stayed there frequently. She could relax, even amid the explosive tantrums and rows that broke out every five minutes among the children. Nina and Martin never minded her being there, or so they said, and her nieces and nephew clearly adored having her about the place. It was the kind of loving, nurturing environment that Flick could never imagine having for herself, so the idea that Nina and Martin's long marriage could be in trouble filled her with consternation.

She had her own key, but didn't like to use it – didn't want to give anyone the impression that she was taking their hospitality for granted – and when she rang the bell Martin opened the door immediately.

'Hi,' she said. 'Off out?'

'Yeah.' He plunged one arm into a North Face jacket as he searched the pockets of another coat on the banister.

Martin was an architect who worked on local government building projects. Flick had known him for nearly two decades now, since her sister came home months early from her gap-year world tour to drop the bombshell that she had married an Aussie she met in Goa just three weeks previously. Nobody had expected it to last five minutes, let alone nineteen years, but Nina and Martin's marriage had always appeared rock solid, not that Flick claimed to be any kind of expert on the subject. Martin was a charming husband, and a kind and thoughtful father who spent hours playing with his kids, and Flick loved him to bits, but he had been evasive on the phone that morning, and she was convinced he was avoiding her eye as he stomped towards the kitchen, calling: 'Nina, where's my keys?'

'I haven't seen them,' she heard her sister shout, and then their voices dropped to an irritable whisper. Flick didn't want to eavesdrop, but couldn't help herself, and was kind of relieved when all she could hear was the *tap, tap, tap* of claws on the floorboards. An old Labrador shambled towards her, tail thumping against the wall. Flick stroked its smooth head, pulling her face clear of its slathering tongue, and tried to pretend Nina and Martin weren't rowing. 'Hey, Lulu, nice breath.'

Moments later, Martin rushed back down the hallway, keys in his grasp. 'Got a poker game,' he said, and left.

'I'm in here,' called Nina.

Flick found her sister in the kitchen. A long counter swung in a gentle curve towards a dining table spotted with lumps of candle wax from the numerous evenings Nina and Martin entertained friends. On summer nights the entire rear glass wall opened so that all the shrubs and plants and flowers in the garden appeared to pour inside. The room was personable and tasteful and tidy – all the more remarkable, thought Flick, because Nina and Martin had three exuberant and messy under-tens.

'Since when did your husband play poker?'

'He plays occasionally.' Nina crouched at the dishwasher prodding buttons. 'He's under the mistaken impression it gives him a tough cowboy vibe. Have you eaten?'

'I'm not hungry.'

'Auntie Flick!' called Coral, the seven-year-old, from upstairs. 'Come and see me.'

'I'll be right up,' Flick shouted, and turned to her sister. 'I thought they'd all be asleep by now.'

'She's wearing her princess outfit in bed. Honestly, the pink is an obscenity, but she won't take it off, she's desperate to show you.' Nina slammed shut the dishwasher door and pressed a folded pair of glasses to her nose to read a label on a bottle of red.

'I'm not in the mood for a drink,' said Flick, 'I'm dead on my feet.'

'You're going to want a glass of this.'

Nina padded in her bare feet to a drawer. She was dressed in a loose top and yoga pants, and her strawberry-blonde hair was piled high on her head by an artfully placed pencil. Slim and toned, she was as tall as Flick, but there was no crick in her posture, no apology for her height or her place in the world. She took out a corkscrew.

'This is the real deal.' Nina posed mock seductively with the bottle, as if she were a hostess stroking the top prize on a game show. 'It's from Martin's *special* stash of very expensive wines. The idea was to drink them on momentous occasions.

Each case costs hundreds of your English pounds. Trust me, you're going to want this.'

'I am honoured,' said Flick warily. 'What's the celebration?'

Nina took two long-stem glasses from a cupboard. 'I told him that if I was going to have this conversation with you alone, because Martin couldn't get away fast enough, then he would have to pay a forfeit.' She twisted the corkscrew pensively. The cork eased out with a soft plop.

'If you're trying to terrify me, you're going about it the right way. What's going on?'

Nina poured the ruby-red liquid and pushed a glass across the table. 'Tell me what you think.'

'I don't care about the wine. Is there something wrong between you and Martin? If I've been overstaying my welcome I promise not to stay over again, unless expressly invited.'

'Don't be ridiculous,' said Nina. 'We love you being here, which makes what I have to say all the more hideous.'

'Are you splitting up?' Panic surged in Flick. 'Oh God, you are.'

'No, of course not!' Nina burst into tears.

'Auntie Flick!' shouted Coral.

'Up in a minute!' Flick held her sister. 'Please, just tell me.'

Nina lifted the hem of her top to dab at her eyes. 'It's good news, really it is, but it feels . . . it feels . . .'

What was really upsetting about this whole situation was that it was Flick's older sister who was usually so composed. She was the strong one, the rock, the anchor. When their father left home it was Nina who pulled the young Flick and their mother through the trauma; and when Daniel vanished into thin air, and the weeks and months passed and they heard nothing, she was the one who pressed for the investigation into their brother's disappearance to be kept open. It was Nina who organised their mother's care when she became sick. She dragged the Crowleys kicking and screaming through every family crisis and out the other side.

Flick took her sister's face in her hands. 'Tell me.'

'You haven't even tasted this.' Nina lifted her glass, miserably. 'It's Argentinian.'

'Tell me,' said Flick gently. 'Please.'

''We're going away,' said Nina.

'I see.' Flick was stunned, yes, but she had always expected something like this to happen sooner or later. London was no place for a growing family. She immediately began to do the calculations. Thinking about the best way to see her nieces and nephew if they moved out of the city. It would be a wrench not being able to turn up when she liked, and it would be difficult to see them every weekend because of her unpredictable working hours, but it wouldn't be so bad.

'To Sydney,' said Nina. 'We're going to Australia.'

Flick stared. 'When?'

'Okay, so . . .' Nina turned away to find things to tidy. 'Martin's been offered a job, and school places for the kids have been arranged. It wasn't planned, I swear, it all happened out of the blue. His parents are elderly now, and he's their only child . . . You know he always wanted to go back eventually.'

'I'm happy for you,' said Flick quietly.

Nina's bottom lip quivered. 'I don't know what I'm even saying right now. I'm so sorry, darling.'

Flick picked up her glass. 'You've nothing to be sorry about. The kids will love it out there. The sun, the outdoor life. You'll have a pool, probably, and you'll go to the beach and have barbies and all that. You're going to be so happy, and I'm glad.'

'Then why do I feel so terrible about it?'

'Because you love your sister and don't want to upset her, but you don't have to worry because she's absolutely fine about it.'

'You're not fine about it, but thanks for lying.' Nina gazed at her. 'When I'm not here, maybe you and Dad—'

'That's not going to happen,' said Flick, smiling flatly.

'Someone has to keep an eye on him. You'll have something in common now; you can get together to badmouth me for leaving.' Nina stared at her. 'Please, Flick, I'm struggling for a silver lining here.'

'Don't worry.' Flick did her best to sound happy. 'What an adventure you're going to have.'

She opened her arms and Nina walked into them. They stood like that, holding each other. Flick didn't want to let go of Nina, or any of them. Her sister, thousands of miles away . . .

'You're going to keep a room ready so that I can come and see you.'

'It'll be the very best room, with a view of the opera house or a kangaroo park. We'll get you a koala, a real one. It'll sit on your bed and wait for you.'

'Auntie Flick!' screamed Coral. 'I can't get to sleep!'

'I'd better go up.' Flick stepped away, the tiredness making her light-headed. She was shattered – emotionally, physically – and knew she wouldn't be able to stay on her feet for long, but it didn't stop her gulping the wine down in one mouthful.

She pointed to the glass as she headed out of the room. 'Refill, please.'

24

All the way home, that feeling he was being followed. Drake swung the car into the dark square outside his house. The engine shuddered and died.

On the passenger seat, the phone rang. The caller's name and number was blocked. He put it to his ear, ready this time. 'Yes.'

The electronic voice was aggressive. 'You thought you could hide from me?'

'Who is this?'

'You thought I wouldn't *know* where to find you?'

Drake twisted in his seat to scan the square. 'Why should I speak to you, if you won't identify yourself?'

'Because you're to blame!' The static exploded angrily, the words becoming discordant. 'You're guilty and you're going to pay the price. Don't think for one moment, *one moment*, you won't. You made it happen, *you* made it happen, and you will pay, just like those others.'

'Tell me your name.' Drake swung open the car door, stepping into the cold night to look beyond the yellow spray of the streetlamps.

'I'm many people now, so many people,' said the voice, speaking urgently. 'One, two, twelve, twenty, so many it's difficult to keep count.' Digital glitches gave every word, each vowel, an abrupt glottal slap. 'So don't try to find me, because I'm all around you. I'm close, I'm everywhere.'

'We knew each other.' Turning in a slow circle, Drake's feet crunched on the frost clinging to the road. 'I met you at the home.'

'You can't hide from me,' said the voice bitterly. 'I found you, like I found the others.'

Drake tried to sound calm, reasonable. 'Why don't we meet?'

'Oh, we're going to meet,' the voice screeched. 'You think I don't know where you are, and how to get to you? I know who you are.'

On the other side of the square an indistinct figure approached, phone clamped to its ear, and Drake moved towards it, his feet clipping noisily on the road.

The voice was shouting, smothered by clicks and loops as the connection warped and distorted. 'I – ember – you did – I – saw – fire!'

'I don't know what you think you—'

'You're to bla – and like the oth – you will pay the con–quences!'

The figure – he saw a raincoat, a cap pulled low – increased its stride as Drake accelerated towards it, but then it turned quickly into a gate and fumbled a key at a door. Drake stopped dead on the pavement, recognising his neighbour. The door thudded shut.

'Do you think it's right that everyone should carry on with their lives as if nothing happened?' screamed the voice, the connection stabilising. 'I was alone in that place!'

'Tell me your name.'

'You're going to pay!'

'Tell me who you are,' repeated Drake.

'You think you don't have to face the consequences of your actions. You're wrong and you will pay, you will all pay.'

Moving back towards his own house, Drake saw a slanted shadow across the alley that led to the garden. The side door was ajar. 'You killed them all?'

'Not all, but soon.'

'Then let's meet, let's talk about it.'

'Oh, we'll meet soon enough.' Static flared in Drake's ear. 'Sooner than you think.'

Drake pushed open the side door, peered down the unlit path. 'When?'

'You people, with your happy lives, with your loving families, have no idea. You think you can carry on like nothing happened!'

'Are you here now?' Drake squinted into the blackness of the side alley. 'Are you at my home?'

'Just remember I know who you are, and where you are,' the voice said. 'The wife is already dead, I would have liked to have killed her myself, but the daughter . . .'

'No!' Drake's heart clenched.

'You remember me,' the voice screamed, 'and I know you. The Two O'Clock Boy is coming!'

A car sped past, the heavy thud of bass thumping from its window, making Drake flinch. When he replaced the phone to his ear, the call had been disconnected. He slipped it into his pocket.

The path at the side of the house was usually lit by a security light activated by a motion detector, but when Drake waved a hand beneath the sensor it didn't work. He walked slowly along the narrow corridor, one hand against the cold brick, the light diminishing with every step.

At the edge of the garden, foliage shivered in the wind. Fallen leaves crunched beneath his feet. Then—

Footsteps ran along the alley. Pain detonated in his head, a starburst of light and colour obliterated his vision. His legs crumpled beneath him. Drake had a fleeting sense of someone in front and also behind, and he let the forward momentum barrel him into the waist of his attacker, heaving them against the wall.

Grappling for a hold, Drake lashed out with a fist, but there was no power behind his punch, and another jolting pain in his kidneys took his breath away. He dropped to his knees and slid onto his back beneath a hail of blows. Curled up, covering his head as best he could against kicks and punches. Thudding into his hands, his face and stomach, sending jolting pain along his ribs and spine.

It was all he could do to breathe. A boot stung his cheek. A rib clicked in his chest. With one final fierce kick into his side, the attack stopped. Drake rolled onto his back, groaning, vision spinning. Two figures towered above him, their features obliterated by darting shapes behind his eyes.

One of them crouched. Breath bloomed in Drake's face. 'Cockroach! You're a cockroach!' A finger was pushed hard into his temple, forcing his head to the paving. 'Mind your own fucking business!'

Someone spat on his shirt, and then he heard footsteps clatter away. Craning his neck, he saw the silhouettes of his burly attackers high-fiving, heard the smack of their palms, as they leapt, laughing, exhilarated, on the tilted paving.

When they had gone, Drake lay on the stone patio, letting the pounding in his head subside, watching the stars trail across the sky like meteorites, until the world shifted itself the right way up. His phone vibrated in his breast pocket. Even the gentle buzz of it, the flutter of the slim sliver of metal, was a hammer against his chest. Gingerly, he lifted his arm, gritting his teeth against the jolting shocks crackling down his body, and took it out. Its blue screen flashed in his face.

He didn't want to answer it, just wanted to lie there for a while, let the frost dampen his hair – but knew he had to.

His voice was a croak. 'Ray Drake.'

'DI Drake?' Amelia Troy's voice was tense. 'There's somebody here. I think there's somebody outside my building.'

25

1984

The boy was bright eyed and bushy tailed, and as soon as he saw him, Elliot wanted to smash his face in.

'Who's this, then?' he asked.

'I'm Toby!'

He was the kind of kid you saw on telly shows. A mop of blond hair, a button nose and a big smile – off for adventures all day and back home for tea, the Secret Seven and all that crap. He even dressed like it. He wore a tank top patterned with purple diamonds that looked like someone's blind granny had knitted it. The leather tongue on his sandals curled with age, and his trousers didn't quite reach down to his ankles – he'd grown out of them – revealing ridiculous red woollen socks.

Elliot smirked. 'Where's he been evacuated from?'

A muscle tweaked in Gordon's jaw. 'Shake the boy's hand, lads, like proper gentlemen.'

Connor and Elliot reluctantly took his hand and he shook energetically. But when Gordon turned away, Elliot scowled.

Toby beamed as if he didn't see it. 'I'm on holiday!'

There was something off about him, Elliot decided. He was too tidy, too spirited. He didn't belong here, not in this place.

There was something different about Gordon, too. Recently, he'd been looking increasingly unkempt; his pock-marked face had become blotchy, and he wore the same clothes every day. But this morning he'd made an effort, changed his shirt, pulled on a tie, and for the first morning in a long time didn't stink of spirits. To go and meet the boy's parents, Gordon said, and bring him back here.

'Toby's going to be staying with us, just for a week or two.'

'Yes, sir!' The boy spoke as if being there was the most exciting thing ever. Elliot almost felt sorry for the kid. He was clever, you could tell by his bright eyes, by the way he spoke, but he knew *nothing* about the world.

'I want you two to look after him, and ensure he settles in.' Gordon locked eyes with Elliot. 'Do you hear me? The boy is to be made welcome.' He ruffled Toby's hair. 'He's a happy chappy.'

Elliot favoured the kid with an angry grin. He slapped Toby on the back so hard that the boy staggered forward. 'I'll show you around.'

When the two boys left the office, Gordon pulled down the tie and collapsed into his chair.

'Toby's the son of a couple of old friends.' Taking a bottle from a drawer, his hand trembled as he poured Scotch into a dirty glass. 'I knew his father a long time ago, back when I was still something vaguely respectable in the community. They're good people, Connor. Better than you or I will ever be.' The tendons in his neck snapped taut like rope when he drank. 'The lad's grandma is unwell and lives in Singapore. Do you have any idea where that is, boy?'

'Asia,' said Connor.

'Aye, a world away. Toby's parents have gone to care for her, and Bernard has asked me to look after his son while they're gone because he thinks I'm a good man. What do you think of that? The fool thinks I'm the man to care for his boy.' He rubbed a hand across his bewildered face. 'And like an idiot I said yes, because for one moment I forgot who I really was, I forgot I'm the kind of creature who swims with sharks. Always moving, always looking to feed.' He moved his hand through the air like a fin through the ocean, eyeing Connor. 'You're a little like that, too, I'd say . . . or perhaps you think you're better than me.'

When Connor didn't reply, Gordon jumped up to pace. 'Truth of the matter is, Connor, I've debts. You know what debts are?'

'You owe people money.'

'Big debts, lad. I owe money to some very bad people, and on top of that I've a dirty pig demanding cash I don't have. I could do without having some snotty kid hanging around the place. Because we both know, don't we, that I'm not a good man.' He stopped at the desk to refill the glass. 'Perhaps a long time ago I had the potential to be one, but I made the wrong choices. As you will, too. The last thing I need is for him to run back home telling tales about this place to Ma and Pa. So I'm relying on you and Elliot to keep him happy. If I hear he's sad, if I see tears bulging in his angelic little eyes, I'm going to hold you responsible.'

When Connor turned to leave, Gordon put down the glass and said: 'And do you know another thing about sharks, Connor?'

'No.'

'Sharks never forget, boy. So don't be thinking you got

away with our little confrontation the other night.'

In the kitchen, Connor heard Toby's voice lifting from the bottom of the garden as he animatedly explained something about a bug on a leaf to Kenny and Debs and several others.

'Who does he think he is? He shook everyone's hand.' Elliot put on a posh voice when Connor arrived at his side. '*I'm Toby! How do yew do! How do yew do!*' His foot tapped impatiently, as if eager to stamp the insect into the mud and the new kid along with it. 'If he tries to explain stuff to me, I'll give him something to think about!'

'You'll do nothing.'

Elliot bit down on his response; he owed Connor now.

Ronnie and Gerry were sat fully dressed in the sun with a Monopoly board between them, and no sign of the tins of lager that usually littered the floor beneath their deckchairs. The Dents playing a board game – the world had gone mad.

If Toby Turrell was surprised by the squalor of the house, or the listless behaviour of the children, he didn't show it. Over the next week he was like a ray of sunshine at the Longacre. His delighted singing could be heard all over the house. It was high and reedy like a choirboy's, and even Connor found it soothing, particularly at night when his voice drifted down from the bedroom above. Toby organised games in the garden, and if Connor didn't take part himself, he made a point of rounding up some of the other kids to join in.

Gordon kept mostly to his office. But on the occasions when he did emerge, he would laugh and joke. If there was a spill in the kitchen, or a child broke one of the rules, he wouldn't scream or lash out. He wouldn't lock them for hours in the small room behind the office. At night nobody listened anxiously for the thud of his footsteps on the stairs.

Everyone's mood lifted, even Elliot had to admit that. Nobody understood why it had changed with the arrival of this boy – they were just going to enjoy the freedom while it lasted. The kids hoped Toby would stay there for ever, but he told everyone in his sing-song voice that he was on holiday. His parents would be coming soon to take him home.

Even that Ray kid had stopped hanging around. Connor didn't see him when he was trudging alone around the borough with the brown packages hidden in a bag, and the handcuffs he always kept hidden in his pocket. Alone all day, his mind whirled with painful thoughts and feelings. Sometimes he felt like he was going to snap, like he was going to explode. He didn't understand how he had ended up at that place, or why he stayed. It would be the easiest thing in the world to slip away. The city was big, the country vast, and Gordon couldn't find him in a million years, wouldn't even bother. But at the end of each day, when the bag was empty, something made him go back there – a weird sense of responsibility – even though the other kids avoided him. Sometimes the situation would become too much and would stop him in his tracks. It came out of nowhere, always when he was alone, when nobody could see. An angry loneliness would blast through him like a shockwave, making him dizzy, and he would drop to his knees and wait for it to pass.

Connor wanted to cry, but he couldn't.

When his parents were delayed in Singapore, Toby's stay was extended. A week became two, became three. The strain of having to keep his temper in check was getting to Gordon. Connor could see that. The manager did his best to stay out of the way, but the funk of booze and body odour in his office was almost unbearable on the occasions Connor went in there. Total strangers, mostly Gordon's business associates, trooped in and out as usual, and there was often laughing and music behind the door into the early hours. Once, the copper from the nick, the one whose handcuffs he had stolen, came out without giving him a second glance. When he did emerge from his office, Gordon was snappy and irritable, and didn't care whether Toby saw it or not.

One night, it was Elliot's turn to help Gerry Dent make dinner, sausages and packet mash. Connor was sat between Ricky and Regina at one of the two dining tables. Chatter tumbled anxiously from Toby Turrell, opposite. The novelty of his presence had worn off. Most of the kids had become tired of his incessant stream of conversation and his knowledge about everything under the sun, and stayed out of his way.

And despite the increasingly bored efforts of Ronnie and Gerry to keep order, Toby had seen more than enough of the bullying and tension rife in the home, and spent a lot of time alone reading the books he'd brought with him. He was smiling as he babbled to Kenny, but Connor could sense his puzzlement about still being there.

'My parents are going to come for me, soon. They're coming to take me home. Shall we play a game after this, Kenny?'

'Don't feel like it,' mumbled Kenny, and turned away.

Connor hadn't seen Gordon. Usually, at about teatime, he strode from his office to bark instructions to the Dents, but tonight he was nowhere to be seen. Toby's voice soared above the other conversations at the table, grating on everybody's nerves.

'Daddy builds things.' His attention turned hopefully to Connor. 'And I help.'

Connor watched the kitchen doorway, suspicious. Elliot was walking around with a satisfied look on his face. Something was going on, something was definitely up.

'He likes to teach me things. Carpentry, pottery. Honest work, he calls it. When I'm older, when I'm grown up, I shall make the most beautiful things. Daddy says I will be a very useful chap.'

When Elliot brought the food in, softly placing the plates in front of the kids, there was an angelic expression on his face that had no business being there. Usually, he enjoyed dropping the plates of lumpy mash and gristly sausage hard on the table so that the gravy splashed everywhere. But there was a gentleness about his movements that hardened Connor's suspicions.

Connor was starving, as he always was on his delivery days. He was usually out of the door before breakfast, and back in the afternoon after walking miles. But looking down at the yellow splodge of mash in its puddle of thin gravy, he lost his appetite. He'd eat as much as he could stomach. The other children hungrily forked up their food as soon as it was put in front of them – everyone except Toby who, too busy talking, hadn't realised his plate hadn't arrived yet. Elliot came out of the kitchen with it, his thumb carelessly slipped into the mash.

Placing the plate down, he winked at Connor. 'Here you go.'

Toby didn't notice the food. 'You must be very careful near a lathe, and follow the safety instructions, or you will lose a hand.'

Finally, he picked up his fork and looked down.

The sound of his chair screeching on the linoleum cut through the conversation. Elliot guffawed, and the kids crowded around Toby to look. Scrabbling around the mound of mash, its legs flicking in the gravy, was a cockroach. Everyone giggled, including Connor. It was funny to see the little creature, shiny brown shell glistening with tiny globules of food, antennas jerking and twitching, as it stumbled around.

'Everybody back to your seats.' There were tears of laughter in Elliot's eyes, but his voice was firm. 'So Toby can eat.'

'But there's a . . .'

Debs reached for the plate. 'I'll take it back.'

'Leave it!' Elliot slammed his hand on the table. 'Nobody leaves here until their food is eaten. That's the rules.'

Connor had wondered when something like this was going to happen. Elliot had been spoiling for a fight with the kid since he'd arrived.

Toby gazed bleakly around the table. 'I can't!'

Nobody could take their eyes off the creature leaving trembling indentations in the mash. Elliot raised the plate to Toby's face.

'Eat it!'

'You ain't in charge, Elliot,' said Connor, leaping to his feet.

Sensing his best hope lay with him, Toby edged behind Connor.

'He's going to eat it.' Elliot's eyes flashed with anger. 'Or I'll stuff it down his throat myself! Shouldn't be a problem, his gob's always open!'

Meeting in the middle of the room, their foreheads bumped together hard. This wasn't about the new kid, Connor knew, he was just the excuse. Elliot had been boiling with resentment since he'd given him a hiding.

'You got me by surprise last time,' Elliot said hoarsely. 'But everyone knows I can take you, any time I want!'

'Gordon said we look after the kid,' Connor said.

'He don't get no special treatment!'

Elliot's forehead burned against his own. Connor was ready to teach him another lesson. This time he'd make sure Elliot stayed on the floor. He fancied giving him a hiding.

'What's going on here?'

When Gordon staggered into the room, Connor knew things were going to get worse. A wailing Toby raced to him, burying his head against the manager's chest. Gordon's hand stroked the boy's hair. Toby said something but his voice was muffled against Gordon's shirt, which was wet with his tears. The manager gently pulled back his head.

'Someone . . . put a cockroach . . . in my food!'

Out of the corner of his eye, unwilling to turn his face from Elliot, Connor glimpsed Sally in the doorway.

'Who did this?' Gordon slurred. His eyes moved slowly around the table, from Ricky to David to Debs and Cliff and Amelia. His gaze lingered on Jason. 'Was it you?'

When the boy's eyes nearly popped out of his head in terror, Gordon turned to Elliot.

'No, this smells like you.' Elliot stared back, defiant. 'I distinctly remember asking you to play nice.'

Connor moved towards the knives and forks on the table, but Elliot caught his eye. *Stay out of this.*

Gordon's smile twisted into a spiteful leer. 'I'm going to ask you one more time.'

'Yeah.' Tears welled in Elliot's eyes. He couldn't hide behind Connor, not this time. 'I did.'

'You can't find it in your shrivelled little heart to be kind to a new boy for five minutes? At least you're true to yourself, lad.'

The manager swiped him across the face with the back of his hand. Elliot flew backwards, crashing across the table. Plates and glasses smashed around his head when he hit the floor.

'Gordon!' Sally stumbled forwards.

'Poor Elliot's upset, so he is. He's not getting enough respect around here, isn't that right? So just this one time we're all going to do as King Elliot says.' He grabbed Toby. 'Come here, boy.'

'Gordon, that's enough.'

'Shut up!'

Sally flinched. Toby was crying harder now, his sobs unbearably loud as Gordon picked up the plate. When the kid squirmed, Gordon gripped his neck and forced his head to the food.

'Eat it,' said Gordon softly. The kids watched with a sick fascination as Toby picked up a lump of mash and put it in his quivering mouth. Tears and snot poured down his lips. The cockroach turned exhaustedly on the plate. 'All of it.'

Toby wailed. 'I'm not hungry!'

'Look at you.' The manager's voice was all cheery reason and encouragement, but his sweating, scarlet face told a different story. 'You're all skin and bones. Look how wee you are. What you need is protein. Eat it up.'

'I'm not hungry.'

'Look, I'll help you.' The manager picked up the cockroach, the creature's antennae rotating furiously in his fingers. 'Open wide.' Gordon forced open Toby's mouth and shoved the insect in. 'Now chew.'

The boy closed his mouth. Connor was sickened by the gagging sounds he made, the soft crunching in the heavy silence of the room. He saw Debs staring at him, a pleading look in her eyes, as if he could do something to make it stop. But Connor did nothing. These kids, they didn't care about him. Nobody wanted him there, they hated him – so he didn't lift a finger.

Ronnie Dent exploded with laughter, and Gerry smirked. Karen retched on the floor as Amelia ran from the room.

'That's good, now open your mouth,' Gordon said, forcing open his jaw. Toby's teeth and gums were smeared with brown juice, pulpy flecks of flesh and shell. 'Here's a good boy who does what he's told. The rest of you could learn a lesson from him.'

The plate of food dropped from Gordon's hand and clattered to the floor. He gripped the boy's neck. 'Now, me and Toby are going to my office. You boys and girls eat your dinners.'

Toby wasn't seen again that night.

26

Thistles scratched at Ray Drake's trousers as he stumbled along the side of Amelia Troy's warehouse. Something scampered away in the weeds. Drake pointed the torchlight at a rusted coke can, stepping carefully in the thick tangle. In this kind of place – remote, even in the heart of the city – there could be used syringes on the ground.

On the far side of the building, where scrub and thicket swept towards the train track, he switched off the torch and propped himself against the wall to listen for anything out of the ordinary, ignoring the shooting pains in his ribs. All he heard was the pounding in his own head, the dull ambient hum of the city at night.

After his attackers had fled, Drake had let himself into his house – the old woman was asleep downstairs, thankfully – to swallow pain-relief tablets. Livid bruises were already deepening across his chest and stomach. Pain crackled along his ribs, but he didn't think any were broken. He changed his suit and shirt and splashed water on his face, gingerly avoiding the swelling beneath his eyes.

A train clicked in the distance, a gentle rhythmic cascade. Drake continued along the wall and the tide of rubbish and rusted metal. The ground-floor windows were shuttered and protected by mesh. Steel plates were bolted across disused loading bays. If anyone had been here, stalking around the building, they were probably gone by now. If they *were* still here, the state he was in, he wasn't sure what he'd be able to do about it.

Amelia was standing at the door, silhouetted against the bare bulb, while he placed the torch in the boot of his car.

'Anything?' she called. 'There was definitely someone here, keeping close to the wall.'

Slamming the boot shut, pain knifed down his shoulder and he winced. 'Did you see them?'

'I saw their shadow on the ground.' When Drake approached, her hand flew to her face. 'Christ! What happened to you?'

'Somebody resisting arrest,' he said. 'It happens.'

Amelia stepped aside to let him inside. The heavy door clanged shut. She snapped two deadlocks, turned keys at the top and bottom of the door. Ascending in the wooden lift, Drake saw grey stubs of corridor flicker briefly in the wan bulb's light. This was a grim and foreboding place for anyone to live in, let alone a single woman.

'The other floors are alarmed,' she said, as if reading his mind. 'And the elevator is switched off every night. Nobody can get upstairs.' Her eyes flicked uncertainly to his. 'That's the idea, anyway.'

'I'm not sure you could live in a more insecure environment if you tried,' he said.

Following her out onto the concrete expanse of her floor, he saw the enormous space was lit by a dozen standing lamps, which didn't quite obliterate the pools of darkness in between. Nests of plug boxes snaked across the concrete. The long trestle table in the studio space had been cleared. Isolated in a soft puddle of light, Amelia's living space looked like a theatre set, a weird Pinteresque fever dream. The edges of the sofas were eaten away by shadow, the faceless torso of a wooden tailor's dummy listed on a pole at the edge of light. Somewhere, lost in the darkness, was her bed. Where her husband had died; where Amelia had nearly died.

'Very moody,' he said.

She tugged a cigarette from a packet on the sill. 'I know it's a bit eighties rock video, but it's all I've got left of Ned. I love it here most of the time . . . but maybe not tonight.' She lit the cigarette. 'I'm sorry, would you like a drink?'

'No, thanks,' he said, eyeing the bottle of beer on a coffee table beside a paperback biography of an artist he'd never heard of.

Amelia peered at him through a cloud of smoke. 'Of course, you're on duty. Or is that a myth about drinking on duty?'

'I just don't want to,' he said.

The paintings leaned against radiators looked ominous, the deep reds turned jet black in the gloom. When Amelia lifted the cigarette to her mouth, Drake saw her hand tremble.

'Tell me again,' he said.

She let out a deep breath and pointed down at his car. 'He ran across the gravel towards the door. He was moving fast, but I saw his shadow stretch along the ground. There's no reason to come down this end of the road unless you're here to visit any of the businesses on the way and they're shut, obviously. Occasionally kids hang about, but never this late.'

Drake shoved his hands in his pockets. 'You think it was a man.'

'In my experience, crazy stalkers tend to be men.'

'What time was this?'

'Uh.' She picked at the label on the bottle. 'It was about eleven o'clock. I haven't been . . . Well, earlier, I wasn't altogether truthful to you and your colleague. You gave me something of a shock, and I didn't say anything because I suppose I was feeling a bit defensive, but . . . I think someone's been watching me. It's nothing I can put my finger on. A strange feeling when I'm out, sometimes, or an odd miscall.'

'What kind of miscall?'

'When I answer, the caller hangs up. I've had three or four in the last few days. I can count on one hand the number of people who have my number. It could be some robot trying to sell insurance, of course.'

'Does the caller say anything?' Amelia shook her head. 'For your own piece of mind it might be a good idea to move out for a couple of days. Is there anybody you could stay with?'

'There's no one.'

'A hotel.'

'No, I want to stay here.' Her eyes flashed angrily, and she folded her arms across her chest. 'I'm sorry; I'm a bit on edge.'

'Of course.' Drake turned away. There were so many shadows you could hide a whole army of intruders. 'Do you mind if I look around?'

'Be my guest.' Smoke poured from her nostrils as she mashed the cigarette in an ashtray. 'By the way, I have something for you.'

Amelia looked through a pile of papers on a sill, and he walked around the windows, checking they were secure, and that the exit to the roof was locked. Eight floors up, it was unlikely anybody could get in, but after what happened to Ryan Overton . . .

'What does your wife feel about your working all hours of the night?' Amelia was standing behind him. Her gaze dropped to his wedding band, and he put his hand in his pocket. 'I'm sorry, there's probably some strict rule about asking policemen personal questions.'

'There's no rule about asking,' Drake said. 'But I've got one about answering.'

'DI Drake, have we . . . met before?' she asked. 'When you came this afternoon I had an overpowering sense that I knew you. You seem so . . . familiar to me.'

He began to move. 'Not as far as I know.'

'Were you one of the policemen who found Ned and me, perhaps? My memory of that time is a touch unreliable on account of my mostly, you know, being in a coma. And let's not forget the dissociative amnesia.' He sensed her keeping pace behind him. 'But maybe you came to the hospital.'

'No,' he said. 'We've never met.'

'That's a shame.' She swung round in front of him, touched his arm.

Her hand, hot and clammy, in his.

Head pulsing.

Fingers clawing at him.

'Because I don't get this feeling often, Detective Inspector.'

He nodded at the windows. 'Everything seems secure.'

'Good.' She let out a dramatic breath. 'I feel much better now that you've discharged your duty to your satisfaction. You'll probably be relieved to get away from the mad woman and home to the wife.'

'She died.' It was the last thing he should have said, but

the words slipped out unbidden. He was sickened by the urge he had to tell her.

'That explains why I feel I know you. You're another lost soul doomed to carry your dead spouse around with you. We're two peas in a pod.' When he looked away, she winced. 'Sorry, my morbid small talk isn't quite hitting the mark tonight. The truth is I'm scared.'

'You have no reason to be.'

'Don't I?' she said quickly. 'Every time I think everything's going to be okay . . . I thought my husband would keep me safe, but he used to . . . Ned was . . .' She smiled sadly. 'Well, I imagine you know all about Ned.'

Drake nodded. 'Yes.'

'That's past now, my husband will never touch me again, but I can't seem to be able to leave everything behind. And the worst thing is I don't even know what it is, who it is, that I should be scared of.'

They stood there for a long moment, and then she took his hand.

'Thank you for coming,' she said.

Smoke bulging beneath the door.

Threats, obscenities, in his ear.

Her hand, hot, in his.

She withdrew her hand and rubbed her calloused fingertips self-consciously. 'One of the problems of being an artist, I'm afraid. Paints and detergents play havoc with your skin.'

'If you feel safer now . . .'

'Time for bed,' she said. 'I'll take something to knock myself out.' Amelia held up her hands quickly, smiling. 'Oh, don't worry, DI Drake, these days it's strictly prescription.'

'Then I'll go.'

'Wait,' she said. 'The last time you were here you and your colleague asked if I had been in contact with anyone from the home. I remembered today that someone wrote to me.' She gave him a slip of paper with a name on it, Deborah Yildiz, and an address in South London. 'This woman has written to me several times saying that she was at the Longacre and asking to meet. I never replied. I get a lot of mail from people and, well, they often ask for money . . . and you know how I feel about that place.'

On the way down, they stood beneath the yellow wash of the elevator bulb.

'If you hear anything else, or if anything else occurs to you,' he said, 'call me.'

'And I've DS Crowley's number.'

'Call me,' he said, and she smiled.

On the ground floor Amelia unlocked the steel door and pulled back the deadbolts. When he stepped outside she gave him a curious look.

'You don't seem like the kind of man who shares information about himself very often, DI Drake. I'm sorry, I've already embarrassed you, so, in for a penny . . . You look like a man with a lot of stuff packed down tightly. I just wanted to say . . . it doesn't work. Take it from somebody who knows.' In the gloom, Drake thought he saw tears glisten in her eyes. 'Just let go of whatever it is or you will never be free.'

He stared as she closed the door on him.

Outside, listening to the locks snap into place, Drake took out the slip of paper and read the name and address.

The name Deborah only registered very dimly. There

were so many kids in that place, so many faces. But Kenny's cuttings included the name Deborah Willetts. It would very difficult for Flick to trace her if Yildiz was her married name.

He only hoped the man who called himself the Two O'Clock Boy hadn't found her first.

27

Rusting appliances were stacked against a metal fence outside the scruffy ground-floor maisonette on an estate in Somers Town. Rubbish spewed from the gaping mouth of a wheelie bin. Flick stepped over the carcass of a cooked chicken, heard the rasping thump of heavy bass coming from an upstairs window.

Despite a good night's sleep at her sister's – not even the three young children screaming up and down the hallway at the crack of dawn could wake her – she felt drained. When her phone alarm went off she took a shower, dressed and slipped out of the house while everyone was having breakfast. The kids chattered, and she heard Nina's patient voice trying to keep some semblance of order – *move your chair so others can sit down, Coral; who wants juice?* – while a cheerful pop song played on the radio. The smell of eggs and coffee made Flick hesitate at the door, but she couldn't face a repeat of the previous night's conversation. She'd managed to avoid bursting into tears then, but more apologies from Nina would only her upset her again. And her sister would bring up Harry, insisting Flick should let bygones be bygones with their father. Flick wasn't in the mood for a repeat of that conversation.

She rang the bell, and the door was opened by a woman wearing a tartan onesie and flip-flops. Her thin, undernourished hair was feathered around her face, and her bottled tan, which looked positively terracotta in the morning sun, streaked at the nape of her neck.

The woman's eyes flashed with expectation beneath long false lashes. 'You from social services?'

'Police.' Flick took out her ID. 'Detective Sergeant Flick Crowley.'

The woman threw her head back, exasperated. 'I thought we'd got all this sorted. Either take him away or leave us alone.'

'I don't know what you think this is about, but I was hoping to talk to Mr Ronnie Dent.'

'Is that right? Whatever it is you think he's done, you're wrong. Because he ain't left the house for three godawful years.'

'I wanted to talk to him about somewhere he worked years ago. He may be able to provide information.'

'A cold case!' The woman's eyebrows shot up. 'Like on the television.'

'Yes,' said Flick. 'That's exactly it.'

'You ain't come to take him away, then? Because it won't take me long to pack his stuff. He don't have much to his name; anything he owned was sold years ago.'

'Not today.'

The woman's sour attitude returned. 'Better come in.'

The hallway was crowded with cardboard boxes and supermarket bags, and smelled of old socks and pork chops. The pounding bass made the light shade sway. She led Flick upstairs, a cigarette packet outlined in a pocket against one buttock and a mobile phone in the other.

'I'm his granddaughter, by the way. Julie. I've been going on about getting him moved to a home for years. I told the social workers but it's murder getting them to listen. The way Grandad is now,' she whispered fiercely, 'he's driving us mental.'

'Us?' asked Flick.

'Me and that brother of mine.' At the top of the stairs, Julie Dent rapped on a door with the edge of a bulky ring. 'Turn that bloody music down!' A voice returned fire inside, but the volume edged down. 'We're only kids, really. It ain't fair that we have to put up with it.'

Flick had presumed Julie was approaching middle age, but looking closer, saw that she was a lot younger, in her mid-twenties, perhaps.

'Gran died years ago. Gerry went out in a blaze of glory, downed three bottles of Duty Free.' She nodded appreciatively. 'He don't leave his room no more, except to piss. His lungs have almost packed in. There must be somewhere they can take him; he finds it a strain here, poor soul. We do our best, course we do, but he does our heads in most of the time.'

The walls of Ronnie Dent's bedroom were painted a depressing beige colour and stained with damp, the worn carpet moth-eaten. The smell was diabolical. Julie cracked a window.

'Jesus, Grandad, it's like someone died in here.'

An old man lay in bed, his emaciated body outlined beneath a single sheet. He was peering up at a portable television atop a wardrobe. His granddaughter quickly pulled the sheet over his arms. 'Look at you, you exhibitionist, showing off all your saggy bits. You got a visitor.'

Thud, thud, thud. The bass throbbed next door.

The old man ignored them both.

'Mr Dent, I'm Detective Sergeant Flick Crowley. I was wondering if I could ask you a few questions.'

Perching on the end of the bed, she tried not to look at the twisting brown nails on his yellow feet, which poked from beneath the sheet like jagged shards of broken pottery. Dent was watching a children's show, all primary colours, baby voices and trilling xylophones. 'It's about the Longacre home in Hackney. You worked there in the nineteen eighties, I understand.'

'Probably don't remember, do you, Grandad?' Julie returned Flick's look. 'He can barely remember what day it is, or his grandson's name.'

'It's Liam, you silly cow,' Dent snarled. 'And it's Tuesday.'

'But it ain't, is it?' Julie surged forward, teeth bared. 'It ain't Tuesday! See what I mean? He winds me right up!'

The old man scowled. 'Get me a tea! Four sugars.'

'I'll get you something in a minute!' Julie spat, and shot a crafty glance at Flick. 'We like a bit of banter, don't we, Grandad?'

Flick noticed discolouration at the top of the old man's arms. Pulling the sheet down, she saw cloudy bruises.

'How did you get those, Ronnie?'

'He falls over. His balance ain't good,' Julie said. 'Is it, Grandad?'

'My balance ain't good.'

'We do our best, but we're busy people, I got a part-time job. And him next door is useless, well, he's only a kid. I've said it once, I've said it a thousand times, Grandad should be in a home. We love him, of course we do, but it's not like we're close or anything.'

Thud, thud, thud. The music was so loud Flick could barely hear herself think.

'The Longacre . . .' The deep creases in the old man's

forehead crinkled. 'Yeah, I worked there. Me and Gerry.'

'You never told me you worked at a children's home?' said Julie. 'What the fuck do you know about kiddies?'

Ronnie Dent narrowed his eyes. 'There's plenty you don't know about me.'

'I bet there fucking is!' Julie erupted. 'No secret money stashed away, though, aye? No pot of gold! You're a drain on the house, you eat my food, use my electricity!' Her voice was shrill. 'Soil your clothes!'

'You're a hateful person!'

Thud, thud, thud, through the walls.

'I got cause! You're a vampire sucking the life out of me. They should put you down!'

'Get away from me!' *Thud, thud, thud.*

Flick stood. 'Julie, would you do me a favour and ask . . . ?'

'His name is Liam.'

'Would you ask Liam to turn down the music?'

Julie sucked air through her teeth. 'I'll see what I can do, but I ain't promising anything. He don't listen to me, nobody does in this house.'

Flip-flops slapping on the carpet, she left. Flick sat back down on the bed. The old man's eyes were clamped on the television.

'You worked at the Longacre, Mr Dent . . .'

'Did I?' His eyes narrowed. 'Maybe. I don't remember.'

Flick grabbed her notebook. 'You said you and your wife worked there, Mr Dent.'

He sighed. 'I miss her.'

'I bet the pair of you had some happy times.' Both the Dents had recorded offences going back years, including ABH, fraud, various drugs, shoplifting and a few motoring misdemeanours. Happy times, indeed. 'I'm going to read out the names of children at the home to see if you remember them . . . Deborah Willetts.'

His attention drifting back to the TV, Dent shook his head vaguely. The bass next door was joined by the growl of a furious argument between Julie and Liam.

'David Horner,' Flick said, watching him closely. 'Karen Smith.'

Thud, thud, thud. Thud, thud, thud.

Snatching up the remote, Dent lifted it at the television. The volume went up, competing against the bass and the argument.

'Toby Turrell,' Flick said loudly. 'Ricky Hancock . . . Jason Burgess . . .'

This was no good. She was getting nowhere.

'Kenny Overton . . . Elliot Juniper . . . Amelia Troy . . .'

The old man stared at the television.

'Connor Laird,' she said.

His Adam's apple jerked. His hand shot out to grab at her wrist.

'Connor Laird,' Dent whispered. His tongue darted between his teeth. His grip was feeble but his papery touch was repulsive.

Leaning close to hear him better, she asked: 'Do you remember him, Ronnie?'

And then he bellowed in her face, a bovine wail that drowned out the TV, the music and voices. Flick lurched back.

The thin sheet covering the old man dropped from his bony chest as he jerked upright to let out another scream. Within a moment, Julie Dent was back in the room, along with an acne-scarred kid in a baseball cap, who laughed. 'He's off again!'

'Now look!' shouted Julie, over the old man's wail. 'I knew this would happen!'

'Connor Laird,' said Flick. 'Do you remember him?'

The old man's distress increased. The boy doubled over. 'Go on, Grandad,' he jeered. 'Let it all out!'

Julie grabbed Flick by the shoulders. 'Look what you've done!'

'He recognises the name,' said Flick. The hairs on the back of her neck stood up.

The missing kid: Connor Laird. Dent was terrified of him.

'He don't know fuck all about anything.' Julie's face twitched with anger. 'He's a senile old fool and I've had it with him.' She reeled towards the old man, holding a hand above her head. 'Up to here!'

The kid in the cutting: Connor Laird.

Thud, thud, thud.

'Having a bad trip, Grandad, yeah?' The boy walked out, laughing.

Something about that cutting.

Ronnie Dent screamed: 'Don't let him near me!'

Flick moved closer. 'Who, Ronnie? Connor Laird?'

The old man's pigeon chest heaved. 'Don't let him near!'

'I think you'd better leave!' said Julie Dent.

'Keep him away!'

Flick needed to get out of there. Without looking back – the music and wailing in her ears, the boy's cruel laughter – she clattered down the stairs, cracking her shin on a side table at the bottom.

Julie followed her down, shouting as Flick heaved open the door. The knocker juddered. 'You tell the social services to come and get him! Or I'll dump him on the motorway, you see if I don't!'

When the door slammed behind her, and she'd made it all the way down the path in one piece, Flick placed her hands on her hips and breathed out slowly to calm herself.

That name repeating in her head. Connor Laird.

The kid from the missing photograph.

The torn cutting.

The boy in that cutting.

Connor Laird.

Something about that cutting.

28

He'd barely pulled past Loughborough Junction, with its railway bridges cutting across the roofs in every direction, when he saw water pour from a turning and gush into the drain, thick black smoke tumbling above it. And he knew he was already too late.

Drake rolled his Mercedes past the turning, stopping on Coldharbour Lane, just past the junction, to watch the fire engines, patrol cars and ambulances blocking off a street. Evacuated residents stood watching in slippers and dressing gowns as firefighters dragged hoses back and forth beneath the black smoke rolling from the first-floor window of a mansion block.

There was no point in staying. He sensed already what had happened in this South London street. The body of Deborah Yildiz, formerly Willetts, would be found in that building – and her family, if she had any.

The last thing he needed was local police asking awkward questions and making a note of his car and registration. So he quickly scanned the openings to the crooked alleys sliced into the junction, with their walkways and shuttered businesses – the auto repair shops and joineries and design companies wedged into the narrow spaces – and decided to leave. Reaching for the ignition, his eyes whipped past the side mirror –

And caught sight of the figure by the entrance of the overground train station.

It wore dark clothes and a woollen hat pulled low, and the instant Drake saw it, it started moving.

Drake accelerated into the next turning to circle back, past the grinding pumps and the shouts of the firemen, towards the station. Adrenalin spiked in his veins, washing away the pain. He gunned the engine beneath the bridge, turning into the road he thought the figure had disappeared along.

And he thought: What next?

What would he do when he caught the Two O'Clock Boy?

He didn't want to contemplate what had to be done, and was almost relieved when he lost sight of the tall man. Drake cruised slowly along the road, tower blocks looming beyond a green space on the left, twisting in his seat to find him. But the pavements on either side were empty. The figure could have doubled backed behind the station, or vanished into the maze of surrounding streets.

But then he saw a flicker of movement in the rear-view, saw the top of the woollen hat bobbing behind a row of cars in the narrow alley beneath the arches of a railway bridge. Drake pumped the brakes. Reversed back, swerving with a screech so that the nose of his car was pointed down the alley.

And there was the guy, the so-called Two O'Clock Boy, running down the middle towards a dead end. Drake saw a flash of pale flesh as the figure darted a look over his shoulder.

And then he put his foot down.

The car surged forwards. A high chain-link fence blocked off the far end. The row of cars on the park side were bumper to bumper. Drake would be on him in less than a minute. He saw the figure thicken in his vision, saw it dart another look over its shoulder, its features hidden beneath the hat. The road was empty of people. Drake debated what to do. He could injure the guy, knock him over the roof of the car, and then tip him into the boot . . .

Or he could finish it.

The shuttered businesses built into the arches flew past – Drake swerved to miss a concrete block in the road – keeping pace with the loping figure, still deciding what to do. The answer came to him, and it was obvious.

End it now. Here on this long, empty lane.

He accelerated, gaining ground quickly, and the figure loomed closer, its arms and legs pumping ineffectually. The man panicked, tried to jump over a car bonnet, but misjudged the leap and bounced off its door, going down in the road. And Drake pressed his foot hard on the pedal, the engine roaring in his ears, bearing down on him.

He'd drive into him, send him flying into the air so that he fell to the floor in a heap of broken bones. He'd dump the body somewhere. The whole nightmare would be over. April would be safe.

It was the only way.

The figure scrambled to its feet as Drake's car hurtled at him, and spun. Drake glimpsed a pale whirl of face just as one of the wheels bumped over a brick. The car's suspension lifted, and when it dropped—

The figure was gone.

Drake slammed his foot on the brake, gripping the wheel

as the Mercedes drifted, tyre rubber burning, and came to a screeching halt. He jumped from the car.

Door alarm pulsing: *ping ping ping.*

There was nothing in front of the car – nobody.

He kicked the door shut and moved stiffly to the pavement. The businesses were padlocked, the man nowhere to be seen. A few yards further along one arch hadn't been developed, providing a cut-through beneath the bridge. Light poured in from the other side. Drake ducked beneath the curling corner of wire mesh that covered the opening. He moved quickly over the accumulation of stinking rubbish, and out the other side into another set of arches. The space on this side was much wider and the bridge opposite soared higher. At the far end, a group of men loaded planks of wood onto a lorry.

When Drake heard a noise coming from behind a protruding wall to his left, he plucked a brick from the floor and swung round the other side, his arm up, ready to fight. Saw a group of young men – two white, two black. Money changing hands – some kind of drug deal. They stared at Drake and the brick.

'What the—?' The kids stepped back in shock.

'Where is he?' said Drake.

'Who the fuck are you?' one of them stammered.

A couple edged away, a couple moved forward. Drake didn't have time for this. 'The man who came through here.'

One of the kids stomped towards him, and Drake drew back his arm, ready to pound the brick into his face, in no mood to take another beating. The kid thought better of it, and fled. Spooked, the others followed, bolting towards the entrance of the road.

Drake dropped the brick, slapped the dust from his fingers, walking into the wide, open space filled with diggers and skips of scrap metal. The Two O'Clock Boy was gone, if he had even come this way in the first place. Drake made his way back beneath the arch. The brickwork roared around him as a train trundled above. His head was filled with sound, and a sudden, unwelcome memory of the track that ran behind the Longacre.

He climbed into his car and sat behind the wheel, thinking he had lost the last, best chance to get the man he had briefly known decades ago, and whose fragile emotional state had tipped into a murderous psychosis. Taking out his phone, Ray Drake thought briefly about trying to speak to April again, but immediately pocketed it. And then he smelled the tang of something in the compartment.

Petrol.

Before he could react, a hand whipped from behind to pull his head back, and a blade was placed against his throat. Drake sucked down a breath, fully expecting to never get the chance to let it out again. Expecting to see his own hot blood spurt across the dash and windscreen. When the blade slashed his jugular he would bleed to death in a matter of minutes. Even quicker, if the carotid artery was sliced open.

His quick, shallow breaths masked the excited, rasping exhalations of the man hidden in the back. Drake's eyes lifted to the rear-view mirror, but his assailant was safely hidden out of sight.

'So this is it,' said Drake. 'You're going to kill me.'

What he felt, more than anything, was anger at a wasted opportunity. If he had pressed his foot on the accelerator earlier, he would have killed the man who called himself the Two O'Clock Boy. He should have finished the job. Instead, he was going to die and the realisation sickened him . . . April would be next.

The blade tightened against his throat. He felt it nick into his skin.

'Like you killed those others.' Drake's heart clattered against his chest. His eyes lifted to the empty mirror. 'Tell me about them.'

He felt hot breath in his ear, smelled the trace of a familiar scent. But nobody spoke.

A horn blasted, he heard an engine. A van pulled up behind his own car, a voice calling: 'Move it!'

'Kill me and this is finished. You leave everybody else alone. I'm the one you want, right? I saved your life, I kept you alive, I'm responsible. Nobody else needs to get hurt.'

The gloved hand tightened around his forehead. His head was yanked back hard. The tip of the blade probed the flesh at his throat. Drake imagined the torn meat of his trachea suddenly flopping onto his chest, followed by a deluge of his blood. He closed his eyes, and thought of how much he loved his daughter and how much he loved his wife.

'Kill me, but leave my daughter. *Please*, leave my daughter. All you have to do is say yes.'

The breath pumped, quick and eager.

'Come on, mate,' called the voice in the van, 'move!' The horn blasted again.

'Let me hear you say it. *Yes*.' But the man in the back didn't speak, he didn't want to be identified, and it gave Drake a glimmer of hope. 'You'd better finish the job now, or I will come for you and I will kill you. Do you understand me?'

He heard a smack of lips, and the blade was pressed so hard against his Adam's apple that he could barely swallow.

'Don't be shy,' said Drake. 'Just say yes.'

Then a door slammed on the van, and footsteps approached. Drake's head was released. The knife glinted past his eyes as it whipped away. The back door opened, and Drake hit his door release to stumble into the alley. But the van driver was already in front of him, remonstrating. 'Come on, fella, shift the car, some of us have work to do.'

Legs shaking, Drake slumped against the door to watch the Two O'Clock Boy, face hidden by the woollen hat, escape across the park.

29

When she arrived in the Incident Room, Flick was mortified to see Eddie Upson at the whiteboard. She'd phoned to warn her team that she'd be late, but he had already taken the daily meeting, held first thing every morning, in her absence. Vix Moore eyed her walking past and murmured something to Kendrick. In contrast, Millie Steiner, bless her heart, gave Flick an encouraging nod.

'Sorry I'm late,' Flick told Eddie, who followed her into her office. 'I had someone to go and see on the way in.'

'No problem,' he said, 'but we may need a new whiteboard.'

Flick slapped the space bar on her keyboard to awaken the screen. 'Why?'

Eddie held up a marker pen. 'I thought this was a magic marker, but it's permanent ink.'

'You need alcohol.'

Upson rolled his eyes. 'Tell me about it.'

'To clean the whiteboard,' she said.

'Yeah, that's what I meant.'

'Do me a favour, Eddie,' said Flick, as he turned to go. 'I need an address.'

'I'll get Vix to do it. Wait, I'll *try* to get Vix to do it.'

'No,' said Flick. The last thing she needed was DC Moore asking awkward questions. 'I'd rather you did it. It's Elliot—'

But then Ray Drake walked in and she blinked, astonished, at the livid yellow bruises beneath one eye, the red nick across his throat.

'Juniper?' Eddie was unaware of Drake behind him. 'The name you mentioned yesterday, do you still want it?'

'Please,' she said, but she must have looked a picture because Eddie followed her gaze, seeing the DI's terse expression, closing the door behind him.

'What on earth happened?'

'It was nothing.' Drake lowered himself stiffly into a chair. 'Some kids attempted to relieve me of my wallet last night, shoved me the ground. They got in a couple of kicks and ran.'

'Did you report it?'

'No point, it was too dark to get a good look at them. Anyway . . .' Drake seemed agitated to Flick. 'Where are we on the investigation?'

Several of the plastic pockets containing the newspaper articles were peeking from a drawer of her desk. She'd not put them back in the Property Room, but had closed the drawer when she'd left yesterday.

'Has anybody been working in here?'

'The cleaners were in my office, so I used your desk earlier,' said Drake. 'I trust that's okay.'

Drake in the basement, stepping forward.

A cough – another sound.

Tucking the plastic inside, she closed the drawer. 'Of course.'

'Holloway's people need to get a move on with the forensic reports,' he said. 'And there's plenty of CCTV still to get through. Steiner's doing her best, but she's snowed under.'

'I'll get someone to help her.'

'Ryan Overton had links with some people who steal scrap metal and sell it on, did you know that?'

'I'll get up to date as soon as I get my email working.'

Drake stood to go, but then turned irritably. 'Why do you want Elliot Juniper's address?'

She prodded at her mouse. 'Is your email down?'

'Flick,' Drake said quietly, 'tell me you've dropped the other stuff, this children's home nonsense.'

'Why?' She struggled to keep the shrillness out of her voice. 'All these years you've told me to trust my instincts, told me to think less like a bureaucrat and more like a detective. Now I am, and you're annoyed.'

Drake came around the desk. There was a splash of mud on one of his shoes. He wasn't the kind of man who wore dirty shoes. But then, the whole world seemed to be turning on its head, these days.

'Amelia Troy was a dead end. She knew nothing about this home you've become obsessed with.'

'Because she can't remember a thing!'

'What have you been doing?'

'Connor Laird,' she barked at him, and Drake flinched, as if she'd shot him in the chest. 'The boy named in the caption of the missing—'

'I recognise the name.'

'There's an old man called—'

'Flick—' Drake pinched the bridge of his nose in exasperation.

'Just hear me out.' Her heart was pumping. 'There's an old guy called Ronnie Dent who worked at the Longacre home. When I mentioned Connor Laird's name he became hysterical. He was ranting and raving, and terrified of the boy even after all these years. I've tried to look him up, guv, but there's no record of a Connor Laird anywhere. No convictions, no social security or national insurance, no driving license, nothing. The boy disappeared into thin air.'

'So he's dead, or emigrated.' Drake folded his arms. 'It's been three decades.'

'Maybe.' She took the cutting with the photo torn from it out of the drawer, and slipped it across the desk. 'Or maybe not. All I know is that all the other children in that caption are dead.'

'Except Amelia Troy.'

'Yes.'

'And, as far as we know, Deborah Willetts.' He plunged his hands into his pockets, turned to the window. 'She's probably married now, living out her life in quiet obscurity.'

'But everybody else . . .' she said quickly. 'I'd like to speak to your—'

'I've told you, absolutely not. She's a frail old lady.'

'Then I'll speak to Elliot Juniper.'

'Right now, DS Crowley,' he said, 'the best thing you could do is concentrate on your job while you still have one. Because, to be honest, I'm running out of patience with this . . . farce.'

'I'll go in my free time.'

'You're investigating four murders, you have *no* free time.'

As he strode to the door, Flick jumped up so quickly that her chair rolled into the radiator behind. 'What were you doing in the Property Room?'

A muscle ticked in Drake's jaw. 'I'm going to forget you spoke to me like that.'

Then he left, slamming the door behind him.

Flick's face burned. She had the terrifying, and oddly liberating, feeling that she had gone too far. The sensible thing to do would be to go next door to rally the troops, get up to speed on the morning's developments. If need be, she'd hold the meeting all over again, just to show who was in charge. For the moment, at least, she was still leading this damned investigation.

But instead she picked up the article about the visit of the Drakes to the home, let the plastic sheet flap gently in her fingers.

There was something about this particular cutting that gnawed at her.

A cough, another sound, Drake stepped forward.

A cough, a *tearing* sound.

The surprise on his face – no, the *shock* – when he saw her.

Flick fumbled the half-page back into the pocket, put it in a drawer. She took a small key from the shallow plastic tray where she kept staples and paperclips, and locked it.

Just as the office door flew openly so violently that it bounced against the wall and shuddered. Drake stood there.

'Come on,' he said.

'Where are we going?'

'To finish this once and for all.'

30

The journey out of London took far too long because of endless northbound roadworks. By the time the motorway snarl cleared, Drake had twenty minutes of hard, fast cruising before he eased his Mercedes off the M11.

Once again Flick spent most of the journey on her phone, keeping on top of things in the office and filling Drake in on developments – if you could even call them that. In particular, Kendrick and Moore had tried to link the Overton murders with a series of burglaries that had recently plagued the borough. But the modus operandi was completely different, and that line of inquiry stalled quickly. It didn't stop Vix from speaking at great length about all the work she had put in.

Ray Drake had come to keep an eye on Flick, and also to put to bed once and for all her obsession with the Longacre. But there was another reason. He wanted to get the measure of Elliot after all these years. Wanted to see him, but not be seen.

After all, Elliot had been one of Gordon's Two O'Clock Boys.

In between calls, Flick gazed tensely out of the window, and Drake thought of that journey from the police station to the Longacre in Sally's car – the stifling heat, the stench of tobacco smoke – all those decades ago.

Following the navigation system's instructions, they drove

past a war memorial on a village green the size of a billiard table, and along a series of winding lanes, past woods and fields. Drake kept an eye on the rear-view mirror, half expecting a murderous face to pop up in the back.

'Not long now,' he said, turning into a lane that was almost hidden from the main road. The car's suspension bounced on the uneven surface. Drake eased past Elliot Juniper's cottage, alongside a listing barn set back from the road, and reversed up the drive, cranked the handbrake on the steep slope. Smoke billowed from the chimney of the cottage.

When Flick opened her door, he said, 'I'll stay here.'

'Aren't you coming in?' she asked, surprised.

'I've some calls to make,' he lied. 'You go ahead.'

She hesitated a moment, then climbed out. Drake adjusted the side mirror to get a better view of the cottage door, watched her climb the drive and knock.

It had been a long time since Drake had seen Elliot Juniper, but he hadn't changed, not really. Much of his bulk had slid down his torso in middle age: a bulging stomach drooped over the belt of his jeans. His hair was shaved, perhaps because there wasn't much left to grow. From this distance, Elliot's flattened nose appeared to spiral on his face, like an optical effect.

Drake cracked the window, but Flick and Elliot were too far away for him to hear anything above the shiver of the leaves on the wall of trees in the lane.

Inside. Drake watched them linger on the doorstep. *Go inside.*

But instead Elliot left the door ajar behind him and walked with Flick halfway down the slope. Drake heard her voice, but not her words. Shoulders slumped, the big man crossed his arms and listened, that same anxious expression etched into his face all these years later.

Don't mention my name, Drake thought.

Flick nodded at the car. Elliot glanced towards the Mercedes. Ray Drake was safely hidden behind his headrest, but Elliot stooped as he tried to see inside. *Not my name.* She said something, and Elliot responded. His eyes widened and he bent his knees, once again trying to see inside.

'Damn it,' said Drake, annoyed that he couldn't hear a thing. He pushed open the car door, crunched across the stony ground towards them. As he approached, Flick was saying: '. . . to know if you have seen Connor Laird.'

Looking from Flick to Drake, Elliot laughed in astonishment. 'Is this some kind of joke?'

Drake took out his ID and held it up, kept it suspended in front of Elliot's face to let the name and the photo fully sink in. 'DI Ray Drake.'

'Is that right?' Elliot gaped at the contusions and bruises on his face, the angry red dash at his throat. 'You look like you've been through the wars, if you don't mind me saying.'

'Answer the question, please,' said Drake. 'Have you lately seen a man called . . .' he turned to Flick. 'What is he called again? Connor . . .'

'Laird,' she said.

Elliot shook his head, bewildered. 'I don't . . .'

'Have you?' Drake asked tersely.

'No,' said Elliot, staring at Drake.

'Or anybody else from the Longacre?' Flick said.

'Ain't been in touch with any of that lot for years. It's all ancient history.' He turned finally to her. 'And as I told you, I haven't been in trouble with the law for donkey's.'

'Nobody's suggesting you have, sir.'

Elliot's gaze kept returning to Drake. 'You said this was to do with Kenny Overton's death?'

'So you haven't heard from Kenny?' asked Flick.

Hesitating, the big man turned his phone in his fingers. But standing out of Flick's sightline, Drake shook his head slowly, emphatically. The answer is: *no*.

'I only know what I saw on television, about him and his family. A terrible business. But what's it got to do with me?'

'Nothing. It's a routine visit,' said Drake. 'We're speaking to anybody who may have known Kenny.'

'You're going a hell of a way back.'

'What was he like?' asked Flick.

'Who? Kenny?'

'Connor Laird.'

Elliot crossed his arms. 'As I say, it was a long time ago. We was kids.'

'What do you remember about him?'

'I remember he did this to my nose.' Elliot held a finger up to his face and laughed, bleakly. 'Everyone was scared of good old Connor. He was cold, unpredictable. You never knew what he would do next.'

'Would you recognise him if you saw him?' asked Flick.

Elliot looked at her in surprise, but before he could answer, a teenager came up the slope, a pair of bulky headphones folded over his head. He walked backwards, admiring the Mercedes unexpectedly parked there. When he saw Elliot with two strangers, he pulled the phones to his shoulders. Music ticked from the earpads.

'This is my boy,' said Elliot bashfully. 'Dylan.'

How do you do, Dylan?' Flick held out her hand. 'Detective Sergeant Flick Crowley.'

'Police,' said Dylan flatly.

'A clever boy, takes after his old man.' Elliot winked at Dylan. 'It ain't nothing to worry about. They're asking about stuff that happened a long time ago, when I was your age. I'll see you inside.'

Dylan looked uncertainly at them and then trudged to the house.

'Nice kid,' said Flick.

'Couldn't ask for better,' said Elliot. 'Was there anything else?'

Flick was about to speak, but Drake said impatiently, 'No, we'll leave you alone. Thank you for your cooperation.'

He held out his hand. Elliot considered it doubtfully, then shook, and Drake walked to the car to wait for Flick to follow him back.

'He's lying,' said Flick, pulling her seat belt around her. 'You can tell.'

'About what?' Drake reached for the ignition.

'I don't know exactly,' she said. 'But he was as pale as a ghost.'

'He's a man with a criminal record who's just received an unexpected visit from two Met police officers,' said Drake. 'That fear of the law never goes away.'

He flung open the door suddenly. Flick asked, 'Where are you going?'

'Forgot to give him a card.' Drake reached into his jacket. 'Won't be a moment.'

He walked back to the cottage, beneath the swaying trees.

A gust of wind sent a spurt of leaves flying around his head like demented bats.

Before he even knocked on the door, it opened. There was an edge of panic in Elliot's voice: 'All these years later and imagine my surprise at who comes knocking. What the fuck is going on?'

'Step inside,' said Drake. 'We don't have much time.'

A fire crackled in the room, which was small and tidy. Smoke tumbled against the blackened brick and pulled into the chimney.

When Drake started to speak, Elliot put a finger to his lips, nodded upstairs. 'The walls in this house are as thin as a fag paper.'

'Where were you this morning? At about six a.m.?'

'Where do you think? I was in bed.' Elliot looked annoyed, but also afraid, and Drake believed him. Elliot's conviction sheet didn't exactly scream *criminal genius*.

'We're in trouble.'

Elliot laughed bleakly. 'I figured you'd grow up to be many things, but a copper wasn't one of them.'

'I've got a certain skill at it.'

'I bet you have at that.'

'Listen to me.' Drake stepped forward. 'People we knew from the Longacre are being killed. Kenny and his wife and sons are just the latest.'

'One son.' Elliot blinked. 'The news said one son.'

'The second was murdered last night. Thrown off a tower block.'

Elliot blinked. 'Who else, then?'

'People from the home.'

'*Which* people from the home?'

'Most of them.' Elliot's eyes bulged in horror. Drake lifted the net curtain in the window to peer down the drive. 'Jason, David, Regina, Karen, Ricky. Debs was killed this morning. They're just the ones I know about.'

'And who do you figure for this?'

Drake dropped the curtain. 'He calls himself the Two O'Clock Boy.'

'Fuck, fuck, fuck.' Elliot dragged his hands down his face. 'You are fucking kidding me.'

'I think we're next.' There was a movement on the floorboards above, and Drake lowered his voice. 'I think he's coming after us.'

'I *know* him.' Elliot groaned. 'Calls himself Gavin.'

'He calls himself a lot of things these days.'

'He told me about Kenny. I gave him money.'

'Money?'

'Lots of money. Is that what this is about, money? If that's what he wants, he can keep it.'

'What does he look like, this Gavin?'

'I don't know, like some bloke.' Elliot grimaced, thinking. 'Uh, tall.'

'He had a clear opportunity to kill me this morning, but he didn't.' Lifting the curtain again, Drake saw Flick climb from the car and look up at the cottage. 'I think he's left us last for a reason.'

'And why's that?' Elliot snatched a packet of cigarettes off the arm of a sofa, fumbled one from the packet.

'Because he hates us, because he blames us for what happened to him,' said Drake, 'because he's insane. He's methodical, patient and very angry. He's killed those people and their families over a long period of time. Found them, murdered them, left no trace – until now. He wants us to know what he's doing.'

'Us?'

'He's got something special planned for you and me, I think.'

'He was a basket case back then, no question. But a murderer?'

Drake watched Elliot light the cigarette and take quick, nervous puffs. 'You married, Elliot?'

'I've a partner. Dylan's my stepson.'

'He'll kill them, too. It's what he does.'

Elliot tried to keep the panic from his voice. 'What am I going to say to Rhonda? What am I going to tell her?'

'You don't tell her anything. You all go away for a while, don't tell anybody where, till I can get to him.'

'I told you, I've got *no* money, he took it all, and I just happen to be all out of magic fucking beans.'

'I need a gun,' said Drake. 'Do you have one?'

'Me? No!' Elliot grimaced. 'What would I do with one of those? What are you going to do, shoot him?'

'Yes.'

Cigarette smoke danced in front of Elliot's face as he lifted his hand to rub his eyes. 'I could do without all this right now, to be honest.'

'You smoking?' called Dylan at the top of the stairs.

Elliot jumped at the sound of his voice. 'Sorry, I'm putting it out now.'

He opened the door and threw out the cigarette, which bounced and sparked on the stony drive. Drake saw Flick waiting impatiently by the car and turned to go, but Elliot grabbed his arm.

'That place, I'll never get it out of my system, I've always known that. It's like a bullet embedded near my heart, slowly working its way in. I've always known that one day it'll be the end of me. It's going to kill me stone dead. But right now I've got a good life, a family, something I never thought would be for the likes of me. And just as I start to feel a little peace, a little . . . normality, you come back into my life, you along with that, that . . .' He shook his head bitterly. 'I don't believe it, after all this time . . .' Elliot snorted miserably. 'Connor Laird.'

'Remember what he told you the last time you saw him.' Drake leaned close. 'Connor Laird is *gone*. Let's keep it that way.'

And then he turned, strode down the drive without looking back. Flick watched him approach over the top of the car.

'You were a long time,' she said.

'You'll have to forgive an old man's prostate.' Drake climbed in, placed his hands on the wheel. 'This is finished, yes – it's over?'

'Yes,' said Flick, looking away. 'It's over.'

He started the car, and glancing in the rear-view, saw the curtains twitch in Elliot's cottage.

31

As they dropped back onto the North Circular, the pips beeped on the radio at the top of the hour. A newscaster said: 'Police in South London are investigating the deaths of a couple in their home this morning. Mehmet and Deb—'

Drake switched off the radio, and when Flick looked at him, said: 'Do you mind? We've enough murders on our hands. I don't particularly want to hear about any more.'

The traffic ahead thickened. Drake eased up behind an estate car to wait for the tailback to get moving. Hands clasped in her lap, Flick made a face. 'This is going to sound like a really crass question.'

'Let's hear it, then.'

'What's the thing you miss most about Laura?'

Drake blew out his cheeks. 'I don't even know how to start answering that question. It's too big.'

She shifted in her seat towards him. 'A small thing, then.'

Drake thought about it. 'She kept me sane.'

'That sounds like a pretty big thing.'

'She kept me from – how would April put it? – from losing my shit.'

'You don't seem a particularly mad person.'

'That,' he said, the edges of his mouth curling into a tight smile, 'is because I am a very good actor.'

The traffic crawled forward and he nosed the car into

the stream of traffic in the left-hand lane, ready for the Tottenham turn-off.

'So what stops you now?' she asked eventually. 'Going mad, I mean?'

'I've April to worry about.' His fingers drummed on the top of the wheel. 'She's still angry about her mother dying, she's . . . vulnerable. I'm not her favourite person right now. I don't like it, but I understand why, because I'm a useful punchbag. But she'll come round. Sooner or later she's going to need me, and I've got to be there for her.' He glanced at her. 'Something on your mind, Flick?'

'It's not the same, and I'm certainly not comparing it to . . . your loss. But my sister's going away with her family, to Australia. We're close, and I know I can visit once a year, or twice maybe, but without them here . . .'

She shook her head, wished she'd never started the conversation. But right now, despite everything, Drake was the only person she felt able to talk to. This murder investigation had driven a wedge between them for reasons she didn't fully understand, but when all was said and done, he had supported her so much more than her own father. Drake's family was important to him, she knew, and he would understand.

'I think I've relied on her too much, taken for granted that Nina would always be there when I needed her, and nothing would ever change.'

'It's tough.'

'If I'm being honest,' she said, and felt a hard lump in her throat, 'I've turned thirty and they're all I've got.'

'There's your father.'

'We don't get on.' She shrugged. 'The usual torturous

family stuff. He left Mum for another woman when I was young and we hardly saw him. A lot of things happened after that. My older brother walked out of the house one day and we never saw him again, you know about that, it hit us all very hard. Then when Mum got dementia Dad didn't lift a finger. He infuriates me, always has. I don't know how long it's been since I saw him last. But Nina has made the effort.' She frowned. 'He's in a home now, a good one, and she pays for it, would you believe.'

'And how do you feel about that?'

'It's none of my business what she does with her money.' She hesitated. 'I told you Dad was a copper.'

Drake nodded. He knew all about Harry Crowley. Let's face it, mostly everyone at the station did.

They didn't speak again until they were cruising past White Hart Lane, just a few minutes from the station. 'Do you miss your own dad?' she asked.

'Leonard . . . my father died when I was eighteen. I didn't know him very well, not really. I wish I'd got to know him better; I have a lot to thank him for. Look, it's none of my business, but maybe you should go and see your father. Make peace. Before, you know . . .'

'Before it's too late.'

'I didn't want to say that,' Drake said. 'But one day he won't be there and . . . well, you know the rest.'

'Sorry to bring it up.' Flick felt guilty about talking about death, not when he had so recently lost his wife. 'Your mother is still going strong!'

'Oh, Myra will outlive us all.' He threw her a sideways glance. 'She tells me she has no intention whatsoever of dying, and I believe her.'

Flick watched the shops and cafés flash by on the High Road. 'Perhaps I will go to see him. There's stuff we need to talk about.'

'There you go.'

But you won't like it, she thought, if you knew what I want to talk to him about: the Longacre, the night it burned down, and the boy called Connor Laird.

She thought, once again, about Drake down in the Property Room. She wanted to know what he was doing there in the dead of night. The noise she heard.

A cough, and then something else – another sound, like—

'What?' Drake asked her, and she realised she had been staring at him.

As soon as she got into her office, Flick unlocked the desk drawer and took out the article about the visit of Leonard and Myra Drake to the Longacre, slipped it from the plastic sheaf. She turned it over in her fingers. Checked the date, reread the names.

She reached into her bag for a pair of nitrile gloves. Snapping them over her wrists, she gently teased the clipping onto the desk. Despite the sun streaming in behind her, Flick clicked on the anglepoise lamp and positioned it above the sheet. Something about this cutting . . .

The next thing she heard was her office door open. When she looked up, Vix Moore was stood there.

'I want to make a complaint about DC Upson.'

Flick stared. 'What kind of a complaint?'

'Detective Constable Upson has a very unfortunate manner. We're the same rank, but he's always telling me what to do. He asks me for an update on my work every five – no, every two minutes – and is frankly very rude.' Vix stepped forward. 'Furthermore, I don't feel that the work I'm being given is helping me progress as a detective.'

'What have you been doing?'

'Leafleting,' she said bitterly.

Half a page from a local newspaper, dated 31 July 1984.

The photograph was torn away.

Flick tried to keep the impatience out of her voice. 'I'll speak to DS Upson, you leave it with me.'

A cough, another sound, the look of shock on Drake's face in the Property Room.

A cough, another sound.

But DC Moore didn't move, and she asked: 'Was there something else?'

'I'd like some media training. One day I'm going to be interviewed – by the papers or by television – and I want to be prepared. I think I'd be very good on the media communications side of things, an asset.'

'Good idea, we'll look into it. Thanks, Vix.'

Flick put her head down. A few moments later, she heard the door slam. The fibre of the old newspaper was stiff and brown. Examining the torn edge, she saw it had wisps of pulp along it, very fine, almost translucent against the dark veneer of the desk. This half-page of newspaper was over thirty years old. The edges on three sides were worn, blunted. Yet the torn edge had tiny shreds of paper still attached. That didn't make sense after thirty years. It would have worn smooth long ago.

Which meant it had been torn recently.

Drake in the basement. As she'd moved into the aisle she'd heard a noise. His cough, yes, but something else as he'd stepped quickly to the shelf to smother her view. Her pulse quickened.

Her office door swung open again and Eddie Upson stormed into the room. 'What was Vix saying about me?'

A cough, another sound, Drake stepped forward.

A cough, a *tearing* sound.

He tore it.

Ray Drake tore the photo away, and took it.

'Get your coat.' Flick stood quickly. 'We're going out.'

32

Sick of the secrets multiplying in his head, exhausted after a sleepless night, Elliot resolved to come clean and tell Rhonda he'd lost their savings.

He had spent the hours before dawn watching the black night dissolve into tepid daylight, trying to work out the best way to do it, and decided to fall on her mercy. And since the shocking visit of a man he'd known briefly a long time ago and had never imagined he'd see again, who was now a *cop*, he was petrified.

Kids from the Longacre killed, and their loved ones slaughtered, by someone calling himself the Two O'Clock Boy. If the copper was right, he would as sure as hell come after Elliot. They had to get away. He had to convince Rhonda and Dylan to take a long holiday, just till this whole fucked-up situation blew over. But even if by some miracle she said, *Sure, let's drop everything, I'll call work to say I'll be back in a few weeks or months, whatever,* she'd find out they had no savings left. The only way he could convince her to come away with him was to come clean about the money.

So Elliot went the whole hog. He kneeled before her like a penitent knight while she sat on the sofa, her small hands in his.

'There was a guy, down the pub.' He winced, the whole thing sounded like the beginning of a bad joke. 'We were going to start a business together, selling burgers. He said we needed to pay a deposit and then I'd get the money back. I didn't ask you because I thought you would say no.'

He waited for her to get angry or upset, but she just frowned at him.

'So, yeah.' He swallowed.' I handed it over to him.'

'All of it?'

He nodded. 'Every penny.'

She untangled her hands from his, placed them in her lap, a small gesture that made him feel wretched.

'Why would you do that?'

'Because I'm Elliot the idiot, and I've a special kind of talent for messing up.' He grimaced. 'Always have had, always will.'

'And who did you give it to?'

'A bloke called Gavin.'

'A bloke called Gavin,' she repeated.

'Well, he said his name was Gavin.' The last thing he could tell her was that he may have given all their hard-earned cash – *Rhonda's* hard-earned cash – to a multiple murderer. He didn't want to terrify her, not on top of everything else. 'I wanted to prove I could make a go of my own business. I wanted to surprise you.'

'Well.' Rhonda smiled bitterly. 'Mission accomplished.'

'I wanted you to know that I can . . .' His voice trailed away. What was the point in telling her what she already knew, that he couldn't be trusted That no matter how much he tried to kid himself, he would always make a mess of any given situation, nailed on?

'Tell me you didn't spend the money on drugs or gambling, or prostitutes—'

'No!' It sickened him that she could think that. 'I'd never –'

'You would never what?' she spat. 'Because you seem to get up to an awful lot without my knowledge, Elliot.'

'Why don't we go away?' he said. 'Take that holiday?'

'You just lost all our money,' she said, and stood suddenly.

'Where are you going?'

'To get a glass of water,' she said. 'If that's okay with you?'

'I'll get it.'

'No.' She waved him off. 'I'll go. I have to do everything else around here.'

When she was gone, he thrust his hands in his pockets and stood at the window, looking miserably at the abandoned barn next door.

That barn was the first thing he saw every morning, on the days he managed to get out of bed before midday – if he had no work to go to, he often didn't – and every day it was a little bit nearer to collapsing. Insects munched on the timber day and night and weeds forced themselves further into the grain of the dry, brittle planks. Every day, without anyone really noticing, the edifice was weakened a little bit more.

That was what his memories of the Longacre were doing to Elliot, eating away at him. Other kids from the home, they could probably handle their memories. But they hadn't seen half of what Elliot had, and he didn't know how to cope with his thoughts, so he did his best to bury them.

So many memories . . . Of Tallis's heavy tread on the stairs, and the time he made Turrell eat the cockroach, and what happened to Sally, and Connor Laird's cold, implacable anger in those final, harrowing hours at the home, a night that would be forever imprinted into Elliot's DNA like a white-hot iron seared into flesh. Those were the memories that ate away at him, as surely as the weeds and insects that patiently consumed that dilapidated barn.

And what was worse, they weren't just memories any more. The terror of the Longacre, a place he thought was done with him, had re-emerged to torment him once more. People he never thought he would see again, never *cared* to see again, had resurfaced, and one of them wanted to kill him. And kill Rhonda and kill Dylan.

The tap gushed in the kitchen. He heard water splash into a glass.

This was his moment to get it all off his chest. The time was right to tell Rhonda everything: about the violence and the abuse, and the crimes he committed when he was too young to know any better. When he was manipulated and bullied by Tallis. When he was a child – a frightened, terrified boy. And then he would tell her about Connor and Sally and Turrell, and about Ray Drake – about what happened all those years ago – and about the terrible danger they were in now, decades later.

Finally he would get it all out. All those other kids, they were dead, or so he was told. But Elliot was alive and he had to move forward, and the only way to do that was to tell Rhonda. Let it all come tumbling into the daylight where it couldn't do any more damage, and where they could examine it. Rhonda would know what to do, how to put him back together. Elliot pressed a hand to his face and decided to take that chance.

The time was now. He took a deep breath.

But.

This scared him, terrified him – she might leave him when she found out about the cold-blooded murders. He hadn't done them, they weren't his fault, but he had been there, and had said nothing about them. Not to anyone, ever. Because he was still the same scared little kid. If what he had done was wrong, then he was sorry, but he had only been a kid and he wasn't to blame for what went on in that place.

She'll know the kind of man you are.

Don't burden her with all your selfish shit. Just suck it up.

So when she came back into the room, instead of telling her the truth, what he said was: 'I can get it back.'

'What?' she asked warily. 'What can you get back?'

'The money. I can get it back.'

And it was a lie, another one to add to all the other lies he had told in his lifetime. Elliot was good with lies, always had been. He wasn't good at much, but he was a natural born liar.

She sipped the water. 'You said this man, this Gavin, has gone.'

'I think . . . I think I know where I can find him.' He held her gaze. 'It just occurred to me. Tell you what, why don't you and Dylan get away for a few days, and let me get everything sorted?'

'What's going on, Elliot? Why are you so keen for us to go away?'

There's this man, he's a psychopath and he's killed before. Kenny, Jason, Karen, so many others. He's trying to kill me – and you, too. But, oh yeah, I can't tell you about that, can't tell you the truth, because I'm gutless, I'm a coward.

And if you . . . *oh God, if you leave me . . .*

'Nothing's going on.' He sounded unconvincing, even to himself. 'It was just, you know, a suggestion. You haven't seen your mum for – how long is it now, nearly a year?'

'We're not going anywhere.'

'I can get the money, and then when you come back—'

'I *work*,' she snapped. 'I bring in money so that you can give it away to complete strangers. Dylan is at school. We can't just drop everything.'

His face burned with shame at her words. 'Right.'

Rhonda put on her coat. 'I've got one child, Elliot, and I really don't need another one. There's something you're not telling me, and I want to know what it is. I thought we had got past this kind of behaviour.'

'We have, but—'

'I'm late for work; we'll talk when I get home.' She picked up her bag. 'I don't know, I'm going to have to think about a few things.'

'What things?' he asked, in alarm.

'But, Elliot . . .' She opened the front door. 'Get that money back.'

'Yes,' he said quickly.

As soon as she drove off in her Ford Focus, he took out the business card he still had in his jeans pocket with a heavy heart, and pressed a number into his phone.

'It's Elliot Juniper,' he said, when Owen Veazey answered.

'Elliot, how nice.' That damned fruit machine hooted and bleeped in the background. Owen was at his usual table.

'That job . . . is the offer still open?'

'It is, as a matter of fact. You've left it a bit late, but . . . why not?'

'And the money—'

'Will be paid into your account as soon as it's done. Interest free, for as long as you need it.' Owen paused. 'Within reason, of course.'

Elliot closed his eyes. 'When?'

'Perry will pick you up later,' said Owen.

Lies upon lies upon lies.

33

1984

Screams and shouts and the sound of crashing furniture came from behind the door to Gordon's office. The children melted into the furthest parts of the house. Ricky and Cliff pulled up weeds in the garden and flung them at each other. Amelia disappeared into the eaves. Some of the others, Kenny and Jason among them, flew from room to room, playing tag.

Elliot was warned by Connor to stay away from Toby, who sat against a tree, head bowed, knees pulled up to his face. Elliot resented being told what to do by Connor, but knew he'd gone too far. Since the cockroach incident several days ago, and since Gordon had started taking him into the small room behind his office of a night, Toby had become withdrawn, distant. He stayed as far from the other children as he could. It was wrong that he was here in the first place. His parents were idiots for not seeing the kind of man Gordon was.

'He got what was coming to him,' Elliot insisted, as they stood looking down the garden at him. 'He deserves everything he gets.'

Connor didn't care what happened to any of them. 'I'm out of here.'

Elliot turned to Connor, incredulous. 'You can't.'

'You don't tell me what I can do.'

But then he saw Elliot thinking about what would happen next. Things would go back to the way they used to be. He would get his delivery job back, be at Gordon's side again. Good luck to him. Connor had stayed for too long, for no good reason. Everybody was scared of him, they'd be happy to see him go. Anyway, Gordon was losing the plot. Something bad was going to happen, Connor sensed that very clearly.

'See ya, then.' Elliot poked a finger into Connor's chest. 'Shame you won't be around to see that fart get what's coming to him.'

'Think about it.' Connor resisted the urge to snap off Elliot's finger. 'Toby ain't like us, he's got family. What do you think he's going to say when he gets out of this place? What do you think he's going to say about what happened?'

Brain cranking into gear, Elliot's eyes snapped wide.

'That's right.' Connor lowered his voice as Karen squeezed past them. 'And then they're gonna look at what else goes on here. They'll find out about your deliveries for Gordon.'

'And yours!'

'I ain't going to be here.' He would just disappear. It was the one thing he had learned to do in his short life. Vanish into the world; keep moving from place to place. Nobody would see him; nobody would know him. 'I'll be gone, and they'll never find me.'

Elliot swallowed. 'And then what'll happen?'

'They'll close this place down and you'll get sent to prison or borstal. You ain't gonna live the good life there, not from what I've heard. You got to make sure Gordon stays away from the kid.'

'How am I gonna do that?' said Elliot, panicking. 'I don't want to go to those places. I definitely don't.'

Now he'd made the decision, Connor just wanted to go. 'Not my problem.'

Down the hallway, the front door opened. Ronnie Dent came in carrying a bag clinking with bottles and knocked on the office door, disappearing inside.

'Gordon ain't gonna listen to me, he never does.' Elliot stared. 'But he'll listen to you.'

Connor shook his head. 'I'm out of here.'

If Elliot or those other kids wanted help they could get that do-gooding Ray kid to come and give them a big hug. Good riddance to the lot of them.

'If you tell him, he'll leave the kid alone.' When Connor turned to go, Elliot grabbed him. 'You gotta help me out. Tell him what you told me. Make him realise, get him to apologise.'

Connor remembered the trouble Elliot had made for him, and for Toby, and angrily slapped his hand away. 'Don't touch me.'

'You're a mate.' Elliot's voice cracked. 'The only one I got.'

When Connor thought about it, he realised he had nothing to lose. He'd made up his mind to go. He would speak to Gordon, and if the manager lost his temper he'd walk out the door and never look back.

'All right,' he said finally, 'I'll do it. But you're coming with me.'

Gordon barked something when they knocked on the door of the office. On his way out, Ronnie Dent stepped aside to let them into the gloomy room. The curtains in the bay window were closed. A sickly stench hung in the air. Slumped on the sofa, Sally barely lifted her head when they walked in, but Gordon jumped up from behind his desk.

'What can I do for you, lads?'

Elliot nudged Connor forward. 'We wanted . . . a word.'

'Have as many as you like.'

Connor said: 'You gotta leave the kid alone.'

Gordon frowned. 'Sorry, son. I'm not with you.'

'Toby.'

'Ah, young Master Turrell.'

'The kid's parents . . .'

'What about them?'

'They ain't gonna like it if you . . .'

'If I what, Connor?'

Gordon's voice was calm, reasonable, but Connor knew to tread carefully. Behind him, Elliot stared at the floor.

'You've got to leave him alone.'

The manager leaned against the desk, feet crossed at the ankles.

'And what do I care about those people? They handed their precious boy to me without considering the consequences.'

'Don't listen to him.' Sally slurred from the sofa. 'He's a drunken fool. He's losing his mind.'

'Be quiet, dear Sal, this doesn't concern you.'

Hauling herself off the sofa, Sally jabbed a dirty fingernail at Gordon. 'Just you be careful, or I'll go – and then you'll be sorry.'

'How will I be sorry, exactly?' Gordon laughed. 'Will I be sorry that you're not here to use all my merchandise? Will I be sorry that you're not sucking me dry?'

Sally shot him a ghastly smile. 'You'll be surprised.'

Gordon's hand shot out to grab her neck. 'So surprise me, Sal.'

'Let her go.' Connor moved forward, the hairs on his arms standing on end, his skin crackling. Part of him was thinking: it doesn't matter, *just go*. But part of him had wanted this moment for a long time. Gordon needed teaching a lesson, needed taking down a peg, and nobody else was going to do it.

'So, finally, the wee man makes his big move.' Gordon pushed Sally away. 'You know, Connor, I've been waiting for this moment. We've been doing this dance for too long now, you and me.' He clicked his fingers, swayed his hips. 'And what about you, Elliot, care to join in? Perhaps together you'll give old Gordon a hiding. Let's find out. Come on, lad, the more the merrier.'

Sally slapped him hard across the face. 'I know people.'

Gordon blinked in surprise. Touching at his cheek, he spoke softly: 'And who is it, you know, Sal, to make me scared? That weakling cousin of yours?'

'His father, he's a judge. I'm going to tell him.'

'Tell him what?'

'Things.'

Gordon's voice lifted angrily. 'Tell him what? Be clear, woman!'

'I'll tell him everything.'

'What's everything?'

'About this place, about what goes on here.'

'I forget sometimes how far you have fallen in life, Sal.' Gordon picked up the glass paperweight from the desk and tossed it from one hand to the other. 'You have to watch

Sally, boys. Watch her carefully or she'll sting you like a scorpion.'

She threw an imploring look at Connor: *get out*, and he turned. He'd done what he came to do, he'd done his best for Elliot, and for the Toby kid, but when he left none of this would mean anything to him. He was going somewhere far away – he wasn't the kind of person, he decided, who was going to spend his life in one place – he'd keep moving, to different cities, different countries, where he didn't have to answer to anybody.

As he stepped to the door, Elliot looked stricken.

'Bye then, lad,' called Gordon.

All Connor had to do was fling open the door and he'd be gone, but his hand froze on the handle. Before he left he wanted more than anything to pound Gordon into the dust, to make him suffer. When he turned back to the room, Gordon smirked.

'Now look, he's staying. He fancies his chances against me. What do we think? Connor's a strong lad, but how far is he willing to go?' He looked at Sally, at Elliot. 'What are his limits, I wonder? I fancy myself a great judge of character.'

Gordon propped his hands on his knees to look deeply into Connor's eyes, as if he was gazing into his very soul. 'I see anger and resentment and confusion, and so much pain . . . and yes, there it is . . . I see the potential for great cruelty.'

He walked away, smacking the paperweight between his palms. 'But what do you think, Connor? Do you think you can match me?'

Connor's nerves, his muscles, screamed. Wanting to leap at Gordon and smash his fists into him. Destroy him.

'Do you think, for example,' he asked, 'that you could kill someone? I have, lad, and I'm comfortable with the fact.'

Sally stepped forward. 'Gordon—'

'Are you willing to kill? I want to hear it.'

But Connor didn't answer, couldn't think straight. An unbearable pressure built in his head, and he stood on the balls of his feet, ready to fly at Gordon.

The manager leered. 'Do you think, boy, that you could do *this*?'

Then Gordon lifted the paperweight high above his head, and in a swift motion, he dashed it down onto the crown of Sally's head. Her legs crumpled like pipe cleaners and she collapsed onto the rug.

Connor and Elliot stared, stunned. Sally laid face down, hair fanned around her head.

'Now look what you've made me do,' Gordon said, with a sick smile.

Get on your feet, thought Connor. *That's enough, now.*

But Sally didn't move. Gordon retreated behind his desk to pour a drink with a shaking hand. Liquid spilled down his chin when he drank. The paperweight slid from his grip, rolled across the desk and off the edge.

'Come on, Sal,' he said, over his shoulder. 'You've made your point.'

But Sally didn't move. Gordon squatted beside her, lifted one of her wrists to feel for a pulse.

'What's wrong with her?' Elliot's face was drenched in sweat. 'Is she gonna be all right?'

'No, she isn't going to be all right.' Gordon climbed to his feet, smiling bitterly. 'She very much isn't going to be all right.'

Right at that moment the door opened and Toby Turrell came in, hands pressed to his face, which was wet with tears. He had barely begun to beg to be able to call his parents, to be allowed to go home, when he saw the pale, shocked expressions of the two boys in the room, and of Gordon.

Only then did he see Sally's body at his feet, blood pumping from the hole in her shattered skull and sliding down her long hair, to curve around the sole of his sandal.

34

Eddie Upson's car was a pigsty. The back seat was a shelf for old tabloids and tossed chocolate wrappers and coffee cups. The atmosphere was a smelly funk of soured milk, and Flick felt queasy all the way to Islington. She cracked the passenger window, while Upson complained to her about Vix Moore.

'I ask her to do something, I ask nicely, and she huffs and puffs.'

'All I'm saying—'

'I'm on eggshells around her. She treats me like a bad smell.'

Sometimes, when Eddie had dodged the deodorant in the morning, there *was* a bad smell in the room. She wound the window lower. 'Apologise and that'll be the end of it.'

Eddie lifted his hands from the wheel in exasperation. 'I've done nothing wrong!'

'Pull over here,' she said.

'Fine, I'll apologise, but it won't do any good.' He swung the car to the kerb in the Islington Square. 'What are we doing here?'

'Never you mind. I'll be five minutes.'

The wind was picking up, shivering the spindly, leafless trees on the pavement, as she climbed the steps to Ray Drake's door. She'd rather not have brought Upson, but she didn't want Drake to think she was pursuing her own investigations again.

Flick had encountered many vicious criminals in her job, had sat in rooms with people who would tear your ears off if you glanced away, but she was terrified at the prospect of speaking to this one old lady. Laura Drake's funeral was a heartfelt occasion, held at a pretty church packed with flowers and wreaths. Every pew was crammed with musician friends of Laura's – a string quartet played – but Flick had found Myra Drake a cold and forbidding woman who sat with her nose in the air as her granddaughter fell to pieces and Ray Drake stared, ashen-faced, at the coffin. She had seemed a chilling and ambivalent presence.

And right now she was the only person who could provide Flick with any information about the Longacre. The consequences of this visit would be severe when Drake found out. But if the DI was, as she suspected, tampering with evidence – it was possible a remorseless killer was at large, and yet Drake was seemingly covering the murderer's tracks – she wanted to know why.

Myra Drake opened the door as soon as Flick rang the bell. Even in her eighties, she was still a tall and imposing figure, with a crook in her spine that made her look like a vulture in a cardigan.

'Mrs Drake, we met briefly at—'

'I know who you are.' The old woman's gaze was steady. 'My son isn't here.'

'I'm not here to see DI Drake; I wanted to talk to you.'

'That won't be possible,' she said, and was about to close the door, but Flick placed her hand on the frame.

'It's about the Longacre. You and your husband visited the home in—'

'I'm perfectly aware of what I have and haven't done. Does my son know you're here, Miss . . .?'

'Crowley. No, he doesn't.' Flick sensed her opportunity slipping away. 'May I come in?'

'Please remove your hand.'

She said quickly: 'Do you remember a boy at the home called Connor Laird?'

Flick saw surprise, and something else – something like *fear* – drop momentarily down the old woman's face, like a glitch on a television screen.

'Connor Laird,' she repeated. 'A boy called Connor Laird?'

Myra Drake tugged at a locket around her neck with a gnarled hand. 'My son will sack you when he discovers you are here.'

'He can't sack me, Myra.' She didn't care for the way the old woman had behaved in the church, refusing to comfort her son or granddaughter. She didn't care if she was reprimanded or even dismissed, because for the first time in a long time Flick felt the excitement of police work coursing through her veins, and annoying this condescending old woman was the icing on the cake. 'You remember him, don't you?'

'I don't care for your attitude or your questions about that boy.'

'Did you know him? Connor Laird.' Every time she said his name, Myra seemed to shrink a little bit more.

'Take your hand off my door.'

'Connor Laird, Myra.'

Myra's shoulders slumped and she looked confused. Flick

remembered how old she was, how frail and vulnerable. She had the awful feeling she was bullying this old woman and removed her hand from the door.

And with a triumphant smile, Myra Drake slammed it in her face.

Annoyed that she had been played for a fool, Flick wanted to jam her finger on the bell and keep it there, but the stubborn old mare, she knew, wouldn't open the door. She imagined Myra was already dialling her precious son. From her reaction to Connor Laird's name, she clearly remembered the boy. In all likelihood she had already discussed him with Ray Drake.

Upson was slapping his hands on the wheel to a song on the radio when Flick climbed back in the car. He turned the ignition.

'That was quick.' He drove out of the square. 'Heading back now?'

'No,' she snapped.

The indicator ticked at a junction, a tense metronome in the interior, and Upson clicked it off. A car beeped behind them as he cranked the handbrake.

'Eddie, please,' she said. 'Just drive.'

He lifted his hands in exasperation. 'I don't know where we're going.'

'Hackney,' she said, blushing. 'We're going to Hackney.'

Upson sighed. 'Have I got *punchbag* written on my forehead today?'

An empty can in the footwell tumbled over her shoes whenever he took a corner and she threw it over her shoulder. Embarrassed by her outburst, Flick persisted with questions about his family, and by the time they reached Mare Street she had even managed to squeeze some terse conversation from him.

When they arrived Flick was relieved to leave the car's cloying atmosphere of curdled dairy and resentment. 'Get yourself a coffee,' she told him.

The weekly *Hackney Express* had closed fifteen years ago, a casualty of the declining fortunes of the local newspaper industry. For a while its name lived on in the tangerine masthead of a free sheet called the *Hackney Argent and Express*, but a mouthful in a diminishing market, the title was shortened to the *Hackney Argent*.

The reception, with its stacks of newspapers and cardboard cutouts of grinning celebrities, managed to be both sparse and untidy. A sales team spoke on headsets behind the counter. When Flick asked about the *Express*, the teenage receptionist was dismissive.

'This is the *Argent*,' she said.

'But it used to be the *Express*.'

The girl's expression hardened. 'What's it about?'

'I'm looking for a report from nineteen eighty-four.'

Flick may as well have asked her about Tudor England. 'That was *way* before I was born.'

'I was hoping there'd be copies of the *Express* on computer or microfiche.'

Please not microfiche, thought Flick. It was cumbersome to use. The Met had long ago transferred its microfiche files onto a computer database. But she needn't have worried, the girl clearly didn't have the faintest idea what she was talking about.

'Micro . . . ?'

'Fiche,' Flick told her, growing impatient.

'Micro . . . fish.'

'It's like camera film, which you run through a machine and read off a screen.'

The girl's face was incredulous. 'I got all my photos on my phone.'

'We don't have anything as sophisticated as that, I'm afraid.' A middle-aged woman came bustling to the counter, a mug of tea swinging carelessly in her fist. Her glossy black hair was cut into a bulbous helmet around her plump face. Beneath a long sweater, leggings as thick and straight as artillery shells disappeared into Ugg boots. 'What is it that you're looking for?'

'I'm investigating four murders,' said Flick, showing her ID.

The young girl leaned forward, interested now. 'Wow.'

'You can be my assistant,' Flick said, but the girl favoured her with a look that suggested she didn't care to be anybody's assistant.

'Do you have an exact date?'

'July thirty-first, nineteen eighty-four.'

The woman, who said her name was Diane, wrote down the date and gave Flick an appraising look. 'It's just as well you've got long legs.'

Ushering her behind the counter, Diane led Flick downstairs to an ill-lit corridor, which smelled of bleach.

'This is where we keep all the old binders.' Diane opened a door and pressed a switch. Fluorescent lights buzzed into life. 'Good luck in getting to them.'

The entire room was filled with office furniture and equipment dumped every way up. Tables and desks, filing cabinets, a photocopier, beige computer drives and monitors, all gathering dust. It was impossible to step in any direction without having to clamber over something.

'Over there.' The entire length of the wall was lined with shelves full of tall volumes. Diane pointed to the far corner.

Tossing clutter out of her way, Flick hesitantly moved forwards. Nearly twisting her ankle while straddling a fax machine, she saw the embossed gold lettering on the spines of the leather books, archives of a host of long-defunct newspapers. Halfway across the room, her phone buzzed. She saw a text from April Drake. Biting down her excitement, she tucked away the phone.

Finally reaching the back of the room, Flick climbed on upturned drawers to reach the highest shelf. Each of the *Hackney Express* volumes contained six months' worth of newspapers. The *Jul–Dec 1984* binder was against the wall. The drawers wobbled precariously beneath her as, balancing like a surfer riding a wave, she plucked at the lip of the binding. The volume was squeezed tight. It wouldn't shift. The drawers teetered. Locking her knees, she tried again. The cheap leather of the book shifted with a dry snap, separating from the wall and the adjacent volume. Flick prised the heavy book from the space.

Climbing carefully off the drawers, she opened the cover, as heavy as the lid of a box, and turned the dry, brittle pages.

'Found what you wanted?' called Diane from the doorway.

'Yes, thank you!' said Flick.

Anticipation rose in her. After about ten minutes, she found it. The newspaper was dated 6 August 1984. The front-page headline said: LOCAL HERO KILLED IN CHILDREN'S HOME BLAZE.

A children's home manager died a hero when a blaze ripped through the building to which he had devoted his life.

Gordon Tallis (44) made the fatal decision to return one last time to the burning building and was overwhelmed by flames.

This was the article in Kenny Overton's clippings, with the photograph of the blackened remains of the home below. A caption beneath it, missing from Kenny's file, credited the photograph to Trevor Sutherland.

Flick turned to the previous week's edition, 31 July 1984. The front-page headline was about an outbreak of graffiti in the borough. She carefully scanned each page in the news section, then the features section, the classifieds, the sports pages at the back.

And that was it.

Somehow she'd managed to miss the story of the Drakes' visit to the home and the accompanying photograph, so she flipped back to the front of the paper and started again, counting the page numbers.

One sheet, pages seven and eight, was missing. It had been removed. A thin strip of paper raced down the spine, straight and sharp to the touch.

Another dead end.

'You will put it back where you found it, won't you?' called Diane.

Flick slammed the volume shut. Dust exploded into the air, and she sneezed. Balancing precariously on the drawers again, she replaced it on the shelf and made her way carefully back across the room, as if negotiating a minefield.

'Has anyone else been down here recently?'

'Not as far as I recall,' said Diane. 'I've always thought it pointless keeping those silly volumes, but it's a kind of heritage, isn't it?'

'Nobody has asked to do research for a book or a university paper?'

Someone sliced out that page, covering their tracks, someone who didn't want to be identified.

'In my time here nobody has shown any interest in anything to do with the *Express*. Tell me what you're after, and I'll ask in editorial.'

Flick told her about the article detailing Leonard and Myra Drake's visit to the Longacre home. Diane wrote down the date and page number of the edition in a pad and tore it out. The sound made Flick shudder. It was the noise she'd heard down in the Property Room when she interrupted Ray Drake.

When he tore the photograph from the cutting.

Tampering with evidence, hiding something.

Connected somehow, implicated in a way she didn't understand, to the deaths of an untold number of people.

35

Ray Drake stayed away from pubs if he could help it. He was forced to go to them occasionally for work functions, like the celebration bash the other night. But alcohol was for other people. He'd never smoked, never taken drugs, avoided caffeine. He and Laura often ate out and dined with her friends, but there was nothing in this cave of wood and mirror, imbued with a sharp vinegar tang, to make him a good man, a better man. And that's all he had ever wanted to be.

His instincts had pulled him towards police work, but his home life had given him balance. It was quiet and loving, ordered and nourishing, Laura had blessed him with that. But she was gone now, and he was forced to face this situation alone. His vivid memories of his wife were fading, swept away by the recent storm of events, and now he was in danger of losing April. It was unthinkable; it would be catastrophic. If something happened to his daughter, he sensed he would unravel. He had to keep his daughter safe, his life on track. The Two O'Clock Boy could strike at any time. Drake had to stop him.

Easier said than done, but Drake didn't have the luxury of doing nothing. All it took was for Flick Crowley to voice her suspicions about the Longacre in the office and the investigation could swing in that direction.

Getting a gun from the station was out of the question. He didn't have the authorisation to access the firearms locker. Ray Drake knew plenty of criminals who would supply one for the right price, but most of those people could cheerfully hold you to account for it later.

His repeated attempts to call April came to nothing. Her phone was switched off, or went to voicemail. So Drake pocketed his mobile and took a table in the pub in Bethnal Green to wait for Amelia Troy. She'd texted him this morning, and when he phoned back, she asked to meet.

Somewhere public, she said. Somewhere busy.

A pair of regulars chatted at the bar. A boisterous group of builders in overalls flopped noisily at a nearby table.

Shading his eyes against the low winter sun, he saw Amelia Troy approach along the high street. Hair pulled back, wearing sunglasses, a yellow hoodie beneath a battered leather jacket; hands thrust into the pockets of her jeans, which tapered into dirty white plimsolls. Something was clamped beneath an arm. When she slumped into the seat opposite, a curled book covered in crepe paper fell to the table, specks of glitter working into the grain of the wood. Drake couldn't take his eyes off it.

'Drink?'

She ignored the question, nodded towards the swelling on his face: 'You never really explained how you got that.'

'I thought I did. Somebody resisting arrest, a fellow we needed to talk to about some robberies.'

'You investigate robberies as well as murders?'

'If necessary,' he said. 'Is everything okay?'

'I had another call last night. Five, maybe ten minutes, after you'd left.'

Drake placed his juice to the side. 'Why didn't you—'

'The voice was electronically altered. You know, like a robot's.'

He nodded, wary. 'What did it say?'

'It said that I had to remember where I had come from, and then I would know why I must . . . why I must die. It said I was to blame.' She laughed, a skittering sound that filled Drake with foreboding. 'But like I told you, I *can't* remember, it the one thing I can't do. So I asked what I had to remember, and you know what it told me?' She watched him carefully. 'It told me to ask you.' Drake shifted in his seat. 'Do you have any idea what it was talking about, DI Drake?'

He forced his gaze from the sketchbook. 'No. How could I?'

'So, as we know, I've no idea what happened back then. But I've always recorded my experiences. I've dozens of books like this, though not quite as old.' More specks of glitter drifted to the table when she tapped the cover. 'All through my shitty life, the drugs, the suicide attempts, the husband who hurt me, I've worked hard. Last night I searched for any drawings I did as a kid. I hire storage, one of those places with twenty-four-hour access. I keep all my preliminary sketches there.'

Her fingers scratched across the crepe.

'I spent the rest of the night there, going through my sketchbooks. The truth is, I didn't feel safe at home and I was too embarrassed to ask you to return. At this storage place, I didn't feel so alone. I found many projects I started and abandoned. Perhaps I'll pick up a few of them again, see if the old magic is still there.'

'It's an idea,' said Drake.

'You look tense, Ray. Can I call you Ray? I feel I know you, I said that last night, didn't I, that your face is familiar to me.' She picked up the sketchbook, the kind of cheap stationery found in any newsagent, her name in neat bubble writing on the cover, and turned the pages with a thumb. 'This is one of the sketchbooks I had as a kid. I don't remember it, but it's very old, as you can see. I was amazed when I saw some of the illustrations. I was pretty good even back then, if I say so myself.' She slid it towards him. 'Take a look.'

'Amelia—'

'Look at it, please.'

Drake opened it to see the drawings and patterns she had done as a child. He remembered her, the book against her knees, a pencil dancing in her hand, lost in her own world. On every page the designs became more elaborate. Sketches of people appeared. There was Gerry Dent. The likeness was clumsy, Amelia still had much to learn about life drawing, but she had caught the essence of the woman: her slovenliness, her dull, predatory gaze.

'I've no idea who she is.' Amelia swiped through the pages. 'Or any of these other people.'

Other kids from the Longacre. She'd captured them playing, laughing, crying. He recognised a boy called Cliff who had a compulsion to eat dirt, and Lena, a girl whose mattress was lumpy from the stolen toys she hid underneath it.

'I wonder where those children are now. Are they getting on with their lives somewhere or, like Kenny, are they . . . ?'

Her voice trailed away when he turned a page – and saw

a drawing of himself, sitting on the steps outside the home. She had captured his sad, troubled expression. The unruly hair, the jagged plummet of his cheeks.

'That's you, yes?' Her voice cracked. 'I'd say that's definitely you.'

'Amelia.' He pushed the book away.

'Explain why I drew you in one of my sketchbooks thirty years ago.'

'It's just a kid, your mind—'

'Please don't tell me I'm paranoid. These days I know the difference between illusion and reality.' She looked stricken. 'I have nightmares. I see a room on fire. I see children, and a crazed man with a beard. I see him shouting and pulling at me, I feel his breath on my face. He hates me and wants to kill me, wants to kill us all. I wake up drenched in sweat, my sheets sopping. So if that's you,' she tapped the image, 'I really would like to know why you've been lying to me.'

The door to the street burst open and more builders swaggered in, laughing.

Drake swallowed. 'That's me.'

Amelia giggled nervously. 'I don't understand.'

Drake leaned forward. 'It's complicated but, yes, I—'

'I have to go.'

'Amelia, please.'

Her thighs banged against the underside of the table when she stood, and Drake's glass shattered on the floor. Someone at the bar cheered. 'Why have I been scared since I saw that drawing? Is it because when I turned on the radio this morning I discovered a woman called Deborah Yildiz was burned to death just hours after I gave you her address?'

'It's not what you think.'

He reached out, but she yanked her hand away. 'Stay away from me!'

'Everything all right over here?' A group of builders came over and crowded behind Drake's chair.

'We're fine, thanks,' he said, without looking up.

'Yeah?' One of the men, hair coated with plaster dust, nodded at Amelia. 'Cos the lady looks like she wants to leave.'

Amelia flew out of the door. Drake watched her throw the hood over her head and melt into the crowd.

'You might want to get that deposit back, chum,' the guy said. 'From the charm school!'

The men turned away, laughing. Drake looked again at his own glowering portrait, then slipped the sketchbook into his pocket.

Minutes later, he sat in his car, which was parked in a quiet residential street, and thought about playing one of Laura's concertos. But he knew it wouldn't do any good. He wouldn't hear her music. That silent roar inside of him, those troubled memories, would drown it out.

He felt anger spiking inside him with every hour that passed, like the agitated head of a seismograph jumping on paper. Felt it rising ever more strongly, filling the empty space his wife left inside him the day she died.

36

'They're next door listening to the Cornetto man,' said the receptionist at Valleywell Retirement Village. 'Pop on in, he's used to all the comings and goings.'

Flick headed towards the baritone rendition of 'O Sole Mio' blasting from the lounge, slipping inside to see the singer belting out the song to a room of elderly men and women. He was an incongruous sight on a weekday in Finchley, in his dinner jacket, bow tie and scarlet cummerbund, hair slicked back in the Mafioso style. Flick scanned the room for Harry, but it wasn't easy when all she could see was an ocean of grey hair. The receptionist had been certain he would be there – 'the ladies and gentlemen love their opera' – but her father's appreciation of music, Flick remembered, went as far as a bit of Dolly.

As soon as he saw her, the singer picked up a red rose from a pile next to the CD player providing his orchestral backing tracks, and threaded his way through the clutter of sofas and chairs to drop to one knee in front of Flick and serenade her. *'Ma n'atu sole, Cchiù bello, oje ne', O sole mio, Sta 'nfronte a te!'*

Dying a little inside, Flick politely accepted the rose. She was relieved to spot Harry at a patio table in the garden, and quickly skirted around the edge of the room. If her father was pleased that his youngest daughter had unexpectedly walked back into his life, he didn't show it.

'Ladies,' Harry vaguely gestured to two women at the table, 'this is my daughter.'

Flick was surprised to see how much weight he had lost. Harry's wavy silver hair still curdled over his head, but his skin sucked in sharply below the cheeks, and a trembling fin of skin hung beneath his jaw. He wore a lurid Hawaiian shirt, long shorts and desert boots. A trilby was placed on the table in front of him.

'Sit yourself down.' He gestured to a chair. 'Becca, Claire, meet Felicity.'

Inside, the backing track changed to a jolly tune Flick recognised from a million TV ads. The baritone pumped his arms as he sang.

'That's not your daughter,' said one of the women.

'You're thinking of my eldest. I got two daughters. This is Felicity, she's followed in her old man's footsteps. She's a constable, a Murder Detective!'

'I'm a DS now,' corrected Flick, but he would have known that, Nina would have told him.

'The single one,' said Claire. 'Can't keep a man.'

'She'd have more success with men if she smiled,' said Becca.

'Can we talk?' Flick asked her father, impatient.

'Perhaps she's not interested in men. Perhaps she's one of those.'

'What have I told you about reading those magazines?' Harry wagged a finger at Becca. 'Putting ideas into your head!' He tilted the hat quickly onto his head as if trapping a mouse beneath it. 'Now, ladies, I expect Felicity won't be staying long, so perhaps you could excuse us.'

The two women took an age pulling on their cardigans

and gathering up their things – Flick had cleared crime scenes more quickly – and clung to each other as they made the treacherous journey inside.

'My harem.' Harry laughed, as Flick took in the view of the landscaped garden and new-build bungalows on either side. 'Don't pay no mind. At their age, they get the wrong end of the stick. You're still with that Alex, of course.'

'We broke up,' said Flick. Years ago, as he well knew.

'Play the field while you can, girl, but remember the clock's ticking. You don't want to end up on your own.'

'I'm not here to talk about that,' she said quickly. 'When you were based at Hackney nick in the eighties there was a children's home.' She took out her notebook and pen. 'Run by a man called Gordon . . .'

'Tallis.' Harry sipped from a mug. 'That's a name that takes me back.'

'What can you tell me about him?'

'He was a squalid little man who ran a squalid little home on a squalid little street. It would have been closed down in a heartbeat these days. The whole area was bulldozed and redeveloped a long time ago. It's all swanky apartments now, and vegan restaurants.'

'He was abusive?'

'Not only that, but he used the kids to shift heroin around North London.'

'How do you know that?'

'Everyone knew. Well, certain people did.' Harry took off the hat to pat his hair, tipped it back in place. 'You hate me because I've never lived up to standards you consider acceptable, but you have to remember it was a different world back then. Yes, I was on the take, but I wasn't the only one.

Tallis paid money to keep certain officers off his back. I was the conduit, the channel, if you will. He delivered cash to me and I distributed it to cops, councillors and numerous petty officials, who would turn a blind eye to his using the home to move drugs. A clever little operation, nobody would suspect a children's home, not back then. A vulnerable young woman called Sally Raynor came to make the payment. She was upper class but preferred the gutter, and you couldn't get more lowlife than Gordon Tallis. Nice girl but a mess, an addict. She disappeared off the face of the earth.'

'You think Tallis had something to do with it.'

'He was a combustible chap.' He drilled a finger into his temple. 'Not right upstairs. A creepy fellow with a smile that made your skin crawl.'

'And he died in a fire at the home.'

'The Longacre burned to the ground, with him inside. Not a great loss to society. I imagine the kids did a jig for joy.'

'Was it started on purpose?'

'Word is, Gordon's friends in the drugs business were becoming very unhappy with the way he was running things. When his body was found inside it was handcuffed to a radiator.'

Flick sat bolt upright. 'Handcuffed?'

'Yeah.' Harry winced. 'My handcuffs, as it happens.' When she stared, he said, 'Don't look at me like that, they were stolen.'

'By whom?' asked Flick.

'By a nasty little shit called Connor Laird.'

Flick felt the blood accelerate around her veins. Inside, the baritone threw his hands up at the climax to the song, and his audience clapped.

'Connor Laird. Do you know what became of him?'

'Oh, yeah.' Harry smiled at her eager question. 'He also burned to death in that fire.'

Inside, the backing track on the opera singer's CD player changed, and the singer's baritone soared over the first notes of 'Nessun Dorma'.

'What a racket.' Harry shook his head. 'We have to listen to that every week. It's terrible what they do to pensioners. Take my advice, Felicity, don't get old.' He sighed at his daughter's obvious impatience. 'Look, we didn't have the fancy forensics you people rely on these days. An unidentified body was found next to Tallis, and Connor Laird was the only kid not to come out of that home. All the others, every single one of them, were accounted for.'

'You're absolutely sure it was him?'

'As sure as we could be.'

'But how do you *know*?'

'Because,' said Harry patiently, 'Tallis and Connor had got into some kind of conflict that escalated out of control, and it looks like he took the kid with him.'

'And this fire, these deaths, were never investigated; why?'

'There would be a few coppers, my love, with prosperous retirements to look forward to, who would have to answer some very difficult questions if their relationship with Gordon Tallis was put under a microscope. There was no paperwork connected to Connor, no birth certificate, no family or dependents. He came out of nowhere and he died.' He tugged at the pouch of skin beneath his jaw. 'And nobody cared, because it was in a lot of people's interests, mine included, that they didn't.'

'And what if he wasn't dead?'

'He's dead.'

'Hypothetically, what would become of him?'

He thought about it. 'Connor Laird was a bad seed. I met him once, I looked into his eyes and they were – what's the word? – *feral*. He was full of contempt for the world, and everyone in it. Nothing good would come of him. If he grew up . . . well, woe betide anybody who got in his way.' Harry narrowed his eyes. 'I remember the fire occurred just after that judge and his wife visited the place.'

Flick gripped her pen. 'Leonard Drake?'

'That was him. One of our detectives went to his house for a statement and the old boy told him in no uncertain terms to sling his hook.'

'I've got to go.'

'Already?' asked Harry. 'Got what you wanted and now you're going?'

'Yes.'

'Listen to that.' Harry smiled at the baritone, whose hands were clasped to his chest as he serenaded an old couple on a sofa. 'He's singing something slow and sad and lonesome. Must be for us, Felicity.'

So Nina had already told him she was going to Australia.

'I'm too old for all this nonsense,' he said. 'I don't want to go on fighting this war, can't we call a truce? It makes me sad that Nina can find it in her heart to forgive and you can't.'

'I'm going.'

'I'm holding out an olive branch here,' he said, exasperated.

'You couldn't even be bothered to see mum.' Flick threw the notebook and pen in her bag. 'I asked and asked, but you didn't go. You took no interest in us,' Flick said bitterly, 'in me or Nina or Daniel.'

'Look,' Harry said softly, 'the affairs, leaving your mum, not taking an interest when she was ill, and, of course, my misadventures in uniform – I've never lived up to your lofty standards and never will. But let's be honest. What you really hate me for is the one thing that I could do nothing about. Dan.'

'That's not true,' she said, and her phone went off in her bag. By the time she snatched it up, it had rung off.

'Well, let me tell you something.' His expression darkened. 'He was your brother, but he was my *son*, my only son, and you will never know what it's like to lose a child. To spend every day wondering whether he's out there somewhere or buried in a shallow grave.'

'I'm not listening to this.'

It had always been like this between them, they couldn't spend more than twenty minutes in each other's company without the usual resentments rising to the surface.

'Nina, who is a loving and caring person, has always known how much his disappearance hit me, *here*.' Harry thumped his chest. 'So don't for one second believe you've got a monopoly in suffering. And I'll tell you something else: she deserves a life away from me and from *you*.'

Flick flinched. 'That's not true, she loves—'

'Me and you, we're parasites, Felicity.' He always knew how to play on her anxieties. 'And as far as I'm concerned, she and that family of hers deserve every happiness.' Harry looked at the residents and staff enraptured by the singer's performance. 'And one last thing, Flick—'

'Don't call me that.'

'When you get all twisted up about how much you dislike me, just remember, I got people around me night and day. I sometimes have to go and sit in my room to get away from the hectic social whirl. So, yeah, I'll regret not seeing you if that's the way it has to be, but I will never be lonely. Can you honestly say the same?'

Right at that moment, the singer reached the big climax of 'Nessun Dorma', and there was a smattering of applause. He bowed low and moved around the room giving out roses. The patio doors opened and a female staff member stood at the door. 'Everything okay, Harry?'

'Grand, love.' A big smile lit up his face. 'Got a visitor.'

Flick waited for him to say, *my daughter*. But he didn't.

'You missed the performance,' said the woman.

'I'll catch it next week, or maybe the week after that.' He winked. 'I'm just coming in now.'

When the woman left, Harry sidled up to his daughter. 'Pop in again if you're in the neighbourhood. Make it a longer visit next time.'

Before he'd taken two steps inside he was grinning and laughing, the life and soul, surrounded by a group of residents. Flick was wondering if there was another way she could get to reception when her phone rang again.

37

Ray Drake rubbed his eyes wearily. 'You're being unreasonable.'

Myra perched on the edge of a frayed and tatty sofa that had been in the house since before she was born. When Laura refurbished, Myra insisted it stayed. It was good for her spine, she said, but everyone knew she was just being bloody-minded. She folded the *Telegraph* she had been reading and dropped it beside her.

'Remind me again why I should leave my home?'

'The matter we spoke about the other night.'

'The killings,' she said. 'Children from *that* place.'

'We're looking into it, but—'

'I trust you are.' She watched him pace restlessly over the top of her reading glasses. 'That policewoman came to see me today.'

Drake stopped dead. 'Flick Crowley.'

'You invited her to the funeral, I recall, although goodness knows how it was any of her business.'

Flick was proving stubborn in her determination to look into the Longacre. He'd speak to Harris about getting her removed from the investigation, but knew that if Amelia Troy had already contacted her, his life would spiral out of control very quickly.

'What did she say?'

'She asked me about the home. I sent her away with a flea in her ear. My advice to you, Raymond, is to sack her immediately.'

'You haven't answered me. Will you go away, just for a short while? I'm not going to be able to be here all the time.'

Myra took off the glasses. 'And what does that matter to me?'

She was forcing him to say it out loud. 'You may be in danger, Myra.'

The old woman rubbed the scuffed metal of the oval locket around her neck. 'But where would I go?'

'Out of town,' he said. 'To family. Take a holiday.'

'I'm eighty-seven years old. A holiday would finish me off.'

'There must be people you can . . .' He racked his brains, annoyed that he still knew so little about this infuriating and intensely private woman. Many years ago, after what happened at the home, she'd cut herself off from family – or, at least, the few family members she had been on speaking terms with. Most of those had, presumably, died of old age.

'I'll take my chances here.'

'I'd rather you—'

'Stop. You're talking to me now, Raymond, not some idiot colleague.' When she heaved herself from the sofa, Drake went to help but she waved him off. 'Is that why you look like you've been dragged through a bush backwards? Did someone attack you?'

'It's just . . . a precaution.'

'Now you listen to me. When Leonard and I became involved with the fallout from that damned home, we understood the consequences of what we were doing. I'm not going to leave everything behind because some pipsqueak is threatening me.'

She'd never given an inch. Never compromised, never backed down.

'He's killed many times, Myra. He's dangerous.'

'And I have great faith in your ability to stop him.'

'At least let me get someone to stay with you.' It wouldn't be impossible to hire some discreet muscle. He knew people who could ensure her safety. 'Just until I can sort out this problem.'

'I will not have strangers in my home.'

'He's coming for me and he'll come for you, too.'

'And how do you know that?'

'Because he told me,' he snapped. 'I'm begging you, be reasonable.'

'I didn't bring you up to be the kind of man to beg,' she hissed.

She touched the edges of her hair. Once upon a time it was a fierce helmet, a towering Thatcheresque construction. Now there were large patches where Drake could see her scalp, plastered with scurf.

'My grandparents lived in this house,' she said quietly. 'I've lived here all my life, and I hope you will remain here when I am gone, even though I know you've been unhappy here lately.' That, he knew, was the nearest she'd get to mentioning Laura. 'I will not run away, it is simply not in my nature.'

He nodded at the locket. 'May I see?'

After a moment's consideration, she said: 'If you wish.'

She lifted the wisps of fine hair drifting down the back of her neck and Drake stepped behind her to undo the tiny clasp. Myra opened the locket. Inside was a small photograph, its edges clipped in a rough hexagonal. He'd never seen it before and she'd never offered to show it. Her crooked finger trembled over the photo, as if she were afraid to touch it, afraid the image would fade beneath her touch.

'I've never thanked you,' he said. 'For everything you've done for me.'

A look that he'd never seen before, the faintest suggestion of vulnerability, passed across Myra's face, and she turned away.

'You were not the easiest boy, but Leonard was very fond of you. He may not have shown it, but be sure of it. And I have . . . loved you, I hope, in my own way.' She snapped the locket shut and her voice hardened. 'The most important thing now is that you protect your daughter. April needs you, even if the selfish child doesn't realise it. She must be your only responsibility.'

'All my life,' he bit down on his annoyance, 'I've done what you said.'

Her mouth twitched in distaste. 'You're embarrassing yourself, Raymond.'

'And now I want you to do as I tell you.'

'This is my—'

'You'll do as I say!'

She considered him, coldly.

'There's a nephew,' she said finally. 'He lives in Kent. I shall telephone to inform him he shall have the pleasure of my company for a few days. I can only imagine his surprise. Does that suit?' Drake nodded, but a part of him wasn't convinced of her intentions. 'In the meantime, I've something that you may find useful.'

She went to a drawer and took out a folded piece of cloth, carefully unwrapped the fabric . . .

To reveal a small handgun.

He stepped forward. 'Where on earth did you get that?'

'We've had it many years. Leonard brought it back from the war.'

Drake removed the magazine from the grip, which was full. Snapped it back in.

'It's a Beretta, I believe,' said Myra, watching him weigh the pistol in his hand. 'It should work; he took very good care of it. I hope for your sake it does.'

'Myra, you're a marvel.' He shook his head in amazement. 'Why didn't you tell me about this before?'

'It would not have been very wise to let you play with such an object when you were younger.' She fixed her gaze on his. 'Do what you have to do, Raymond, so that we can get back to normal.'

38

Perry drove two wheels onto the verge and cranked the handbrake. A necklace of light moved across the darkness at the top of the field opposite, traffic snaking along the M11.

He reached across to the glove compartment, digging his elbow into Elliot's ribs, to take out two balaclavas and then something that made Elliot nearly shit himself with fear.

'Why the hell did you bring a gun?' Ignoring him, Perry slapped the dash shut and palmed the weapon, a squat, ugly thing, into his pocket. 'I asked why—'

'What does it matter?' Perry swung round, nostrils flaring. He had barely spoken on the way, not that Elliot was clamouring for conversation, but his surly silence had frayed Elliot's nerves.

'What does it *matter*?' Elliot tried to keep the rising panic from his voice. 'You said nobody would be here, you said they were on holiday!'

'I didn't say anything like that,' Perry sneered. 'If Owen wants to spin you a line it's his call. And, anyway, it's just two old people; try not to wet your knickers.'

'I'm not coming in.' Breaking and entering, burglary, that was bad enough, but this was a home invasion, aggravated assault with a deadly weapon, and Elliot wasn't going to cross that line. That's not the kind of man he was. Not now, not ever.

'You're coming in,' insisted Perry, pulling the balaclava over his head, 'or Owen will have something to say about it.'

No way, no fucking way was Elliot going inside. He spoke very slowly, so there was no misunderstanding him: 'You're on your own.'

Perry leaned in close to intimidate, his eyes small, hard pellets inside the black fabric of the balaclava. 'Fine, you can drive. Just make sure you're ready as soon as I come out.' He snatched a rucksack from the back seat and winked. 'Back in a mo.'

Elliot watched anxiously as Perry walked up the lane towards the big house, half hidden by swaying pampas grass, at the top of a long, curving drive. No good was going to come of this, he knew that much. When Owen found out Elliot had refused go in with Perry he would withhold the money. Elliot hadn't held up his end of the bargain, he'd say, hadn't played his part. Elliot would be back to square one. He'd promised Rhonda he would get the money. They needed it to get away.

On top of that, Perry's body language, the casual way he sauntered up the drive, told him everything he needed to know about what was going to happen inside.

Minutes later, Elliot thought he heard a scream.

He slammed his hand on the dashboard – this couldn't be happening! – and yanked the balaclava over his head. The wool pricked his scalp. He could barely breathe.

Elliot ran up the drive, the front of the house jumping in his eyeholes, and saw the front door was ajar. There wasn't another home in sight, but – he heard raised voices, a moan – it was stupid to take such a chance. In the hallway he rushed towards the sitting room, but getting the angles wrong inside the mask, he ill-judged the turn, cracking his shoulder on the doorframe.

An elderly man in a cardigan cringed in a chair. Seen through the narrow eyeholes of Elliot's balaclava, the room swerving all over the place, the man looked as if he was clinging to the armrests as the chair was swept about on a turbulent sea.

'No!' pleaded the man. 'My wife!'

Elliot's heart leapt into his mouth when he saw Perry standing over an old woman. The scene swung up and down, visible only in fragments. The woman on her knees, arms lifted protectively above her head, long hair spilling from a clip onto a shoulder. Perry, jabbing the weapon, screaming: 'Open it!'

'No,' she moaned. 'I don't know what you're—'

'Open – the – fucking – safe!' Perry grabbed her neck. Pressed her to the floor, stuck the gun at the back of her head.

Elliot turned, fleetingly seeing the old man's pale, rigid face whip past the eyeholes. And when he spun back, sweating beneath the hot, itchy fabric, panic rising in his chest, he couldn't find Perry and the old woman. He could only hear Perry screaming: 'Open it, open it, open—'

And then, from behind Elliot: 'Please! Don't hurt my wife!'

'Open the safe, or I'm going to—'

Eyes flashing with anger, Perry pressed the weapon into the woman's neck. Her moans were lost in the thick carpet. Elliot couldn't see a safe, couldn't see a thing, couldn't breathe, had to do something.

'You! Move it!' Perry jerked the gun towards a cabinet, and Elliot realised that he was screaming at him. He stumbled forward, catching his foot on the tasseled edge of a rug. His chest was about to burst. There wasn't enough air in the room, not enough oxygen in the world, to fill his lungs. He pushed the cabinet along the shagpile to reveal a safe set into the wall.

'We've got a problem here,' said Perry to the old man, who rocked backwards and forwards on the chair, 'because I'm going to need a code, we ain't got a code—'

'Then let's go,' said Elliot urgently.

'We ain't going till we've got the code.' Perry's head snapped up. 'Or these two old farts are dead!'

He wrenched at the woman's shoulder, dragging her head off the floor, the weapon's barrel swinging carelessly in his other hand. 'I'm going to count from five and if that safe isn't open when I get to zero you're going to die.'

The man wept, tears pouring down the hands covering his face, wetting the cuffs of his shirt and glistening on the plain gold wedding band he had worn for thirty, forty, fifty years or more.

'Ain't no time for tears, fella,' snarled Perry, 'just numbers.'

'Perry,' Elliot stepped forward, 'don't.'

Perry's eyes burned with rage at Elliot's use of his name. 'Five!'

'Don't do this!'

'Four!'

The old man pressed his hands together as if in prayer, as Perry traced the gun barrel along his wife's hairline and down her temple, resting it in the hollow of her wet eye socket.

And the woman said something, but Elliot couldn't hear what it was. Burning up, he pulled the balaclava off his head. They could see him now and he didn't care.

'Put it back on!' screamed Perry.

But it was too late, because the old man, white with fear, with dread, looked Elliot full in the face. And Elliot wondered how long they had been married, this couple. A lifetime, judging by the framed photos of kids and grandkids around the room, by the numerous mementoes of a marriage, a union cemented more strongly with every minute, month, decade.

'Three!'

And Elliot, angry now – enraged by the old fool's stubbornness, his willingness to get himself and his wife killed for cash and stupid trinkets that don't mean a thing if you're lucky enough to possess the love and companionship of another person, just one person, to help you through this terrible, shitty life, to pick you up when you fell – surged forward. 'For fuck's sake, tell him! Tell him the code!'

'Two!'

Then the old man squeezed his eyes shut, and his mouth opened and closed – but nothing came out. A mewling sound came from the carpet. Elliot lurched to Perry. 'She's trying to tell us, she's trying to—'

But Perry, insensible with rage, was leaning over the woman. 'You are this close, *this* close, from getting your brains blown out!' And then he straightened his gun arm, execution-style.

Elliot shouted: 'No!'

And the old man tipped forward, slammed face down into the rug, a stuttering moan coming from his mouth, a froth of spittle arcing across his cheek. His arms and legs thrashed, his body was wracked by spasms.

'Please,' wailed the woman. 'He's having a fit.'

Elliot kneeled to take her trembling, anguished face in his hands, looking her in the eyes, almost in tears himself.

'Please,' he whispered desperately, the smell of petrol, of soil, filling his nostrils. 'Tell us and we'll go.'

And she told him – seven eight four nine seven one, seven eight four nine seven one – between juddering sobs, before crawling on her hands and knees to the jerking body of her husband.

And Perry flew to the safe.

39

1984

In the dead of night they carried Sally's body to the bottom of the garden, along the narrow path beneath the copse of trees. Gordon held the front of the rug and Elliot and Connor struggled with the other end. Toby walked behind, snivelling. The moon and stars disappeared as they stumbled with the heavy load beneath the canopy of leaves and reappeared above the wall at the bottom. A petrol canister was propped there, a pair of spades.

Gordon had earlier locked the three boys in the office with the body while he went to fetch the equipment, and to tell the Dents to get the other kids to bed early. Connor, Elliot and Toby couldn't help but stare at the body and the fingers of blood probing every crack in the floorboards. Toby didn't stop weeping. Finally, Elliot gave up telling him to pack it in.

Taking a torch from his pocket, Gordon ran a beam of light along the length of the rolled-up rug. Sally's feet hung limply out the bottom, the chipped varnish on her toes catching the light. He threw the torch down and sat on the rug, slipping off a shoe to rub his foot, emitting little smacking noises of satisfaction.

'You lads are doing me a mighty favour, and I appreciate

it.' Gordon took out a flask. 'The thing is, Sally wanted it both ways. She wanted everything I had, but she wanted me to change, she expected me to be something I'm not. I'm not excusing what I did, but it's the truth. When you boys are older you'll realise that you'll always be stuck with yourself.'

Connor asked: 'What do we do now?'

'You're going to dig a bloody great hole is what you're going to do, against that wall.' He clapped his hands together. 'Come on, chop-chop.'

Connor and Elliot dug at the dry earth, which crumbled easily beneath the spades. They worked in silence as Gordon sat and watched, drinking steadily.

'You boys have been good friends to me. You don't know how difficult it can be, the burden I carry.' His fingers absently stroked the rug. 'I loved that girl, but she had a mouth on her. I'm a patient man, but she pushed me too far.'

Below the topsoil the ground was damp, and they lifted great chunks of it. Elliot tore ferociously into the earth. His shoulders ached as he dug the spade into the earth. Lifted a clump of mud, dropped it onto the pile. Dug the spade into the earth, lifted the soil, placed it on the heap.

'I won't forget this.' Planting his legs apart, Gordon lowered his head into his hands. 'This is a special moment, so it is. We're bonding, the four of us, because we're in this together now, for all time. You're my late-night buddies,' he glanced at his watch, 'you're my Two O'Clock Boys. That's what we are, we're pals for life, the Two O'Clock Boys.'

Then Elliot became lost in robot labour – digging the spade into the earth and tipping it to the side, the smell of soil filling his nostrils – and it was a while before he realised Connor had stopped digging, and was listening to Gordon's snores.

'Come on, let's get this done.'

There was a cold gleam in Connor's eye that Elliot understood immediately. 'We'll do it now, while he's asleep, and then we'll go.'

'You can't!' said Elliot.

'We do it now.'

'What about the kid?' Elliot stammered. 'He'll tell his parents and then what?'

But Connor climbed from the hole and stood over Gordon.

'Connor!' Elliot lunged forward. 'You can't just—'

'Shut up!' Connor hefted the spade, turned it in his hands so that the dull metal edge would cleave Gordon's skull into two. 'We'll never have a better time.'

'You can't!'

Elliot grabbed at him, but Connor pushed him off. Gordon's chest heaved with each guttural snore. Connor lifted the spade above his head, his arms shaking violently, damp palms slick on the wooden shaft.

And he still hadn't swung it down when Gordon's head snapped up to leer at Connor and the spade trembling above his head.

'Finally, let's see what you're made of,' he said quietly. 'I believed you had it in you to go the whole way, lad, but you're just like those others. Weak, like Elliot. A victim, like our friend Toby. I thought I saw something in those cold eyes of yours, Connor; I really thought you would be different.'

Gordon lifted himself from the rug, taking a moment to

brush down his trousers before taking the spade from Connor. 'You want to see how it's done again, do you, boy? Let me show you.'

He walked to Toby and threw him into the trench, then picked up the canister to slop petrol all over the boy. The stench of the liquid lifted into the air, making Elliot's eyes sting. He stumbled back, blinking. Toby screamed, scrabbling around on the mud like the cockroach on his plate. Gordon poured the petrol until the boy's hair, skin and clothes were drenched.

'Watch me.' Gordon pulled a lighter from his pocket, flicking open the lid to spark the flint. A long, flickering flame whipped in the night air. '*This* is how to do it.'

'Don't,' said Connor.

Toby screeched. Elliot shook violently. Connor stepped forward. 'He's got family, Gordon, people who love him and who are waiting for him!'

Gordon swayed above the trench. A shelf of mud gave way beneath his feet and he almost toppled forward. There was a deafening rush of noise and a mail train hurtled past a few feet away, shaking the trees. Elliot saw, but couldn't hear, Toby's frenzied shriek. The flame danced violently in Gordon's hand.

'He can't go home, Connor,' said Gordon, when it had passed. 'Not now.'

'Yeah,' said Connor quickly. 'You're right, but we'll talk about it tomorrow, when you're . . . when you've got a clear head.'

Elliot heard the bones in Gordon's neck crack. Then the lid of the lighter snapped shut, and he threw it at Connor. When the boy caught it, it was hot to the touch.

'Get him out of there.' Gordon stared at Sally's body.

'Burn her and then fill in the hole. Cover it with leaves and branches. When I come back tomorrow, I don't want to be able to see it. I'll make sure the kids stay out of the garden for a few days.'

Then he stumbled back through the trees to the house, and Elliot scrambled into the hole to pull Toby out. 'Get back to the house and wash, and stop crying.'

'Leave your clothes,' said Connor.

The boy undressed, shivering with cold and fear. They threw his clothes into the trench and Toby went whimpering up the path. Elliot and Connor dragged the rug containing Sally's body into the hole, splashed petrol onto it and set it alight.

Smoke and sparks lifted into the air between them. Connor pulled his T-shirt over his nose against the smell of burning flesh.

'You gonna have a family, Connor?' asked Elliot, as they slumped against the wall listening to the crack and fizz of the fire. Entranced by the flames leaping off the rug, Connor didn't answer.

'I'm gonna have a wife,' continued Elliot. 'And loads of kids. I'll bring them up right; they ain't ever gonna be afraid of nothing. I'll be a dad, a proper dad . . .' He threw a stick into the flames. 'Just got to get out of this place first.'

Neither of them spoke for the rest of the night. They dozed. By the time the sky began to swell, and the stars faded in the sky, the flames had dwindled. They shovelled mud back into the trench, smothering the last embers, avoided looking at the smouldering corpse. When the hole was filled, they covered the fresh soil with leaves, branches and large stones as best they could.

At dawn, shouts drifted down from the house – the other kids were awake – and Gordon came along the garden with a bucket of hot water so they could wash. He stared at the disturbed earth, made the sign of the cross on his chest, and left without saying a word.

Exhausted, the two boys walked up the path beneath the trees towards the house, in the cloudy grey wash of the morning.

40

They accelerated up the narrow lane, flew along it, headlight beams carving out the way beneath the thick canopy of trees. Too fast along a road barely wide enough for a single vehicle.

Elliot braced himself against the dash as Perry wrestled with the tight turns, wanting to be as far away from the house as quickly as possible. He felt sickened. This wasn't who he was. How could he have been so stupid? Now he could never look Rhonda or Dylan in the face again.

But he didn't want to die, and they were taking the bends too fast, the wheels shuddering off the green verges, Perry barely paying attention to the road as he screamed at Elliot.

'They saw you! You used my name!' His face was scrunched tight with anger, the cords in his neck snapped taut. Flecks of his spittle spotted Elliot's cheek. 'She saw your face! You said my name! You said my—'

He gunned the engine harder, and the car swerved. The sharp fingers of an overhanging tree tore at the roof. Elliot, filled with terror, shouted: 'Watch the road, watch the—'

And on a bend he had a split second – no more than that – to register a vehicle coming the other way. 'Car! Car!'

Perry swore, jerking the wheel to the left, the angry blare of a horn bearing down on them, and the car careened up the verge. Elliot was thrown against Perry's shoulder as the passenger side lifted. Perry's hands clenched the wheel, wrestled to regain control as it jerked left and right and left. Foot scrabbling frantically for the brake pedal, finding the accelerator instead.

The engine moaned. Shrubs and bushes hurtled towards them, sticks and branches cracked against the windscreen, obscuring their view as the car plunged over the verge and into the undergrowth. Perry found the brake – and pressed hard.

Both men were propelled forward. Elliot's head flew into the dash. His neck whiplashed. Perry's chest smashed against the wheel.

The car spun on the soft earth and careened to a halt.

Elliot stared into the gloom, through the mess of leaves and twigs heaped across the windscreen, a swirl of shapes and colours dancing in his eyes. Stunned, unsure of where he was, or even for a few short moments, who he was. Perry moaned. When Elliot turned his head, an electric jolt of pain crackled down his neck. He pressed his weight against the door, fumbling for the release, and tipped onto the damp, muddy earth. He stood, hands propped on his knees. A wall of trees hemmed them in on the slope, it was a miracle the car hadn't smashed into any of the ancient trunks. Elliot, not wearing his seat belt, would have gone through the windscreen. Would be dead, for sure.

'We . . . got . . . back.' A voice behind him.

Tremors of shock vibrated up his spine when Elliot stood. 'What?'

'We got to go back.' Perry slumped against the car.

'Why?' Elliot wanted to laugh at the insanity of the suggestion.

'Because . . .' Perry clutched his chest, grimacing. 'They saw your face and you used my name.'

He had taken a knock to the head. That was the only explanation.

'The police will be there.' Elliot felt his anger swell. He'd taken part in an armed robbery, and there was nobody to blame but himself. Rhonda was never going to forgive him – he could barely believe it himself. He thought of the old man wrenching on the carpet, flapping like a fish on dry land, his wife kneeling beside him, pleading in his ear. *It'll be okay, it's all going to be okay.* Just thinking of her husband despite the terror she must have felt, as Perry slid the contents of the safe, money and valuables, into the rucksack.

'They saw your face, you said my name.' Perry's voice dripped with contempt. 'They can identify us.'

'The house will be crawling with police.' Elliot couldn't believe what he was hearing. If he was going to go back, it would be to return the money and fall on the mercy of the cops. Not to, not to—

'We're in the shit if we don't.' Perry pressed the heel of his hand against his bleeding forehead.

'You were going to kill her!'

'Didn't, though, did I?' Perry took the gun from his pocket. 'But it ain't too late. We've no choice now.'

'I'm not going back.' Elliot reeled forward on the uneven ground, twigs snapping beneath his feet. 'And you ain't either!'

'This is all because of you.' Perry lifted the gun to Elliot's head. 'Perhaps I should shoot you.'

'You were going to kill her,' repeated Elliot. Blood gushed in his head, like rapids through a rock fissure, a deafening roar in his ears. When he turned his neck, his nerves shrieked.

'Get in the car.'

'Let's just get home.' Elliot clapped his hands down his sides.

Rhonda would tell him the right thing to do. He didn't know any more, he couldn't be trusted. 'I just want to go home!'

'Get in the car, or I'll do you here,' snapped Perry.

Elliot laughed bitterly. 'Then you'll just have to do it.'

Hesitation rippled down Perry's face, then he squeezed the trigger.

And Elliot flinched.

They stood there for a moment, both of them wondering why nothing had happened, and then Perry fumbled with the safety catch on the weapon. And Elliot realised that he had to do something, or in a few, short seconds he'd be dead. Perry was going to shoot him and his body would rot here in the middle of the woods.

So he ran forward, his pumping legs creating a chain reaction of screaming muscle, and went in low. Head down, charging like a rhino, piling into Perry's chest. Pain exploded inside his head, whipping like naked electric cables down his body as Perry smashed the butt of the gun on his shoulder.

And they went down, rolling along the ground, leaves and clumps of mud spinning off them as they scrabbled at each other's arms and legs, trying to get a grip, trying to get the upper hand. Elliot felt the gun fly from Perry's fingers, and a fist swipe across his cheek. But Elliot was bigger and heavier than Perry. Rolling onto him, he spread his weight and pinned him to the floor. Struggling, Perry's mouth twisted in a rictus of impotent rage.

Elliot lifted his fist—

Saw the old woman crawling along the floor towards her husband, her face contorted by anguish.

And drove it down into Perry's face. Lifted it high again—

And saw Dylan popping a mint onto his tongue, felt

Rhonda's head against his chest, her hair tangled in his thick fingers.

Smashed the fist down into Perry's face – blood exploded from his nose, but Elliot didn't care – raised his fist high—

He knew he would lose her, because he had let everybody down, because he hadn't changed, not really. He was just the same man, the same pathetic Elliot, and always would be.

The fist came down.

He would never change. He would lose her, and he would lose Dylan, and he would be alone, because his old man was right, he was nothing, he was shit, he was scum. Tallis was right, he deserved nothing from this life. He had watched Sally Raynor die, had burned her corpse in an unmarked grave, and she was lost long ago, and he deserved nothing, not happiness, not peace and not love.

She'll know the kind of man you are.

A bully, a thief, a lowlife.

Screaming with fury, he smashed his fist down into Perry's face again and again. But Perry was gone and instead it was Gordon beneath him, who laughed and laughed in his face.

They were better off without him. Because no matter how hard he tried he could never change, when all he wanted was a quiet life with the woman he loved and her boy – *his* boy, *his* family.

And Elliot drove his fist into Gordon again and again and again, his nostrils filled with the stench of soil and petrol and burning flesh, until he could barely see who it was, the face was so covered with blood and mud and mucus and phlegm.

He lifted his fist one final time high above his head—

Bully, bully, bully.

And it trembled there, because he saw Gordon was gone. Instead Perry's head slumped to the side, eyes slits in his bloody, swollen cheeks. With a growing sense of horror, Elliot realised that Perry wasn't moving. He lowered his fist. Slumped against the man's chest, and sobbed.

I've killed him, he thought.

Elliot rolled off Perry's body onto the cold ground. Birdsong trilled as he stared up at the trees swaying high above, leaves spinning down towards him. After a moment he stood, cleared the mulch and mud off him as best he could. There was no going back from this, no leading a normal life, no playing happy families.

I've killed him.

A vehicle blipped past on the road, only yards away.

Elliot staggered to the car and popped the boot. He grabbed Perry's ankles and dragged him to the rear of the vehicle, twigs and berries and leaves gathering in the dead man's armpits. Pain lashing down his neck, Elliot wrapped his arms around Perry's chest and tipped him into the boot. Slammed it shut.

The faint sound of a siren on the wind made him freeze. Then he picked up the gun, muddy and slippery, and stuffed it into the rucksack, which he pulled from behind the front seat of the car. Hefted it over his shoulder, ignoring the shooting pains, and set off through the woods.

The voice of the Two O'Clock Boy – the only man in the world who knew that Elliot could never change – going round and round in his head.

She'll know the kind of man you are.

41

If Drake knew what she was doing, he'd go ballistic. Doorstepping the old woman was one thing; secretly pressing his beloved daughter for information was taking Flick's betrayal to a whole new level. But there was something Drake wasn't telling her, something that involved him and Myra and that home, and it was important enough to make him steal evidence. While she was still clinging to the investigation by her fingertips, she was determined to discover what it was.

And besides, she was only fulfilling a promise she'd made to the girl. At Laura's funeral Flick had told April that she would be a shoulder to cry on any time she wanted – she remembered Ray Drake had been grateful for the offer. Now she was making good on her word. When Flick had returned her call, still shaken from her meeting with Harry, April had sounded upset – she didn't know who to talk to, she said – and they arranged to meet immediately.

When she arrived at the Pret in Camden Town, grateful to peel away from the army of tourists marching towards the Lock, April was already there, looking very pretty and very miserable in an expensive cashmere coat, and clutching in her lap the kind of bag Flick could only dream of affording. All this designer stuff, she presumed, a perk of being with that City boy of hers.

Flick leaned in for an awkward hug, feeling the treachery lift off her like vapour, and asked April if she wanted coffee. The girl shook her head. Flick bought them both sparkling water.

'I hear you've moved out,' she said, cracking the cap on her bottle.

The girl mumbled. 'Yes, to Jordan's.'

'You know I'm a detective sergeant now?'

'How's it going?'

'Let's just say it's a learning curve.' Flick smiled. 'Your dad is worried about you.'

'I'm sure he is.'

'You don't sound like you believe it.'

'He probably is in his own way but . . .' April shrugged. 'Well, everyone thinks they know him, but they don't.'

'I'm not going to go running back to him; this is strictly between you and me.'

'He's so controlling, suffocating. Secretive, you know?'

Flick took a casual sip of water. 'In what way?'

'He came to Jordan's apartment and he keeps calling and calling. It's like he won't let me have my own life.'

Controlling, suffocating. That didn't sound like the Ray Drake she knew, but then the memory of him in the Property Room popped into her head. Taking that photo, stealing evidence.

'Has he hit you or . . . hurt you in any way?'

'Hit me?' April looked shocked. 'Of course he hasn't!'

'I'm sorry.' Flick held up her hands. 'I was just trying to—'

'He's just not an easy man to know, he keeps everything . . . in.'

'A lot of men do.'

'Sometimes I think he's going to, I don't know . . . explode. He went off the rails when he was younger; I bet you didn't know that.'

'Oh?'

'Gran took him out of school.'

'Why?'

'I don't know, something happened, raging teenage hormones. I asked Gran about it and she said he was challenging, whatever that means. Getting Gran to talk about anything is *challenging*.'

'Your father sounds like a chip off the old block.'

'You can say that again. I think he's turning into Gran. She scares the shit out of me sometimes.' April laughed, but there was no humour in it. 'That's not right, is it, being scared of your own gran?'

'It's probably not as unusual as you think.'

'She's the coldest person you ever met. He's turning into her and maybe one day I'll turn into him, and on it goes . . .' Tears bulged in the girl's eyes, and Flick went to the counter to get a napkin. The girl wept quietly for a minute, turning her engagement ring on her finger. 'Jordan hates him – and now he hates me.'

'Is that why you wanted to see me, April?'

The girl dabbed at her eyes. 'He asked me to move in, but now he says he's never loved me, never wanted to be with me. He told me to get out.'

Flick squeezed April's hand, which tightened around the soggy balled napkin. 'Why don't you go home? Your dad just wants you back.'

April shook her head. 'I can't!'

'Why not?'

She took a deep, shuddering breath. 'Because I've been awful to him.'

'He doesn't care about that. He just wants you to be happy. Your mum's death knocked you both for six, and you're finding it difficult to talk. You're both hurting, both grieving, and you need each other. Whatever you do, don't . . .' She felt her chest tighten. 'Don't fall out with your dad.'

'I don't understand it. When Mum was still . . . Jordan loved me. He was there for me. I love him.'

'Is he at home now?' asked Flick.

'He's at work. He'll be home later . . . maybe. He usually goes out after work, to pubs and clubs – who knows where else? – and gets in at all hours.' She met Flick's eyes, reproachfully. 'Or not at all.'

'You're welcome to stay with me.'

'I've a friend I can go to.'

'Give your friend a call; tell them you're coming over.'

'I don't have any clothes with me.'

'That can wait till tomorrow. Let Jordan calm down, let him consider his actions. Call me if you want me to go and pick up anything. And if you want me to speak to your father . . .'

'I'll call him later.' April pushed the unopened water bottle away. 'I promise.'

Taking the cue, Flick said: 'I'd better go.'

Outside on the street, Flick stuck out her arm and a cab immediately pulled up beside them. She crouched at the window, while the driver was leaned away straightening the side mirror.

'Docklands, please, the lady will give you the address.'

Flick and April shared a long hug. The girl clung to her

tightly, reluctant to let go, and Flick was grateful for the physical contact. Then April climbed into the back of the cab. When it drove off, Flick answered a call from Eddie Upson's mobile.

'Eddie.' She heard the chatter of the Incident Room. 'What news?'

'I've been told to tell you to get back here,' he said. She sensed the anxiety in his voice and dread detonated in her gut. 'You're off the case.'

42

The road rushed towards him with a dizzy clarity. A time was coming soon when this life would be over and he could sleep, the boy sensed that very clearly. Good riddance to it, he was sick of it.

Glancing in the mirror at the girl speaking into her phone, he considered that it was at times like this when he felt most alive. All he'd ever wanted was to punish those people who had allowed the sickness to fester inside him, who had let him become – it wasn't too strong a word – a monster. When he was finally released from his life's work, when he had meted out justice to the guilty, he would step gratefully into oblivion.

His foot squeezed the accelerator of the stolen cab. He felt a quickening in his pulse. He would be at peace, reunited with his own family at last. Then, perhaps, he would know happiness. If not, if no one waited for him on the other side, as he suspected, he would at least know the comfort of the void.

When the girl finished her call, he took off his baseball cap, his appearance meant nothing to her so there was little point in wearing it, and ran a hand over his scalp.

He caught her eye in the mirror. 'You look sad.'

She smiled faintly, absorbed in her own thoughts. 'Family worries.'

'Oh, I know all about those,' he said, not without sympathy. Her phone lay on the seat beside her, he saw.

In years gone by, he had told himself that once his work was done, the rest of his days could be lived happily enough. But he realised long ago that there would be no happiness in this world for him. His adult life had consisted of three drives: to eat, to sleep and to kill, and he derived little pleasure from any of them.

The boy ate healthily because he had to keep physically and mentally able. His life was busy and demanding – with every new persona he was obliged to alter his body shape, which required a strict fitness and diet regime. His sleep was fitful because that was where his dreams and nightmares merged. Every night his sins soaked more heavily into his soul, like water into a sponge.

His mind only made room for the information that would allow him to complete his life's work. Years of study gave him a multitude of professional qualifications, the mastery of a skill or command of a new identity. Money, possessions, held no appeal. The exception was the small collection of mementoes he'd taken from his victims, every new trophy a reminder that he was a step closer to his own release. They sat on the top of the fridge in his rented house.

There was the tobacco tin he had taken only this morning from the flat of Deborah Willetts before he torched her. Beside it was the horseshoe he'd picked up when working as an animal feed salesman visiting the Australian stud farm where David Horner lived. Propped behind that was a torn coaster from the pub where he'd befriended Jason Burgess. Then there was a bicycle pump he'd borrowed from Ricky Hancock when he'd been his sponsor in Alcoholics Anonymous. And the china figurine he'd slipped in his pocket before he gutted Kenny Overton's wife.

As Gavin, he'd stolen an air freshener shaped like a pine tree from Elliot Juniper's van. As well as all that money, which he passed on to third parties in pursuit of Juniper's ultimate humiliation. Juniper, of course, was unfinished business. The boy wanted him to suffer, wanted to take everything from him, so that in the end he would understand how contemptible he was, and had always been.

There were other objects, so many objects.

But from the policeman, when the time came, he'd take nothing. There was only one thing he required from him.

With his life's work almost complete, the boy would probably never go back to that house, never again touch those trophies, but he didn't care. That place was never a home, it was just one of a succession of temporary addresses where he slept and prepared and planned. He moved from place to place as required, had lived in so many cities as so many people, and soon his long journey would be over.

A car edged out of a junction and he politely gestured for the driver to pull out, *go ahead.*

All those lives he'd lived. All the people he had been. If you put all of his identities in a room together, if such a metaphysical act were possible, you wouldn't believe they were all the same person. They would bicker and take an immediate dislike to each other. He had no real sense of self, not any more, which is why perhaps it was so easy for him to become someone else.

His consciousness was as shattered as the bones of Kenny's brat when he fell to his death. It was always a relief to step into the skin of another person, and another, and then another.

Physically, he'd learned to alter every aspect of his appearance and personality: his gait, the very cadence of his speech. He'd mastered new accents and mannerisms, taken jobs up and down the country and abroad.

Say what you like about the boy, grind his reputation into the dirt, but he'd always been clever.

Years ago, he'd discovered it was easy to ingratiate yourself into other people's lives. Nobody remembered the child he'd been, nobody wanted to remember him or the home. Damaged and unhappy, those people smeared their fear and paranoia onto everybody who came into their orbit, so that it was easy for him insinuate himself into their lives. As a social worker, a well-heeled neighbour or work colleague, a friend in the pub. It was sickening the way they threw themselves at him, leeching comfort, love – and money, always money. He hardly had to do anything. These people, the kids who had let him kill his parents – caused him to stove in their skulls until the head of the hammer was matted in hair, gristle, splinters of bone – circled him like ravenous hyenas, darting in to greedily snatch what they wanted. Their lives were as useless as boneless limbs. When you thought about it, he was doing them a favour, putting them and their dismal kin out of their misery. It wasn't right that they were able to live their lives as if nothing had happened, and he had nothing. They were guilty, every single one of them.

It had been easy for him to find the people from the Longacre. They left a paper trail – of institutions, criminal records, benefit claims – and Amelia Troy lived a life in plain view. The boy looked long and hard, he never gave up, and eventually he found them all, with a single agonising exception.

There was only one person who had managed to evade him, and his absence left a massive, angry hole. The boy had come to the conclusion that he was dead – a bitter pill to swallow. And it was only by blind luck, or perhaps it was destiny, that the boy discovered him.

Short weeks after he'd driven Ricky and his family into the river, he'd been sitting in a café vacantly staring at a television. The news was on, a report about the completion of a criminal case. A high-ranking policeman was making a statement outside a court building. News cameras pressed forward, microphones jutted into the scene, flashes exploded.

We are pleased to get a conviction, blah, blah, blah, justice has been done. The policeman's chest puffed out. *The end of a long and difficult investigation, and so on, thanks to Detective Inspector Raymond Drake . . .*

Detective Inspector Drake looked none too pleased about being identified. He stood at the edge of the throng, trying to melt into the background. Physically shrinking from the attention. Mesmerised by that grim expression, the boy felt a surge of joy, a moment of rapture the likes of which he'd never dared to hope to experience.

And then the report ended. The boy tried to organise the euphoric feelings that ricocheted around inside him. There was no TV in the bedsit he lived in at that time, so that night he stood in the sheeting rain to watch a bank of televisions in the window of an electrical retailer. He was petrified that the story would be dropped for the evening bulletin. But there it was again, the same footage: the bustle outside the court, the high-ranking policeman droning on – and the man identified as Ray Drake trying to make himself invisible by the sheer force of his will.

The boy stood outside that shop and wept. He felt complete, even as his tears of happiness, tears of powerful rage, were washed away in the deluge.

Take my hand. Take it.

You're alive.

You can go home.

If the policeman had let the boy die that day, if he had let the flames consume him, then all those others would be alive. All those men, all those women, all those children.

This, then, was the endgame.

As he shifted up a gear to slip past a green light, he accepted his own imminent death. The Two O'Clock Boy was tired, he didn't want to live. If people believed he had sailed through life without a thought to what he had done, and what he had become, they were sorely mistaken.

He was ready.

'This isn't the way,' said a voice.

Blinking, he remembered the girl in the back – April Drake. She perched forward, reading the street signs. He smiled in the rear-view mirror.

The conclusion was near, and it would be sweet.

43

The call came from April's phone. It barely rang once before Drake snatched it up, expecting to hear her. Instead, the electronic voice said: 'I have your daughter.'

Drake's stomach churned. Phone clamped to his ear, he stumbled against his desk. 'Where is she?'

'Remember what I told you,' said the Two O'Clock Boy, his anger twisting and surging in the synthetic swirl. 'You are to blame.'

'Please, don't hurt her.' His own voice was faint, as if it were coming from the end of a long tunnel.

'I wanted to die. If you had let me go to sleep, those others would still be alive. Say it.'

'I'm to blame,' said Drake. 'I'm guilty. Let me talk to her, just let—'

The line went dead and his mind whirled. The gun Myra had given him was in the boot of his car – if he only knew where to go, how to find April. But when he turned, Flick Crowley was standing in the doorway, hands on her hips.

'Why have I been taken off the investigation?' she asked.

Drake scooped up his car keys. They scraped loudly along the desk in the quiet of his office.

'I don't have time for this,' he said.

But Flick blocked his way. 'I've a right to know.'

'Not now,' he said, stepping forward.

'You can't just—'

'April is gone,' Drake said. 'She's—' He stopped himself saying it, wanted to get out of there and find his daughter.

If *he* had her – *oh God.*

The fear, the anger, made his head swim.

'What are you talking about?'

'Never mind,' he said, but she wouldn't step aside.

'I was with her this afternoon.'

'Where?' Drake grabbed her upper arm.

Flick stared at his hand. 'We met at a café in Camden. Jordan's thrown her out. She needed to talk to someone but was too afraid to contact you; she thought you'd be angry with her.'

'Where?' His mouth was dry. 'Where did she go?'

'To a friend's.' Flick warily absorbed the alarm in his voice. 'I put her in a cab.'

I have your daughter.

He pushed her against the doorframe, fingers pressing into her shoulders. 'Do you know what you've done?'

Flick cringed in shock and disgust, and Drake's head dropped. He closed his eyes to stop the room spinning. April could be anywhere by now. Could be dead by now.

He killed all those others. Men, women, children. Didn't think twice about it.

'Who is Connor Laird?'

Flick's question jolted him back into the room. When he opened his eyes, she was looking straight at him.

'I think he's alive,' she said. 'I think Myra is afraid of him, and I believe you are, too.'

'No.' He wanted to tell her everything, but couldn't. For the first time in his life he had no idea what to do.

'Who is Connor Laird?' she repeated.

'The investigation is drifting.' He cleared his throat, tried to sound authoritative. 'Upson told me you led him on a wild goose chase around town. I'm taking over.'

'Who is Connor Laird? Why were you tampering with evidence?'

'I told you to leave Myra alone.'

'Who is Connor Laird?' She kept hammering him with that question. All he heard was that damned name in his head. He couldn't focus, couldn't concentrate. 'Why did you destroy that cutting?'

'You're not—'

'Why did you tear out that photograph?'

He needed to be out of there, looking for April, for his daughter. 'You're not making any progress.' It was all he could think to say. 'We need to get the investigation back on—'

'What was in that photo, Ray? What was in it that you don't want anybody to see?'

'Go home, Flick.'

'Or what?' She didn't look away. 'What will happen?'

Drake didn't have time for this, didn't—

'Who is Connor Laird?'

Drake stared.

'Is he alive?' she barked.

'He's *gone*,' whispered Drake, his fingers digging into her shoulders. 'Long gone.'

'I don't think so,' she said softly. 'He's out there, and he's very dangerous, and I think you know who he is. Tell me.'

'You don't understand . . . the Two O'Clock Boy . . .' Drake needed to find his daughter, had no time to spare, but he was weary – his life was fragmenting, shattering into a thousand pieces – and all the secrets, all the lies . . . it wasn't worth it any more.

He would tell her. 'Connor Laird is—'

'What's going on here?' asked a voice. Peter Holloway stood in the corridor. His gaze dropped to Drake's grip on Flick's shoulders. 'Take your hands off her, please.'

When Drake let go, Flick quickly slipped past Holloway and out of the room. He heard her slam through the fire door along the corridor.

'What on earth is going on?' asked Holloway.

'It's none of your concern.'

Drake moved to go, but Holloway held a hand to his chest. 'On the contrary, it looked to me very much that—'

There was a knock on the door and Holloway turned irritably to see Frank Wanderly, knuckles raised to the wood, a scrap of paper in his other hand.

'Sorry to barge in, gents. I was looking for DS Crowley.'

'Not now,' said Holloway.

'I've been asked to give her a message.'

'She's not here, Frank,' Holloway snapped.

Wanderly blinked, his gaze moving from the CSM to Drake, who pushed roughly past him.

'DI Drake, wait!' Drake swung open the fire door to drop into the stairwell, flew downstairs as fast as he could. But Holloway kept pace behind him. 'Ray! Is there anything I can do? Please stop and talk.'

Drake didn't look back. 'Mind your own business, Peter.'

'I heard how you spoke to DS Crowley, and you can be sure I'll be taking this further.'

At the landing Drake whirled. 'Do what you have to do.'

'You can speak to me, Ray, I'm a friend. And now Laura is gone . . .'

When Holloway attempted to place a hand on his shoulder, Drake jerked away.

'I appreciate your concern, Peter. But there's nothing you can do. My daughter, she . . . I wish I'd taken more care of her.'

'Let's go to the canteen,' Holloway said kindly. 'My shout.'

Drake ran down the rest of the stairs, leaving Holloway behind.

In the car park, he opened the boot and took out a plastic bag containing the gun, slipped it in his pocket. Climbing behind the wheel, he called April's phone again. It rang and rang and rang.

Drake smashed his hands again and again against the dashboard. When a pair of uniforms came through the gate, he fired up the engine and accelerated onto the High Road.

Flick said Jordan had thrown April out. Hours later, she'd been taken. Drake didn't believe in coincidences. Besides, he had a score to settle with the kid.

He drove to the Docklands, hands shaking on the wheel, willing the phone on the passenger seat to ring. The evening traffic was thick. Drake forced himself not to panic, to stay focused, as he edged forward, each slow yard of the commuter snarl pure torture.

44

The first thing she would do when she got home was get it all on paper. Ray Drake in the Property Room; his old mother's connection to the home; the way he pressured Flick to ignore the cuttings. And how he lost control in his office. Holloway had seen everything, so she had a witness – that episode, at least, wasn't a figment of her imagination. She would hand her report to DCI Harris and he could decide what action to take. Whatever happened to her, it was clear to Flick that Drake was losing the plot. He was still grieving for his wife, that much was clear; he was in no fit mental state. He needed to take compassionate leave, seek medical help.

Taking long, calming breaths, trying to get her head on straight, she just wanted to get out of the station as quickly as possible. But slamming through a fire door, her heart sunk when she heard Millie Steiner's voice behind her.

'Ma'am, wait up. Flick!'

Flick composed herself and forced a smile onto her face.

'I was hoping to catch you,' said Steiner. 'I'm so sorry. I feel like we just haven't been able to deliver for you.'

'It's nobody's fault,' said Flick. Her removal from the investigation was obviously big news by now. 'We haven't been looking in the right direction.'

If Steiner had asked her to elaborate, she would have

blurted it all out there and then, shared her concerns and suspicions, but instead the young detective said: 'DS Kendrick is going to take charge with DC Upson assisting, that's what we've been told, and DI Drake will give us more of a steer.'

Drake will take you in completely the wrong direction, thought Flick. He'll let the investigation go cold, let it fade away. Because there's something about the death of Kenny Overton and countless others at the hands of a remorseless predator that he doesn't want you, or any of us, to know about.

Drake had been ranting about April going missing and somebody called the Two O'Clock Boy, she remembered that now, and it made her uneasy.

'What are you going to do?' asked Steiner.

'Go home, take a bath, drink wine.' Too shocked after her encounter with Drake, she wasn't going to get anything done here. She wanted to talk to Nina. Her sister would know exactly what to do. 'I'll catch you later, Millie.'

Buzzing out of the exit, Flick took out her mobile to call her sister – it would also provide a useful human shield if anybody else tried to speak to her, but there was no answer on the home number – which was unusual. Nina was like an old person with her mobile, she regarded it strictly as something to be used in emergencies, if she broke down on the motorway or if there was some kind of alien apocalypse, but Flick tried it anyway.

The phone rang and rang. Flick was nearly at her car when the call connected. Nina spoke loudly, as she always did when she had a couple of drinks inside her.

'Hello, darling!'

'Are you in?'

'We're out tonight,' said Nina, over loud conversation in the background. 'Meeting bigwigs from Martin's new company. They're visiting from Down Under. Oh, Flick, I was really worried about moving to the other side of the world and knowing hardly anyone, but they seem really nice people.'

'Who's looking after the kids?'

'They're on a sleepover at Imogen's next door.'

'I can pick them up and stay over if it helps.'

'Oh, thank you, darling.' Nina's voice was almost lost against a burst of laughter at her end. 'But they've been so looking forward to it.'

Flick climbed into her car, slammed the door. The traffic noise from the High Road dulled.

'Dad said he saw you,' said Nina. 'Said you looked great. He was so happy, Flick, he was so excited.'

'Nina, we didn't—'

'You don't know how pleased I am, what a weight it is off my mind to know the pair of you are talking again. Thank you so much. I feel much better about everything. Oh Christ, someone's put *another* glass of champagne in my hand. The last thing I want to do is get pissed. Tell me to watch my step.'

'Three glasses and then you're on the water.'

'Got it. I want to see you as much as possible in the next month.'

'Month?'

'We're leaving in a month. Not much notice, is it? But they're keen for Martin to start work as soon as possible.' She hesitated. 'Is everything okay there, you sound . . . quiet.'

'I'm fine,' said Flick. 'You'd better go.'

'I'm sorry, I'll call tomorrow and we can talk properly. Love you.'

Flick threw the phone on the passenger seat and turned on the heater. It throbbed loudly. The gate rattled open and a patrol car pulled in.

She'd go home, change into her pyjamas and try to relax. Write up those notes. Then she'd message some people on Facebook, maybe even arrange a few catch-ups. There was a sudden rap on the window, and she flinched in momentary terror when she saw Frank Wanderly hunched there, bald head ghoulishly haloed against the sodium lamps in the car park. He spun his fist – *wind down the window.*

The glass lowered with a whine, and Wanderly stuck his head in. 'Glad I caught you. Someone's been trying to get in touch.'

He handed her the scrap of paper. Above a number was a name: Trevor Sutherland. She stared at it, expecting it to make some kind of sense. She'd no idea who it was.

'Thanks, Frank.'

'You're very welcome.' He waved over his shoulder as he headed towards the gate, and out of the station.

Flick dropped the paper beside the phone, started the engine, wincing again at the sudden, unwelcome memory of her confrontation with Drake in his office, and drove to the gate. As it trundled open, the penny dropped and she snatched up the note.

Trevor Sutherland, the photographer who took the image at the Longacre all those years back.

She called him straight back.

45

The Thames churned angrily, a speedboat bumping across the choppy water, as Drake arrived outside Jordan's apartment building. He flew into reception.

'You can't just . . .' The porter stepped forward, but Drake headed straight to the elevator.

On Jordan's floor he heard the throb of music inside. He knocked on the door, stepping aside to avoid being seen through the spyhole, and when it opened, Drake kicked at it, sending Jordan stumbling backwards.

Back-heeling the door shut, he yanked Jordan to his feet, gripped the back of his neck to push him into the living room. The kid wore a vest top and underpants. His spray tan glowed faintly in the winter glare of the tall windows and the impressive panorama of the broiling brown river below. On a table of white glass was a smear of pale dust, an open wrap of coke. Yanking a power cable from it socket, Drake killed the music. He forced Jordan's face to the table. A faint spurt of breath blossomed on the glass beneath his nose.

'What did I tell you would happen if I caught you with that stuff?'

The kid's fingers were splayed rigid on the surface. 'Mr Drake! Let me . . . let me . . .'

On top of everything else, April had been exposed to

drugs, had maybe even taken them with Jordan. The certainty of it ignited his fury. He jerked back the young man's head and smashed his nose down hard. Strings of blood spurted along the glass. Jordan cried out. Drake took gloves from his jacket pocket. The kid lifted himself from the table, cupping his bloody nose in his hands.

'And I haven't thanked you for the visit.'

'What you talking about?' Babbling now, terror and coke popping goosebumps on his skin. 'I've no idea what you're saying!'

'Those thugs you sent to beat me up. That was above and beyond the call of duty.' Drake stretched the left glove tight over his hand. 'I'm guessing that was your own idea.'

'My nose!' Blood poured through his fingers, pattering into the thick weave of the cream carpet. 'This is police brutality!'

'You don't realise how often I've dreamed of this moment, Jordan. How long I've wanted to go to work on someone. You were right; it's a relief to let it out. The fact that it's you I'm going to beat unconscious makes me very happy.'

When Drake balled his fists and moved forward, Jordan cowered. 'Woah, woah! All right! I hired a couple of guys to do you over! Thought I'd teach you a lesson. You were giving me grief!' He nodded at Drake's face. 'But no harm done, it don't look so bad.'

'I don't care about my face, Jordan, or that you paid men to kick me around. We'll let bygones be bygones about that. But I want to know about the *other* thing.'

'What other thing?' Jordan hopped from foot to foot. 'I don't know what you're talking about!'

'Someone paid you to keep my daughter from me.' Drake

cuffed the top of his peroxided head. Jordan was soft, snide, weak, no amount of gym time could compensate for that. 'This isn't a game. Someone's trying to kill April.'

Jordan flinched. 'I don't know what you're—'

'Shut up.' Drake slapped his cheek. 'My guess is that you were made an offer. This person came to you because they very much want to keep me apart from my daughter.' Drake nodded at the spectacular view from Jordan's apartment, the swell of the Thames, the skyline of skyscrapers and bridges and monuments at twilight; at the expensive furniture and decor, the biggest television screen he'd ever seen. 'I imagine the sports car and the horse, the drugs, all the rest of it, cost a fortune.'

Jordan gawped. 'Kill her?'

'Someone's trying to kill April, and kill me.' Drake clenched Jordan's throat, dragged him close. 'And when he's done that, I imagine he's going to want to tie up a few loose ends. You, for example. Because this man, he's killed many, many people, Jordan, and he won't think twice about offing a preening little squirt like you.'

Jordan's eyes bulged. Drake released his throat and he slumped on the table. Gingerly dabbed at the blood streaming from his nose.

'He said he'd help me out.' Jordan gulped down air. 'I got debts, Mr Drake. I made some bad investments. He said he'd look after me if I treated April nice, and kept her away from you. And I did, Mr Drake, I treated her very well.'

'Till you couldn't stand it any more, and threw her out.'

'I don't want to get tied down. I'm a young guy, my whole life ahead, and I don't need the grief.' Jordan looked up warily. 'I swear, Mr Drake, she hasn't done any drugs, not with me. She's not interested in anything like that.'

'She just wanted to be with you,' said Drake.

'Yeah.' Jordan swallowed. 'She loved me.'

'You told him where she was going when she left?'

'I told him I was through.' He wiped his nose along his arm, leaving a streak of blood. 'I let him know I was gonna do it this afternoon.'

'By phone?'

'I've got an email address.'

'Tell me about him.'

'I met him just after I'd started seeing April. I wasn't all that into her, to be honest.' He eyed Drake's clenched fists. 'She's too classy for the likes of me.'

'That's the first truthful thing you've said.'

'We got talking in a pub. I thought I was going to lose it all and he said he could help. He wanted me to get April away from you. It was a wind-up, he said. I presumed it was someone you'd banged up in the past. He offered a lot of money, no questions asked.'

Drake rubbed his temples. 'And you thought, yeah, it'll be easy getting this girl to fall for me, it'll be a laugh.'

'It weren't easy, Mr Drake. She liked me, yeah, but she weren't interested in . . . going further.' Mucus and blood strung between Jordan's lips. 'But when her mum died, and things weren't so good between you, it . . . got easier.'

'This man who came to you,' said Drake, tired, 'what's his name?'

'Mr Smith. Well, that was what he said.'

'Describe him.'

'I can do better than that.' Jordan stumbled to an android phone on a cabinet. 'I took a sneaky photo of him one night. Just in case, like.'

He swiped a thumb across it, smearing a blob of blood that had dropped from his nose onto the screen, just as Ray Drake's own phone rang. His stomach lurched when he saw the call was from his daughter's phone. Turning away from Jordan, he said: 'Please, don't hurt her.'

'Your daughter?' The electronic laugh howled in his ear. 'I don't have your daughter any more.'

The thought that she was already dead sent him staggering to the window to press his forehead against the cold glass, before his legs gave way. The room, the glow of the golden river and the city at twilight, melted away. Drake tried to focus, gripping the phone in both hands to keep it steady.

The thought of what he would hear next terrified him.

She was gone: killed, tortured.

He imagined April's screams of terror, her agonising last moments. His legs nearly buckled. If he fell, he didn't know how far he would drop. When Drake tried to respond, his lips moved but nothing came out.

'I'm visiting another old friend of ours,' the voice said triumphantly. 'And we're waiting for you.'

Drake heard screams in the background. 'Ray, oh God! Help me!'

The call disconnected and Drake flew towards Jordan.

'Show me!' he screamed.

46

1984

When a couple of days went by and Sally didn't phone, Ray tried not to panic. She had things to do, he reasoned. She was a grown woman with responsibilities, and he had to respect that. She had made him a solemn promise that she would stay in contact, would call him when she was able. But more days passed, a week, and he knew something was wrong.

That home was the last place he wanted to go, but he had no choice. He would wait outside, he decided, until Sally came out and he would ask her why she hadn't called, why she had made him so worried. But when he arrived he saw her car was gone, and swallowed down the panic he felt.

He waited all day at the bottom of the street, and well into the evening, but he couldn't – wouldn't – wait any longer. A red sky was flattening across the slope on the other side of the train track when he hammered on the door of the Longacre.

'Can I help you, lad?' asked Gordon, when it opened.

'Where is she?' Ray tried to look over his shoulder into the home. 'Where's Sally?'

Gordon told Ray politely that he was very sorry but he

had no idea where she was. She was gone, he said, had decided to leave. It all happened very suddenly; Sally just got up and left. Somewhere up north, he said.

'No.' Ray felt the ground lurch beneath his feet. 'She wouldn't go without telling me. She wouldn't just leave.'

'I don't know what to tell you,' said Gordon sadly. 'If I knew any more . . .'

'You're lying.' Ray pushed past Gordon and into the office. When he didn't see her there, he opened the door to the small room at the back. The only light came from a dirty skylight above a mattress. Sheets lay tangled on top of the bedding, and a petrol canister, its pungent fumes overwhelming in the small space, was placed beside a green radiator.

'I'm going to have to ask you to leave,' said Gordon, the kids crowding behind him to watch the commotion.

'Amelia!' He saw the girl he had met on his last visit. 'Where's Sally?'

But the girl just stared. A band of steel coiled tighter around his chest.

'She left one morning,' said Gordon. 'Got a better offer, she said. You know how she is, Raymond, a free spirit.'

'I don't believe you.' Ray was on the verge of tears. 'You're lying.'

'I'm sorry, son. I don't claim to understand what goes on in that woman's head.'

'She wouldn't go away without telling me.'

Ray walked to the office door, thinking about bolting upstairs, but he saw Elliot stood with Connor and knew he wouldn't get far.

'Where is she?' Ray demanded, but Elliot wouldn't meet his eyes.

'I wouldn't ask Elliot,' said Gordon quietly. 'He'll not tell you anything. He's one of my pals, one of my Two O'Clock Boys.'

'Where is she?' Ray turned to Connor, and thought he saw something unfamiliar in the kid's defiant stare, something he didn't understand. Connor's fists were clenched, the skin of his knuckles stretched white.

'She left,' said Ronnie Dent, storming out of the kitchen with his wife, 'pissed off without telling anyone; and you can do the same.'

'I want to hear it from him.' Ray prodded Connor in the chest. 'I want to hear Connor say it.'

At Gordon's nod, the Dents moved to either side of Ray to lift him off the floor. He tried to escape, kicking his legs, screaming 'get off me' at the top of his voice, but they were too strong and Ray was hurled out the door. He fell down the steps, just managing to stick out his arms to break his fall. His stinging palms were red raw where the skin scraped on the pavement. Ronnie and Gerry laughed.

'I'm sorry for you, son, and for your loss,' said Gordon at the door, 'but stay away now. There's nothing for you here no more.'

Ray wasn't finished. He stood to force his way back inside, he wasn't going to leave until he discovered where she had gone – but Connor blocked his way.

'Go,' he said.

'Tell me where she is.'

'Get away from here or . . .'

'Or what?' Ray's cheeks were wet with tears. 'What will happen?'

'You don't want to mess with Connor, lad.' Gordon made

himself comfortable on the top step, like an emperor taking his seat at the Colosseum. 'He'll eat you for breakfast.'

Connor could smash him to bits, Ray had no doubt about that, but he didn't care, he wanted to know where Sally was. He had never in his life felt such anger.

'She wouldn't go!' he cried. 'She wouldn't leave me!'

The heel of his hand shot into Connor's chest. It felt good to lash out, but Ray expected to go down instantly, expected Connor to knock him to the floor and punch and kick him. But Connor didn't move – and Ray went in swinging.

Screaming in fury, he surged forward, hitting Connor again and again – in the chest and arms, in the face – making him stagger into the road. Connor hunched against Ray's blows – but he didn't hit back. Insensible with rage, Ray roared, and the other kids poured onto the street to watch.

And just as suddenly, Ray stopped. Exhausted, fists throbbing, head pounding. Connor's face was cut and bruised, his teeth blood red from a split lip. Ray covered his eyes and sobbed, right there in the middle of the street, in front of them all.

Because Sally was gone, and there was nothing he could do about it.

'I'm coming back.' Ray pointed a trembling finger at Gordon. 'And I'm going to bring my parents.'

And he would do it. Ray would make Leonard and Myra listen to him. They might not care about the poor kids in this place, or about Sally, but for first time in his life he would make them listen to what he had to say.

'You do that, lad.' The manager lifted himself off the step and went inside, taking most of the children with him.

Amelia remained, and Kenny and David and Elliot, and a small blond boy Ray had never seen before. And Connor was in front of him, eyes bulging with intense emotion.

'Where is she?' Ray asked, but he didn't expect a reply. His hands pulsed with pain, but he didn't care.

Connor shook his head.

'*Please*,' said Ray.

'Gone,' said Connor, in a voice barely louder than a whisper.

'Connor, come on, son,' called Gordon, at the door. All the others had already disappeared inside.

Ray nodded at the home. 'You can do something,' he told Connor. 'Why don't you do anything?'

'Let's go,' said Gordon, more loudly.

Just before Connor left, Ray saw it on the boy's face again, just for a second. That look of . . . what? Confusion, bewilderment, and something else – something that was both frightening and frightened.

And then Ray Drake was left alone in the street with the terrible certainty that he would never see Sally again, and that something inside of him had changed for ever.

47

The plan was to clean up. He would stash his mud-spattered clothes and the rucksack, and take a shower. Stand under the steaming hot spray and wash off the filth and the blood, scrub his skin till it was pink, maybe put on some aftershave.

It wasn't going to do him any good, because splashing on a bit of Paco Rabanne wouldn't conceal the stench of guilt and shame lifting off him, Elliot knew that. There was no going back from beating a man to death and stuffing his corpse in the boot of a car. But maybe he wouldn't frighten the life out of Rhonda when she got home.

And it would give him time to work out what to do next. He would convince her to leave with him – he'd make up some cock and bull story, if he could clear enough space in his head to think of one – and they would go far away, the three of them. Start all over again.

But what he wasn't banking on was Rhonda being home when he came in, covered in mud from head to toe, his fist red and raw and smeared with dried blood. Elliot stared in shock at the sight of her sitting on the sofa, and a voice spoke behind him.

'What the . . . ?'

When he turned, twisting his body at the waist so that he didn't suffer searing neck pain, he saw Dylan at the window.

‘What’s that?’ Rhonda pointed at the rucksack. Elliot dropped it as if it was white hot.

‘Why don’t you leave me and your mum for a few minutes, Dylan, mate?’ If he had intended to say it casually, like they had boring home insurance to discuss, he failed miserably. His terror instantly transmitted to the boy, whose eyes darted to Elliot’s spattered clothes, his bloody hand, the bag pulsing at his feet.

Rhonda asked again: ‘What’s in the bag, Elliot?’

‘Dylan,’ Elliot said, ‘do us a favour and—’

But the teenager rushed to the rucksack. Elliot stiffly tried to reach it first – ‘Leave it!’ – but Dylan whipped it away by the straps, and plunged his hand inside to lift out a fistful of money. An ornate necklace hung off his fingers.

‘I said I’d get the money back,’ Elliot explained, but Rhonda’s face was set hard. And that was even before Dylan gasped and pulled the gun from the bag, lifting it gingerly between two fingers.

‘Put it down,’ whispered Rhonda. Dylan worked the weapon into his hand so that his finger rested on the trigger guard. ‘I said put it down!’

Her son dropped the gun back into the rucksack. ‘Is this why the police were here earlier?’

‘The police?’ asked Rhonda.

‘No,’ said Elliot. ‘That . . . that’s not . . .’

Rhonda stood. ‘Dylan, go and pack a bag.’

Elliot’s nose throbbed, his hand, his neck. ‘I know what it looks like.’

‘Will someone tell me what’s going on?’ Dylan’s voice quivered with fear. For once, when his phone vibrated in his pocket he ignored it.

'Go upstairs, Dylan. Right now!'

The boy backed away, staring at Elliot, soaking up the desperation in his face, and ran up the stairs. They heard his heavy footfalls above, drawers slamming open.

Rhonda nodded at the bag. 'Where did you get it?'

He opened his mouth to answer, but nothing came out. Elliot couldn't tell her what he had done, because it would be the end if he confessed. After all, he had killed a man. Beaten him to death and left him to rot. And there was no going back from that. Not now, not ever.

So he just had to let the scene play out to its bitter conclusion.

Rhonda crouched over the bag. She touched the jewellery – some of it very old, inlaid with sparkling gemstones – and the money, and the personal items that Perry had swept from the safe, the deeds of property and other documents. 'This isn't our money, Elliot. This isn't our savings. Whose it is?'

He shook his head.

'Tell me,' she said. 'Tell me what you've done.'

He'd had plenty of opportunity to tell Rhonda all the things he'd done in the past, but never had. It occurred to him with a sinking heart that if he had told her what had happened to him as a boy, when he was a child and didn't have a choice, she would have forgiven him, supported him, because it was all so long ago. But all those secrets, all those lies, were nothing compared to murdering a man in cold blood.

She shouldn't be near him. Dylan shouldn't be near him. He was despicable, toxic, and deserved their contempt and hatred. His old man had made him that, and that creep

Tallis. Both of them long dead, but both still gleefully pulling his strings, making him dance to their tune.

All he could think to say, even though he knew it was the understatement of the century, was: 'I messed up.'

'Tell me what you did.' Her eyes dropped to his bloody fist, which throbbed on the end of his arm. He wished she wouldn't keep repeating it. 'Tell me what you did.'

'I can't,' he said, voice hoarse, because it would be the end.

'Tell me.'

Elliot shook his head.

Dylan clattered down the stairs with a bag, and Rhonda told him to get to his room. She needed to pack some things before they left.

'Where are we going?' asked the boy. 'What's going on with Elliot?'

'Go back upstairs.'

'I didn't mean what I said, about him being just some passing bloke.'

'It's not your fault.' Elliot's voiced cracked with emotion. 'And don't you ever think it is. None of it.'

'Go to your room!' snapped Rhonda, and the boy thumped back upstairs, a strangled little noise coming from his throat. 'We can work this out. Whatever you've done, or think you've done, we can get past it.'

'Not this.' His tongue felt swollen. 'We can't get past this.'

'Tell me what you've done.'

Wild horses couldn't drag it out of him. After a lifetime of lies, to himself and everybody else, they had become such a part of him that he barely knew where they ended and where the real Elliot Juniper began. The Two O'Clock Boy had always known the truth about Elliot, had known the kind of man he was.

'You have to take responsibility for yourself,' Rhonda told him. 'If you can't do it for me or for Dylan, then do it for yourself. Because if you don't, you will never be happy.'

'I'll never be happy without you.'

'You should have thought about that earlier. Before you brought this, whatever this is,' she kicked the rucksack with her foot, 'into my home.' She didn't raise her voice, that wasn't Rhonda's style, but it was full of quiet contempt. 'Congratulations, Elliot, you've finally gone too far. You've brought it into our home, Elliot, *our* home, and you can't even be truthful with me.'

'That's me.' He laughed miserably. 'Elliot the idiot.'

'Ask yourself how you can make it stop, all the unhappiness you carry with you, because I don't think I'm enough. I hoped I would be, that Dylan would be, but we're not.'

'This isn't your fault.'

'No,' she said bitterly, 'it isn't. You're the only one who can stop reacting to the world like a bullied little boy and become a grown-up. And you can start by taking responsibility for this.' She nodded at the bag. 'Will you do that, Elliot?'

He whispered, 'I hope so.'

'Then tell me what you've done,' she said. 'Tell me why there's a gun in my home and I promise we will get through this.'

He wanted to tell her, but he had killed a man, and there were some things that could never be, *should* never be, forgiven.

She shouldn't be around him, neither of them should.

The one sliver of hope was that he would get them away from that maniac, and they would be safe.

And so he said: 'Just go.'

And Rhonda gave him a cold, reproachful look that obliterated all his hopes and dreams of a future, any kind of future, and climbed the stairs.

48

Ray Drake's car skidded to a stop outside Amelia Troy's warehouse. He killed the engine and lights.

Amelia's floor was dark. The steel door was ajar. Edging inside the building, he called the lift. The mechanism boomed into life high above him. He raised the handgun, but when the elevator arrived, its innards lit by the sallow bulb, it was empty.

Drake stepped inside, pulling the metal cage shut, and hit the button. In this tiny box he would be a sitting duck when it reached the top, but it was the only way up. Unscrewing the hot bulb above his head, Drake plunged the lift into darkness. He crunched the bulb beneath his foot. The upper floors passed dimly, infused faintly with an ambient glow.

The lift thunked to a halt at Amelia's floor. Inches of speckled floor were visible at his feet, and the lights of the city in the windows, but the space in between was a blank. Careful to keep his gun raised, he rattled open the cage and called: 'Amelia!'

Stepping out, Drake could just about make out the surface of the long table. The rectangular canvas frames loomed black against the sills, like portals into space. His careful steps scraped on the concrete floor as he swung round the side of the elevator, back pressed against the shaft. The furnished area of the space was smothered in gloom, the lamps switched off. Drake wished he'd brought a torch.

'Anyone here?' A rustle in the darkness. 'Amelia?'

He moved forward and bumped his knees against the sofa. Drake found the metal pole of the standing lamp and scrabbled with the switch – but it didn't come on.

There was a muffled sound of distress. Pistol raised, Drake took out his phone with his free hand and touched the screen to bathe the area in front of him – a foot, perhaps, no more – with a faint blue light. Gun pointed, phone light sprayed ahead, he rounded the sofa.

A figure was seated in the dark, just beyond the circle of light. He heard the shuffle of plastic, a muffled cry. Drake stepped forward, stumbling over the lip of a rug, and the figure in the chair was revealed.

Amelia bound in layers of clinging plastic.

As soon as she saw him, she strained in the chair. Drake moved forward. And the phone light whipped across someone rushing towards him in the darkness.

Drake lifted the weapon, bracing with both hands against the recoil, and fired. Once, twice.

The explosions were deafening in the dark. The windows vibrated in their frames, a toneless buzz, and the figure was flung backwards. Drake lifted the phone and edged forward, small pigeon steps in the dark, to see the featureless face of the tailor's dummy on the floor. Jagged splinters splayed from its wooden chest. The upended wheels spun on their stand.

Drake retreated to Amelia and tore at the plastic over her mouth. Her eyes stared at him in terror. He was getting nowhere fast with the gun in his hand, and shoved it beneath his armpit to fumble in his pocket for his keys, using a serrated edge to cut the material. It tore away, shreds of it corkscrewing around her cheek.

'It's going to be okay,' he told her, 'just stay still.'

When her mouth was free, Amelia was almost hysterical. 'He's . . . he's—'

Then she screamed.

A blur of movement at the edge of the tiny circle of light.

A metal bar swung out of the darkness. Instinctively, Drake lifted his arm high to protect his head. His shoulder went dead. The gun dropped to the floor. Another stinging blow to the thigh dropped him to his knees. Reaching for the gun he swung it up, but the weapon was knocked from his hand and skittered into the darkness. Drake's arms and legs propelled him backwards. He scuttled like a crab as a shape – a mass, a weight barely heavier than the blackness surrounding it – moved with him, bringing down the steel rod. Sparks flew up from the concrete floor in the space between his legs.

At any moment, one of those blows would find his skull and it would be game over. Drake kicked blindly with his leg into the dark, and the mass stumbled. He heard the metal bar clatter on the concrete.

A faint rectangle of light lay behind him, the phone upside down on the rough floor. Drake rolled on his side, scrabbling the last few inches to snatch it. Holding the phone to the floor, its glow revealing an inch of racing blue concrete, he scrambled to where the gun had disappeared.

Behind him, he heard the metal rod scrape as it was picked up. The gun appeared in the phone's scant light and Drake lunged for it, rolling onto his back and pulling the trigger.

The gun discharged three times. He heard the rod hit the floor with a discordant clang.

When the echo of the shots had died, he lay there – trying not to pass out from the juddering pain that rippled through his already beaten body. The rod rolled out of the blackness and touched his foot. Drake listened to his own rapid breath, heard the elevator cage open.

'Not yet!' that familiar voice echoed. 'Soon, though. Very soon.'

The cage door shut. The elevator chuntered into life and descended.

Amelia screamed in the chair, rocking from side to side in a frenzy.

'I'm here,' said Drake, climbing wearily to his feet. 'I'm here.'

49

There it was again, that noise, barely louder than the squeak of a mouse.

Myra Drake had lived in this house all her life and was familiar with its every wheeze and sigh. People presumed that the older you got, the more your senses degraded, but she had always had excellent hearing. Her eyes weren't what they once were, and these days everything tasted the same, but her ears were as sharp as ever.

Raymond insisted that she leave, but she had always intended to stay, despite her promise to him. This was her home, and she was not going to let anybody scare her away. Besides, she didn't even know if she still had a suitcase. At Myra's age it was sensible to assume your next trip would not require luggage.

A few months ago, Raymond had given her a mobile phone with his number programmed into it, in case of an accident. She held it now. The small plastic rectangle felt insubstantial in her palm. Raymond had told her how to operate it, explaining the buttons in a loud and condescending manner. She was a pensioner, she had told him, not an imbecile. But no matter how many times she pressed the *On* button, the screen remained blank. The battery on the device had died. She had never recharged it. So she sat on the sofa and listened. Seconds later, a loose tile on the parquet rattled outside the door.

'Stop that creeping around, I can hear you.' It was a big house, and easy to get lost. 'In here.'

A man walked in, dressed in black from head to toe, and wearing a balaclava. He held a long knife in his hand.

'Take that off,' she said. 'You look ridiculous.'

The intruder's eyes bulged. Then he pulled off the woollen garment, brushing a hand over his scalp to remove any clinging fibres.

'Careful.' Myra's smile was brittle. 'You don't want to leave any DNA around the place.'

'It's too late to worry about that,' said the boy. He walked around the room, hands clasped behind his back. Perusing the bookcase, the items on the mantelpiece, taking a great interest in everything, as if he were a tourist at a stately home. 'Do you remember me?'

Myra considered him. 'You appear to be an eminently forgettable person. Should I?'

For so many years he had strived to be invisible to others, as insubstantial as vapour – that was how he was able to go about his business so successfully – and yet her response made his blood boil. He perched on the arm of a chair, sensing it would irritate her, even as she was facing death.

'We met a long time ago.'

'And you are here to kill me.'

'Yes. And then your granddaughter will die. And, of course . . .' His grin was sarcastic. '*Your boy*.'

Myra Drake's thumbs spun restlessly in her lap. 'I doubt that. Raymond is a better man than you in every way. He has more intelligence and more guile. He will not allow himself to be murdered, by you or any other person.'

What the boy could tell her, the supercilious old crone,

was how he could have killed him twice already; how he had placed a knife to his throat only this morning, was so close he could see the tendons in his neck glide beneath the skin; how he had toyed with him in the warehouse only this evening. He could also tell her just how many people had died at his hands. That would wipe the sneer off her face. 'After everything you have done for him, and he's allowed you to die.'

'It is not his place to allow me to do anything. Besides, it's something of a relief. Since the death of my husband, I confess I've found life somewhat trying.'

'I can understand that. My time is also coming to an end.'

'Well,' the corners of her mouth twitched, 'that's something, I suppose. And how do you intend to kill me?' He placed the long blade, its polished edge gleaming, across his knees. Myra pulled her cardigan around her shoulders. 'Will it be quick?'

'I'm afraid not. I'll take my time and you will die in agony. I harbour a lifetime's resentment against your family.'

Myra's stare glittered with contempt. 'I remember you now. There was something off about you even then. It was those dead eyes.'

'I was just a boy!' he shouted.

'And you are now a dismal little man.'

A tear ran down his cheek. He wiped it away with the back of his hand. 'I'm not the man I should be, that's true enough.'

'Well, if nothing else, you're not self-deceiving.'

The man checked his watch and jumped up. 'Well, let's get on.'

Myra nodded bleakly. When he stepped forward, lifting the knife, she raised a shaking hand.

'Please,' she said, and he stopped.

Myra Drake took off her glasses and folded them neatly on the occasional table, beneath the ornate lamp and beside her copy of Trollope, as she had done every night for fifty, sixty years.

Routine was important to Myra Drake and, looking back, considering all the turbulent events she had experienced, the people she had lost . . . well, it hadn't been a bad sort of life. She clicked open the locket to look one last time at the photograph inside. Running a trembling thumb over it, she thought of her boy, Raymond. Then she folded her hands in her lap and shut her eyes. Whatever happened in the next few seconds, she would not open them again. She nodded.

Myra felt a faint breeze as her murderer swung the blade high above his head. She clenched her teeth, determined not to cry out . . .

And then there was a knock on the front door. Her eyes snapped open. Myra was ready to shout, but the man lifted the tip of the blade to her jaw.

Another knock, and someone called. The man's eyes slid towards the hallway, and the smile that lit up his face was ghastly.

'I'm going to enjoy this.'

50

1984

Leonard and Myra Drake arrived unexpectedly on the doorstep of the Longacre with Ray and a photographer from the local newspaper.

'I hope we haven't come at an inopportune time.' Myra's faint smile to Gordon Tallis suggested that she didn't much care one way or the other what he thought. 'My son was keen for us to see the work you do here. And Mr Sutherland from the local newspaper has agreed to record the occasion.'

'Of course,' said Gordon, biting down on his panic. 'It will be my pleasure to talk to you, and perhaps give you a tour. However,' he said, eyeing Ray, 'your son can't come in. I'm afraid he attacked one of our children. I don't know what he's told you—'

'He's told us enough,' said Leonard, looking unhappy about leaving his car in such an unsavoury area.

'I will vouch for my son's behaviour,' Myra said.

'I'm afraid I'm going to have to insist that he remains outside. The rest of you are welcome to come in.'

Myra Drake considered Gordon. 'Very well,' she said eventually.

'I want to come in,' said Ray, annoyed. 'I want to hear what he says.'

'Wait in the car,' his mother told him. 'And we'll talk afterwards.'

Ray pressed forward. 'I'm not staying outside.'

'Raymond,' said Myra Drake quietly. A single look from her silenced him. And no wonder, Gordon decided. It was a look that could fell a charging elephant. 'Go to the car.'

The boy threw an angry glance at Gordon, and pushed past the photographer down the steps, throwing himself against the Daimler parked below.

'Come in.' Gordon led them into the office, Myra taking her older husband's free arm – he leaned heavily on a cane with the other – to help him inside.

Gordon was panicking. There had been no warning, no time to make the home look halfway presentable. All he could do was command the Dents to tidy the place as best they could in the time available. But Ronnie and Gerry had never had a talent for moving quickly, and to his frustration he knew the house wasn't going to be miraculously transformed in a few, short minutes.

'Which of the little bastards look presentable enough to meet them?' He surveyed the kids roaming the garden.

'There's the new one,' said Gerry. 'The little fella's going home soon, so he'll be in a good mood.'

Toby Turrell sat cross-legged, staring at the ground. Listening nearby, Connor saw Gordon tense at the thought of the boy returning home, and knew he wouldn't – couldn't – allow that, not after what the kid had seen. Someone like Sally, estranged from her family and with few ties to the world, could disappear, but not a boy with devoted parents. Gordon must see that no more harm could come to him. Trouble was, these days his thinking was all over the place.

The manager grabbed Connor. 'Round up some of the ones you trust to keep their mouths shut and come to my office.' When Connor turned to leave, Gordon pulled him back. 'But not the boy.'

Connor found Amelia, and Jason and Kenny, and Elliot. And, despite Gordon's strict instructions, he went to get Toby.

'Please go away,' pleaded the kid.

'You're coming with me.' Connor hauled him to his feet. If Toby was going to get out of this place alive, the more people who knew about him the better. He needed to be seen by adults, important people – and they were taking a photo for the local newspaper.

'Please!'

'Listen to me.' Connor shook his arm. 'You're gonna go in there and talk to the judge and tell him you're going home.'

He pushed Toby to the office. Gordon scowled when he saw the boy, but bit down on his anger in front of the visitors. He'd made an effort with his appearance, but the long hair slicked neatly inside his collar jarred with the clammy sheen on his forehead.

Connor had never met anyone like Leonard Drake. A giant of a man in a three-piece suit, he dominated the room, towering over the other adults despite a stoop. A thick mane of hair surged back from his heavy brow, as he looked around him in barely concealed disgust. Myra Drake was scarcely shorter than her husband and stood stiffly, looking down the slope of her nose at the children.

'Raymond is very attached to his cousin,' she said, 'and he's concerned about her whereabouts.'

'As we all are.' Gordon pressed his hands together, as if in prayer. 'I'm afraid Sally stole money from me, so I would very much like to know where she is.'

'Have you told the police?'

'I'm very fond of Sal and would rather not get the local constabulary involved. Despite everything, she's always welcome here. Ain't that right, kids?' He wiped his slick forehead with a sleeve. 'But she's a handful, that lass, so who knows where she's got herself off to.'

'What is your name?' Myra asked each of the children in turn. When she came to Connor, she eyed him curiously, perhaps because he brazenly stared right back. 'And who are you?'

'Connor Laird,' he said, and her attention lingered on him.

Gordon gestured at the photographer's camera. 'Many of our children lack confidence, and you'll give them a fright with that thing, Mr . . . ?'

'Sutherland,' said the man, cleaning the camera lens. 'Trevor.'

'Why don't you stay here, Trevor, and relax. We'll be back soon.'

Leaving Sutherland in the office, the group walked around the house. The kids trailed behind the adults as Gordon stammered his excuses about the state of the home. The judge and his wife listened solemnly as he explained that, despite the homely nature of the place – 'it could do with the odd nail here and there!' – the children adored the Longacre.

But even Connor could see there was a huge gulf between the praise Gordon heaped on the home and the reality of the squalid, characterless rooms. Children were positioned carefully in front of some of the worst patches of damp, or sat on beds to hide ripped mattresses. All the best furniture had been moved hastily to the two or three bedrooms Gordon allowed Myra to see inside. Unable to climb the stairs, her husband waited at the bottom with the Dents, who watched beneath the banisters like trolls beneath a bridge.

The judge took the time to survey each ground-floor room carefully, despite Gordon's desperate efforts to hurry him. Aside from asking a few terse questions, he said little. Every now and then, Connor would catch Myra looking at him.

'Why are there no doors?' asked Leonard Drake.

'The children get scared when they bang in the night.' Gordon smiled. 'So we thought it best to remove them.'

The tour lasted less than fifteen minutes. When they returned to the office, the photographer jumped up, asking to get some quick shots before he rushed to another job. He was in a hurry, he said, because the paper was going to press that evening. He placed them in a line, the kids and the adults, on the very spot where Sally had died.

Connor didn't want to be photographed. Call it instinct, call it some innate protective urge, he positioned himself at the very edge of the group.

As the camera flash whined and popped, and the room was soaked in a fluttering light – 'Let's have some big smiles from the little ones!' – he swung away from the others. The photographer frowned, disappointed with the framing of his shots. But he was late for his next job, he said, and after getting brief quotes from Gordon and Leonard Drake, and jotting down everyone's name, he left.

'A glass of wine, perhaps?' Gordon asked the judge.

Leonard Drake leaned grimly on his cane. 'Of course not, it's midday.'

'You must understand, my son was very insistent that we come here, Mr Tallis,' said Myra Drake. 'To see . . . the work that you do.'

'And what about you children?' The judge's eyes swept around the room. 'Are you happy here?'

Seeing Gordon's expression, Jason, Amelia and Kenny nodded.

'Don't look at him,' Myra told Jason. 'My husband asked *you* the question.'

'I just want to go home,' whined Toby. Tears fell down his cheeks.

Myra turned to him. 'You have a home, child?'

Gordon stepped between them. 'Connor! Toby's not feeling well, why don't you take the poor mite up to bed?'

Toby wrung his hands together. 'We dug in the garden.'

'Why don't—'

'Wait.' Myra Drake spoke over Gordon. 'You've a home, child?'

The other kids became agitated at Toby's weeping. Kenny and Jason looked like they would do anything to get away. Elliot couldn't tear his eyes from the spot where Sally had laid, blood blooming from the crown of her head across the floorboards.

'He's upset, aren't you Toby, lad?' Gordon tousled the boy's hair. 'I think this momentous occasion has been too much for him.'

'We dug a hole,' said Toby, between sobs.

'Connor, take—'

'Be quiet,' Myra told Gordon. 'And why did you do that, boy?'

Toby stared at her, dismally. 'We buried a rug.'

'What a curious thing to say.'

'Take him away,' Gordon hissed at Connor, but the boy didn't move.

'He's going home soon, ain't that right, Gordon?' Connor said. 'You promised him he'd be going home to his folks.'

'The boy doesn't belong here?' asked Myra Drake.

Gordon pressed a handkerchief to his forehead. 'He's staying with us, temporarily.'

'Toby wants to see his people again,' said Connor. 'His parents.'

'Temporarily?' Leonard Drake scowled. 'That sounds very unorthodox.'

Connor met Gordon's stare. 'He's going home.'

'That's right; the lad's soon to go home.' Gordon swallowed. 'To his folks. And we'll miss him, because we're a happy family here.'

'I doubt that very much.' The rubber tip of Leonard Drake's cane squeaked on the floor as he bore down on Gordon. 'I think we've seen enough. This home is a disgrace.'

'Let me—'

'*You* are an absolute disgrace. I shall ensure that this cesspit is closed.'

'Your Honour . . .'

The judge stood close to Gordon, who cringed beneath his steady gaze. 'And you will inform us where Sally is as soon as you hear from her.'

Gordon frantically followed Leonard Drake outside.

'You're a spirited one,' said Myra to Connor. Something

caught her eye at the skirting as she turned to leave, and she bent to pick up the paperweight. She placed it on the desk, chipping at a stain on its glass surface with a thumbnail. Then she plucked at his T-shirt to pull him closer.

He felt her hot breath on his ear when she whispered: 'This place deserves to burn.'

When she left, Connor joined the others at the window to watch the manager circle the judge as he reached the pavement, while Myra went to her son. Ray Drake listened while his mother spoke to him, slowly, firmly. His face was red with rage, but she wouldn't allow him to speak, and when she finished, he flung up his arms in impotent fury and ran off down the street. His mother watched him go, impassive. A chauffeur jumped out of the car to open the rear doors. Leonard and Myra climbed in, ignoring Gordon's panicked protestations.

Connor dropped the curtain and turned to see the others – Kenny, Jason, Elliot, Amelia and Toby – staring tensely at him.

Moments later, Gordon stepped back in the room. Hoping to disappear back amongst all the other kids, Kenny went to leave, but the manager blocked his way.

'Where do you think you're going?' Eyes jerking in their sockets, Gordon slammed the door. 'Let's not break up the party, not while the day's still young!'

51

Flick had never seen anything like it. She always presumed gardens were drab places in the winter but the grass was lush and green. The plants packed in the borders were colourful and vibrant in the dusk, and water trickled in a pretty pond. The wind was blowing hard now, but she couldn't spot a single leaf on the lawn, or on the rippling surface of the water.

'The wife's the gardener.' Trevor Sutherland stepped carefully across the neat paving embedded in the lawn towards a garden shed. 'I hardly set foot out here if I can help it. My life wouldn't be worth living if I damaged the grass.'

He was a sprightly man, with one shoulder hunched lower than the other. From carrying a heavy camera bag for half his life, he said. Keys of all shapes and sizes jangled at his waist, hanging from a solid brass ring a medieval jailer might fear too sinister. He lived in a quiet street in Barnet, in a modest two-up, two-down, with his wife and a pair of yapping dogs. Reaching the shed he considered the keys beneath tangled eyebrows, while Flick waited impatiently.

In the circumstances, this was the last place she should be. She should have washed her hands of the whole thing, should be at home with her feet up, writing notes about Ray Drake's conduct, not standing outside a stranger's shed in the suburbs.

'This used to be my darkroom,' he said. 'Now it's Shirley's Gardening HQ.'

'Do you miss it?' asked Flick. 'The job?'

'Not much, but these days it's a lot easier. You take a picture, and bang, the images are sent electronically to the news desk.' Trevor's fingers slipped from the key he'd finally located on the ring, and to Flick's frustration he began his search all over again. 'In my day you spent hours in the dark fiddling with chemicals – what a palaver! But it weren't all bad, back then all the journalists loved to drink and swap stories.' He winked. 'So it was a good excuse to snatch a few hours down the pub.'

'I'm amazed you remember the Longacre,' she said, fishing for detail.

'I didn't work local papers for long. I had a talent, you see. Not for photography, any monkey can point a camera, but for getting in people's faces. Lizzie Taylor, Princess Margaret, Stallone.' His eyes twinkled. 'They all knew me. I've always kept scrapbooks of my work. So when Diane from the *Argent* rang and said you were looking for something, I knew I could help.'

Her phone rang and she checked the screen: Peter Holloway. Wanting to discuss what happened in Ray Drake's office, no doubt. It could wait.

'I could have gone to Iraq and Afghanistan, trotted the globe winning awards.' Trevor fumbled keys against the padlock. 'But I don't care for crocodiles or war zones.'

Flick waited, anxious to intervene. 'Can I help you?'

'I can manage, luv, it's one of these little ones, and my motor skills ain't what they used to be.' He peered for a long time at a small silver key and then inserted it. The padlock bar pinged open. 'Been a while since I've been in here.'

When Trevor snapped a switch inside the door, the shed was bathed in red light. Gardening equipment was stacked against the walls, a lawnmower, a shovel and hoe. Bottles of weed killer and lawn feed sat on a shelf. At the back was a makeshift darkroom. Two sinks set into a counter, trays piled with brushes and stained Marigolds and plastic tubs.

Trevor looked around in wonder, as if he'd found the Holy Grail. 'You wouldn't believe how many hours I spent in here.' He picked up a chipped mug. 'I wondered where that'd got to.'

Flick's attention was grabbed by box files piled on top of a filing cabinet. 'In one of these?'

'Nah. That far back, it'll be in the cabinet.'

Flick tugged at the cabinet's handle but it was locked, and she had to stifle a groan when Trevor frowned at the key ring.

'Here we go again.' He held the keys close to his face beneath the soft red light, and by some miracle managed to quickly find a tiny key, turn it in the slot. The top drawer opened with a metallic shiver.

'When I was younger, I'd cut out my photos from the paper, stick 'em in a book. Let's take a look.'

He took out an old scrapbook, bloated by damp, the thick reams of paper stuck into it decades ago. Licking a forefinger, Trevor turned the pages, lingering nostalgically over articles and images. School fêtes; the opening of municipal buildings; long-dead authors giving talks in long-closed libraries.

'There you are.' He tapped at a page and handed the book to Flick. She read: JUDGE VISITS LOCAL CHILDREN'S HOME.

> Noted High Court judge Leonard Drake dropped in to meet the kids at the Longacre Children's Home, this week.
>
> Mr Drake and his wife Myra visited in his role as Chairman of the Hackney Children's Protection League to meet manager Gordon Tallis and his dedicated staff.

Her eyes dropped to the photograph beneath, and she grabbed the cabinet.

'You all right, love?'

She barely heard him, as she matched faces to names from the caption.

A tall man stood in the middle of the group lined up in a nondescript office, a thick mane of hair swept back over his head. Leonard Drake. Died of natural causes years ago.

Beside him stood a snooty-looking woman, Myra Drake, tall and rigid, dressed in a frumpy frock. But no locket around her neck, Flick noticed. That penetrating gaze was unmistakable.

At the far left was a man with a lopsided smile, Gordon Tallis. Fists clenched in a threadbare corduroy suit and flared-collared shirt, lank hair sliding to his shoulders. His face, hidden behind a scruffy beard, was bloated and shifty. Tallis died hours after this photo was taken.

The smiles of the children between them were strained. Kenny Overton, a plump, red-headed boy with an awkward smile. Tied to a chair and slaughtered with his family only days ago.

Next to him was another small boy, Toby Turrell, his expression blank, and then came Jason Burgess, who stared aggressively into the camera lens. He was murdered decades later with his family, the deaths recorded as a murder–suicide.

Beside Jason was Elliot Juniper, a sullen boy with surly, reproachful eyes, and then Amelia Troy, her fingers tugging at his sleeve.

And – finally – there was the last boy, rearing back at the edge of the shot. Caught in swift movement. A single pixelated eye, angry and intense, flashing at the camera. That night he would use the chaos caused by the blaze to disappear into the night.

The one that got away.

She knew now, with gut-wrenching certainty, that Connor Laird was very much alive.

Jason, Ricky, David, Karen, God knows how many others, dead . . .

'Yeah, you see, that's the kind of mistake an inexperienced photographer makes.' Trevor pointed at the shadows edging the image. 'But I ain't done so badly in the years, considering.'

Flick pushed past him to stumble into the garden. The red light still pulsed in her vision when she propped her hands on her knees to vomit into a flowerbed.

'I'm not going to enjoy explaining this to the wife,' said Trevor, watching. 'But at least you didn't do it over the koi. Would you like a glass of water?'

She nodded. 'Please.'

Trevor hopped back up the pathway while Flick felt hot needles of sweat on her forehead cool in the wind.

Connor Laird was alive.

Men, women and children. Burned, shot, drowned, stabbed.

Her mobile rang and she fumbled it from her pocket. Holloway again. When she hit the button she did her best to sound alert and engaged.

'Peter, what can I do for you?'

'I'm outside Ray Drake's house,' he said. 'I was worried about him after your . . . altercation tonight. But, DS Crowley . . . I think there's something terribly wrong.'

52

Emotion scraped in Ray Drake's chest like a nail. He had his daughter back. He didn't understand how, he didn't understand why, but she was with him and that was all that mattered. April gripped his hand as staff stacked tables and chairs in the café on the cavernous concourse of St Pancras train station, preparing to close for the night.

'Tell me again.'

Bewildered, April looked from her father to Amelia, who stared at the table. 'He dropped me off at Susie's house.'

'And he never touched you?'

'He helped me out of the cab. I thought it was a bit weird,' she said. 'That's when he must have taken my mobile.'

'Did he talk to you?'

'He asked me in the car why I was sad.' April glanced at Amelia again. 'I was upset, I'd just been talking to Flick about . . . Jordan.'

Drake saw the engagement ring was gone from her finger. 'Did you tell him anything about yourself?'

'No.'

She was going to call him, until she realised her phone was gone. Drake had received her call, from her friend's number, at Amelia's warehouse. April put a finger to her cheek. Her face was puffy with tears. She was more beautiful, more precious, to him than ever.

The girl looked at Amelia, confused as to why her father was with this strange woman. 'Why are you asking me about the cab driver?'

Drake's gaze restlessly swept the concourse. A steady flow of people passed, even at this late hour. He'd have liked to spend time with April, but time was the one thing neither of them had. Both women were lucky to be alive. Their safety was paramount. His reconciliation with his daughter, all the things he wanted to say, would have to wait.

'I think he may be linked to an investigation I'm working on.'

'An investigation?' April shook her head, uncomprehending.

The less she knew about the situation the better. 'It's . . . complicated. Threats have been made to officers involved in the case.'

She looked at the cuts on Amelia's face. 'What happened to you?'

'It's nothing.' Amelia's face was pale and strained. She wore a yellow windbreaker and red jeans, dirty white trainers. An overnight bag sat at her feet. 'It looks worse than it is.'

'Amelia is a witness in the case.'

'You're not telling me everything.' April frowned. 'What's going on, Dad?'

That word, *Dad*. He couldn't remember the last time she'd called him that. It filled him with gratitude, relief – and hope for the future.

'I want you to go away for a couple of days,' he said.

'What does any of this have to do with me?'

'April . . .' Amelia took a deep breath. 'Someone very dangerous attacked me tonight, and your father saved my life. I have absolutely every reason to trust his judgement. I'm as much in the dark about what's happening as you are, but as I understand it, there's a slim chance that this person may try to get revenge against your father. The last thing he wants is for you to be placed in any danger.'

'I know somewhere you can go, out of the city,' said Drake. 'You'll be comfortable there. You'll have space to think about what you want to do next, whether you want to come back to live with me and your gran, or . . .' He didn't want to consider other possibilities. 'Whatever you decide, I'll support you.'

'So I am in danger.'

'Probably not, but it's better to be safe than sorry.' Amelia smiled. 'Believe me, I know.'

'I can't, there's Jordan – what if he tries to make contact?'

'Forget Jordan,' Drake said shortly.

'There you go again.' April removed her hand.

Drake rubbed his face. 'I'm sorry, I—'

'I loved him, Dad.'

'I know,' he said, and she slipped her hand back into his.

For the first time he imagined a scenario where everything would be okay. Now he knew the assumed identity of the Two O'Clock Boy. One look at Jordan's phone and he saw, with shock, who it was. All this time the murderer had been close, *too* close. But now Drake knew where to start looking for him. April was here with him, safe and sound. His daughter was back, and it was a start.

'And what about Gran, isn't she coming?' she asked.

'She's away, visiting relatives.'

When she blinked, Drake sensed the enormity of the situation hitting home to her. April knew that Hell would have to freeze over before Myra agreed to leave her precious house.

'We can look after each other,' said Amelia warmly. 'Trust me, I've plenty of experience of unsuitable men, and I'm a good listener. And like you, I could really do with a friend.' She turned to him. 'Give us a moment, Ray.'

Drake scraped back his chair and walked onto the concourse. Someone was playing one of the upright pianos placed along the crowded precinct. Drake watched April and Amelia talk, heads bowed across the table, and scanned the jostling crowd of commuters who marched past him. When he returned to the two women, Amelia threw him a reassuring glance.

'So I'll be under police protection?' asked April.

'No,' he said. 'I'm the only person who'll know where you are.'

Amelia nodded encouragingly. Drake wished he could tell April more, but it was impossible. Well, when all this was over, that would change. He would do everything in his power to make things better between them. She would be his main, his only, priority in life.

'When do we leave?'

Amelia stood. 'No time like the present, my car's around the corner.'

'Can I go to the toilet first?' asked April.

'Rather now than in my car.' Amelia laughed. 'I've just had it valeted.'

Drake wanted to escort his daughter to the toilet at the rear of the café, but Amelia touched his arm, *leave her*. He watched April all the way to the door.

'I haven't had the chance to say thank you,' said Amelia.

'If you hadn't got there in time . . . I still don't know why he didn't kill me.'

'He wanted me there.' Drake reluctantly tore his eyes from the door. 'He wanted us to watch each other die. It's what he did with the Overtons, I think, and probably the others.'

'I don't understand,' she asked, bewildered. 'Why does he want to kill us?'

'His experiences at the Longacre unhinged him. He . . . went through things.'

'But why target us?'

'He blames the kids he knew back then for what happened to him.'

To his surprise she slipped her fingers into his. 'And am I to blame?'

'None of this is your fault. He's sick, deranged.'

'And what about you? Are you to blame for what happened to him?'

Drake thought about that last catastrophic night at the Longacre, a night that changed the lives of those who survived it for ever. 'Yes, I am.'

'I doubt it. I married a violent man, but I'm not to blame for that. If Ned hadn't died when he did I'm sure he would have ended up killing me eventually. Well . . . my husband will never touch me again. I'm sorry I freaked out on you at the pub, I was scared. Were we . . . friends, back then?'

'Yes.' Drake decided that, whatever happened, he wanted to see Amelia Troy again. He looked away. 'We were friends.'

'Where did you get that gun?' she asked. 'I didn't think the police . . .'

'When all this is over, I'll explain it to you.'

She smiled. 'And what if I don't want to know?'

'Then I won't.'

She smiled. 'Decisions, decisions.'

She was a tough lady, Amelia, thought Drake. The vulnerable young girl with the precocious artistic talent had been knocked down so many times in life, and yet she kept going. 'You're a survivor.'

'Yes, I am.' She nodded, as if it had only just occurred to her. 'Hooray for me. But I'm not sure I want to know anything about the Longacre. When this whole nightmare is finally over, I just want to enjoy the rest of my life; I don't want to look back.'

'It'll all be over soon.'

Amelia squeezed his hand. 'Yes, it will.'

He wondered if that meant she wouldn't want to see him again, and the idea jolted him. Drake felt an unexpected affinity with Amelia. She was a survivor, but he was too.

When he blushed, she smiled wryly. 'Let's just see what happens?'

'Let's do that.'

'Where are we going?'

'There's someone who knows what's going on, he was at the home.' Drake didn't want to send them there, it was difficult to know how far to trust the weak-minded, anxious man he once knew, but he didn't know what else to do. At least now the so-called Two O'Clock Boy was in his sights. 'You'll have safety in numbers there.'

The toilet door opened and their hands separated.

'Right, then,' Amelia said to Drake and April. 'What now?'

'We're going to get you out of the city,' he said, 'and when you come back, I promise it'll all be over.'

He was about to take his phone out of his pocket when his daughter threw her arms around his neck. She held him tight, clung to him, sending shooting pains through his battered body that he barely noticed.

53

What nobody had expected, least of all Elliot, was that he would be left all on his lonesome with a gun at his disposal. Slumped on the sofa, the ugly thing rising and falling on the crest of his stomach, he thought about what to do next.

One thing came to mind.

He couldn't understand how everything had spiralled out of control so quickly. Just a few days ago he was letting that madman smooth talk him into handing over thirty grand. Just a deposit, the man calling himself Gavin had cheerfully explained. Elliot had never been so excited about anything, had believed it was a beginning for him, a successful new phase, which would prove, once and for all, that he was marching triumphantly forward in life.

But Elliot shouldn't be allowed to tie his own shoelaces, let alone make his own decisions. He had always hidden behind other people – Rhonda was just the latest – because he couldn't be trusted to do the right thing. Everything had been looking up – he had a home, a family, everything he needed – but then he had to cozy up to a multiple murderer, a man who wished him dead. Now, here he was, days later, and Rhonda was gone, Dylan was gone. He had killed a man. It would have been better if Perry had put him out of his misery.

There was no future that he could see.

She'll know the kind of man you are.

But at least he had a way out. The gun was not at all like the muscular-looking things in the movies, but it would do a job. So, sprawled there, smoking a last cigarette – because smoking inside the house was the least of his worries – Elliot decided that if the Two O'Clock Boy was so keen to kill him . . . well, he would save him the trouble.

All he had to do was flick off the safety; he wasn't going to repeat the same mistake that Perry had made. The trick was to stick the gun in his mouth, not to press it against the side of his head where it could slip. He'd heard the horror stories of the poor souls who botched it. Blown half their brains out and spent the rest of their days drooling vegetables hooked up to beeping machines. That would be typical of Elliot.

He had to focus on the tension of his finger against the trigger, concentrate on that, and nothing else, and then . . .

It would all be over.

All his memories of the Longacre would be gone. Of those summer days delivering Gordon's drugs; of a tearful Turrell gagging on the cockroach, the crunch of its shell in his mouth, the brown juices dribbling down his chin; of Tallis dashing the paperweight on Sally's head; of him and Connor burning her body, the smell of soil and petrol and burning flesh filling his nostrils, to this day as vivid a memory to Elliot as anything else in his life.

And that final, terrifying night in Gordon's office when he held them prisoner—

His phone rang.

Owen's number. Elliot killed the call.

His fist throbbed from pounding it into Perry's face. He

would never truly accept that the Two O'Clock Boy was right about him. That wasn't the kind of man he was – he couldn't be. He wasn't a bully, or a murderer.

Except he was.

The phone rang again, and he was going to turn it off, because he was sick and tired of the endless calls from Owen. But when he saw who was calling – and although it didn't matter now, nothing could make Rhonda come home, or Perry return from the dead – something, a faint glimmer of responsibility, made him answer.

'I need you to look after my daughter,' said the cop.

'Still ain't got this thing done?' Elliot had at least hoped that lunatic would be taken out of the equation.

'I'm working on it. But I need to think of my daughter's safety. Get her out of town till it's over. I'd be grateful if you could put her up for the night, maybe two. You'll be safer together.'

'Sure.' Elliot massaged his temples. 'Why not?'

'Unless explaining to your family—'

'That's not going to be a problem. They're gone, I sent them away.' One more night on Earth wouldn't make a difference. He touched the gun. 'She'll be safe here.'

'She'll be coming with Amelia Troy.'

'Amelia,' Elliot grunted. It was turning out to be something of a reunion. 'Be nice to see her after all these years.'

'Everything okay, Elliot?' Maybe the policeman could detect the weariness in his voice, the exhaustion.

'Yeah,' he said quickly. He didn't want to let him down, didn't want to get on his wrong side, not him, not on top of everything else. 'I'm good.'

Elliot scrambled off the sofa. He'd have to tidy the place,

get a fire going. He should shower, spray on some Lynx. That would be a start.

'And, Elliot . . . She doesn't know about *me;* she can never know.'

'I got that.'

'Make sure you do. He's coming for us, Elliot. If we let our guard down, he'll kill us all. Me, you, Amelia, the people we love.'

'If he dares to show his face here,' he said, trying to sound confident, 'I'll finish it.'

Elliot had killed a man already, had beaten him to death. But if it came to it, if he was forced to protect April Drake and Amelia Troy, he hoped to God that he could find the strength in himself to do it again.

54

Peter Holloway was sitting on the front steps of Ray Drake's house when Flick arrived. The side-panel lights on her vehicle winked when she locked it.

'What are you doing here, Peter?'

He stood. 'Since your . . . episode, DI Drake has been ignoring my calls. He's usually very prompt in getting back, and I'm concerned. He's my friend, DS Crowley.'

For the first time Flick detected a tension, an edge of vulnerability to the man. Maybe the officious Holloway was more human than she'd given him credit for. 'You old softy.'

'Myra Drake rarely leaves the house,' he said. 'I rang and rang on the doorbell but there was no answer.'

'When I knocked yesterday she came to the door pretty sharpish.'

Holloway regarded her curiously as they approached the door. 'You were here?'

'Long story,' she said. 'Perhaps she's gone out.'

'I could have sworn I heard somebody moving about inside, and . . . you should take a look around the back.'

'Stay here,' she told him, and walked down the alley at the side of the house. The glass in the patio doors at the rear had been smashed, the door forced.

'You understand now?'

Jumping in terror at the voice, she turned to see Holloway behind her. 'I told you to wait, Peter.'

'I would never let a lady go in alone. It's not in my nature.'

'Have you been inside?'

He held up his hands and Flick saw he was wearing nitrile gloves. 'I'm a very good boy, DS Crowley, and decided it best to wait for you.'

She'd left her own gloves in the car, but Holloway took out a spare pair and she snapped them on. 'This time, stay where you are.'

'Not a chance,' he said.

She led them into the big kitchen, which was more sleek and modern than she expected, and spotlessly clean, calling as she went, 'Myra! Myra, are you there?'

A door led into a long central hallway. More doors led off either side Flick knew the old woman lived in a basement flat below the main house. The internal connecting door was sure to be one of those. Holloway drifted ahead. Flick recalled his comment about hearing somebody in the house and was about to call him back, when he shouted her name.

When she followed him into a spacious reception room, she saw Myra Drake on a sofa, hands folded in her lap.

'Myra?'

The old woman didn't answer. When Flick came closer, she saw she was trembling. 'Myra, speak to me.'

Myra's hooded eyes were wide and round. Her lips moved, but nothing came out. Holloway crouched to check her pulse. 'She's in shock,' he said. 'Lay her down.'

'No,' croaked the old woman. Her arms fluttered as Flick tried to ease her shoulders down.

'Make her comfortable, I'll get a blanket.' Holloway left

the room. Flick heard his shoes clip across the parquet floor in the hallway and up the stairs.

'Peter,' said Flick, alarmed. 'Wait!'

Myra resisted Flick's attempts to lay her down and snatched at Flick's wrist, pulling her close. 'Listen to me, you must—'

'Is Ray here?' Flick tried to free her hand, but Myra's grip was surprisingly firm.

'It's not safe.' The old woman's eyes bored into hers. 'He's here!'

'Who's here, Myra? Ray?' Flick barked over her shoulder, urgently, 'Peter!'

Myra's fingers rubbed anxiously at her locket. 'You must go!'

'Let's get you out of here.'

Her bag, with her phone, was at her feet. She'd leave it. The priority was to get Myra outside. Myra swayed unsteadily when Flick helped her up. They moved slowly, taking small, hesitant steps into the gloomy hallway. The front door was just ahead. Something creaked on the floor above.

'Keep going, almost there,' said Flick in as calm a voice as she could manage.

Crossing the parquet, she peered up the stairs, which doubled back out of sight. A vase surrounded by photo frames stood in an alcove on the half-landing.

Flick rattled the handle of the door, but it was locked. 'The key.'

'The key?'

'Where do you keep it?'

The old woman blinked. 'He's here.'

'The key, Myra . . . Never mind.' She turned, intending

to lead Myra out the back, when a shadow moved across the half-landing. Making sure the old woman was upright against the door, Flick went to the bottom step. 'Peter!'

Gripping the banister, trying to avoid looking at the happy family photos of Drake, Laura and April on the wall, she called again. But there was no answer. The shadow shifted. Flick planted a foot on the bottom step, but thought better of going up. Myra stood, ashen, against the door.

What was that she heard above her – a voice?

'Peter, what is it?'

Against her better judgement, heart clattering in her chest, Flick climbed a couple of steps.

'Peter, is that you?'

Footsteps stumbled along the landing hidden above, and she edged back down.

Moments later, Holloway appeared at the turning, standing very tall and straight, his features hidden in the gloom.

'Peter!' She let out a sigh of relief at the sight of him, but when he didn't respond, she asked angrily: 'Have you called the Incident Room?' Holloway swayed gently, snorting loudly through his nose. 'Peter, don't play silly buggers!'

Holloway lifted his arms and stumbled to the edge of the landing. Knees buckling, he tipped down the stairs, fell forward onto her. His forehead slammed into hers, and she crumpled beneath him. Her spine jarred painfully against the parquet beneath Holloway's dead weight. Too stunned to feel the impact, stars bursting in her eyes, Flick scrambled from under him, scrabbling away on her hands and heels, sliding in the blood seeping from him, smearing it into the tile. Holloway lay face down, unmoving.

And when she looked up, there was somebody else standing in his place on the landing, face obscured in the dark.

'Ray?' she said.

'No, not him.' The figure stepped slowly downstairs, the shape of his bald head, the features of his face, that shy smile, solidifying as he moved into the light.

'Frank?' said Flick. Her limbs began to shake at the sight of the blood-smeared knife that Frank Wanderly clenched in his fist.

'Not Frank. That's not my name.'

Tap.

His upper lip trembled like a snarling wolf's and she glimpsed his white teeth, as he trod lightly down the stairs towards her, gently tapping the blade along the banister.

Tap, tap.

'Let me come down and I'll introduce myself properly.'

55

The skeletal trees lining the pavement shivered in the wind as Drake stuffed the gun into his belt at the small of his back and climbed from his car, walked to the address where the Two O'Clock Boy, or so he called himself, had lived under the name of Frank Wanderly.

He considered phoning Myra, but if she had any sense she would already be in the sticks, settling a few ancient scores with unlucky relatives. Just as April and Amelia would be en route to the safety of Elliot's home.

The address in Hornsey had been easy enough to find. The small, terraced house sat in the middle of an anonymous row, nothing to distinguish it from the houses on either side except the number embossed in bulging red tile above the door. The curtains on the ground floor were drawn. A security alarm was fixed beneath the bedroom window, but the dummy box was old, the telephone number on it prefixed with the long redundant 0171. Ray Drake glanced along the street to make sure nobody was about and then slipped round the back into a neglected garden.

At the kitchen window, he cupped his eyes against the glass to see a kitchen furnished with beige Formica units. The door was locked, but the frame was rotten. Drake leaned hard into it and the wood splintered. Inside, the kitchen was bare, nondescript, except for a curious collection of objects on top of the fridge. Among them, a horseshoe, a beer mat, an egg timer with mauve sand. There was a replica of Blackpool Tower, a bicycle pump and a china figurine of a maid with a bonnet and a milk pail, similar to the ones in the Overtons' bedroom.

Drake opened the door to the living room, which was dark behind the closed curtains, and flicked on the light. Dust burned on the bulb beneath a wicker shade. Everything in the room was impersonal, second hand, the atmosphere musty. There was an old sofa and a sideboard. Inside were textbooks, a single, upturned wine glass on a doily, a neat pile of newspapers, a box of matches.

Drake pocketed the matches and was climbing the stairs when his phone vibrated. One eye on the landing, he checked the Caller ID. Flick. She'd already left several messages, he saw, and there were others from Peter Holloway. Upstairs, the bathroom was empty except for a bar of soap, a deodorant, a toothbrush and towel. Strings of dust trembled along the skirting of an empty rear bedroom, below cartoon animals parading on faded wallpaper. No effort had been made to make this house anything resembling a home.

Walking into the main bedroom, he saw a single bed, diminished in a sea of carpet. The duvet was a perfect rectangle, the crisp white sheet beneath tucked with precision. On a bedside cabinet was a lamp and an encyclopedia.

Drake turned to the wall opposite, which was covered its entire length, from ceiling to floor, with photographs and newspaper clippings and documents. Sheets of information detailing victims clustered in groups; images of men and women, photographed going about their daily business; floor plans of properties; street maps; social-media screen grabs;

work schedules; diary excerpts. Keys labelled with passcodes hung from pins. Lengths of string raced across the wall, tacking in every direction, mysteriously linking clusters of pages.

Many of the names and some of the faces were familiar to Drake, others he didn't recognise. Maybe they had all been at the home, or perhaps in his murderous obsession, the Two O'Clock Boy had given innocent men and women an obscure, fatal relationship to the Longacre that they didn't deserve.

His eyes flitted from one newspaper cutting to another:

> . . . twins were last night killed in a blaze that ripped through a sheltered housing . . .
>
> . . . attached a rubber hose to the exhaust of their car on 12 November last year, and died of carbon . . .

Lifting the cuttings, he found others beneath.

> . . . blamed faulty brakes for the fatal crash, which killed a family of . . .
>
> . . . impaled on railings, causing massive internal . . .

Drake followed the trail of paper until he found his own name contained in a satellite of clippings isolated at the edge of the wall, along with Elliot Juniper and Amelia Troy.

There were photos of Elliot, sitting in the snug of a pub, and walking along a country lane with his stepson. A black-and-white image of Amelia – pale, sad – in a hospital bed after her overdose. And he himself was photographed from a window overlooking the car park at the station, and with his daughter exiting from a restaurant. There he was again with Laura, helping her into the car, probably taking her to a hospital appointment in the weeks before she died. He tugged the photo off the wall – the tack popped out and flew over his head – and pocketed it. Finally, there was a photo of him with the man he had known as Frank Wanderly at some police function.

Drake stepped back to take in the elaborate design in its entirety, its sheer scale. The last thing the Two O'Clock Boy saw before he closed his eyes, and the first thing he saw when he opened them, was this macabre montage of death and conspiracy. Its mass loomed over him as he slept, imprinting itself into his dreams and nightmares. The conspiracy was overwhelming. All the people he had killed, men, women and children – and all the people he was going to kill. He would stare at it, absorbing it, his plans shifting and sliding in the dark, slotting together in his head like elaborate pieces of machinery.

Dead centre on the wall, separated from the other clusters of information by a thin moat of space, was a photograph: Toby Turrell as a small boy, taken at the coast. Wrapped in a windcheater, a big smile on his face, hair plastered to his head by rain. The boy held the hands of his happy parents. In the distance, a rainbow speared the horizon.

Drake looked one last time at the sprawling design, an insane representation of the inside of the Two O'Clock Boy's head, and went downstairs.

He opened the front door and walked to his car, checking he was alone in the street, and took from the boot a petrol canister. Back inside, he set to work, pouring the liquid across the bedroom, staining the perfect white duvet, and sloshing it on the wall, careful not to splash any on his shoes.

The cold canister ignited memories of that last horrific night at the home – and the lonely death of the boy who had saved him from Gordon, and whom he barely knew. A boy from whom he had taken so much.

For decades he had hidden behind a façade, the smiling face of a man few people really knew. Laura knew him and loved him, despite everything. He missed his wife, but she was gone and he was afraid that Ray Drake, too, would soon slip away.

When the canister was empty, its contents splashed in the kitchen and living room, he took out the matches at the front door.

Drake's phone rang again – his home number – and some instinct made him answer the call. 'Yes.'

'I'm ready now,' said the voice, this time undisguised by any electronic filter. 'I'm ready for you to finish what you started.'

Propping the phone between his ear and his shoulder, Drake pinched three matches together.

'You tell me when you want me to kill you,' said Drake, 'and I'll happily oblige.'

'It's time now, I think. Yes, I think so. We're waiting for you.'

Drake cut the call. He struck the matches and tossed them, watched fire blossom in an orange inferno at his feet, Gordon Tallis's agonising last moments flickering momentarily on the wall like a shadow play.

He considered how he was right back where he had started. How everything he had strived for would soon come to an end.

'See you soon, Toby,' he said.

56

Here they were, Amelia Troy and April Drake, pulling up the drive in a fancy sports car. He didn't want them here – couldn't stop thinking about what he had done, what he was going to do – but Elliot had made a promise. One more night wasn't going to make a difference when you were staring eternity in the face.

The wind chime was going nine to the dozen. Elliot loved its gentle tinkle in a soft breeze, but tonight the fierce wind was blowing the tops of the trees sideways – the gales were steadily picking up strength – and its incessant clinking, like a furious warning, made him want to rip it down.

'Ladies,' he said, forcing a smile, 'welcome.'

Elliot felt strangely emotional at the sight of Amelia Troy. He'd expected some butch old painter in dungarees, but when she climbed from the car he saw she was slim and pretty. She hugged him, and he smelled cigarettes on her, which made him like her all the more.

'Thanks for having us, Elliot.'

They'd gone through the wars together years ago, him and Amelia, but she looked like she'd come out the other side in better shape. She was worth more money than he could imagine – with millions in the bank! – all because she chucked paint at a canvas. Once, Elliot had gone to a gallery to see her paintings, had found them too . . .

disturbing. Elliot preferred more uplifting pictures, like that dancing couple with the butler. Life was hard enough without hanging depressing stuff on your walls.

When Amelia looked up at the cottage, with its peeling paint and rotting frames, Elliot grimaced. 'Not up to your usual standards; it ain't exactly a mansion.'

'It's comfortable.' She touched his arm. 'And, believe me, my place isn't exactly a palace. This is April, Ray Drake's daughter.'

He nodded, hanging back, not wanting to frighten the girl. She was a beauty in all her designer gear. Her dad's princess, no doubt. It couldn't be easy for her to be here, cowering from a deranged killer in a ramshackle cottage in the middle of nowhere, alongside an oaf.

'I've a son myself,' said Elliot. 'Well, a stepson, sort of thing.' A lump formed in his throat when he realised he'd never see Dylan again. 'Shall we get inside?'

April smiled, flatly. 'Do you have a . . . ?'

Elliot blinked, and Amelia prompted: 'We drank a *lot* of water on the way.'

'Of course! Bathroom's upstairs, first door.'

They watched the girl climb the stairs, disappearing out of sight. Elliot had made a fire, which crackled and hissed, throwing warmth into the small room.

'I hope it's not too much of an inconvenience to have us here. Your family aren't going to be put out?'

'They're away,' said Elliot quickly. 'Staying with friends. Thought it would be best, you know, in the circumstances.'

Amelia nodded thoughtfully, her gaze dropping to his injured hand. 'I'm sure we were good friends back at the home, but I don't remember much about back then.'

'Yeah,' said Elliot, uncomfortable. 'We were pals.'

'Then it's good to meet again, even if the circumstances aren't so jolly.'

He caught sight of himself in the mirror. He'd never been a handsome man, what with the nose smeared across his face like gravy across a plate, and he was carrying a few more pounds than he should, but he looked wretched right now. Dark rings cupped his eyes, his skin was grey. Emotion pressed against his ribs. He had given her hell back in the home, her and those others – particularly Turrell, who was now going about murdering all and sundry – and she had every right to hate him. 'This is my fault.'

'What are you talking about?'

'I just want you to know that I'm not the same person you knew back then.' He gripped her arm. 'I treated you wrong, I'm sorry. I was scared, I was . . . That's not me any more. I got a partner who loves me, and a son. That's me now, that's who I am.'

A look fell down her face – discomfort, maybe even fear. He realised his fingers were digging into her skin, and let go.

'It sounds like you love them very much.'

He closed his eyes, overwhelmed by his own stupidity. Rhonda and Dylan were the only good things that had ever happened to him.

'Yes.' His voice was barely a whisper. 'I do.'

'Whatever you're thinking,' said Amelia, 'I promise you it's not that bad.'

But it is, he thought. He couldn't tell her about the dead man hidden in a car boot, and the stolen money, an old couple's savings, stashed in his wardrobe. He just had to get through this night. Stay focused. He was expected to protect these girls. 'Look at me, this ain't no way to welcome an old friend. Let's have some tea . . . something stronger.'

'Tea would be good.' Amelia smiled. 'I mean it, Elliot. It's good to see you. One last time.'

'You're safe until our friend—' He checked himself. It didn't feel right saying the policeman's name, he would have to be careful about what he said in front of the girl. 'Until everything's good for you to go home.'

'I just . . .' Amelia nodded, her cheerful façade cracking. 'I just want it to be over.'

'Do you trust him?' he asked quietly, nodding up the stairs to where April had disappeared. Her father had changed a lot since Elliot had last seen him, on the night of that fatal fire more than three decades ago.

'Yes, I do.'

The way she said it, with a quiet confidence, made him feel slightly better about the whole fucked-up situation. He heard the toilet flush and the tap running. The pipes shuddered. An old cottage like this, you heard everything that went on in every room. Then April stepped downstairs.

'There's plenty in the fridge,' Elliot said, 'but we're out of foie gras.'

'I'm afraid that's utterly unacceptable.' Amelia tapped a finger on his chest. 'And I promise there will be serious consequences for you.'

It was dark now, they were a long way from street lamps and the evening dropped like a blackout curtain. The night sky was filled with lumbering cloud. He didn't like the idea that the poor, insane Toby Turrell was out there somewhere watching, waiting for his moment.

The women sat at the kitchen table while Elliot brewed tea, but the conversation was stilted. The girl, in particular, was subdued. Amelia did her best to put everybody at ease, asking Elliot about his family and his life. But he was nervous in front of April, unsure of how much he could say to her. He didn't want to tell them Rhonda had left him, and the information that he intended to kill himself just as soon as they were safe would add the finishing touch to an already strained atmosphere.

'I know you're frightened.' He placed a steaming mug in front of April. 'But your dad – he'll fix this. He'll, er, arrest this guy.'

April cocked her head. 'How do you know him?'

'An old investigation he worked on,' said Amelia quickly. 'Isn't that right, Elliot?'

'Correct.' Elliot cleared his throat. 'Way back in the mists of time.'

The girl stared doubtfully, looked like she was about to say something, when the doorbell rang. Two angry bursts. April's hand immediately searched for Amelia's across the table.

'Are you expecting anyone?'

'A salesman, probably.' Elliot smothered his anxiety with a grin. 'Get a lot of them around here. You girls stay here, relax.' He placed a biscuit barrel on the table. 'Help yourself.'

At the door, Elliot stifled a groan when he saw the shape on the other side of the patterned glass. Slipping his grazed fist into his pocket, he opened the door.

'Owen!' he said loudly. 'What a pleasure!'

The old man was watching leaves blow across the bonnet of Amelia's sports car. 'Evening, Elliot.' He nodded at the vehicle. 'Been splashing the cash already?'

'Good one,' said Elliot tensely.

Amelia called from the kitchen doorway: 'Who is it?'

'Just a mate,' said Elliot, over his shoulder. 'Nothing to worry about, I'll be back in a minute.'

Owen tried to look inside but Elliot stepped out, closing the door behind him. The black wall of trees across the lane hunkered against the relentless wind. The barn creaked and cracked.

'Nice to see you, Owen.'

'Is it?' asked Owen, dabbing at one of his watery eyes with a knuckle. 'Is it nice to see me, Elliot?'

'Course it is.' Elliot's laugh was brittle.

Owen nodded at the closed door. 'A bad time, then?'

'Got some friends round, that's all.' Looking down, he saw the old man's trousers were neatly tucked into a pair of wellingtons. 'What can I do for you?'

'Sorry for the inconvenience, Elliot, but I want to know where he is.'

'Where who is?'

'I haven't heard from Perry since he left to pick you up. Everything go as planned?'

'Yeah.' That bloody chime clanging in his ears. 'Like clockwork.'

'Then where is he?'

'Please, Owen. I've people here.'

'Well, we don't want to spoil the party. Why don't we head to the barn? We can talk about it there.'

'Sure.'

Elliot followed Owen down the drive.

'Thing is, Elliot, I'm worried.' Owen's small frame braced against the wind as they walked. 'It's odd for Perry not to get in touch. He usually sticks to me like glue.'

'He dropped me off and then sped away,' Elliot said quickly. 'That was the last I saw of him.'

'You don't think he's trying to pull a fast one, do you, and taken all the money for himself?'

Elliot let out a long breath. 'He seemed pretty fired up. Angry, you know, volatile. And . . .'

Owen stopped outside the barn. 'And what?'

'Well, he had a few choice things to say about you.'

'What did he say?' Owen blinked. 'Tell me.'

'Nothing.' Elliot folded his arms. 'It's not stuff you would want me to repeat.'

'Son of a bitch,' said Owen quietly. 'How could he do it, Elliot? He's worked for me for years. Perry has been like a son to me.'

'Last I saw, he was driving off with the rucksack.' Elliot sighed. 'Sorry, Owen, it looks like he's done a runner.'

A branch cracked in the darkness. They heard it crash to the floor.

'Can't trust anyone, these days,' said Owen sadly. 'You really can't.'

'No,' agreed Elliot, 'you can't.'

'If only Perry were here to put his side of this.' Eyes fixed sourly on Elliot, the old man prodded open the barn door with his foot.

When Elliot looked into the gloom, he saw a figure standing in the empty space: Perry. The man's eyes, those small, hard pellets, almost hidden in his swollen face, glittered with hatred.

Owen placed a hand on the small of Elliot's back and guided him inside.

57

The first thing Drake saw when he entered his house was Toby Turrell, the man he knew as Frank Wanderly, waiting in the hallway, a long knife down at his side.

Flick Crowley sat tensely on the bottom step of the staircase. On the floor in front of them both, face down in a pool of blood, was a body.

'It's Peter Holloway,' said Turrell helpfully.

Closing the door, Drake saw the old woman against the wall, her arms crossed over her chest as if she had already been entombed. 'Myra?'

Lips pursed tightly, she nodded.

'We thought you'd never get here.' The way Turrell listlessly rubbed his scalp made Drake lower his gun. 'Don't do that,' Toby snapped. 'You'll need it in a moment.'

Drake took a good look at the man. In all the time that Frank Wanderly had worked at the station – several years now – Drake had never recognised him. Turrell's features from that chaotic time had always been muddy in his memory, and there was little to connect Wanderly to the boy from the Longacre. Wanderly was tall and bland, a happy, amiable man who Drake saw for a few seconds each day. Toby Turrell had been small and slight, with a mop of thick, blond hair. All he remembered about him was the misery and terror etched onto his face that last night at the home. The forgettable child had grown up to be a forgettable adult, the kind of man who slipped from your memory the moment you turned your back on him. Which, of course, was exactly how he went about his murderous business.

'All those people, Toby, all those families.'

'And why should they have people to love?' Turrell made a face. 'Sons, daughters, wives, husbands – and I have nothing! I worshipped Mary and Bernard, I adored them. None of you stopped me, and I have had to live with the consequences of what . . . I did.'

'You killed your parents,' said Drake quietly.

'You should have let me die at that home,' said Turrell. 'If you had, I wouldn't have done it, or killed any of those other people. In a way, all this is entirely because of you.'

'It's always someone else's fault with you, isn't it?' said Myra, from the corner.

'But I'm going to give you the opportunity to do the right thing. Kill me now, put right what was made wrong all those years ago, and I promise I'll let your daughter live.'

'She's out of your grasp now, Toby.'

Turrell smirked. 'You tried to run me down in your car; you came to kill me at Amelia's.'

Drake paced the hallway, trying to think of one good reason to blow his head off, in spite of Flick. 'Why didn't you kill me when you had the chance, Toby? Why didn't you kill Amelia or April?'

'Because I've been waiting for this moment,' said Turrell. 'Waiting for you and me to meet, face to face. You set all this bloodshed into motion, and it's your responsibility to finish it.' He pointed with the knife. 'I have chosen *you* to do it.'

In any other circumstances Drake would be happy to oblige Toby Turrell. But with Flick Crowley present, killing him in cold blood was out of the question. 'I'm not going to kill you, Toby.'

'You must! I want to be with Mary and Bernard. Go on, right here.' He pulled back his arms and puffed out his chest. 'Shoot me in the heart.'

When Drake didn't move, Turrell grabbed Flick's hair, dragging her to her feet. She cried out, and Drake snapped his gun towards him.

'That's more like it.' Turrell's eyes flashed. 'That's more like the old *you*. I really thought I'd lost you, so you can imagine my joy when I found you – hiding in plain sight! It's all so perfect. I want to die, and you want to kill me. Look, I'll show you how.'

Pulling Flick to him, he traced the knife in a slow pantomime from her throat to her stomach, the tip snagging on the cotton of her shirt, to show Ray Drake the bloody journey of the blade if he chose to slice her open.

'I discovered a long time ago that killing is easy. Believe me, I'm very good at it, I've had a *lot* of practice. I've always been good at things.' He laughed in delight. 'Mummy and Daddy always said I was a clever little boy.'

'Your parents left you in the Longacre, Toby,' said Drake.

'My parents loved me!'

'They left you there.'

'They didn't know what went on at that place!' Spittle flew from Turrell's mouth.

'Are you absolutely sure about that?' asked Drake. 'Because they didn't hurry to take you away, they took their own good time about it. They left you there as long as possible, with

Gordon, with all those kids, and let those things happen to you. They were terrible people, Mary and Bernard, selfish and cruel and thoughtless, and they deserved to die.'

'Shut up!'

'They hated you so much they sent you to that place.'

'Shut your fucking mouth!' Turrell screamed. 'They loved me!' He covered his face with his knife hand and howled. His shoulders heaved, snot bubbled from his nose. 'They weren't like that!'

'But that's what you've always suspected, isn't it?' Drake tapped his chest. 'In here, Toby, you've never been able to rid yourself of the nagging feeling that they hated you so much that they left you there on purpose.'

'Call it in, Ray,' said Flick, through gritted teeth.

'That's a cruel thing to say!' whined Toby. 'They loved me, and they made a mistake! You're just like all the rest. No fancy home, no snooty mother or spoilt brat of a daughter makes you any different. You're just the same as Elliot and Kenny and Jason and that other scum.'

Drake stepped forward. He was no marksman, and Flick was too close to Turrell. 'You killed your parents. No one else is responsible.'

'But I didn't want to.' The hallway echoed with Turrell's sobs. 'I miss them so much!'

'Call it in, Ray.'

'I know you do, Toby,' said Drake. 'But it's over. April is safe, Amelia is safe, it's just you and me now.'

'No, it's not over.' A nasty smiled twisted on his face. 'It's all worked out just the way I planned it. Elliot, your daughter—'

'Are safe,' said Drake.

'Make the call, Ray,' said Flick, her voice cracking.

Pushing Flick away, Turrell clamped his eyes shut. 'I'm ready now, you can shoot me.' But Drake didn't move. 'I said I'm ready!'

'I'm not going to kill you, Toby,' said Drake. His free hand tapped rapidly against his thigh as he tried to fit together the sequence of events. Turrell took his daughter, and attacked Amelia. But they both survived. All those others died.

'Why didn't you kill April? Why didn't you kill Amelia when you had the chance?'

Turrell leered. 'Kill me and I'll tell you.'

'It doesn't make sense, Toby.'

'So you're not going to kill me?'

'You're going to prison. It's over,' Drake said. 'For both of us.'

'I understand,' said Toby bitterly. 'But there's one thing I have to do first.'

And then, shrieking at the top of his voice, Turrell lunged towards Drake with the knife raised above his head.

Ray Drake lifted the gun in a precise, fluid movement and fired at point-blank range into his chest. Turrell's feet lifted into the air and he flew back against the stairs and slid to the floor.

Drake dropped the weapon and went to Flick, who was crying and shaking. He took her in his arms and she clung to him.

'It's over,' he told her, desperately wanting to believe it. 'It's all over.'

Myra stepped away from the wall to nudge Turrell's body with her foot. 'He's dead, Raymond.'

Flick pushed Drake away and staggered to the old woman, her face full of rage.

'Don't call him that!' She swung to face him. 'That's not who he is!'

58

1984

Ranting and swigging from a bottle, Gordon Tallis worked himself into a fury.

Forced to listen to his bitter tirade, they sat in the room – Connor and Elliot, Kenny and Jason, Amelia and Toby – anxious and fearful. Each of them was accused of trying to destroy him. But mostly it was the Turrell boy who bore the brunt of his drunken anger. Toby sat with his face pressed into his knees, unresponsive to Gordon's threats.

Huddled against the wall, Amelia reached for Connor's hand, and he took it. Her grip was hot and clammy. Elliot darted glances in his direction, as if expecting him to do something, anything.

Life at the home carried on as usual outside the room. Connor heard the Dents shout commands in the kitchen; the chirp and chatter of conversation over the evening meal; the bedtime stampede, feet thundering on the floorboards above.

'It's all over for me.' Gordon paced, flinging out his arms. 'I've associates breathing down my neck, and a high court judge on my back. It's all right for you people, you've your whole lives ahead, but who's looking out for Gordon? All the effort I put into this place, the commitment. All that good work ruined because of a stupid bitch.'

He stopped in front of Connor. Liquid plinked in the bottle as it dropped from his fist and rolled on the floor. 'What do you think, lad? What should Gordon do next?'

'You should let us go, Gordon. We just want to sleep.'

'But where's the fun in that?' Gordon's lips curled back, revealing his jumble of teeth. 'After everything I've done for you, and you let me down!' Lurching forward, he grabbed Toby. The boy hung limply in his grip, his eyes had lost all focus. 'And this is the one who's caused it all. I do people a favour out of the goodness of my heart, and this is what happens.'

'Put him down.' Connor jumped to his feet.

'Yes.' The manager threw Toby down, wiped his palms down his sides. 'Let's get this over with.'

He pushed Connor, who nearly fell over Jason's outstretched legs, stumbling into the room at the back. Connor saw the threadbare mattress, the petrol canister beside it, and the green ribbed radiator.

'I've been waiting for this, boy.' Gordon slammed the door shut. 'It's time for us to settle our differences, one way or the other.'

Connor was pinned against the radiator. 'Promise you won't hurt them.'

'I can't do that.' Gordon giggled. 'This anger inside me has been building, building. I've nothing to lose no more. The boy ain't going home, I'll tell you that much.' He ran his fingers through Connor's hair, and his face was pressed so close that the boy could smell his fetid breath. 'You've been a big disappointment to me, lad. I thought we were chums, partners. I thought we shared something special.'

Connor reached for the manager's hand, felt his calloused fingers, and whispered: 'I've been waiting for this moment.'

Gordon stared, as if in a trance. 'You and me both, boy.'

Then Connor let go of his hand, and slid out from against the radiator. Gordon's hand snapped towards him angrily – and jerked to a stop. He was handcuffed to the radiator piping. Gordon yanked at the cuff, then lunged at Connor, clawing with his free hand, but the boy stepped out of his reach.

'Get these off!' Straining against the radiator, the cuffs jangling against the metal strut, Gordon's face twisted with rage. 'Sooner or later I'm going to get free. You may be long gone, I don't expect you to stick around, but the others will be here.' His laugh was laced with bile. 'And, believe me, boy, I'm going to make those cunts pay.'

And it was at that moment Connor knew what he had to do. Knew why he had stayed in this place. Maybe he had always known why. With shaking hands, he picked up the canister and unscrewed the cap.

Gordon sneered. 'Oh, come on now, you're not going to—'

He reared back as Connor lifted the canister and slopped the contents all over him.

'What do you think you're doing?' The petrol soaked his chest and legs; Connor threw it into his face and he spluttered. 'What the fuck are you doing?'

The pungent liquid spattered onto the diamond-patterned carpet. Connor splashed it over the walls, and it soaked into the mattress as Gordon hurled threats, obscenities, working himself into a frenzy. Then he threw down the canister. Its contents gulped onto the manager's feet.

Connor's head pulsed with cold, hard contempt.

He took out the lighter he'd kept from the night before. Thumbed the flint. Sparks flew off it.

'You ain't gonna do it!' snarled Gordon. 'You wouldn't dare! You and me are pals!'

Connor swayed on his heels, the fumes making him light-headed, and lost his balance. Stumbling too close, Gordon grabbed his wrist. Connor screamed as his arm was wrenched behind his back, and he was pulled close against Gordon, who lifted his arm around the boy's neck.

'Drop it!' screamed Gordon, who couldn't snatch the lighter with his free arm and instead tightened the crook of his elbow around the boy's throat and squeezed with all his might. Connor felt air trap in his lungs, blood bulge in his head, as he struggled to keep the lighter at arm's length. He plucked ineffectually at Gordon's arm with his free hand. The lack of oxygen, the stench of petrol in his nostrils, made the room warp and bend and his thoughts became sluggish.

And just as his outstretched arm ached and he was afraid that he would drop the lighter, he had a fleeting sense of glass shattering in the skylight and a figure dropping into the room.

And then Ray Drake was pulling at Gordon's arm, digging his fingers into his flesh. The lighter fell from Connor's hand and bounced across the floor. Gordon released his arm from Connor's throat to punch Ray in the side of his head, sending the boy flying into a corner.

Connor fell to his knees and crawled to the lighter – gulping for air, colour and shapes rolling in his vision – to spark the flint. The flame took, and as the manager struggled in panic, Connor lunged towards him – pressed it into his face.

Flame crackled across Gordon's skin, sizzling greedily into his hair and collar.

Connor stood back and saw him burn. Watched his body erupt into flame. Fire leapt from Gordon, igniting the curtains, and racing across the floor to the mattress.

Gordon screamed and thrashed in agony, frenzied hands clawed in submission, his skin cooking. Then Connor snapped out of his trance – knew they had to get out of there. He shouted to Ray in the corner, who climbed unsteadily to his feet. But his path was blocked by the burning mattress on one side and Gordon's flaming body on the other.

'Quick!' Connor held out his arm, and Ray moved forward, cringing against the heat, to pass close to Gordon—

Whose hand thrashed out, knocking Ray behind the rising wall of fire.

'No!' Connor tried to get to him, but was forced back. Flames rippled to the ceiling. Smoke rolled into every corner. When he tried again to get to Ray a hand held him back.

'No!' Connor wept tears of rage and frustration. 'No! No! No!'

'You can't,' shouted Elliot, as Ray Drake disappeared behind the thickening fire and smoke. Connor angrily shrugged off Elliot and surged forward, but couldn't find a way through the intense heat.

Connor's last memory, as he was dragged from the room, was of Gordon, a fireball shaped like a man, on his knees, his last agonising screams lost in the snap of the fire.

And Ray Drake's eyes, imploring, terrified, vanishing behind a black curtain of smoke.

Back in the office, Kenny and Jason pounded desperately

at the locked door to the hallway. Toby was still slumped against the wall.

'Help us!' screamed Elliot, but Connor stood dazed in the middle of the room.

The two biggest boys, Elliot and Jason, picked up the desk chair and threw it at the window, smashing the glass. Cold night air sucked inside. Flame and smoke billowed greedily from the back room. Elliot kicked out the shards of glass around the frame, and one by one the children climbed onto the sill and jumped to the pavement.

'Connor!' Elliot shouted, and Connor lifted Amelia in his arms. The children from upstairs poured onto the street from the front door. People from the squat opposite came to watch. Connor swung Amelia out of the window and climbed out after her, falling to the pavement. He sat on his haunches in the road to watch the fire take hold of the building.

'Where's Gordon?' Ronnie Dent stumbled through the crowd of kids. He angrily hauled Connor to his feet. 'Where is he?'

'He's dead,' Connor said softly. 'I killed him.'

Dent flinched from the boy's calm stare and disappeared quickly back into the crowd.

Elliot came up behind him. 'Where's Toby?'

Connor looked everywhere, but couldn't see him. When he moved towards the house, Elliot grabbed at him. 'You can't—'

But Connor shrugged him off and ran up the steps. Smoke poured from the window, clawing at his eyeballs. He covered his mouth and pressed inside, the image of Ray Drake's final, terrified look as he disappeared behind the whirling flame and smoke repeating in his mind's eye. In the hallway

Connor kicked at the office door, pumping his leg against the lock.

The door splintered. Smoke and heat rolled towards him, forcing him back. He dropped to his hands and knees and crawled inside. Orange flame climbed every wall. The desk was alight on one side, the sofa on the other. Toby was curled into a ball when Connor reached him. He tugged at the kid's arm, barely able to open his stinging eyes, or to breathe.

'No,' mumbled Toby.

'Take my hand,' Connor said. 'Take it.'

He bunched the kid's jumper in his fist, tugging him towards the door, blind from the smoke, which burned his lungs and throat. Connor's limbs became sluggish, heavy. Toby's body was limp, his feet dragged. The kid made no effort to escape or even move. The door was so close – but Connor collapsed, hardly able to breathe.

And then he felt the boy rise out of his grip, the weight lifted. Squinting up, he glimpsed Elliot stumble to the door with Toby over his shoulder. Connor crawled out after them, tumbling down the steps, rolling onto the pavement just as the upstairs windows exploded from the intense heat. Connor fell across Toby as glass rained down around them. All the children screamed in terror.

'You're alive,' Connor gasped. 'You can go home.'

The boy lay on the road, staring at the sky.

In the distance they heard sirens. Connor pushed his way through the crowd, the screams and shouts and distant sirens muffled in his head, as if he were underwater. Amelia and Kenny, all the other children, sat on the pavement watching the house burn.

Elliot stared when Connor told him: 'You'll never see me again.'

At the dead end of the road he used his last vestiges of strength to scrabble over the wall and into the cool darkness. The burble of excited voices faded as he stumbled across the train track, and up the verge on the other side.

Connor collapsed on the grass to watch the night sky consume the smoke pumping from the windows. A wave of flashing blue light, police cars and fire engines, poured towards the home. Flame threw flickering shadow over the uniformed men moving urgently among the kids.

He had killed a man.

He'd poured petrol over Gordon Tallis and set him alight.

Watched him burn.

The truth was, once he had decided to do it, it had felt right.

But Ray Drake had also died. Connor told himself it wasn't his fault. Ray had tried to save him, and instead had been killed. He shouldn't have been there.

Connor's anger had gone now, but he knew with a sickening certainty it would return. The whirling chaos inside of him would eat him alive him if he allowed it.

He needed to tell them, the judge and his wife, that it wasn't his fault. Tell them Ray had saved him. And now he was dead. Their son was dead.

When Elliot saw him on the other side of the tracks, barely a shadow against the night, Connor turned and walked into the night.

They wouldn't meet again for another thirty years.

59

'The decades since my boy died have seemed like a dream. We waited for Raymond to come home, we waited for days, but he never did. And then Connor found his way here and told us what happened, and it was the most terrible, the most awful, thing to know our son was dead.' Myra Drake swallowed. 'And that I was in some way responsible. He died because he cared too much and his parents cared too little.' She lifted the wisps of fine hair drifting down the back of her neck. 'Do you mind?'

Drake stepped behind her to undo the tiny clasp, and Myra offered the locket to Flick, who took it. Inside was a small photograph of her dead son, its edges clipped in a rough hexagonal. In the photo he was seven or eight years old, and he straddled a turnstile in the countryside, smiling easily, eyes burning with a fierce intelligence.

'It's the only photo I have here,' said Myra. 'There are one or two in a safety deposit box, but the others were destroyed. Ray was a good boy, a popular child. I wish I had got to know him better, I wish Leonard and I had taken more time to listen to him before he . . .'

Myra shook her head, as if she had said enough. Stunned, Flick sat back in her chair. The boy who had been Connor Laird and was now called Ray Drake paced the kitchen, willing his mobile to ring. The bodies of Peter Holloway and Toby Turrell lay undisturbed in the hallway.

'And when Connor came to you . . .?' prompted Flick.

'Everybody believed him dead, so when he turned up on our doorstep, Leonard and I . . . well, we took him in. We understood the consequences of what we did. The boy had a fire in him, an anger, and we knew it wouldn't be easy, but we felt such anguish, such guilt, you see, so it was a kind of penance. There's no doubt in my mind it is what Raymond would have wanted. If he had lived, he would have helped people, in the same way he was desperate to help that wretched cousin of his.' The old woman's hooded eyes followed Drake around the room. 'We cut family ties, and, of course, he couldn't go to school, so he was taught here. We lost quite a few tutors along the way, I can tell you, he was a difficult young man, to say the least. Life was a challenge for a number of years. But also . . . oddly exhilarating.'

And it hadn't been easy for Myra, thought Drake. But she'd never compromised, never backed down. When he was young, when the anger blasted off Connor Laird like heat off a furnace, she never flinched. She stood her ground. His guilt and rage threatened to engulf them all but she never showed any weakness, any fear.

'He'll never be my son, he'll never be my boy, he understands that. But I'm proud of him, and proud of what he has achieved.' Myra turned to Flick. 'He's come so very far in life. He's a different person now, I think, to the youth we took in.'

When Drake had tried to call April's phone it was switched off, the same with Amelia's phone. When he tried Elliot's number the call went to voicemail.

Myra reached for the locket, the thin chain slithering across the table, to click shut the image of the son she lost many years ago. She closed her fist around it.

'I thought it was you,' Flick told Drake. 'I thought you killed all those people.' She took out the cutting with the photo of Connor Laird cringing from the camera and placed it on the table.

'Yes, that was Connor.' Myra tapped the image as if it was a different person entirely from the man she raised. But Drake didn't look, his eyes remained fixed on his phone, a nameless anxiety seeping through him.

'Look at the photo,' Flick told him, and when he ignored her, she said it again. '*Look at it.*'

Finally, he picked up the cutting to gaze for a long moment into the flashing eye of Connor Laird. Then he dropped it and tried Elliot's number again. It went to voicemail, so he called Amelia's number. He would keep calling for as long as it took.

'Tell me,' Flick said to Drake.

Myra sighed. 'I've told you everything you need to—'

'Shut up, Myra,' snapped Flick. The old woman blinked. 'I want to hear it from him.'

So Ray Drake told her about his life as Connor Laird, and about the Longacre home. It all tumbled from him. He told her of Gordon's murder of Sally, and how Connor and Elliot and Toby Turrell had been forced to bury her, something inside of Turrell becoming corrupted in the process. He recounted Leonard and Myra Drake's visit, and said that a fire broke out later that night; told her how he stumbled, filthy and feverish, across the city, and found his way, days later, to Myra and Leonard, who took him in; and how the judge used his wealth and influence to ensure Connor Laird took the identity of their dead child, Raymond Drake.

He explained how he had long ago destroyed any evidence

– every file and photo – that linked Connor Laird to that place, burying the past, his former identity, as best he could; removing files and destroying documents about the Longacre. He took every copy of the article about Leonard and Myra's visit from newspaper offices and libraries and destroyed it. Or so he had thought. God only knows where Kenny had found that article about the visit of the Drakes to the Longacre.

Finally, he told her about Turrell's manipulation of Jordan, and how he himself had saved Amelia's life earlier in the evening, and sent her and April to Elliot's cottage in the middle of nowhere, where they would be safe, or so he hoped.

He told her everything that happened at the Longacre on that last night.

Or almost everything . . .

What he didn't say was how he had cuffed Gordon Tallis to the radiator and soaked him in petrol and burned him alive. Myra knew, and she would take that secret to her grave. Laura had known, but she accepted the person he had been because she loved the man he had become. But Laura was gone now, as the real Ray Drake had died decades ago, and Sally Raynor, and so many others.

'What will you do?' Myra asked Flick.

'Peter Holloway is dead.'

'Killed by Turrell.'

'And Toby Turrell is dead.'

This is where Drake expected it to end. The lie he had been living since he arrived on her doorstep had been blown wide apart. But he had much to be thankful for in his life. He had been given an education, a career. And he had a family of his own, a loving wife and daughter. April might never understand why her father kept the truth from her, but the most important thing was that she was safe. Turrell was dead.

She was safe. He kept telling himself that, but the sudden nature of Turrell's death nagged at him.

'You helped Toby get out alive from that place,' Flick said.

'And if I had let him burn,' Drake said, 'all those people would be alive.'

'Give me the gun.'

He placed it on the table.

'We'll call the office.' Flick ran a hand down her face. 'And you can make a statement.'

'*I* killed Turrell,' said Myra tersely. 'In self-defence. This has nothing to do with Ray, and everything to do with me. He has already lost his wife, and if you take this further, he will lose his daughter, his livelihood and his reputation. I am asking you to consider very carefully what you do next. If you feel any compassion for him at all do not destroy his life for something that has absolutely nothing to do with him.'

Flick scraped back her chair. 'I need to think about this.'

'Of course.' Myra smiled sourly. 'You must do what you believe is right.'

Drake lifted himself from the wall, agitated. An image churned in his head: a jaunty red hoodie disappearing at the corner at Ryan Overton's estate. He heard Amelia's voice.

My husband will never touch me again.

When he came to the table, his fingers dabbed anxiously at the surface.

'What?' asked Flick.

'It doesn't make sense,' he said. 'Turrell had the opportunity to kill me more than once. He could have killed Amelia and taken April anywhere, knowing how important she is to me, and yet he let her go. At one time or the other, he could have killed us all. Why?'

'Turrell had a death wish. He was obsessed with you killing him.'

'He spent many years murdering those people, and he hated me and Elliot more than any of them.' Drake winced. 'All that intricate planning, and yet he chooses to die before his task is finished?'

He tried Elliot's number again, his stomach tightening with every unanswered ring.

'Where did he get the money for the endless changes of identity and location?' he said. 'Or the money to pay Jordan? He's been saving something special for us both, he – oh, God . . . He's got everyone just where he wants them.'

She's out of your grasp now, Drake had said, and Turrell had smirked.

Drake scooped up the gun.

Flick jumped to her feet. 'Ray, you have to stay here. We'll call—'

His face drained of colour. It wasn't over; he was a fool for ever believing it was.

'Turrell was content to die in the knowledge that his work would be completed after his death. The intention was always for Elliot and me to die together. We were the other Two O'Clock Boys; we were always together at the home, that's how he remembered us. And April . . .'

'An armed response unit will get there quicker than we can,' said Flick.

'No, if police approach the house, April will die.' His voice was a whisper. 'Please help me.'

Flick looked at him impassively, and then stormed into the hallway, stepping around the corpses. As Drake followed her, Myra hooked a finger around his wrist.

'Do you trust her to do the right thing?'

'Whatever happens, happens,' said Ray shortly.

'We have come too far to allow our lives to fall apart. Do whatever you must to safeguard your daughter's future, and your own reputation.'

'Myra—'

'Wake up, boy!' She slapped him hard across the face. 'Wake up!'

His bruised cheek stung, but the blow crashed through his body like a shockwave. All these years, the old woman had never raised a hand to him, not once. She hadn't needed to. She could chill the blood in his veins with a single contemptuous look.

'There are times when I miss our friend Connor, his vitality and passion. Connor would never let events unravel like this.' Moisture shone in her eyes, a greasy film that could be no more than another sign of her failing eyesight. He had never seen her cry, and knew he never would. 'I have lost one child, and I will not lose another. Come home, Raymond.'

When he left, she went to the cutting to look at the image of Connor Laird one last time. And then, igniting the hob, she set fire to the paper, let it blacken and burn to the tips of her fingers.

60

'Whatever happens next,' said Owen, voice low against the wind moaning through the warped planks of the barn, 'is entirely up to you. Because the fact is, son, you're in big trouble. Perry here is keen to beat the shit out of you, and I can't say I blame him. He's very unhappy at being locked in the boot of a car, particularly as he gets very claustrophobic. Ain't that right, Perry?'

Perry, leaning on a cricket bat, his swollen face almost unrecognisable in the dark, muttered something.

'It's lucky he had his mobile with him,' continued Owen. 'Or he'd still be in there. It's not going to be good for you. You understand that, don't you?'

'Yes,' said Elliot, pale with shock. He lurched forward on the muddy ground; wanted to touch Perry, to make sure he was real. The flatulent crack of Perry's grip tightening on the rubber handle of the bat made him snort. His stomach convulsed, his heart raced. He felt . . .

Joy.

Elliot experienced such a grateful release of tension that despite the danger of the situation – there was no doubt Perry and Owen would make him pay for what he had done – he couldn't help burst out laughing.

The truth was, Elliot wanted to plant a smacker on Perry's lips and hug him. Tell him how happy he was. He propped his hands on his knees and laughed and laughed till his sides ached. Tears of relief dropped from his cheeks, spotting the hard floor.

'I don't think you've got much to laugh about,' said Owen angrily. 'You're in big trouble.'

And then just as quickly, Elliot fell to his knees and wept. The sobs came so hard that he was barely able to breathe. All the guilt and dread, all that toxic shit locked inside him for so long, poured out.

'That's more like it,' said Owen, not understanding.

Because Elliot felt blessed. Everything was going to work out. The worst hadn't happened. Perry was alive. He was flesh and blood, standing in front of Elliot. Angry, dangerous, as ugly as sin, but alive and kicking. And Elliot knew that whatever they did to him, Perry and Owen – and it would be very bad indeed – it didn't matter.

None of it mattered, because now he could look Rhonda in the eye, hug Dylan to him, and ask for their forgiveness. It wasn't too late. He could put it all behind him, this whole nightmare scenario, and start again.

The worst hadn't happened. His mind whirled with new beginnings and possibilities. He was friends with Amelia now, and she had money, plenty of it. And that copper Drake – his mad, bad old mate Connor Laird – owed him *big time* now.

He picked himself up. Owen's face was twisted with revulsion, as if Elliot had revealed something about himself, something unsavoury.

'Just let me do him,' Perry growled.

'We'll get the money first, and then you can set to work on him. I'm looking forward to giving you a hand,' said Owen, rolling up the sleeves of his jumper with great care.

'You know what, Elliot, I can see a pattern emerging here.'

'Yeah?' Elliot wasn't bothered by what Owen had to say. He was only thinking about Rhonda and Dylan. He would fall on their mercy. Tell them about what happened at the Longacre – Connor Laird be damned. If he had to do time for the robbery, or the assault, he would do it willingly, wipe the slate clean and start all over again.

'Bloke called Gavin came to me a few days ago.' Owen circled him. 'Bren brought him to me. Said he'd taken your money. Gave half to me, half to Bren, your *good mate*.' Owen mimed reeling in a fish. 'He told us to hook you in, get you on a job. Scratch the surface, he said, and you were a rotter, a scumbag, said you're a thief and a bully. I've never heard the like of it. He really despises you, Elliot. You always struck me as strictly pound shop, a little man, but he was quite insistent. I don't know what you did to Gavin, son, but he's got it in for you real bad.'

'His name's not Gavin,' said Elliot, wiping the tears from his eyes. 'It's Toby.'

Gavin – Turrell – was wrong about him. He wanted to get on with the rest of his life now, was impatient to be with Rhonda and Dylan, and he just had to get through this night.

'Where's the money, Elliot?'

'In my bedroom.'

When Owen moved towards the door, Elliot stepped in front of him.

'Please – my guests. Let me go get it. I swear I'm not going to make any trouble, or try to leave. I'll come right back, you have my word.'

'Your word.' Owen rubbed his chin thoughtfully. 'Five

minutes, then. Any later and Perry will introduce his cricket bat to your lady friends.'

Perry rested the bat on his shoulder, as if in readiness for a long night's work.

Elliot ran into the howling wind, the gale lifting his heels. Cloud raced across the moon. Leaves flew around his head like demented bats. He sensed Owen watching at the barn door. The wind chime was turned sideways, its metal threads thrashing, white noise in his head.

Inside the cottage, the final embers of the fire clung to blackened logs. The kitchen door was closed. Elliot took the stairs two, three, at a time, and slipped into his bedroom.

Grabbing the rucksack from the wardrobe, he unzipped it, took out the gun. Part of him wondered whether he should hold Owen and Perry at gunpoint and call the police – give himself up, then and there – but he didn't want anything to do with the weapon. Just wanted it gone, and them gone. Elliot dropped it into the bag with disgust and zipped it up.

He was about to go back downstairs – five minutes, Owen had said – but couldn't help himself. He took out his phone and called Rhonda's number. It rang and rang and dropped to voicemail. Elliot wanted to assure her that the worst hadn't happened. Everything was going to be all right, he was free now, and they could be together.

'I've done a terrible thing,' he said, 'some terrible things, and I want to tell you about them. From now on I'm going to tell you *everything*.' At the window he lifted the net curtain, thought he saw a figure slip into the barn. 'I'll never keep anything from you or Dylan again, that's a promise. If you decide it's all over between us, I will accept it. But—' He pressed his fingers into his eyes. 'If you can find it in your heart to forgive me, I will do everything in my power to make you both happy. That's a promise, Rhonda. I've never felt as sure about anything in my whole life. I will do *anything*. I love you both. Please call me back, let me make things better.'

He cut the call. The phone rang immediately and his heart leapt. But when he looked he saw a string of miscalls from Connor. Not now, he thought, let's deal with one fucking problem at a time, and threw it on the bed.

The kitchen door was still closed when he crept downstairs. Elliot crunched down the drive. The trees swayed and creaked above him. His spine chilled where sweat popped on his back and froze.

'Take it.' He strode into the barn and threw the bag on the dirty floor. 'The gun is in there, too.'

No one replied.

For one brief moment, Elliot thought Owen and Perry had gone. But above the moaning wind he heard a curious gurgling sound. Stepping carefully through the shards of silver light pouring in through loose planks in the roof, his foot hit something.

Perry was sprawled on the ground, perfectly still. Face pale, almost luminous, a final glimmer of light fading from his swollen eyes. Blood, jet black in the moonlight, ticked gently from his gaping throat, like a water feature in a rockery, pooling around his shoulders. A hiss of escaping air whispered from the exposed piping in his neck.

'Christ almighty.' Elliot's legs buckled, and he fell to his hands and knees into the warm, sticky blood. He smothered a cry, smearing his face in Perry's blood, frantically wiped his hands down his jeans.

He found Owen a few moments later, behind hardened

sacks of clay. The old man's hands loosely cupped the remains of his throat, the meat of it bulged between his fingers, strings of blood and tissue hanging from the yawning wound. His wellington boot jerked, and went still.

The barn door banged against the frame, and Elliot turned quickly.

'Hello?'

A cloud passed in front of the moon and the barn was plunged into darkness. Elliot listened to the wind howl through the rotten planks, then rushed forward.

Stumbling over Perry's leg, he fell, throwing his arms forward to protect himself, jarring his elbows on the cold, hard mud. He had no idea if he was alone or – oh God, if Turrell was still in the barn.

He could be in here, could be standing right over him.

Elliot swept a hand in front of him, scrabbling for the rucksack, desperate for it. Finding fabric, grabbing it. He unzipped it with shaking hands, shoulders cringing against a sudden blow to the head, or a knife slicing out of the darkness. Elliot tipped out the contents and snatched up the gun, flicked off the safety, and pointed it at the banging door.

He edged towards it, swinging the gun wildly, not knowing from which direction he would be attacked. Waiting for any movement, any tiny change in the density of the dark. Then he barged through the door to run towards the cottage, trying to keep his balance on the uneven ground.

'Amelia! April! Get out,' he called, but his shouts were lost in the blast of the wind. 'Get outside!'

Elliot ran inside and shouldered open the kitchen door. Cups of tea sat on the table, untouched. He stomped upstairs, shouting hoarsely, 'Amelia! April!'

He raced into every room, one after the other, and then into the front bedroom. Empty. He looked out of the window. With that sick maniac Turrell roaming about the place, he hoped desperately that the two women had got away into the woods.

Owen dead, Perry dead. He struggled to think. Focused on the fact that his family was waiting for him. Everything was going to work out fine, he felt it in his bones. He wasn't going to die now, not now.

Emboldened by the heft of the weapon in his fist, he felt a surge of fury and chambered a bullet.

'Elliot?'

He whirled, his finger squeezing the trigger. Amelia Troy let out a frightened whimper in the doorway, lifted her hands above her head.

'Jesus! You scared the shit out of me!' Elliot took her wrist and lowered her to the bed. 'Where've you been?'

'We've been looking for you,' she said, gawping at the weapon. 'You went outside and didn't come back.'

'He's here!' he hissed.

Amelia stared. 'Who?'

'Turrell – he's in the house!'

'Oh my God!' Her hand flew to her mouth.

The last thing he needed was for her to start screaming the place down. He had to take the heat out of the situation, asked quietly, 'Where's the girl?'

'Downstairs,' she said. 'In the living room.'

'She's not,' Elliot whispered urgently. 'I was just there.'

The idea that April was alone somewhere frightened him. Christ, if Connor's girl disappeared . . . he didn't want to think of the consequences. All he had to do was get through this.

Rhonda was waiting for him, Dylan was waiting.

'We've been everywhere looking for you!' Tears filled Amelia's eyes; she was starting to get hysterical.

He pulled her off the bed, waved the gun in front of her face. 'We're going to get out of this. We find April and get in the car and drive away, do you understand?'

She nodded.

'Do you have your keys?'

'Yes.' Her voice trembled.

'All you've got to do is stay behind me, okay?' He squeezed her arm. 'Good girl, you're doing great,' and added: 'We both are.'

He led her out of the bedroom and onto the landing, pointing the gun ahead, holding a protective arm in front of Amelia. At the bottom of the stairs, the front door shuddered. He leaned over the banister, but couldn't see anything.

Elliot called down: 'April, you there?' There was no response. A log shifted in the grate, sending up a billowing cloud of sparks.

'Elliot,' Amelia spoke low behind him.

He needed to listen, needed all his wits about him, put a finger to his lips: 'Quiet!'

She said it again: 'Elliot.'

'What?' He turned to face her, and Amelia pressed a knife into his gut and twisted it, this way and that, her face straining with concentration.

And when she calmly lifted her gaze to his, all Elliot had time to do was stare in shock, let out a brief grunt, and feel his legs give way, sending him toppling backwards down the stairs.

61

They drove in silence, threading slowly through the late-night traffic and accelerating at the edge of the city, both lost in their own thoughts. Drake stared ahead, reflected street lights pulling silently down his face, focused on his daughter's safety. When they left the motorway and drove deeper into the countryside, the tall trees a blank wall on either side, the car scythed a knife of light on the black road. Something with shining eyes skittered across the head-lights and plunged into the verge.

'You didn't have to come,' he said, as they approached Elliot's cottage.

'No, I didn't.'

'Then why did you?'

Flick watched the canopy of trees fold above them, as if the car was going down a tunnel beneath the earth. When the branches parted, they saw the silhouette of the barn. Elliot's cottage, its lights off, was barely an outline beneath the cloud. Drake eased the car to a stop and killed the engine, the lamps. They sat in silence.

'Why was Gordon Tallis handcuffed to a radiator?'

'Tallis was unstable, unpredictable. He killed himself in front of us.'

'Hell of a way to do it,' said Flick.

'Yes.'

'He was trapped by handcuffs *you* took from my father.'

Drake grunted in surprise. She saw the harsh plummet of his cheeks in profile and a pinprick of light in one eye, and it reminded her of the image of Connor Laird cringing from the flash of the camera. 'I'm different now, I'm a different person.'

'Are you?' she asked. When he didn't answer, she held his hand. Badly needed the reassurance of his touch. 'You asked why I'm here. It's because right now you're the only person I have left. Because I can't bear to lose anybody else from my life.'

'Thank you,' he said, 'for—'

She dropped his hand, snapped off her seat belt. 'Let's just do this.'

'No, stay here.' Drake reached for the door release. 'Lock the door. I'm going to look around. If I'm not back in ten minutes, call for back-up.'

And then he climbed out, slamming the door behind him. Flick watched him trot up the drive.

As soon as he was gone, nausea washed over her in the silent compartment, turning her stomach, slipping along her skin like a clammy chill, as all the terror of the night hit her. She had watched Peter Holloway and Toby Turrell die; had been convinced she was going to be killed. And now, here she was, sitting alone in the middle of nowhere in the dark, every muffled sound making her tense with fear. A minute passed, and then another, and the longer she sat there, the more she realised how wrong it all was. She was scared – and confused. Well, enough was enough.

Flick scrambled for her phone. Its blue light bathed the

interior. Out here, the signal was weak, a single flat bar – if the call even connected it would be a miracle. But the device managed to find a mast somewhere, and the call was blasted to a satellite thousands of miles above the woodland. After a few moments a phone rang somewhere in the city.

'Fli –' Eddie Upson's voice dropped out almost immediately.

'Eddie, I'm at Elliot Juniper's.'

'Wha –' Upson's voice kept disappearing. '– ick, is tha –'

She clamped the phone tightly to her ear, said: 'I need a response unit, Eddie . . .'

'A what? I can't – you, Fli – ere are – ?'

'A response unit, Eddie! Now! Elliot Juniper!' she cried.

'Ell –'

'It's Ray Drake, Eddie.' She gripped the dash. 'He's – '

'Eddie's voice said: '—per,' and the line went dead.

Flick threw the phone down in frustration. She cracked the window. Wind howled into the gap. Somewhere, an owl hooted. She'd try Steiner next, was bending over to pick up the mobile when the bushes quivered on the verge ahead, and a figure stepped onto the road.

Flick held her breath, leaned forward to see who it was – and was relieved to see Drake approach beneath the moonlight, a silver ghost. He came along the passenger side and rapped on the glass.

'It's difficult to see inside,' he said. 'All the lights are off. And in the barn . . .'

She stepped unsteadily from the car. 'In the barn, what?'

'Never mind.' He hesitated. 'The cottage looks empty, but—'

Flick's hands flew to her face. When she pulled them

away, her palms were wet with tears. 'Jesus Christ, Ray!' she said bitterly.

Ray Drake nodded. 'I understand. You don't have to come inside.'

'No.' Her hands clapped her sides. 'Let's get this over with.'

If anything happened to April she would never forgive herself. All she hoped was that Upson had heard her, and help was on its way.

Drake reached into his pocket and took out the pistol. He snapped the magazine from the grip and slapped it in again.

'You can't use it,' she told him.

His eyes flashed. 'My daughter is in there, Flick.'

She held out her hand. 'Leave it here or I call this in right now.'

Drake handed her the weapon. She opened the door and threw it under the seat.

'When you get April out of there, drive away and keep going.' He pressed the car key into her palm. 'If I'm not with you, don't wait. Just get to safety.' He touched her arm. 'Are you ready?'

Flick nodded, but barely heard him. She strained to hear sirens, the sound of distant engines, but the wind crashing through the trees obliterated every noise.

Staying close to the verge, they walked along the lane, leaves churning around them. A hundred yards ahead, the drive rose steeply.

62

The windows of the cottage reflected the swaying wall of trees. A saucer of moonlight struck the glass and vanished. A wind chime lifted sideways in the wind, clinking like crazy.

'Go round the back and keep your head down. And be careful.'

Flick nodded, and disappeared around the side. There was little point in creeping around, Drake decided. He stood tall, crunching up the drive, his tie dancing in the wind like an angry viper.

The front door was unlocked. When he walked into the dark and closed the door, the sound of the chime, the whistling wind, was muffled. The window frames shuddered. Definition bleeding into his vision, the layout of the room slowly emerged. He could make out the fireplace, its final embers fading. LED lights glowed on a television, a Wi-Fi router and stereo. He heard the loud thrum of a boiler, and something else . . . a rasping breath on the floor.

'April?' he called. 'Elliot?'

A voice rattled wetly in reply. Somebody lay at the bottom of the stairs. Elliot. His shirt – and the carpet around him – was jet black and sticky.

'Lights?' asked Drake.

'By . . . the door.'

Drake pressed the switch. Light illuminated the space. Elliot's face was drained of colour and soaked in oily sweat. Black rings circled his eyes, which were swollen blood red by broken capillaries. His body was drenched in the blood ticking patiently from the gaping wound in his guts.

'Finally.' His lips smacked together. 'The cavalry.'

'Where is she?' Drake leaned close to Elliot. 'Where's April?'

Elliot's eyelids fluttered. Two figures appeared at the top of the stairs. Drake's heart leapt when he saw the gun held at his daughter's throat. Amelia jammed the muzzle into April's windpipe as they moved together down the steps.

'It's a crying shame Toby isn't here,' said Amelia brightly. 'He would have enjoyed seeing this. But the poor man was desperately tired, and so eager to be gone. I assured him that he could leave it all to me, that I would complete his magnificent obsession. I presume he's . . . ?'

Drake focused on his daughter, who trembled violently in Amelia's grip, and her stricken eyes were fastened on his. 'He's dead,' he said.

'I'll miss him, but it's what he wanted.' Amelia sighed. 'There was no talking him out of it. The truth is Toby was too sensitive a soul to survive in this stinking world.'

Elliot's throat hacked a wet laugh.

'Why?' asked Drake. 'Why are you doing this?'

'I loved him.' Amelia's eyes filled with tears. 'He saved me. He taught me how to live my life without pain, without torment, and you can't imagine how much of a release that was, how much of a revelation.'

'He killed your husband, and very nearly killed you.'

'He meant to kill us both, of course he did. I was never meant to survive that overdose. We discussed it like grown-ups. When I woke up in hospital my memories of the Longacre were gone and I felt free. For the first time I could begin to enjoy life. They came back eventually, of course they did, in bits and pieces, but they held no power over me. The death of my hateful husband, the abusive man who made my life a perfect misery, gave me hope that I could finally live. And Toby assured me that when it's all over, when I leave here tonight, I will be reborn. I will live without fear, somewhere far away.' Tears slid down her cheeks. 'I'm for ever in his debt for what he's done for me. In another life I believe he would have achieved many great things, and I'm grateful to have been at his service. To be honest, I believe he was happy for the company on his difficult journey.' The corners of her mouth lifted in a repugnant smile. 'Not all of us can do the Lone Wolf thing, Connor.'

'By killing all of those people?'

'Well,' she said modestly, 'I helped, just a little bit.'

'Ryan Overton.' Drake sensed movement in the corner of his eye, Flick edging through the kitchen door.

'Yes, that was me,' said Amelia. 'I've always been super supple, I used to love climbing the trees in the garden at the home, and Toby had to work that evening. But mostly I financed his work. Provided documentation, identities, forged qualifications, that kind of thing. None of that stuff is cheap, believe me. I like to think of myself as more of a facilitator, a sponsor. It was actually kind of fun.'

'I can help you,' said Drake, edging forward.

'You could have helped me at the home,' she spat. 'But you never did. Ray was the only one to make any effort, the only one who ever took an interest in my welfare. But you killed him, and took his future for yourself.'

'Whatever Turrell told you, it's wrong.'

'That poor, sweet boy burned to death, and you didn't save him. You forget, Connor, I was there.'

'Toby said he'd let April go if I killed him.'

Amelia gave him a sympathetic look. 'I'm afraid I didn't get that memo. But I tell you what . . .' She took a knife from her belt and threw it at his feet. 'I'll consider letting your precious little girl live if you save me the trouble and kill yourself right now.'

'How do I know you'll let her go?'

'Oh, you don't! I could just kill her anyway, but you're going to have to trust me. I'm a very trustworthy person, and trusting in return. Ask Toby, ask my beautiful, brutal husband, may he rot in hell.' She nodded. 'Don't be coy, Connor. Pick up the knife and gut yourself. I've seen the things you can do when you put your mind to it.'

Flick moved closer behind Amelia as Drake crouched over the knife.

'Don't do this, Amelia.'

'I'm waiting.' She shuffled backwards, April whimpering in her grip.

He flipped the knife in his hand so that the tip of the blade was pressed to his stomach. 'We'll get you help,' he said.

'But I don't want help.' Amelia's eyes bulged. 'I've never felt better!'

When he stepped forward again, Amelia jammed the barrel of the gun up into the soft flesh beneath April's jaw. 'Just do it!'

Drake stood hunched over the knife as if to disembowel himself, and Amelia shivered with expectation.

He shouted: 'Now!'

Flick lunged to grab Amelia's gun hand, wrenching it away from April. Plaster exploded in the ceiling when Amelia squeezed off a shot, but Drake flew forward, sending them both to the floor.

'Get out!' he shouted, and April ran screaming out the door. Drake slammed Amelia's gun hand against the floor and the weapon went off again, splintering the wooden stairs above Elliot's head. Drake crunched her wrist again, and the gun leapt from her hand.

A furious wind blew in through the open door. Amelia and Drake rolled towards the fireplace, tumbling over each other, her nails clawing at his face, his eyes, as she scrabbled on top of him. Screaming, clawing, slapping and punching his temples and cheeks. A riot of colour swam in his vision.

Flick flew at her, but Amelia stretched to pump the knife into her left side in three quick stabs, *in, in, in,* and when Flick's body stiffened in shock, she swung her against the fireplace. Flick's head cracked against the mantelpiece and she slumped against the wall.

Amelia dropped back onto Drake, and he glimpsed the flash of the blade – a searing pain ripped through his shoulder. She pressed down on it with a banshee shriek, wrenching the knife around in his flesh, leaning on it with both hands, opening the wound. Arching so low that her lips brushed against his, and he thought he was going to black out. Then he felt the knife suck from the wound and Amelia sat bolt upright, holding the blade high, ready to bring it down into his face.

She stroked his cheek tenderly, said: 'Goodbye, Connor.'

Then there was an explosion, and chips of stone flew from the fireplace. Amelia flinched at the gunshot, giving Drake the moment he needed. He twisted his fingers into her hair and smashed her head down into the stone surround with all the force he could muster. He heard a crack as her skull splintered, and Amelia went slack on top of him.

Trying to avoid the weight of her lifeless body pressing on his wound, he pushed her aside and lay against the warm edge of the fireplace. Elliot made a feeble smacking sound in his throat. Drake climbed to his feet.

'Shit,' Elliot mumbled. The gun dropped from his hand. 'Missed.'

When Drake crouched beside him, Elliot said: 'You get him?'

Drake nodded, gingerly pulling the jacket from the wound in his shoulder. The slick dome of Elliot's scalp was sallow, and his breath rattled, as if his lungs were flapping loose inside.

'Ain't lost your touch, have you? Turrell, the girl . . . and Gordon. I remember your first one.' Elliot winced at a shooting pain. His pupils were almost obliterated behind a sea of clotted red. 'You ever think about it, Connor . . . what you did to Tallis?'

Drake said: 'He deserved to die.'

'You did him good. In cold blood. The look in your eyes, the way you torched him, it was ice cold. I ain't ever forgotten it. But it's got to stop now. All these lies, all these secrets.' He attempted a slack smile. 'They'll be the death of me.'

Drake glanced at Flick, unconscious against the wall, blood seeping from the ragged wounds in her side.

Faintly in the distance, the sound of sirens.

'She's coming back to me, my Rhonda,' said Elliot. 'I know she is – and the boy. I'm getting a second chance . . . and I'm going to tell her everything. Get it all out where it can't hurt me any more.'

Blood spurted from his mouth. Chances are, Elliot wasn't going to last much longer, he had lost too much blood. But stranger things had happened. Drake reached into his pocket, took out a pair of disposable gloves.

'They're probably on the way back now, and I'm gonna tell 'em everything. About the home, and what happened there . . . and what became of us. It's the only way. Me and you, we'll tell the truth for the first time in our lives, and the lies won't hurt us no more. And then . . . we'll be free, at last.' Drake crouched, snapping the gloves over his fingers. 'What do you say, Connor? A new start for the both of us.'

'I think it's a fine idea, Elliot,' said Drake, and he pinched Elliot's nostrils together, cupping the hand over his mouth. Elliot tried to struggle, his hands scrabbled weakly at Drake's wrist for a few moments as his mouth filled with blood. Eyes fastened on Drake, his arms swayed slowly like reeds in a gentle stream, then fell to his sides. A short time after that he stopped moving – and his dead eyes stared blankly.

Drake stood, pulling the gloves off his fingers, and when he turned, Flick was staring at him.

Right at him.

63

What did you see?

Drake was leaning over her when she came to, pressing a towel into the wounds in her side. Flick's head swam; she was ice cold and shook uncontrollably: her muscles, her nerves, her whole body. 'Am I . . .?'

'Easy,' he said, glancing towards the door. 'They're here.'

The sound of vehicles outside. Doors slamming and shouts. Lights, blue and yellow, refracted off the windows and whirled across the ceiling.

'What did you see, Flick?' he asked. Her mouth was dry, despite the icy sweat dripping into her lips. She tried to speak, but couldn't. She felt pain, but didn't know where it was coming from. He smeared her sopping fringe away from her eyes. Drake's face was close to hers, and he spoke quickly. 'What did you see?'

There was blood everywhere. His own suit jacket was sodden. Amelia Troy was face down beside the fire, Elliot Juniper's body by the stairs.

'We're good, aren't we, Flick? We're going to get through this, me and you together.' Drake smiled gently. 'What did you see?'

Then the bodies were surrounded by uniformed men and women as paramedics and police poured inside. Drake called: 'Over here!'

She heard shouts, urgent commands, and then Eddie Upson was standing over her. She heard him ask Drake if there was anything he could do. His voice echoed, as if from the far end of a long pipe.

'Let us through, please!'

A pair of paramedics kneeled beside her and started barking questions. Talking in slow, loud voices as they unpacked equipment. One of them moved Drake aside to press hard on the sopping wound – Flick's body couldn't stop juddering – and fired questions at her.

'Are you cold?'

'Can you breathe properly?'

'Tell me your name.'

'She's in shock,' said Drake.

One of them held up a hand, irritably. 'Move away, please. Let us work.'

Drake stepped back, and Flick dimly registered some kind of dispute as more paramedics surrounded him. He didn't want treatment, didn't want to leave her.

And minutes later, when an oxygen mask had been placed over her face, and a clotting agent applied to her wounds and bandaged, she was lifted onto a trolley and brought out of the cottage. The breeze cooled her burning face. The furious winds of the night before had subsided and the wall of trees on the other side of the lane had emerged from the dark. She sensed Drake keeping pace with the trolley.

He had asked: *What did you see?*

And the question kept going round in her head, but she didn't understand it. Her head was groggy with the throbbing pain and the cold that coated her bones. Images repeated in her mind, each one layered transparently on top of the other like a double exposure. She saw Amelia Troy's twisted leer as she gleefully stabbed at her; Peter Holloway falling on the stairs, arms outstretched; and Ray Drake crouched over Elliot, doing something with his mouth, as Juniper's hand plucked ineffectually at his sleeve.

'We're taking you to a trauma centre.' She barely heard the paramedic as she was secured on the ambulance. 'You'll go straight into surgery.'

She tried to speak, wanted to say goodbye to Nina and Martin and the kids. Needed them close, now more than ever, but knew she had to let them go.

'Do you want someone with you?' asked the woman.

Eddie Upson and Millie Steiner and Vix Moore crowded at the back door of the vehicle. 'Is she going to be okay?' Steiner asked.

'We'll need one of you with her,' the woman said.

And she heard Drake say: 'Let me go.'

Flick said, *No*. She didn't know why, but she didn't want him near. Needed time to order the images in her head. *No, please*. But nobody heard her, because her voice was muffled and weak beneath the mask, and her head swam, and she had no idea if she'd even spoken.

Millie Steiner climbed on board and took Flick's hand. The throb of the engine pulsed through her. Beyond the doors, she glimpsed the patrol cars and ambulances, the uniforms scattering across the drive, and saw the boy called Connor Laird staring at her, oblivious of all the commotion around him.

And she had no idea what he was thinking.

A last glimpse of racing cloud, a whirl of flashing blue light across the gravel, and the ambulance doors slammed shut.